Virtual Lab CD-ROM with Virtual Lab Manual

More than 170 modules, including animations, experiments, and demonstrations

For the first time accompanied by its own manual, the Virtual Lab CD-ROM for *Sensation and Perception* is designed to help students get the most out of your course.

Virtual Lab CD-ROM
by Colin Ryan, John Baro, and Bruce Goldstein

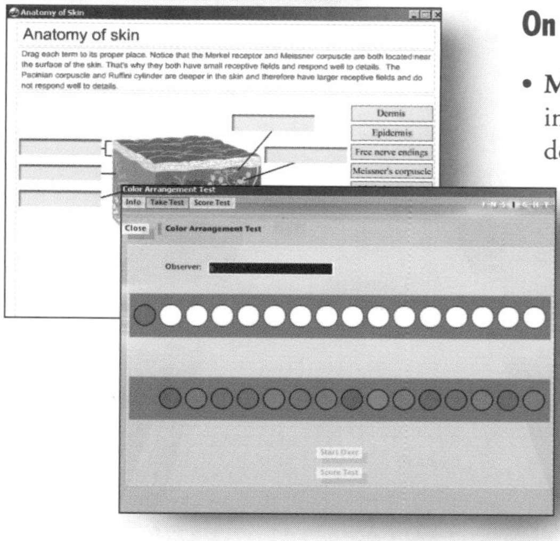

On the CD-ROM:

- **Media Interactions** include drag-and-drop animations, experiments, and interactive exercises illustrating principles in this book, as well as auditory demonstrations, which are newly updated.
- **Media Experiments and Demonstrations** are designed so students can practice gathering data, varying many parameters to determine how changes to parameters affect perception, and analyzing the results.
- **New! Seven Demonstration Videos from NASA** include topics like biological motion, convergence, motion parallax, and stereo vision.

In the accompanying Virtual Lab Manual:

Written by Jan Proctor of Purdue University, this newly published manual includes worksheets for the Virtual Lab experiments to help students take a closer look at the labs and engage in analysis of the results. Students can tear out the perforated pages and submit them to the instructor as homework assignments. The worksheets will also be available online in PDF format for Perception PsychologyNow, WebTutor, and on the Book Companion Website as an instructor resource.

WebTUTOR™ Advantage

WebTutor™ Advantage on Blackboard and WebCT

Online course management . . . includes Virtual Labs

Ready to use as soon as you log on, this complete course management system and communication tool is pre-loaded text-specific content, including extensive quizzing with full-rejoinders, learning objectives, detailed chapter outlines, chapter summaries, glossary, flashcards, and weblinks. WebTutor Advantage also includes all elements from the Virtual Lab CD-ROM (with corresponding worksheets from the Virtual Lab Manual) plus additional interactive modules. *Authored by Deborah Briihl of Valdosta State University.*

Package these exciting media options with the textbook!

Simply contact your local Thomson Wadsworth representative to create the package that's just right for your class.

Full color **at an affordable price... because Goldstein *is* the gold standard.**

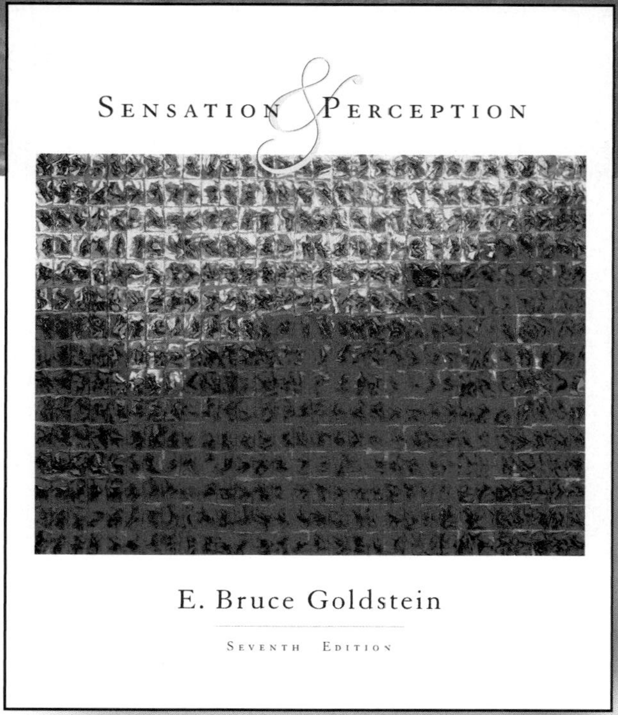

Never has there been an easier-to-understand, more student-friendly book for the sensation and perception course. And yet, with this Seventh Edition, Goldstein further raises the bar for teachability and clarity with:

- ***Full color that effectively promotes learning***—almost every illustration, diagram, and photograph is now in teachable, vivid full color.
- ***Streamlined presentation***—every chapter has been thoroughly revised with an eye to accessibility and student-friendliness.
- ***The latest research***—culled from hundreds of new references.
- ***Complete media integration***—with the book's Virtual Labs accessible in three easy ways: on the Virtual Lab CD-ROM, online through Perception PsychologyNow™, and online via WebTutor™ Advantage. The choice is yours!

And there's more good news . . . *You'll be surprised at this edition's affordable price!* It is a value-packed dynamo, featuring cutting-edge material, meticulous updating, and a student-friendly style. This edition has the most innovative media resources and tools available with any text for this course.

A fantastic value when packaged with this book:

PERCEPTION Psychology Now™

Perception PsychologyNow™
A powerful, assignable online learning companion that assesses each student's study needs through diagnostic tests and builds focused *Personalized Study Plans*. A great timesaver for students *and* instructors!

Virtual Lab CD-ROM with Manual
More than 170 modules, including animations, labs, experiments, demonstrations, updated audio interactions, new media, and seven new "stimuli" videos from NASA, plus a NEW accompanying lab manual.

Request either or both of the above items when placing your adoption order.
For details and package order numbers, please contact your local Thomson Wadsworth representative.

Turn the page to begin your tour →

THOMSON WADSWORTH™

Your preview of the 7th Edition

Now in full color throughout

With vivid, pedagogically directed *full color*, it's so much easier for students to understand concepts

Hundreds of new full-color illustrations

Under Goldstein's expert, hands-on direction, nearly every illustration in this book has been re-thought and re-drafted, using color. Wherever possible, the narrative and its accompanying illustration appear on the same page or same spread. There are more than 480 illustrations and photographs in this edition.

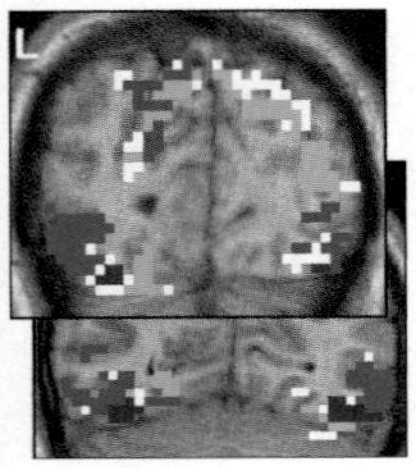

Figure 4.28 ▮ fMRI responses of the human brain to various types of stimuli: (a) areas that were most strongly activated by houses, faces, and chairs; (b) all areas activated by each type of stimulus.

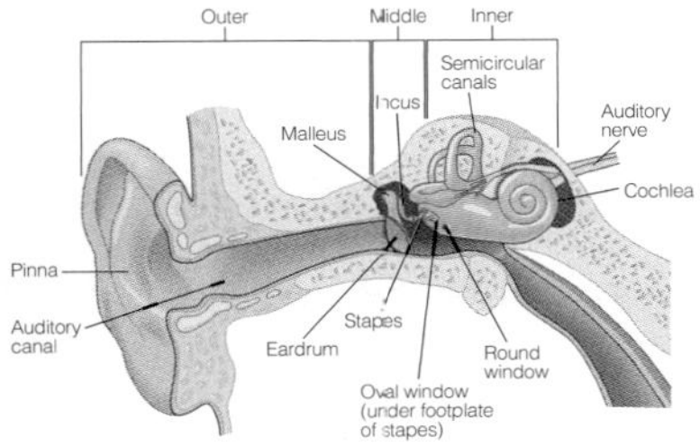

Figure 11.11 ▮ The ear, showing its three subdivisions—outer, middle, and inner.
Redrawn by permission from Human Information Processing, by P. H. Lindsay and D. A. Norman, 2nd ed. 1977, p. 229. Copyright © 1977 by Academic Press, Inc.

Colorful, in-text prompts guide students to Virtual Labs located on the CD and online

Located throughout every chapter, easy-to-spot **VL** icons prompt students to visit the media-rich Virtual Labs, which bring to life specific sections in the textbook with drop-and-drag animations, experiments, interactive exercises, and demonstrations.

VIRTUAL LAB VL

Your Virtual Lab is designed to help you get the most out of this course. The Virtual Lab icons direct you to specific media demonstrations and experiments designed to help you visualize what you are reading about. The number beside each icon indicates the number of the media element you can access through your CD-ROM, Perception PsychologyNow, or WebTutor resource at http:now.ilrn.com/goldstein_7e.

The following are the lab exercises covering what you've just learned in this chapter:

1. *Cortical Areas* Functions of each of the primary sensory receiving areas of the cortex.

2. *3D Virtual Brain* A 3D picture of a brain that you can rotate and dissect. Also indicates the functions of different areas.

3. *Structure of a Neuron* Functions of different parts of a neuron.

4. *Oscilloscopes and Intracellular Recording* How nerve potentials are displayed on an oscilloscope.

5. *Resting Potential* Demonstrates the difference in charge between the inside and outside of the neuron when it is not conducting impulses.

6. *Phases of Action Potential* How sodium and potassium flow across the axon membrane during the action potential.

Events at the Synapse

Early in the 1900s, it was discovered that the action potentials themselves do not travel across the synapse. Instead, they trigger a chemical process that bridges the gap between the sending neuron (the *presynaptic neuron*) and the receiving neuron (the *postsynaptic neuron*). When the action potential reaches the end of the presynaptic neuron, it causes the release of chemicals called **neurotransmitters** that are stored in synaptic vesicles in the presynaptic neuron (Figure 2.7).

VL 8, 9

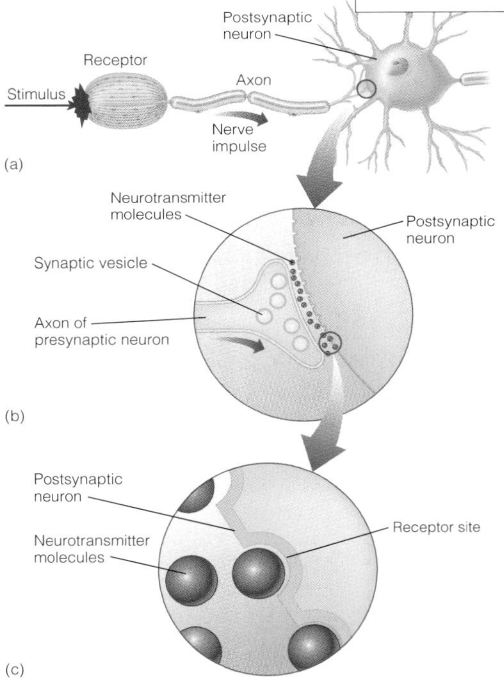

Figure 2.7 ▮ Synaptic transmission from one neuron to another. (a) A signal traveling down the axon of a neuron reaches the synapse at the end of the axon. (b) The nerve impulse causes the release of neurotransmitter molecules from the synaptic vesicles of the presynaptic neuron. (c) The neurotransmitters fit into receptor sites and cause a voltage change in the postsynaptic neuron.

Learning tools enhanced with *full color* give students new ways to reinforce the material

NEW *Method* sections

Included whenever a new research method is first introduced, *Method* sections place the description of the method conveniently in the text, where it is first applied. The book's new full-color design integrates the *Method* sections into the flow of the narrative, so students are efficiently guided through complex material.

METHOD ▪ Brain Imaging

Brain imaging enables researchers to create images that show which areas of the brain are active. One of these techniques, **positron emission tomography (PET)**, was introduced in 1976 (Hoffman et al., 1976; Ter-Pogossian et al., 1975). In the PET procedure a person is injected with a low dose of a radioactive tracer that is not harmful. The tracer enters the bloodstream and indicates the volume of blood flow. The basic principle behind the PET scan is that changes in the activity of the brain are accompanied by changes in blood flow, and monitoring the radioactivity of the injected tracer provides a measure of this blood flow (Figure 4.5).

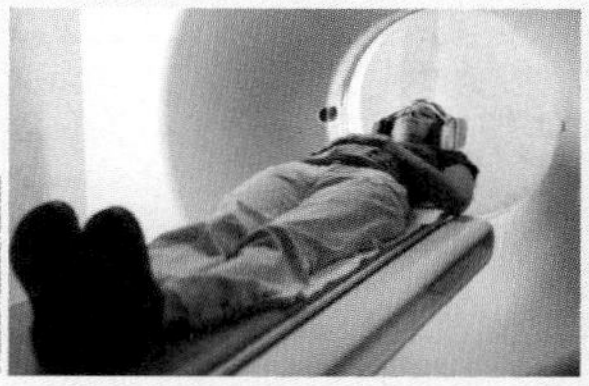

Figure 4.5 ▮ A person in a brain-imaging apparatus.

NEW full-color photos and graphs

This edition's full-color images reinforce adjacent text to help students master the material.

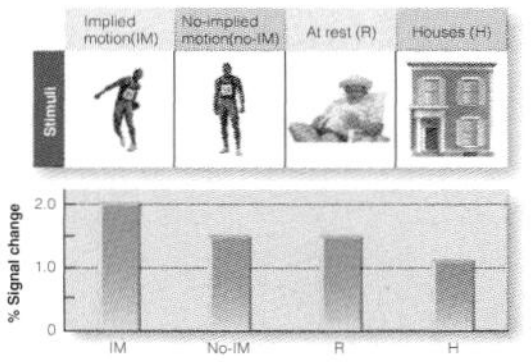

Figure 9.25 ▮ Examples of pictures used by Kourtzi and Kanwisher (2000) to depict implied motion (IM), no implied motion (no-IM), "at rest" (R), and a house (H). The height of the bars below each picture indicates the average fMRI response of the MT cortex to that type of picture.
(Kourtzi, Z. and Kanwisher, N. Activation in human MT/MST by static images with implied motion. Journal of Cognitive Neuroscience, 12, 48–55, MIT Press (2000).)

Figure 4.19 ▮ A neuron in the monkey's IT cortex that responds to face stimuli but not to nonface stimuli. (Based on data from Rolls & Tovee, 1995.)

NEW *If You Want to Know More* features offer topics for further study

Appearing at the end of each chapter, these new features present key references to help students get started in their searches. For example, in Chapter 7, "Perceiving Color," the *If You Want to Know More* feature gives students direction in exploring color vision in animals and the adaptive nature of animal coloration.

IF YOU WANT TO KNOW MORE

1. ***Color Vision in Animals.*** What does your cat or dog see? Are there animals other than humans who have trichromatic vision? Are there animals who have better color vision than humans?

   Jacobs, G. H. (1993). The distribution and nature of colour vision among the mammals. *Biological Review, 68,* 413–471.

   Neitz, J., Geist, T., & Jacobs, G. H. (1989). Color vision in the dog. *Visual Neuroscience, 3,* 119–125.

   Varela, F. J., Palacios, A. G., & Goldsmith, T. H. (1993). Color vision of birds. In H. P. Zeigler & H-J. Bishof (Eds.), *Vision, brain and behavior in birds* (pp. 77–98). Cambridge: MIT Press.

2. ***The Adaptive Nature of Animal Coloration.*** Some birds have bright plumage to attract mates. This could be dangerous if these colors also made these birds more obvious to predators. It has been shown that Swedish songbirds reflect light in the ultraviolet area of the spectrum, which other songbirds can see. However, these wavelengths are not very conspicuous to potential predators.

NEW *Test Yourself* questions that encourage active review

Appearing midway through each chapter and at the end of the chapter, these new questions don't simply repeat main points in the text, but require students to review the material in active ways.

NEW *Something to Consider* sections and *Think About It* exercises

Located near the end of each chapter, these new pedagogical features encourage students to focus beyond specific chapter content and think more deeply about the material.

SOMETHING TO CONSIDER: THE INTELLIGENCE OF HUMAN OBJECT PERCEPTION

We are now ready to consider why humans are so much more successful than computers at solving the problem of object perception. If we were to answer the question

ception may be determined by neurons that are loc[…] the brain, the nature of the perceptions that the bra[…] ates are influenced by events that occur as light[…] flected from objects, enters the eye, is focused, and […] transformed into electricity. Each of these steps […] mines the nature of the information that will be tra[…] ted out of the eye and which will eventually rea[…] brain. In the next chapter, we will consider how th[…] processes the information that it receives from th[…]

SOMETHING TO CONSIDER: TRANSFORMATIONS AND RECEPTORS

We have seen that perception involves transformations. A tree is transformed into reflected light and becomes an image on the retina, which is then transformed into electrical signals by the receptors. This means that what we perceive depends on the nature of the transformation. For example, what we see with our rods may be different from what we see with the cones because the rod and cone pigments regenerate at different rates and absorb light in different parts of the spectrum.

To carry this idea a step further, we can consider perception in other animals. Figure 2.30 shows the absorption spectra of the honeybee's visual pigments. Although the honeybee has three cone pigments like the human, there is an important difference: the honeybee's pigments are more spread out, so the "honeybee visible spectrum" is broader than the human's. Also, the pigment at the short-wavelength end of the spectrum absorbs ultraviolet light. These wavelengths below 400 nm, which humans can't see, are strongly reflected by the flowers on which the honeybee depends for its survival.

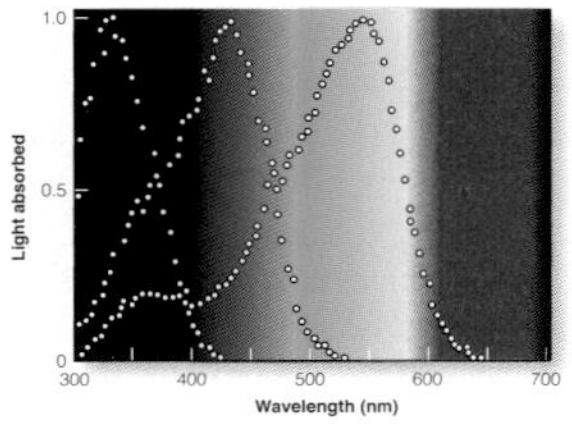

Figure 2.30 ▮ Absorption spectra of honeybee's visual pigments. The pigment at the far left absorbs light below the wavelength range that is visible to humans.

can influence our perceptions.

TEST YOURSELF 2.2

1. Where on the retina does a researcher need to put a stimulus to test dark adaptation of the cones? How can adaptation of the rods be measured without any interference from the cones?
2. Describe how rod and cone sensitivity changes starting when the lights are turned off and how this change in sensitivity continues for 20–30 minutes in the dark.
3. What happens to visual pigment molecules when they (a) absorb light and (b) regenerate? What is the connection between visual pigment regeneration and dark adaptation?
4. What is spectral sensitivity? How is a cone spectral sensitivity curve determined? A rod spectral sensitivity curve?
5. What is an absorption spectrum? How do rod- and cone-pigment absorption spectra compare, and what is their relationship to rod and cone spectral sensitivity?
6. What are the two answers (one "simple" and the other "profound") to the question, "Why is our perception of colors and details worse in dim illumination than in bright illumination?"
7. What does it mean to say that our perception depends on transformations? Give an example from human perception and an example from honeybee perception of how different transformations can result in different perceptions.

THINK ABOUT IT

1. Because the long axons of neurons look like electrical wires, and both neurons and electrical wires conduct electricity, it is tempting to equate the two. Compare the functioning of axons and electrical wires in terms of their structure and the nature of the electrical signals they conduct.
2. In the demonstration "Becoming Aware of What Is in Focus" on page 31, you saw that we see things clearly

Think About It 41

Now in full color throughout

At the field's cutting edge

Goldstein intrigues students with current, important research

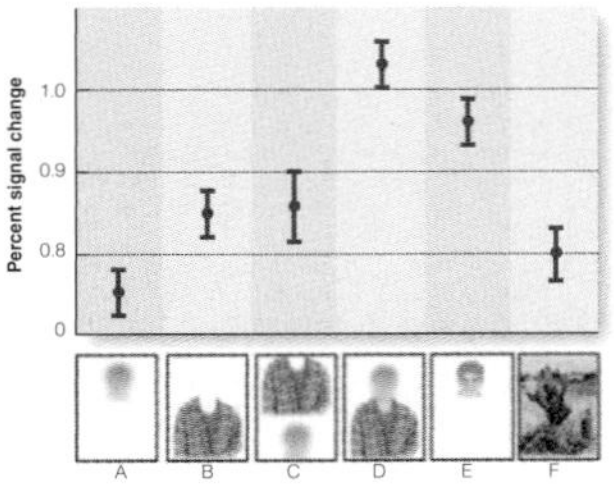

Figure 4.21 ▮ fMRI response of the human fusiform face area. Activation occurs when a face is present (E) or is implied (D) but is lower when other stimuli are presented (A, B, C, F). *(Reprinted with permission from Cox, D., Meyers, E., Sinha, P. (2004). Contextually evoked object-specific responses in human visual cortex. Science, 304, 115–117.)*

however, to pictures that did not imply the presence of a face (A, B, C, and F).

In addition to the FFA, which contains neurons that are activated by faces, two other specialized areas in the temporal cortex have been identified. The **parahippocampal place area (PPA)** is activated by pictures indicating indoor and outdoor scenes like those shown in Figure 4.22a

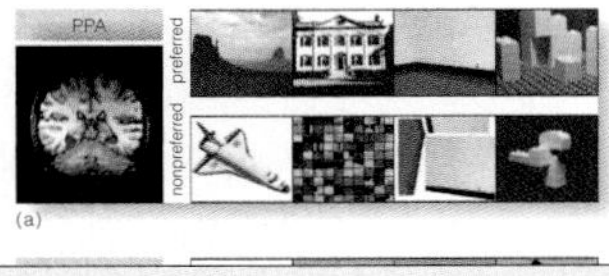

(Aguirre et al., 1998; R. Epstein et al., 1999; R. Epstein & Kanwisher, 1998). Apparently what is important for this area is information about spatial layout because increased activation occurs both to empty rooms and rooms that are completely furnished (Kanwisher, 2004). The other specialized area, the **extrastriate body area (EBA)**, is activated by pictures of bodies and parts of bodies (but not by faces), as shown in Figure 4.22b (Downing et al., 2001).

EVOLUTION AND PLASTICITY: HOW DO NEURONS BECOME SPECIALIZED?

When researchers began describing neurons that were specialized to fire to specific stimuli, such as faces, places, and bodies, they naturally wondered how this specialization might have occurred. One possibility is that these neurons became specialized by a process of biological evolution, which causes people to be born with selective neurons. Another possibility is that these neurons became specialized by a process involving a person's experience as they perceived common objects in their environment.

Is Neural Selectivity Shaped by Evolution?

According to the **theory of natural selection**, genetically based characteristics that enhance an animal's ability to survive, and therefore reproduce, will be passed on to future generations. Thus, a person whose visual system contains neurons that fire to important things in the environment (like faces, for example) will be more likely to survive and pass on his or her characteristics than will a person whose visual system does not contain these specialized neurons. Through this evolutionary process, the visual system may have been shaped to contain neurons that respond to faces and other important perceptual information.

There is no question that evolution has shaped the functioning of the senses, just as it has shaped all of the other physical and mental characteristics that have en-

This best-selling author's meticulous review of research is apparent in his cutting-edge coverage of every topic. Goldstein has updated every chapter and every page of this edition. There are more than 200 references from 2000–2005, most of them new to this edition. He writes with clarity and impact, helping students appreciate the impressive advances that researchers have made toward understanding perception.

Effects of Attention on Perception

One possible way to measure the *perceptual response* to seeing a stimulus is shown in Figure 6.17a. An observer views two stimuli and is instructed to pay attention to one of them and decide whether it is brighter than the other, unattended, stimulus. The stimuli could be presented at different intensities from trial to trial, and the goal would be to determine whether observers report that the attended stimulus appears brighter on trials when the two stimuli have the same intensity.

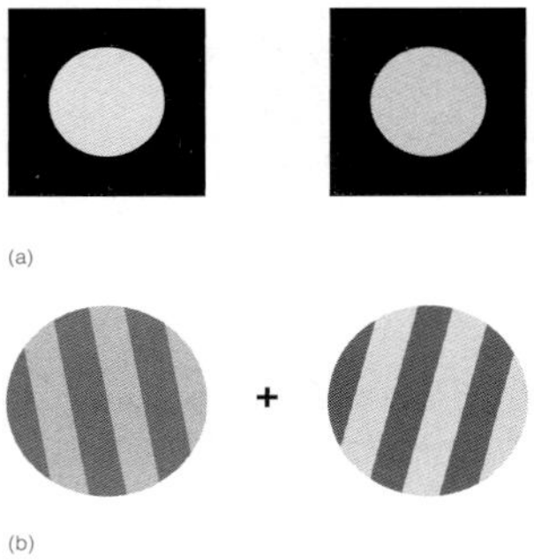

Figure 6.17 ▮ (a) Stimuli to measure how attention might affect perception. (b) Stimuli used by Carrasco et al. (2004).

This procedure is a step in the right direction because it focuses on what the observer is seeing rather than on how fast the observer can react to the stimulus. However, can we be sure that the observer is accurately reporting his or her perceptions? If the observer has a preconception that paying attention to a stimulus should make it stand out more, this might influence the observer to report that the attended stimulus appears brighter, when, in reality, the two stimuli may appear equally bright (Luck, 2004).

A recent study by Marissa Carrasco and coworkers (2004) has eliminated this possible source of bias by devising a clever procedure that avoids directly asking the observer to judge the object's appearance. Carrasco used grating stimuli with alternating light and dark bars, like the one in Figure 6.17b. She was interested in determining

port that the attended stimulus appears brighter, when, in reality, the two stimuli may appear equally bright (Luck, 2004).

A recent study by Marissa Carrasco and coworkers (2004) has eliminated this possible source of bias by devising a clever procedure that avoids directly asking the observer to judge the object's appearance. Carrasco used grating stimuli with alternating light and dark bars, like the one in Figure 6.17b. She was interested in determining

SOMETHING TO CONSIDER: ARE THERE GRANDMOTHER CELLS AFTER ALL?

Although the idea of a highly specific "grand
has generally not been accepted by researche
velopment has brought this idea back to li
Quiroga and coworkers (2005) recorded fro
the brains of eight patients with epilepsy. T
had electrodes implanted in their hippocar
precisely localize where their seizures origin
aration for surgery (Figure 4.29a).

Patients saw a number of different view
individuals and objects plus random pictu
things, such as faces, buildings, and animals.
ingly, a number of neurons responded to s
stimuli. What was surprising, however, w
neurons responded to a number of different
one person or building. For example, on
sponded to all pictures of the actress Jenn

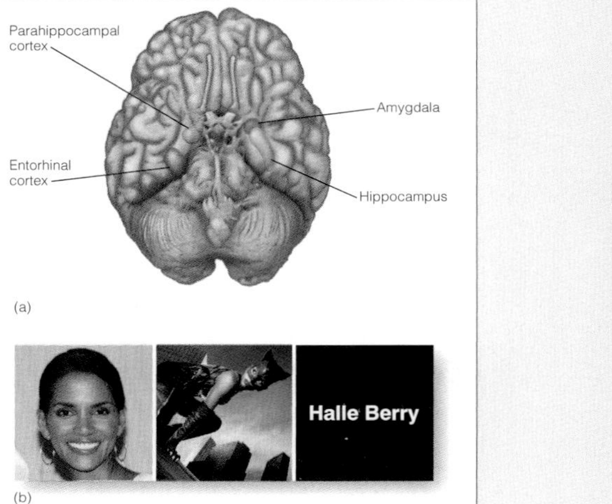

Figure 4.29 ▮ (a) Location of the hippocampus and some of the other structures that were studied by Quiroga and coworkers (2005); (b) Some of the stimuli that caused a neuron in the hippocampus to fire.
(Left photo: © Evan Agostini/Getty Images; Right photo: © Doane Gregory/Warner Bros./Bureau L.A. Collections/CORBIS)

This edition intrigues students with late-breaking research, such as this fascinating 2005 study that reopens the question of whether "grandmother cells" exist.

A streamlined book that engages students with the latest research

CHAPTER 6

VISUAL ATTENTION

Chapter Contents

ATTENTION AND PERCEIVING THE ENVIRONMENT
Why Is Selective Attention Necessary?
How Is Selective Attention Achieved?
Scanning a Scene

IS ATTENTION NECESSARY
When Can Perception Occur
When Is Attention Necessary
Demonstration: Change

TEST YOURSELF 6.1

DOES ATTENTION ENHAN
Effects of Attention on Inform
Effects of Attention on Percep

ATTENTION AND EXPERIEN
Why Is Binding Necessary?
Feature Integration Theory
Method: Searching for C
The Physiological Approach t

THE PHYSIOLOGY OF ATTENTION

SOMETHING TO CONSIDER: DO NEURONS NOTICE STIMULI?

TEST YOURSELF 6.2

This photo of PNC Park show progress and the city in the dots and red lines indicate e one person looked in the firs picture. The eye-movement r directed attention to the ball looked somewhere else, dep what attracted his or her att (Eye movement record courtesy

Scanning a Scene

The first task in the study of eye movements is to devise a way to measure them. Early researchers measured eye movements using devices such as small mirrors and lenses that were attached to the eyes, so the cornea had to be anesthetized (Yarbus, 1967). However, modern researchers use camera-based eye trackers, like the one in Figure 6.3, that track the position of the eye without attaching anything to the eye (Henderson, 2003; Morimoto & Mimica, 2005).

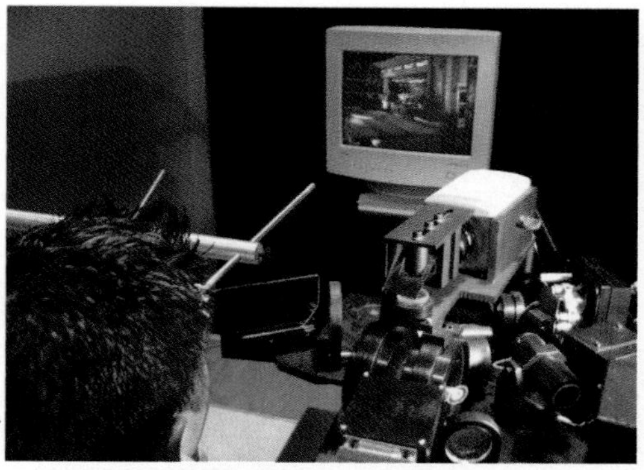
Dan Gajewski

A brand-new Chapter 6, "Visual Attention"

This completely new chapter reflects the importance of attentional processes in perception with new material on eye movement, how attention can enhance perception, and the role of attention in binding.

SOMETHING TO CONSIDER: THE INTELLIGENCE OF HUMAN OBJECT PERCEPTION

We are now ready to consider why humans are so much more successful than computers at solving the problem of object perception. If we were to answer the question

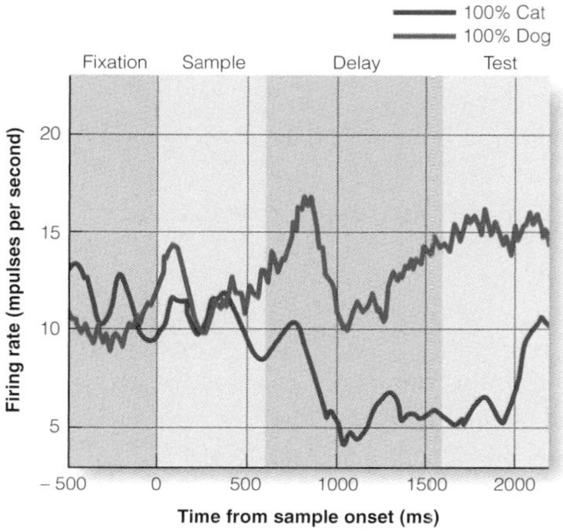

(b) PF neuron

CHAPTER 16

PERCEPTUAL DEVELOPMENT

Chapter Contents

BASIC VISUAL CAPACITIES
Visual Acuity
Methods: Preferential Looking and Visual Evoked Potential
Contrast Sensitivity
Perceiving Color
Method: Habituation
Perceiving Depth

PERCEIVING FACES
Recognizing Their Mother's Face
Is There a Special Mechanism for Perceiving Faces?

TEST YOURSELF 16.1

PERCEIVING OBJECT UNITY

HEARING
Threshold for Hearing a Tone
Recognizing Their Mother's Voice

PERCEIVING SPEECH
The Categorical Perception of Phonemes
Experience and Speech Perception

INTERMODAL PERCEPTION

OLFACTION AND TASTE

SOMETHING TO CONSIDER: THE UNITY OF PERCEPTION
Method: Paired Comparison

TEST YOURSELF 16.2

THINK ABOUT IT

IF YOU WANT TO KNOW MORE

KEY TERMS

VISIT YOUR COMPANION WEBSITE FOR THIS BOOK

Caption to come?

351

Cognitive material increased throughout

The Seventh Edition focuses greater attention on cognition, reflecting the field's current interest in cognitive processes. Examples of cognitive topics in this edition include:

- **Chapter 5:** the Gestalt laws as heuristics; the intelligence of object perception
- **Chapter 6:** attention and perceiving the environment; the effect of attention on information processing
- **Chapter 8:** how distance perception can be influenced by cognition
- **Chapter 9:** motion perception and experience; implied motion
- **Chapter 13:** cognitive dimensions of speech perception
- **Chapter 14:** cognitive and experiential aspects of pain perception
- **Chapter 16:** intermodal perception in infants

WebTUTOR™ Advantage

PERCEPTION Psychology Now™

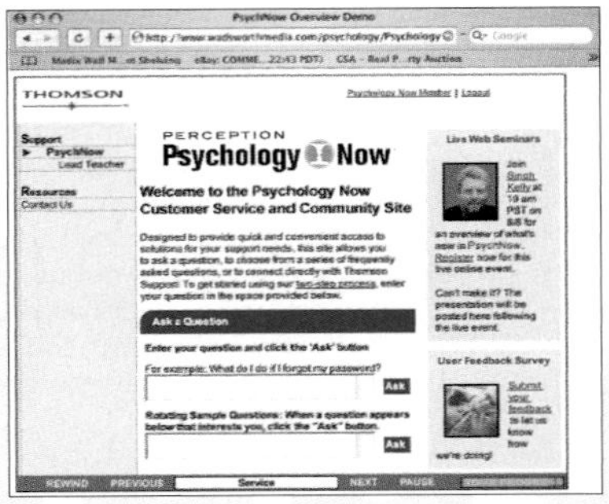

Choose from 3 GREAT WAYS to link this book to Virtual Labs and other media!

Online and CD-ROM integration

1 Perception PsychologyNow™

PERCEPTION Psychology Now™

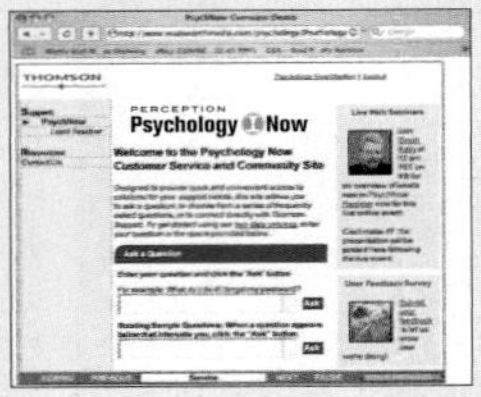

Including all elements from the Virtual Labs, this powerful, easy-to-use tool is correlated chapter-by-chapter with Goldstein's text. A powerful, assignable online learning companion, Perception PsychologyNow assesses each student's study needs through diagnostic tests and builds focused *Personalized Study Plans.* A great timesaver for students *and* instructors! As soon as students log on, the system's simple, browser-based format is evident—as easy as surfing the web:

- **The Pre-Test** is a diagnostic quiz that helps students test their understanding of the chapter they've just read.
- **The Personalized Study Plan** is based on results of the *Pre-Test.* It outlines those topics that require review—guiding students to the program's Virtual Labs, which include animations, experiments, demonstrations, and videos.
- **The Post-Test** ensures that students have mastered the concepts in each chapter. Perception PsychologyNow also includes an Instructor Grade Book, which assists instructors in tracking grades and monitoring student progress.

2 Virtual Lab CD-ROM with Manual

For the first time accompanied by its own manual, the Virtual Lab CD-ROM for *Sensation and Perception* is designed to help students get the most out of your course.

The CD-ROM's more than 170 modules include:

- Goldstein Media interactions, including drag-and-drop animations, experiments, and interactive exercises that illustrate principles in this book, as well as auditory demonstrations, which are newly updated.
- Insight™ Media labs and demonstrations, utilizing John Baro's Insight Media Lab experiments and demonstrations. Designed so students practice gathering data, varying many parameters to determine how changes to parameters affect perception, and analyzing the results.
- New! Seven demonstration videos from NASA, including topics like biological motion, convergence, motion parallax, and stereo vision.

The Virtual Lab Manual includes worksheets for the Virtual Lab experiments. The perforated pages can be torn out and submitted to the instructor as homework assignments.

3 WebTutor™ Advantage on WebCT® and Blackboard®

Ready to use as soon as you log on, this complete course management system and communication tool is pre-loaded text-specific content, including extensive quizzing with full-rejoinders, learning objectives, detailed chapter outlines, chapter summaries, glossary, flashcards, and weblinks. WebTutor Advantage also includes all elements from the Virtual Lab CD-ROM (with corresponding worksheets from the Virtual Lab Manual) plus additional interactive modules. *Authored by Deborah Briihl of Valdosta State University.*

Also available:

The robust Book Companion Website
http://psychology.wadsworth.com/goldstein7e/
Correlated with every textbook chapter. Includes audio flashcards, tutorial quizzes, weblinks to informative sites offering more information on chapter topics, and a glossary.

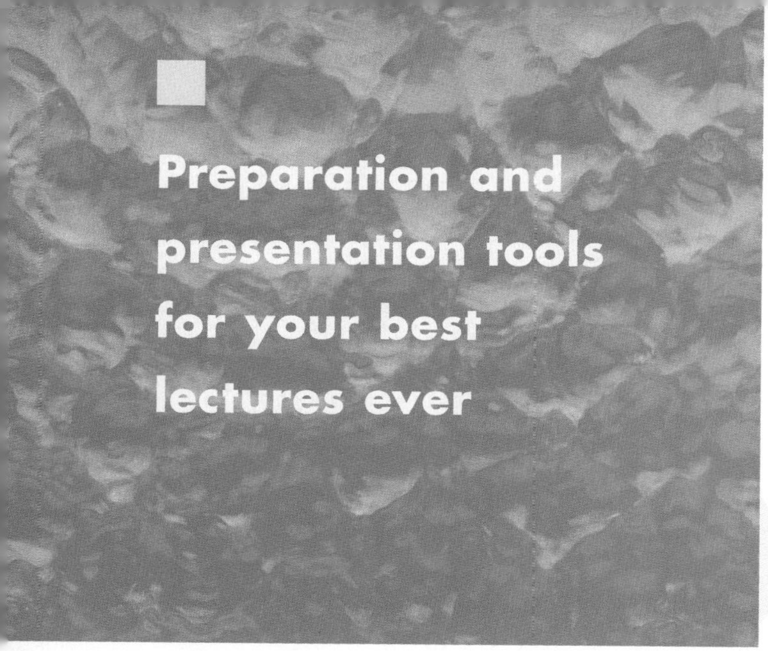

Multimedia Manager Instructor's Resource CD-ROM A Microsoft® PowerPoint® Tool

0-495-03138-0

With this one-stop digital library and presentation tool, you can assemble, edit, and present custom lectures with ease. Multimedia Manager contains preassembled PowerPoint lecture slides for each chapter in Goldstein's text—with all available art integrated into the PowerPoint outlines, authored by Terri Bonebright of DePauw University. Also included are animations and NASA videos. You can use the material as is or add your own material for a truly customized lecture presentation in the classroom or online for student reference and distance learning. Microsoft® Word® files of the *Instructor's Manual with Test Bank* (which contains the Resource Integration Guide) are also included. *Please consult your local representative for details.*

JoinIn™ on TurningPoint®

for Goldstein's *Sensation and Perception,* Seventh Edition

0-495-18751-8

Transform any lecture into an interactive experience for students with JoinIn on TurningPoint software—offering book-specific content created especially for use with personal response systems. Combined with your choice of several leading keypad systems, JoinIn turns an ordinary PowerPoint application into powerful audience response software. With just a click on a handheld device, your students can respond to multiple-choice questions, short polls, interactive exercises and peer review questions. You can take attendance, collect student demographics to better assess student needs, and even administer quizzes without collecting paper or grading. Please consult your local sales representative for details or visit **http://turningpoint.thomsonlearningconnections.com**

Instructor's Manual with Test Bank

Comprehensive— includes the Resource Integration Guide

0-495-03136-4

by Stephen Wurst, SUNY at Oswego.

Completely updated for the Seventh Edition of Goldstein's text, the manual contains the following ***for each text chapter:***

- A detailed chapter outline
- Learning objectives
- A general overview/summary of the chapter
- Virtual Lab integration
- Demonstrations, activities, and lecture topics
- Topic-related weblinks
- Integration of mainstream movie clips

The extensive section of *Test Bank* questions includes the following ***for each chapter:***

- Thirty-five to sixty multiple-choice questions— with correct answers, page references, and question type
- Five to ten essay questions

Also included is the Resource Integration Guide, which is organized by chapter to help you integrate any or all of your student and instructor ancillaries into your course.

ExamView®

Computerized testing with online capabilities

Microsoft® Windows®/Macintosh®:

0-495-03137-2

Contains all Test Bank questions electronically. Helps you create and customize tests in minutes! You can easily edit and import your own questions and graphics, edit and maneuver existing questions, and change test layouts. Tests appear on screen just as they will when printed. ExamView offers flexible delivery and the ability to test and grade online.

Due to contractual reasons, certain ancillaries are available only in higher education or U.S. domestic markets. Minimum purchases may apply to receive the ancillaries at no charge. For more information, please contact your local Thomson Wadsworth sales representative.

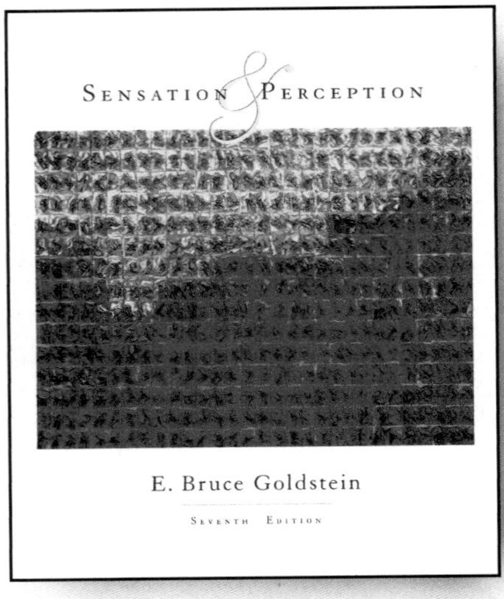

Custom publishing made easy— your course, your needs, your personalized solutions

Your course, your way!

As you consider the Seventh Edition of Goldstein's *Sensation and Perception*, keep in mind that **Thomson Custom Publishing** can help create personalized learning solutions for instructors like you—no matter what your course needs may be. There are times when your teaching needs are not fulfilled by a traditional text alone; and that is where custom publishing can help. With custom publishing, you can teach sensation and perception your way.

http://www.textchoice.com brings textbook customization to your desktop.

TextChoice®, Thomson Custom Publishing's digital library, provides the fastest, easiest way for you to create your own learning materials. You may easily preview and select content from this as well as hundreds of other best-selling titles, choose material from one of our databases, and add your own material. Getting exactly what you want has never been so easy.

Experience the advantages

- Database of content includes materials suitable for virtually every course
- Chapters can be mixed and matched from multiple titles
- Automatic repagination and indexing
- Instant, printable Table of Contents
- Online viewing, page by page, within minutes
- Your original material can be incorporated

You can add your own material—course notes, supplements, lecture outlines, articles, study guides, problems, exercises, out-of-print books, and more—at the beginning or end of any chapter. **TextChoice** can insert blank pages wherever you wish to place your content, then your Thomson representative will collect the material from you. It's that easy.

Start today at http://www.textchoice.com

SENSATION AND PERCEPTION

SEVENTH EDITION

E. Bruce Goldstein
University of Pittsburgh

THOMSON
WADSWORTH

Australia • Brazil • Canada • Mexico • Singapore
Spain • United Kingdom • United States

THOMSON
WADSWORTH

Sensation and Perception, **Seventh Edition**
E. Bruce Goldstein

Publisher: *Vicki Knight*
Acquisitions Editor: *Marianne Taflinger*
Development Editor: *Kate R. Barnes*
Assistant Editor: *Jennifer Keever*
Editorial Assistant: *Lucy Faridany*
Technology Project Manager: *Darin Derstine*
Marketing Manager: *Raghu Reddy*
Marketing Assistant: *Natasha Coats*
Marketing Communications Manager: *Kelley McAllister*
Project Manager, Editorial Production: *Lori Johnson*
Creative Director: *Rob Hugel*
Art Director: *Vernon Boes*
Print Buyer: *Doreen Suruki*
Permissions Editor: *Kiely Sisk*
Production Service: *Nancy L. Shammas, New Leaf Publishing Services*
Text Designer: *Tani Hasegawa*
Art Editor: *Lisa Torri*
Photo Researcher: *Sabina Dowell*
Copy Editor: *Mary Anne Shahidi*
Illustrator: *Precision Graphics*
Cover Designer: *Cheryl Carrington*
Cover Image: *Photo by Petronella Ytsma of original artwork by Tim Harding, "Oro y Rojo"*
Text and Cover Printer: *Transcontinental Printing/Interglobe*
Compositor: *G&S Book Services*

Printed in Canada
1 2 3 4 5 6 7 10 09 08 07 06

Library of Congress Control Number: 2005936745

ISBN 0-534-55810-0

Thomson Higher Education
10 Davis Drive
Belmont, CA 94002-3098
USA

For Barbara

ABOUT THE AUTHOR

E. Bruce Goldstein is a member of the Department of Psychology at the University of Pittsburgh and is Adjunct Professor of Psychology at the University of Arizona. He has received the Chancellor's Distinguished Teaching Award for his classroom teaching and textbook writing. He received his Bachelor's degree in chemical engineering from Tufts University, his PhD in experimental psychology from Brown University, and he was a post-doctoral fellow in the Biology Department at Harvard University before joining the faculty at the University of Pittsburgh. Bruce has published papers on a wide variety of topics, including retinal and cortical physiology, visual attention, and the perception of pictures. He is the author of *Cognitive Psychology* (Wadsworth, 2005) and the editor of the *Blackwell Handbook of Perception* (Blackwell, 2001) and the forthcoming *Encyclopedia of Perception* (Sage). He currently teaches undergraduate courses in cognitive psychology, sensation and perception, introductory psychology, and the psychology of visual art, as well as a graduate seminar on the teaching of psychology.

BRIEF CONTENTS

CONTENTS

INTRODUCTION TO PERCEPTION 3

INTRODUCTION TO THE PHYSIOLOGY OF PERCEPTION 21

3

NEURONS AND PERCEPTION 45

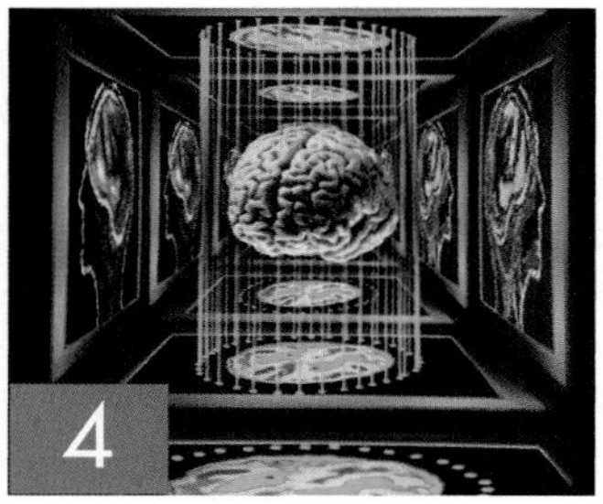

4

THE ORGANIZED BRAIN 71

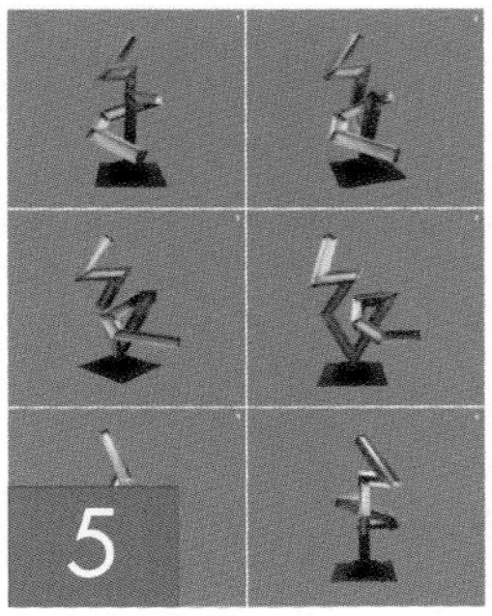

5

PERCEIVING OBJECTS 93

6

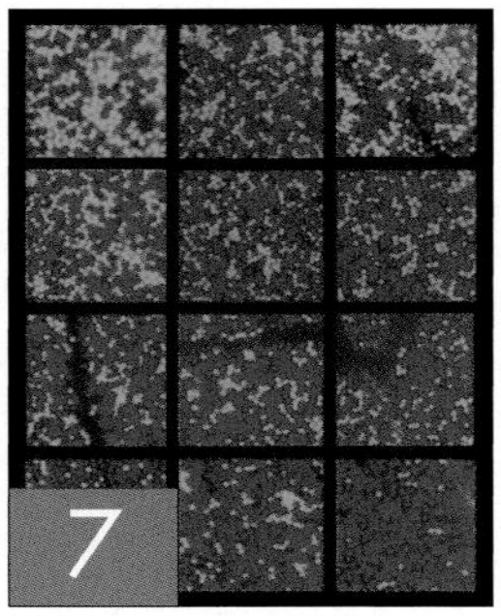
7

PERCEIVING DEPTH AND SIZE 167

PERCEIVING MOVEMENT 195

PERCEPTION AND ACTION 215

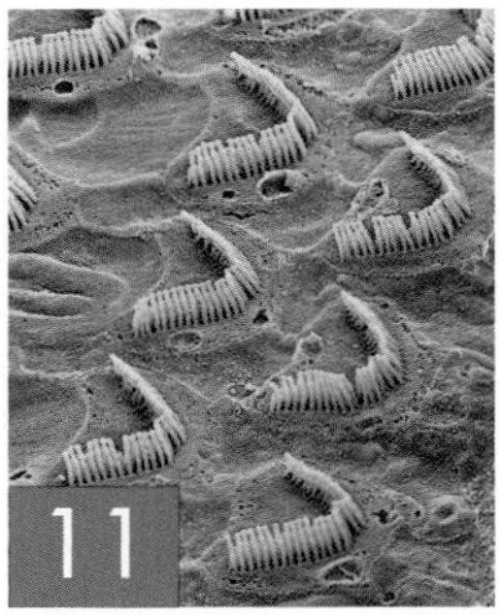

SOUND, THE AUDITORY SYSTEM, AND PITCH PERCEPTION 233

12

SOUND LOCALIZATION AND THE AUDITORY SCENE 265

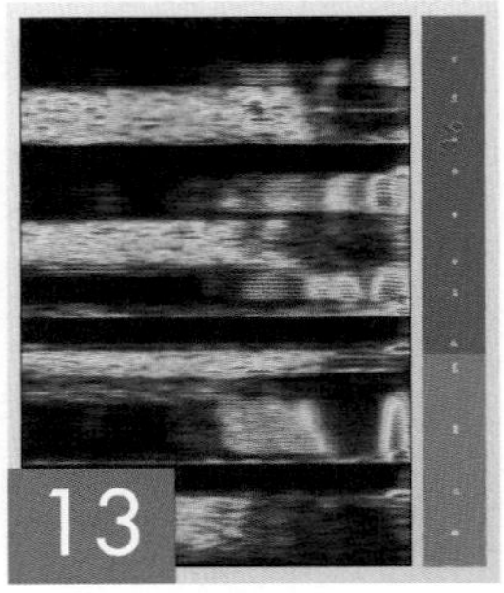

13

SPEECH PERCEPTION 285

14

THE CUTANEOUS SENSES 303

15

THE CHEMICAL SENSES 327

16

PERCEPTUAL DEVELOPMENT 351

Appendix
SIGNAL DETECTION: PROCEDURE AND THEORY 373

VIRTUAL LAB CONTENTS

Chapter 5

Chapter 6

Chapter 7

Chapter 8

Chapter 9

DEMONSTRATIONS

PREFACE

When I first began working on this book, Hubel and Wiesel were mapping orientation columns in the striate cortex and were five years away from receiving their Nobel Prize; Amoore's stereochemical theory, based largely on psychophysical evidence, was a prominent explanation for odor recognition; and one of the hottest new discoveries in perception was that the response properties of neurons could be influenced by experience. Today, specialized areas in the human brain have been mapped using brain imaging, olfactory receptors have been revealed using genetic methods, and the idea that the perceptual system is tuned to regularities in the environment is now supported by a wealth of both behavioral and physiological research.

But some things haven't changed. Teachers still stand in front of classrooms to teach students about perception, and students still read textbooks that reinforce what is being discussed in the classroom. Another thing that hasn't changed is that teachers prefer texts that are easy for students to read, that present both classic studies and up-to-date research, and that present both the facts of perception and overarching themes and principles.

When I began teaching perception, I felt that such a textbook did not exist. That is why I decided to write this one, and why I have continued to revise it over the years. My goal for each revision has been to create the "best text ever," and I hope you will agree that this edition accomplishes that goal. My goal in this preface is to tell you about some of the things that are new to this edition.

Telling the Story of Perception

In writing *Sensation and Perception,* I have tried to follow the advice I give to the graduate students in my Teaching of Psychology seminar. I tell them that the first step in putting together a lecture is to create a story. I focus on the story aspect of lecturing because one property of good stories is narrative flow—one idea flows from another to create a plot that engages the reader. Thinking in terms of narrative flow when creating a lecture or writing a textbook can go a long way toward ensuring that explanations are clear, that the transitions from one idea to the next make sense, and that a bigger picture emerges from the string of ideas. Here are some of the changes in this edition that have been made to enhance the way the story of perception is told.

- *Improved Organization:* The organization of material within every chapter has been evaluated with an eye toward improving clarity of presentation. An example of one outcome of this evaluation is shown in the following table, which compares the organization of Chapters 2–4 in the 6th and 7th Editions. In the 6th Edition this sequence of chapters was organized by following the visual pathway from retina to extrastriate cortex; in the 7th Edition, these chapters still retain some of the retina-to-higher-level sequence, but are organized more in terms of function. The result is a smoother flow because basic principles such as retinotopic mapping and parallel processing streams, which hold at different levels of the visual system, are now described together.

	6th Edition	7th Edition
Chapter 2	Receptors and Neural Processing	Introduction to the Physiology of Perception
Chapter 3	The Lateral Geniculate Nucleus and Striate Cortex	Neurons and Perception
Chapter 4	Higher-Level Visual Processing	The Organized Brain

- *Streamlining the Book:* In approaching this edition, I realized that the book had grown in length over time from one edition to the next. Since teachers don't have more weeks in a term, and students have no more time to devote to their studies than they ever did, I focused my energies on making the book leaner and tighter. The result is a book that has smaller, more student-friendly units but that still covers both basic principles and the latest developments.

- *Integrating Boxed Material Into the Text:* In the 6th Edition, material in the following three areas was included in boxes: (1) brain imaging (*Brain Scan*); (2) experience-dependent plasticity (*Plasticity of Perception*); and (3) multi-modal perception and similarities across the senses (*Across the Senses*). These boxes have been eliminated to help reduce length and improve flow, but much of this material, as well as new developments in these areas, has been integrated into the text.

Embellishing the Story

The other advice I give my students in the teaching seminar is that once they have created the story, they should *embellish* it. What this means for a classroom lecture is adding active learning experiences, real-life examples to illustrate concepts, demonstrations and films to create "changes of pace," and material on the *how* and *why* of psychology to ensure that the lecture isn't just a series of facts. Just as these extras help improve a lecture, they are also important in a textbook. Here are a few of the features that help embellish the story in this text:

- ***Demonstrations:*** Demonstrations have been a popular feature of this book for many editions. They are integrated into the flow of the text and are easy enough so they can be carried out with little trouble, thereby maximizing the probability that students will do them. This edition contains most of the old demonstrations plus a few new ones.

- ***Methods:*** It is important not only to present the facts of perception, but to also make students aware of how these facts were obtained. Methods have always been described in *Sensation and Perception,* but in this edition they are introduced in a highlighted *Methods* section. These highlighted sections, which are integrated into the ongoing discussion, emphasize the importance of methods, and the highlighting makes it easier to refer back to them when referenced later in the book.

- ***Something to Consider:*** This new end-of-chapter feature offers the opportunity to consider an especially interesting new finding (for example, Chapter 4: *Are There Grandmother Cells After All?*), wrap up an argument (Chapter 5: *The Intelligence of Perception*), or highlight a practical application (Chapter 11: *Cochlear Implants: Where Science and Culture Meet*).

- ***Test Yourself:*** End-of-chapter study questions have long been a feature of this book. But in keeping with the less-is-more philosophy of this edition, fewer, more general questions are now placed in *Test Yourself* sections that are located in the middle and at the end of each chapter. Fewer questions reduces students' "overwhelm" factor and require that students unpack these questions themselves, thereby making them more active participants in their studying.

- ***Think About It:*** A new *Think About It* section at the end of each chapter poses questions that require students to apply what they have learned and that takes them beyond the material in the chapter.

- ***If You Want to Know More:*** A new section, *If You Want to Know More,* appears at the end of each chapter. This section invites students to look into topics that were not covered in the chapter. A specific finding is described and key references are presented to provide a starting point for further research. In some cases, material that was eliminated from the 6th Edition is referenced in this section.

- ***Virtual Lab:*** The *Virtual Lab* feature of this book enables students to view demonstrations and become participants in mini-experiments. There are now over 170 Virtual Lab exercises, animations, and demonstrations. Each item is indicated in the chapter by this numbered icon: VL Using this system, students can access their Virtual Lab through a number of forms: the CD-ROM, Perception PsychologyNow, or WebTutor resource at http:now.ilrn.com/goldstein_7e.

- ***Full-Color Illustrations:*** Perception, of all subjects, should be illustrated in color, and after six editions of black and white color has finally arrived! What pleases me about the illustrations is not only how beautiful the color looks, but how well it serves pedagogy. The 485 figures in this edition include photographs, which use color to illustrate perception in real-world contexts; graphs and diagrams, which use color-coding to help students understand what the data mean; anatomical diagrams, which use color to highlight key structures; and the results of brain-imaging experiments, which use color to indicate the locations and magnitudes of neural activation.

If you have used this book before, you will notice that the final chapter of the 6th Edition, *Clinical Aspects of Vision and Hearing,* is no longer in the book. This chapter, which had to be eliminated to make room for other material, such as the new chapter on visual attention, described how vision and hearing can become impaired, what happens during eye and ear examinations, and some of the medical procedures that have been used to deal with these problems. This chapter is posted on the book's website at http://psychology.wadsworth.com/goldstein7e.

Updating the Research

In addition to the many new features designed to increase "teachability," this edition also contains a wealth of new material reflecting research that has been published since the last edition, as well as some earlier research. Here are a few of these new additions, listed in the order they appear in each chapter:

Chapter 3: Neurons and Perception

Neurons that respond to objects such as houses (Kreiman et al., 2000)

Chapter 4: The Organized Brain

Brain imaging and the magnification factor in humans (Dougherty et al., 2003)

Connection between cortical area and acuity (Duncun & Boynton, 2003)

Behavioral demonstration of action stream (Dyde & Milner, 2002)

Brain activation by implied faces (Cox et al., 2004)

Place and body areas in the brain (Downing et al., 2001; Kanwisher, 2004)

Distributed activation of cortex (Ishai et al., 2001; Tanaka, 2004; Tsunoda et al., 2001)

"Halle Berry" neuron in the hippocampus (Quiroga et al., 2005)

Chapter 5: Perceiving Objects

Lower region and figure–ground perception (Vecera et al., 2002)

Border ownership and figure–ground perception (Baylis & Dirver, 2001)

Perception and regularities in the environment (Furmananski & Engel, 2000; Coppela et al., 1998)

Object recognition and brain activity (Grill-Spector et al., 2004)

Brain responses to categorization (Freeman et al., 2003)

Chapter 6: Visual Attention

Basic characteristics of eye movements (Henderson, 2003)

Saliency and attention (Parkhurst et al., 2002)

Task-based scanning (Land & Hayhoe, 2001)

The effect of attention on perceived contrast (Carasco et al., 2004)

Neural firing to objects during free viewing (Sheinberg & Logothetis, 2001)

Chapter 7: Perceiving Color

Lightness perception and perceptual organization (Anderson & Winawer, 2005)

Chapter 8: Perceiving Size and Depth

Neurons that respond to pictorial depth (Tsutsui et al., 2002, 2005)

Disparity-tuning curves (Uka & DeAngelis, 2003)

Microstimulation and depth perception (Cohen & Newsome, 2004)

The effect of perceived effort on distance perception (Proffit et al., 2003; Witt et al., 2004)

Chapter 9: Perceiving Movement

Real movement neurons (Galetti & Fattorie, 2003)

The aperture problem (Pack & Born, 2001)

Biological motion update (Grossman & Blake, 2001)

Inferred motion (Kourtzi & Kanwisher, 2000)

Representational momentum (David & Senior, 2000; Freyd, 1983; Reed & Vinson, 1996)

Brain activation to implied motion (Kourtzi & Kanwisher, 2000)

Chapter 10: Perception and Action

Microstimulation and optic flow (Britten and van Wezel, 2002)

Brain activation and navigation (Maguire et al., 1998; Janzen & van Turenout, 2004)

How dogs catch Frisbees (Shaffer et al., 2004)

How optic ataxia affects reaching behavior (Schindler et al., 2004)

Audio-visual mirror neurons (Kohler et al., 2002)

Brain activity elicited by watching a Clint Eastwood movie (Hasson et al., 2002)

Chapter 11: Sound, the Auditory System, and Pitch Perception

What and where streams for hearing (Alain et al., 2001; Clarke et al., 2001)

Role of auditory cortex in pitch perception (Tramo et al., 2002)

Effect of training on tuning of auditory neurons (Fritz et al., 2003)

Chapter 12: Localization and the Auditory Scene

Binaural cues, virtual auditory space (Wightman & Kistler, 1992, 1998)

Effect of ear molds on pinnae cues for localization (Hoffman et al., 1998)

How visual movement can affect the perception of auditory localization (Soto-Faraco et al., 2004)

How sound can affect vision (Sekuler et al., 1997)

Chapter 13: Perceiving Speech

Cues and speech segmentation (Sanders & Neville, 2000)

What and where streams and speech perception (Scott & Johnsrude, 2003)

Physiological evidence for experience-dependent plasticity (Rivera-Gaxiola et al., 2005)

Audio-visual mirror neurons and motor theory (Kohler et al., 2002)

Linking perception and production (Watkins et al., 2003)

Chapter 14: The Cutaneous Senses

Methods for measuring tactile acuity (Cholewaik & Collins, 2003)

The duplex theory of texture perception (Hollins et al., 2001, 2002)

Perceiving texture with a tool (Klatzky et al., 2003)

Different types of pain (Scholz & Woolf, 2002)

Where the unpleasantness of pain is represented in the brain (Hoffauer et al., 2001; Rainville, 2002)

Chapter 15: The Chemical Senses

Methods for measuring thresholds (Dalton, 2002)

Genetic techniques for identifying olfactory receptors (Buck, 2004)

Olfactory bulb activation by odorants (Linster et al., 2001; Uchida et al., 2000)

Piriform cortex activation by odorants (Zou et al., 2001)

Genetic techniques for identifying taste receptors (Mueller et al., 2005; Zou et al., 2003)

Is taste coding specific or distributed? (Smith & Scott, 2003)

Individual differences in taste sensitivity (Bufe et al., 2005; Delwiche et al., 2001)

Chapter 16: Perceptual Development

Is there a special mechanism for face recognition? (Farah et al., 2000)

Newborn preference for the mother's face (Bushnell, 2001; Turati et al., 2002; Sai, 2005)

Infant perception of object unity (Johnson et al., 2004)

Plasticity of face perception during the first year (Pascalis et al., 2002)

ACKNOWLEDGMENTS

It is a pleasure to acknowledge the following people who worked tirelessly to turn my manuscript into an actual book! Without these people, this book would not exist, and I am grateful to all of them.

- Marianne Taflinger, my editor, for her commitment to this book and especially for her guidance regarding the extensive changes that were made in this edition. This included making the full-color illustration program possible, suggesting ways to streamline the book to make it both more affordable and more effective for student-learning, obtaining extensive reviews for every chapter, and developing the Virtual Lab program. I thank Marianne for her efforts in all of these areas, plus her unstinting support of my textbooks over many years.
- Kate Barnes, my developmental editor, who not only provided excellent suggestions on my presentation and writing, but also shepherded the book through the production process. I thank Kate for all of the things she did that I know about and also for the many "behind the scenes" things that I am unaware of. Her efforts contributed greatly to the quality of this book.
- Lucy Faridany, Marianne Taflinger's editorial assistant, who saw to it that requests for reviews went out and that I received them in a timely way. When I needed something and asked Lucy, I knew it was going to happen right away. Thanks, Lucy.
- Nancy Shammas, of New Leaf Publishing Service, who I communicated with on an almost daily basis during the production of this book. Nancy was in charge of much of the nuts-and-bolts process of turning my manuscript into a book. I especially thank her for all of the care she put into accomplishing this, for putting up with many of my concerns that came up along the way, and for her creative solutions, which helped keep me sane and created a better book.
- Lisa Torri, the book's art editor, who has worked on so many of my books, that I would feel at a loss without her. I thank Lisa for her humor, which often helped me get through some of the "things" that inevitably come up during the production process, for her artistic taste, and for her ability to know how to present illustrations for maximum teaching effectiveness.
- Mary Anne Shahidi for her expert (and fast!) copy editing.
- Lori Johnson, the editorial production project manager, who coordinated all of the elements of the book during production and made sure everything happened when it was supposed to so the book would get to the printer on time.
- Vernon Boes, art guru, who directed the design for the book. Thanks, Vernon, for helping create the great cover, and for having taste in art and design that pretty much matches mine.
- Thanks to Tani Hasegawa for the elegant design and to Cheryl Carrington for the striking cover.
- Jennifer Keever, the assistant editor in charge of the book's ancillaries, who created the great package that accompanies this book. When I heard that Jennifer was going to coordinate the ancillaries I knew they would be done right, because I have worked with her on other projects. Thanks again, Jennifer.
- Darin Derstine, technology project manager, whose great skill in producing and coordinating the com-

plex and technically demanding media program has resulted in the Virtual Lab feature that accompanies the book.

- Kiely Sisk, permissions editor, for obtaining the permissions.
- J. C. Morgan of Precision Graphics, who coordinated the creation of the graphs, diagrams, and drawings. The feat of creating this art program is all the more impressive, considering the sometimes hard-to-decipher sketches that I often provided.
- Stephen Wurst, SUNY Oswego, for creating the Instructor's Manual and Test Bank, and for keeping in touch with me along the way, both to ask questions and offer suggestions.
- Terri Bonebright, DePauw Univeristy, for creating the Multimedia Manager Instructor Resource CD-ROM.
- Deborah Briihl, Valdosta State University, for her work on WebTutor™ Advantage on WebCT® and on Blackboard®.
- Janet Proctor for creating the Virtual Lab Manual.
- David Kobus, San Diego State University, for creating the pre- and post-tests for Perception PsychologyNow.
- Nathan Fullerton and Tom Nuchels of the Apple Store in Pittsburgh (Shadyside) who expertly and patiently showed me how to use Adobe® Photoshop® to process a number of the book's photographs.

In addition to the help I received from all of the above people on the editorial and production side I also received a great deal of help from researchers and teachers. One of the things I have learned in my years of writing is that other people's advice is crucial. The field of perception is a broad one, and I rely heavily on the advice of experts in specific areas to alert me to emerging new research and to check my writing for accuracy. Equally important are all of the teachers of perception, who rely on textbooks in their courses. They have read groups of chapters (and in a few cases, the whole book), with an eye both to accuracy of the material and pedagogy. I owe a great debt of thanks to this group of reviewers for their advice about how to present the material to their students. The following is a list of those who provided expert and teaching advice on this edition of the book.

Rhianon Allen
Long Island University

Ira Bernstein
University of Texas, Arlington

Erik Blaser
University of Massachusetts

Susan Borsky
University of North Florida

Paul Breslin
Monell Chemical Senses Center

Bruce Bridgeman
University of California, Santa Cruz

Kenneth Carter
University of Southern Indiana

Ellen Covey
University of Washington

Massimiliano Di Luca
Brown University

Joan DiGiovanni
University of Arizona

Velma Dobson
University of Arizona

Marion Frank
University of Connecticut Health Center

Melvyn Goodale
University of Western Ontario

Peter Gerhardstein
Binghampton University

Jane Gwiazda
New England College of Optometry

Randy Hammond
University of Georgia

John Henderson
Michigan State University

Mark Hollins
University of North Carolina

Mark Huebener
Max Planck Institute, Germany

Kenneth Johnson
Johns Hopkins University

Scott Johnson
New York University

J Scott Jordan
Illinois State University

Donald Katz
Brandeis University

Roberta Klatzky
Carnegie Mellon University

Timothy Klitz
Washington and Jefferson College

Michael Landy
New York University

Lou Lianggang
Grand Valley State University

Kristen Macuga
Univeristy of California, Santa Barbara

Mortimer Mishkin
National Institutes of Health

Donald Mitchell
Dalhousie University

Eriko Miyahara
California State University, Fullerton

Ken Nakayama
Harvard University

John Neuhoff
College of Wooster

Crystal Oberle
Arizona State University

Elizabeth Olds
Wilfrid Laurier University

Mary Peterson
University of Arizona

Jeannin Pinto
Lafayette College

Thomas Sanocki
University of South Florida

Harvey Schiffman
Rutgers University

William Schmidt
SUNY, Buffalo

Robert Shaw
University of Connecticut

David Smith
University of Tennessee

John Sparrow
University of New Hampshire, Manchester

Steven Specht
Utica College

Theron Stimmel
Texas State University

Kenneth Tangen
University of California, Irvine

Michael Tarr
Brown University

Shaun Veccera
University of Iowa

Jeffrey Wagman
Illinois State University

Robert Weathersby
Eastern University

Catherine Weir
The Colorado College

Fred Wightman
Univerisity of Louisville

Teresa Wilcox
Texas A & M University

William Yost
Loyola University of Chicago

I am also grateful to the following people who kindly provided photographs, brain scan results, and other materials that have greatly enhanced the presentation of the results of research throughout the book.

Claude Alain
University of Toronto

Stuart Anstis
University of California, San Diego

Stephanie Clarke
CHUV, Switzerland

Robert Dougherty
Stanford University

David Freedman
Massachusetts Institute of Technology

Jonathan Fritz
University of Maryland

W. D. Gates
Lawrence, Kansas

Kalanit Grill-Spector
Stanford University

Uri Hasson
Weizmann Institute, Israel

John Henderson
Michigan State University

Alumit Ishai
National Institutes of Health

Gabriele Janzen
Max Plank Institute, Nijmegen, The Netherlands

Nancy Kanwisher
Massachusetts Institute of Technology

Zoe Kourtzi
Massachusetts Institute of Technology

Daniel Levin
Vanderbilt University

Christiane Linster
Cornell University

Thomas Macaulay
Kent State University

Eleanor Maguire
University College London

Anthony Movshon
New York University

Ernst Neibur
Johns Hopkins University

Olivier Pascalis
University of Sheffield, UK

David Pisoni
Indiana University

David Sheinberg
Brown University

Maggie Shiffrar
Rutgers University

Daniel Simons
University of Illinois

Pawan Sinha
Massachusetts Institute of Technology

Evan Tahler & the Red Team
Carnegie-Mellon University

James Tanaka
Oberlin College

Manabu Tanifuji
Institute of Physical and Chemical Research
Saitama, Japan

Naoshige Uchida
Cold Spring Harbor Laboratory

Alex Wade
Smith Ketterwell Institute

Bilhenry Walker
Milwaukee, Wisconsin

David Williams
University of Rochester

Jonathan Winawer
Massachusetts Institute of Technology

TO THE OWNER OF THIS BOOK:

I hope that you have found *Sensation and Perception,* 7th Edition, useful. So that this book can be improved in a future edition, would you take the time to complete this sheet and return it? Thank you.

School and address: ______________________________

____

Department: ______________________________

Instructor's name: ______________________________

1. What I like most about this book is: ______________________________

____

____

2. What I like least about this book is: ______________________________

____

____

3. My general reaction to this book is: ______________________________

____

____

4. The name of the course in which I used this book is: ______________________________

____

5. Were all of the chapters of the book assigned for you to read? ______________________________

   If not, which ones weren't? ______________________________

6. In the space below, or on a separate sheet of paper, please write specific suggestions for improving this book and anything else you'd care to share about your experience in using this book.

____

____

____

____

____

____

____

TAPE HERE.
DO NOT STAPLE.

TAPE HERE.
DO NOT STAPLE.

FOLD HERE

THOMSON ™
WADSWORTH

NO POSTAGE
NECESSARY
IF MAILED
IN THE
UNITED STATES

BUSINESS REPLY MAIL
FIRST-CLASS MAIL PERMIT NO. 102 MONTEREY CA

POSTAGE WILL BE PAID BY ADDRESSEE

Attn: Marianne Taflinger, Psychology

Wadsworth / Thomson Learning
60 Garden Ct Ste 205
Monterey CA 93940-9967

FOLD HERE

OPTIONAL:

Your name: ______________________ Date: ______________

May we quote you, either in promotion for *Sensation and Perception,* 7th Edition, or in future publishing ventures?

Yes: __________ No: __________

Sincerely yours,

E. Bruce Goldstein

SENSATION AND PERCEPTION

SEVENTH EDITION

EXIT
CASUAL CORNER
PETITE SOPHISTICATE

CHAPTER 1

INTRODUCTION TO PERCEPTION

Chapter Contents

Why do we perceive this picture as a three-dimensional scene even though it is on a flat page? This is just one of the many questions about perception we will consider in this book.
Photo by Bruce Goldstein

VL *The Virtual Lab icons direct you to specific animations and videos designed to help you visualize what you are reading about. The number beside each icon indicates the number of the clip you can access through your CD-ROM or your student website.*

Some Questions We Will Consider:

- Why should you read this book (p. 4)
- How are your perceptions determined by processes that you are unaware of? (p. 5)
- What is the difference between perceiving something and recognizing it? (p. 7)
- How can we measure perception? (p. 12)

Imagine that you have been given the following hypothetical science project.

Science project:
Design a device that can locate, describe, and identify all objects in the environment, including their distance from the device and their relationships to each other. In addition, make the device capable of traveling from one point to another, avoiding obstacles along the way.

Extra credit:
Make the device capable of having conscious experience, such as what people experience when they look out at a scene.

Warning:
This project, should you decide to accept it, is extremely difficult. It has not yet been solved by the best computer scientists, even though they are equipped with the world's most powerful computers.

Hint:
Humans and animals have solved the problems above in a particularly elegant way. They use two spherical sensors, which contain a light sensitive chemical, to sense light; two detectors on the sides of the head, which are fitted with tiny vibrating hairs to sense pressure changes in the air; small pressure detectors of various shapes imbedded under the skin to sense stimuli on the skin; and two types of chemical detectors to detect gases that are inhaled and solids and liquids that are ingested.

Additional note:
Designing the detectors is just the first step in designing the system. An information processing system is also needed. In the case of the human, this information processing system is a "computer" called the brain, with 100 billion active units and interconnections so complex that they have still not been completely deciphered. Although the detectors are an important part of the project, the design of the computer is crucial, because the information that is picked up by the detectors needs to be analyzed. Note that operation of the human system is still not completely understood and that the best scientific minds in the world have made little progress with the extra credit part of the problem. Focus on the main problem first, and leave conscious experience until later.

The "science project" above is what this book is about. Our goal is to understand the human model, starting with the detectors—the eyes, ears, skin receptors, and receptors in the nose and mouth—and then to move on to the computer—the brain. We want to understand how we sense things in the environment and interact with them. The paradox we face in searching for this understanding is that although we still don't understand perception, perceiving is something that is easy for us to do. In most situations, we simply open our eyes and see what is around us, or listen and hear sounds, without expending any particular effort.

Because of the ease with which we perceive, many people see perception as something that "just happens," and don't see the feats achieved by our senses as complex or amazing. "After all," the skeptic might say, "for vision, a picture of the environment is focused on the back of my eye, and that picture provides all the information my brain needs to duplicate the environment in my consciousness." But the idea that perception is not that complex is exactly what misled computer scientists in the 1950s and 1960s to propose that it would only take about a decade or so to create "perceiving machines" that could negotiate the environment with humanlike ease. That prediction, made over 45 years ago, has yet to come true, even though a computer defeated the world chess champion in 1997. From a computer's point of view, perceiving a scene is more difficult than playing world championship chess.

In this chapter we will begin by introducing some basic principles to help us understand the complexities of perception. We will first consider a few practical reasons for studying perception, and then how perception occurs in a sequence of steps and, finally, how to measure perception.

WHY READ THIS BOOK?

The most obvious answer to the question "Why read this book?" is that it is required reading for a course you are taking. Thus, it is probably an important thing to do if you want to get a good grade. But beyond that, there are a number of other reasons for reading this book. For one thing, the material will provide you with information that may be helpful in other courses and perhaps even your future career. If you plan to go to graduate school to become a researcher or teacher in perception or a related area, this book will provide you with a solid background to build on. In fact, a number of the research studies you will read about were carried out by researchers who were introduced to the field of perception by earlier editions of this book.

The material in this book is also relevant to future studies in medicine or related fields, since much of our discussion is about how the body operates. A few medical applications that depend on knowledge of perception are devices to restore perception to people who have lost vision or hearing, and treatments for pain. Other applications include robotic vehicles that can find their way through unfamiliar environments, speech recognition systems that can understand what someone is saying, and highway signs that are visible to drivers under a variety of conditions.

But reasons to study perception extend beyond the possibility of useful applications. Because perception is something you experience constantly, knowing about how it works is interesting in its own right. To appreciate why, consider what you are experiencing right now. As you look around, or perhaps touch the page of this book, you probably get the feeling that you are perceiving exactly what is "out there" in the environment. After all, touching this page puts you in direct contact with it, and it is likely that you feel that what you are seeing is what's actually there. But one of the things you will learn as you study perception is that everything you see, hear, taste, feel, or smell is filtered through the mechanisms of your senses. This means that what you are perceiving is determined not only by what is "out there," but also by the properties of your senses. This concept has fascinated philosophers, researchers, and students for hundreds of years, and is even more meaningful now because of recent advances in our understanding of the mechanisms responsible for our perceptions.

Another reason to study perception is that it can help you become more aware of the nature of your own perceptual experiences. Many of the everyday experiences that you take for granted—such as listening to someone talking, tasting food, or looking at a painting in a museum—can be appreciated at a deeper level by considering questions such as "Why does an unfamiliar language sound as if it is one continuous stream of sound, without breaks between words?" "Why do I lose my sense of taste when I have a cold?" and "How do artists create an impression of depth in a picture?" Reading this book will not only answer these questions but will consider other questions that you may not have thought of, such as "Why don't I see colors at dusk?" and "How come the scene around me doesn't appear to move as I walk through it?" Thus, even if you aren't planning to become a physician or a robotic-vehicle designer, you will come away from reading this book with a heightened appreciation of both the complexity and the beauty of the mechanisms responsible for your perceptual experiences, and perhaps even with an enhanced awareness of the world around you.

In one of those strange coincidences that occasionally happen, I received an e-mail from a student (not one of my own, but from another university) at exactly the same time that I was writing this section of the book. In her e-mail, "Jenny" made a number of comments about the book, but the one that struck me as being particularly relevant to the question "Why read this book?" is the following: "By reading your book, I got to know the fascinating processes that take place every second in my brain, that are doing things I don't even think about." Your reasons for reading this book may turn out to be totally different than Jenny's, but hopefully you will find out some things that will be useful, or fascinating, or both.

THE PERCEPTUAL PROCESS

One of the messages of this book is that perception does not just happen, but is the end result of complex "behind the scenes" processes, many of which are not available to your awareness. An everyday example of the idea of behind-the-scenes processes is provided by what's happening as you watch a play in the theater. While your attention is focused on the unfolding drama created by the characters in the play, another drama is unfolding backstage. An actress is rushing to complete her costume change, an actor is pacing back and forth to calm his nerves just before he goes on, the stage manager is checking to be sure the next scene change is ready to go, and behind the glass window above the last row of the audience, the lighting director is getting ready to make the next lighting change.

Just as the audience sees only a small part of what is actually happening during a play, your effortless perception of the world around you is only a small part of what is happening as you perceive. One way to illustrate the behind-the-scenes processes that are involved in perception is to consider perception as involving a sequence of steps, which we will call the **perceptual process**. We will describe this process, which is diagrammed in Figure 1.1, by considering each of the steps in the perceptual process.

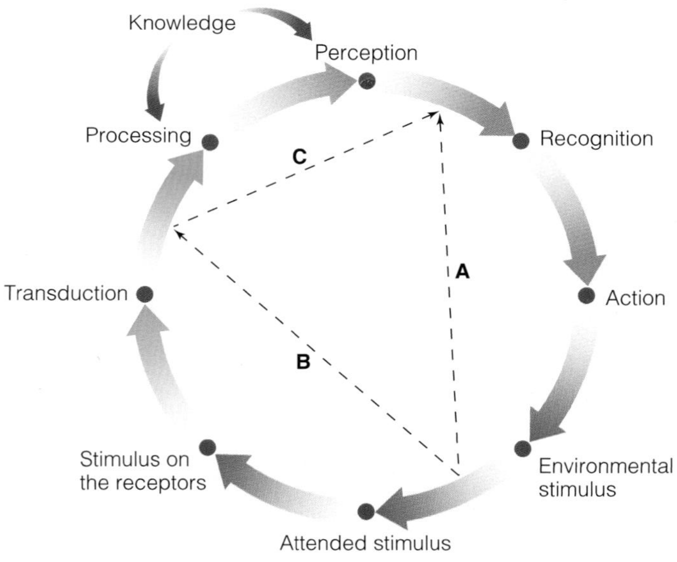

Figure 1.1 ▌ The perceptual process. The steps in this process are arranged in a circle to emphasize the fact that the process is dynamic and continually changing. Blue arrows point to stimuli; green to processing; red to perceptual responses. Arrows A, B, and C indicate three important relationships that researchers measure.

Environmental Stimuli and Attended Stimuli

The **environmental stimulus** is all of the things in our environment that we can potentially perceive. Consider, for example, the potential stimuli that are presented to Ellen, who is taking a walk in the woods. As she walks along the trail she is confronted with a large number of stimuli (Figure 1.2a)—trees, the path on which she is walking, rustling noises made by a small animal scampering through the leaves. Because there is far too much happening for Ellen to take in everything at once, she scans the scene, looking from one place to another at things that catch her interest.

When Ellen's attention is captured by a particularly distinctive looking tree off to the right, she doesn't notice the interesting pattern on the tree trunk at first, but suddenly realizes that what she had at first taken to be a patch of moss was actually a moth (Figure 1.2b). When Ellen focuses on this moth, making it the center of her attention, it becomes the **attended stimulus**. The attended stimulus changes from moment to moment, as Ellen shifts her attention from place to place.

Figure 1.2 ▮ (a) We take the woods as the starting point for our description of the perceptual process. Everything in the woods is the environmental stimulus. (b) Ellen focuses on the moth, which becomes the attended stimulus.

The Stimulus on the Receptors

When Ellen focuses her attention on the moth, she looks directly at it, and this creates an image of the moth and its immediate surroundings on the receptors of her retina, a 0.4-mm thick network of light-sensitive receptors and other neurons that line the back of the eye (Figure 1.3a). (We will describe neurons in more detail in Chapter 2.) This step is important because it is a transformation of the stimulus—the moth—into another form: an image on Ellen's retina. But this transformation from "moth-on-a-tree" to "image-of-moth-on-the-retina" is a small transformation compared to what happens next: The image on the retina is transformed into electrical signals in the receptors by a process called transduction.

Transduction

Transduction is the transformation of one form of energy into another form of energy. For example, when you touch the "withdrawal" button on the screen of the automated teller machine at the bank, the pressure exerted by your finger is transduced into electrical energy, which

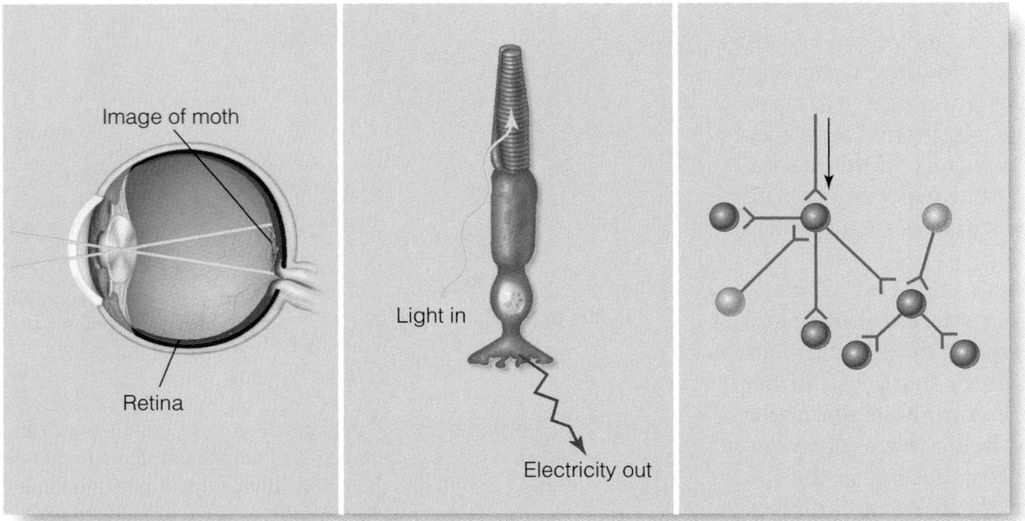

Figure 1.3 ▮ (a) An image of the moth is formed on Ellen's retina. (b) *Transduction* occurs when the receptors create electrical energy in response to light. (c) This electrical energy is *processed* through networks of neurons.

signals a device that uses mechanical energy to push your money out of the machine. Transduction occurs in the nervous system when energy in the environment—such as light energy, mechanical pressure, or chemical energy—is transformed into electrical energy. In our example, the pattern of light created by the moth on Ellen's retina is transformed into electrical signals in thousands of her visual receptors (Figure 1.3b).

Neural Processing

After the moth's image has been transformed into electrical signals in Ellen's receptors, these signals activate other neurons, which in turn activate more neurons. These neurons are organized in interconnected pathways far more complex than the map that would be created if we could shrink the entire U.S. highway system down to the size of this page. It is along these pathways that electrical signals travel, first from the eye to the brain and then within the brain itself. During their travels through this network of neurons, the electrical signals undergo neural processing (Figure 1.3c).

Neural processing refers to operations that change the electrical responses of neurons in various ways. In Chapter 3 we will describe exactly how these electrical responses are processed, but we can understand processing on a simple level by imagining that we are hovering above the city in a traffic helicopter looking down on the traffic patterns on a network of busy city streets at rush hour. We see one place where traffic from three or four other streets is flowing into a single street that has become totally clogged and almost looks like a parking lot; another street that has stop-and-go traffic because there are traffic lights at each intersection; and a third on which traffic is flowing smoothly because it is a limited-access highway. It is apparent from this scene that the way different streets are laid out and the number of traffic signals affects the flow of cars through the city.

In Chapter 3 we will see that a similar situation occurs in the nervous system. The way the pathways of the nervous system are laid out and the nature of the interconnections between the various pathways can affect the flow of electrical signals. This is extremely important because it is this flow of signals that creates the next step in the perceptual process—perception.

Perception

Perception is conscious sensory experience. It occurs when the electrical signals that represent the moth are somehow transformed by Ellen's brain into her experience of seeing the moth (Figure 1.4a).

In the past, some accounts of the perceptual process have stopped at this stage. After all, once Ellen *sees* the moth, hasn't she perceived it? The answer to this question is yes, she has *perceived* it, but other things have happened as well—she recognized the form as a "moth" and not a "butterfly," and she took action based on her perception, as when she walked closer to the tree to get a better look at the moth. These two additional steps—recognition and action—are behaviors that are important outcomes of the perceptual process.

Recognition

Recognition is our ability to place an object in a category, such as "moth," that gives it meaning (Figure 1.4b). Although we might be tempted to group perception and

(a) Ellen perceives something on the tree.

(b) Ellen realizes it is a moth.

(c) Ellen walks toward the moth.

Figure 1.4 ■ (a) Ellen has conscious perception of the moth. (b) She recognizes the moth. (c) She takes action by walking toward the tree to get a better view.

Figure 1.5 ▮ See Perceiving a Picture in the Demonstration box for instructions.
(Adapted from "The Role of Frequency in Developing Perceptual Sets," by B. R. Bugleski and D. A. Alampay, 1961, Canadian Journal of Psychology, 15, *205–211. Copyright © 1961 by the* Canadian Psychological Association. *Reprinted with permission.)*

recognition together, researchers have shown that they are separate processes. For example, consider the case of Dr. P., a patient who is described by neurologist Oliver Sacks (1985) in the title story of his book *The Man Who Mistook His Wife for a Hat.*

Dr. P., a well-known musician and music teacher, first noticed a problem when he began having trouble recognizing his students visually, although he could immediately identify them by the sound of their voices. But when Dr. P. began misperceiving common objects, for example addressing a parking meter as if it were a person or expecting a carved knob on a piece of furniture to engage him in conversation, it became clear that his problem was more serious than just a little forgetfulness. Was he blind, or perhaps crazy? It was clear from an eye examination that he could see well and, by many other criteria, it was obvious that he was not crazy.

Dr. P.'s problem was eventually diagnosed as visual form **agnosia**—the inability to recognize objects—that was caused by a brain tumor. He perceived the parts of objects but couldn't identify the whole object, so when Sacks showed him a glove, Dr. P. described it as "a continuous surface unfolded on itself. It appears to have five outpouchings, if this is the word." When Sacks asked him what it was, Dr. P. hypothesized that it was "a container of some sort. It could be a change purse, for example, for coins of five sizes." The normally easy process of object recognition had, for Dr. P., been derailed by his brain tumor. He could perceive the object and recognize parts of it, but couldn't perceptually assemble the parts in a way that would enable him to recognize the object as a whole. Cases such as this show that perception and recognition are not the same.

Action

Action includes motor activities such as moving the head or eyes and locomoting through the environment. In our example, Ellen looks directly at the moth and walks toward it (Figure 1.4c). Some researchers see action as an important outcome of the perceptual process because of its importance for survival. David Milner and Melvyn Goodale (1995) propose that early in the evolution of animals the major goal of visual processing was not to create a conscious perception or "picture" of the environment but to help the animal control navigation, catch prey, avoid obstacles, and detect predators—all crucial functions for the animal's survival.

The fact that perception often leads to action, whether it be an animal's increasing its vigilance when it hears a twig snapping in the forest or just deciding to look more closely at something that looks interesting, means that perception is a continuously changing process. For example, the scene that Ellen is observing changes every time she shifts her attention to something else, or moves to a new location, or when something in the scene moves.

The changes that occur as people perceive is the reason the steps of the perceptual process in Figure 1.1 are arranged in a circle. Although we can describe the perceptual process as a series of steps that "begin" with the environmental stimulus and "end" with perception, recognition, and action, the overall process is so dynamic and continually changing that it doesn't really have a beginning point or an ending point.

Knowledge

In our diagram of the perceptual process, just above "neural processing" and "perception" is **knowledge**—any information that the perceiver brings to a situation. Knowledge is placed outside the circle because it can affect a number of the steps in the perceptual process. Information that a person brings to a situation can be things learned years ago, such as when Ellen learned to tell the difference between a moth and a butterfly, or knowledge obtained from events that have just happened. The following demonstration provides an example of how perception can be influenced by knowledge that you have just acquired.

DEMONSTRATION

Perceiving a Picture

After looking at the drawing in Figure 1.5, close your eyes, turn to page 10, and open and shut your eyes rapidly to briefly expose the picture in Figure 1.7. Decide what the picture is, and then open your eyes and read the explanation below it.

Do this now, before reading further. ■

Did you identify Figure 1.6 as a rat (or a mouse)? If you did, you were influenced by the clearly rat- or mouse-like figure you observed initially. But people who first

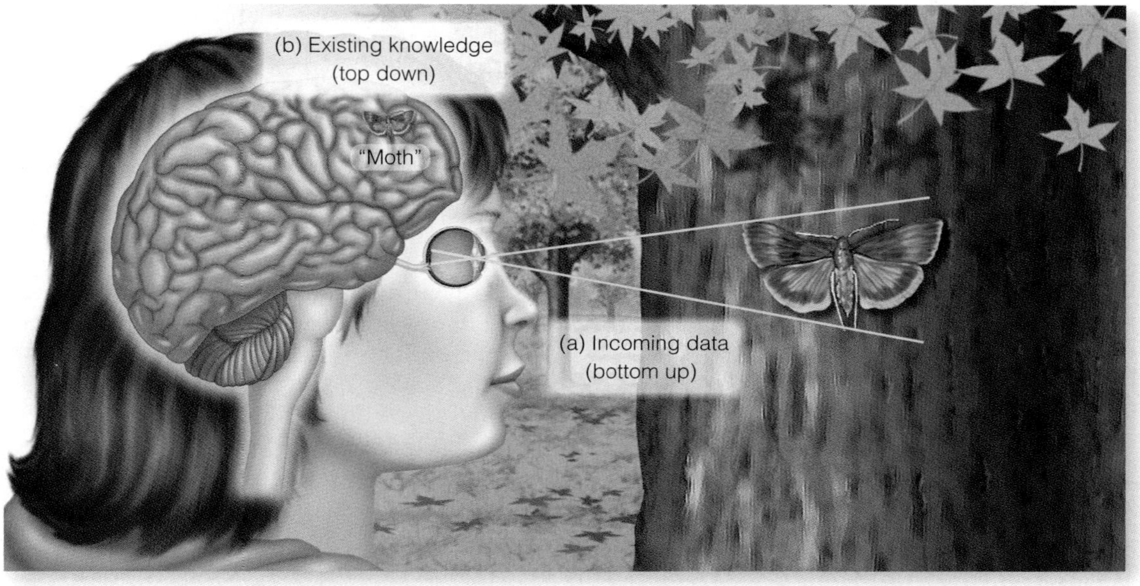

Figure 1.6 ▌ Perception is determined by an interaction between bottom-up processing, which starts with the image on the receptors, and top-down processing, which brings the observer's knowledge into play. In this example, (a) the image of the moth on Ellen's retina initiates bottom-up processing, and (b) her prior knowledge of moths contributes to top-down processing.

observe Figure 1.9 (page 12) instead of Figure 1.5 usually identify Figure 1.7 as a man. (Try this on someone else.) This demonstration, which is called the **rat–man demonstration**, shows how recently acquired knowledge ("that pattern is a rat") can influence perception.

VIRTUAL LAB **1, 2**

An example of how knowledge acquired years ago can influence the perceptual process would be the ability to categorize objects. Thus, Ellen can say "that is a moth" because of her knowledge of what moths look like. In addition, this knowledge can have perceptual consequences because it might help her distinguish the moth from the tree trunk. Someone with little knowledge of moths might just see a tree trunk, without becoming aware of the moth at all.

Another way to describe the effect of information that the perceiver brings to the situation is by distinguishing between bottom-up processing and top-down processing. **Bottom-up processing** (also called **data-based processing**) is processing that is based on incoming data. Incoming data is always the starting point for perception because if there is no incoming data, there is no perception. For Ellen, the incoming data is the pattern of light and dark on her retina that is created by light reflected from the moth and the tree (Figure 1.8a). **Top-down processing** (also called **knowledge-based processing**) refers to processing that is based on knowledge (Figure 1.8b). For Ellen, this knowledge includes what she knows about moths. Knowledge isn't always involved in perception but, as we will see, it often is—sometimes without our even being aware of it.

Bottom-up processing is essential for perception because the perceptual process usually begins with stimulation of the receptors.[1] Thus, when a pharmacist reads what to you might look like an unreadable scribble on your doctor's prescription, she starts with bottom-up processing, which is based on the pattern that the doctor's handwriting creates on her retina, but she also uses top-down processing, which makes use of her knowledge of the names of drugs and perhaps past experience with this particular doctor's writing, to help her decipher the prescription.

HOW TO APPROACH THE STUDY OF PERCEPTION

The goal of perceptual research is to understand each of the steps in the perceptual process that lead to perception, recognition, and action. (For simplicity, we will use the term *perception* to stand for all of these outcomes in the discussion that follows.) The approach we will use to achieve this understanding involves an idea called levels of analysis.

[1]Occasionally perception can occur without stimulation of the receptors. For example, being hit on the head might cause you to "see stars," or closing your eyes and imagining something may cause an experience called "imagery," which shares many characteristics of perception (Kosslyn, 1994).

Figure 1.7 ▌ Did you see a "rat" or a "man"? Looking at the more ratlike picture in Figure 1.5 increased the chances that you would see this one as a rat. But if you had first seen the man version (Figure 1.9), you would have been more likely to perceive this figure as a man.
(Adapted from "The Role of Frequency in Developing Perceptual Sets," by B. R. Bugelski and D. A. Alampay, 1961, Canadian Journal of Psychology, *15, 205–211. Copyright © 1961 by the Canadian Psychological Association. Reprinted with permission.)*

Levels of Analysis

The idea behind **levels of analysis** is that we can observe processes at different scales. We can illustrate this idea of different levels, or scales, by returning to the traffic situation we described when we considered neural processing. High above the traffic, in our helicopter, we were observing the "big picture." This vantage point enabled us to see how the flow of automobiles is affected by the way the streets are laid out, the locations of traffic lights, and other things we can see from high above the streets.

But if we want to understand the operation of an individual automobile, we would need to zoom in to street level and consider an individual car and perhaps take it out for a road test that might include determining performance measures like acceleration, braking, and handling. We could also zoom in even further by looking under the hood to gain an understanding of the inner workings of the automobile's engine. The point is that studying the automobile at each of these levels gives us a much deeper understanding of automobiles than we would get from studying them only at one level.

The same reasoning applies to our study of perception. In this book we will gain a broad understanding of perception by studying it at two different levels of analysis. We will consider how a person's perception is related to stimulation in the environment. This is achieved through the **psychophysical level of analysis**, which focuses on the *stimulus–perception relationship*, indicated by arrow A in the diagram of the perceptual process in Figure 1.1.

The term psychophysics was introduced by Gustav Fechner, a physiologist who published *Elements of Psychophysics* (1860), which described a number of methods for precisely measuring relationships between the stimulus (*physics*) and perception (*psycho*). These methods are still used today to measure quantitative relationships between stimuli and perception. Because there are also a number of other, nonquantitative, methods that are used to measure the relationship between the stimulus and perception, we will use the term **psychophysics** more broadly in this book to refer to any measurement of the relationship between the stimulus and perception. An example of research at the psychophysical level would be an experiment in which an experimenter asks an observer to decide whether two very similar patches of color are the same or different (Figure 1.8a).

We will also consider how a person's perception is related to physiological processes that are occurring within the person. This is called the **physiological level of analysis**, and it focuses on the *stimulus–physiology relationship* (Figure 1.1, Arrow B) and the *physiology–perception relationship* (Figure 1.1, Arrow C).

An example of measuring the stimulus–physiology

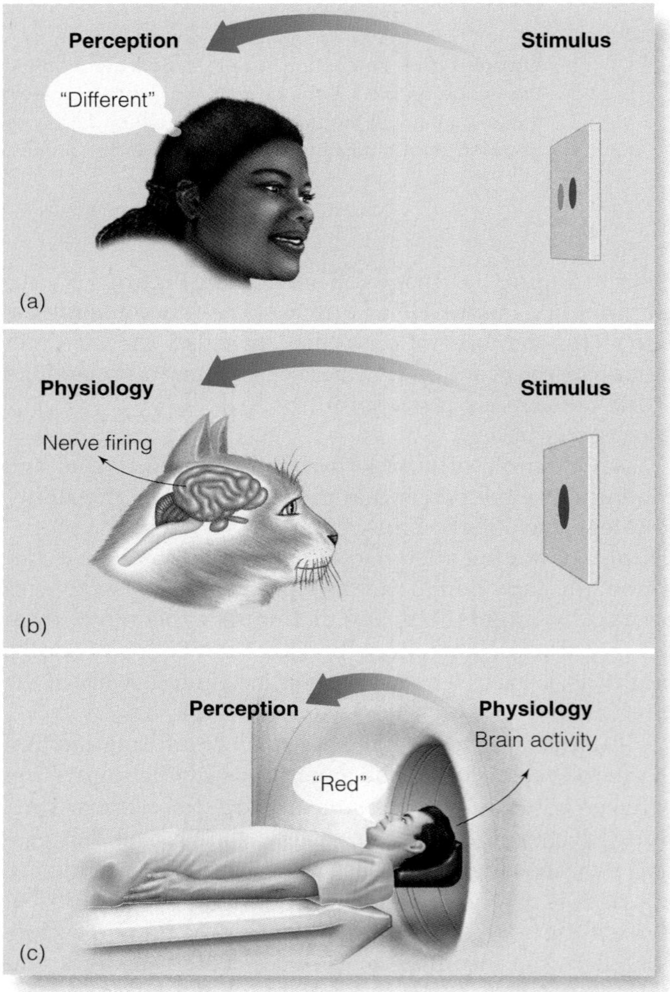

Figure 1.8 ▌ Experiments that measure the relationships indicated by the arrows in Figure 1.1. (A) *Stimulus–perception:* Two colored patches are judged to be different. (B) *Stimulus–physiology:* A colored light generates a neural response in the cat's cortex. (C) *Physiology–perception:* Brain activity is monitored as a person indicates what he is seeing.

relationship is an experiment in which the electrical activity generated by neurons in a cat's cortex is measured in response to the presentation of different colored lights (Figure 1.8b).[2] An example of measuring the physiology-perception relationship would be a study in which a person's brain activity is measured as the person describes the color of an object he is seeing (Figure 1.8c). (See Tables 1.1 and 1.2.)

Table 1.1 ▮ *Levels of analysis in the study of perception*

Level of Analysis	Type of Information	Relationships
Psychophysical level	Stimuli in the environment	Stimulus → Perception
Physiological level	Physiological processes in the body	Stimulus → Physiology Physiology → Perception

Table 1.2 ▮ *Methods of studying relationships in the perceptual process*

Relationship	How Studied?
A. Stimulus → perception	Psychophysically. Present a stimulus and determine the person's response.
B. Stimulus → physiology	Physiologically. Present a stimulus and measure the electrical response in the nervous system.
C. Physiology → perception	Physiologically and psychophysically. Measure physiological and perceptual responses to the same stimuli.

As we study perception at both the psychophysical and physiological levels, we will also be concerned with how the knowledge, memories, and expectations that people bring to the situation influence their perceptions. These factors, which we have described as being the starting place for top-down processing, are called **cognitive influences on perception**. Researchers study cognitive influences by measuring how knowledge and other factors, such as memories and expectations, affect each of the three relationships in Figure 1.1.

[2]Because a great deal of physiological research has been done on cats and monkeys, students often express concerns about how these animals are treated. All animal research in the United States follows strict guidelines for the care of animals established by organizations such as the American Psychological Association and the Society for Neuroscience. The central tenet of these guidelines is that every effort should be made to ensure that animals are not subjected to pain or distress. Research on animals has provided essential information for developing aids to help people with sensory disabilities such as blindness and deafness and for helping develop techniques to ease severe pain.

For example, consider the rat–man demonstration. If we were to measure the stimulus–perception relationship by showing just Figure 1.7 to a number of people, we would probably find that some people see a rat and some people see a man. But by adding some "knowledge" by first presenting the more ratlike picture in Figure 1.5, most of the people say "rat" when we present Figure 1.7. Thus, in this example, knowledge has affected the stimulus–perception relationship. Notice in Figure 1.1 that the arrows from "Knowledge" in the perceptual process point both to perception and to physiological aspects of the process. As we apply the levels of analysis approach, we will see that knowledge can affect both a person's perceptions and physiological responding in their nervous system.

Communication Between the Levels of Analysis

One of the things that becomes apparent when we step back and look at the psychophysical and physiological levels of analysis is that each one provides information about different aspects of the perceptual process. Thus, to truly understand perception, we have to study it at both levels. It is important, however, to realize that even though we are distinguishing between these two levels, there is a great deal of communication, or "cross-talk," between them. That is, they are intimately related to one another. Just as the mechanical characteristics of a car's engine affect the car's performance, the physiological characteristics of a person's perceptual system affect his or her perceptions.

One consequence of the close relationship between the psychophysical and physiological levels of analysis is that we can learn about one level by studying the other (Goldstein, 2001a). For example, consider a patient who has suffered a stroke caused by blockage of one of the arteries serving his brain. When we test the patient's vision, we find that he has trouble seeing objects that are located in an area off to his left. This measurement of the relationship between stimulus (an object on the left) and perception (the ability to see the object) suggests that there is a problem in a particular area in the right hemisphere of the patient's brain (since the right hemisphere is responsible for vision in the left visual field). We can then check this guess by doing a brain scan that creates a picture of the brain's physiological operation.

This example shows that even without looking inside the person, we can use psychophysical measurements to obtain clues regarding the person's inner workings. Later in the book we will have a number of opportunities to see how researchers have used perceptual information to provide important clues about what is going on physiologically, both for abnormal perception, as in our patient with brain damage, and for normal perception as well.

To understand how we study perception at the two levels of analysis, we need to know something about the

Figure 1.9 ▮ Man version of the rat–man stimulus. *(Adapted from "The Role of Frequency in Developing Perceptual Sets," by B. R. Bugelski and D. A. Alampay, 1961,* Canadian Journal of Psychology, 15, *205–211. Copyright © 1961 by the Canadian Psychological Association. Reprinted with permission.)*

procedures we use to measure the relationships in Figure 1.1. In the remainder of this chapter we will describe some ways to measure perception at the psychophysical level. In Chapter 2 we will describe measurement at the physiological level.

MEASURING PERCEPTION

We have seen that the psychophysical approach to perception focuses on the relationship between the *physical properties of stimuli* and the *perceptual responses to these stimuli.* We can respond to stimuli in a number of different ways. Here are some examples taken from experiences that might occur while watching a football game.

- *Describing:* Indicating characteristics of a stimulus. "All of the people in the student section are wearing red."
- *Recognizing:* Placing a stimulus in a specific category. "Number 22 is the other team's quarterback."
- *Detecting:* Becoming aware of a barely detectable aspect of a stimulus. "That lineman moved slightly just before the ball was snapped."
- *Perceiving magnitude:* Being aware of the size or intensity of a stimulus. "That lineman looks twice as big as our quarterback."
- *Searching:* Looking for a specific stimulus among a number of other stimuli. "I'm looking for Susan in the student section."

We will now describe some of the methods that perception researchers have used to measure these ways of responding to stimuli.

Description

When a researcher asks a person to describe what he or she is perceiving or to indicate when a particular perception occurs, the researcher is using the **phenomenological method.** This method is a first step in studying perception because it describes what we perceive. This description can be at a very basic level, such as when we notice that we can perceive some objects as being farther away than others, or that there is a perceptual quality we call "color," or that there are different qualities of taste, such as bitter, sweet, and sour. These are such common observations that we might take them for granted, but this is where the study of perception begins, because these are the basic properties that we are seeking to explain.

Recognition

When we categorize a stimulus by naming it, we are measuring recognition.

METHOD ▪ Recognition

Every so often we will introduce a new method by describing it in a "Method" section like this one. Students are sometimes tempted to skip these sections because they think the content is unimportant. However, you should resist this temptation because these methods are essential tools for the study of perception. These "Method" sections will help you understand the experiment that follows and will provide the background for understanding other experiments later in the book.

The procedure for measuring recognition is simple: A stimulus is presented, and the observer indicates what it is. Your response to the rat–man demonstration involved recognition because you were asked to name what you saw. This procedure is widely used in testing patients with brain damage, such as the musician Dr. P., with visual agnosia, whom we described earlier. Often the stimuli in these experiments are pictures of objects rather than the actual object (thereby avoiding having to bring elephants and other large objects into the laboratory!).

▪ ▪ ▪

Describing perceptions using the phenomenological method and determining a person's ability to recognize objects provides information about what a person is perceiving. Often, however, it is useful to be able to establish a quantitative relationship between the stimulus and perception. One way this has been achieved is by methods designed to measure the amount of stimulus energy that is necessary for detecting a stimulus.

Detection

In Gustav Fechner's book *Elements of Psychophysics,* he described a number of quantitative methods to measure the relationship between stimuli and perception. These methods—limits, adjustment, and constant stimuli—are called the **classical psychophysical methods** because they were the original methods that were used to measure the stimulus–perception relationship.

The Absolute Threshold The **absolute threshold** is the smallest amount of stimulus energy necessary to detect a stimulus.

METHOD ▪ Determining the Absolute Threshold

To measure the threshold by using the **method of limits**, the experimenter presents stimuli in either ascending or descending order, as shown in Figure 1.10, which indicates the results of an experiment that measures a person's threshold for seeing a light. VL 3

Intensity	1 ↓	2 ↑	3 ↓	4 ↑	5 ↓	6 ↑	7 ↓	8 ↑
103	Y		Y		Y		Y	
102	Y		Y		Y		Y	
101	Y		Y		Y		Y	Y
100	Y	Y	Y	Y	Y		Y	Y
99	Y	N	Y	N	Y	Y	Y	Y
98	N	N	Y	N	N	N	N	Y
97		N	N	N		N		N
96		N		N		N		N
95		N		N		N		N
Crossover values	98.5	99.5	97.5	99.5	98.5	98.5	98.5	97.5

Threshold = Mean of crossovers = 98.5

Figure 1.10 ▮ The results of an experiment to determine the threshold using the method of limits. The dashed lines indicate the crossover point for each sequence of stimuli. The threshold—the average of the crossover values—is 98.5 in this experiment.

On the first series of trials, the experimenter presents a light with an intensity of 103, and the observer indicates by a "yes" response that he sees the light. This response is indicated by a Y at an intensity of 103 on the table. The experimenter then decreases the intensity, and the observer makes a judgment at each intensity until he responds "no," that he did not see the light. This change from "yes" to "no" is the crossover point, and the threshold for this series is taken as the mean between 99 and 98, or 98.5. By repeating this procedure a number of times, starting above the threshold half the time and starting below the threshold half the time, the threshold can be determined by calculating the average of all of the crossover points. VL 4

In the **method of adjustment**, the observer or the experimenter adjusts the stimulus intensity in a continuous manner (as opposed to the stepwise presentation for the method of limits) until the observer can just barely detect the stimulus. This just barely detectable intensity is then taken as the absolute threshold. This procedure can be repeated several times and the threshold determined by taking the average setting. VL 5

In the **method of constant stimuli**, the experimenter presents five to nine stimuli with different intensities in random order. The results of a hypothetical determination of the threshold for seeing a light are shown in Figure 1.11. The data points in this graph were determined by presenting six light intensities 10 times each and determining the percentage of times that the observer perceived each intensity. The results indicate that the light with an intensity of 150 was never detected, the light with an intensity of 200 was always detected, and lights with intensities in between were sometimes detected and sometimes not detected. The threshold is usually taken as the intensity that results in detection on 50 percent of the trials, so in this case the threshold is an intensity of 180. VL 6, 7

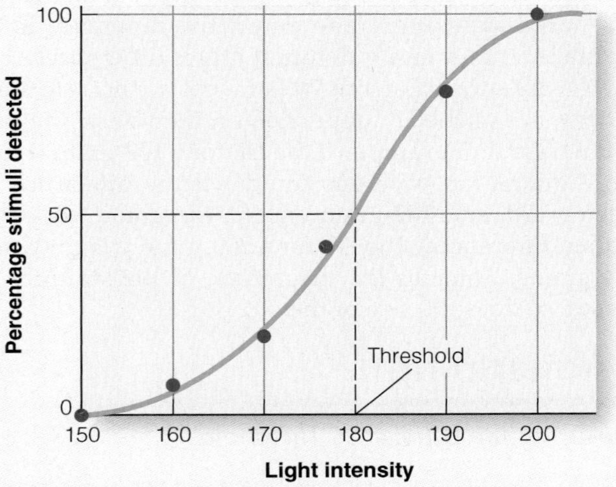

Figure 1.11 ▮ Results of a hypothetical experiment in which the threshold for seeing a light is measured by the method of constant stimuli. The threshold—the intensity at which the light is seen on half of its presentations—is 180 in this experiment.

The choice among the methods of limits, adjustment, and constant stimuli is usually determined by the accuracy that is needed and the amount of time available. The method of constant stimuli is the most accurate method but takes the longest time, whereas the method of adjustment is the least accurate but the fastest.

▪ ▪ ▪

When Fechner published *Elements of Psychophysics,* he not only described his methods for measuring the absolute threshold but also described the work of Ernst Weber (1795–1878), a physiologist, who, a few years before the publication of Fechner's book, measured another type of threshold, the difference threshold.

The Difference Threshold The **difference threshold** (called DL from the German *Differenze Limen,* which is translated as "difference threshold") is the smallest difference between two stimuli that a person can detect. VL 8, 9

METHOD ▪ Determining the Difference Threshold

To measure the difference threshold, one of Fechner's methods, described earlier, can be used, except instead of asking participants to indicate whether or not they detect a stimulus, they are asked to indicate whether they detect a *difference* between two stimuli. For example, to measure the difference threshold for sensing weight, Weber had observers lift a small "standard" weight and then lift a slightly heavier "comparison" weight and judge which was heavier.

▪ ▪ ▪

Weber found that when the difference between the standard and comparison weights was small, his observers found it difficult to detect the difference in the weights, but they easily detected larger differences. That much is not surprising, but Weber went further. He found that the size of the DL depended on the size of the standard weight. For example, if the DL for a 100-gram weight was 2 grams (an observer could tell the difference between a 100- and 102-gram weight, but could not detect smaller differences), the DL for a 200-gram weight would be 4 grams. Thus, as the magnitude of the stimulus increases, so does the size of the DL.

DEMONSTRATION

Measuring the Difference Threshold

By doing a simple experiment with some pennies, you can show that the DL gets larger as the standard stimulus gets larger. Have a friend place 10 pennies on a small paper plate (the standard) and 11 on another plate (the comparison). Comparing the weights with your eyes closed, try to decide which one is heavier. After making this judgment, repeat this procedure; if you can't correctly judge which is heavier on three out of three trials, have your friend place another penny on the comparison plate, and try again. Continue this procedure until you can consistently judge which weight is heavier. If, for example, you can consistently tell that the comparison weight is heavier when it contains 12 pennies, then the DL equals 2 pennies. Now repeat the above procedures, but start with 20 pennies for the standard and 21 for the comparison. Since the DL gets larger as the weight of the standard gets larger, you should find that the DL for the 20-penny standard is larger than the DL for the 10-penny standard. ▪

Research on a number of senses has shown that over a fairly large range of intensities, the ratio of the DL to the standard stimulus is constant. This relationship, which is based on Weber's research, was stated mathematically by Fechner as $DL/S = K$ and was called **Weber's law.** K is a constant called the **Weber fraction,** and S is the value of the standard stimulus. Applying this equation to our example of lifted weights, we find that, for the 100-gram standard, $K = 2/100 = 0.02$, and that, for the 200-gram standard, $K = 4/200 = 0.02$. Thus, in this example, the Weber fraction (K) is constant. In fact, numerous modern investigators have found that Weber's law is true for most senses, as long as the stimulus intensity is not too close to the threshold (Engen, 1972; Gescheider, 1976). VL 10, 11

The Weber fraction in our example, 0.02, means that a stimulus must be changed by 2 percent before a change can be detected. Thus, the Weber fraction indicates a sensory system's sensitivity to detecting changes. For a given sense, the Weber fraction remains relatively constant, but each type of sensory judgment has its own Weber fraction. For example, from Table 1.3 we can see that people can detect a 1 percent change in the intensity of an electric shock, but that the intensity must be increased by 8 percent before they can detect a change in light intensity.

Table 1.3 ▮ *Weber fractions for a number of different sensory dimensions*

Electric shock	0.01
Lifted weight	0.02
Sound intensity	0.04
Light intensity	0.08
Taste (salty)	0.08

Source: From Teghtsoonian (1971).

Fechner's proposal of three psychophysical methods for measuring the threshold and his statement of Weber's law for the difference threshold were extremely important events in the history of scientific psychology because they demonstrated that mental activity could be measured quantitatively. This was a notable achievement because in the 1800s many people thought that it was impossible to measure mental activity. But perhaps the most significant thing about these methods is that even though they were proposed in the 1800s, they are still used today. In addition to being used to determine thresholds in research laboratories, simplified versions of the classical psychophysical methods have been used to measure people's detail vision when determining prescriptions for glasses or measuring people's hearing when testing for possible hearing loss.

The classical psychophysical methods were developed to measure absolute and difference thresholds. But what about perceptions that occur above threshold? Most of our everyday experience consists of perceptions that are far above threshold, when we can easily see and hear what is happening around us. To measure these above-threshold perceptions involves a technique called magnitude estimation.

Magnitude Estimation

If we double the intensity of a tone, does it sound twice as loud? If we double the intensity of a light, does it look twice as bright? Although a number of researchers, including Fechner, proposed equations that related perceived magnitude and stimulus intensity, it wasn't until 1957 that S. S. Stevens developed a technique called scaling, or **magnitude estimation**, that accurately measured this relationship (S. S. Stevens, 1957, 1961, 1962).

METHOD ■ Magnitude Estimation

The procedure for a magnitude estimation experiment is relatively simple: The experimenter first presents a "standard" stimulus to the observer (let's say a light of moderate intensity) and assigns it a value of, say, 10; he or she then presents lights of different intensities, and the observer is asked to assign a number to each of these lights that is proportional to the brightness of the light. If the light appears twice as bright as the standard, it gets a rating of 20; half as bright, a 5; and so on. Thus, each light intensity has a brightness assigned to it by the observer. There are also magnitude estimation procedures in which no "standard" is used. But the basic principle is the same: The observer assigns numbers to stimuli that are proportional to perceived magnitude. VL 12

■ ■ ■

The results of a magnitude estimation experiment on brightness are plotted as the red curve in Figure 1.12. This graph plots the means, for a number of observers, of the magnitude estimates of the brightness of a light versus the intensity of the light. You can see from the way this curve bends down that doubling the intensity does not necessarily double the perceived brightness. Doubling the intensity causes only a small change in perceived brightness, particularly at higher intensities. This result is called **response compression**. As intensity is increased, the magnitude increases, but not as rapidly as the intensity. To double the brightness, it is necessary to multiply the intensity by about 9. VL 13

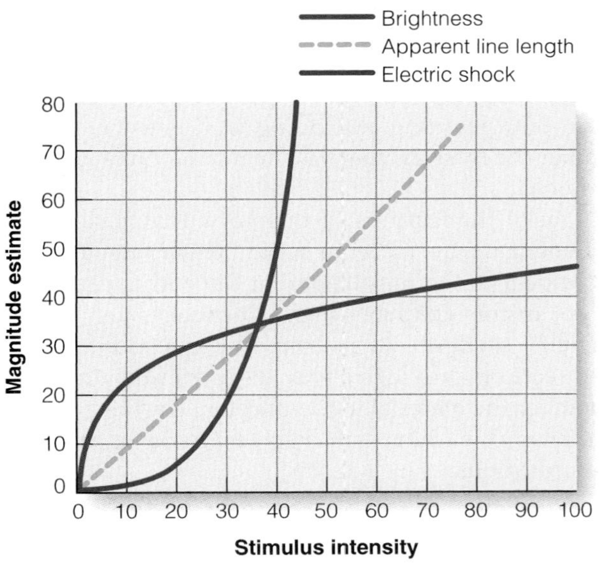

Figure 1.12 ▮ The relationship between perceived magnitude and stimulus intensity for electric shock, line length, and brightness.
(Adapted from "The Surprising Simplicity of Sensory Metrics" by S. S. Stevens, 1962, American Psychologist, 17, 29–39. Copyright © 1962 by American Psychological Association.)

Figure 1.12 also shows the results of magnitude estimation experiments for the sensation caused by an electric shock presented to the finger and for the perception of length of a line. The electric shock curve bends up, indicating that doubling the strength of a shock more than doubles the sensation of being shocked. This is called **response expansion**. As intensity is increased, perceptual magnitude increases more than intensity. The curve for estimating line length is straight, with a slope of close to 1.0, so the magnitude of the response almost exactly matches increases in the stimulus (i.e., if the line length is doubled, an observer says it appears to be twice as long).

The beauty of the relationships derived from magnitude estimation is that the relationship between the intensity of a stimulus and our perception of its magnitude follows the same general equation for each sense. These functions, which are called **power functions**, are described by the equation $P = KS^n$. Perceived magnitude, P, equals a constant, K, times the stimulus intensity, S, raised to a power, n. This relationship is called **Stevens's power law**.

If we plot the logarithm of the magnitude estimates in Figure 1.12 versus the logarithm of the stimulus intensities, all three curves become straight lines (Figure 1.13). The slope of each of these lines indicates n, the exponent of the power law. Remembering our discussion of the three types of curves in Figure 1.12, we can see that the curve that shows response compression has a slope of less than 1.0, the straight line has a slope of about 1.0, and the curve that shows response expansion has a slope of greater than 1.0. Thus, the relationship between response magnitude and stimulus intensity is described by a power law for all senses, and the exponent of the power law indicates whether doubling the stimulus intensity causes more or less than a doubling of the response.

These exponents not only illustrate that all senses follow the same basic relationship, they also illustrate how the operation of each sense is adapted to how organisms function in their environment. Consider, for example, your experience of brightness. Imagine you are inside looking at a page in a book that is brightly illuminated by a lamp on your desk. Now imagine that you are looking out the window at a bright sidewalk that is brightly illuminated by sunlight. Your eye may be receiving thousands of times more light from the sidewalk than from the page of your book, but because the curve for brightness

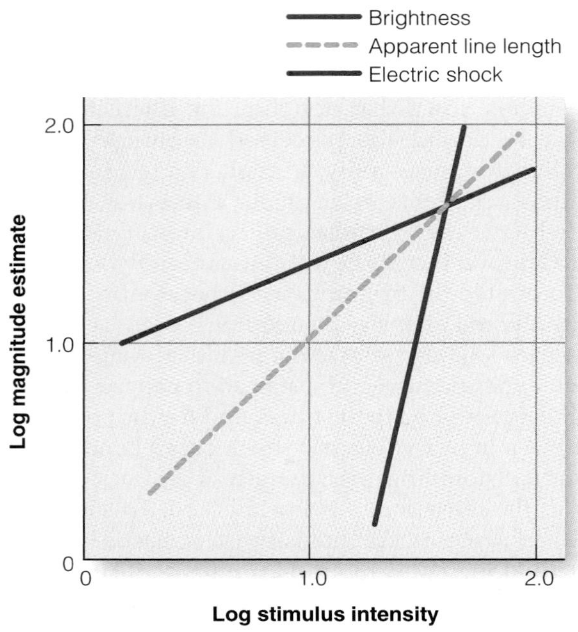

Figure 1.13 ▮ The three functions from Figure 1.12 plotted on log-log coordinates. Taking the logarithm of the magnitude estimates and the logarithm of the stimulus intensity turns the functions into straight lines.
(Adapted from "The Surprising Simplicity of Sensory Metrics" by S. S. Stevens, 1962, American Psychologist, 17, *29–39. Copyright © 1962 by American Psychological Association.)*

bends down (exponent = 0.6), this large increase in intensity causes a smaller change in brightness, and you aren't blinded by the sunlit sidewalk.[3]

The opposite situation occurs for electric shock, which has an exponent of 3.5 so that just small increases in shock intensity cause large increases in pain. This rapid increase in pain even to small increases in shock intensity serves to warn us of impending danger, and we therefore tend to withdraw even from weak shocks.

Search

So far, we have been describing methods in which the observer is able to make a relatively leisurely perceptual judgment. When a person is asked to indicate whether he or she can see a light or tell the difference between two weights, the accuracy of the judgment is what is important, not the speed at which it is made. However, some perceptual research uses methods that require the observer to respond as quickly as possible. One example of such a method is **visual search**, in which the observer's task is to find one stimulus among many, as quickly as possible.

[3]Another mechanism that keeps you from being blinded by high-intensity lights is that your eye adjusts its sensitivity in response to different light levels.

An everyday example of visual search would be searching for a friend's face in a crowd. If you've ever done this, you know that sometimes it is easy (if you know your friend is wearing a bright red hat, and no one else is), and sometimes it is difficult (if there are lots of people and your friend doesn't stand out). When we consider visual attention in Chapter 6, we will describe visual search experiments in which the observers' task is to find a target letter that is hidden among a number of other letters. We will see that measuring **reaction time**—the time between presentation of the stimulus and the observer's response to the stimulus—has provided important information about mechanisms responsible for perception.

Other Methods of Measurement

Numerous other methods have been used to measure the stimulus–perception relationship. For example, in some experiments, observers are asked to decide whether two stimuli are the same or different, or to adjust the brightness or the colors of two lights so they appear the same, or to close their eyes and walk, as accurately as possible, to a distant target stimulus in a field. We will encounter methods such as these, and others as well, as we describe perceptual research in the chapters that follow.

SOMETHING TO CONSIDER: HOW TO GET THE MOST OUT OF THIS BOOK

As you start your sensation and perception course, one of your goals is probably to do well in the course and perhaps learn something along the way! Of course, one key to both learning and doing well is to be able to remember the material that you hear in lectures and read in this book.

One of the features of this book that is designed to help you learn the material is the "Test Yourself" sections that appear in the middle and at the end of each chapter (except in this chapter, in which there is just one "Test Yourself" section). Answering the questions posed in these sections provides a way to determine whether you remember the material in the chapter. The following basic principles of learning will help you make optimal use of these questions.

Principle 1: It is important to know what you really know.

A lament that professors often hear from students is "I came to the lecture, read the chapters a number of times, and still didn't do well on the exam." Sometimes this statement is followed by ". . . and when I walked out of the exam I thought I had done pretty well." If this is something that you have experienced, then the root of the problem may be that you didn't have a good awareness of what you knew and what you didn't know. The problem is that if you think you know the material but actually don't, you might stop studying or might continue studying in an ineffective way, with the net result being poor understanding and an inability to remember what you need to know, come exam time.

Principle 2: Don't mistake ease and familiarity for knowing.

One of the main reasons that students may think they know the material, even when they don't, is that they mistake familiarity for understanding. Here is how it works: You read the chapter once, perhaps highlighting as you go. Then later, you read the chapter again, perhaps focusing on the highlighted material. As you read it over, the material is familiar because you remember it from before, and this familiarity might lead you to think, "OK, I know that." The problem is that this feeling of familiarity is not necessarily equivalent to knowing the material and may be of no help when you have to come up with an answer on the exam. In fact, familiarity can often lead to errors on multiple-choice exams because you might pick a choice that looks familiar, only to find later that it was something you had read, but it wasn't really the best answer to the question.

Principle 3: The pathway to learning is often paved with mistakes.

This principle may sound counterintuitive, but research has shown that one of the most effective ways to learn material is to attempt to remember that material, even if you fail the first time or two. For example, reading a chapter once is a good idea, but then simply doing things that increase your familiarity with the material without pushing yourself to practice remembering it is not the most effective way to study. So rather than reading the chapter a second time, try answering the "Test Yourself" questions. The key is to try answering them *before* you look back at the book to find the answer. If you find you don't know the material, that's good information because it tells you what to study, and whether you realize it or not, the very act of *trying* to answer a question increases the chances you will be able to answer it when you try again later. Answering questions is an effective way to study because of an important cognitive principle: *Generating* material is a more effective way of getting information into memory than simply *reviewing* it.

After you have tried to generate an answer, go back over the material, keeping in mind that an effective strategy is to rest (take a break or study something else) before studying more and then retesting yourself. Research has shown that memory is better when studying is spaced out over time, rather than being done all at once. Repeating this process a number of times—attempting to remember an answer, checking back to see if you were right, waiting, attempting to remember the answer again, and so on— is a more effective way of learning the material than simply looking at it and getting that warm, fuzzy feeling of familiarity, which may not translate into actually knowing the material when you are faced with questions about it on the exam.

TEST YOURSELF 1.1

1. What are some of the reasons for studying perception?
2. Describe the process of perception as a series of steps, beginning with the environmental stimulus and culminating in the behavioral responses of perceiving, recognizing, and acting.
3. What is the role of higher-level or "cognitive" processes in perception? Be sure you understand the difference between bottom-up and top-down processing.
4. What does it mean to say that perception can be studied at different levels of analysis?
5. Describe the different ways that the behavioral responses in the perceptual process can be measured.
6. Why does your author claim that being familiar with the material that you have studied is not always a good thing?

THINK ABOUT IT

1. This chapter argues that although perception seems simple, it is actually extremely complex when we consider "behind the scenes" activities that are not obvious as a person is experiencing perception. Cite an example of a similar situation from your own experience, in which an "outcome" that might seem like it was achieved easily actually involved a complicated process that most people are unaware of.
2. We introduced the idea of levels of analysis by describing a number of ways we might study the automobile. Apply the idea of levels of analysis to another topic by identifying at least three "levels" at which you would study that topic.

3. Describe a situation in which you initially thought you saw or heard something, but then realized that your initial perception was in error. What was the role of bottom-up and top-down processing in this process of first having an incorrect perception and then realizing what was actually there?

IF YOU WANT TO KNOW MORE

1. ***History.*** The study of perception played an extremely important role in the development of scientific psychology in the first half of the 20th century.

   Boring, E. G. (1942). *Sensation and perception in the history of experimental psychology.* New York: Appleton-Century-Crofts.

2. ***Disorders of recognition.*** Dr. P.'s case, in which he had problems recognizing people, is just one example of many such cases of people with brain damage. In addition to reports in the research literature, there are a number of popular accounts of these cases written for the general public.

   Sacks, O. (1985). *The man who mistook his wife for a hat.* London: Duckworth.

   Kolb, B., & Whishaw, I. Q. (2003). *Fundamentals of human neuropsychology* (5th ed.). New York: Worth. (Especially see Chapters 13–17, which contain numerous descriptions of how brain damage affects sensory functioning.)

3. ***Phenomenological method.*** David Katz's book provides excellent examples of how the phenomenological method has been used to determine the experiences that occur under various stimulus conditions. He also describes how surfaces, color, and light combine to create many different perceptions.

   Katz, D. (1935). *The world of color* (2nd ed., R. B. MacLeod & C. W. Fox, Trans.). London: Kegan Paul, Trench, Truber.

4. ***Top-down processing.*** There are many examples of how people's knowledge can influence perception, ranging from early research, which focused on how people's motivation can influence perception, to more recent research, which has emphasized the effects of context and past learning on perception.

   Postman, L., Bruner, J. S., & McGinnis, E. (1948). Personal values as selective factors in perception. *Journal of Abnormal and Social Psychology, 43,* 142–154.

   Vernon, M. D. (1962). *The psychology of perception.* Baltimore: Penguin. (See Chapter 11, "The relation of perception to motivation and emotion.")

KEY TERMS

Absolute threshold (p. 12)
Action (p. 8)
Agnosia (p. 8)
Attended stimulus (p. 6)
Bottom-up processing (data-based processing) (p. 9)
Classical psychophysical methods (p. 12)
Cognitive influences on perception (p. 11)
Difference threshold (p. 13)
Environmental stimulus (p. 6)
Knowledge (p. 8)
Level of analysis (p. 10)
Magnitude estimation (p. 15)
Method of adjustment (p. 13)
Method of constant stimuli (p. 13)
Method of limits (p. 13)
Neural processing (p. 7)
Perception (p. 7)
Perceptual process (p. 5)
Phenomenological method (p. 12)
Physiological level of analysis (p. 10)
Power function (p. 15)
Psychophysical level of analysis (p. 10)
Psychophysics (p. 10)
Rat–man demonstration (p. 9)
Reaction time (p. 16)
Recognition (p. 7)
Response compression (p. 15)
Response expansion (p. 15)
Stevens's power law (p. 15)
Top-down processing (knowledge-based processing) (p. 9)
Transduction (p. 6)
Visual search (p. 16)
Weber fraction (p. 14)
Weber's law (p. 14)

VISIT YOUR COMPANION WEBSITE FOR THIS BOOK

http://psychology.wadsworth.com/goldstein7e

Check out this companion website where you'll find online resources—glossary, flashcards, web links, multiple-choice and essay questions, and much more!

VIRTUAL LAB

Your Virtual Lab is designed to help you get the most out of this course. The Virtual Lab icons direct you to specific media demonstrations and experiments designed to help you visualize what you are reading about. The number beside each icon indicates the number of the media element you can access through your CD-ROM, Perception PsychologyNow, or WebTutor resource at http:now.ilrn.com/goldstein_7e.

The following lab exercises cover what you've just learned in this chapter:

1 *Rabbit–Duck Demonstration* A picture of a figure that, like the rat–man demonstration in Figures 1.5, 1.7, and 1.9, can be seen in two ways.

2 *Young Girl–Old Woman* Another picture that can be seen in two ways.

3 *The Method of Limits* How a "typical" observer might respond using the method of limits procedure to measure absolute threshold.

4 *Measurement Fluctuation and Error* How our judgments of size can vary from trial to trial.

5 *Adjustment and PSE* Measuring the point of subjective equality for line length using the method of adjustment.

6 *Method of Constant Stimuli* Measuring the difference threshold for line length using the method of constant stimuli.

7 *Measuring Illusions* An experiment that enables you to measure the size of the Muller-Lyer, horizontal-vertical, and simultaneous contrast illusions using the method of constant stimuli. The simultaneous contrast illusion is described in Chapter 7, and the Muller-Lyer illusion is described in Chapter 8.

8 *DL by the Method of Limits* Measuring the difference threshold for the size of triangles using the method of limits.

9 *Just Noticeable Difference* Measuring the just noticeable difference (roughly the same thing as difference threshold) for area, length, and saturation of color.

10 *Weber's Law and Weber Fraction* Plotting the graph that shows how Weber's fraction remains constant for different weights.

11 *DL vs. Weight* Plotting the graph that shows how the difference threshold changes for different weights.

12 *Scaling Vision* Magnitude estimation experiments in which you can judge the whiteness of a dot pattern, the length of lines, and the brightness of gray patches.

13 *Response Compression and Expansion* Plotting the functions that demonstrate response compression and response expansion in magnitude estimation.

FAST FOOD NATION
The Dark Side of the All-American Meal
Eric Schlosser
the blue bedspread
BEATTIE
PICTURING WILL
IDORU
William Gibson
NEW YORK TIMES BESTSELLING AUTHOR
THE UNBEARABLE LIGHTNESS OF BEING
MILAN KUNDERA
WORLD'S FAIR
E.L. DOCTOROW
BEL CANTO
ANN PATCHETT
The Blind Assassin
MARGARET ATWOOD
Abbey One Life at a Time, Please
WHEREVER YOU GO, THERE YOU ARE
JON KABAT-ZINN
THE BEST AMERICAN SHORT STORIES 2002
SUE MILLER, EDITOR
Jeanette Winterson
THE PASSION
Ron Carlson At the Jim Bridger
the curious incident of the dog in the night-time
BRAZZAVILLE BEACH
WILLIAM BOYD
JONATHAN FRANZEN
THE CORRECTIONS
PICADOR USA
THE SEVILLE COMMUNION
ARTURO PÉREZ-REVERTE
Michael Chabon Wonder Boys
PICADOR USA
NATIONAL BESTSELLER
COYOTE WAITS
TONY HILLERMAN
ELMORE LEONARD
CITY PRIMEVAL
COLD MOUNTAIN
FRAZIER
THE MONKEY WRENCH GANG
EDWARD ABBEY
Coyote in the Maze
edited by Peter Quigley
UTAH
NICK HORNBY
about a boy
ALIAS GRACE
ELMORE LEONARD
BARBARA EHRENREICH
Nickel and Dimed
Don DeLillo
WHITE NOISE
WRITTEN ON THE BODY
LAURA HILLENBRAND
SEABISCUIT
HAMILL
A DRINKING LIFE
THE BEAN TREES
BARBARA KINGSOLVER
Barbara Kingsolver Prodigal Summer
FORD
Rock Springs
A CONFEDERACY OF DUNCES
The House on Mango Street
Sandra Cisneros
ANIMAL DREAMS
KINGSOLVER
Michael Chabon Werewolves in Their Youth
Italo Calvino
Difficult Loves
The Inner Circle
THE SHARPSHOOTER BLUES
A Walk in the Woods
Bill Bryson
IN A SUNBURNED COUNTRY
BILL BRYSON

CHAPTER

2

INTRODUCTION TO THE PHYSIOLOGY OF PERCEPTION

Chapter Contents

The shift from colorful, sharp vision to the black-and-white blurred vision that occurs as illumination is decreased is caused by a shift from cone vision to rod vision. Visual perception is determined both by what is "out there" and by the physiology of the perceptual system.

Photo by Bruce Goldstein

VL *The Virtual Lab icons direct you to specific animations and videos designed to help you visualize what you are reading about. The number beside each icon indicates the number of the clip you can access through your CD-ROM or your student website.*

Some Questions We Will Consider:

- *How are physiological processes involved in perception? (p. 28)*
- *How is light transformed into electricity in the eye? (p. 32)*
- *How is what we see determined by the properties of the receptors in our retinas? (p. 36)*

Imagine that you are standing in a room. You can see everything clearly, especially the colored bindings of the books lining the shelves on your right. When you turn out the lights, the room is still illuminated by moonlight streaming in through the window, but now you can see only large forms, like the outline of the bookcase. After some time in the dark, you begin to see individual books on the shelves as well as some of the other objects in the room, although they are not very clear and you can't see any color. Everything is in shades of gray.

You may not be surprised by this description because you've probably experienced something similar. But let's look a little more closely at what happens when the lights go out. You wouldn't expect to see things very well in the lower illumination of the moonlight, but why does the color go away, and why don't you see sharp details anymore?

The answer to these questions is both simple and profound. The simple answer is that you have two types of visual receptors: cones, which control vision under high illuminations, and rods, which control vision under low illuminations. The cones are able to resolve fine details and extract information that enables you to see colors. The rods are poor at resolving details and are not able to extract information for color. In the light, you are using your cones to see details and colors. Under dim illuminations, you are using your rods, and although they slowly become more sensitive, so you can begin to see things better as you stay in the dark, they are unable to pick up details or create colors. Thus, the simple answer to the question "Where did all the colors and details go?" is that you use different visual receptors in the light and in the dark.

The more profound answer to our questions is that our perception of the environment depends not only on the properties of objects in the environment, but on the properties of our visual system as well. One of the main messages of this chapter is that we do not just perceive what is out there. We perceive what is out there *as filtered through the properties of the visual system.* This message is important because it holds not only for seeing but also for hearing, feeling with the skin, tasting, and smelling.

The idea that what we see depends on the properties of the visual system isn't really surprising when we consider the perceptual process, which we introduced in Figure 1.1 (page 5). Remember that perception is created from a series of transformations, beginning when an image of the environment is formed on the retina and then proceeding as light is transduced into electrical signals and these electrical signals are processed by other neurons in the visual system.

This chapter focuses on the initial processes of transformation in which an object in the environment becomes "transformed" into electricity in the nervous system. After introducing some facts about two basic components of sensory systems—neurons and the brain—we will describe how a stimulus in the environment, such as a tree, becomes transformed, first into an image on the retina, then into electrical signals in the visual receptors. Finally, we will return to the problem posed at the beginning of the chapter and describe how properties of these receptors determine our perceptions.

THE BRAIN: THE MIND'S COMPUTER

Today we take it for granted that the brain is the seat of the mind: the structure responsible for mental functions such as memory, thoughts, language, and—of particular interest to us—perceptions. But the idea that the brain controls mental functioning is a relatively modern idea.

Early History of the Physiological Approach

Our modern ideas about the physiological basis of perception are descended from a long line of speculation and research regarding the physiological workings of the mind. Early thinking about the physiology of the mind focused on determining the anatomical structures involved in the operation of the mind. In the 4th century B.C. the philosopher Aristotle (384–322 B.C.) stated that the heart was the seat of the mind and the soul (Figure 2.1).

The Greek physician Galen (ca. 130–200 A.D.) saw human health, thoughts, and emotions as being determined by four different "spirits" flowing from the **ventricles**—cavities in the center of the brain (Figure 2.1b). This idea was accepted all the way through the Middle Ages and into the Renaissance in the 1500s and early 1600s. In the early 1630s the philosopher Rene Descartes, although still accepting the idea of flowing spirits, specified the **pineal gland**, which was thought to be located over the ventricles, as the seat of the soul (Zimmer, 2004).

In 1664 the brain started to move to center stage, with the publication of the first major work on the brain, *The Anatomy of the Brain*, by Thomas Willis, a physician at the University of Oxford. In this book, which presented the results of dissections of the brains of humans, dogs, sheep, and other animals, Willis stated that the brain was responsible for mental functioning, that different functions were located in different regions of the brain, and that disorders of the brain were disorders of chemistry (Figure 2.1d). Although it would be a long time before researchers would begin to understand the specific mechanisms of brain functioning, Willis's observations and

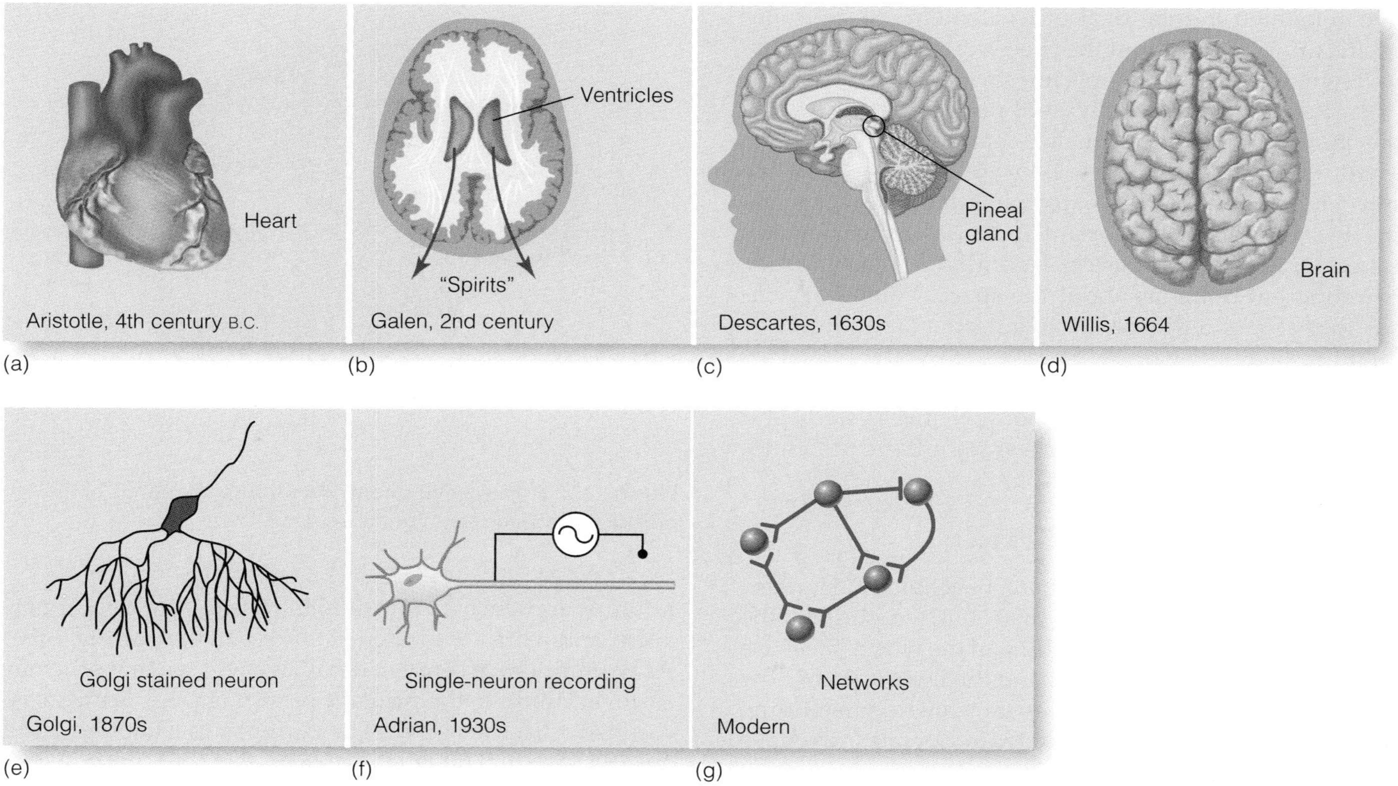

Figure 2.1 ▌ Some notable ideas and events regarding the physiological workings of the mind.

speculations were a beginning. Progress was slow, however, because many discoveries about the brain had to await the development of new technologies that would enable researchers to see the brain's microstructure and record its electrical signals.

Significant advances in anatomical techniques—specifically more sophisticated microscopes and the development of the technique of **staining**, which enabled researchers to inject dyes into the nervous system that were taken up by individual cells—led to the visualization of **neurons**, the cells that form the communication and information processing network of the nervous system. In 1873, the Italian anatomist Camillo Golgi developed a chemical technique that stained some neurons and left most unstained, thereby revealing the structure of single neurons in pictures (Figure 2.1e).

By the late 1800s, researchers had shown that a wave of electricity is transmitted down the nerve. To explain how these electrical signals result in different perceptions, Johannes Mueller in 1842 proposed the **doctrine of specific nerve energies**, which stated that our perceptions depend on "nerve energies" reaching the brain and that the specific quality we experience depends on which nerves are stimulated. Thus he proposed that activity in the optic nerve results in seeing, activity in the auditory nerve results in hearing, and so on. By the end of the 1800s, this idea had expanded to conclude that nerves from each of these senses reach different areas of the brain. This idea of separating different functions was to become a central principle of nervous system functioning.

Further details about how neurons operate had to await the development of electronic amplifiers that were powerful enough to make visible the extremely small electrical signals generated by the neuron. When this equipment became available in the 1920s, researchers began recording these electrical signals, called nerve impulses, and began to understand the chemical basis of nerve signals (Adrian, 1928, 1932) (Figure 2.1f).

The ability to record electrical signals from neurons ushered in the modern era of brain research, and by the 1960s the development of more sophisticated electronics and the availability of computers and the electron microscope made more sophisticated analysis of how neurons function possible. Most of the physiological research we will describe in this book had its beginning at this point, when it became possible to create pictures of networks of neurons and to determine how individual neurons respond to stimuli in the environment (Figure 2.1g).

We can appreciate the importance of being able to record from single neurons by considering the following analogy: You walk into a huge room in which there are thousands of delegates to a political convention who have just heard a speech. There is a great deal of noise and commotion in the room as people react to the speech. However, based on just hearing this "crowd noise," all you can say about what is going on is that the speech seems to have generated a great deal of excitement. To get more specific information about the speech it is necessary to listen to what individual people are saying.

Just as listening to individual people provides valuable information about what is happening in a large crowd, recording from single neurons provides valuable information about what is happening in the nervous system. It is, of course, important to record from as many neurons as possible because just as individual people may have different opinions about the speech, different neurons may respond differently to a particular stimulus or situation.

We will now briefly describe the overall layout of the brain, to give you an overview of the entire system, and then will zoom in to look in detail at some basic principles of neuron structure and operation.

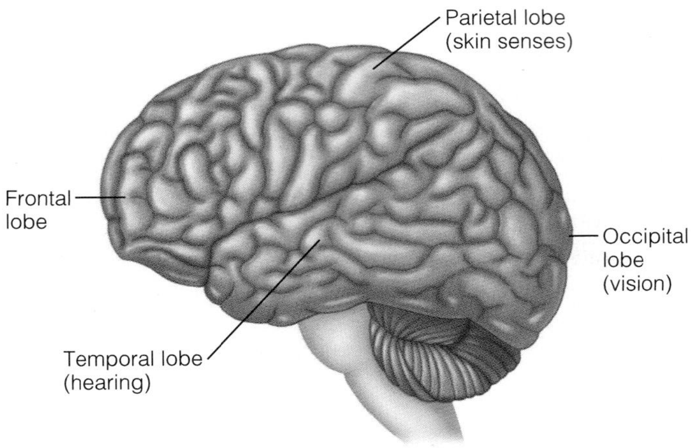

Figure 2.2 ▌ The human brain, showing the locations of the primary receiving areas for the senses.

Basic Structure of the Brain

In the first American textbook of psychology, Harvard psychologist William James (1890/1981) described the brain as the "most mysterious thing in the world" because of the amazing feats it achieves and the intricacies of how it achieves them. Although we are far from understanding the vast complexity of how the brain operates, we have learned a tremendous amount since James's time about how the brain determines our perceptions. Much of the research on the connection between the brain and perception has focused on activity in the cerebral cortex, the 2-mm-thick layer that covers the surface of the brain and contains the machinery for creating perception, as well as for other functions, such as language, memory, and thinking. A basic principle of cortical function is **modular organization**—specific functions are served by specific areas of the cortex.

VIRTUAL LAB 1, 2

One example of modular organization is how the senses are organized into **primary receiving areas**, the first areas in the cerebral cortex to receive the signals initiated by each sense's receptors (Figure 2.2). The primary receiving area for vision occupies most of the **occipital lobe**; the area for hearing is located in part of the **temporal lobe**; and the area for the skin senses—touch, temperature, and pain—is located in an area in the **parietal lobe**. As we study each sense in detail, we will see that other areas in addition to the primary receiving areas are also associated with each sense. For example, in Chapters 3 and 4 we will see that there is an area high in the temporal lobe concerned mainly with the perception of visual movement, and an area lower in the temporal lobe concerned with the perception of form. We will consider the functioning of various areas of the brain in more detail later. For the rest of this chapter we will be concerned with the properties of neurons.

NEURONS: COMMUNICATION AND PROCESSING

The key components of neurons are shown in Figure 2.3. The **cell body** contains mechanisms to keep the cell alive; **dendrites** branch out from the cell body to receive electrical signals from other neurons; and the **axon**, or **nerve**

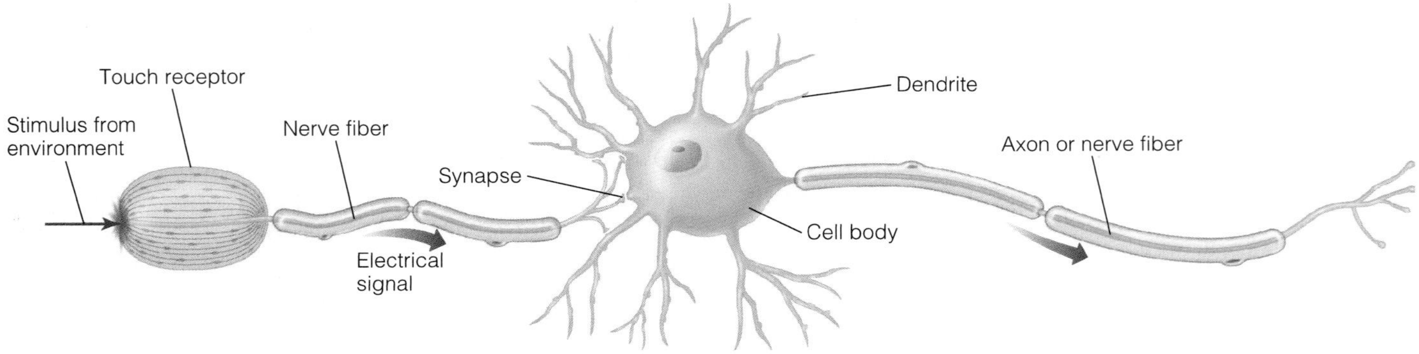

Figure 2.3 ▌ The neuron on the right consists of a cell body, dendrites, and an axon, or nerve fiber. The neuron on the left that receives stimuli from the environment has a receptor in place of the cell body.

fiber, is filled with fluid that conducts electrical signals. Neurons that are specialized to receive information from the environment are called **receptors** because they have receptor structures that are specialized to respond to different kinds of energy—light energy for seeing; mechanical deformation for touch and pain; pressure changes in the air for hearing; molecules in the air for smell; and molecules in liquid for taste. For our purposes, we are most interested not in the neuron's structure, but in the nature of the electrical signals that travel in these neurons. VL 3

Recording Electrical Signals in Neurons

What kinds of electrical signals are transmitted by neurons? When most people think of electrical signals, they imagine signals conducted along electrical power lines or along the wires used for household appliances. Unlike the electrical wires of your television set, however, neurons are bathed in liquid. Some people find this fact disconcerting because we are taught that we should keep electricity and water separated. However, as we shall see, the body has devised ways to create electrical signals within a liquid environment.

The key to understanding the "wet" electrical signals transmitted by neurons is to understand the components of the neuron's liquid environment. Neurons are surrounded by a solution rich in **ions**, molecules that carry an electrical charge. Ions are created when molecules gain or lose electrons, as happens when compounds are dissolved in water. For example, adding table salt (sodium chloride, NaCl) to water creates positively charged sodium ions (Na^+) and negatively charged chlorine ions (Cl^-). The solution outside the axon of a neuron is rich in positively charged sodium (Na^+) ions, whereas the solution inside the axon is rich in positively charged potassium (K^+) ions (Figure 2.4). These and other ions create electrical signals in the neuron when they flow across the cell membrane of the axon. We can see how this works by measuring electrical signals as they are conducted down the axon and by observing the connection between these potentials and the charged ions.

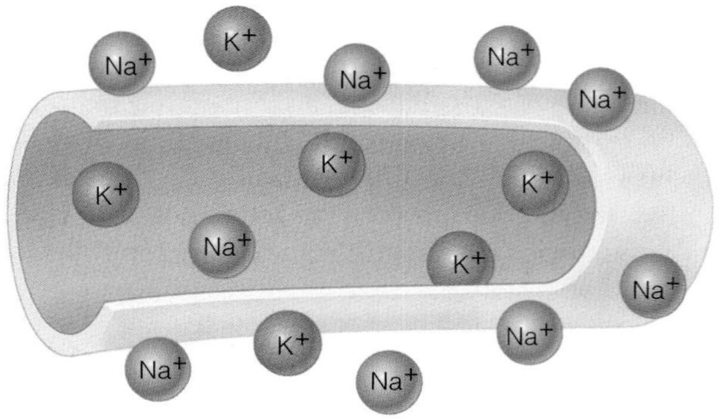

Figure 2.4 ▮ A nerve fiber, showing the high concentration of sodium outside the fiber and potassium inside the fiber. Other ions, such as negatively charged chlorine, are not shown.

METHOD ▪ Recording From a Neuron

To measure electrical signals in a neuron, we use **microelectrodes**, small shafts of glass or metal with tips small enough to pick up the electrical signals from a single neuron. Two electrodes are used to record signals: one recording electrode, shown on the left in Figure 2.5a, and one reference electrode, shown on the right. The recording device, called an oscilloscope, measures the difference in charge, measured in millivolts (where 1,000 millivolts = 1 volt), between the two electrodes and displays the results on a screen. The reference electrode is positioned far away from any electrical activity, and so records a stable baseline. The tip of the recording electrode is positioned in or near the neuron that will be activated, so any change in charge near the electrode's tip will be represented as a change in the difference in charge between the two electrodes.

Usually, signals that are picked up by the recording electrode are fed to the oscilloscope, to a computer that records and analyzes the signals, and to a sound amplifier and loudspeaker that changes the electrical signals into sounds so the researchers can tell when a neuron is firing without looking at the oscilloscope screen. VL 4

▪ ▪ ▪

Figure 2.5a shows a pressure-sensitive receptor and its nerve fiber with two microelectrodes positioned to record signals from the axon. The tip of the recording electrode is positioned inside the fiber, and the tip of the null electrode is positioned outside the axon.[1] The difference in charge between the two electrodes is –70 millivolts (mV; 1 mV = 1/1,000 volt), which means that the inside of the neuron is 70 mV more negative than the outside of the neuron. This –70 mV charge inside the neuron, which is typical of most neurons, is called the neuron's **resting potential** because it is the neuron's charge when it is at rest (Figure 2.6a). VL 5

Now that we have measured the resting potential, we are ready to push on the axon's pressure-sensitive receptor. If we push hard enough, we measure the rapid change in charge shown in Figure 2.5b. The charge inside the fiber rapidly increases from –70 mV to +40 mV compared to the outside and then returns back to the resting potential, all within about 1 millisecond (ms, or 1/1,000 seconds). This rapid increase in positive charge is called the **nerve impulse**, or **action potential**. (There are also smaller electrical potentials in nerve fibers, but we are going to focus

[1] In practice, most recordings are achieved with the tip of the electrode positioned just outside the neuron because it is technically difficult to insert electrodes into the neuron, especially if it is small. However, if the electrode tip is close enough to the neuron, the electrode can pick up the signals generated by the neuron.

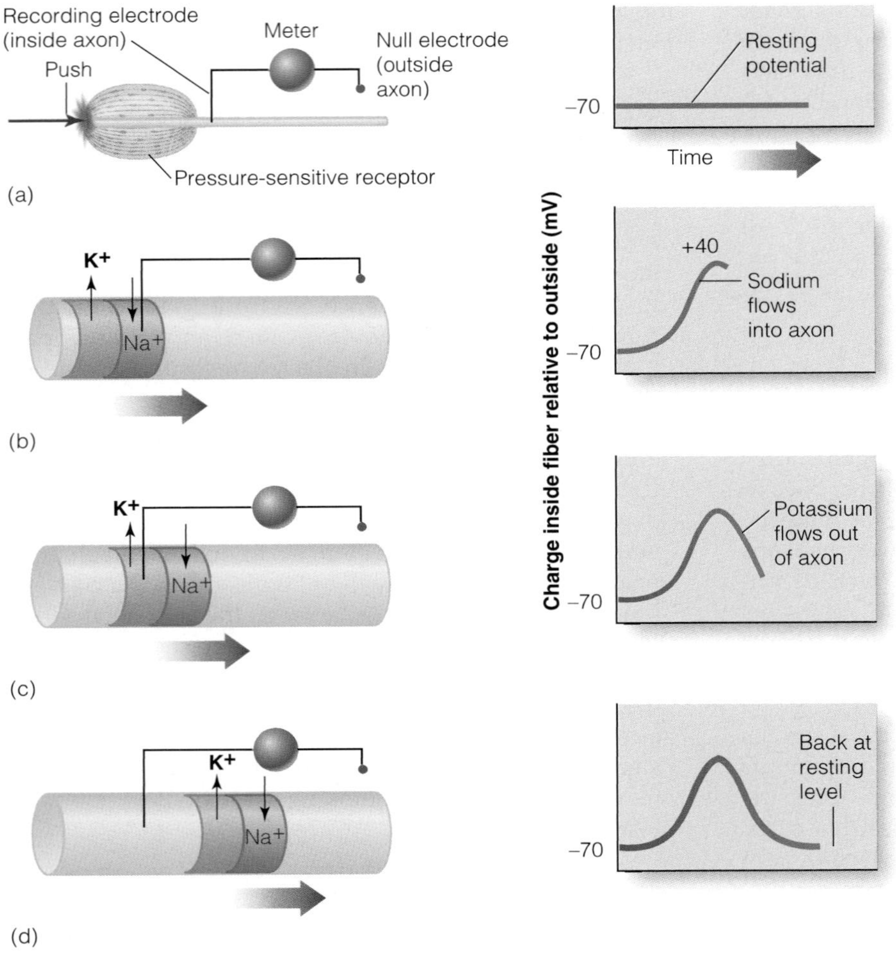

Figure 2.5 ▮ (a) Before the receptor is stimulated, so the nerve fiber is at rest, there is a difference in charge of −70 mV between the inside and the outside of the fiber. (b) When the receptor is pushed, an action potential is generated. As the action potential passes by the recording electrode, on its way down the fiber, sodium flows in, (c) potassium flows out, and (d) the fiber returns to its resting state. This series of events causes the charge inside the fiber to change, as shown on the right.

on action potentials because they are the most relevant electrical response for perception.)

If we observe the Na^+ and K^+ ions in the vicinity of the recording electrode, we see that positively charged sodium ions (Na^+) rush into the fiber at the beginning of the action potential. This Na^+ inflow is what causes the inside of the fiber to become more positive and creates the rising phase of the action potential (Figure 2.5b). This inflow of Na^+ is followed by an outflow of positively charged potassium (K^+). This K^+ outflow is what causes the inside of the fiber to become more negative and creates the downward phase of the action potential that brings the charge back to its original level (Figure 2.5c and d).

These rapid changes in sodium and potassium flow that create the action potential are caused by changes in the fiber's permeability to sodium and potassium. **Permeability** is a property of the cell membrane that refers to the ease with which a molecule can pass through the membrane. Before the action potential occurs, the membrane's permeability to sodium and potassium is low, so there is little flow of these molecules across the membrane. Stimulation of the receptor triggers a process that causes the membrane to become permeable to sodium. Sodium pours across the membrane to the inside of the axon for about 1 ms, and then the membrane's permeability to sodium decreases and its permeability to potassium increases, causing potassium to flow out of the axon for about 1 ms.[2] VL 6

This process creates the rapid increase and then decrease in positive charge inside the axon, which lasts about 1 ms at the electrode. The signal that is picked up by the electrode is the change in charge caused by the action potential as it passes by the electrode on its way down the axon. The fact that the action potential travels down the axon means that it is a **propagated response**—once the response is triggered it travels all the way down the axon without decreasing in amplitude. This is an extremely important property of the action potential because it enables neurons to transmit signals over long distances.

[2]After hearing this description of how Na^+ flows into the axon and K^+ flows out, students often wonder whether sodium would accumulate inside the axon and if potassium would accumulate outside the axon. This accumulating is prevented by a mechanism called the sodium-potassium pump, which continuously returns sodium to the outside of the axon and potassium to the inside, thereby maintaining sodium and potassium concentrations at their original levels so the axon can continue to generate nerve impulses.

Basic Properties of Action Potentials

As an action potential propagates down the axon, it remains the same size no matter how far it has traveled and no matter how intense the stimulus is. We can demonstrate this by determining how the neuron fires at different stimulus intensities. Figure 2.6 shows what happens when we do this. Each action potential appears as a sharp spike in these records because we have compressed the time scale to display a number of action potentials.

The three records in Figure 2.6 represent the axon's response to three intensities of stimulation. Figure 2.6a shows how the axon responds to gentle stimulation applied to the skin, whereas Figures 2.6b and 2.6c show how the response changes as the stimulation is increased. Comparing these three records leads to an important conclusion: Changing the stimulus intensity does not affect the size of the action potentials but does affect the rate of firing. VL 7

Although increasing the stimulus intensity can increase the rate of firing, there is an upper limit to the number of nerve impulses per second that can be conducted down an axon. This limit occurs because of a property of the axon called the **refractory period**—the interval between the time one nerve impulse occurs and the next one can be generated in the axon. Because the refractory period for most neurons is about 1 ms, the upper limit of a neuron's firing rate is about 500 to 800 impulses per second.

Another important property of action potentials is illustrated by the beginning of each of the records in Figure 2.6. Notice that action potentials occur even before the pressure stimulus is applied. This firing in the absence of stimuli from the environment is called **spontaneous activity**. Although you may wonder why an axon would be designed to fire in the absence of outside stimulation, you will see later that this spontaneous activity can play an important role in determining our perceptions.

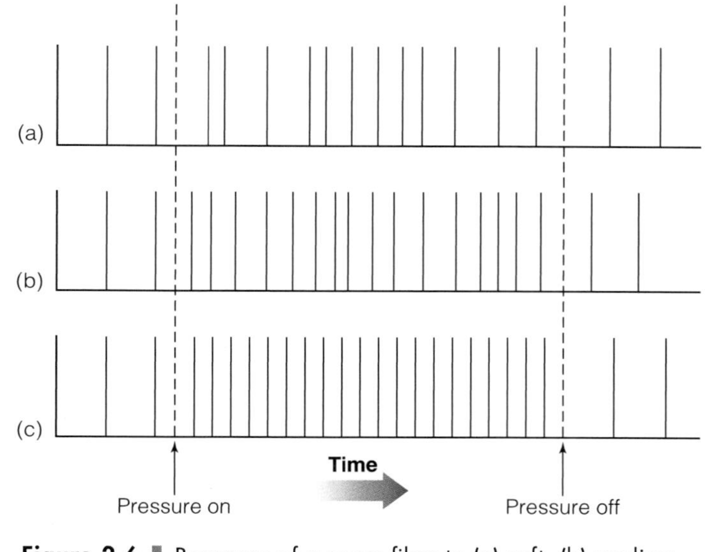

Figure 2.6 ▌ Response of a nerve fiber to (a) soft, (b) medium, and (c) strong stimulation. Increasing the stimulus strength increases both the rate and the regularity of nerve firing in this fiber.

What do these properties of the action potential mean in terms of their function for perceiving? The action potential's function is to communicate information. We have seen that pushing harder on a pressure receptor increases the rate of nerve firing. Thus, these increased rates of nerve firing carry information about the intensity of the stimulus. But if this information remains within a single neuron, it serves no function. In order to be meaningful, this information must be transmitted to other neurons and eventually to the brain or other organs that can react to this information.

The idea that the action potential in one neuron must be transmitted to other neurons poses the following problem: Once an action potential reaches the end of the axon, how is the message that the action potential carries transmitted to other neurons? The Spanish anatomist Santiago Ramon y Cajal (1852–1934) showed that there is a very small space between the neurons, known as a **synapse** (Figure 2.7). The discovery of the synapse raised the question of how the electrical signals generated by one neuron are transmitted across the space separating the neurons. As we will see, the answer lies in a remarkable chemical process that involves molecules called neurotransmitters.

Events at the Synapse

Early in the 1900s, it was discovered that the action potentials themselves do not travel across the synapse. Instead, they trigger a chemical process that bridges the gap between the sending neuron (the *presynaptic neuron*) and the receiving neuron (the *postsynaptic neuron*). When the action potential reaches the end of the presynaptic neuron, it causes the release of chemicals called **neurotransmitters** that are stored in synaptic vesicles in the presynaptic neuron (Figure 2.7). VL 8, 9

The neurotransmitter molecules flow into the synapse to small areas called **receptor sites** on the postsynaptic neuron that are sensitive to specific neurotransmitters. These receptor sites exist in a variety of shapes that match the shapes of particular neurotransmitter molecules. When a neurotransmitter makes contact with a receptor site matching its shape, it activates the receptor site and triggers a voltage change in the postsynaptic neuron. Thus, a neurotransmitter is like a key that fits a specific lock. It has an effect on the postsynaptic neuron only when its shape matches that of the receptor site.

At the synapse, then, an electrical signal generates a chemical process that, in turn, triggers a change in voltage in the postsynaptic neuron. The direction of this voltage change depends on the type of transmitter that is released and the nature of the cell body of the postsynaptic neuron. **Excitatory transmitters** cause the inside of the neuron to become more positive, a process called **depolariza-**

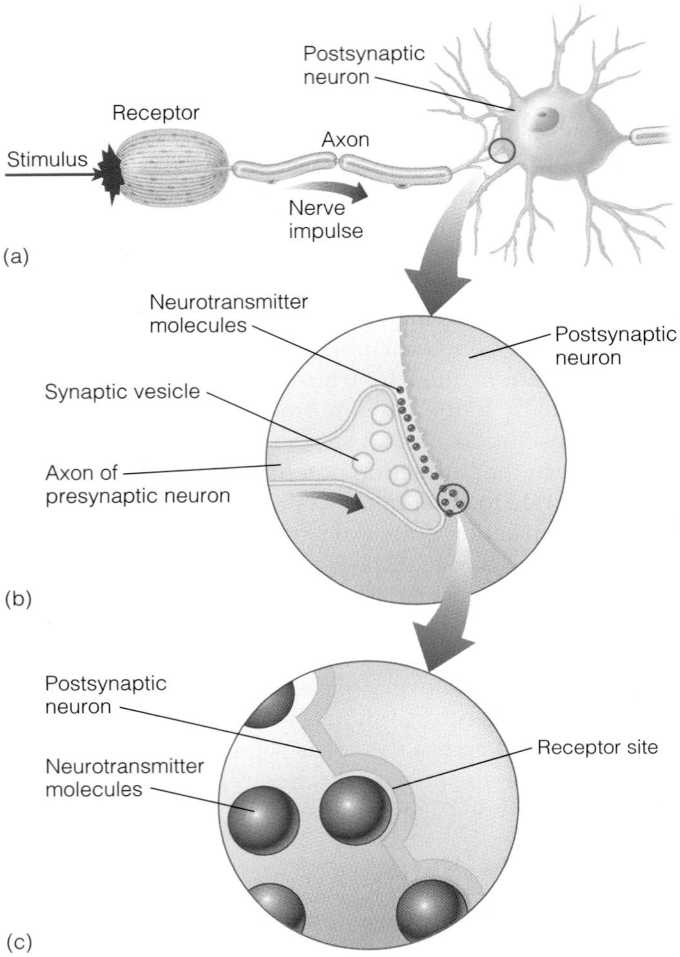

Figure 2.7 ▮ Synaptic transmission from one neuron to another. (a) A signal traveling down the axon of a neuron reaches the synapse at the end of the axon. (b) The nerve impulse causes the release of neurotransmitter molecules from the synaptic vesicles of the presynaptic neuron. (c) The neurotransmitters fit into receptor sites and cause a voltage change in the postsynaptic neuron.

tion. This depolarization is considered to be an **excitatory response** because sufficient depolarization can lead to the generation of action potentials in the postsynaptic neuron. **Inhibitory transmitters** cause the inside of the neuron to become more negative, a process called **hyperpolarization.** Hyperpolarization is considered an **inhibitory response** because it can prevent depolarization from reaching the level needed to generate action potentials. VL 10

We can summarize this description of the effects of excitatory and inhibitory transmitter as follows: The release of excitatory transmitter onto a neuron increases the chances that the neuron will generate action potentials and is associated with high rates of nerve firing. Conversely, the release of inhibitory transmitter onto a neuron decreases the chances that the neuron will generate action potentials and is associated with lowering rates of nerve firing.

Why does inhibition exist? If one of the functions of a neuron is to transmit its information to other neurons, why would the action potentials in one neuron trigger a process that decreases or eliminates nerve firing in the next neuron? The answer to this question is that the function of neurons is to transmit information *and* to process it, and that both excitation and inhibition are necessary for this processing. In Chapter 3, you will see how both excitation and inhibition help create this processing when we describe how synapses use both inhibition and excitation to control the flow of information through the nervous system.

Our story up to now has established the overall layout of the brain, and the structure and functioning of neurons. We will now introduce additional physiological principles, but rather than describing neurons in general, we will use examples from the visual system. Later in the book, we will see that many of the principles we will introduce in this chapter also apply to neurons in other sensory systems.

VISION BEGINS IN THE EYE

We see objects in the environment because light is reflected from these objects into the eye. The eye is where vision begins, because it is here that the reflected light is focused into a sharp image and where the light in the image is transformed into electrical signals in the visual receptors.

The **eye** consists of a focusing mechanism in front, the lens and cornea, and the retina, which contains the receptors for vision, lining the back of the eye (Figure 2.8). As light enters the eye through the pupil, it passes through the transparent cornea and lens, which are the eye's focusing elements. The cornea and lens create a focused image on the **retina**, which lines the back of the eye, and the light in this image stimulates the receptors. VL 11

As we noted at the beginning of the chapter, there are two kinds of visual receptors, **rods** and **cones**, which have different properties. These receptors contain light-sensitive chemicals called **visual pigments**, which react to light and trigger electrical signals. These signals flow through a network of neurons shown in Figure 2.8, and eventually emerge from the back of the eye in the **optic nerve**, which conducts signals toward the brain. The elements of the eye—the cornea and lens and the receptors and various other neurons—all play important roles in shaping what we see. As you will see in this chapter, they all contribute to the transformations that occur at the beginning of the perceptual process. VL 12, 13, 14

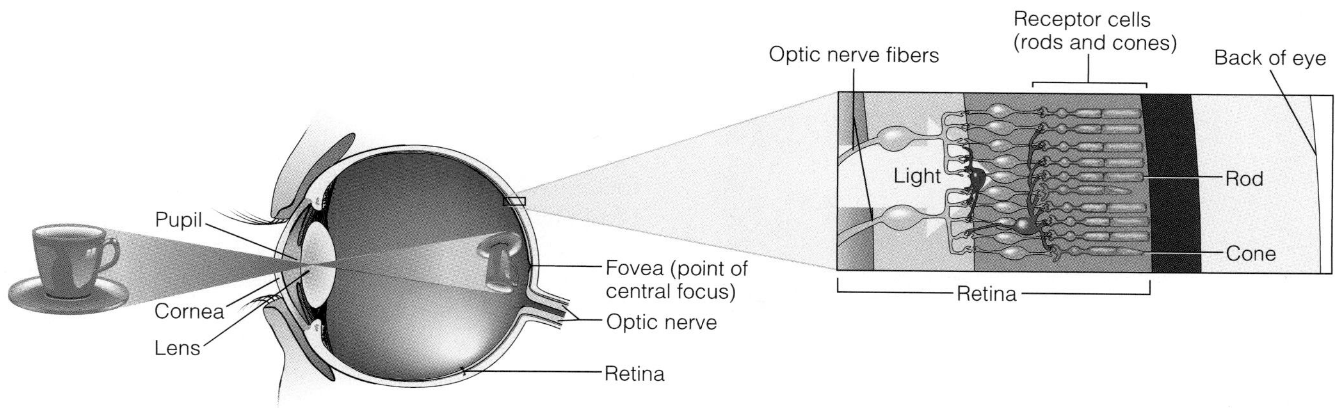

Figure 2.8 ▮ An image of the cup is focused on the retina, which lines the back of the eye. The close-up of the retina on the right shows the receptors and other neurons that make up the retina.

Light Is the Stimulus for Vision

Vision is based on visible light, which is a band of energy within the electromagnetic spectrum. The **electromagnetic spectrum** is a continuum of electromagnetic energy, which is energy produced by electric charges that is radiated as waves (Figure 2.9). The energy in this spectrum can be described by its **wavelength**—the distance between the peaks of the electromagnetic waves. The wavelengths in the electromagnetic spectrum range from extremely short–wavelength gamma rays (wavelength = about 10^{-12} meters, or one ten-billionth of a meter) to long-wavelength radio waves (wavelength = about 10^{+4} meters, or 10,000 meters).

Visible light, the energy within the electromagnetic spectrum that humans can perceive, has wavelengths ranging from about 400 to 700 nanometers (nm), where 1 nanometer = 10^{-9} meters. For humans and some other animals, the wavelength of visible light is associated with the different colors of the spectrum. Although we will usually specify light in terms of its wavelength, light can also be described as consisting of small packets of energy called photons, with one photon being the smallest possible packet of light energy.

A light's wavelength and number of photons are important properties that can be related to perception, as we will see shortly. Another property of light that is important for perception is that light is reflected from objects in the environment. In fact, the majority of your perceptual experience is due to this property of light, because we see objects when light is reflected from the object into our eye.

For example, as Sofia looks out the window at the tree in Figure 2.10a, she sees the tree and becomes aware of its properties because light is reflected from the tree into her eyes. She sees the leaves of the tree as green because the leaves reflect light from the middle of the visible spectrum. She sees the texture created by the leaves because of the way reflected light is structured by the leaves.

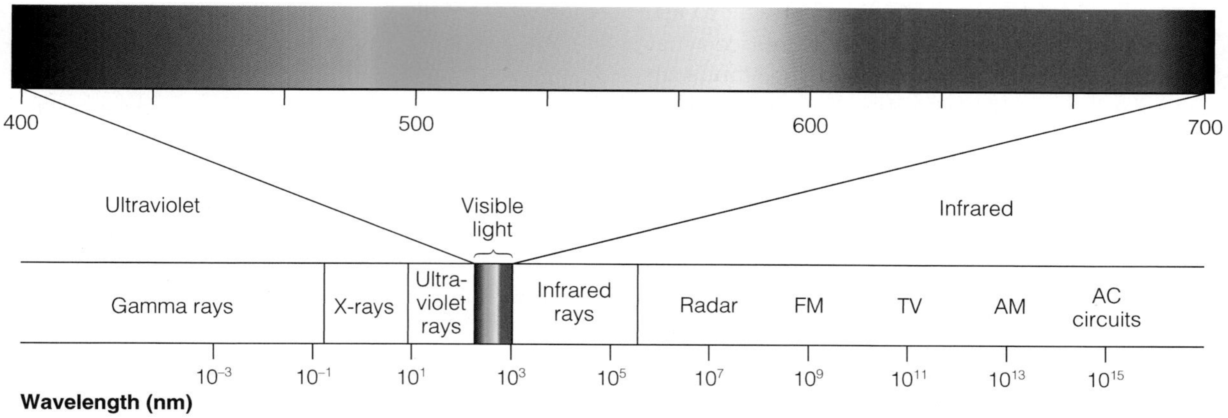

Figure 2.9 ▮ The electromagnetic spectrum, showing the wide range of energy in the environment and the small range within this spectrum, called visible light, that we can see.

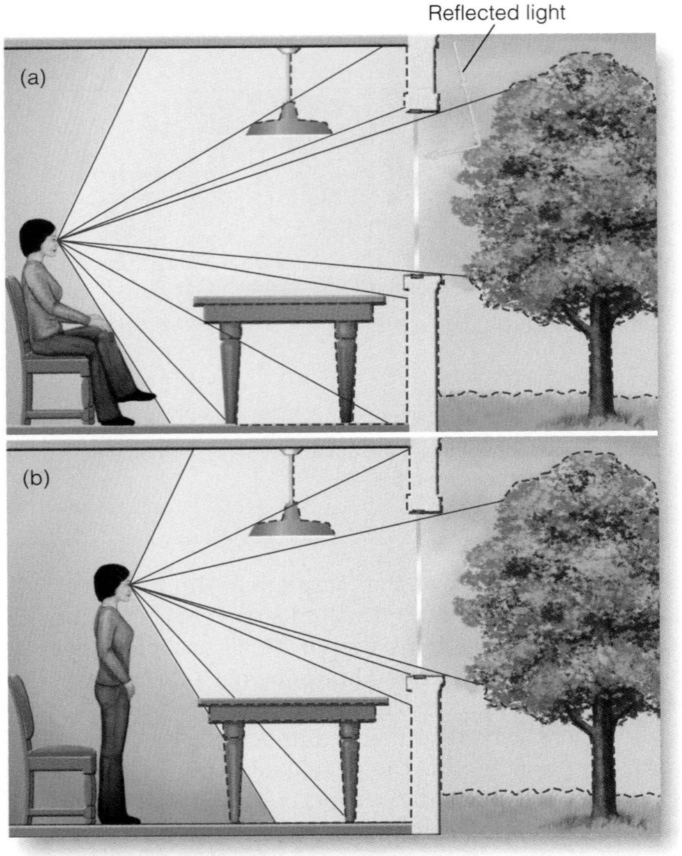

Figure 2.10 ▮ Sofia only sees objects like the tree that reflect light into her eyes. The light Sofia receives is structured both by characteristics of the environment and by the position of her eye in relation to the environment. Panels (a) and (b) show how the light reaching Sofia's eyes changes when she changes her viewpoint. For example, when she stands up she can no longer see the front leg of the table.

Another example of how light is structured by the environment is provided by the way light is reflected from various surfaces inside the room. The easiest way to appreciate the idea of "structured light" is to notice what happens to Sofia's view of the room when she stands up (Figure 2.10b). The rays in these figures show how light is structured by the borders of surfaces and objects in the room, and how a change in viewpoint can reveal portions of the scene that were previously hidden and can obscure parts that were originally visible.

The important thing about how light is reflected from objects and how its structure depends on the observer's viewpoint is that Sofia sees the inside of the room and the tree because *information* about the tree and the room is carried by reflected light that gets into her eyes. Thus, as we study the processes involved in vision, we will be concerned both with the actual stimulus in the environment *and* with the nature of the *information* about this stimulus that is received by the observer.

Images Are Focused on the Retina

Once light is reflected from an object into the eye, it needs to be focused. The **cornea**, the transparent covering of the front of the eye, accounts for about 80 percent of the eye's focusing power, but it is fixed in place, so can't change its focus. The **lens**, which supplies the remaining 20 percent of the eye's focusing power, changes its shape to adjust the eye's focus for stimuli located at different distances.

We can understand how the lens works by first considering what happens when we look at an object that is located more than 20 feet away. Light rays that reach the eye from this distance are essentially parallel (Figure 2.11a), and these parallel rays are brought to a focus on the retina. If, however, we move the object closer to the eye, the rays that enter the eye are no longer parallel and the focus point is pushed back, to a point behind the retina (Figure 2.11b). Of course, the light never comes to a fo-

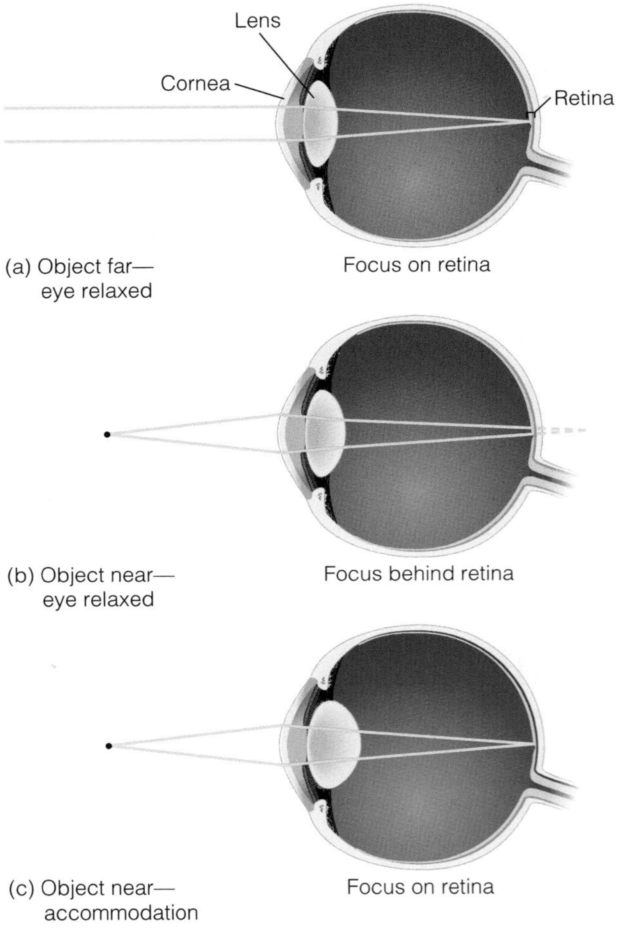

Figure 2.11 ▮ Focusing of light rays by the eye. (a) Parallel rays from a light source farther than 20 feet from the eye. Focus point: on retina; (b) nonparallel rays from a light source closer to the eye. Eye relaxed. Focus point: behind retina; (c) nonparallel rays. Eye accommodated (indicated by fatter lens). Focus point: on retina.

cus in this situation because it is stopped by the retina, and if things remain in this state, both the object's image on the retina and our perception of the object will be out of focus.

To bring the image into focus, the eye increases its **focusing power** by a process called **accommodation**, in which tightening muscles at the front of the eye increases the curvature of the lens so that it gets thicker (Figure 2.11c). This increased curvature bends the light rays passing through the lens more sharply so the focus point moves forward and creates a sharp image on the retina. The beauty of the process of accommodation is that we don't have to think about it; the lens's focusing power is constantly being adjusted to keep the image of the object we are looking at in focus.

DEMONSTRATION

Becoming Aware of What Is in Focus

Accommodation occurs unconsciously, so you are usually unaware that the lens is constantly changing its focusing power so you can see clearly at different distances. This unconscious focusing process works so efficiently that most people assume that everything, near and far, is always in focus. You can demonstrate that this is not so by holding a pencil point up, at arm's length, and looking at an object that is at least 20 feet away. As you look at the faraway object, move the pencil point toward you without actually looking at it (stay focused on the far object). The pencil will probably appear blurred.

Then move the pencil closer, while still looking at the far object, and notice that the point becomes more blurred and appears double. When the pencil is about 12 inches away, focus on the pencil point. You now see the point sharply, but the faraway object you were focusing on before has become blurred. Now, bring the pencil even closer until you can't see the point sharply no matter how hard you try. Notice the strain in your eyes as you try unsuccessfully to bring the point into focus. ■

When you changed focus during this demonstration, you were changing your accommodation. Accommodation enables you to bring both near and far objects into focus but objects at different distances are not in focus at the same time. But accommodation has its limits. When the pencil was too close, you couldn't see it clearly, even though you were straining to accommodate. The distance at which your lens can no longer adjust to bring close objects into focus is called the **near point**. The distance of the near point increases as a person gets older, a condition called **presbyopia** (for "old eye"). The near point for most 20-year-olds is at about 10 cm, but it increases to 14 cm by age 30, 22 cm at 40, and 100 cm at 60 (see Figure 2.12). This loss of ability to accommodate occurs because the lens hardens with age, and the ciliary muscles, which control accommodation, become weaker. These changes make it more difficult for the lens to change its shape for vision at close range. Though this gradual decrease in accommodative ability poses little problem for most people before the age of 45, at around that age the ability to accommodate begins to decrease rapidly, and the near point moves beyond a comfortable reading distance. There are two solutions to this problem. One is to hold reading material farther away, perhaps even at arm's length, and the other is to wear glasses to provide the necessary focusing power to bring light to a focus on the retina.

The combined action of the fixed focus of the cornea and the variable focus on the lens creates a focused representation of the environment inside the eye. The idea that our perception is based on a representation is an important one that bears repeating: As Sofia observes the inside of the room and the tree outside the window, *the room and the tree do not get into her eye.* Instead, a *representation* of the room and the tree are created by light that is reflected from the room and the tree, and this representation is what gets into her eye, in the form of an image on her retina. As we will now see, this representation in the form of an image is changed into another form when the light that falls on the retina is transformed into electricity by the visual receptors.

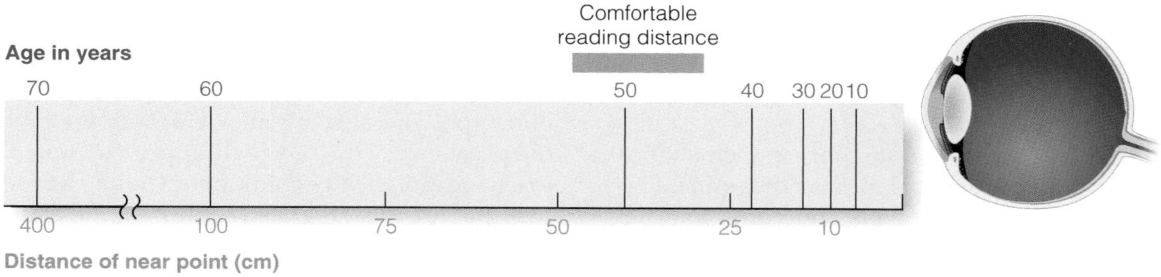

Figure 2.12 ■ Vertical lines show how the distance of the near point increases with increasing age (green numbers). When the near point becomes farther than a comfortable reading distance, corrective lenses (reading glasses) become necessary.

TRANSFORMING LIGHT INTO ELECTRICITY

How is light changed into electricity? The answer to this question involves the rods and the cones, which are the receptors for vision. Before considering how the rods and cones react to light, we will describe them.

The Rod and Cone Receptors

The structural differences between the rods and cones that gives them their names was first noticed by Max Schultze, who in 1865 looked through his microscope and saw large rod-shaped receptors and smaller cone-shaped receptors. Figure 2.13a shows modern drawings of the rods and cones, and Figure 2.13b is a picture created by a scanning electron microscope.

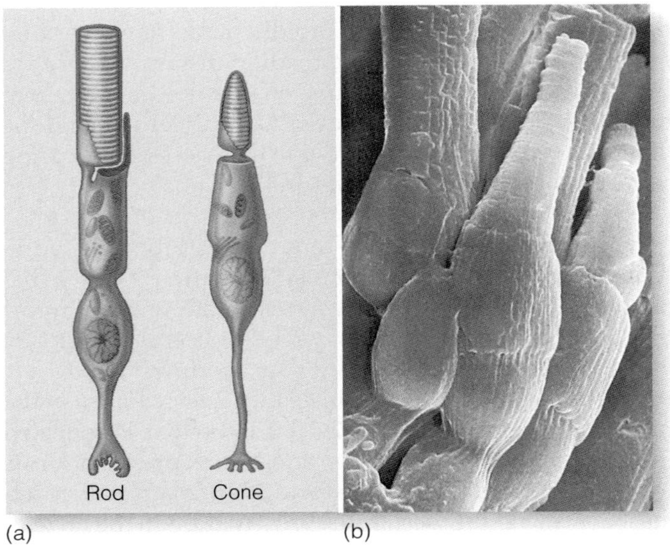

Figure 2.13 ▮ (a) Drawing of the rod and cone receptors. (b) Scanning electron micrograph showing the rod and cone outer segments. The rod outer segment on the left extends out of the picture, but the cylindrical shape of the rods and the tapered shape of the cones can be clearly seen.
(From "Scanning Electron Microscopy of Vertebrate Visual Receptors," by E. R. Lewis, Y. Y. Zeevi, & F. S. Werblin, 1969, Brain Research, *15, 559–562. Copyright © 1969 Elsevier Science Publishers, B. V. Reprinted with permission.)*

The rods and the cones differ not only in their shapes but also in the way they are distributed on the retina. Figure 2.15, which shows how the rods and cones are distributed, reflects a number of the retina's properties.

- There is one small area, the **fovea**, that contains only cones.
- The **peripheral retina**, which includes all of the retina outside of the fovea, contains both rods and cones. It is important to note that although the fovea is the only place where there are *only* cones, *most* of the cones are in the peripheral retina. This occurs because the fovea is so small (about the size of this "o"), that it contains only about 1 percent, or 50,000, of the 5,000,000 cones in the retina (Tyler 1997a, 1997b).
- There are many more rods in the peripheral retina than cones because most of the retina's receptors are located there and because there are about 120 million rods and 5 million cones. The preponderance of rods in the peripheral retina is shown in Figure 2.16, which indicates the "mosaic" of receptors created by the rods (small green circles) and the cones (large yellow and green circles).
- There is one area in the retina where there are no receptors. This is the place where the optic nerve leaves the eye, so all of the receptors are swept to the side, as shown in Figure 2.17. This area is called the **blind spot**. Although you are not normally aware of the blind spot, you can become aware of it by doing the following demonstration.

DEMONSTRATION

"Seeing" the Blind Spot

You can demonstrate the existence of the blind spot perceptually by closing your right eye and, with the cross in Figure 2.14 aligned with your left eye, looking at the cross while moving the book (or yourself) slowly back and forth. When the book is 6 to 12 inches from your eye, the circle disappears. This is the point at which the image of the circle is falling on the blind spot.

Figure 2.14 ■

Why aren't we usually aware of the blind spot? One reason is that the blind spot is located off to the side of our visual field, where objects are not in sharp focus. Because of this and because we don't know exactly where to look for it (as opposed to the demonstration, in which we are focusing our attention on the circle), the blind spot is hard to detect.

But the most important reason that we don't see the blind spot is that some mechanism in the brain "fills in" the place where the image disappears (Churchland & Ramachandran, 1996). Think about what happened when the spot in the demonstration disappeared. The place where the spot used to be wasn't replaced by a hole or by nothingness—it was filled in by the white page. VL 15, 16

One way to appreciate the fact that the rods and cones are distributed differently in the retina is by considering what happens when functioning receptors are missing

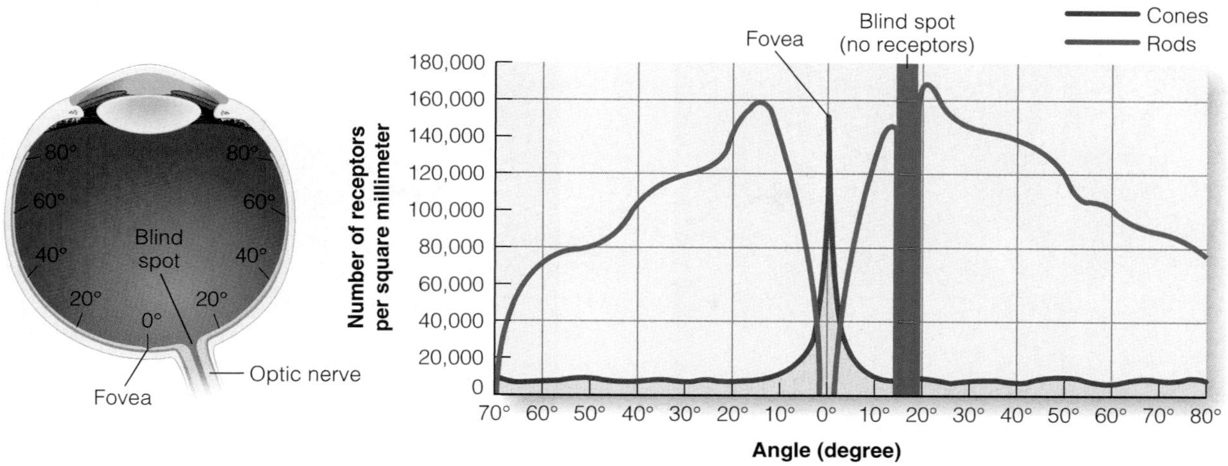

Figure 2.15 ▌ The distribution of rods and cones in the retina. The eye on the left indicates locations in degrees relative to the fovea. These locations are repeated along the bottom of the chart on the right. The brown bar near 20 degrees indicates the place on the retina where there are no receptors because this is where the ganglion cells leave the eye to form the optic nerve.
(Adapted from Human Information Processing, *by P. Lindsay and D. A. Norman, 1977, 2nd ed., p. 126. Copyright © 1977 Academic Press, Inc. Adapted with permission.)*

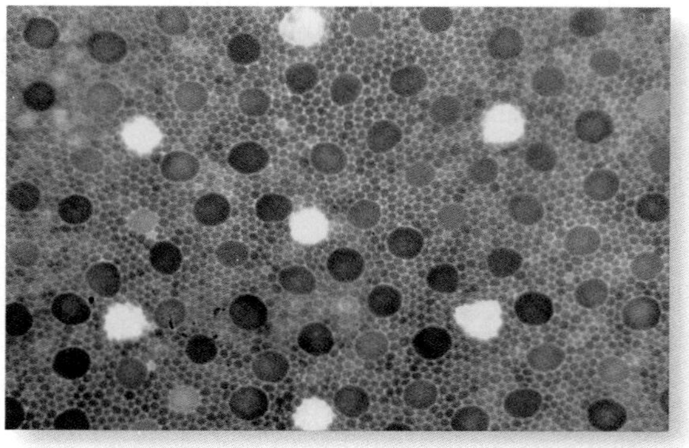

Figure 2.16 ▌ The mosaic of rods and cones in the peripheral retina of a monkey. The small circles are rods and the larger ones, cones. The cones appear larger because the retina has been sliced across the receptor's inner segments, which are fatter for the cones compared to the rods, in the peripheral retina. The cones that are stained yellow contain a visual pigment that absorbs shorter wavelength light than the pigment in the other cones.
(From deMonasterio et al., 1981.)

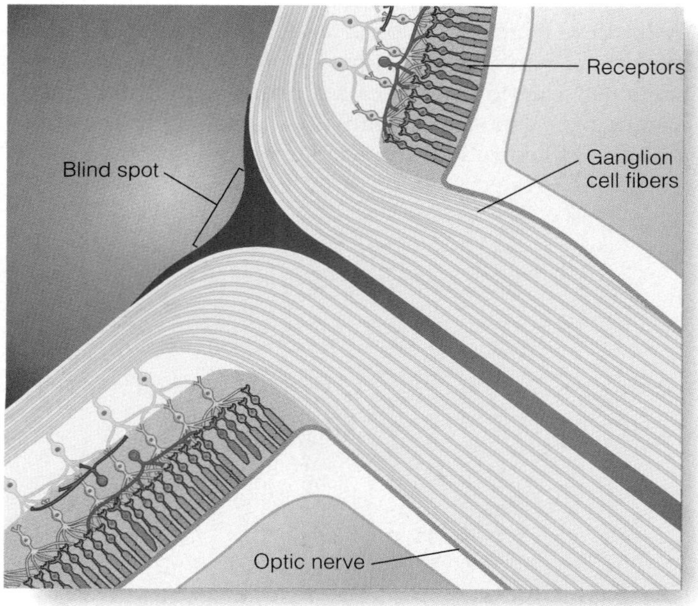

Figure 2.17 ▌ There are no receptors at the place where the optic nerve leaves the eye. This enables the receptor's ganglion cell fibers to flow into the optic nerve. The absence of receptors in this area creates the blind spot.

from one area of the retina. A condition called **macular degeneration**, which is most common in older people, destroys the cone-rich fovea and a small area that surrounds it. This creates a "blind spot" in central vision, so when a person looks at something he or she loses sight of it (Figure 2.18a).

Another condition, called **retinitis pigmentosa**, is a degeneration of the retina that is passed from one generation to the next (although not always affecting everyone in a family). This condition first attacks the peripheral rod receptors and results in poor vision in the peripheral visual field (Figure 2.18b). Eventually, in severe cases, the foveal cone receptors are also attacked, resulting in complete blindness.

Transduction of Light Into Electricity

The part of the receptors called the **outer segments** are the center of action for the visual receptors, because it is here that the light acts to create electricity. These outer segments contain stacks of discs (Figure 2.19a), which

Figure 2.18 ▮ (a) In a condition called macular degeneration, the fovea and surrounding area degenerates so the person cannot see whatever he or she is looking at. (b) In retinitis pigmentosa, the peripheral retina initially degenerates and causes loss of vision in the periphery. The resulting condition is sometimes called "tunnel vision."

contain **visual pigment molecules** (Figure 2.19b). These molecules, which loop back and forth across the disc membrane seven times (Figure 2.19c), have two components: (1) a large protein called **opsin** with a molecular weight of about 40,000, and (2) a small light-sensitive molecule called **retinal** (molecular weight = 268).

Retinal, which is attached to the opsin at the point shown, reacts to light and is therefore responsible for **visual transduction**—the transformation of light energy into electrical energy. The transduction process begins when the light-sensitive retinal absorbs one photon of light. (Remember that a photon is the smallest possible

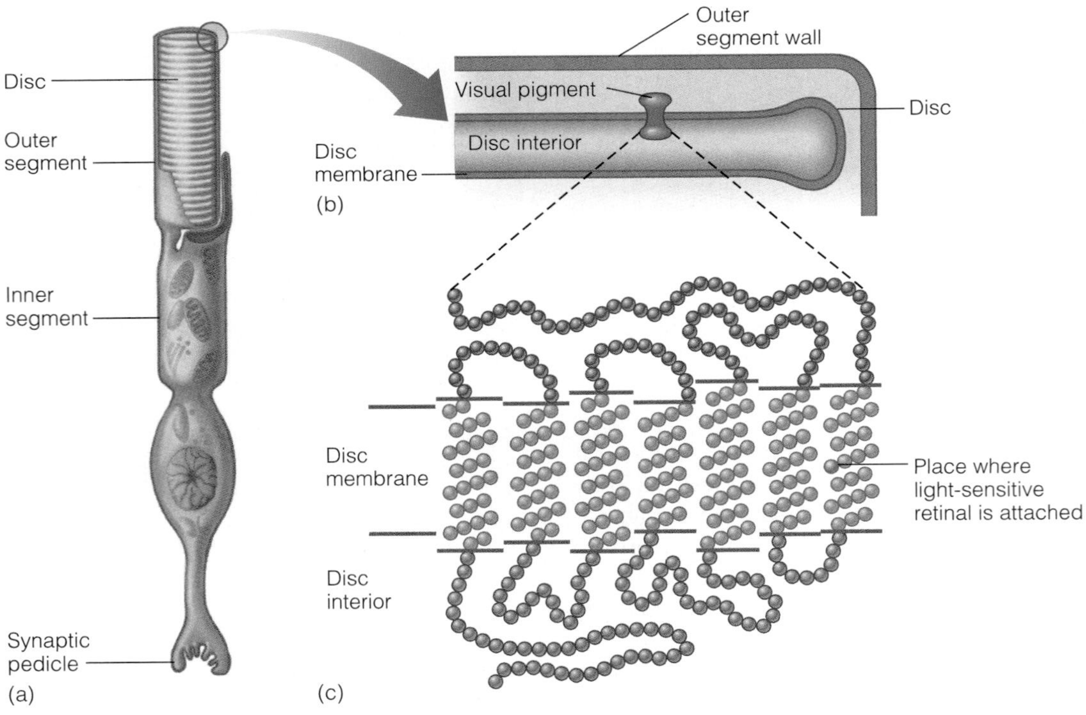

Figure 2.19 ▮ (a) Rod receptor showing discs in the outer segment. (b) Close-up of one disc showing one visual pigment molecule in the membrane. (c) Close-up showing how the protein opsin in one visual pigment molecule crosses the disc membrane seven times. The light-sensitive retinal molecule is attached at the place indicated.

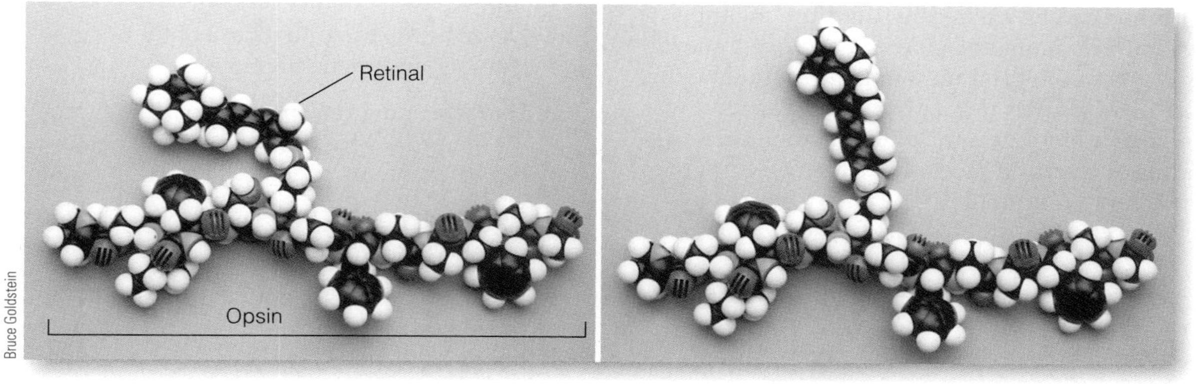

Figure 2.20 ▮ Model of a visual pigment molecule. The horizontal part of the model shows a tiny portion of the huge opsin molecule near where the retinal is attached. The smaller molecule on top of the opsin is the light-sensitive retinal. The model on the left shows the retinal molecule's shape before it absorbs light. The model on the right shows the retinal molecule's shape after it absorbs light. This change in shape is one of the steps that accompanies the generation of an electrical response in the receptor.

packet of light energy.) When the retinal absorbs this photon it changes its shape (Figure 2.20), a process called **isomerization**.

How does this isomerization result in an electrical signal? This question has been approached in two ways, psychophysically and physiologically. You may wonder how it is possible to study a chemical process such as isomerization using psychophysics. After all, psychophysics involves measuring the relationship between the stimulus and perception, and *not* with chemicals in the eye.

The fact that psychophysics can provide information about physiological processes is so important that we are going to describe, in some detail, a psychophysical experiment by Selig Hecht, Simon Shlaer, and Maurice Pirenne (1942), in which they determined that a rod receptor can be excited when just one of the visual pigment molecules in the receptor is isomerized. The idea behind this experiment was simple: Determine the absolute threshold for detecting a light, and then determine how many visual pigment molecules this threshold-level light would affect.

Using a precisely calibrated light source, Hecht determined that the threshold for seeing the light was 100 photons. Of these 100 photons, 50 bounce off the surface of the cornea before entering the eye or are reflected or absorbed by the lens, just inside the eye, or by the jellylike vitreous humor that fills the inside of the eye (Figure 2.21). Of the remaining 50 photons, only about 7 are actually absorbed by visual pigment molecules. The rest either slip between the receptors or pass through a receptor without hitting the light-sensitive part of a visual pigment molecule. Thus, Hecht determined that when 7 visual pigment molecules are activated, a person can see the light. (See also Sackett, 1972.)

But Hecht wasn't satisfied just to show that activating 7 visual pigment molecules causes a person to see the light. He reasoned that because the flash of light seen by

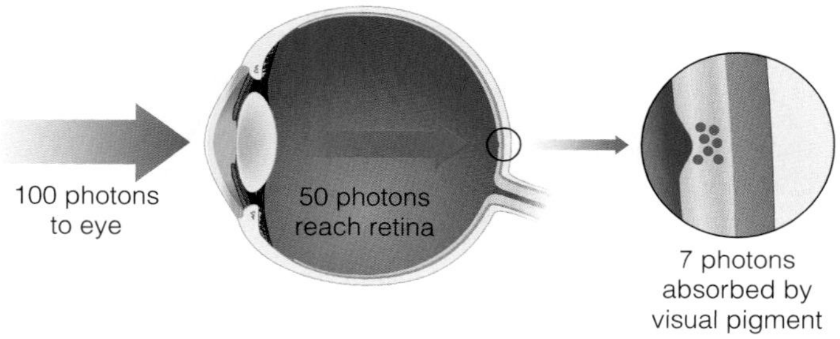

Figure 2.21 ▮ The observer in Hecht et al.'s (1942) experiment could see a spot of light containing 100 photons. Fifty photons reached the retina, and 7 photons were absorbed by visual pigment molecules. Each of these visual pigment molecules were most likely contained in different rods. Hecht concluded that (1) it takes only 1 photon to activate a rod receptor and (2) we see the light when 7 rod receptors are activated simultaneously.

his observer covered about 500 receptors, it is highly unlikely that more than 1 of the 7 activated visual pigment molecules would be in the same receptor. Look at it this way: If you were in a helicopter hovering high above an array of 500 small cylinders, and you released 7 ping pong balls, what is the probability that 2 of these balls would fall into the same cylinder? The answer is "very small." Similarly, it is equally unlikely that of the 7 visual pigment molecules that absorbed light in Hecht's experiment, 2 of them would have entered the same receptor. Hecht therefore concluded that only one visual pigment molecule per receptor is isomerized. This means that a rod receptor can be excited by 1 photon of light and that we see the light when 7 rod receptors are activated simultaneously. Thus, Hecht's psychophysical measurements provided information about the physiology of the visual receptors (see Goldstein, 2001a).

About 30 years after Hecht, Shlaer, and Pirenne concluded that a rod can be excited by the isomerization of only one visual pigment molecule, physiologists began uncovering the physiological mechanisms that make this amazing feat possible. What the physiologists found was that isomerizing a single visual pigment molecule triggers thousands of chemical reactions, which, in turn, trigger thousands more (Figure 2.22).

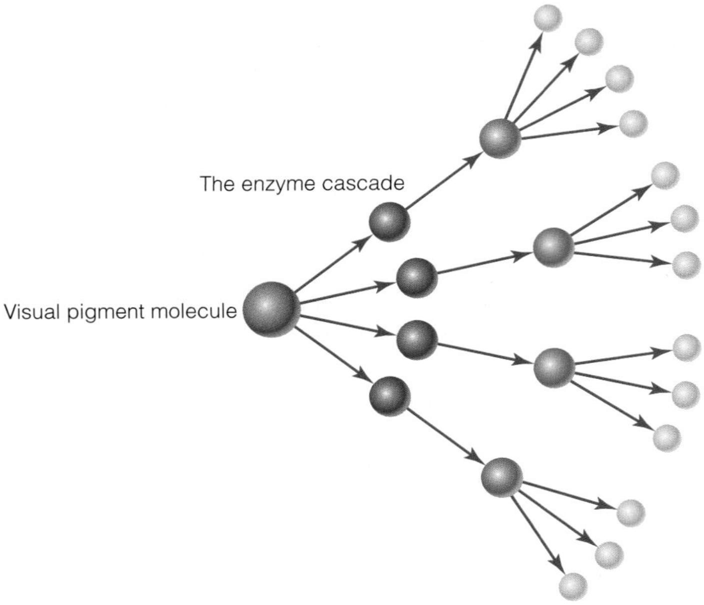

Figure 2.22 ▮ This sequence symbolizes the enzyme cascade that occurs when a single visual pigment molecule is activated by absorption of a quantum of light. In the actual sequence of events, each visual pigment molecule activates hundreds more molecules, which, in turn, each activate about a thousand more molecules. Thus, isomerization of one visual pigment molecule activates about a million other molecules.

A biological chemical that in small amounts facilitates chemical reactions in this way is called an enzyme, and the sequence of reactions triggered by the activated visual pigment molecule is therefore called the **enzyme cascade**. Just as pulling your bathtub drain plug can empty the entire tub, isomerizing one visual pigment molecule can cause a chemical effect that is large enough to activate the entire rod receptor. For more specific details as to how this is accomplished, see "If You Want to Know More" at the end of this chapter.

The visual pigments play an essential role in vision by triggering the electrical response in the receptors. As we will see in the next sections, the properties of these visual pigments also determine a number of the basic properties of vision.

TEST YOURSELF 2.1

1. How did people's conception of the physiological basis of the mind change between the time of the ancient Greeks and the 1800s?
2. Describe the basic structure of the brain in terms of its lobes and their functions.
3. Describe a neuron in terms of (a) its structure and (b) the properties of the action potentials transmitted by the neuron.
4. What happens when an action potential reaches the end of an axon?
5. Describe the process that starts with light being reflected from an object, continues as a structured image is focused on the retina, and culminates in generation of electrical potentials in the receptors.
6. What are the two types of visual receptors, and how are they distributed across the retina?
7. Describe the psychophysical experiment that showed that it takes one photon to excite a rod, and the physiological mechanism that explains how this is possible.

PIGMENTS AND PERCEPTION

In our example at the beginning of the chapter, we noted that it is often difficult to perceive objects in a dimly illuminated room, but as you spend more time in dim illumination, you eventually begin to see light that you hadn't noticed before and can begin to make out forms that were previously difficult to detect. These perceptions reflect a process called **dark adaptation**—the increase in sensitivity that takes place as the eyes stay in the dark. Dark adaptation, which enables people to function in dim illuminations, illustrates an important difference between the rods and the cones.

Dark Adaptation of the Rods and Cones

Although you might be aware that your eye becomes more sensitive as you spend time in the dark, it is probably not obvious that the increase in sensitivity takes place in two distinct stages: an initial rapid stage and a later, slower stage. These two stages are revealed by measurement of the **dark-adaptation curve**—a plot of how visual sensitivity changes in the dark beginning just after the lights are extinguished. VL 17

We will now describe three ways of measuring the dark adaptation curve that show that the initial rapid stage is due to adaptation of the cone receptors and that the second slower stage is due to adaptation of the rod receptors. We will first describe how to measure a two-stage, dark-adaptation curve that is caused by both the rods and the cones. We will then measure the dark adaptation of the cones alone and of the rods alone and will show how the different adaptation rates of the rods and the cones can be explained by differences in their visual pigments.

In all of our dark-adaptation experiments, we ask our observer to adjust the intensity of a small, flashing test light so he or she can just barely see it. This is similar to the psychophysical *method of adjustment* that we described in Chapter 1 (see p. 13). In the first experiment, our observer looks at a small fixation point while paying attention to a flashing test light that is off to the side. Because the observer is looking directly at the fixation point, its image falls on the fovea, and the image of the test light falls in the periphery (Figure 2.23). Thus, the test light stimulates both rods and cones, and any adaptation measured with this test light should reflect the activity of both the rod and the cone receptors. The procedure for measuring the dark-adaptation curve is as follows:

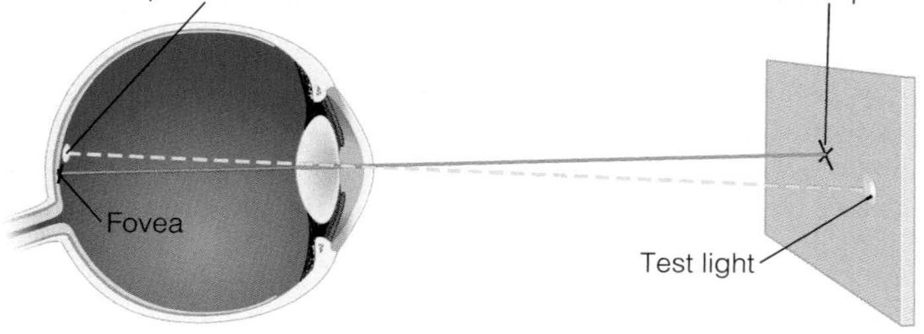

Figure 2.23 ▮ Viewing conditions for a dark-adaptation experiment. The image of the fixation point falls on the fovea, and the image of the test light falls in the peripheral retina.

METHOD ▪ Measuring Dark Adaptation

The first step in measuring dark adaptation is to light adapt the observer by exposure to an intense light. While the light is on, the **light-adapted sensitivity** is measured by having the observer adjust the intensity of the test light so he or she can just barely see it. Once the light-adapted sensitivity is determined, the intense light is extinguished to begin the process of dark adaptation. The course of dark adaptation is usually measured by giving the observer control over the intensity of the test light and asking the observer to continually adjust its intensity so he or she can just barely see it. The result, shown as the red curve in Figure 2.24, is a dark-adaptation curve.

▪ ▪ ▪

The dark-adaptation curves show that as dark adaptation proceeds, the observer becomes more sensitive to the light and so slowly turns down its intensity. Note that lower intensities are at the bottom of this graph, so as the curve moves downward, this means that the observers' sensitivity is increasing.

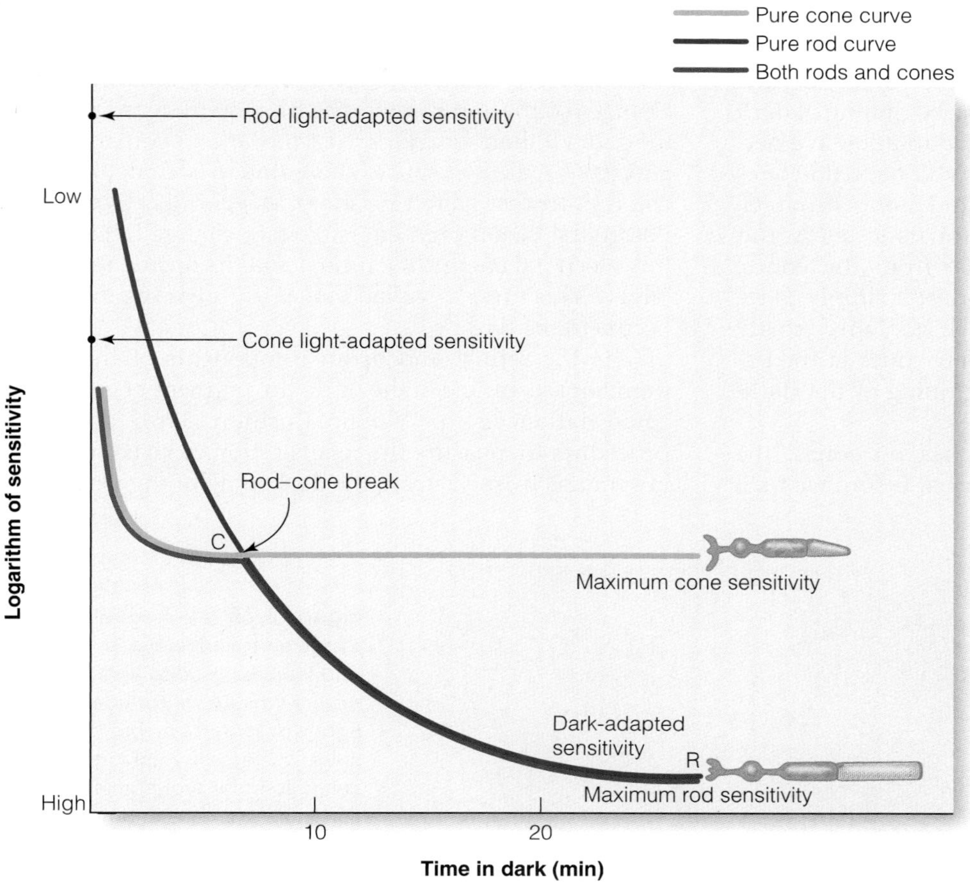

Figure 2.24 ▮ Three dark-adaptation curves. The red line is the two-stage dark-adaptation curve, with an initial cone branch and a later rod branch. The green line is the cone-adaptation curve. The black line curve is the rod-adaptation curve. Note that the downward movement of these curves represents an *increase* in sensitivity. The curves actually begin at the points indicating "light-adapted sensitivity," but there is a slight delay between the time the lights are turned off and when measurement of the curves begins. *(Partial data [pure rod curve] from "Rhodopsin Measurement and Dark Adaptation in a Subject Deficient in Cone Vision," by W. A. H. Ruston, 1961,* Journal of Psychology, 156, *193–205. Copyright © 1961 by the Psychological Society, Cambridge University Press.)*

The dark-adaptation curve indicates that the observer's sensitivity increases in two phases. It increases rapidly for the first 3 to 4 minutes after the light is extinguished and then levels off, until after about 7 to 10 minutes, sensitivity begins increasing again and continues to do so for another 20 to 30 minutes. The sensitivity at the end of dark adaptation, labeled **dark-adapted sensitivity**, is about 100,000 times greater than the light-adapted sensitivity measured before dark adaptation began.

Measuring Cone Adaptation To measure dark adaptation of the cones alone, we have to ensure that the image of the test light stimulates only cones. We achieve this by having the observer look directly at the test light so its image will fall on the all-cone fovea, and by making the test light small enough so its entire image falls within the fovea. The dark-adaptation curve determined by this procedure is indicated by the green line in Figure 2.24. This curve, which reflects only the activity of the cones, matches the initial phase of our original dark-adaptation curve but does not include the second phase. Does this mean that the second part of the curve is due to the rods? We can show that the answer to this question is "yes" by doing another experiment.

Measuring Rod Adaptation We know that the green curve of Figure 2.24 is due only to cone adaptation because our test light was focused on the all-cone fovea. Because the cones are more sensitive to light at the beginning of dark adaptation, they control our vision during the early stages of dark adaptation, and so we don't see what is happening to the rods. In order to reveal how the sensitivity of the rods is changing at the beginning of dark adaptation, we need to measure dark adaptation in a person who has no cones. Such people, who have no cones due to a rare genetic defect, are called **rod monochromats**. Their all-rod retinas provide a way for us to study rod dark adaptation without interference from the cones. (Students sometimes wonder why we can't simply place the test flash in the periphery, which contains mostly rods. The answer is that there are a few cones in the periphery, which will influence the beginning of the dark-adaptation curve.)

Because the rod monochromat has no cones, the light-adapted sensitivity we measure just before we turn off the lights is determined by the rods. The sensitivity we determine, which is the "rod light-adapted sensitivity," is much lower than the light-adapted sensitivity we measured in the original experiment. Once dark adaptation begins, the rods increase their sensitivity and reach their final dark-adapted level in about 25 minutes (Rushton, 1961).

We can summarize the process of dark adaptation in a normal observer as follows: As soon as the light is extinguished, the sensitivity of both the rods and cones both begin increasing. However, since the cones are more sensitive at the beginning of dark adaptation, they control our vision and determine the early part of the dark-adaptation curve. After about 3 to 5 minutes, the cones are finished adapting and their curve levels off. Meanwhile, the rods are still increasing their sensitivity, and by about 7 minutes of dark adaptation, the rods catch up to the cones and then become more sensitive than the cones. When this occurs, the rods begin controlling vision because they are now more sensitive, and the dark adaptation curve now reflects rod adaptation. The place where the rods begin to determine the dark adaptation curve is called the **rod-cone break**.

Why do the rods take about 20 to 30 minutes to reach their maximum sensitivity (point R on the curve), compared to only 3 to 4 minutes for the cones (point C)? The answer to this question involves a process called visual pigment regeneration, which occurs with different speeds in the rods and the cones.

Visual Pigment Regeneration When the visual pigment absorbs light, the light-sensitive retinal molecule changes shape and triggers the transduction process (Figure 2.20). It then separates from the larger opsin molecule, and this separation causes the retina to become lighter in color, a process called **pigment bleaching** (Figure 2.25). Before the visual pigment can again change light energy into electrical energy, the retinal and the opsin must be rejoined. This process, called **visual pigment regeneration**, occurs in the dark.

As the retinal and opsin components of the visual pigment recombine in the dark, the pigment begins to become darker again. William Rushton (1961) devised a procedure to measure the regeneration of visual pigment in humans by measuring the darkening of the visual pig-

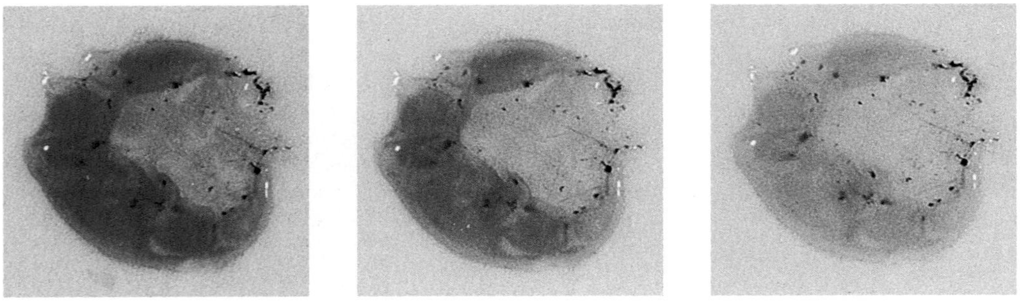

Bruce Goldstein

(a) (b) (c)

Figure 2.25 ▮ A frog retina was dissected from the eye in the dark and then exposed to light. (a) This picture was taken just after the light was turned on. The dark red color is caused by the high concentration of visual pigment in the receptors. As the pigment bleaches, the retina becomes lighter, as shown in (b) and (c).

ment during dark adaptation. Rushton's measurements showed that cone pigment takes 6 minutes to regenerate completely, whereas rod pigment takes over 30 minutes. When he compared the course of pigment regeneration to the rate of psychophysical dark adaptation, he found that the rate of cone dark adaptation matched the rate of cone pigment regeneration and the rate of rod dark adaptation matched the rate of rod pigment regeneration.

Rushton's result demonstrated two important connections between perception and physiology:

1. Our sensitivity to light depends on the concentration of a chemical—the visual pigments.
2. The speed at which our sensitivity is adjusted in the dark depends on a chemical reaction— the regeneration of the visual pigments.

We can appreciate the fact that the increase in sensitivity we experience during dark adaptation is caused by visual pigment regeneration by considering what happens when the visual pigments can't regenerate because of a condition called **detached retina**. A major cause of detached retinas is traumatic injuries of the eye or head, as when a baseball player is hit in the eye by a line drive. When the retina becomes detached, it has become separated from a layer that it rests on, called the pigment epithelium, which contains enzymes that are necessary for pigment regeneration. The result is that once pigments are bleached, so the opsin and retinal are separated, they can't be recombined, and the person becomes blind in the part of the visual field served by that area of the retina.

Spectral Sensitivity of the Rods and Cones

Another way to show that perception is determined by the properties of the visual pigments is to compare rod and cone **spectral sensitivity**—an observer's sensitivity to light at each wavelength across the visible spectrum.

In our dark-adaptation experiments, we used a white test light, which contains all wavelengths in the visible spectrum. To determine spectral sensitivity, we use flashes of **monochromatic light**, light that contains only a single wavelength. We determine the threshold for seeing these monochromatic lights for wavelengths across the visible spectrum. For example, we might first determine the threshold for seeing a 420-nm (nanometer) light, then a 440-nm light, and so on, using one of the psychophysical methods for measuring threshold described in Chapter 1. The result is the curve in Figure 2.26a, which shows that the threshold for seeing light is lowest in the middle of the spectrum; that is, less light is needed to see wavelengths in the middle of the spectrum than to see wavelengths at either the short- or long-wavelength ends of the spectrum.

We can change threshold to sensitivity by the formula, sensitivity = 1/threshold, and when we do this, our threshold curve of Figure 2.26a becomes the sensitivity curve of Figure 2.26b, which is called a **spectral sensitivity curve**. We measure the cone spectral sensitivity curve by having people look directly at the test light, so that it stimulates only the cones in the fovea. We measure the rod spectral sensitivity curve by measuring sensitivity after the eye is dark adapted (so the rods are the most sensitive receptors) and presenting test flashes off to the side of the fixation point.

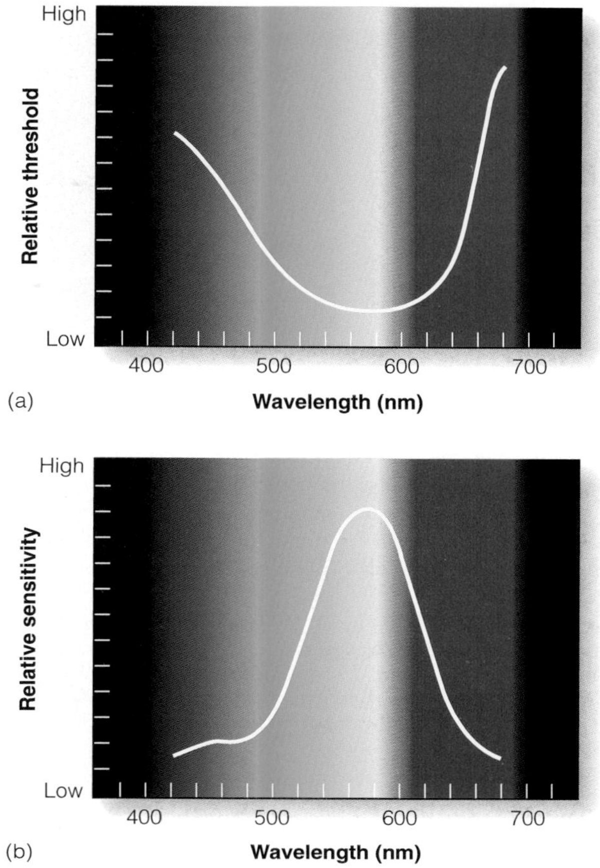

Figure 2.26 ▮ (a) The threshold for seeing a light versus wavelength. (b) Relative sensitivity versus wavelength—the *spectral sensitivity curve.*
(Adapted from "The Receptors of Human Color Vision," by G. Wald, 1964, Science, *145, p. 1009 and 1011. Copyright ©1964 by the American Association for the Advancement of Science. Adapted with permission.)*

The cone and rod spectral sensitivity curves in Figure 2.27 show that the rods are more sensitive to short-wavelength light than are the cones, with the rods being most sensitive to light of 500 nm and the cones being most sensitive to light of 560 nm. This difference in the sensitivity of the rods and the cones to different wavelengths means that as vision shifts from the cones to the rods during dark adaptation, we become relatively more sensitive to short-wavelength light—that is, light nearer the blue and green end of the spectrum.

You may have noticed an effect of this shift to short-wavelength sensitivity if you have observed how green

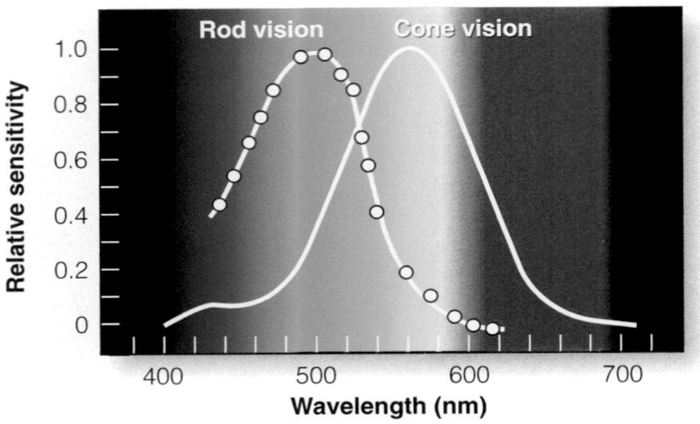

Figure 2.27 ▮ Spectral sensitivity curves for rod vision (left) and cone vision (right). The maximum sensitivities of these two curves have been set equal to 1.0. However, the relative sensitivities of the rods and the cones depend on the conditions of adaptation: the cones are more sensitive in the light, and the rods are more sensitive in the dark. The circles plotted on top of the rod curve are the absorption spectrum of the rod visual pigment.

(From "Human Rhodopsin," by G. Wald and P. K. Brown, 1958, Science, 127, p. 222–226, figure 6, and "The Receptors of Human Color Vision," by G. Wald, 1964, Science, 145, p. 1007–1017. Copyright © 1964 by the American Association for the Advancement of Science. Adapted with permission.)

Figure 2.28 ▮ Flowers for demonstrating the Purkinje shift. See text for explanation.

foliage seems to stand out more near dusk. This shift from cone vision to rod vision that causes this enhanced perception of short wavelengths during dark adaptation is called the **Purkinje** (Pur-kin'-jee) **shift**, after Johann Purkinje, who described this effect in 1825. You can experience this shift in color sensitivity that occurs during dark adaptation by closing one of your eyes for about 5–10 minutes, so it dark adapts, and then switching back and forth between your eyes and noticing how the blue flower in Figure 2.28 is brighter compared to the red flower in your dark-adapted eye.

The difference between the rod and cone spectral sensitivity curves is caused by differences in the absorption spectra of the rod and cone visual pigments. An **absorption spectrum** is a plot of the amount of light absorbed by a substance versus the wavelength of the light. The absorption spectra of the rod and cone pigments are shown in Figure 2.29. The rod pigment absorbs best at 500 nm, the blue-green area of the spectrum.

There are three absorption spectra for the cones because there are three different cone pigments, each contained in its own receptor. The short-wavelength pigment absorbs light best at about 419 nm; the medium-wavelength pigment absorbs light best at about 531 nm; and the long-wavelength pigment absorbs light best at about 558 nm. VL 18

The absorption of the rod visual pigment closely matches the rod spectral sensitivity curve (Figure 2.29), and the short-, medium-, and long-wavelength cone pigments that absorb best at 419, 531, and 558 nm, respectively, add together to result in a psychophysical spectral sensitivity curve that peaks at 560 nm. Because there are fewer short-wavelength receptors and therefore much less of the short-wavelength pigment, the cone spectral sensitivity curve is determined mainly by the medium- and long-wavelength pigments (Bowmaker & Dartnall, 1980; Stiles, 1953).

It is clear from the evidence we have presented that the rod and cone sensitivity in the dark and sensitivity to different wavelengths are determined by the properties of the rod and cone visual pigments. Thus, even though per-

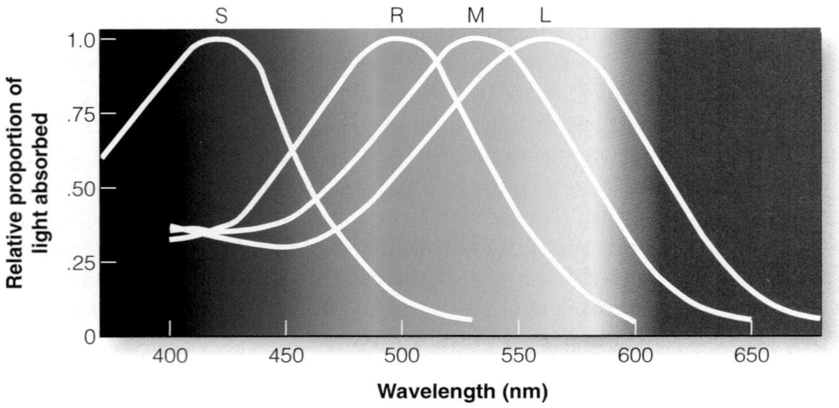

Figure 2.29 ▮ Absorption spectra of the rod pigment (R), and the short- (S), medium- (M), and long-wavelength (L) cone pigments.

(From J. K. Bowmaker and H. J. A. Dartnall, "Visual Pigments of Rods and Cones in a Human Retina," Journal of Physiology, 298, 1980, 501–511. Copyright © 1980. Reprinted with permission of the author.)

ception may be determined by neurons that are located in the brain, the nature of the perceptions that the brain creates are influenced by events that occur as light is reflected from objects, enters the eye, is focused, and is then transformed into electricity. Each of these steps determines the nature of the information that will be transmitted out of the eye and which will eventually reach the brain. In the next chapter, we will consider how the brain processes the information that it receives from the eyes.

SOMETHING TO CONSIDER: TRANSFORMATIONS AND RECEPTORS

We have seen that perception involves transformations. A tree is transformed into reflected light and becomes an image on the retina, which is then transformed into electrical signals by the receptors. This means that what we perceive depends on the nature of the transformation. For example, what we see with our rods may be different from what we see with the cones because the rod and cone pigments regenerate at different rates and absorb light in different parts of the spectrum.

To carry this idea a step further, we can consider perception in other animals. Figure 2.30 shows the absorption spectra of the honeybee's visual pigments. Although the honeybee has three cone pigments like the human, there is an important difference: the honeybee's pigments are more spread out, so the "honeybee visible spectrum" is broader than the human's. Also, the pigment at the short-wavelength end of the spectrum absorbs ultraviolet light. These wavelengths below 400 nm, which humans can't see, are strongly reflected by the flowers on which the honeybee depends for its survival.

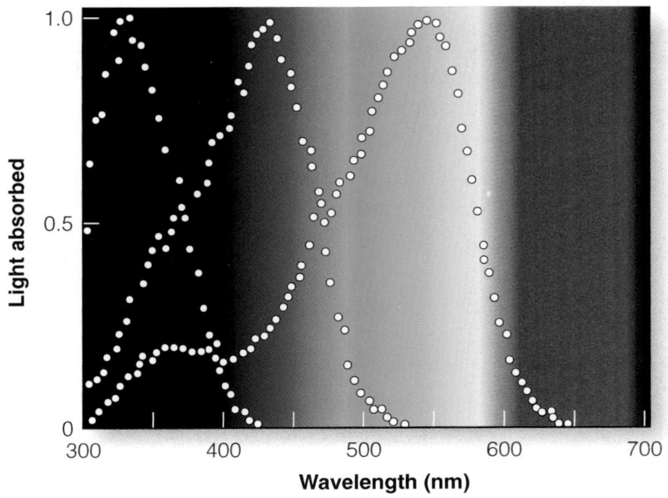

Figure 2.30 ▌ Absorption spectra of honeybee's visual pigments. The pigment at the far left absorbs light below the wavelength range that is visible to humans.

Although we have no way of knowing what the honeybee is experiencing from these short-wavelengths, we do know that it has access to different information about the flower than we have. The honeybee's transformations are different so it receives different information and, perhaps because of this, experiences the world differently. In the next chapter, we will take this idea of transformations a step further by showing how transformations of the electrical signals caused by interactions between neurons can influence our perceptions.

TEST YOURSELF 2.2

1. Where on the retina does a researcher need to put a stimulus to test dark adaptation of the cones? How can adaptation of the rods be measured without any interference from the cones?
2. Describe how rod and cone sensitivity changes starting when the lights are turned off and how this change in sensitivity continues for 20–30 minutes in the dark.
3. What happens to visual pigment molecules when they (a) absorb light and (b) regenerate? What is the connection between visual pigment regeneration and dark adaptation?
4. What is spectral sensitivity? How is a cone spectral sensitivity curve determined? A rod spectral sensitivity curve?
5. What is an absorption spectrum? How do rod- and cone-pigment absorption spectra compare, and what is their relationship to rod and cone spectral sensitivity?
6. What are the two answers (one "simple" and the other "profound") to the question, "Why is our perception of colors and details worse in dim illumination than in bright illumination?"
7. What does it mean to say that our perception depends on transformations? Give an example from human perception and an example from honeybee perception of how different transformations can result in different perceptions.

THINK ABOUT IT

1. Because the long axons of neurons look like electrical wires, and both neurons and electrical wires conduct electricity, it is tempting to equate the two. Compare the functioning of axons and electrical wires in terms of their structure and the nature of the electrical signals they conduct.
2. In the demonstration "Becoming Aware of What Is in Focus" on page 31, you saw that we see things clearly

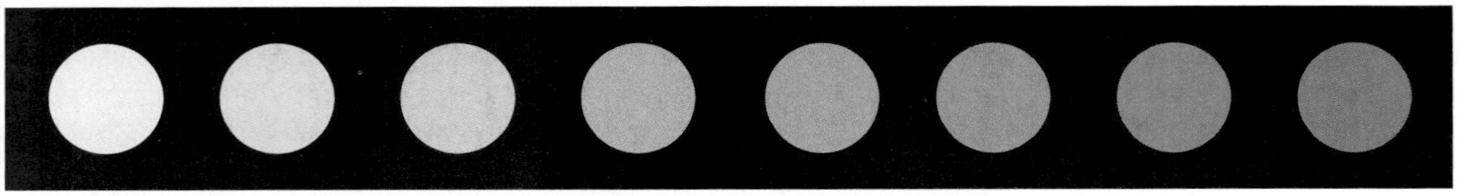

Figure 2.31

only when we are looking directly at them so that their image falls on the cone-rich fovea. But consider the common observation that the things we aren't looking at do not appear "fuzzy," that the entire scene appears "sharp" or "in focus." How can this be, in light of the results of the demonstration?

3. Here's an exercise you can do to get more in touch with the process of dark adaptation: Find a dark place where you will make some observations as you adapt to the dark. A closet is a good place to do this because it is possible to regulate the intensity of light inside the closet by opening or closing the door. The idea is to create an environment in which there is dim light (no light at all, as in a darkroom with the safelight out, is too dark). Take this book into the closet, opened to this page. Close the closet door all the way so it is very dark, and then open the door slowly until you can just barely make out the white circle on the far left in the Figure 2.31, but can't see the others or can see them only as being very dim. As you sit in the dark, become aware that your sensitivity is increasing by noting how the circles to the right in the figure slowly become visible over a period of about 20 minutes. Also note that once a circle becomes visible, it gets easier to see as time passes. If you stare directly at the circles, they may fade, so move your eyes around every so often. Also, the circles will be easier to see if you look slightly above them.

IF YOU WANT TO KNOW MORE

1. ***Disorders of focusing.*** Many people wear glasses to compensate for the fact that the optical system of their eye does not focus a sharp image on their retinas. The three most common problems are farsightedness, nearsightedness, and astigmatism.

   Goldstein, E. B. (2002). *Sensation and perception* (6th ed.). Belmont, CA: Wadsworth. (See Chapter 16, "Clinical aspects of vision and hearing," which is also available on the website for this book.)

2. ***Transduction.*** The molecular basis of transduction, in which light is changed into electrical energy, is a process that involves sequences of chemical reactions.

   Burns, M., & Lamb, T. D. (2004). Visual transduction by rod and cone photoreceptors. In L. M. Chalupa & J. S. Werner (Eds.), *The visual neurosciences.* Cambridge, MA: MIT Press.

3. ***A disorder of dark adaptation.*** There is a rare clinical condition called Oguchi's disease, in which adaptation of the rods is slowed so that it takes 3 or 4 hours for the rods to reach their maximum sensitivity in the dark. What makes this condition particularly interesting is that the rate of rod visual pigment regeneration is normal, so there must be a problem somewhere between the visual pigments and the mechanism that determines sensitivity to light.

   Carr, R. E., & Ripps, H. (1967). Rhodopsin kinetics and rod adaptation in Oguchi's disease. *Investigative Ophthalmology, 6,* 426–436.

4. ***Animal perception.*** The idea that perception is determined by the functioning of our nervous system is illustrated by differences between human and vision and animal vision, like the case of the honeybee described in this chapter. A large amount of research has determined the basic perceptual capacities of animals.

   Collett, T. S., & Harkness, L. I. K. (1982). Depth vision in animals. In D. J. Ingle, M. A. Goodale, & R. J. W. Mansfield (Eds.), *Analysis of visual behavior* (pp. 111–176). Cambridge, MA: MIT Press.

   Fernald, R. D. (2000). Evolution of eyes. *Current Opinion in Neurobiology, 10,* 444–450.

KEY TERMS

Absorption spectrum (p. 40)
Accommodation (focus) (p. 31)
Action potential (p. 25)
Axon (nerve fiber) (p. 24)
Blind spot (p. 32)
Cell body (p. 24)
Cones (p. 28)
Cornea (p. 30)
Dark adaptation (p. 36)
Dark-adaptation curve (p. 36)
Dark-adapted sensitivity (p. 38)
Dendrites (p. 24)
Depolarization (p. 27)
Detached retina (p. 39)
Doctrine of specific nerve energies (p. 23)
Electromagnetic spectrum (p. 29)
Enzyme cascade (p. 36)
Excitatory response (p. 28)
Excitatory transmitters (p. 27)
Eye (p. 28)
Focusing power (p. 31)
Fovea (p. 32)
Hyperpolarization (p. 28)

Inhibitory response (p. 28)
Inhibitory transmitters (p. 28)
Ions (p. 25)
Isomerization (p. 35)
Lens (p. 30)
Light-adapted sensitivity (p. 37)
Macular degeneration (p. 33)
Microelectrode (p. 25)
Modular organization (p. 24)
Monochromatic light (p. 39)
Near point (p. 31)
Nerve impulse (action potential) (p. 25)
Neuron (p. 23)
Neurotransmitter (p. 27)
Occipital lobe (p. 24)
Opsin (p. 34)
Optic nerve (p. 28)
Outer segments (p. 33)
Parietal lobe (p. 24)
Peripheral retina (p. 32)
Permeability (p. 26)
Pigment bleaching (p. 38)
Pineal gland (p. 22)
Presbyopia (p. 31)
Primary receiving areas (p. 24)
Propagated response (p. 26)
Purkinje shift (p. 40)
Receptor (p. 25)
Receptor sites (p. 27)
Refractory period (p. 27)
Resting potential (p. 25)
Retina (p. 28)
Retinal (p. 34)
Retinitis pigmentosa (p. 33)
Rod (p. 28)
Rod-cone break (p. 38)
Rod monochromat (p. 38)
Spectral sensitivity (p. 39)
Spectral sensitivity curve (p. 39)
Spontaneous activity (p. 27)
Staining (p. 23)
Synapse (p. 27)
Temporal lobe (p. 24)
Ventricles (p. 22)
Visible light (p. 29)
Visual pigment (p. 28)
Visual pigment molecules (p. 34)
Visual pigment regeneration (p. 38)
Visual transduction (p. 34)
Wavelength (p. 29)

VISIT YOUR COMPANION WEBSITE FOR THIS BOOK

http://psychology.wadsworth.com/goldstein7e

Check out this companion website where you'll find online resources—glossary, flashcards, web links, multiple-choice and essay questions, and much more!

VIRTUAL LAB

Your Virtual Lab is designed to help you get the most out of this course. The Virtual Lab icons direct you to specific media demonstrations and experiments designed to help you visualize what you are reading about. The number beside each icon indicates the number of the media element you can access through your CD-ROM, Perception PsychologyNow, or WebTutor resource at http:now.ilrn.com/goldstein_7e.

The following lab exercises cover what you've just learned in this chapter:

1. *Cortical Areas* Functions of each of the primary sensory receiving areas of the cortex.

2. *3D Virtual Brain* A 3D picture of a brain that you can rotate and dissect. Also indicates the functions of different areas.

3. *Structure of a Neuron* Functions of different parts of a neuron.

4. *Oscilloscopes and Intracellular Recording* How nerve potentials are displayed on an oscilloscope.

5. *Resting Potential* Demonstrates the difference in charge between the inside and outside of the neuron when it is not conducting impulses.

6. *Phases of Action Potential* How sodium and potassium flow across the axon membrane during the action potential.

7. *Nerve Impulse Coding and Stimulus Strength* How neural activity changes as the intensity of a stimulus is varied.

8. *Synaptic Transmission* How electrical signals are transmitted from one neuron to another.

9. *Lock and Key Neurotransmitter Action* How the shape of a neurotransmitter determines its effect on the postsynaptic neuron.

10. *Excitation and Inhibition* How excitation and inhibition interact to determine the firing rate of the postsynaptic neuron.

11. *The Human Eye* A drag-and-drop exercise to test your knowledge of parts of the eye.

12. *Cross Section of the Retina* A drag-and-drop exercise to test your knowledge of the neurons in the retina.

13. *Anatomy of the Eye* Short film showing what happens when light enters the retina and activates the rods and cones.

14. *Visual Path Within the Eyeball* How electrical signals that start in the rods and cones are transmitted through the retina and out of the back of the eye in the optic nerve.

15. *Mapping the Blind Spot* A demonstration that enables you to determine the location of your blind spot.

16. *Filling in the Blind Spot* A demonstration of how fading caused by the presence of the blind spot is "filled in."

17. *Dark Adaptation of the Rods and Cones* Plots the dark adaptation curve for rods and cones, cones only, and rods only.

18. *Types of Cones* Plots of the absorption spectral of pigments in each of the types of cone receptors.

CHAPTER
3

NEURONS AND PERCEPTION

Chapter Contents

Processing by the nervous system accentuates borders between light and dark areas, such as the stripes on the lighthouse.

VL *The Virtual Lab icons direct you to specific animations and videos designed to help you visualize what you are reading about. The number beside each icon indicates the number of the clip you can access through your CD-ROM or your student website.*

Some Questions We Will Consider:

- *How does neural processing determine what we see? (p. 62)*
- *What happens to an animal's visual system when it is raised in an abnormal environment, such as being exposed only to horizontals or only to verticals? (p. 65)*
- *What do we mean when we say that perception is indirect? (p. 66)*

Let's return to Sofia looking at the tree, from Figure 2.10. We know that the tree creates a pattern of light on her retina. But what actually causes her to perceive the tree? She doesn't perceive the "picture" of the tree on her retina because the retina alone can't perceive anything. The retina registers information about the tree and transforms this information into electrical signals. These signals travel through the network of neurons in the retina and then out the back of the eye in the fibers of the optic nerve. Only after these signals have reached Sofia's brain, where they are transmitted through additional networks of neurons, does perception somehow occur.

We say "somehow" because researchers have not yet completely figured out how the electrical impulses that travel in neurons become transformed into our experience of seeing a tree, or anything else. But we do know quite a lot about how these neurons participate in the process of perception, and in this chapter we begin telling the story of how researchers have studied the relationship between neural firing and perception by showing how perception depends on the interactions between neurons.

CONVERGENCE: MANY NEURONS SENDING SIGNALS TO ONE NEURON

Neurons do not operate alone. The brain contains 180 billion neurons, 80 billion of which are involved in cognitive processes (Kolb & Wishaw, 1990). But the large numbers of neurons isn't what's important. What's important is how the neurons interact with each other, and there are plenty of interactions because each neuron in the brain receives signals from about 1,000 other neurons. This means that there are more synapses in the brain than the number of stars in the Milky Way!

All of these interactions between neurons means that the response of a particular neuron depends on the signals it receives from many other neurons. To understand how this process works, we will show how a process called **convergence**, in which many neurons send signals to one neuron, occurs in the retina.

Convergence in the Retina

Figure 3.1 shows the relationship between the five basic types of neurons in the retina. The rod and cone receptors (R) send their signals to **bipolar cells** (B), which, in turn, synapse onto **ganglion cells** (G). The axons of the ganglion cells form the fibers that travel out of the eye in the optic nerve. Because there are 1 million ganglion cells in the retina, there are 1 million fibers in each optic nerve. VIRTUAL LAB 1

The receptors, bipolar cells, and ganglion cells transmit the signals that originate in the receptors *vertically* through the retina and out the back of the eye, to begin the journey to the brain. In contrast, the **horizontal cells** (H) and **amacrine cells** (A) transmit signals *horizonally* across the retina. For example, from Figure 3.1 we can see that signals generated by the rods on the left can be transmitted through the horizontal cell to affect receptors and bipolar cells on the right.

A great deal of convergence occurs in the retina because there are 126 million receptors, but only 1 million ganglion cells. Thus, on the average, each ganglion cell receives signals from 126 receptors. It's easy to see that each of the ganglion cells in Figure 3.1 receives signals from a number of receptors by picking a ganglion cell and tracing its connections backward through the bipolar cells to the receptors.

We can show how convergence can affect perception by returning to the comparison of the rods and cones that we began in Chapter 2. An important difference between the rods and cones is that the signals from the rods converge more than do the signals from the cones. We can appreciate this difference by noting that there are 120 million rods in the retina, but only 6 million cones. On the average, about 120 rods pool their signals to one ganglion cell, but only about six cones send signals to a single ganglion cell.

This difference between rod and cone convergence becomes even greater when we consider the foveal cones. (Remember that the fovea is the small area that contains only cones.) Many of the foveal cones have "private lines" to ganglion cells, so each ganglion cell receives signals from only one cone, and there is no convergence. The greater convergence of the rods compared to the cones translates into two differences in perception: (1) the rods result in better sensitivity than the cones, and (2) the cones result in better detail vision than the rods.

Why Rods Result in Greater Sensitivity Than Cones

One reason rod vision is more sensitive than cone vision is that it takes less light to generate a response from an individual rod receptor than from an individual cone receptor (Barlow & Mollon, 1982; Baylor, 1992), but there is another reason as well: The rods have greater convergence than the cones.

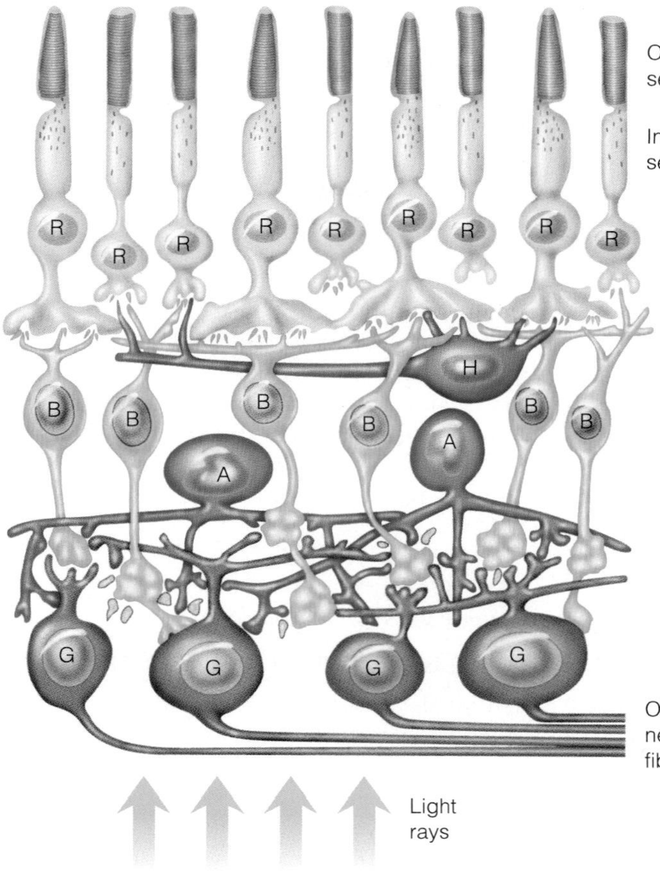

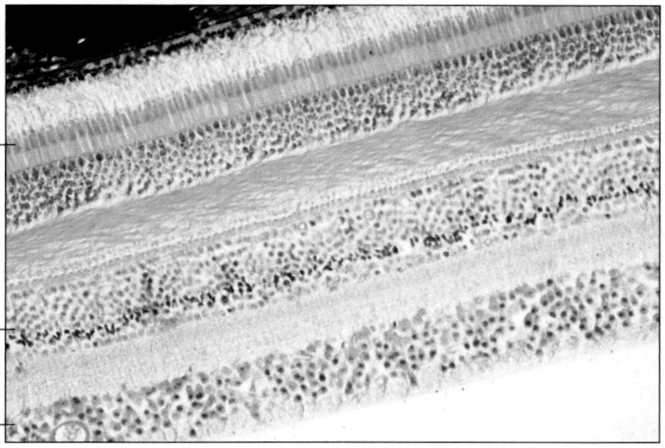

Figure 3.1 ▮ (a) Cross section of the primate retina showing the five major cell types and their interconnections. R: receptors; B: bipolar cells; G: ganglion cells; H: horizontal cells; A: amacrine cells. *(Based on "Organization of the Primate Retina," by J. E. Dowling and B. B. Boycott,* Proceedings of the Royal Society of London, B, *1966, 166, p. 80–111. Used by permission of the Royal Society of London and John Dowling.)* (b) Cross section of a monkey retina, which has been stained to show the various layers. Light is coming from the bottom. The red circles are cell bodies of the receptors, bipolar cells, and ganglion cells.

We can understand why the amount of convergence is important for determining sensitivity by expanding our discussion of neurotransmitters from Chapter 2 (see page 27). We saw that the release of excitatory transmitter at the synapse increases the chances that the postsynaptic, or receiving, neuron will fire. This means that receiving excitatory transmitter from a number of neurons increases the chances that a neuron will fire.

Keeping this basic principle in mind, we can see how the difference in rod and cone convergence translates into differences in the maximum sensitivities of the cones and the rods by considering the two circuits in Figure 3.2. In these circuits, five rod receptors converge onto one ganglion cell and five cone receptors each synapse onto their own ganglion cells. We have left out the bipolar, horizontal, and amacrine cells in these circuits for simplicity, but

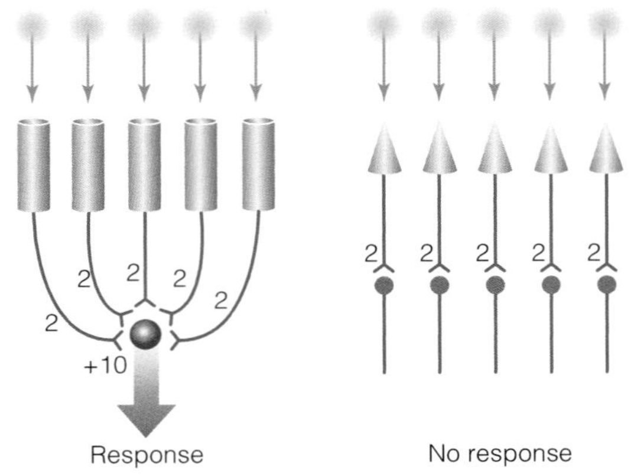

Figure 3.2 ▮ The wiring of the rods (left) and the cones (right). The spot and arrow above each receptor represents light that stimulates the receptor. The numbers represent the number of response units generated by the rods and the cones in response to a spot intensity of 2.0.

our conclusions will not be affected by these omissions. VL 2

For the purposes of our discussion, we will assume that we can present small spots of light to individual rods and cones. We will also make the following additional assumptions:

1. One unit of light intensity causes the release of one unit of excitatory transmitter, which causes one unit of excitation in the ganglion cell.
2. The threshold for ganglion cell firing is 10 units of excitation. That is, the ganglion cell must receive 10 units of excitation to fire.
3. The ganglion cell must fire before perception of the light can occur.

When we present spots of light with an intensity of 1.0 to each receptor, the rod ganglion cell receives 5 units of excitation, 1 from each of the 5 receptors, and each of the cone ganglion cells receives 1.0 units of excitation, 1 from each receptor. Thus, when intensity = 1.0, neither the rod nor the cone ganglion cells fire. If, however, we increase the intensity to 2.0, the rod ganglion cell receives 2.0 units of excitation from each of its five receptors, for a total of 10 units of excitation. This total reaches the threshold for the rods' ganglion cell, it fires, and we see the light. Meanwhile, at the same intensity, the cones' ganglion cells are still below threshold, each receiving only 2 units of excitation. For the cones' ganglion cells to fire, we must increase the intensity to 10.0.

The operation of these circuits demonstrate that one reason for the rods' high sensitivity compared to the cones' is that because of the rods' greater convergence, many rods summate their responses by feeding into the same ganglion cell, but only one or a few cones send their responses to a single ganglion cell.

Why We Use Our Cones to See Details

Have you ever found it difficult to locate a friend's face in a crowd? Unless your friend attracted your attention by wearing a distinctive color of clothing or by shouting your name, you probably found it necessary to scan the crowd, looking at one face after another, until you finally came upon your friend's face.

The reason you needed to scan the crowd was that to see enough detail to recognize a face you need to focus the image of your friend's face on your fovea, which contains only cones. Only all-cone foveal vision has good **visual acuity**—the ability to see details. The high acuity of foveal vision means that the particular face at which you are looking is seen in enough detail to be recognized, whereas the rest of the faces in the crowd fall on the rod-rich peripheral retina and can't be recognized.

DEMONSTRATION

Foveal Versus Peripheral Acuity

D I H C N R L A Z I F W N S M Q P Z K D **X**

You can demonstrate that foveal vision is superior to peripheral vision for seeing details by looking at the X in the line of letters and, without moving your eyes, seeing how many letters you can identify to the left. If you do this without cheating (no fair moving your eyes!), you will find that although you can read the letters right next to the X, which are imaged on or near the fovea, you can read only a few of the letters that are off to the side and which are imaged on the peripheral retina. ■

Visual acuity can be measured in a number of ways, one of which is to determine how far apart two dots have to be before a space can be seen between them. We make this measurement by presenting a pair of closely spaced dots and asking whether there are one or two dots. We can also measure acuity by determining how large the elements of a checkerboard or a pattern of alternating black and white bars must be for the pattern to be detected. Perhaps the most familiar way of measuring acuity involves the eye chart in an optometrist's or ophthalmologist's office.

In the demonstration above, we showed that acuity is better in the fovea than in the periphery. Because you were light adapted, the comparison in this demonstration was between the foveal cones, which are tightly packed, and the peripheral cones, which are more widely spaced. Comparing the foveal cones to the rods results in even greater differences in acuity. We can make this comparison by measuring how acuity changes during dark adaptation. When we do this, we find that visual acuity drops (that is, details must be larger in order to be seen) as vision changes from cone function to rod function during dark adaptation. This poor acuity of the rods is why the details of the books in the bookcase vanished when you turned out the lights in the example at the beginning of

Chapter 2, and is also why it is difficult to read in dim illuminations.

We can understand how differences in rod and cone wiring explain the cones' greater acuity by returning to our rod and cone neural circuits. As we stimulate the receptors in the circuits in Figure 3.3 with two spots of light, each with an intensity of 10, we will ask the following question: Under what conditions can we tell that there are two separate spots of light? We begin by presenting the two spots next to each other, as in Figure 3.3a. When we do this, the rod ganglion cell fires, and the two adjacent cone ganglion cells fire. The firing of the single rod ganglion cell provides no hint that two separate spots were presented, and the firing of the two adjacent cone ganglion cells could have been caused by a single large spot. However, when we spread the two spots apart, as in Figure 3.3b, the output of the cones signals two separate spots, because there is a silent ganglion cell between the two that are firing, but the output of the rods' single ganglion cell still provides no information that would enable us to say that there are two spots. Thus, the rods' convergence decreases their ability to resolve details (Teller, 1990). VL 3

We have seen that convergence can influence how we perceive sensitivity to light and the ability to perceive details. We will now show how inhibition can influence how we perceive light and dark.

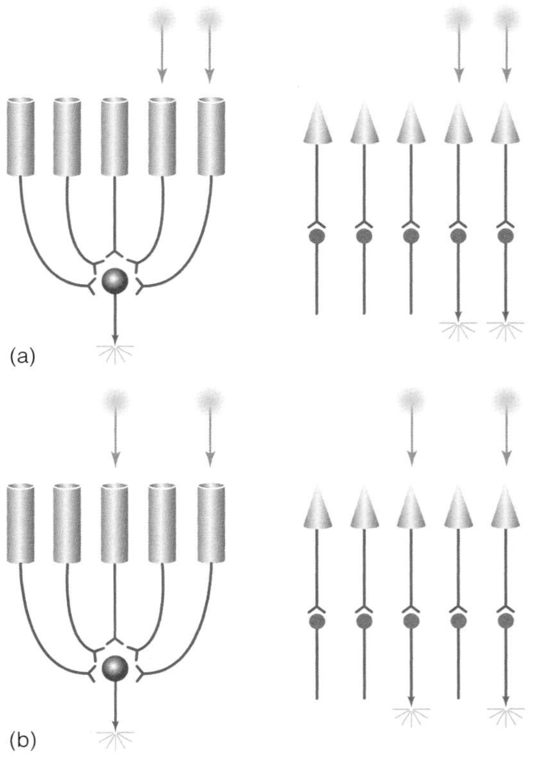

Figure 3.3 ▌ Neural circuits for the rods (left) and the cones (right). The receptors are being stimulated by two spots of light.

INHIBITION: HOW ACTIVITY IN ONE NEURON CAN DECREASE ACTIVITY IN ANOTHER ONE

Inhibition occurs when one neuron releases inhibitory neurotransmitter onto another neuron. To understand how this inhibition can affect neural firing, we will look at an experiment that demonstrated the effect of inhibition in the eye of a primitive animal called the *Limulus*, which is more familiarly known as the horseshoe crab (Figure 3.4).

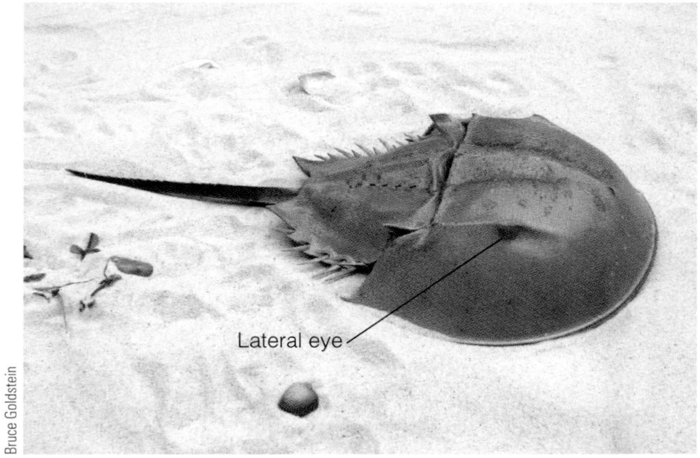

Figure 3.4 ▌ A *Limulus*, or horseshoe crab. Its large eyes are made up of hundreds of ommatidia, each containing a single receptor.

What the Horseshoe Crab Teaches Us About Inhibition

In an experiment that is now considered a classic, Keffer Hartline, Henry Wagner, and Floyd Ratliff (1956) used the *Limulus* to demonstrate how stimulating one neuron can decrease the response in another neuron. They chose the *Limulus* because of the structure of its eye. The *Limulus* eye is made up of hundreds of tiny structures called **ommatidia**, and each ommatidium has a small lens on the eye's surface that is located directly over a single receptor. Each lens and receptor is roughly the diameter of a pencil point (very large compared to human receptors), so it is possible to illuminate and record from a single receptor without illuminating its neighboring receptors.

When Hartline and coworkers recorded from the nerve fiber of receptor A, as shown in Figure 3.5, they found that illumination of that receptor caused a large response. But when they added illumination to the three nearby receptors at B, the response of receptor A decreased (Figure 3.5b). They also found that increasing the illumination of B further decreased A's response (Figure 3.5c). Thus, illumination of the neighboring receptors inhibited the firing of receptor A. This inhibition is called **lateral inhibition** because it is transmitted laterally, across the retina. Lateral inhibition is transmitted across the Limulus' eye by the fibers of the *lateral plexus*, shown in Figure 3.5. VL 4

Remember that signals are transmitted across the human retina by the horizontal cells and amacrine cells. Does this mean that lateral inhibition occurs in humans and, most important, that it can influence perception? We will now see that there is evidence that lateral inhibition may, in fact, influence how we perceive light and dark.

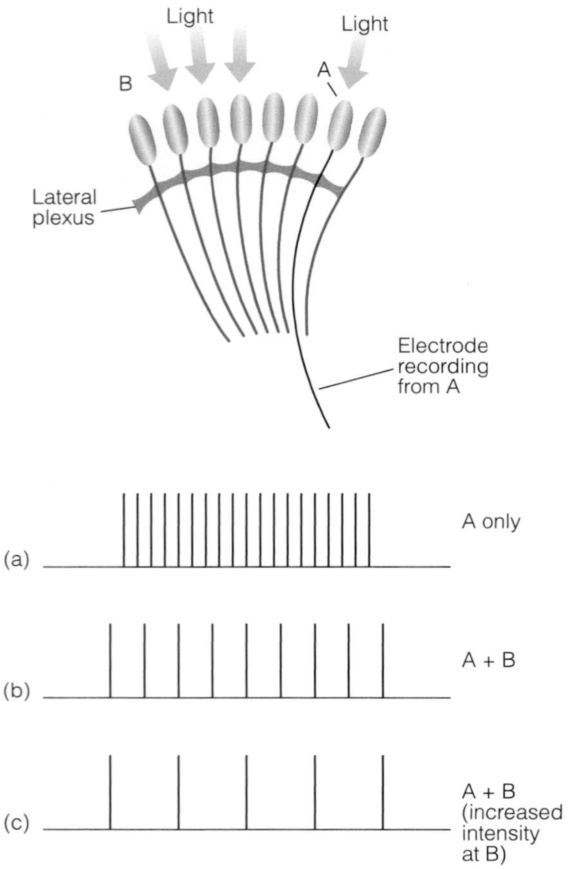

Figure 3.5 ▮ A demonstration of lateral inhibition in the *Limulus.* The records on the right show the response recorded by the electrode in the nerve fiber of receptor A: (a) when only receptor A is stimulated; (b) when receptor A and the receptors at B are stimulated together; (c) when A and B are stimulated, with B at an increased intensity.
(From Mach Bands: Quantitative Studies on Neural Networks in the Retina, *by F. Ratliff, 1965, figure 3.25, p. 107. Copyright ©1965 Holden-Day, Inc. Reprinted with permission.)*

Lateral Inhibition and Lightness Perception

We will now describe three perceptual phenomena that have been explained by lateral inhibition. Each of these phenomena involves the perception of lightness—the perception of shades ranging from white to gray to black.

The Hermann Grid: Seeing Spots at Intersections Notice the ghostlike gray image at the intersection of the white "corridors" in the display in Figure 3.6, which is called the **Hermann grid**. You can prove that this grayness is not physically present by noticing that it is reduced or it vanishes when you look directly at an intersection or, better yet, by masking off the four squares that surround one intersection. VL 5, 6

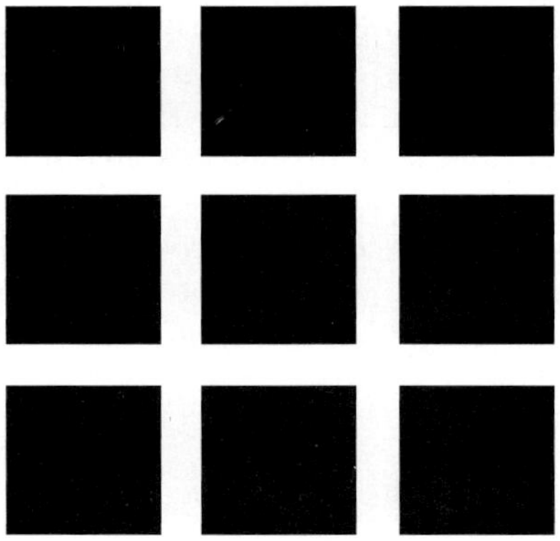

Figure 3.6 ▮ The Hermann grid. Notice the gray "ghost images" at the intersections of the white areas, which decrease or vanish when you look directly at the intersection.

Figure 3.7 shows how the dark spots at the intersections can be explained by lateral inhibition. Figure 3.7a shows the four squares of the grid and five receptors. Receptor A is at the intersection of two of the white corridors, where the gray spot is perceived, and the surrounding receptors are located in the corridors. Figure 3.7b shows another view of the grid and the receptors, which indicates that each receptor sends its signals to a bipolar cell and that each of the bipolar cells sends lateral inhibition, indicated by the arrows, to receptor A's bipolar cell. The thickness of the arrows indicates the strength of the inhibition.

Figure 3.7c shows another array of five receptors. In this example, receptor B is in the corridor between two black squares, and the other receptors surround it. The key difference between this group of receptors and the ones in Figure 3.7a is that in this group the receptors to the left and right, L and R, are illuminated less because they are under the black squares.

Our goal is to compare the responses of the bipolar

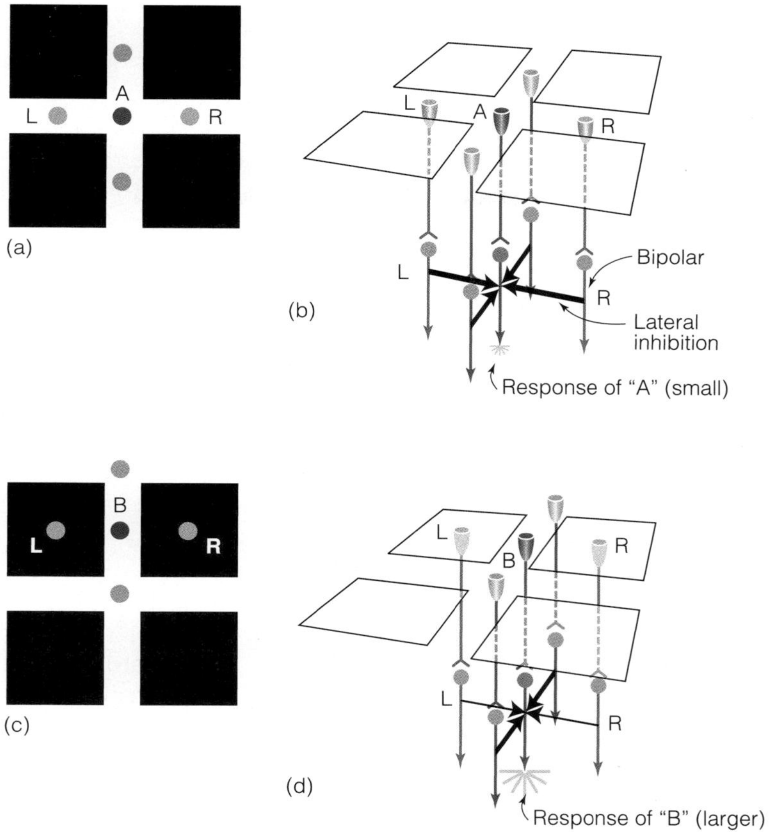

Figure 3.7 ▮ How lateral inhibition can explain the dark "ghosts" at the intersections. (a) View of four squares of the grid showing the position of receptor A, at the intersection, and the surrounding receptors in the "corridors." (b) Perspective view of the squares and receptors in (a), showing that each receptor connects to a bipolar cell, and that the bipolar cells that surround A all send a large amount of lateral inhibition to A's bipolar cell (indicated by the thick arrows). (c) and (d) Same as (a) and (b) above, but focusing on receptor B, which is located in the corridor of the grid.

cells for receptors A and B because we are assuming, for the purposes of this example, that our perception of the lightness at A and at B is determined by the responses of these bipolar cells. (It would be more accurate to use ganglion cells because they are the neurons that send signals out of the retina, but to simplify things for the purposes of this example, we will focus on the bipolar cells.)

The size of the bipolar cell responses depends on how much stimulation each one receives from its receptor and on the amount that this response is decreased by the lateral inhibition it receives from its neighboring cells. Because receptors A and B are both illuminated by white areas of the grid, they send the same amount of stimulation to their bipolar cells. However, the bipolar cells of A and B receive different amounts of lateral inhibition, as indicated by the thickness of the horizontal arrows coming from the neighboring bipolar cells. As shown in Figure 3.7b, A's bipolar cell receives a large amount of lateral inhibition from each of its neighboring cells because all four of their receptors are strongly illuminated by the white corridors. However, as shown in Figure 3.7d, B's bipolar cell receives less inhibition from the cells associated with receptors L and R because these receptors are under the black squares and so are only weakly illuminated.

A's bipolar cell receives more lateral inhibition than B's bipolar cell, so it will fire less than B, and this lower rate of firing is translated into the gray spots we see at the intersections. These gray spots provide a good example of the principle we introduced in Chapter 2: *We do not just perceive what is out there. We perceive what is out there as filtered through the properties of our visual system.*

Mach Bands: Seeing Borders More Sharply Ernst Mach was an Austrian physicist and philosopher. His research in physics resulted in the *Mach number,* which is the ratio of an object's speed to the speed of sound, so an airplane traveling at Mach 2 would be going twice the speed of sound. Mach was also interested in the psychology of sensation and expressed the idea in his book *The Analysis of Sensations* (1897) that all of our knowledge is caused by the stimulation of our senses. One of his psychological discoveries was a perceptual effect that has come to be called **Mach bands,** which is a tendency to see light and dark bars near the borders between light and dark areas. For example, if you look closely at the display in Figure 3.8, you may be able to see a faint light band on the left of the border (at B) and a faint dark band on the right (at C).

VL 7, 8

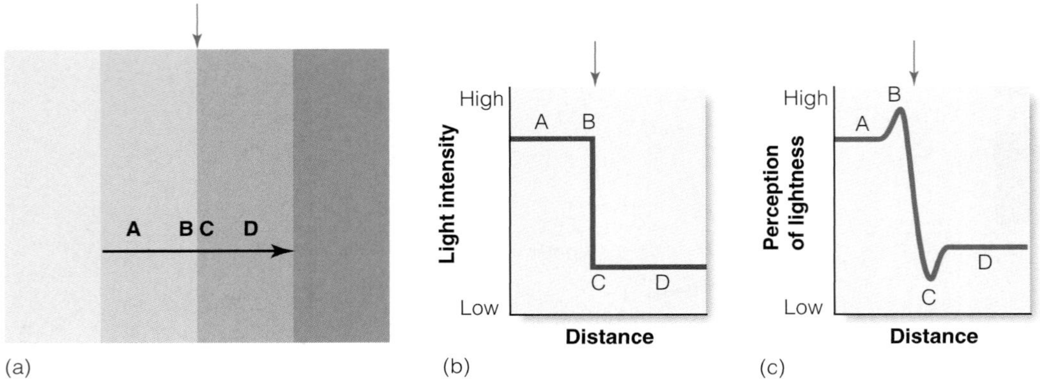

Figure 3.8 ■ (a) Mach bands at a contour. Just to the left of the contour, near B, a faint light band can be perceived, and just to the right at C, a faint dark band can be perceived. (b) The physical intensity distribution of the light, as measured with a light meter. (c) A plot showing the perceptual effect described in (a). The bump in the curve at B indicates the light Mach band, and the dip in the curve at C indicates the dark Mach band. The arrows in each panel indicate the location of the contour between B and C. The bumps that represent our perception of the bands are not present in the physical intensity distribution.

DEMONSTRATION

Creating Mach Bands in Shadows

Mach bands can be demonstrated using gray stripes, as in Figure 3.8, or by casting a shadow, as shown in Figure 3.9. When you do this, you will see a dark Mach band near the border of the shadow and a light Mach band on the other side of the border. The light Mach band is often harder to see than the dark band.

Figure 3.9 ■ Shadow-casting technique for observing Mach bands. Illuminate a light-colored surface with your desk lamp and cast a shadow with a piece of paper. ■

The reason Mach bands are interesting is because, like the spots in the Hermann grid, they are an illusion—they are not actually present in the pattern of light. We can demonstrate this by measuring the intensity across the stripes in Figure 3.8a with a light meter, starting at A and measuring the amount of light reflected as we move along the line between A and D. When we do this, we obtain the result shown in Figure 3.8b. The intensity distribution across each stripe is flat, so the same amount of light is reflected across the entire distance between A and B, and the same amount is reflected between C and D.

Because the intensities remain constant across the light stripe on the left and the dark stripe on the right, the bands we perceive on either side of the border must be illusions. Our perception of these illusory bands is represented graphically in Figure 3.9c, which indicates the lightness that we actually perceive across the two stripes.

How can we explain our perception of Mach bands in terms of lateral inhibition? We will answer this question by considering the hypothetical neural circuit in Figure 3.10. We use the same reasoning we did for the Hermann grid. Each of the six receptors in this circuit sends signals to bipolar cells, and each bipolar cell sends lateral inhibition to its neighbors on both sides. Receptors A, B, and C receive intense illumination, and D, E, and F receive dim illumination. This is what would occur if we illuminated all six receptors equally and then cast a shadow on receptors D, E, and F.

Let's assume that receptors A, B, and C generate responses of 100, whereas D, E, and F generate responses of 20, as shown in Figure 3.10. Thus, without inhibition, A, B, and C send the same responses to their bipolar cells, and D, E, and F send the same responses to their bipolar cells. If perception were determined only by these responses, we would see a bright bar with equal intensity across its width in the area served by receptors A, B, and

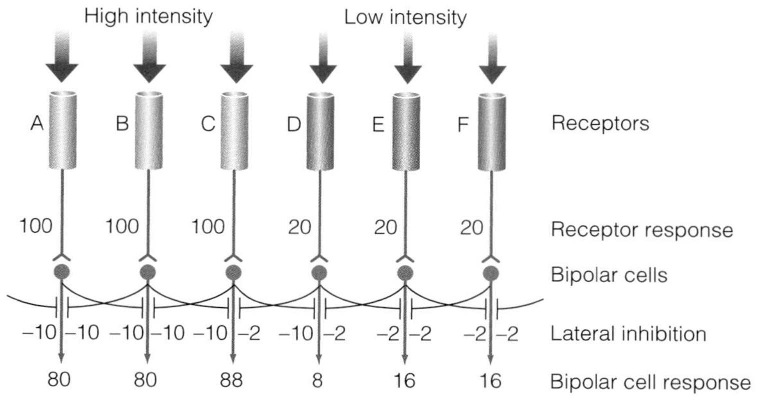

Figure 3.10 ▮ Circuit to explain the Mach band effect based on lateral inhibition. The circuit works like the one for the Hermann grid in Figure 3.6, with each bipolar cell sending inhibition to its neighbors. If we know the initial output of each receptor and the amount of lateral inhibition, we can calculate the final output of the receptors. (See text for a description of the calculation.)

C and a dim bar with equal intensity across its width in the area served by D, E, and F. The following calculation shows how lateral inhibition would modify these initial responses to produce a physiological effect that would result in the perception of Mach bands:

1. Start with the response received by each bipolar cell: 100 for A, B, and C, and 20 for D, E, and F.
2. Determine the amount of inhibition that each bipolar cell receives from its neighbor on each side. For the purposes of our calculation, we will assume that each cell sends inhibition to its neighbor equal to one-tenth of that cell's initial output. Thus, cells A, B, and C will send $100 \times 0.1 = 10$ units of inhibition to their neighbors, and cells D, E, and F will send $20 \times 0.1 = 2$ units of inhibition to their neighbors.
3. Determine the final response of each cell by subtracting the amount of inhibition from the initial response. Remember that each cell receives inhibition from its neighbor on either side. (We assume here that cell A receives 10 units of inhibition from an unseen cell on its left and that F receives 2 units of inhibition from an unseen cell on its right.) Here is the calculation for each cell:

Cell A: Final response	$100 - 10 - 10 = 80$
Cell B: Final response	$100 - 10 - 10 = 80$
Cell C: Final response	$100 - 10 - 2 = 88$
Cell D: Final response	$20 - 10 - 2 = 8$
Cell E: Final response	$20 - 2 - 2 = 16$
Cell F: Final response	$20 - 2 - 2 = 16$

The graph of these neural responses in Figure 3.11 looks similar to Figure 3.8c, where there is an increase in brightness on the light side of the border at C and a decrease in brightness on the dark side at D. The lateral inhibition in our circuit has therefore created a neural pattern that looks like the Mach bands we perceive. A circuit similar to this one, but of much greater complexity, is probably responsible for the Mach bands that we see. VL 9

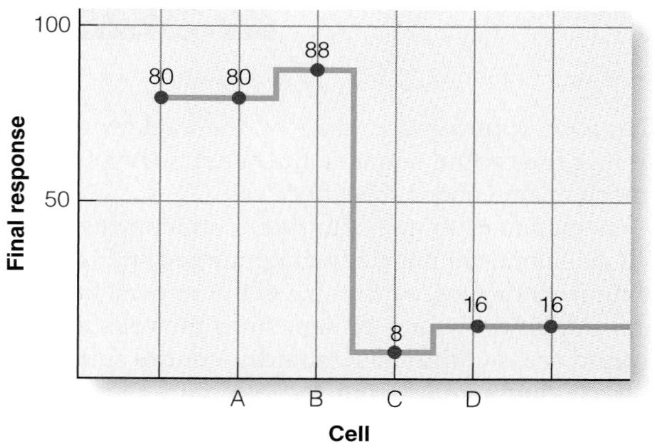

Figure 3.11 ▮ A plot showing the final receptor output calculated for the circuit of Figure 3.10. The bump at B and the dip at C correspond to the light and dark Mach bands, respectively.

Lateral Inhibition and Simultaneous Contrast **Simultaneous contrast** occurs when our perception of the brightness or color of one area is affected by the presence of an adjacent or surrounding area. VL 10, 11, 12

DEMONSTRATION

Simultaneous Contrast

When you look at the two center squares in Figure 3.12, the one on the left appears much darker than the one on the right. Now, punch two holes 2 inches apart in a card or a piece of paper, place the two holes over the squares, and compare your perception of the squares, as seen through the holes. ■

You may have been surprised to see that the two squares look the same when viewed through the holes, even though they look different when the whole pattern is visible. This is the simultaneous contrast effect. Based on the results of this demonstration, we can say that si-

Figure 3.12 ❚ Simultaneous contrast. The two center squares reflect the same amount of light into your eyes but look different because of simultaneous contrast.

multaneous contrast is caused by the backgrounds surrounding the central squares. But what is the physiological mechanism behind this effect?

An explanation for simultaneous contrast that is based on lateral inhibition is diagrammed in Figure 3.13. This figure indicates, by the size of the arrows, how much lateral inhibition would be sent from the cells under the surround areas to the cells under the central squares. The cells receiving signals from the receptors under the left surround are intensely stimulated, so they send a large amount of inhibition toward the cells in the center (large arrows). The cells receiving signals from the receptors under the right surround are less intensely stimulated, so they send only a small amount of inhibition to the cells in the center (small arrows). Because the cells under the left square receive more inhibition than the cells under the right square, their response is decreased more, they fire less than the cells under the right square, and the left square therefore looks darker.

The above explanation based on lateral inhibition makes sense and is still accepted by some researchers, although it is difficult for lateral inhibition to explain the following perception: If we start at the edge of the center square on the left and move toward the middle of the square, the lightness appears to be the same, all across the square. However, because lateral inhibition would affect the square more strongly near the edge, we would expect that the square would look lighter near the border and darker in the center. The fact that this does not occur suggests that lateral inhibition cannot be the whole story behind simultaneous contrast. In fact, psychologists have created other displays that result in perceptions that can't be explained by the spread of lateral inhibition.

Displays That Can't Be Explained by Lateral Inhibition

Look at the two triangles in Figure 3.14, which is called the **Benary cross** (Benary, 1924). Triangle B looks slightly lighter than triangle A, even though both reflect the same amount of light. Notice that both triangles are surrounded by dark areas on two sides and a light area on one side. This means that they both should receive the same amount of lateral inhibition. Nonetheless they look different.

The idea that our perception of light and dark may

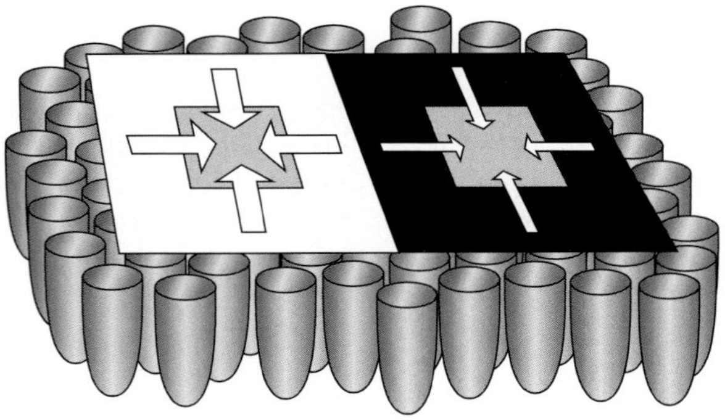

Figure 3.13 ❚ How lateral inhibition has been used to explain the simultaneous contrast effect.

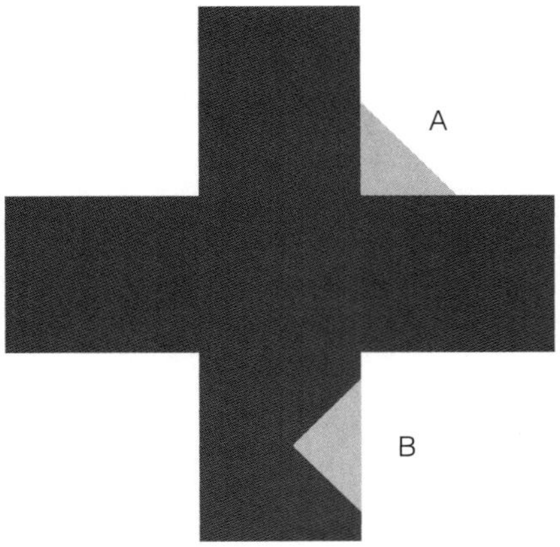

Figure 3.14 ❚ The Benary cross.

not be determined solely by lateral inhibition in the retina is also supported by our perception of the display in Figure 3.15, which is called **White's illusion** (White, 1981). This display looks like a light gray rectangle (rectangle B) and a dark gray rectangle (rectangle A). However, the bars that create each rectangle reflect exactly the same amount of light. You can demonstrate this to yourself by masking off everything but one of the horizontal bars in each rectangle. When you do this, you will see that they look the same.

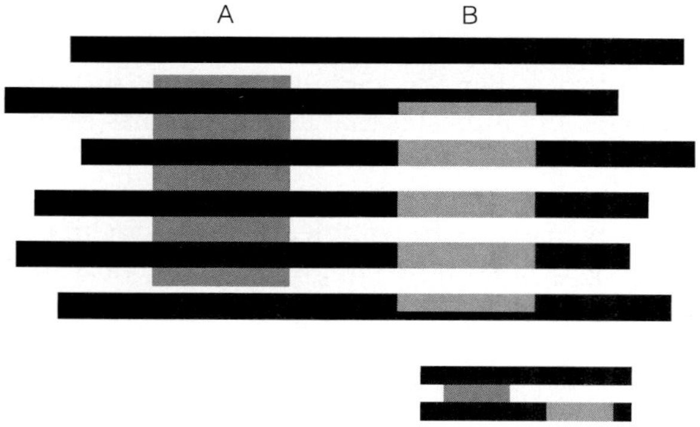

Figure 3.15 ▌ White's illusion.
(From Perception, *1981, 10, p. 215–230, fig 1a, p. 216. Reprinted with permission from Pion, Ltd., London.)*

Let's look at this display in terms of what lateral inhibition would predict. The cells stimulated by the bars of rectangle B receive a lot of lateral inhibition from the bordering white areas, which would make them appear darker. The cells stimulated by the bars of rectangle A receive less inhibition because of the bordering black areas, so they should appear lighter. However, as you can see, the opposite happens. The areas receiving the most inhibition look the lightest! Clearly, lateral inhibition can't explain White illusion.

What's happening here, according to Alan Gilchrist and coworkers (1999) is that our perception of lightness is influenced by a principle called **belongingness**, which states that an area's appearance is influenced by the part of the surroundings to which the area appears to belong. For example, in the Benary cross, triangle B "belongs" to the dark cross because it is located within it, but triangle A "belongs" to the white area outside the cross. Thus, the dark cross makes triangle B appear lighter, and the light background makes triangle B appear darker. White's illusion works the same way because rectangle B "belongs" to the dark bars and rectangle A "belongs" to the white background.

Whether or not this idea of belongingness holds up for other types of displays, there is no question that some mechanism other than lateral inhibition is involved in our perception of the Benary cross, White's illusion, and many other displays (see Adelson, 1993; Knill & Kersten, 1991; Williams, McCoy, & Purves, 1998). Contrary to what perception researchers once thought, the mechanism behind many contrast effects appears to be based not only in the retina, but also farther upstream, probably in the cortex, although at this point we don't know what the physiological mechanism is.

So it appears that the neural processing that occurs in the retina helps determine some of the properties of rod and cone vision and probably perception at the intersections of the Hermann grid and the perception of the lightness at edges, as in the Mach band effect. Although inhibition plays a very important role in perception, it isn't surprising that there are perceptions we can't explain based just on what is happening in the retina. There is still much more processing to be done before perception occurs, and this processing happens later in the visual system, in the visual receiving area of the cortex and beyond.

TEST YOURSELF 3.1

1. What is convergence, and how can the differences in the convergence of the rods and cones explain (a) the rods' greater sensitivity in the dark, and (b) the cones' better detail vision?
2. Describe the experiment that demonstrated the effect of lateral inhibition in the *Limulus.*
3. How can lateral inhibition explain the "spots" that are perceived at the intersections of the Hermann grid?
4. What are Mach bands, and how can lateral inhibition explain our perception of them? Be sure to understand the calculations used in conjunction with the circuit in Figure 3.10.
5. What is simultaneous contrast? How has it been explained by lateral inhibition? What are some problems with this explanation?
6. How do the Benary cross and White's illusion demonstrate that there are some perceptual "lightness" effects that lateral inhibition cannot explain? What does this mean about the location of the mechanism that determines lightness perception?

NEURAL PROCESSING: INTERACTIONS BETWEEN NEURONS

We have seen that excitation is necessary to cause neurons to fire and that inhibition can decrease the firing of individual neurons in ways that can cause perceptual effects such as Mach bands or spots in the Hermann grid. We are now ready to look more closely at how excitation and inhibition work together in groups of interconnected neurons called **neural circuits**.

We are going to introduce neural circuits by describing the operation of a few simple circuits. But don't let this simplicity fool you because the basic principles we are going to demonstrate with these simple circuits also hold for the more complex circuits that are responsible for our ability to perceive objects and scenes in our environment.

Excitation, Inhibition, and Neural Responding

Neural circuits can be very simple, consisting of a few neurons connected by excitatory synapses, or extremely complicated, consisting of hundreds or thousands of neurons that are interconnected in complex ways by both excitatory and inhibitory synapses. To illustrate how neural circuits can process electrical signals, we will compare how three different neural circuits affect a neuron's response to a bar-shaped light stimulus of different lengths.

We begin with a simple neural circuit and then increase the complexity of this circuit in two stages, noting how this increased complexity affects the circuit's response to the light. In these circuits we represent receptors by ellipses (⬭), cell bodies by circles (o), nerve fibers by straight lines (–), excitatory synapses by Y's (≺) and inhibitory synapses by T's (⊣). For this example, we will assume that the receptors respond to light, although the principles we will establish hold for any form of stimulation. VL 13

First, let's consider the circuit in Figure 3.16. This circuit contains no convergence—the signal generated by each receptor travels straight to the next neuron, and no other neurons are involved. Also, notice that all six of the synapses in this circuit are excitatory. We stimulate the circuit by first illuminating receptor 4 with a spot of light. We then change this spot into a bar of light by adding light to illuminate receptors 3, 4, and 5 (3 through 5), then receptors 2 through 6, and finally receptors 1 through 7. When we measure the response of neuron B and indicate this response in the graph to the right of the circuit, we find that neuron B fires when we stimulate receptor 4 but that stimulating the other receptors has no effect on neuron B because it is still receiving exactly the same input from receptor 4. For this circuit, therefore, the firing of neuron B simply indicates that its receptor has been stimulated and doesn't provide any information about the length of the bar of light.

We now increase the complexity of the circuit by adding convergence, as shown in the circuit in Figure 3.17. In this circuit, receptors 1 and 2 converge onto neuron A; 6 and 7 converge onto C; and 3, 4, and 5, and A and C converge onto B. As in the previous circuit, all of the synapses are excitatory; but, with the addition of convergence, cell B now collects information from all of the receptors. When we monitor the firing rate of neuron B, we find that each time we increase the length of the stimulus, neuron B's firing rate increases, as shown in the graph in Figure 3.17. This occurs because stimulating more receptors increases the amount of excitatory transmitter

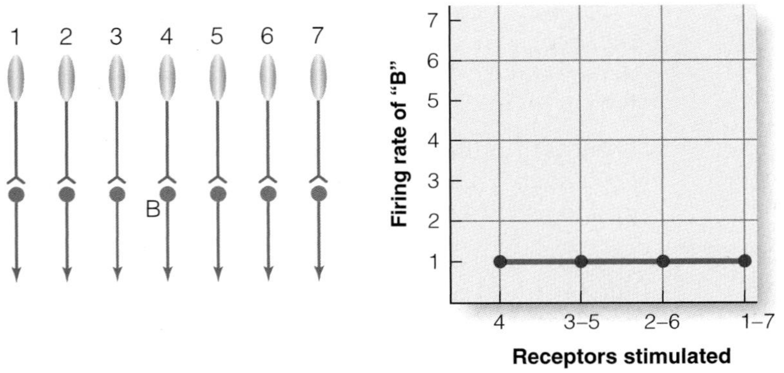

Figure 3.16 ▌ Left: A circuit with no convergence. Right: Response of neuron B as we increase the number of receptors stimulated.

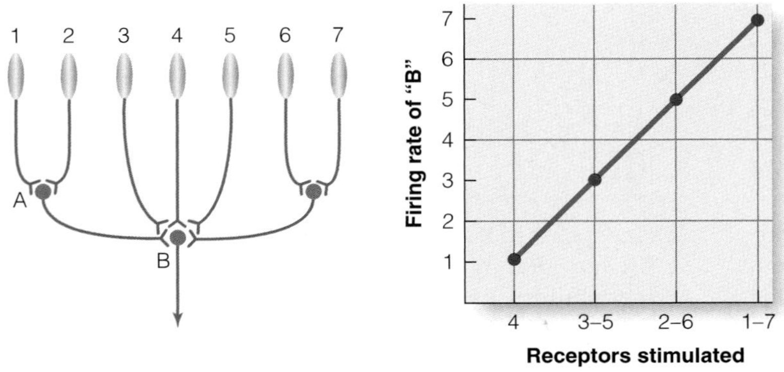

Figure 3.17 ▌ Circuit with convergence added. Neuron B now receives inputs from all of the receptors, so increasing the size of the stimulus increases the size of neuron B's response.

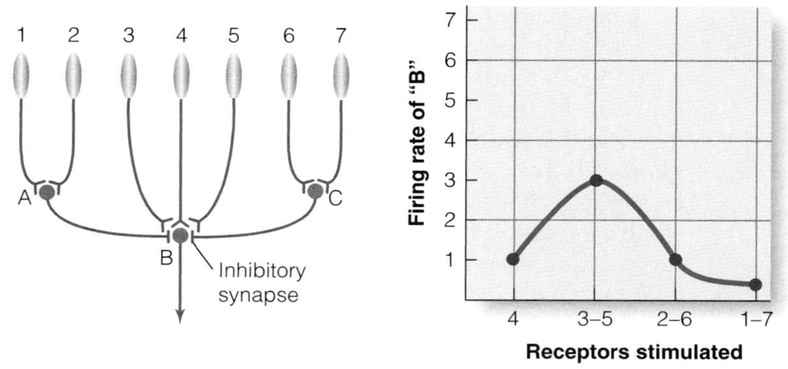

Figure 3.18 ▌ Circuit with convergence and inhibition. Because stimulation of the receptors on the side (1, 2, 6, and 7) sends inhibition to neuron B, neuron B responds best when just the center receptors (3–5) are stimulated.

released onto neuron B. Thus, in this circuit, neuron B's response provides information about the length of the stimulus.

We now increase the circuit's complexity further by adding two inhibitory synapses to create the circuit in Figure 3.18, in which neurons A and C inhibit neuron B. Now consider what happens as we increase the number of receptors stimulated. The spot of light stimulates receptor 4, which, through its excitatory connection, increases the firing rate of neuron B. Extending the illumination to include receptors 3 through 5 adds the output of two more excitatory synapses to B and increases its firing. So far, this circuit is behaving similarly to the circuit in Figure 3.17. However, when we extend the illumination further to also include receptors 2 through 6, something different happens: Receptors 2 and 6 stimulate neurons A and C, which, in turn, inhibit neuron B, decreasing its firing rate. Increasing the size of the stimulus again to illuminate receptors 1 through 7 increases the inhibition and further decreases the response of neuron B.

In this circuit, neuron B fires weakly to small stimuli (a spot illuminating only receptor 4) or longer stimuli (illuminating receptors 1 through 7) and fires best to a stimulus of medium length (illuminating receptors 3 through 5). The combination of convergence and inhibition has therefore caused neuron B to respond best to a light stimulus of a specific size. The neurons that synapse with neuron B are therefore doing much more than simply transmitting electrical signals; they are acting as part of a neural circuit that enables the firing of neuron B to indicate the size of the stimulus falling on the receptors. We will now see how the kind of neural processing shown in Figure 3.18 can be demonstrated in the visual system by introducing the concept of the receptive field.

Introduction to Receptive Fields

The **receptive field** of a neuron in the visual system is the area on the retina that influences the firing rate of the neuron.

METHOD ▪ Determining a Neuron's Receptive Field

A neuron's receptive field is measured using a setup like the one shown in Figure 3.19, in which stimuli are presented on a screen at which the animal (a cat, in this case) is looking. The cat's eye is kept stationary, so presenting stimuli on the screen is equivalent to shining lights on different places on the retina. Thus, for each point on the screen, there is a corresponding point on the cat's retina.

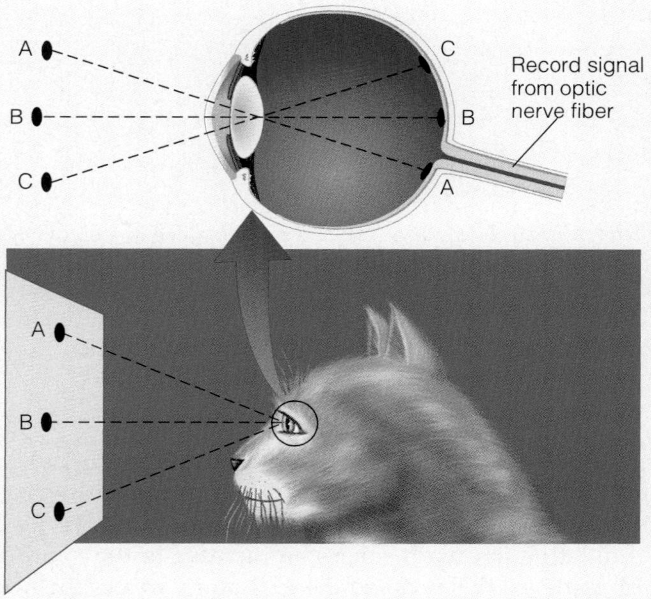

Figure 3.19 ▌ Recording electrical signals from a fiber in the optic nerve of an anesthetized cat. Each point on the screen corresponds to a point on the cat's retina.

The first step is to position an electrode so it is picking up signals from a single nerve fiber. In this example, we are recording from a single fiber in the optic nerve. (Remember that optic nerve fibers are the axons of ganglion cells (see Figure 3.1a), so recording from an optic nerve fiber is equivalent to recording from a ganglion cell in the retina.) Then, a small spot of light is flashed on the screen. As shown in Figure 3.20a, this flash can cause (A) no effect (the firing shown is spontaneous activity), (B) an increase in the neuron's firing rate, or (C) a decrease in the neuron's firing rate. The spot is flashed at many places on the screen, and the result is indicated by marking the screen with a + if there is an increase in firing and with a − if there is a decrease in firing. The areas marked with +'s and −'s indicate the extent of the neuron's receptive field. VL 14, 15

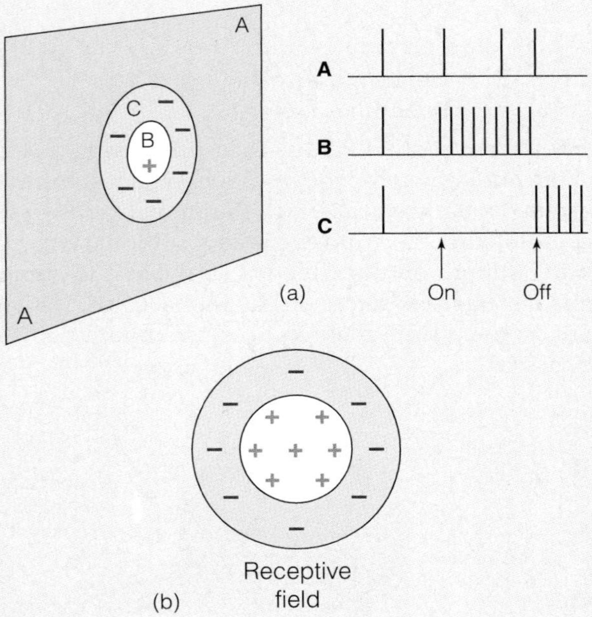

Figure 3.20 ▮ (a) Response of a ganglion cell in the cat's retina to stimulation: outside the cell's receptive field (area A on the screen); inside the excitatory area of the cell's receptive field (area B); and inside the inhibitory area of the cell's receptive field (area C). (b) The neuron's receptive field is shown without the screen.

■ ■ ■

In our example in Figure 3.20, stimulating anywhere in area A causes no change in the activity of our neuron, so this area is not part of the neuron's receptive field. Stimulating in area B causes an increase in the neuron's firing rate, so this is called the **excitatory area** of the neuron's receptive field. Stimulating in area C causes a decrease in firing rate, so this is called the **inhibitory area** of the neuron's receptive field.

The receptive field in Figure 3.20 is called a **center-surround receptive field** because the areas of the receptive field are arranged in a center region that responds one way and a surround region that responds in the opposite way. This particular receptive field is an **excitatory-center–inhibitory-surround receptive field**, but there are also **inhibitory-center–excitatory-surround receptive fields**.

The fact that the center and the surround of the receptive field respond in opposite ways causes an effect called **center-surround antagonism**. This effect is illustrated in Figure 3.21, which shows what happens as we increase the size of a spot of light presented to the ganglion cell's receptive field. A small spot that is presented to the excitatory center of the receptive field causes a small increase in the rate of nerve firing (a), and increasing the light's size so that it covers the entire center of the receptive field increases the cell's response, as shown in (b). (Notice that we have used the term *cell* in place of *neuron* here. Because neurons are a type of cell, the word *cell* is often substituted for *neuron* in the research literature. In this book, we will often use these terms interchangeably.) VL 16, 17

Center-surround antagonism comes into play when the spot of light becomes large enough so that it begins to cover the inhibitory area, as in (c) and (d). Stimulation of the inhibitory surround counteracts the center's excitatory response, causing a decrease in the neuron's firing rate. Thus, this neuron responds best to a spot of light that is the size of the excitatory center of the receptive field.

The processing we have been describing, which occurs in the retina, is the first in a series of transformations of neural signals that occur before we perceive. Further processing occurs as the signals travel from the retina to the brain and then within the brain itself.

Processing Past the Retina

Figure 3.22a, which is an overview of the visual system, pictures the pathway that the neural signals follow once they leave the retina. Most of the signals from the retina travel out the eye in the optic nerve to the **lateral geniculate nucleus (LGN)** in the thalamus. From here, signals travel to the primary visual receiving area in the occipital lobe of the cortex. The visual receiving areas is also called the **striate cortex** because of the presence of white stripes (striate = striped) that are created within this area of cortex by nerve fibers that run through it (Glickstein, 1988). From the striate cortex, signals are transmitted to other areas of the cortex, which are called, collectively, **extrastriate cortex**. Figure 3.22b shows the visual system as seen from the underside of the brain. In addition to showing the pathway from the eye to LGN to cortex, this view also indicates the location of the **superior colliculus**, an area involved in controlling eye movements and other visual behaviors that receives about 10 percent of the fibers from the optic nerve. This view also shows how signals from half of each retina cross over to the opposite side of the brain. VL 18

Neurons in the LGN have receptive fields with the center-surround configurations like the receptive fields of neurons in the retina. But at the cortex, things become more interesting. The story we are going to tell about the striate cortex is an important one because it demonstrates that (1) neurons in the striate cortex are specialized to respond best to specific aspects of stimuli, such as orienta-

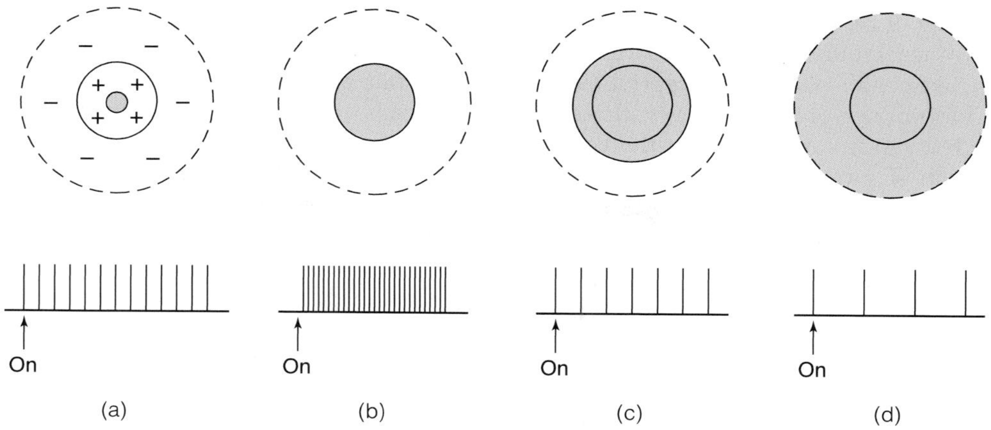

Figure 3.21 ■ Response of an excitatory-center–inhibitory-surround receptive field as stimulus size is increased. Color indicates the area stimulated with light. The response to the stimulus is indicated below each receptive field. The largest response occurs when the entire excitatory area is illuminated, as in (b). Increasing stimulus size further causes a decrease in firing due to center-surround antagonism. *(From "Integrative Action in the Cat's Lateral Geniculate Body," by D. H. Hubel and T. N. Wiesel, 1961,* Journal of Physiology, *155, 385–398, figure 1. Copyright © 1961 by The Physiological Society, Cambridge University Press. Reprinted with permission.)*

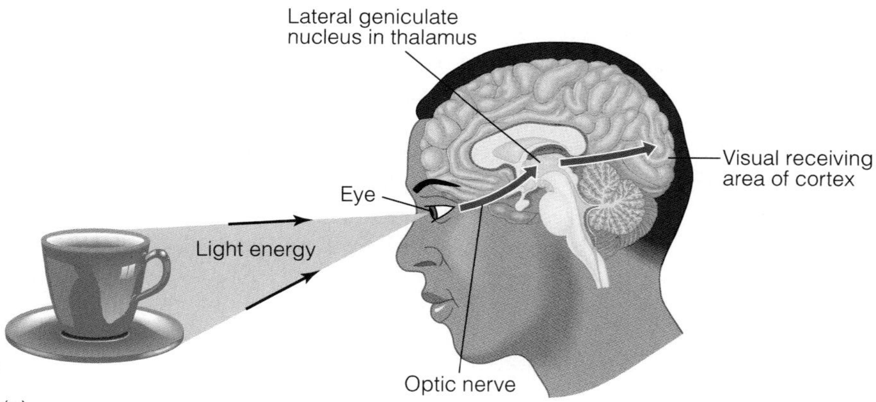

(a)

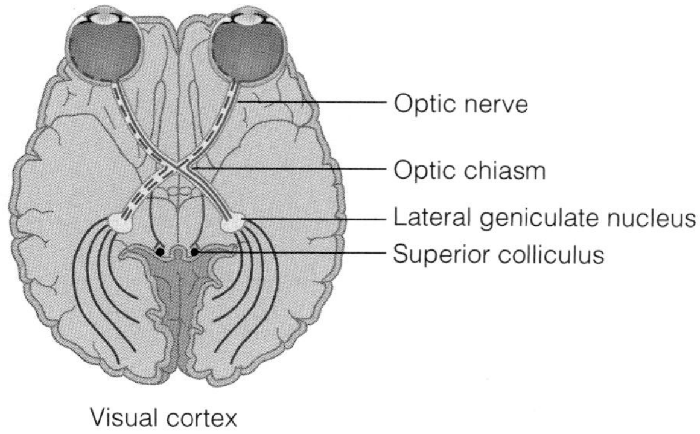

(b)

Figure 3.22 ■ (a) Side view of the visual system, showing the three major sites along the primary visual pathway where processing takes place: the retina, the lateral geniculate nucleus, and the visual receiving area of the cortex. (b) Visual system seen from underneath the brain showing how some of the nerve fibers from the retina cross over to the opposite side of the brain at the optic chiasm.

tion, movement, and size, and (2) we can connect the responding of these neurons with perception by using a psychophysical technique called selective adaptation.

The pioneering work on the physiology of neurons in the striate cortex was done by David Hubel and Torsten Wiesel, who won the 1981 Nobel Prize in Physiology and Medicine for their research. When Hubel and Wiesel began their research on the cortex, it was known that retinal ganglion cells had center-surround receptive fields and responded well to spots of light. Using the procedure of "spot" mapping of receptive fields (described on page 58), Hubel and Wiesel found cells in the cortex with receptive fields that, like center-surround receptive fields, have excitatory and inhibitory areas. However, these areas are arranged side-by-side rather than in the center-surround configuration (Figure 3.23a). Cells with these side-by-side receptive fields are called **simple cortical cells**. VL 19

Because of the side-by-side arrangement of the excitatory and inhibitory areas of the receptive field, a simple cell responds best to a bar of light with a particular orientation. The cell responds best when the bar is oriented along the length of the receptive field (top record) and responds less and less as the bar is tilted away from this best orientation (Hubel & Wiesel, 1959).

This preference of simple cortical cells for bars with particular orientations is shown in the **orientation tuning curve** of Figure 3.23b. This curve, which is determined by measuring the responses of a simple cortical cell to bars with different orientations, shows that the cell responds with 25 nerve impulses per second to a vertically oriented bar and that the cell's response decreases as the bar is tilted away from the vertical, until a bar tilted 20 degrees from the vertical elicits only a small response. We can appreciate the narrowness of this tuning by noting that when a clock indicates that the time is 12:04, the angle between the hour hand and the minute hand is 24 degrees. Although this particular simple cell responds best to a bar with a vertical orientation, there are other simple cells that respond to other orientations, so there are neurons that respond to all of the orientations that exist in the environment.

Although Hubel and Wiesel were able to use small spots of light to map the receptive fields of simple cortical cells like the one in Figure 3.19, they found that many of the cells they encountered in the cortex refused to respond to the small spots of light. In his Nobel lecture, Hubel describes how he and Wiesel were becoming increasingly frustrated in their attempts to get these cortical neurons to fire, when something startling happened: As they inserted a glass slide containing a spot stimulus into their slide projector, a cortical neuron "went off like a machine gun" (Hubel, 1982). The neuron, as it turned out, was responding not to the spot at the center of the slide that Hubel and Wiesel had planned to use as a stimulus, but to the image of the slide's edge moving downward on the screen as the slide dropped into the projector. Upon realizing this, Hubel and Wiesel changed their stimuli from small spots to moving lines and were then able to elicit responses from neurons in the cortex.

Hubel and Wiesel discovered that many cortical neurons respond best to barlike stimuli with specific orientations. **Complex cells**, like simple cells, respond best to bars of a particular orientation. However, unlike simple cells, which respond to small spots of light or to stationary stimuli, most complex cells respond only when a correctly oriented bar of light moves across the entire receptive field. Further, many complex cells respond best to a particular direction of movement (Figure 3.24a). VL 20

End-stopped cells fire to moving lines of a specific length or to moving corners or angles. The cell in Figure 3.24b responds best to a corner that is moving upward across the receptive field. End-stopped cells will not fire if

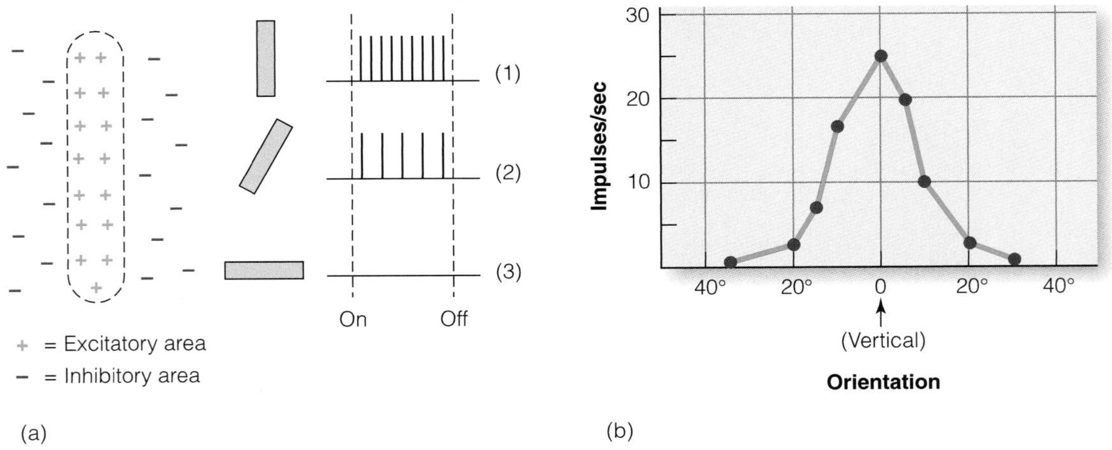

Figure 3.23 (a) The receptive field of a simple cortical cell. This cell responds best to a vertical bar of light that covers the excitatory area of the receptive field. The response decreases as the bar is tilted so that it also covers the inhibitory area. (b) Orientation tuning curve of a simple cortical cell for a neuron that responds best to a vertical bar (orientation = 0).
(From "Receptive Fields of Single Neurons in the Cat's Striate Cortex," by D. H. Hubel and T. N. Wiesel, 1959, Journal of Physiology, *148, 574–591, figure 2. Copyright ©1959 by The Physiological Society, Cambridge University Press. Reprinted by permission.)*

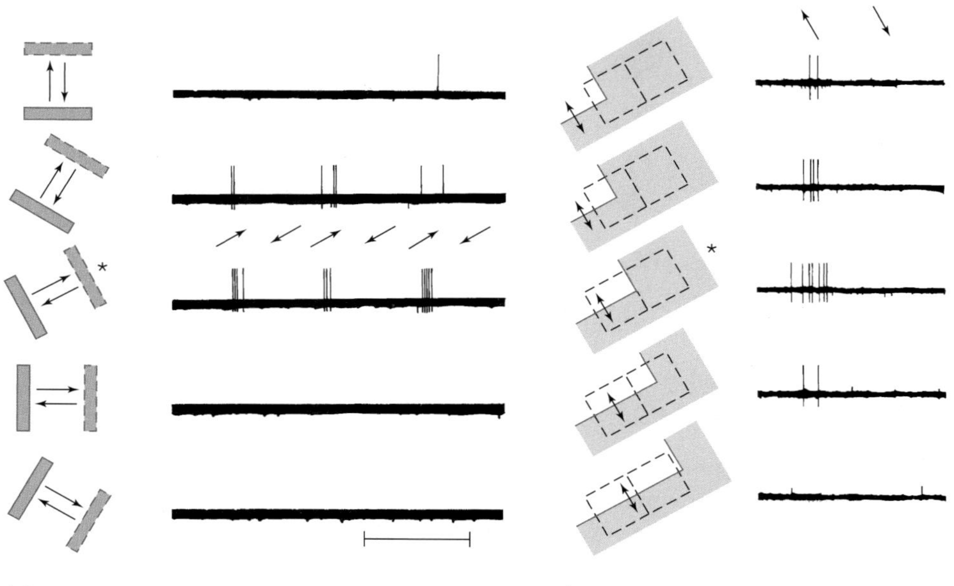

(a) (b)

Figure 3.24 ▮ (a) Response of a complex cell recorded from the visual cortex of the cat. The stimulus bar is moved back and forth across the receptive field. The cell fires best when the bar is positioned with a specific orientation and is moved in a specific direction (*). (b) Response of an end-stopped cell recorded from the visual cortex of the cat. The stimulus is indicated by the light area on the left. This cell responds best to a medium-sized corner (*).

((a) From "Receptive Fields of Single Neurons in the Cat's Striate Cortex," by D. H. Hubel and T. N. Wiesel, 1959, Journal of Physiology, 148, *574–591, figure 2. Copyright ©1959 by The Physiological Society, Cambridge University Press. Reprinted by permission. (b) From "Receptive fields and functional architecture in two non-striate visual areas (18 and 19) of the cat," by D. H. Hubel and T. N. Wiesel, 1965,* Journal of Neurophysiology, 28, *229–289.)*

the stimulus is too long, so if we extend the length of this stimulus, as in the bottom record of Figure 3.24b, the cell no longer fires (Hubel & Wiesel, 1965a).

Hubel and Wiesel's finding that some neurons in the cortex responded only to moving lines was an extremely important discovery because it indicated that neurons in the cortex do not simply respond to "light," but they respond to some patterns of light and not to others. This makes sense because the purpose of the visual system is to enable us to perceive objects in the environment, and many objects can at least be crudely represented by lines of various orientations. Thus, Hubel and Wiesel's discovery that neurons respond selectively to moving lines was an important step toward determining how neurons respond to more complex objects.

Because simple, complex, and end-stopped cells fire in response to specific features of the stimulus, such as orientation or direction of movement, they are sometimes called **feature detectors**. Table 3.1, which summarizes the properties of the four types of neurons we have described so far, illustrates an important fact about neurons in the visual system: As we travel farther from the retina, neurons fire to more complex stimuli. Retinal ganglion cells

Table 3.1 ▮ *Properties of neurons in the optic nerve, LGN, and cortex*

Type of cell	Characteristics of Receptive Field
Optic nerve fiber (ganglion cell)	Center-surround receptive field. Responds best to small spots, but will also respond to other stimuli.
Lateral geniculate	Center-surround receptive fields very similar to the receptive field of a ganglion cell.
Simple cortical	Excitatory and inhibitory areas arranged side-by-side. Responds best to bars of a particular orientation.
Complex cortical	Responds best to movement of a correctly oriented bar across the receptive field. Many cells respond best to a particular direction of movement.
End-stopped cortical	Responds to corners, angles, or bars of a particular length moving in a particular direction.

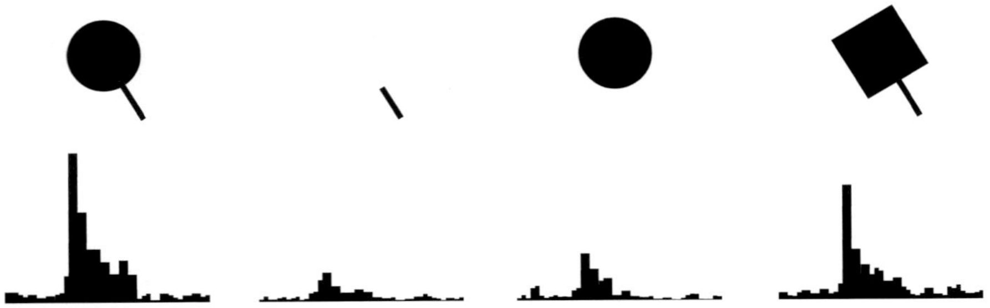

Figure 3.25 ▌ How a neuron in a monkey's temporal lobe responds to a few stimuli. This neuron responds best to a circular disc with a thin bar.
(From "Coding Visual Images of Objects in Inferotemporal Cortex of the Macaque Monkey," by K. Tanaka, H.-A. Siato, Y. Fukada, and M. Moriya, 1991, Journal of Neurophysiology, 66, *170–189. Copyright © 1981 by The American Physiological Society. Reprinted by permission.)*

respond best to spots of light, whereas end-stopped cells respond best to bars of a certain length that are moving in a particular direction.

Researchers who followed in the footsteps of Hubel and Wiesel's pioneering work have discovered neurons that respond to even more complex stimuli. For example, Keiji Tanaka and his coworkers (Ito et al., 1995; Kobatake & Tanaka, 1994; Tanaka, 1993; Tanaka et al., 1991) recorded from cells in the temporal cortex that responded best to complex stimuli such as those in Figure 3.25. This cell responds best to a circular disc with a thin bar but responds poorly to the bar alone or the disc alone. The cell does respond to the square shape and the bar but not as well was to the circle and the bar. Neurons have also been discovered in the temporal lobe that respond best to faces and objects in the environment such as houses (Kreiman et al., 2000; Perrett et al., 1992).

You may wonder how there could be neurons that respond best to things such as faces or houses. We will answer this question in Chapter 4 when we describe these neurons. For now, the important point is that specialized neurons are created by neural processing that involves the same mechanisms of convergence, excitation, and inhibition that we used to create the "small-bar detecting neuron" in Figure 3.18. Of course, the neural circuits involved in creating a "face-detecting" or a "house detecting" neuron must be extremely complex, but remember that each neuron in the cortex receives inputs from an average of 1,000 other neurons. When we consider the vast complexity of the neural interconnections that must be involved in creating a neuron that responds best to your friend's face or to the house on the corner, it is easy to agree with William James's (1890) description of the brain as "the most mysterious thing in the world."

DO FEATURE DETECTORS PLAY A ROLE IN PERCEPTION?

Neural processing endows neurons with properties that make them feature detectors, which respond best to a specific type of stimulus. But just showing that neurons respond to specific stimuli doesn't prove that they have anything to do with the perception of these stimuli. One way to establish a link between the firing of these neurons and perception is by using a psychophysical procedure called selective adaptation.

Selective Adaptation and Feature Detectors

The idea behind **selective adaptation** is that when we view a stimulus with a specific property, neurons tuned to that property fire, and if viewing continues for long enough, these neurons adapt. This adaptation causes two effects: (1) the neuron's firing rate decreases, and (2) the neuron fires less when that stimulus is immediately presented again. According to this idea, presenting a vertical line causes neurons that respond to vertical lines to respond, but as these presentations continue, these neurons eventually begin to fire less to vertical lines. Adaptation is *selective* because only the neurons that respond to verticals adapt, and other neurons do not.

The basic assumption behind a psychophysical selective adaptation experiment is that if these adapted neurons have anything to do with perception, then adaptation of neurons that respond to verticals should result in the *perceptual* effect of becoming less sensitive to verticals. The following procedure for selective adaptation is used to determine whether this decrease in sensitivity does, in fact, occur. We will use orientation as an example, but this same procedure has been used for other stimulus properties as well.

METHOD ▪ Selective Adaptation

Selective adaptation to orientation involves the following three steps:

1. Measure a person's sensitivity to a range of orientations.
2. Adapt the person to one orientation by having the person view an oriented "adapting stimulus" for a minute or two.
3. Remeasure the person's sensitivity to the range of orientations. If adaptation does have a selective perceptual effect, sensitivity to the adapted orientation should decrease, but sensitivity to other orientations should remain unaffected.

▪ ▪ ▪

Now that we know the general procedure for a selective adaptation experiment, let's describe the stimulus that has been used to selectively adapt observers to an orientation.

The Adapting Stimulus How can we adapt an observer to a particular orientation? One way is to use an adapting stimulus with alternating bars, like the ones in Figure 3.26. This type of stimulus is called a **grating**. Gratings have a number of properties, including the thickness of the grating's bars, the orientation of the bars, and the contrast between the bars. For the purposes of our orientation experiment, we will focus on the two properties of orientation and contrast:

- *Orientation:* The **orientation** of a grating is its angle relative to vertical. Gratings may be oriented vertically or may be tilted at various angles (Figure 3.26a).
- *Contrast:* The **contrast** of a grating is related to the difference in the intensity of the light and dark bars. Figure 3.26b shows a series of gratings that vary in contrast, with the high contrast gratings on the left and lower contrast on the right. VL 21

Remember that the basic idea behind selective adaptation is to determine how presentation of an adapting stimulus affects perception. We do this by determining how looking at a grating affects a perceptual property called contrast sensitivity.

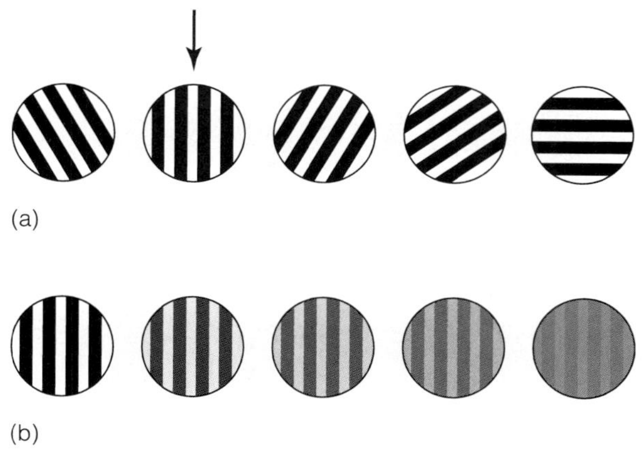

Figure 3.26 ▮ (a) Gratings that vary in orientation. (b) Gratings that vary in contrast.

METHOD ▪ Determining Contrast Sensitivity

Contrast sensitivity is a measure of how sensitive people are to the differences between the light and dark bars. To measure contrast sensitivity, we first measure the **contrast threshold** by decreasing the intensity difference between the dark and light bars of a grating until an observer can just barely tell the difference between the dark and light bars. We can do this by using one of the psychophysical methods for determining thresholds that we described in Chapter 1 (see page 12). The intensity difference at which the bars can just barely be seen is the contrast threshold. After determining the contrast threshold, we can calculate the contrast sensitivity by the formula, sensitivity = 1/threshold. Thus, if a person's contrast threshold is low—that is, they can detect a grating in which there is only a small intensity difference between the light and dark bars—their contrast sensitivity is high. VL 22

▪ ▪ ▪

Selective Adaptation to Orientation We are now ready to describe a selective adaptation experiment, which will provide evidence supporting the idea that orientation-sensitive neurons in the cortex play a role in determining our perception of orientation. We first measure an observer's contrast sensitivity to gratings of a number of different orientations, like the ones in Figure 3.26a. We then adapt the observer to a high-contrast vertical grating, like the one indicated by the arrow in Figure 3.26a, for about 1 minute. Once the observer has been adapted to this grating, we then remeasure the observer's contrast sensitivity to the same orientations that we measured before the adaptation. Figure 3.27a shows how the contrast sensitivity has changed due to the adaptation. Our observer's contrast sensitivity has decreased to vertical gratings and to some nearly vertical orientations but not to orientations far from vertical. This is what we would predict if adapting with the vertical grating decreased the response of neurons that respond best to verticals and also of some neurons that respond best to orientations near vertical. VL 23

The important result of this experiment is that our psychophysical curve shows that adaptation selectively affects only some orientations, just as neurons selectively respond to only some orientations. In fact, comparing the psychophysically determined selective adaptation curve (3.27a) to the orientation tuning curve for a simple cortical neuron (3.27b) reveals that they are very similar. The psychophysical curve is slightly wider because the grating adapts not only neurons that respond best to verticals, but also may affect, although more weakly, some neurons that respond to nearby orientations.

The near-match between the orientation selectivity of neurons and effect of selective adaptation support the idea that orientation detectors play a role in perception. Thus, when you look at a complex scene, such as a crowded shopping mall, feature detectors that are firing to the orientations in the scene are helping to construct our perception of this scene. As we will see in Chapter 4, further processing occurs before we perceive the objects, and as we will see next, selective adaptation also provides evidence for neurons that respond to the *sizes of* different parts of the scene.

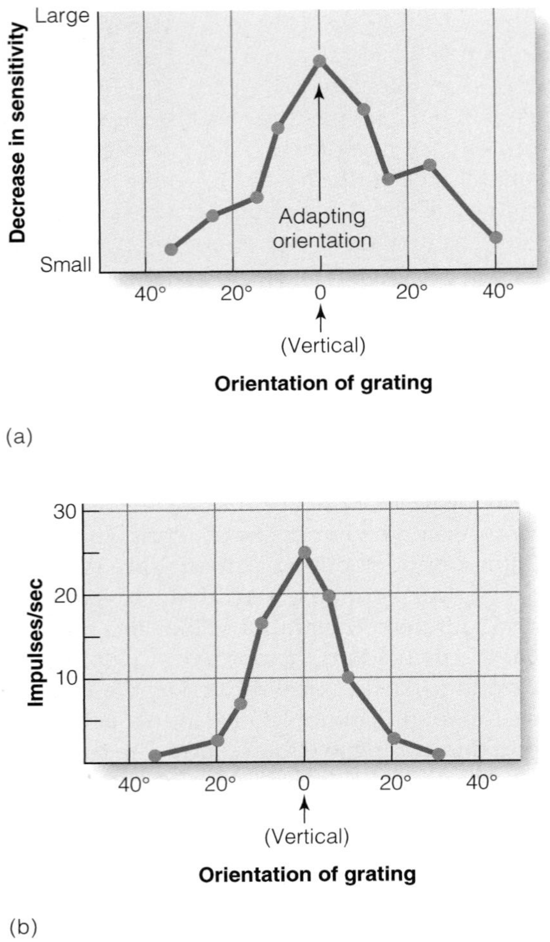

Figure 3.27 ▮ (a) Results of a psychophysical selective adaptation experiment. This graph shows that the participant's adaptation to the vertical grating causes a large decrease in her ability to detect the vertical grating when it is presented again, but has less effect on gratings that are tilted to either side of the vertical. (b) Orientation tuning curve of the simple cortical neuron from Figure 3.23b.

Selective Adaptation to Size Just as we can selectively adapt to a grating's orientation, we can also selectively adapt to the size of a grating's bars. You can experience this for yourself by doing the following demonstration.

DEMONSTRATION

Adaptation to Size

Look at Figure 3.28 by moving your eyes back and forth along the horizontal line between the two gratings on the left for about 60 seconds. This adapts you to the wide bars above the line and to the narrow bars below the line. After this adaptation, shift your gaze to the dot between the two gratings on the right and compare the spacing between the lines of the top and bottom gratings. VL 24

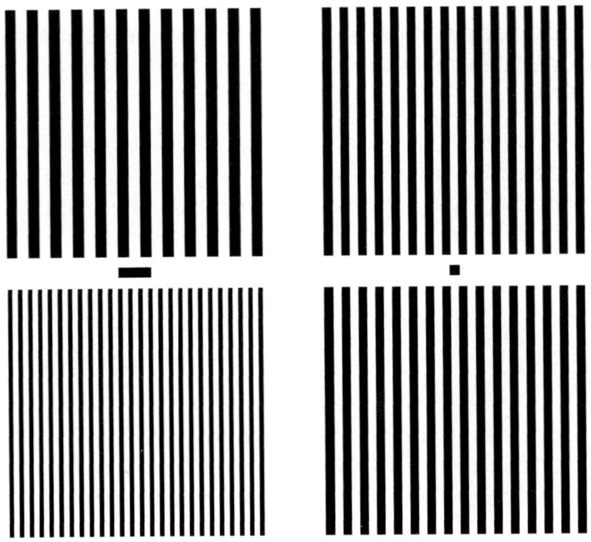

Figure 3.28 ▮ Stimuli for selective adaptation to size. See text for instructions. ■

After adapting to the gratings on the left, the lines of the top right grating may appear more closely spaced than those of the bottom right grating, even though the sizes of the bars are actually the same for both gratings.

Selective Adaptation and Size-Sensitive Neurons We can relate the above perception of the gratings to the activity of neurons that respond best to bars with a specific size. Figure 3.29 plots firing rate versus the size of bars for three neurons. The resulting plots are called **size-tuning**

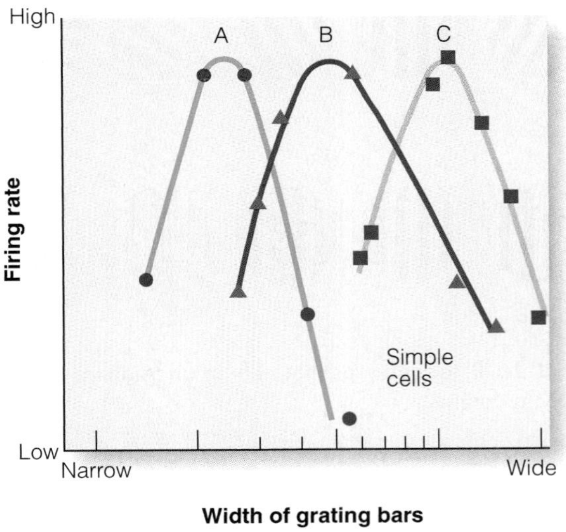

Figure 3.29 ▮ Size-tuning curves for three simple cortical cells to gratings moved across their receptive fields.
(From "The Visual Cortex as a Spatial Frequency Analyzer," by L. Maffei and A. Fiorentini, 1973, Vision Research, 13, *1255–1267, figure 3. Copyright © 1973 with kind permission from Elsevier Science Ltd., The Boulevard, Langford Land, Kidlington OX5 1GB, UK.)*

curves. (Remember that orientation tuning curves, as in Figure 3.27b, plotted firing rate vs. the orientation of the bars.) The tuning curves for these neurons indicate that Cell A responds best to wide bars, cell B to medium-width bars, and C to fine bars (Maffei & Fiorentini, 1973; cf. Albrecht, DeValois, & Thorell, 1980; K. K. DeValois, DeValois, & Yund, 1979; Robson et al., 1988).

To relate the firing of these size-selective neurons to the results of the size-adaptation demonstration, let's first consider how neurons responded to the two gratings on the right before the adaptation. Both of these gratings cause a large response in neurons that are sensitive to the gratings' size, indicated by bar M in Figure 3.30a–b. These gratings also cause some responding of neurons that are most sensitive to bars that are wider (W) and narrower (N) than the bars of the adapting gratings.

You can appreciate what happened during adaptation to the gratings on the left by considering Figure 3.30c–d. Adapting to the wide-bar grating decreased the responding of neurons that respond best to wide bars. Thus, shifting your eyes to the grating on the top right resulted in the response shown in Figure 3.30c, in which the neurons tuned to wide bars responded less than before they were adapted. This pattern of firing, which is weighted toward narrower bars, explains why you may have perceived the top right bars as narrower. In contrast, adapting to the narrow-bar grating decreased the responding of neurons that respond best to narrow bars. Thus, shifting your eyes to the grating on the bottom right resulted in the response shown in Figure 3.30d, in which the neurons tuned to narrow bars respond less than before they were adapted. This pattern of firing, which is weighted toward wide bars, explains why you may have perceived the bottom right bars as wider. Thus, just as selective adaptation to orientation supports the connection between orientation-selective neurons and perception, selective adaptation to size supports the connection between size-selective neurons and perception.

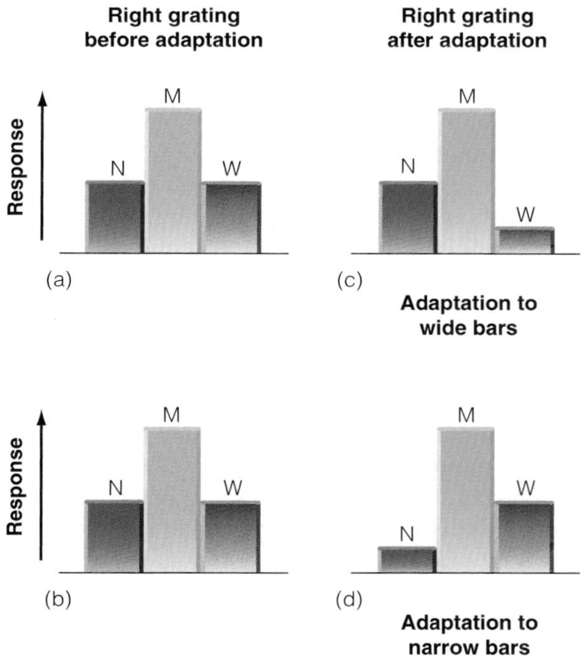

Figure 3.30 ▌ How neurons that respond best to narrow (N), medium (M), and wide (W) bars respond to the medium-bar grating on the right of Figure 3.28. (a–b): Response before adaptation. (c) Response after adaptation to the wide-bar grating at the top left. (d) Response after adaptation to the narrow-bar grating on the bottom left.

Selective Rearing and Feature Detectors

The link between feature detectors and perception has also been demonstrated by taking advantage of a property of the nervous system called neural plasticity. **Neural plasticity** refers to the fact that the response properties of neurons can be shaped by an animal's or person's perceptual experience. One way neural plasticity has been demonstrated is to use a procedure called selective rearing.

The idea behind **selective rearing** is that if an animal is reared in an environment that contains only certain types of stimuli, then neural plasticity will cause the animal to have more neurons that respond best to that type of stimulus. According to this idea, rearing an animal in an environment that contains only vertical lines should result in neurons that respond predominantly to verticals.

In one selective rearing experiment, Colin Blakemore and Grahame Cooper (1970) placed kittens in striped tubes, like the one in Figure 3.31a, so each kitten was exposed to only one orientation, either vertical or horizontal. The kittens were kept in the dark from birth to 2 weeks of age, at which time they were placed in the tube for 5 hours a day; the rest of the time they remained in the dark. Because the kittens sat on a Plexiglas platform, and the tube extended both above and below them, there were no visible corners or edges in their environment other than the stripes on the sides of the tube. The kittens wore neck ruffs to prevent them from seeing vertical stripes as oblique or horizontal stripes by turning their heads; however, according to Blakemore and Cooper, "The kittens did not seem upset by the monotony of their surroundings and they sat for long periods inspecting the walls of the tube" (p. 477).

When the kittens' behavior was tested after 5 months of selective rearing, they seemed blind to the orientations that they hadn't seen in the tube. For example, a kitten that was reared in an environment of vertical stripes would pay attention to a vertical rod but ignored a horizontal rod. Following behavioral testing, Blakemore and Cooper recorded from cells in the visual cortex and determined the stimulus orientation that caused the largest response from each cell. Their results indicate that many of the cells of the vertically reared cats respond best to verti-

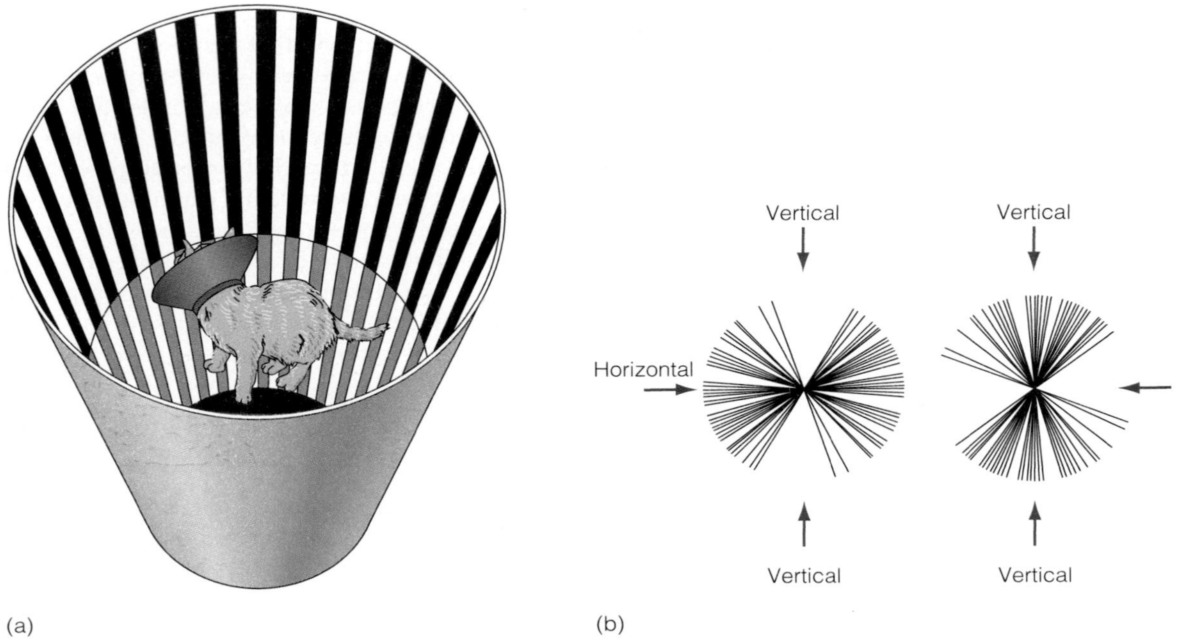

Figure 3.31 ■ (a) Striped tube used in Blakemore and Cooper's (1970) selective rearing experiments. (b) Distribution of optimal orientations for 52 cells from a cat reared in an environment of horizontal stripes, on the left, and for 72 cells from a cat reared in an environment of vertical stripes, on the right.
(Blakemore & Cooper, 1970.)

cal or near-vertical stimuli, but none respond to horizontal stimuli, and the opposite result occurred for the horizontally reared cats (Figure 3.31b). Thus, selective rearing demonstrates a parallel between the orientation selectivity of neurons in the cats' cortex and the cats' behavioral response to the same orientation.

SOMETHING TO CONSIDER: PERCEPTION AS INDIRECT

One of the main purposes of perception is to provide experiences that link us to our environment. But perception does more than that. It gives us the feeling that we are in *direct contact* with the environment. As I look up from my writing, I can tell that there is a coffee cup sitting on the table directly in front of me. I know where the cup is, so I can easily reach for it, and as I pick it up I feel the smooth texture of the cup's ceramic finish. As I drink the coffee, I also sense heat, and also the coffee's taste and smell. But as much as I feel that all of these experiences are due to my direct contact with the coffee cup and the liquid in it, I know that this feeling of directness is largely an illusion. Perception, as we will see throughout this text, is an indirect process.

We have already demonstrated the indirectness of perception by considering the mechanisms responsible for vision. I see the cup not because of any direct contact with it, but because the light that is reflected from the cup is changed into electricity in the retina that is then transmitted in the optic nerve to the lateral geniculate nucleus and the cortex. My experience of the cup therefore depends on the numerous transformations that occur between the time I look at the cup and neurons fire in my brain.

"Well, vision may be indirect," you might say, "but how about the perceptions of heat and texture that occur from picking up the cup? Weren't your fingers in direct contact with the cup?" The answer to this question is, yes, it is true that my fingers were in direct physical contact with the cup, but my perception of the heat of the coffee and the texture of the cup's finish was due to the stimulation of temperature-sensitive and pressure-sensitive receptors in my fingers, which translated the temperature and pressure into electrical impulses, just as the light energy that causes vision is translated into electrical impulses.

Smell and taste are also indirect because these experiences occur when chemicals travel through the air to receptor sites in the nose and tongue. Stimulation of these receptor sites causes electrical signals that are processed by the nervous system to create the experiences of smell and taste. Hearing is the same. Air pressure waves transmitted through the air cause vibrations of receptors inside the ear, and these vibrations generate the electrical signals our auditory system uses to create the experience of sound.

The amazing thing about perception is that despite this indirectness, it seems so real. And it is real, in the sense that our perceptions usually provide us with accurate information about what's out there in the distance or what's up close under our noses or beneath our fingers. But in all of these cases, this information is created through the actions of receptors that change environmental stimulation into electrical signals that eventually, somewhere in the brain, create our sensory impressions of the environment.

TEST YOURSELF 3.2

1. Why is interaction between neurons necessary for neural processing? Be sure to understand how convergence and inhibition work together to achieve processing.
2. What is a neuron's receptive field, and how is it measured?
3. Describe a center-surround receptive field, and explain how center-surround antagonism affects firing as a stimulus spot is made bigger.
4. Describe the response properties of neurons at different levels of the visual system, beginning in the retina and moving into the primary receiving area of the cortex and other areas beyond the primary receiving area.
5. How has the psychophysical procedure of selective adaptation been used to demonstrate a link between feature detectors and (a) the perception of orientation, and (b) the perception of size? Be sure you understand the rationale behind a selective adaptation experiment and also how we can draw conclusions about physiology from the results of this psychophysical procedure.
6. How has the procedure of selective rearing been used to demonstrate a link between feature detectors and perception? Be sure you understand the concept of neural plasticity.
7. What does it mean to say "all perception is indirect"?

THINK ABOUT IT

1. Ralph, who is skeptical about the function of lateral inhibition, says, "OK, so lateral inhibition causes us to see Mach bands and the spots at the intersections of the Hermann grid. Even though these perceptual effects are interesting, they don't seem very important to me. If they didn't exist, we would see the world in just about the same way as we do with them." How would you respond to Ralph if you wanted to make an argument for the importance of lateral inhibition? (Warning: Be sure to consider the possibility that Ralph could be right.)
2. Look for shadows, both inside and outside, and see if you can see Mach bands at the borders of the shadows. Remember that Mach bands are easier to see when the border of a shadow is slightly fuzzy. Mach bands are not actually present in the pattern of light and dark, so you need to be sure that the bands are not really in the light but are created by your nervous system. How can you accomplish this?
3. Cell A responds best to vertical lines moving to the right. Cell B responds best to 45-degree lines moving to the left. Both of these cells have an excitatory synapse with cell C. How will cell C fire to a moving vertical line? To 45-degree lines?

IF YOU WANT TO KNOW MORE

1. ***Beyond "classic" receptive fields.*** We defined a neuron's receptive field as "the area on the retina that, when stimulated, influences the firing of the neuron." But recent research has revealed that for some neurons, there are areas outside of the "classic" receptive field that cause no change in the firing of a neuron when stimulated alone, but can nonetheless influence the neuron's response to stimulation of an area inside the "classic" receptive field.

   Vinje, B. V., & Gallant, J. L. (2002). Natural stimulation of the non-classical receptive field increases information transmission efficiency in V1. *Journal of Neuroscience, 22,* 2904–2915.

   Zipser, K., Lamme, V. A. F., & Schiller, P. H. (1996). Contextual modulation in primary visual cortex. *Journal of Neuroscience, 16,* 7376–7389.

2. ***Specialized neurons.*** The existence of neurons that respond to complex stimuli, such as faces and buildings, is one of the outcomes of neural processing. The pictures in Figure 3.25 are just introductions to the kinds of stimuli to which these neurons respond. As you read Chapter 4, note the additional information that is provided regarding what these neurons respond to and where they are located in the brain.
3. ***Spatial frequency.*** We described neurons that respond to different sizes of grating stimuli. We can also describe stimuli in terms of the spatial frequency of the stimulus. High spatial frequencies correspond roughly to small, detailed stimuli, and low spatial frequencies correspond roughly to larger, less detailed

stimuli. Research has shown that there are neurons that are tuned to respond to different spatial frequencies and that these neuron may play a role in perceiving the different spatial frequencies in the environment.

Campbell, F. W., & Robson, J. G. (1968). Application of Fourier analysis to the visibility of gratings. *Journal of Physiology, 197,* 551–566.

4. ***Spatial frequency analysis.*** On page 64 we discussed selective adaptation to size and size-sensitive neurons. Closely related to the idea that the visual system analyzes stimuli in terms of size, is the idea that the visual system analyzes stimuli in terms of a measure called spatial frequency (see page 355). Roughly speaking, high spatial frequencies correspond to fine details and rapid changes that occur moving across a visual stimulus (as might occur at a border between a light and a dark area), and low spatial frequencies correspond to larger units and slow changes across a visual stimulus. VL 25

Campbell, F. W., & Robson, J. G. (1968). Application of Fourier analysis to the visibility of gratings. *Journal of Physiology, 197,* 551–566.

Graham, N. (1992). Breaking the visual stimulus into parts. *Current Directions in Psychological Science,* 1, 55–61.

KEY TERMS

Amacrine cell (p. 46)
Belongingness (p. 55)
Benary cross (p. 54)
Bipolar cell (p. 46)
Center-surround antagonism (p. 58)
Center-surround receptive field (p. 58)
Complex cell (p. 60)
Contrast (p. 63)
Contrast sensitivity (p. 63)
Contrast threshold (p. 63)
Convergence (neural) (p. 46)
End-stopped cell (p. 60)
Excitatory area (p. 58)
Excitatory-center–inhibitory-surround receptive field (p. 58)
Extrastriate cortex (p. 58)
Feature detector (p. 61)
Ganglion cell (p. 46)
Grating (p. 63)
Hermann grid (p. 50)
Horizontal cell (p. 46)
Inhibitory area (p. 58)
Inhibitory-center–excitatory-surround receptive field (p. 58)
Lateral geniculate nucleus (LGN) (p. 58)
Lateral inhibition (p. 50)
Mach bands (p. 51)
Neural circuit (p. 56)
Neural plasticity (p. 65)
Ommatidium (p. 44)
Orientation (p. 63)
Orientation tuning curve (p. 60)
Receptive field (p. 57)
Selective adaptation (p. 62)
Selective rearing (p. 65)
Simple cortical cell (p. 60)
Simultaneous contrast (p. 53)
Size-tuning curve (p. 64)
Striate cortex (p. 58)
Superior colliculus (p. 58)
Visual acuity (p. 48)
White's illusion (p. 55)

VISIT YOUR COMPANION WEBSITE FOR THIS BOOK

http://psychology.wadsworth.com/goldstein7e

Check out this companion website where you'll find online resources—glossary, flashcards, web links, multiple-choice and essay questions, and much more!

VIRTUAL LAB VL

Your Virtual Lab is designed to help you get the most out of this course. The Virtual Lab icons direct you to specific media demonstrations and experiments designed to help you visualize what you are reading about. The number beside each icon indicates the number of the media element you can access through your CD-ROM, Perception PsychologyNow, or WebTutor resource at http:now.ilrn.com/goldstein_7e.

The following lab exercises cover what you've just learned in this chapter:

1. *Cross-Section of the Retina* A drag-and-drop exercise to test your knowledge of the neurons in the retina.

2. *Receptor Wiring and Sensitivity* When light is presented to the receptors, rod ganglion cells fire at lower light intensities than cone ganglion cells.

3. *Receptor Wiring and Acuity* When spots of light are presented to rod and cone receptors, detail information is present in the cone ganglion cells but not the rod ganglion cell.

4. *Lateral Inhibition* How lateral inhibition affects the firing of one neuron when adjacent neurons are stimulated.

5. *Hermann Grid* A display similar to Figure 3.6, showing the gray spots that occur at intersections in the Hermann grid.

6. *Lateral Inhibition in the Hermann Grid* How lateral inhibition can explain the firing of neurons that cause the "spots" in the Hermann grid.

7. *Mach Bands* A demonstration that enables you to create patterns that result in Mach bands and to see perceived brightness distributions superimposed on these patterns.

8. *Intensity and Brightness* Mapping the physical intensity across a display that produces Mach bands and comparing this intensity to perceived brightness across the display.

9. *Inhibition and Mach Bands* How receptive fields can explain the Mach band illusion.

10. *Simultaneous Contrast* How varying the intensity of the surround can influence perception of the brightness of squares in the center.

11. *Simultaneous Contrast: Static* A simultaneous contrast display like the one in Figure 3.12.

12. *Simultaneous Contrast: Dynamic* How perception of a gray dot changes as it moves across a background that is graded from white to black.

13. *Simple Neural Circuits* Presenting lights to receptors in three neural circuits illustrates how adding convergence and inhibition influences neural responding.

14. *Mapping Receptive Fields* Mapping the receptive field of a retinal ganglion cell.

15. *Receptive Field Mapping* Mapping the receptive fields of ganglion cells, LGN neurons, and cortical neurons.

16. *Stimulus Size and Receptive Fields* How the size of a stimulus relative to the receptive field affects the size of the neural response.

17. *Receptive Fields and Stimulus Size and Shape* How the size of a stimulus and the size of the receptive field influence neural responding.

18. *The Visual Pathways* A drag-and-drop exercise that tests your knowledge of visual structures.

19. *Simple Cells in the Cortex* How the firing rate of a simple cortical cell depends on orientation of a stimulus.

20. *Complex Cells in the Cortex* How the firing rate of a complex cortical cell changes with orientation and direction of movement of a stimulus.

21. *Calculating Grating Contrast* How changing the illumination of bars of a grating affects the grating's contrast.

22. *Contrast Sensitivity* An experiment in which you measure your contrast sensitivity to grating patterns.

23. *Orientation Aftereffect* How adaptation to an orientated grating can affect the perception of orientation.

24. *Size Aftereffect* How adaptation to a grating can affect size perception.

25. *Spatial Vision* Illustrates how an image's appearance is changed by changing the spatial frequencies contained in the image.

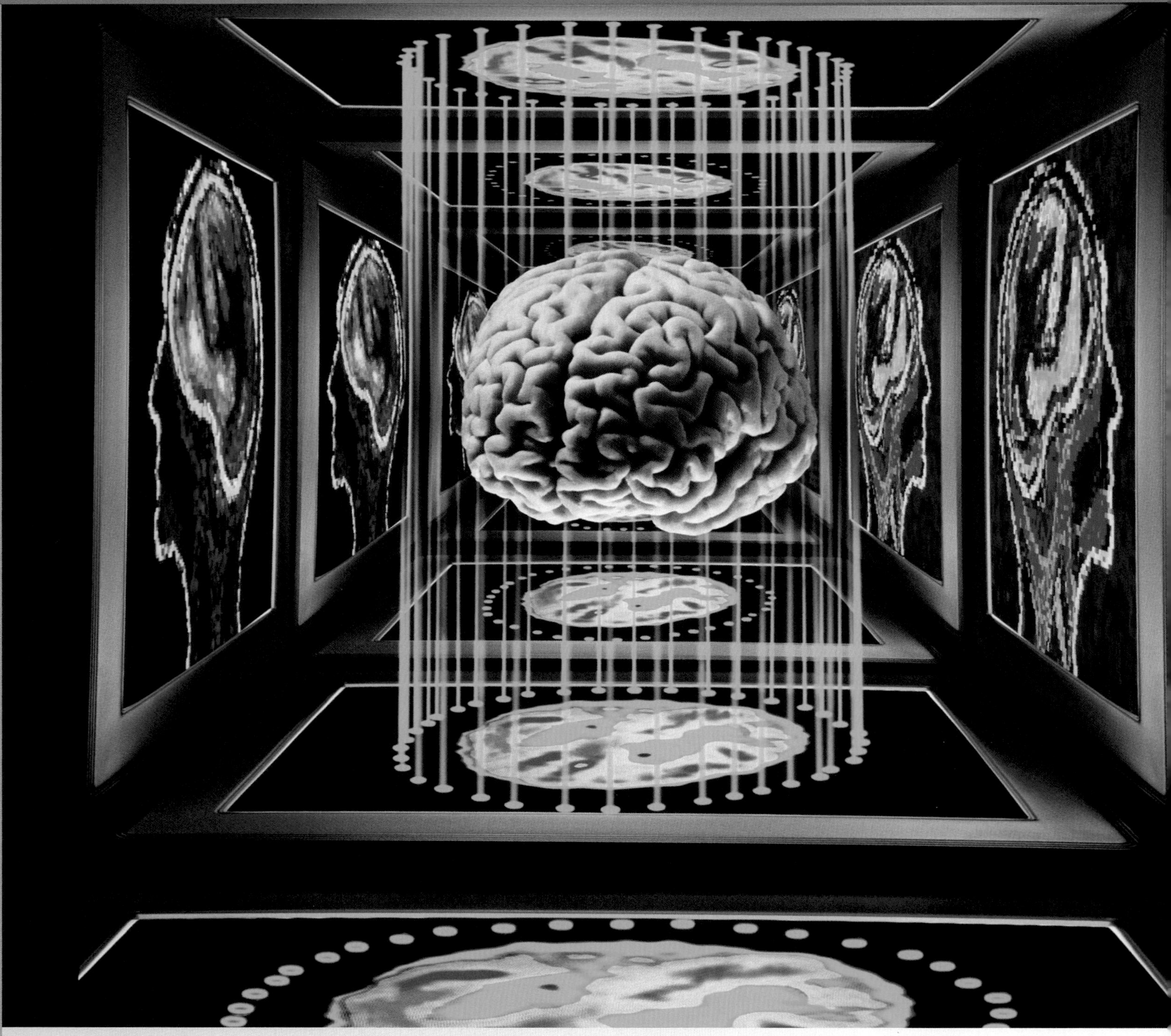

Brain-imaging technology has made it possible to visualize both the structure and function of different areas of the brain.

CHAPTER

4

THE ORGANIZED BRAIN

Chapter Contents

VL *The Virtual Lab icons direct you to specific animations and videos designed to help you visualize what you are reading about. The number beside each icon indicates the number of the clip you can access through your CD-ROM or your student website.*

Some Questions We Will Consider:

- *How can brain damage affect a person's perception?* *(p. 81)*
- *Are there separate brain areas that determine our perception of different qualities?* *(p. 82)*
- *How has the operation of our visual system been shaped by evolution and by our day-to-day experiences?* *(p. 84)*

Remember our example at the beginning of Chapter 2, in which we discussed ways to determine reactions to a speech that had just been given at a political convention (see page 23)? We noted that one way to determine the effect of the speech would be to poll individual people. But another way is by determining how the people in the audience are organized. We might determine, for example, which groups of people have similar political views, whether they are sitting together, and how they have been interacting with groups of people who may have somewhat different views.

Just as we can learn more about what is happening at the convention both by assessing the reactions of individuals and by determining how people are organized, we can also learn about how the brain operates both by measuring the responses of single neurons and by determining how these neurons are organized and how they interact with one another. Thus, our focus in Chapters 2 and 3 was on recording from single neurons in the visual system, but in this chapter we shift our focus to consider how these neurons are organized. To do this, we will describe the following types of organization in the visual system:

- *Maps:* The surface of the retina is *mapped* onto the visual cortex so that adjacent points on the cortex correspond to adjacent areas on the retina.
- *Columns:* Neurons with similar properties are organized in *columns* in the visual cortex.
- *Streams:* Certain sequences of interconnected structures serve specific functions.
- *Modules:* Certain areas are specialized to serve specific functions.
- *Distributed representation:* Objects in the environment are represented by activity in groups of neurons.

MAPS: REPRESENTING SPATIAL LAYOUT

To introduce the idea of spatial maps, we first consider Figure 4.1a. When the man looks at the cup, points A, B, and C on the cup are imaged on points A, B, and C of the retina, and each place on the retina corresponds to a specific place on the lateral geniculate nucleus (LGN). This correspondence between points on the LGN and points on the retina creates a **retinotopic map** on the LGN—a map in which each point on the LGN corresponds to a point on the retina. To determine what this map looks like, we record from neurons in the LGN.

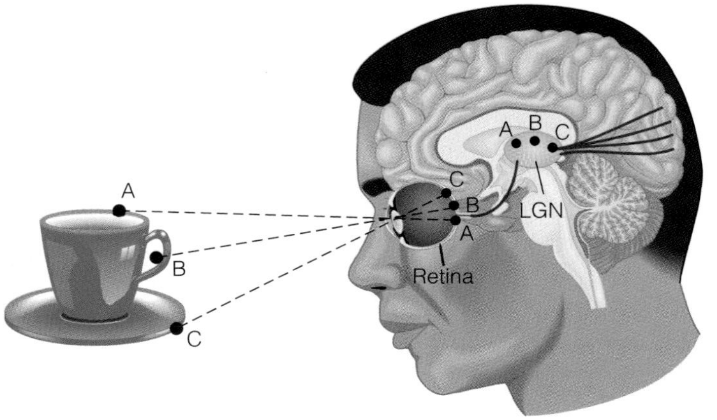

Figure 4.1 Points A, B, and C on the cup create images at A, B, and C on the retina and cause activation at points A, B, and C on the lateral geniculate nucleus (LGN). The correspondence between points on the LGN and retina indicates that there is a retinotopic map on the LGN.

METHOD ▪ Determining Retinotopic Map by Recording from Neurons

The retinotopic map on the LGN has been determined by recording from neurons in the LGN with an electrode that penetrates the LGN obliquely (at an angle to the surface), as shown in Figure 4.2. Notice that the LGN has six layers. We are recording from the neurons at A, B, and C in layer 6 of the LGN.

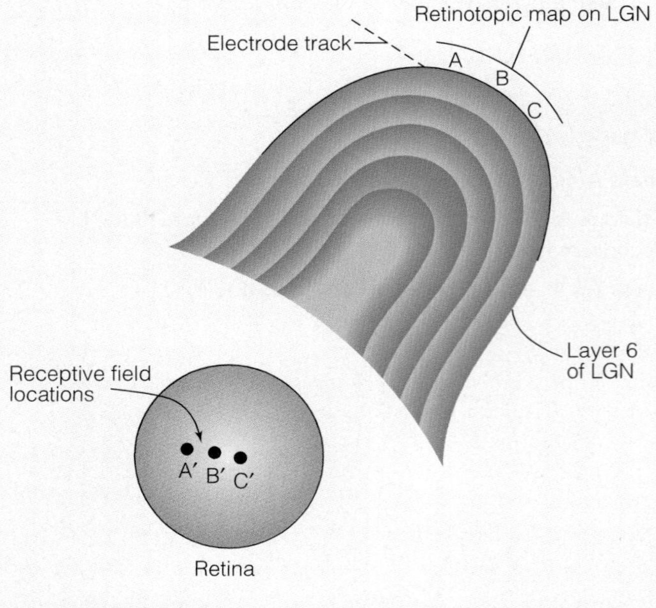

Figure 4.2 Retinotopic mapping of neurons in the LGN. The neurons at A, B, and C in layer 6 of the LGN have receptive fields located at positions A′, B′, and C′ on the retina.

Recording from the neuron at A, we determine the location of the neuron's receptive field on the retina by stimulating the retina with spots of light until the neuron responds. The location of the neuron's receptive field is indicated by A′ on the retina. When we repeat this procedure with an electrode at B and then at C, we find that B's receptive field is at B′ on the retina, and C's receptive field is at C′ on the retina. Results such as those in Figure 4.2 show that stimulating a sequence of points on the retina results in activity in a corresponding sequence of neurons in the LGN. This is the retinotopic map on the LGN.

■ ■ ■

The Map on the Cortex

Using the procedure we have just described, when the recording from neurons in the cortex reveals that just as there is a retinotopic map in the LGN, there is also one in the cortex. Figure 4.3 shows the results of an experiment by David Hubel and Thorsten Wiesel (1965), who recorded from a series of neurons along an oblique electrode track in the cat's visual cortex. They found that the receptive fields of neurons close to each other along the electrode track had receptive fields that were close to each other or overlapping on the retina.

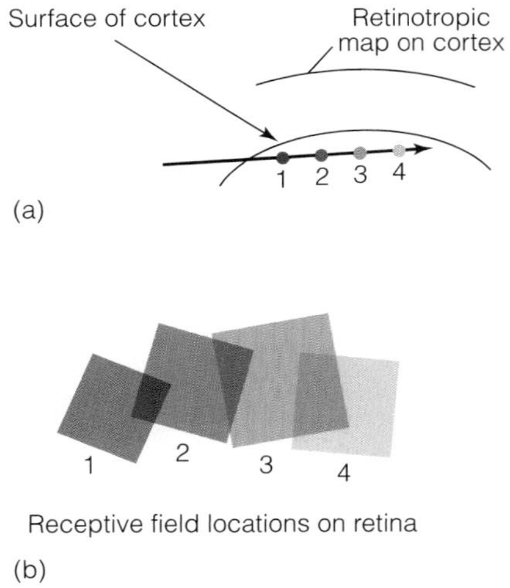

Figure 4.3 ▌ Retinotopic mapping of neurons in the cortex. When the electrode penetrates the cortex obliquely, the receptive fields of neurons recorded from the numbered positions along the track are displaced, as indicated by the numbered receptive fields; neurons near each other in the cortex have receptive fields near each other on the retina.

An important feature of this retinotopic map on the cortex is that the area representing the cone-rich fovea is much larger than one would expect from the fovea's small size. Even though the fovea accounts for only 0.01 percent of the retina's area, signals from the fovea account for 8 to 10 percent of the retinotopic map on the cortex (Van Essen & Anderson, 1995). This apportioning the small fovea with a large area on the cortex is called the **cortical magnification factor** (Figure 4.4).

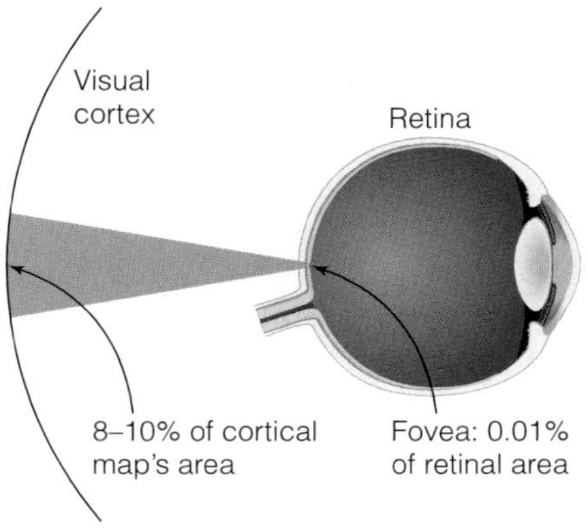

Figure 4.4 ▌ The magnification factor in the visual system: The small area of the fovea is represented by a large area on the visual cortex.

The cortical magnification factor has been determined in humans by using a technique called brain imaging, which can be used to create pictures of the brain's activity. We will describe the procedure of brain imaging and how this procedure has been used to measure the cortical magnification factor in humans.

METHOD ■ Brain Imaging

Brain imaging enables researchers to create images that show which areas of the brain are active. One of these techniques, **positron emission tomography (PET)**, was introduced in 1976 (Hoffman et al., 1976; Ter-Pogossian et al., 1975). In the PET procedure a person is injected with a low dose of a radioactive tracer that is not harmful. The tracer enters the bloodstream and indicates the volume of blood flow. The basic principle behind the PET scan is that changes in the activity of the brain are accompanied by changes in blood flow, and monitoring the radioactivity of the injected tracer provides a measure of this blood flow (Figure 4.5).

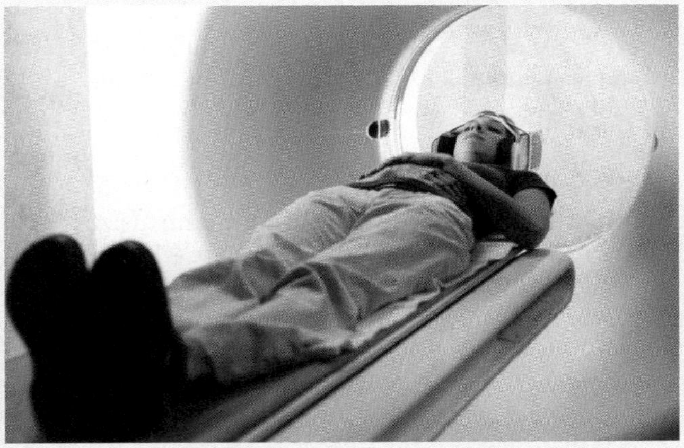

Figure 4.5 ▌ A person in a brain-imaging apparatus.

PET enabled researchers to track changes in blood flow to determine which brain areas were being activated. To use this tool, researchers developed the **subtraction technique**. Brain activity is first measured in a "control state" before stimulation is presented and is then measured while the stimulus is presented. For example, in a study designed to determine which areas of the brain are activated when a person manipulates an object in his or her hand, activity generated by simply placing the object in the hand would be measured first. This is the control state (Figure 4.6a). Then activity is measured as the person manipulates the object. This is the stimulation state (Figure 4.6b). Finally, the activity due to manipulation is determined by subtracting the control activity from the stimulation activity (Figure 4.6c).

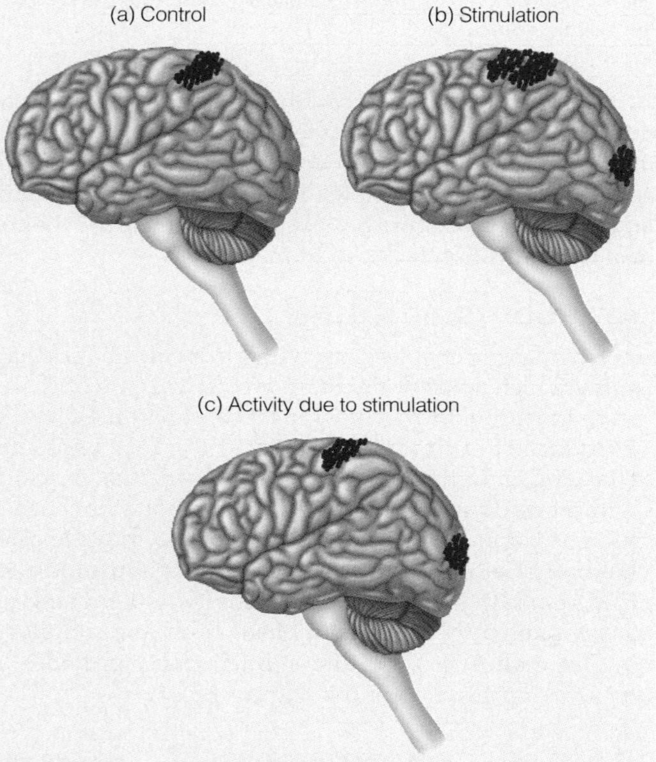

Figure 4.6 ▌ The subtraction technique that is used to interpret the results of brain imaging experiments. See text for explanation.

Recently, another neuroimaging technique called **functional magnetic resonance imaging (fMRI)** has been introduced. Like PET, fMRI is based on the measurement of blood flow. Because hemoglobin, which carries oxygen in the blood, contains a ferrous molecule and therefore has magnetic properties, presenting a magnetic field to the brain causes the hemoglobin molecules to line up like tiny magnets.

fMRI indicates the presence of brain activity because the hemoglobin molecules in areas of high brain activity lose some of the oxygen they are transporting. This makes the hemoglobin more magnetic, so these molecules respond more strongly to the magnetic field. The fMRI apparatus determines the relative activity of various areas of the brain by detecting changes in the magnetic response of the hemoglobin. The subtraction technique described above for PET is also used for the fMRI and, because fMRI doesn't require radioactive tracers and because it is more accurate, this technique has become the main method for localizing brain activity in humans.

■ ■ ■

Robert Dougherty and coworkers (2003) used brain imaging to determine the magnification factor of the human cortex. Figure 4.7 shows that a small area just outside of the fovea (red arc in Figure 4.7a) accounts for more area on the cortex (red area) than the much larger arc located at a distance out from the center of view (blue arc and

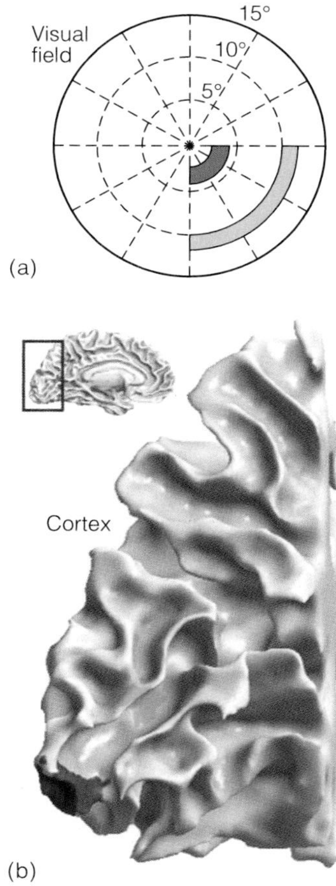

Figure 4.7 ▌ (a) Purple and teal areas show the extent of stimuli that were presented while a person was in an fMRI scanner. (b) Purple and teal indicates areas of the brain activated by the stimulation in (a).

(From Dougherty, R. F. et al. (2003). Visual field representations and locations of visual areas V1/2/3 in human visual cortex. Journal of Vision, 3, *586–598.)*

blue area). The extra cortical space allotted to the foveal cones is available for the extra neural processing needed to accomplish high-acuity tasks such as reading or identifying your friend's face in a crowd (Azzopardi & Cowey, 1993).

The connection between cortical area and acuity has been confirmed by Robert Duncan and Geoffrey Boynton (2003). They measured brain activation with the fMRI and acuity using a psychophysical task. The fMRI indicated that the magnification factor was not the same for all of their observers. Some people had more cortical space for their foveas than other people, and the people with more cortical space had better acuity. This finding supports the idea that a person's ability to see details depends not only on how well images are focused on the retina and how the cones are wired in the retina, but also on how much space in the cortex is allotted to signals that are coming from cones in the fovea.

COLUMNS: ORGANIZING FOR LOCATION, ORIENTATION, AND OCULAR DOMINANCE

Determining the retinotopic map and the magnification factor has kept us near the surface of the LGN and cortex. We are now ready to ask what is happening below the surface. To answer this question, researchers have penetrated structures perpendicularly, as shown for the LGN in Figure 4.8.

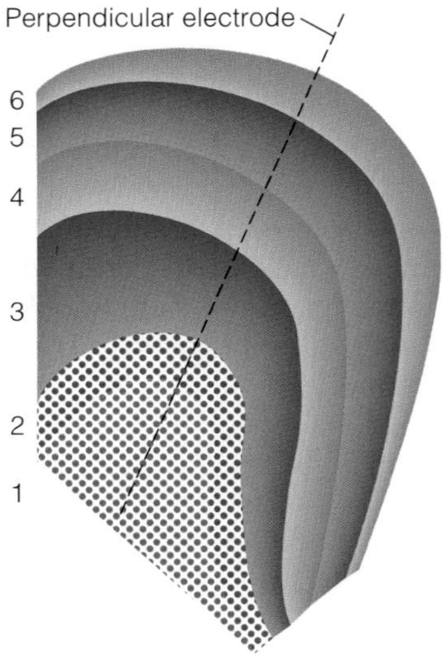

Figure 4.8 ▌ Cross section of the LGN showing layers. Red layers receive signals from the ipsilateral (same side of the body) eye. Blue layers receive signals from the contralateral (opposite side) eye. Solid layers: parvocellular layers. Dotted layers: magnocellular layers. (Parvocellular and magnocellular are described on page 79.) The dashed line represents an electrode inserted perpendicular to the surface.

The LGN "Club Sandwich"

In Figure 4.2 we saw that there are 6 layers in the LGN. The LGN receives signals from both the left and right eyes, but inputs from the two eyes are segregated in different layers. Layers 2, 3, and 5 (Figure 4.8, red layers) receive signals from the **ipsilateral eye**, the eye on the same side of the body as the LGN. Layers 1, 4, and 6 (Figure 4.8, blue layers) receive signals from the **contralateral eye**, the eye on the opposite side of the body from the LGN. Thus, each eye sends half of its neurons to the LGN that is located in the left hemisphere of the brain and half to the LGN that is located in the right hemisphere. Because the signals from each eye are sorted into different layers, the information from the left and right eyes is kept separated in the LGN.

When researchers inserted an electrode perpendicular to the surface of the LGN, as shown in Figure 4.8, they found that all neurons along the same electrode track had receptive fields at about the same place on the retina. This finding prompted the anatomist Gordon Walls (1953) to compare the LGN to a club sandwich because the electrode is like a toothpick piercing a club sandwich's layers.

Because the electrode encounters neurons that have overlapping receptive fields, these neurons all receive information from the same place on the retina (Mollon, 1990). This is an amazing feat of organization: 1 million ganglion cell fibers travel to each LGN, and, on arriving there, each fiber goes to the correct LGN layer and finds its way to a location that is next to other fibers that left from about the same location on the retina. In addition, these fibers are lined up with all of the other fibers that are coming from the same place on the retina, even though these other fibers are in the other layers of the club sandwich!

Location Columns in the Cortex

Using a procedure similar to the one we described for the LGN, Hubel and Wiesel (1965) found that a similar result occurs in the cortex, with neurons along a perpendicular electrode track having receptive fields either on top of each other or very close together on the retina (Figure 4.9). They concluded from this result that the cortex is organized into **location columns** that are perpendicular to the surface of the cortex and that the neurons within a location column have their receptive fields at the same location on the retina.

Orientation Columns in the Cortex

As Hubel and Wiesel were recording from neurons along their perpendicular electrode track in the cortex, they also noted how their neurons responded to orientation. (Remember from Chapter 3 that cortical neurons respond best to bars of light with a particular orientation.) As Hubel and Wiesel lowered their electrodes, they noted not only that the neurons along this track had receptive

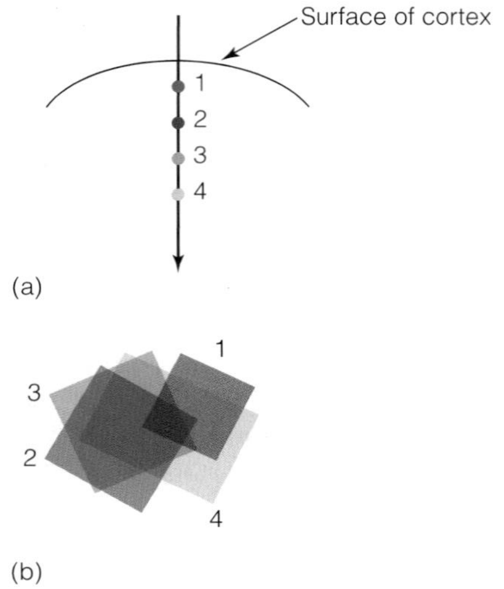

Figure 4.9 ▮ When an electrode penetrates the cortex perpendicularly, the receptive fields of the neurons encountered along this track overlap. The receptive field recorded at each numbered position along the electrode track is indicated by a correspondingly numbered square.

fields with the same location on the retina but that these neurons all preferred stimuli with the same orientations. Thus, all cells encountered along the electrode track at A in Figure 4.10 fired the most to horizontal lines, whereas all those along electrode track B fired the most to lines oriented at about 45 degrees. Based on this result, Hubel and Wiesel concluded that the cortex is organized into **orientation columns**, with each column containing cells that respond best to a particular orientation. (Also see "If You Want to Know More," at the end of the chapter, for another technique for revealing orientation columns.)

Hubel and Wiesel also showed that adjacent columns have cells with slightly different preferred orientations. When they moved an electrode through the cortex obliquely, as in Figure 4.2, so that the electrode cut across orientation columns, they found that the neurons' preferred orientations changed in an orderly fashion, so a column of cells that respond best to 45 degrees is right next to the column of cells that respond best to 40 degrees. Hubel and Wiesel also found that as they moved their electrode 1 millimeter across the cortex, their electrode passed through orientation columns that represented the entire range of orientations.

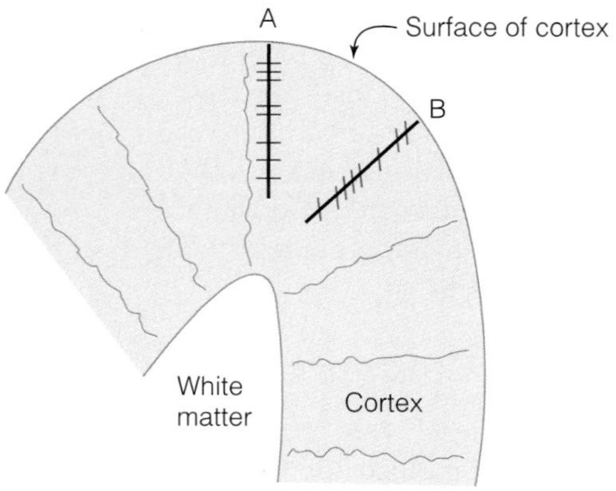

Figure 4.10 ▮ All of the cortical neurons encountered along track A respond best to horizontal bars (indicated by the red lines cutting across the electrode track). All of the neurons along track B respond best to bars oriented at 45 degrees.

Ocular Dominance Columns in the Cortex

Neurons in the cortex are also organized with respect to the eye to which they respond best. About 80 percent of the neurons in the cortex respond to stimulation of both the left and the right eyes. However, most neurons respond better to one eye than to the other. This preferential response to one eye is called **ocular dominance**, and neurons with the same ocular dominance are organized into **ocular dominance columns** in the cortex.

Hubel and Wiesel observed these columns during their oblique penetrations of the cortex. They found that a given area of cortex usually contains cells that all respond best to one of the eyes, but when the electrode was moved about 0.25 to 0.50 mm across the cortex, the dominance pattern changes to the other eye. Thus, the cortex consists of a series of columns that alternate in ocular dominance in a left-right-left-right pattern.

How Is an Object Represented in the Striate Cortex?

Now that we have described how the cortex is organized into maps and columns, we are in a position to take an initial stab at answering the question: How is an object represented in the striate cortex? That is, how does the electrical activity in the cortex *stand for* the object in the environment?

To begin, we will consider a situation in which an observer is viewing a striped peppermint stick, like the one in Figure 4.11. This figure shows that looking at the peppermint stick results in an image on the retina, which then results in a pattern of activation on the striate cortex that looks something like the peppermint stick because of the retinotopic map in the cortex. Notice, however, that the activation is distorted compared to the actual object because the magnification factor allots more space on the cortex to the parts of the image that fall on the observer's fovea.

But the pattern of activation on the surface of the cortex doesn't tell the whole story. To appreciate how the peppermint stick is represented by activity that is occurring under the surface of the cortex, we will ignore the stripes and focus just on the length of the stick, which is essentially a long oriented bar. From what we know about orientation columns, we know that an oriented line activates neurons in the column that corresponds to the

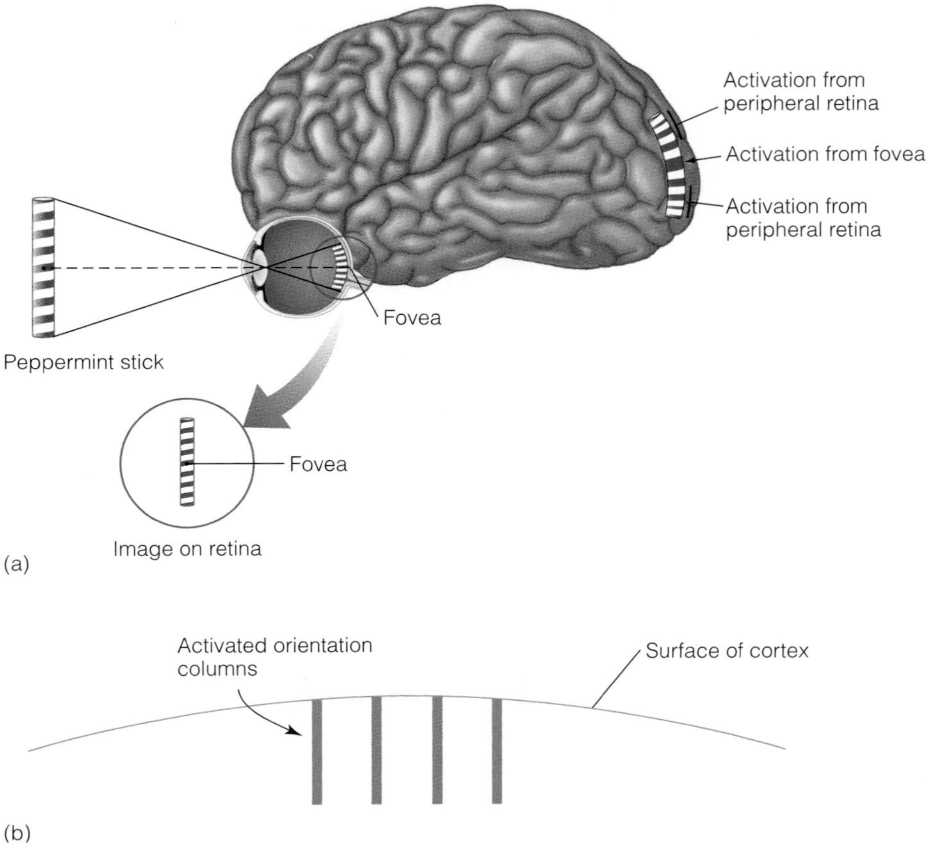

Figure 4.11 ■ (a) How a peppermint stick creates an image on the retina and a pattern of activation on the cortex. (b) How a long peppermint stick would activate a number of different orientation columns in the cortex.

line's orientation and may also cause some activation in nearby orientation columns.

Another thing we know about orientation columns is that each column responds only to stimulation of a small area of the retina. Thus, a large stimulus, which stretches across the retina, will stimulate a number of different orientation columns, which are separated in the cortex. A rough picture of what this activation might look like is shown in Figure 4.11b. The length of the peppermint stick has been translated into activity in a number of orientation columns, and this activity looks quite different than the shape of the stimulus, which is a single continuous bar.

Although it may be surprising that the peppermint stick is represented in a number of separate columns in the cortex, it simply confirms a basic property of our perceptual system: The cortical representation of a stimulus does not have to *resemble* the stimulus; it just has to contain information that *represents* the stimulus. The representation of the length of the peppermint stick in the visual cortex is contained in the firings of neurons in separate cortical columns, and if we were to also consider the stripes, we would observe additional activation in other cortical columns. Of course, this representation in striate cortex is only the first step in representing the peppermint stick. As we will now see, signals from the striate cortex (V1) travel to a number of other places in the cortex for further processing.

STREAMS: PATHWAYS FOR *WHAT, WHERE,* AND *HOW*

Research that began in the late 1950s described how the striate cortex is arranged in columns and how objects can be represented by activity in these columns. But beginning in the 1970s and 80s, another line of research began investigating areas outside the striate cortex. One of the most influential ideas to come out of this research is that there are pathways, or "streams," that transmit information from the striate cortex to other areas in the brain. This idea was introduced in 1982, when Leslie Ungerleider and Mortimer Mishkin described experiments that distinguished two streams that served different functions.

Streams for Information About *What* and *Where*

Ungerleider and Mishkin (1982) used a technique called **lesioning**, or **ablation**, which involves determining how removal of a specific brain area affects an animal's behavior.

METHOD ▪ Ablation

The goal of an ablation experiment is to determine the function of a particular area of the brain. This is accomplished by first determining an animal's capacity by testing it behaviorally. Most ablation experiments have used the monkey because of the similarity of its visual system to the humans' and because monkeys can be trained to indicate perceptual capacities such as acuity, color vision, depth perception, and object perception.

Once perception has been measured, a particular area of the brain is ablated (removed or destroyed) either by surgery or by injecting a chemical at the area to be removed. Ideally, one particular area is removed and the rest of the brain remains intact. After ablation, the monkey is retrained to determine which perceptual capacities remain and which have been affected.

▪ ▪ ▪

Ungerleider and Mishkin presented monkeys with two tasks: (1) an object discrimination problem and (2) a landmark discrimination problem. In the **object discrimination problem**, a monkey was shown one object, such as a rectangular solid, and was then presented with a two-choice task like the one shown in Figure 4.12a, which included the "target" object (the rectangular solid) and another stimulus, such as the triangular shape. If the monkey pushed aside the target object, it received the food reward that was hidden in a well under the object. The **landmark discrimination problem** is shown in Figure 4.12b. Here, the monkey's task is to remove the food well cover that is closest to the tall cylinder.

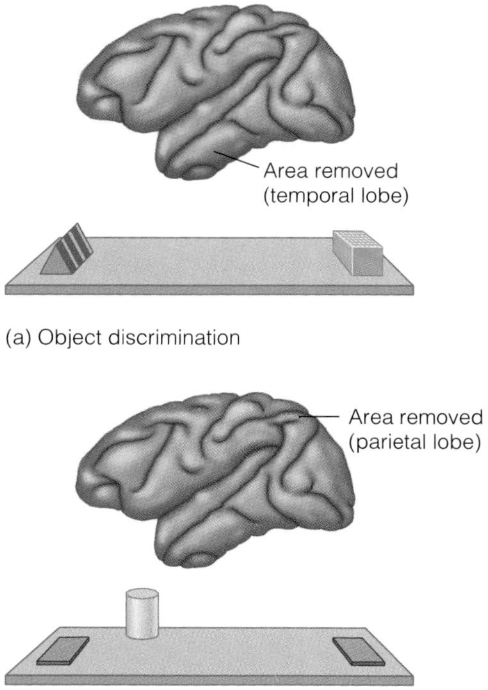

Figure 4.12 ▮ The two types of discrimination tasks used by Ungerleider and Mishkin. (a) Object discrimination: Pick the correct shape. Lesioning the temporal lobe (shaded area) makes this task difficult. (b) Landmark discrimination: Pick the food well closer to the cylinder. Lesioning the parietal lobe makes this task difficult.

(From "Object Vision and Spatial Vision: Two Central Pathways," by M. Mishkin, L. G. Ungerleider, & K. A. Macko, 1983, Trends in Neuroscience, *6, 414–417, figure 2. Copyright © 1983 Elsevier Science Publishers B. V. Reprinted by permission.)*

In the ablation part of the experiment, part of the parietal lobe was removed in some monkeys and part of the temporal lobe was removed in other monkeys. After ablation, behavioral testing showed that monkeys with their temporal lobes removed found the object discrimination problem to be extremely difficult. This result indicates that the pathway that reaches the temporal lobes is responsible for determining an object's identity. Ungerleider and Mishkin therefore called the pathway leading from V1 to the temporal lobe the ***what* pathway** (Figure 4.13). VIRTUAL LAB 1

In contrast, monkeys with their parietal lobes removed had difficulty with the landmark discrimination problem. This result indicates that the pathway that leads to the parietal lobe is responsible for determining an object's location. Ungerleider and Mishkin therefore called the pathway leading from V1 to the parietal lobe the ***where* pathway**.

The *what* and *where* pathways are also called the **ventral pathway** and the **dorsal pathway**, respectively, because the lower part of the brain, where the temporal lobe is located, is the ventral part of the brain, and the upper part of the brain, where the parietal lobe is located, is the dorsal part of the brain. This terminology comes from the

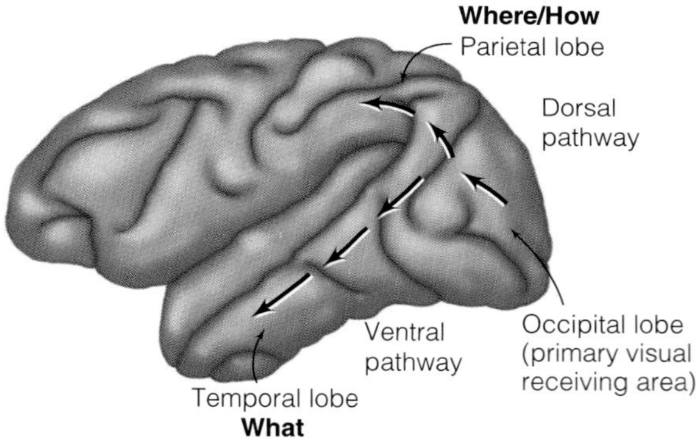

Figure 4.13 ▮ The monkey cortex, showing the *what,* or *ventral,* pathway from the occipital lobe to the temporal lobe, and the *where,* or *dorsal,* pathway from the occipital lobe to the parietal lobe. The *where* pathway is also called the *how* pathway (see page 81). The sequences of arrows indicate that there are a number of synapses along each of these pathways.

(From "Object Vision and Spatial Vision: Two Central Pathways," by M. Mishkin, L. G. Ungerleider, & K. A. Macko, 1983, Trends in Neuroscience, *6, 414–417, figure 1. Copyright © 1983 Elsevier Science Publishers B. V. Reprinted by permission.)*

fact that *dorsal* corresponds to the back or the upper surface of an organism. Thus, the dorsal fin of a shark or dolphin is the fin on the back that sticks out of the water. Figure 4.14 shows that for upright, walking animals such as humans, the dorsal part of the brain is the top of the brain. *Ventral* is the opposite of dorsal, so would be on the lower part of the brain.

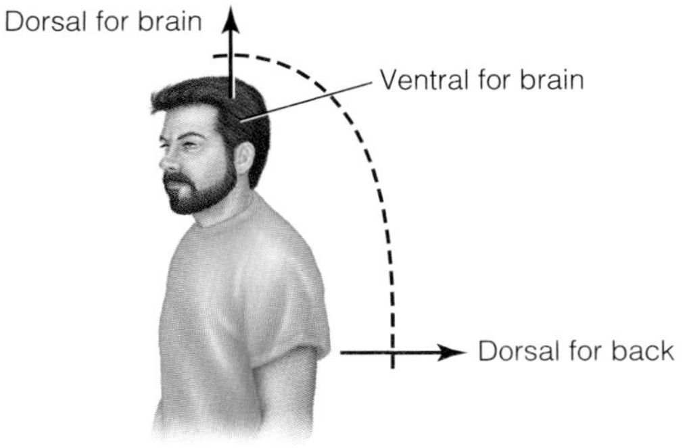

Figure 4.14 ▌ As described in the text, *dorsal* refers to the back surface of an organism. In upright standing animals such as humans, dorsal refers to the back of the body *and* to the top of the head, as indicated by the arrows and the curved dashed line. Ventral is the opposite of dorsal.

The dorsal and ventral pathways originate in the retina and LGN. The dorsal pathway begins in the retina with ganglion cells with large cell bodies, called **M-cells** (Table 4.1). The axons of these M-cells synapse in layers 1 and 2 of the LGN, which together are called the **magnocellular** (or **magno**) **layers** (Figure 4.8, dotted area). The ventral pathway begins in the retina with ganglion cells with small cell bodies, called **P-cells**. The axons of P-cells synapse in layers 3, 4, 5, and 6 of the LGN, which together are called the **parvocellular** (or **parvo**) **layers** (Figure 4.8, solid areas). Peter Schiller and his coworkers (1990) used the ablation technique to show that the magno and parvo layers of the LGN process information that correspond to the cortical dorsal and ventral streams, respectively.

Table 4.1 ▌ *Retinal ganglion cells and their functions*

Type of Ganglion Cell	Destination in LGN	Function
M ganglion cell	**Magnocellular layers** (1 and 2)	Movement
P ganglion cell	**Parvocellular layers** (3, 4, 5, and 6)	Color Texture Depth

Schiller and his coworkers first tested rhesus monkeys behaviorally to determine their ability to perceive movement, pattern, shape, color, and depth. They then anesthetized the monkeys and injected a neurotoxin called ibotenic acid so part of the parvo layers was destroyed in some monkeys and part of the magno layers was destroyed in other monkeys. After recovering from the operation, the monkeys with lesions in the parvo layers had lost their ability to detect color, fine textures and patterns, and the depth of small or finely detailed objects, and the monkeys with lesions in the magno layers had lost their ability to detect movement. Schiller and coworkers therefore concluded that neurons in the parvo and magno layers represent two channels. The parvo channel sends information about color, texture, shape, and depth to the cortex, and the magno channel sends information about motion to the cortex (Table 4.1).

Figure 4.15 shows that the dorsal pathway begins with the retinal M-ganglion cells and the LGN magno layers, and the ventral pathway begins with the retinal P-ganglion cells and the LGN parvo layers. Most of the research that resulted in this diagram was done on monkeys, but research using the technique of brain imaging has confirmed the idea that parallel pathways also exist in humans (Haxby et al., 1994).

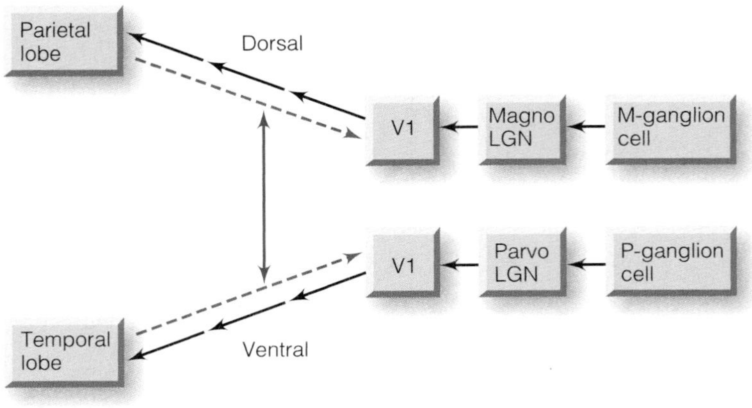

Figure 4.15 ▌ The dorsal and ventral streams in the cortex originate with the magno and parvo ganglion cells and the magno and parvo layers of the LGN. The red arrow represents connections between the streams. The dashed blue arrows represent feedback—signals that flow "backward."

Although there is good evidence that the dorsal and ventral pathways serve different functions, it is important to note that: (1) The pathways are not totally separated because there are connections between them (represented by the red arrows); and (2) signals not only flow "up" the pathway but "back" as well (represented by the dashed arrows; Merigan & Maunsell, 1993; Ungerleider & Haxby, 1994). It makes sense that there would be communication between the pathways because in our everyday behavior we need to both identify and locate objects, and we routinely coordinate these two activities every time we identify something (for example, a pencil) and take action with regard to it (picking up the pencil and writing with it).

The "backward" flow of information, which is called "feedback," provides information from higher centers that can influence the signals flowing into the system. This feedback is one of the mechanisms behind "top-down processing" that we introduced in Chapter 1 (page 9).

Streams for Information About *What* and *How*

Although the idea of dorsal and ventral streams has been generally accepted, David Milner and Melvyn Goodale (1995; see also Goodale & Humphrey, 1998, 2001) have suggested that rather than being called the *where* and *what* streams, the dorsal and ventral streams should be called the *how* and *what* streams. The ventral stream, they argue, is for perceiving objects, an idea that fits with the idea of *what.* However, they propose that the dorsal stream is for taking action, such as picking up an object. Taking this action would involve knowing the location of the object, consistent with the idea of *where,* but it also involves a physical interaction with the object. Thus, reaching to pick up a pencil involves information about the pencil's location *plus* movement of the hand toward the pencil. According to this idea, the dorsal stream provides information about *how* to direct action with regard to a stimulus.

Evidence supporting the idea that the dorsal stream is involved in how to direct action is provided by the discovery of neurons in the parietal cortex that respond (1) when a monkey looks at an object and (2) when it reaches toward the object (Sakata et al., 1992; also see Taira et al., 1990). But the most dramatic evidence supporting the idea of a dorsal "action," or *how* stream, comes from **neuropsychology**—the study of the behavioral effects of brain damage in humans.

METHOD ▪ Dissociations in Neuropsychology

One of the basic principles of neuropsychology is that we can understand the effects of brain damage by studying **dissociations**—situations in which one function is absent while another function is present. To help us understand dissociations, we will consider the example of a broken television (Parkin, 1996). One observation about broken televisions is that they can lose their color but still have a picture. This situation, when one function (color) is absent and the other (picture) is present, is called a **single dissociation**. The existence of a single dissociation indicates that the two functions involve different mechanisms, although they may not operate totally independently of one another.

Demonstrating a single dissociation involves just one TV, like the one we just described with a picture but no color. Now let's consider a situation in which we have two TV sets. Set *A* has no sound but has a picture. Set *B* does have sound but has no picture. A **double dissociation** occurs when we can demonstrate that one function is absent and the other is present in one TV (*A:* no sound, but the picture is OK) and that the opposite can also occur in another TV (*B:* sound OK, but there is no picture; Table 4.2a). When a double dissociation occurs, the two functions—sound and picture, in this example—involve different mechanisms and these mechanisms operate independently of one another. This makes sense for our television example because the television picture is created by the picture tube and the sound is created by the amplifier and speakers.

This same reasoning can be applied in cases of human brain damage. For example, consider a hypothetical situation in which a woman, Alice, who has suffered damage to her parietal lobe, has difficulty indicating where objects are located but has no trouble identifying them (Table 4.2b). Bert, on the other hand, has the opposite problem; he can locate objects but has trouble identifying them. These two cases, which are analogous to our two TVs, represent a double dissociation and indicate that locating objects and identifying them are served by different mechanisms that are independent of one another. Notice that in order to dem-

Table 4.2 ▮ *Double dissociations in TV sets and people*

a. Two TV Sets

	Function 1: Sound	Function 2: Picture
Broken TV set A	No	OK
Broken TV set B	OK	No

b. Two People

	Function 1: Locating objects	Function 2: Identifying objects
Dorsal stream damage (Alice)	No	OK
Ventral stream damage (Bert)	OK	No

onstrate a double dissociation, it is necessary to find two people with opposite problems.

■ ■ ■

The Behavior of Patient D.F. The method of determining dissociations was used by Milner and Goodale (1995) to study D.F., a 34-year-old woman who suffered damage to her ventral pathway from carbon monoxide poisoning caused by a gas leak in her home. One result of the brain damage was that D.F. was not able to match the orientation of a card held in her hand to different orientations of a slot. This is shown in the left circle in Figure 4.16a. Perfect matching performance would be indicated by a vertical line for each trial, but most of D.F.'s responses are widely scattered. The right circle shows the accurate performance of the normal controls.

Because D.F. had trouble orienting a card to match the orientation of the slot, it would seem reasonable that she would also have trouble *placing* the card through the slot because to do this she would have to turn the card so it was lined up with the slot. But when D.F. was asked to "mail" the card through the slot, she could do it! Even though D.F. could not turn the card to match the slot's orientation, once she started moving the card toward the slot, she was able to rotate it to match the orientation of the slot (Figure 4.16b). Thus, D.F. performed poorly in the static orientation-matching task but did well as soon as *action* was involved (Murphy, Racicot, & Goodale, 1996). Milner and Goodale interpreted D.F.'s behavior as showing that there is one mechanism for judging orientation and another for coordinating vision and action.

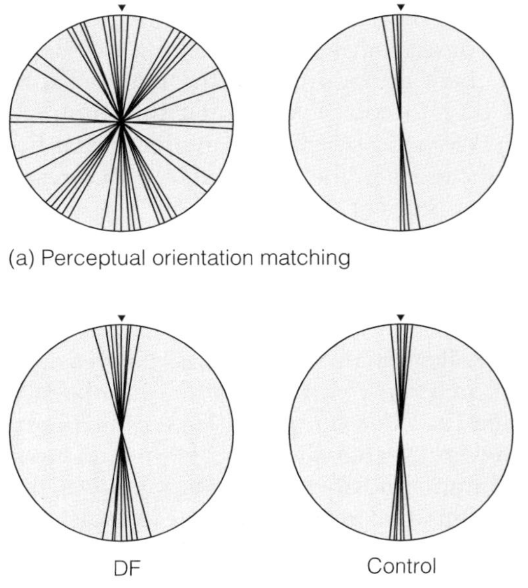

Figure 4.16 ▌ Performance of D.F. and a person without brain damage for two tasks: (a) judging the orientation of a slot; and (b) placing a card through the slot. See text for details.
(From the Visual Brain in Action by A. D. Milner and M. A. Goodale. Copyright © 1995 by Oxford University Press. Reprinted by permission.)

These results for D.F. demonstrate a single dissociation, which indicates that judging orientation and the coordination of vision and action involve different mechanisms. To show that these two functions are not only served by different mechanisms but are also *independent* from one another, we have to demonstrate a double dissociation. As we saw in our TV example, this involves finding a person whose symptoms are the opposite of D.F.'s, and such patients do, in fact, exist. These patients can judge visual orientation, but they can't accomplish the task that combines vision and action. As we would expect, whereas D.F.'s ventral stream is damaged, these other patients have damage to their dorsal streams.

These results suggest that perception and action operate independently in the brain (Table 4.2). Based on these results, Milner and Goodale suggested that the ventral pathway should still be called the *what* pathway, as Ungerleider and Mishkin suggested, but that a better description of the dorsal pathway would be the ***how* pathway**, or the ***action* pathway**, because it determines *how* a person carries out an *action*.

The Behavior of People Without Brain Damage The case of D.F. demonstrated a dissociation between perception and action in a person with brain damage. This dissociation between perception and action has been demonstrated in people without brain damage by measuring their reactions to visual illusions like the one in Figure 4.17a, which is called the **rod-and-frame illusion**. In this illusion, the two small lines inside the tilted squares appear slightly tilted in opposite directions, even though they are parallel vertical lines. **VL 2, 3**

Richard Dyde and David Milner (2002) presented their observers with two tasks: a matching task and a grasping task. In the matching task, observers adjusted the rod located in the "matching apparatus" until it appeared to match the orientation of the rod in the stimulus frame (Figure 4.17b). In the grasping task, observers grasped the rod between their thumb and forefinger (Figure 4.17c). The positioning of the thumb and forefinger was measured using a special position-sensing device attached to the observers' fingers.

The rationale behind this experiment is that because these two tasks involve different processing streams (matching task = ventral, or *what,* stream; grasping task = dorsal, or *how,* stream), they may be affected differently by the presence of the surrounding frames. The results, shown to the right of each condition, confirm this: The matching task was affected by the frame, causing observers to adjust the matching rod about 5 degrees from the actual position of the rod. In contrast, the frame had no effect on the accuracy of grasping. Observers positioned their fingers appropriately for the rods' orientation. In other words, conditions that created a perceptual visual illusion (matching task; ventral stream) had no effect on the person's ability to take action with regard to

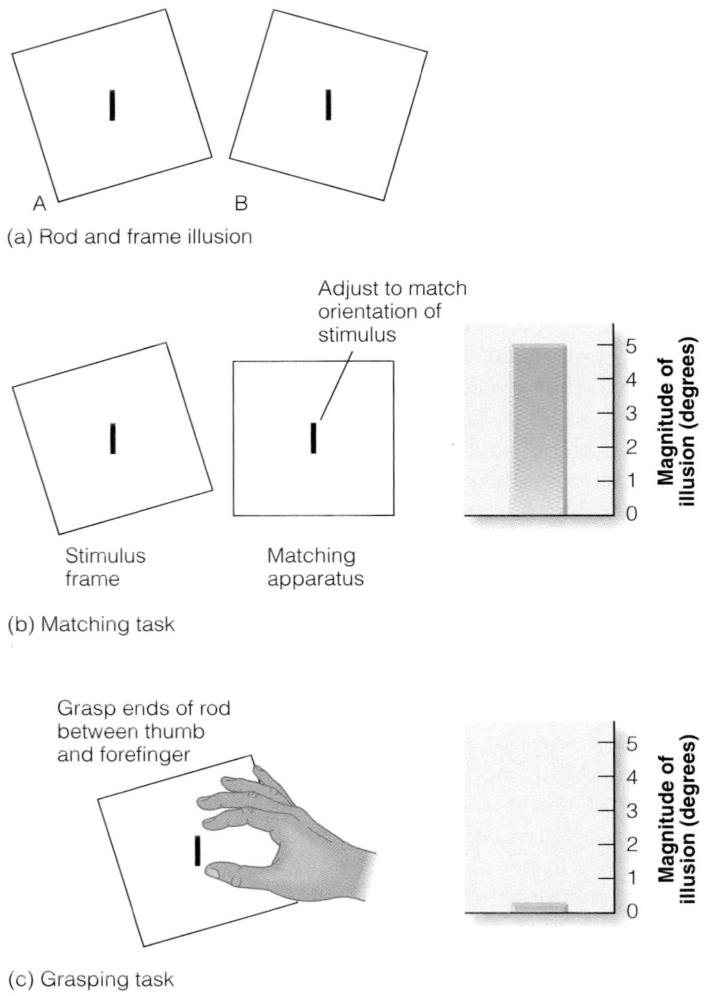

Figure 4.17 ■ (a) Rod and frame illusion. Both small lines are oriented vertically. (b) Matching task and results. (c) Grasping task and results. See text for details.

the stimulus (grasping task; dorsal stream). These results support the idea that perception and action are served by different mechanisms. Thus, an idea that originated with observations of patients with brain damage is supported by the performance of observers without brain damage.

TEST YOURSELF 4.1

1. How is the retina mapped onto the LGN and striate cortex, and how were these maps determined in animals and in humans?
2. What is the cortical magnification factor, and what function does it serve?
3. How was neural recording used to determine the existence of location, orientation, and ocular dominance columns in the striate cortex? How was optical imaging used to determine the layout of orientation columns in the striate cortex?
4. How is a simple object, such as a long bar, represented by electrical activity in the cortex?
5. How has ablation been used to demonstrate the existence of the ventral and dorsal processing streams? What is the function of these streams?
6. How has neuropsychology been used to show that one of the functions of the dorsal stream is to process information about coordinating vision and action? How do the results of a behavioral experiment involving the rod-and-frame illusion support this conclusion?

MODULARITY: STRUCTURES FOR FACES, PLACES, AND BODIES

Our description of the separate streams of Figure 4.13 shows one set of arrows from V1 to the temporal cortex (ventral stream) and another set of arrows from V1 to the parietal cortex (dorsal stream). But what about the individual structures that are located between the visual cortex and the temporal and parietal lobes? There is a great deal of evidence that the structures located along the ventral and dorsal pathways are often specialized to process information about specific visual qualities, an idea called **modularity**.

A structure that is specialized to process information about a particular type of stimulus is called a **module**. When we described neural processing in Chapter 3, we saw that there are neurons in the temporal cortex that respond best to complex geometrical stimuli (see Figure 3.25). We will now present evidence that has identified specific areas in the temporal lobe that respond best to particular types of stimuli.

There Are Face Neurons in the Monkey's IT Cortex

Edmund Rolls and Martin Tovee (1995) measured the response of neurons in an area in the monkey's temporal lobe called the inferotemporal (IT) cortex (Figure 4.18a). When they presented pictures of faces and pictures of nonface stimuli (mostly landscapes and food), they found many neurons that responded best to faces. Figure 4.19 shows the results for a neuron that responded briskly to faces but hardly at all to other types of stimuli. Another example, also in IT cortex, is shown in Figure 4.20. This neuron responds only to the head. Notice that it responds well to a photograph of a whole person and to just the person's head, but stops responding when the head is covered (Wachmuth et al., 1994). Results such as these, and from many other experiments, have led to the proposal that IT cortex is a module for form perception.

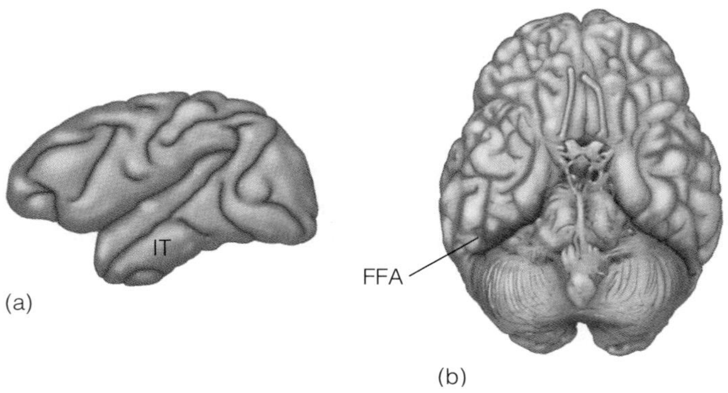

Figure 4.18 ▮ (a) Monkey brain showing location of the inferotemporal cortex (IT) in the lower part of the temporal lobe. (b) Human brain showing location of the fusiform face area (FFA) in the fusiform gyrus, which is located under the temporal lobe.

Figure 4.19 ▮ A neuron in the monkey's IT cortex that responds to face stimuli but not to nonface stimuli. (Based on data from Rolls & Tovee, 1995.)

Damage to the Temporal Lobe Affects a Person's Ability to Recognize Faces

Studies of people with damage to their temporal cortex have found that damage to this area causes **prosopagnosia**—difficulty recognizing the faces of familiar people. Even very familiar faces are affected, so people with prosopagnosia might not be able to recognize close friends, family members—or even their own reflection in the mirror—although they can easily identify the person as soon they hear them speak (Burton et al., 1991; Hecaen & Angelerques, 1962; Parkin, 1996).

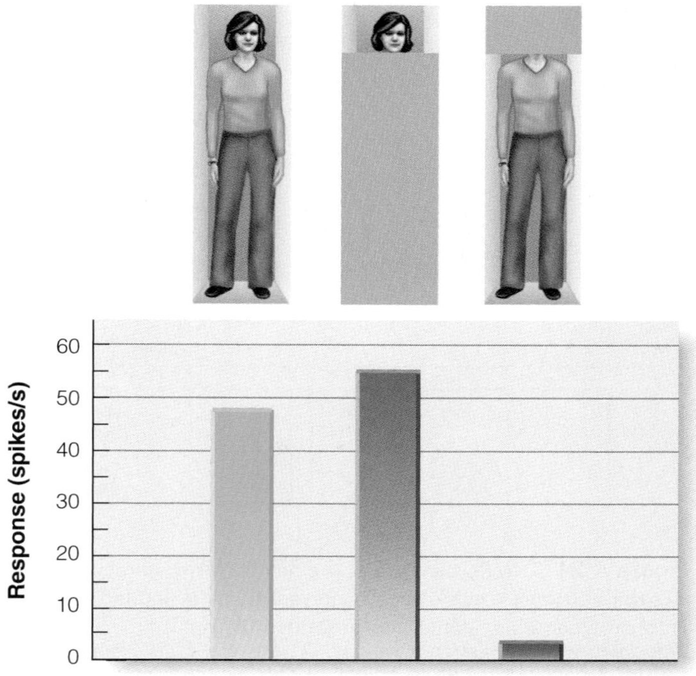

Figure 4.20 ▮ Response of a neuron in IT cortex for which the person's head is an important part of the stimulus because firing stops when the head is covered.
(From "Recognition of Objects and Their Component Parts: Responses of Single Units in the Temporal Cortex of the Macaque," by E. Washmuth, M. W. Oram, and D. I. Perrett, 1994, Cerebral Cortex, 4, *Copyright © 1994 by Oxford University Press.)*

There Are Areas for Faces, Places, and Bodies

Nancy Kanwisher and coworkers (1997) used brain imaging and the subtraction technique described on page 73 to show that neurons within a specific area in the fusiform gyrus in the temporal lobe respond selectively to faces. They first used the fMRI to determine that pictures of faces caused brain activity in the fusiform gyrus and some other structures as well. They then determined the areas activated by other objects, such as pictures of scrambled faces, household objects, houses, and hands. When they subtracted the response to the other objects from the response to the faces, Kanwisher and coworkers found that activity remained in an area in the fusiform gyrus (see Figure 4.18b). They interpreted this result to mean that this area, which in humans is called **the fusiform face area (FFA)**, is specialized to respond to faces.

Recently, David Cox and coworkers (2004) showed that the FFA is activated not only by pictures of faces, but by pictures in which the presence of a face is *implied* by the context. Figure 4.21 shows that the FFA is activated by a picture of a face (E) and a picture of a body with a blurred image where the face should be (D). No activation occurs,

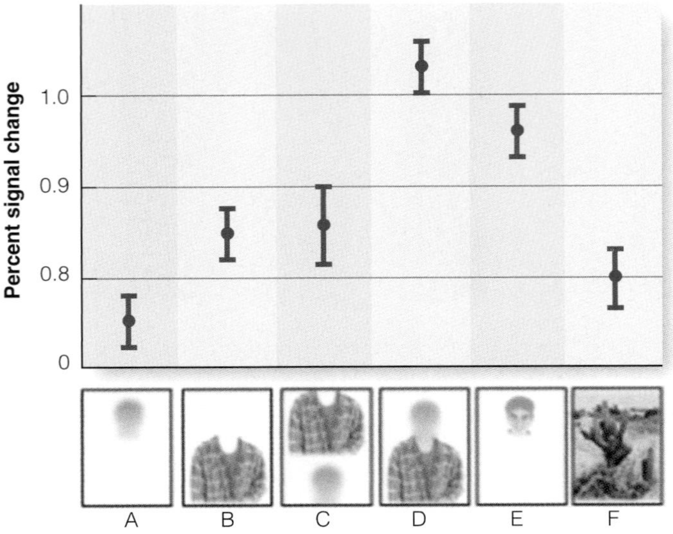

Figure 4.21 ▮ fMRI response of the human fusiform face area. Activation occurs when a face is present (E) or is implied (D) but is lower when other stimuli are presented (A, B, C, F).
(Reprinted with permission from Cox, D., Meyers, E., & Sinha, P. (2004). Contextually evoked object-specific responses in human visual cortex. Science, 304, *115–117.)*

however, to pictures that did not imply the presence of a face (A, B, C, and F).

In addition to the FFA, which contains neurons that are activated by faces, two other specialized areas in the temporal cortex have been identified. The **parahippocampal place area (PPA)** is activated by pictures indicating indoor and outdoor scenes like those shown in Figure 4.22a

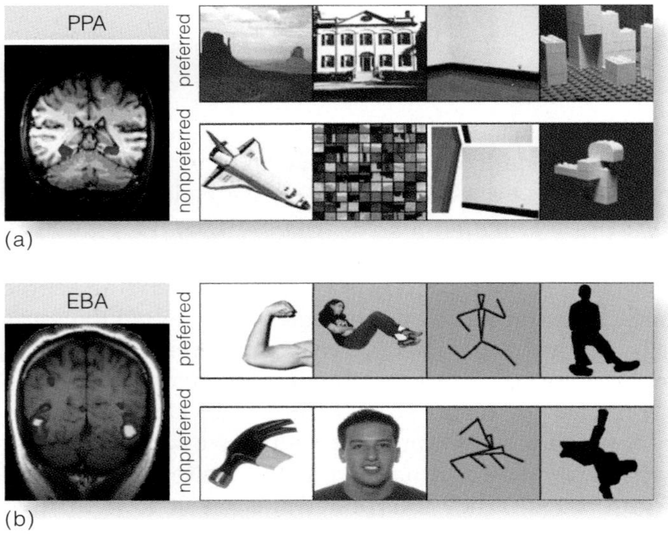

Figure 4.22 ▮ (a) The parahippocampal place area is activated by places (top row) but not by other stimuli (bottom row). (b) Extrastriate body area is activated by bodies (top), but not by other stimuli (bottom).
(Reprinted with permission from Kanwisher, N. (2003). The ventral visual object pathway in humans: Evidence from fMRI. In L. M. Chalupa & J. S. Werner (eds.). The Visual Neurosciences. *(pp. 1179–1190). Cambridge, MA: MIT Press.)*

(Aguirre et al., 1998; R. Epstein et al., 1999; R. Epstein & Kanwisher, 1998). Apparently what is important for this area is information about spatial layout because increased activation occurs both to empty rooms and rooms that are completely furnished (Kanwisher, 2004). The other specialized area, the **extrastriate body area (EBA)**, is activated by pictures of bodies and parts of bodies (but not by faces), as shown in Figure 4.22b (Downing et al., 2001).

EVOLUTION AND PLASTICITY: HOW DO NEURONS BECOME SPECIALIZED?

When researchers began describing neurons that were specialized to fire to specific stimuli, such as faces, places, and bodies, they naturally wondered how this specialization might have occurred. One possibility is that these neurons became specialized by a process of biological evolution, which causes people to be born with selective neurons. Another possibility is that these neurons became specialized by a process involving a person's experience as they perceived common objects in their environment.

Is Neural Selectivity Shaped by Evolution?

According to the **theory of natural selection**, genetically based characteristics that enhance an animal's ability to survive, and therefore reproduce, will be passed on to future generations. Thus, a person whose visual system contains neurons that fire to important things in the environment (like faces, for example) will be more likely to survive and pass on his or her characteristics than will a person whose visual system does not contain these specialized neurons. Through this evolutionary process, the visual system may have been shaped to contain neurons that respond to faces and other important perceptual information.

There is no question that evolution has shaped the functioning of the senses, just as it has shaped all of the other physical and mental characteristics that have enabled us to survive as a species. We know that the visual system is not a "blank slate" at birth. There are neurons in the newborn monkey that respond to the direction of movement and the relative depths of objects (Chino et al., 1997), and 3½-week-old monkeys possess orientation columns that are organized like the adult columns in Figure 4.10 (Blasdel et al., 1995).

Although we have less information about the neural structure of infant humans than about infant monkeys, we do know that babies prefer looking at pictures in which the parts are arranged to resemble a face compared to pictures in which the same parts are scrambled (Johnson et al., 1991; also see Turati et al., 2004). It is likely that this behavior is caused by neurons that respond best to facelike patterns.

Although there is no question that the basic layout and functioning of all of the senses is the result of evolution, it is difficult to prove whether a particular capacity is, in fact, "built in" by evolution or if it is caused by learning (Kanwisher, 2004). There is, however, a great deal of evidence that learning can shape the response properties of neurons that respond best to complex visual features. We will first describe some single-neuron recording experiments that show that neurons in the monkey IT cortex can become tuned by experience to respond best to specific complex objects or geometrical shapes, and we will then describe a study that considers neural activity in the human cortex.

How Neurons Can Be Shaped by Experience

Although it may be important for the visual system to have some specialized neurons at birth, it is also important that the visual system be able to adapt to the specific environment within which a person or animal lives. The nervous system can achieve this adaptation to the environment through a process that causes neurons to develop so they respond best to the types of stimulation to which the person has been exposed. This process is called **experience-dependent plasticity**.

Experience-Dependent Plasticity in Animals The idea of experience-dependent plasticity was first suggested by experiments with animals. For example, we saw in Chapter 3 that when kittens are raised in an environment that contains only verticals, most of the neurons in their visual cortex respond best to verticals (Blakemore & Cooper, 1970; see Figure 3.31 on page 66). Since this early demonstration of experience-dependent plasticity, many more experiments have demonstrated this effect in animals (Merzenich et al., 1998).

An example of experience-dependent plasticity is provided by an experiment in which Nikos Logothetis and Jon Pauls (1995) trained monkeys to recognize a specific view of an unfamiliar object, like the one marked "training" in Figure 4.23a. After training, the monkeys were tested to see if they recognized a number of views of the object. The results, shown in figure 4.23b, indicate that the monkeys recognized the view that they had been trained to recognize, and that recognition declined gradually as the object was rotated from this trained view.

When Logothetis and Pauls repeated the same procedure recording from neurons in IT cortex instead of testing psychophysically, they found many neurons that responded best to the view that the monkeys had been trained to recognize but found no neurons that responded best to views far from the one that the monkeys had been trained to recognize. The tuning curve for a neuron that responded to one of the training stimuli, shown in Figure 4.23c, is very similar to the psychophysically determined recognition curve.

Logothetis and Pauls's experiment is an example of one that measures both the *stimulus-perception relationship*

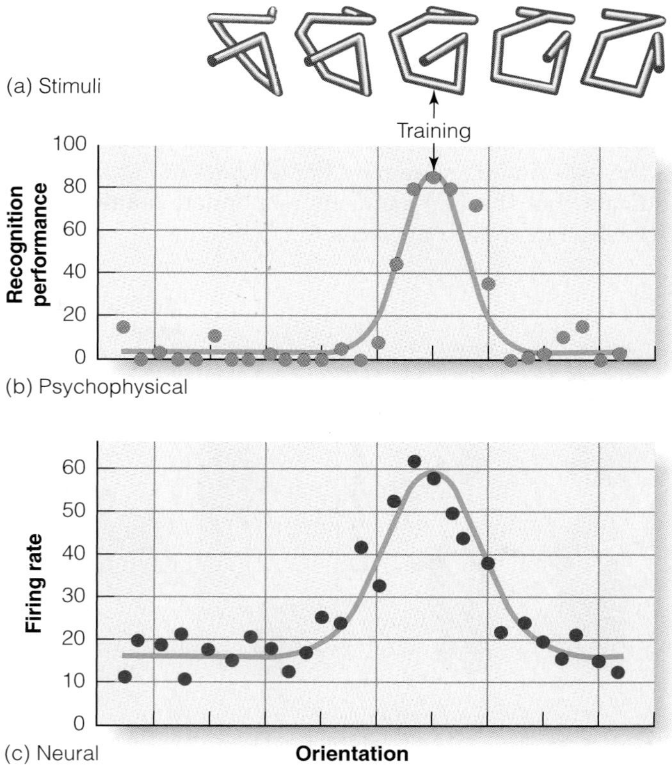

Figure 4.23 (a) Stimuli like those used by Logothetis & Pauls (1995). (b) Monkey's ability to recognize the training shape and rotated views of the shape that were not seen during training. (c) Response of neurons in the IT cortex of the trained monkey to the training shape and the rotated shape.

(Figure 4.23b) and the *stimulus-physiology relationship* (Figure 4.23c) in the same animal. Experiments such as this are particularly useful for studying the relationship between physiology and perception. Based on their results, Logothetis and Pauls concluded that these neurons are involved in perceiving the shapes and also that they must have become "tuned" to the shape that was seen during training. Thus, some cells in IT cortex can apparently "learn from experience" to fire to unusual objects like Logothetis and Pauls's stimuli. (See also Freedman et al., 2002; Kobatake et al., 1998; Rolls, 2004, for other examples of learning by neurons.)

Experience-Dependent Plasticity in Humans There is no doubt that experience causes changes in how neurons are tuned in the human cortex. For example, brain-imaging experiments have shown that there are regions in the human cortex that are specialized to respond to visual letters and word forms (Nobre et al., 1994). Because humans have been reading for only a few thousand years, this specialized responding could not have evolved but must have developed as people learned to read (Ungerleider & Pasternak, 2004).

Brain-imaging experiments have also demonstrated a shift in responding of neurons in the FFA due to training. Isabel Gauthier and coworkers (1999) used fMRI to first determine the level of activity in the fusiform face area

(FFA) in response to faces and to objects called Greebles—families of computer-generated "beings" that all have the same basic configuration but differ in the shapes of their parts (Figure 4.24a). Initially, the observers were shown both human faces and Greebles. The results for this part of the experiment, shown by the left bars in Figure 4.24b, indicate that the FFA neurons responded poorly to the Greebles but well to the faces.

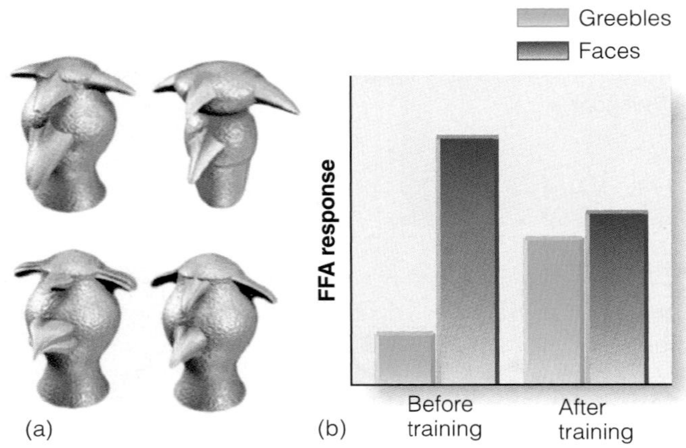

Figure 4.24 ▮ (a) Greeble stimuli used by Gauthier. Participants were trained to name each different Greeble. (b) Brain responses to Greebles and faces before and after Greeble training.
(a: From Figure 1a, p. 569, from Gauthier, I., Tarr, M. J., Anderson, A. W., Skudlarski, P. L., & Gore, J. C. (1999). Activation of the middle fusiform "face area" increases with experience in recognizing novel objects. Nature Neuroscience, 2, *568–573.)*

The participants were then trained in "Greeble recognition" for 7 hours over a 4-day period. After the training sessions, participants had become "Greeble experts," as indicated by their ability to rapidly identify many different Greebles by the names they learned during the training.

The right pair of bars in Figure 4.24b shows how becoming a Greeble expert affected the neural response in the subject's FFA. After the training, the FFA neurons responded about as well to Greebles as to faces. Apparently, the FFA area of the cortex is an area that responds not just to faces but to other complex objects as well. The objects that the neurons respond to are established by experience with the object. In fact, Gauthier has also shown that neurons in the FFA of people who are experts in recognizing cars and birds respond well not only to human faces but to cars (for the car experts) and to birds (for the bird experts; Gauthier et al., 2000). It is important to note that the function of the FFA is controversial: Some researchers agree with Gauthier's idea that the FFA is specialized to respond to complex objects that have become familiar due to experience, and others feel that the FFA is specialized to respond specifically to faces. (See "If You Want to Know More" at the end of the chapter.)

Let's return to the question we posed at the beginning of this section: How do neurons become specialized? It seems that specialized tuning is at least partially the result of neural plasticity. This makes it possible for neurons to adapt their tuning to objects that are seen often and that are behaviorally important. Thus, evolution has apparently achieved exactly what it is supposed to achieve—it has created an area that is able to adapt to the specific environment in which an animal or human lives. According to this idea, if we moved to a new planet inhabited by Greebles or other strange-looking creatures, which contained landscapes and objects quite different from Earth's, our neurons that previously responded well to Earth creatures and objects would eventually change to respond best to the creatures and environment of this new, and previously strange, environment (Gauthier et al., 1999).

THE SENSORY CODE: HOW THE ENVIRONMENT IS REPRESENTED IN THE NERVOUS SYSTEM

We have seen that visual perceptions, such as an object's location and orientation on the retina as well as the object's form and a person's ability to take action with regard to the object, are organized in a number of different ways (Figure 4.25). Now that we have a more complete picture of how the visual system is organized and how neurons in the visual system respond to specific types of stimuli, we are ready to introduce the idea of the sensory code, which provides a more complete answer to our question about how an object is represented in the nervous system.

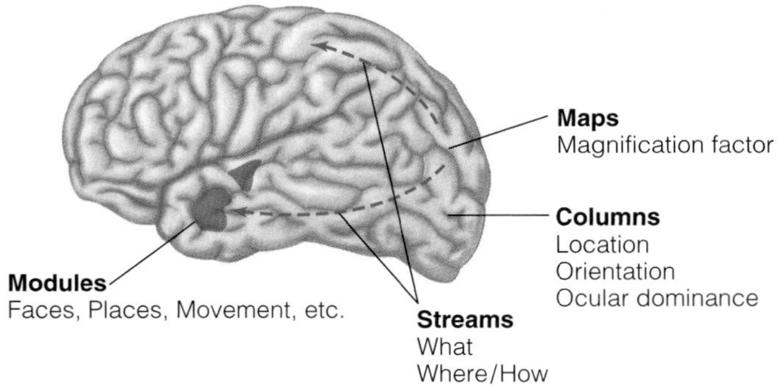

Figure 4.25 ▮ Ways that the brain is organized.

Coding by Neurons and Groups of Neurons

The **sensory code** is the information contained in the firing of neurons, which represents what we perceive. Exactly what is the nature of this information? To answer this question, we will use the example of face perception and consider how a particular face can be represented by the firing of neurons in the IT cortex. Although we are using faces as an example, the answer we will arrive at is true for all experiences, not just for seeing faces.

One possible way that faces could be represented is by **specificity coding**—the representing of a specific stimulus, like Bill's face, by the firing of neurons that are specialized to respond just to this stimulus. According to the idea of specificity coding, each of the faces in Figure 4.26a would be signaled by the firing of a neuron that is tuned to respond to each specific face. Neuron 1 responds only to Bill, neuron 2 only to Samantha, and neuron 3 only to Roger.

The idea that there are single neurons that respond only to a specific stimulus was proposed in the 1960s by Jerzy Konorski (1967) and Jerry Lettvin (see Barlow, 1995; Gross, 2002; Rose, 1996). Lettvin coined the term "grandmother cell" to describe this highly specific type of cell. A **grandmother cell**, according to Lettvin, is a neuron that responds only to a specific stimulus. This stimulus could be a specific image, such as a picture of your grandmother, or a concept, such as the idea of grandmothers in general (Gross, 2002).

But there are problems with this idea: (1) there are just too many different faces and other objects in the environment to assign specific neurons to each one; and (2) although there are neurons that respond only to specific types of stimuli, like faces, even these neurons respond to a number of different faces. Thus, a neuron that responds to Bill's face would also respond to Roger's and Samantha's faces as well. Because of these problems, the idea of a highly specific grandmother-type neuron has not been accepted by researchers. (But see "Something to Consider" on page 89 for a recent development.)

The generally accepted solution to the problem of sensory coding is that a particular object is represented not by the firing of a single neuron, but by the firing of *groups* of neurons. For example, let's consider how the three neurons in Figure 4.26b fire to a number of different faces. Bill's face causes all three neurons to fire, with neuron 1 responding the most and neuron 3 responding the least. Roger's face also causes firing in all three neurons, but the pattern is different, with neuron 3 responding the most and neuron 1 the least. All three neurons also fire to Samantha's face, but with a pattern that differs from the firing to either Bill's or Roger's faces. Thus, each face is represented by a pattern of firing across a number of neurons. This solution to the problem of sensory coding is called **distributed coding** because the code that indicates a specific face is *distributed* across a number of neurons.

One of the advantages of distributed coding is that a large number of stimuli can be signaled by the firing of just a few neurons. In our example, the firing of three neurons signals three faces, but these three neurons could signal other faces as well, such as Grace's and Ellen's, which have their own pattern of firing. How many neurons are actually involved in coding for an object like a face or a perceptual quality like the direction of movement? It depends on the specific object or property. For example, we will see in Chapter 9 that there are neurons that are tuned

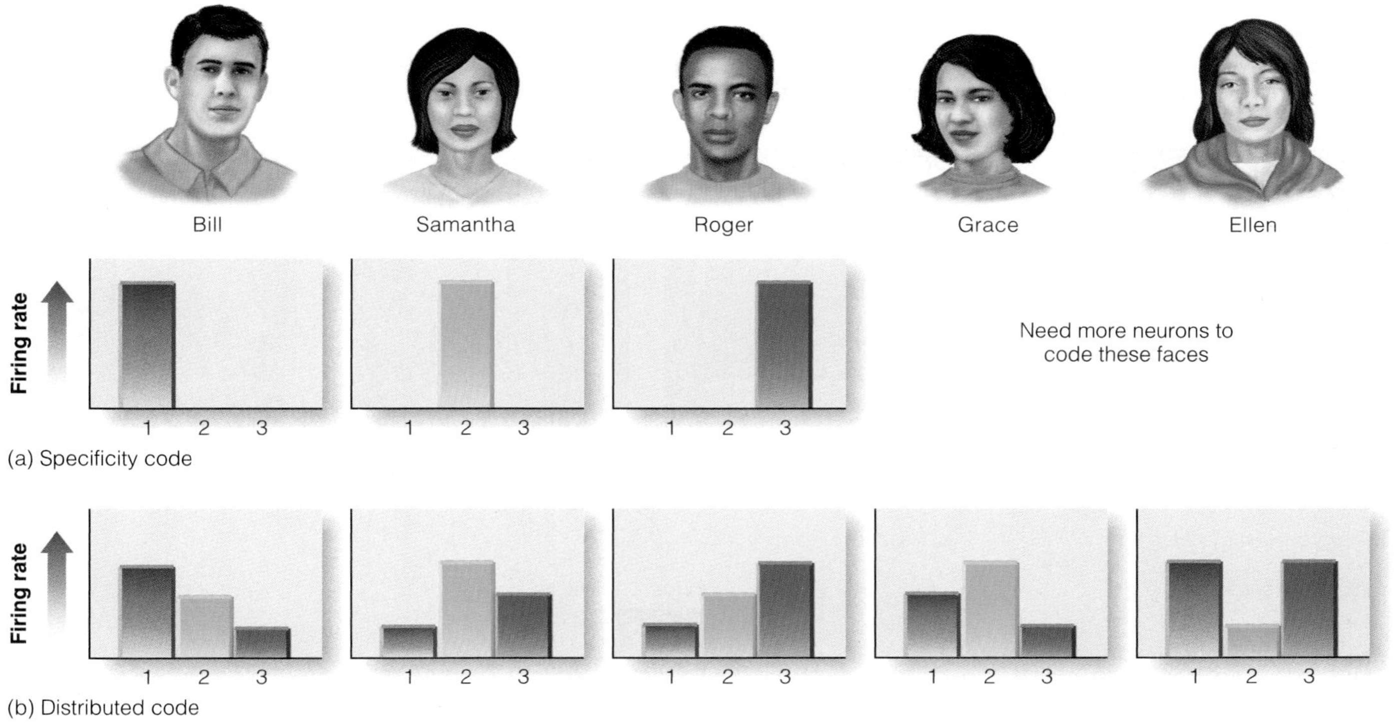

Figure 4.26 ▌ How faces could be coded according to (a) specificity coding and (b) distributed coding. The height of the bars indicates the response of neurons 1, 2, and 3 to each stimulus face. See text for explanation.

so precisely for the direction of movement that the firing of just a few neurons contains enough information to accurately signal the direction in which an object is moving (Newsome et al., 1989). In contrast, more neurons are required to provide enough information to identify complex stimuli such as faces or other environmental objects (Abbott, Rolls, & Tovee, 1996; Rolls & Tovee, 1995).

What all of this means is that our ability to identify and recognize the huge number of different objects in our environment is the end result of distributed cooperation between many neurons. This occurs even for stimuli like faces that are served by specialized neurons that respond just to faces. It may not take many neurons to let you know that you are seeing a face, but a number of neurons work together to signal the presence of one particular face.

Coding by Distributed Activity in the Brain

We've seen that a specific stimulus, like Bill's face, can be represented by the pattern of firing across a number of neurons. We now broaden our perspective from groups of neurons to the entire brain. When we do this, we see that even for simple stimuli, activation is spread over a large area of the brain.

We can see this clearly from the picture in Figure 4.27, which shows the areas of the monkey's IT cortex that are activated by three different stimuli (Tsunoda et al., 2001). These results show that each stimulus activates a number of different areas, and that there is some overlap between the activation caused by the different stimuli (also see Tanaka, 2003, 2004).

What about activation of the human cortex? fMRI experiments on humans reveal that pictures of houses, faces, and chairs cause maximum activation in three separate areas in the IT cortex (Figure 4.28a). This result is consistent with the idea of modules we discussed earlier. However, each type of stimulus also causes substantial activity within the other areas, as shown in the three panels of Figure 4.28b (Ishai et al., 1999, 2000). Thus, houses cause activation that is spread over all of the areas, and the same result occurs for faces and chairs.

It is apparent that although there are areas that respond best to specific types of stimuli, activation is not

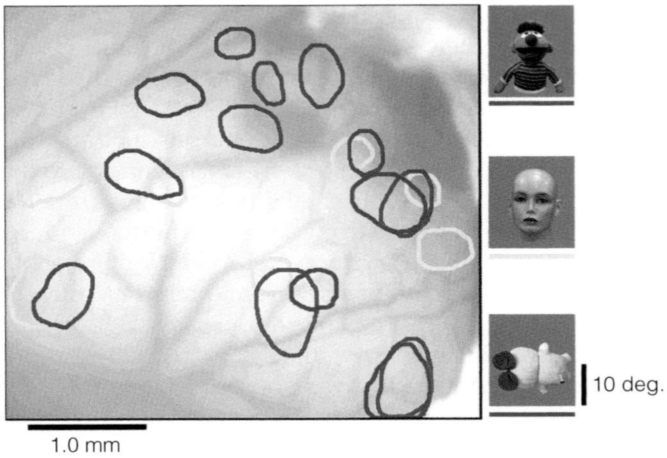

Figure 4.27 ▌ Areas in monkey's IT cortex, determined by a brain scanning procedure, that were activated by Sesame Street's Ernie (red), a doll's face (yellow), and a teddy bear (blue). *(From Tsunoda, K., Yamane, Y., Nishizaki, M., & Tanifuji, M. (2001). Complex objects are represented in macaque inferotemporal cortex by the combination of feature columns.* Nature Neuroscience, 4, *832–838.)*

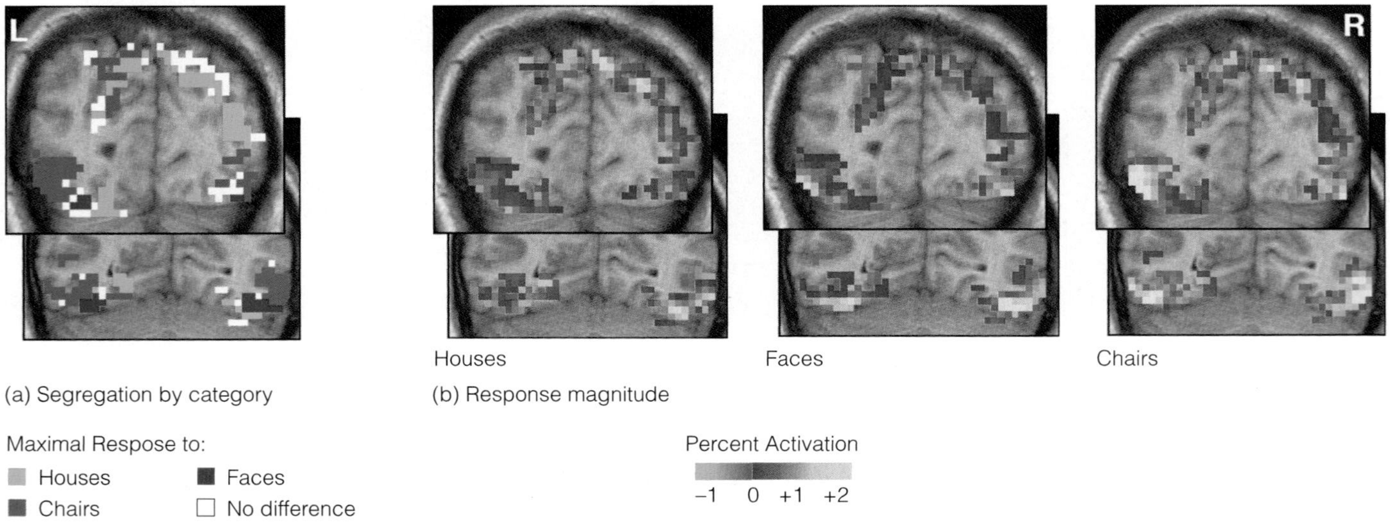

Figure 4.28 ▌ fMRI responses of the human brain to various types of stimuli: (a) areas that were most strongly activated by houses, faces, and chairs; (b) all areas activated by each type of stimulus. *(From Ishai, A., Ungerleider, L. G., Martin, A., & Haxby, J. V. (2000). The representation of objects in the human occipital and temporal cortex.* Journal of Cognitive Neuroscience, 12, *35–51.)*

limited to just these areas—it is distributed over a large area of cortex. Thus, the idea of specialized modules is correct, but shouldn't be carried too far. Objects may cause a focus of activity in a particular area, but they are represented in the cortex by activity that is distributed over a wide area (J. D. Cohen & Tong, 2001; Riesenhuber & Poggio, 2002).

The way a stimulus activates a number of areas in the brain becomes even more dramatic when we consider stimulus qualities in addition to an object's form. We will see in Chapter 7 that an object's color activates specific areas, in Chapter 8 that the location of an object in depth activates other areas, and in Chapter 9 that an object's movement activates yet other areas.

Taking this evidence into account, let's consider what is happening in your cortex as you see a red Corvette drive by: Cells sensitive to complex forms fire in a number of different places in IT cortex, cells sensitive to movement fire in another area, and cells sensitive to color also fire in other areas as well. This distribution of activity across different areas of the brain poses a problem: How are the Corvette's qualities combined so that you perceive a unified perception of it rather than separate, independent qualities? This is an important question because it is part of the main question we want to answer: How does seeing things in the environment—whether it be a red Corvette driving by or a paper clip on the clutter of your desk—result from the electrical signals in the brain?

We will return to the question of how distributed activity in the brain becomes combined to result in a coherent perception of the Corvette in Chapter 6, when we consider attention. To end this chapter, we will consider some recent research that reopens the question of whether there are grandmother cells.

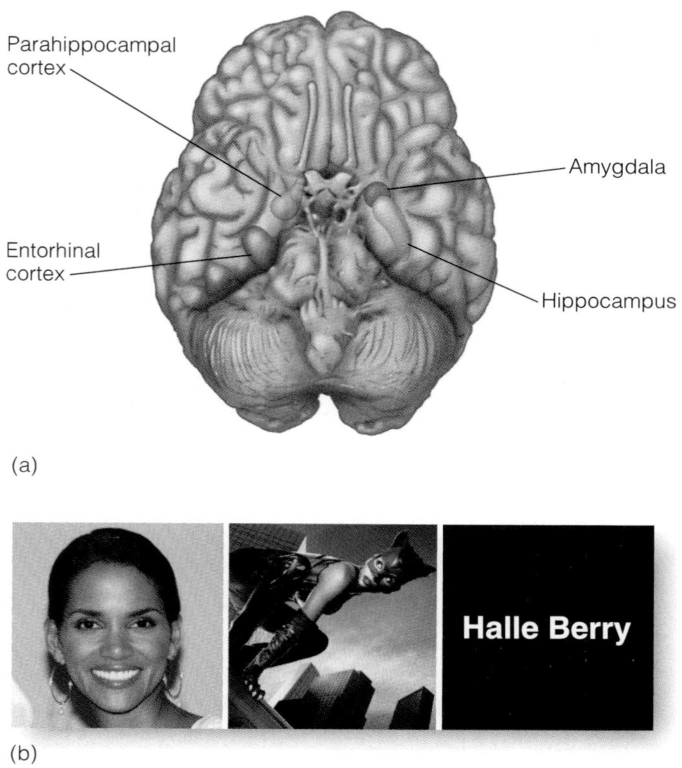

Figure 4.29 ▌ (a) Location of the hippocampus and some of the other structures that were studied by Quiroga and coworkers (2005); (b) Some of the stimuli that caused a neuron in the hippocampus to fire.
(Left photo: © Evan Agostini/Getty Images; Right photo: © Doane Gregory/Warner Bros./Bureau L.A. Collections/CORBIS)

SOMETHING TO CONSIDER: ARE THERE GRANDMOTHER CELLS AFTER ALL?

Although the idea of a highly specific "grandmother cell" has generally not been accepted by researchers, a new development has brought this idea back to life. R. Quian Quiroga and coworkers (2005) recorded from neurons in the brains of eight patients with epilepsy. These patients had electrodes implanted in their hippocampus to help precisely localize where their seizures originated, in preparation for surgery (Figure 4.29a).

Patients saw a number of different views of specific individuals and objects plus random pictures of other things, such as faces, buildings, and animals. Not surprisingly, a number of neurons responded to some of these stimuli. What was surprising, however, was that some neurons responded to a number of different views of just one person or building. For example, one neuron responded to all pictures of the actress Jennifer Aniston alone, but did not respond to other faces of famous people, nonfamous people, landmarks, animals, or other objects. Another unit responded to pictures of actress Halle Berry. This neuron responded not only to photographs of Halle Berry, but to drawings of her, pictures of her dressed as Catwoman from *Batman,* and also to the words "Halle Berry" (Figure 4.29b). A third neuron responded to numerous views of the Sydney Opera House.

Do these neurons qualify as grandmother cells? Quiroga and coworkers are careful to note that presenting more pictures might have revealed additional stimuli that would cause these neurons to respond. But what is amazing about these neurons is how they respond to many different views of stimulus, different modes of depiction, and even words signifying the stimulus. These neurons, therefore, are not responding to visual features of the pictures, but to *concepts*—"Jennifer Aniston," "Halle Berry," "Sydney Opera House"—that the stimuli represent.

It is important to note that these neurons were in the hippocampus—an area associated not with vision but with the storage of memories. Thus, perhaps the highly specialized nature of these neurons depends on the processing that occurs when information about the visual characteristics of objects is transformed into the abstract representation of these objects that are stored in memory.

The journey we have taken through the visual system in Chapters 2–4 began in the receptor's outer segments and has taken us far beyond the primary visual receiving area in the striate cortex. In these chapters, we have spent a lot of time looking "under the hood" at the inner workings of the visual system, and so you now have the background you need to understand the physiological discussions in the rest of the book. With this background in mind, it is now time to zoom out, from inside the neural mechanisms of vision to a whole person who is looking at things in the environment and interacting with them. We begin exploring these aspects of perception in the next chapter, "Perceiving Objects," by considering how researchers have studied perception by focusing on behavior.

TEST YOURSELF 4.2

1. What is modularity, and what is the evidence that there are modules for faces (FFA), for places (PPA), and bodies (EBA)?
2. What is the evidence that the properties of selective neurons are determined by evolution? By experience?
3. Describe the experiments that demonstrated experience-dependent plasticity in (a) monkeys and (b) humans.
4. What is the sensory code? Describe specificity coding and distributed coding. Which type of coding is most likely to operate in the visual system?
5. What is the evidence that an object is represented by activity that is distributed throughout different areas in the brain?
6. Describe the experiment that recorded from neurons that responded to Halle Berry and other very specific stimuli.

THINK ABOUT IT

1. We have seen that the neural firing associated with an object in the environment does not necessarily look like, or resemble, the object. Can you think of situations that you encounter in everyday life in which objects or ideas are represented by things that do not exactly resemble those objects or ideas?
2. Ralph is hiking along a trail in the woods. The trail is bumpy in places, and Ralph has to avoid tripping on occasional rocks, tree roots, or ruts in the trail, he is nonetheless able to walk along the trail without constantly looking down to see exactly where he is placing his feet. That's a good thing because Ralph enjoys looking out at the woods to see whether he can spot interesting birds or animals. How can you relate this description of Ralph's behavior to the operation of the dorsal and ventral streams in the visual system?
3. Although most neurons in the striate cortex respond to stimulation of small areas of the retina, many neurons in the temporal lobe respond to areas that represent as much as half of the visual field (see "If You Want to Know More," below). What do you think the function of such neurons is?
4. We have seen that there are neurons that respond to complex shapes and also to environmental stimuli such as faces, bodies, and places. Which types of neurons do you think would fire to the stimulus in Figure 4.30? How would your answer to this question be affected if this stimulus were interpreted as a human figure? ("Howdy pardner!") What role would top-down processing play in determining the response to a "cactus-as-person" stimulus?

Figure 4.30 ▮ "Howdy pardner!"

IF YOU WANT TO KNOW MORE

1. ***Seeing Columns.*** Location columns can be revealed by using a technique called autoradiography, in which a monkey injected with radioactive tracer views grating with a particular orientation. This makes it possible to see columns that were discovered using single-unit recording.

   Hubel, D. H., Wiesel, T. N., & Stryker, M. P. (1978). Anatomical demonstration of orientation columns in macaque monkey. *Journal of Comparative Neurology, 177,* 361–379.

2. ***Another Kind of Specialized Neuron.*** Neurons called "bimodal neurons" respond to a visual stimulus pre-

sented near a place on a monkey's body, such as the face or the hand, and also to touching that part of the body.

Graziano, M. S. A., & Gross, C. G. (1995). The representation of extrapersonal space: A possible role for bimodal, visual-tactile neurons. In M. S. Gazzaniga (Ed.), *The cognitive neurosciences* (pp. 1021–1034). Cambridge, MA: MIT Press. VL 4

3. ***Wide-Angle Neurons.*** There are maps of the retina in the striate cortex, and neurons in the striate cortex respond to stimulation of a small area of the retina. However, recording from neurons further "upstream" in the visual system, in places such as the temporal cortex, reveals that "maps" like those in the striate cortex no longer exist because neurons in these structures respond to stimulation of very large areas of the retina.

Rolls, E. T. (1992). Neurophysiological mechanisms underlying face processing within and beyond the temporal cortical areas. *Philosophical Transactions of the Royal Society of London, B., 335,* 11–21.

4. ***Invariant Neurons.*** There are neurons at the far end of the ventral stream that continue to respond to objects even when these objects appear in different orientations or their size is changed.

Perrett, D. I., & Oram, M. W. (1993). Neurophysiology of shape processing. *Image and Visual Computing, 11,* 317–333.

5. ***Fusiform Face Area.*** There is a controversy over the role of the fusiform face area: Some researchers feel it is specialized to respond to faces, and others feel that it is specialized to respond to complex objects that we have had experience with. According to this idea, the FFA responds to faces because we see lots of faces.

Kanwisher, N. (2000). Domain specificity in face perception. *Nature, 3,* 759–763.

Tarr, M. J., & Gauthier, I. (2000). FFA: A flexible fusiform area for subordinate-level visual processing automatized by expertise. *Nature, 3,* 764–769.

KEY TERMS

Ablation (p. 77)
Action pathway (p. 81)
Brain imaging (p. 73)
Contralateral eye (p. 75)
Cortical magnification factor (p. 73)
Dissociation (p. 80)
Distributed coding (p. 87)
Dorsal pathway (p. 78)
Double dissociation (p. 80)
Experience-dependent plasticity (p. 85)
Extrastriate body area (EBA) (p. 84)
Functional magnetic resonance imaging (fMRI) (p. 74)
Fusiform face area (FFA) (p. 83)
Grandmother cell (p. 87)
How pathway (p. 81)
Ipsilateral eye (p. 75)
Landmark discrimination problem (p. 78)
Lesioning (p. 77)
Location column (p. 75)
Magnocellular (magno) layer (p. 79)
M-cell (p. 79)
Modularity (p. 82)
Module (p. 82)
Neuropsychology (p. 80)
Object discrimination problem (p. 78)
Ocular dominance (p. 76)
Ocular dominance columns (p. 76)
Orientation column (p. 76)
Parahippocampal place area (PPA) (p. 84)
Parvocellular (parvo) layer (p. 79)
P-cell (p. 79)
Positron emission tomography (PET) (p. 73)
Prosopagnosia (p. 83)
Retinotopic map (p. 72)
Rod-and-frame illusion (p. 81)
Sensory code (p. 86)
Single dissociation (p. 80)
Specificity coding (p. 87)
Subtraction technique (p. 74)
Theory of natural selection (p. 84)
Ventral pathway (p. 78)
What pathway (p. 78)
Where pathway (p. 78)

VISIT YOUR COMPANION WEBSITE FOR THIS BOOK

http://psychology.wadsworth.com/goldstein7e

Check out this companion website where you'll find online resources—glossary, flashcards, web links, multiple-choice and essay questions, and much more!

VIRTUAL LAB

Your Virtual Lab is designed to help you get the most out of this course. The Virtual Lab icons direct you to specific media demonstrations and experiments designed to help you visualize what you are reading about. The number beside each icon indicates the number of the media element you can access through your CD-ROM, Perception PsychologyNow, or WebTutor resource at http:now.ilrn.com/goldstein_7e.

The following are the lab exercises covering what you've just learned in this chapter:

1 *What and Where Streams* Drag-and-drop exercise to test your knowledge of the *what* and *where* pathways.

2 *Tilt Illusion, 25 Degrees* Display showing how the perceived orientation of stripes in a vertical grating are affected by being superimposed on a surround that is tilted at 25 degrees.

3 *Tilt Illusion, 75 Degrees* Same as above, but the surround lines are tilted at 75 degrees.

4 *Bimodal Cell Responding* How bimodal cells respond to visual and tactile stimulation.

1

2

3

4

5

6

CHAPTER

5

PERCEIVING OBJECTS

Chapter Contents

Our perception of objects is complicated by the fact that objects appear different when viewed from different angles. These panels show how the sculpture Khyber (2002) by Bilhenry Walker appears as a person walks around the sculpture in a counterclockwise direction, starting with view 1 and eventually reaching view 6, which is directly opposite view 1.

Photo by Bruce Goldstein

VL *The Virtual Lab icons direct you to specific animations and videos designed to help you visualize what you are reading about. The number beside each icon indicates the number of the clip you can access through your CD-ROM or your student website.*

Some Questions We Will Consider:

- Why do some perceptual psychologists say "the whole differs from the sum of its parts"? (p. 99)
- How do "rules of thumb" help us in arriving at a perception of the environment? (p. 102)
- How do we distinguish objects from their background? (p. 103)
- Why are even the most sophisticated computers unable to match a person's ability to perceive objects? (p. 114)

9:00 A.M., March 13, 2004: Fifteen robotic vehicles are lined up at the starting line in the desert near Barstow, California. Their goal: Be the first to reach to the finish line near Las Vegas, 142 miles across the Mojave Desert. The race: The Defense Advanced Research Projects Agency (DARPA) Grand Challenge for Autonomous Robotic Ground Vehicles.

In place of drivers, each vehicle contains a state-of-the-art computer system designed to perceive terrain, obstacles, and other vehicles, and to keep the vehicles on a course determined by global positioning coordinates that were entered into the vehicles' guidance systems just 3 hours before the start of the race. The course included well-traveled utility roads, switchbacks, severe elevation changes, blind turns, and sheer drops. The vehicles were required to navigate this course without any human intervention, recognizing course obstacles and maneuvering around them based only on their onboard computer systems. The vehicle completing the course most quickly in under 10 hours was to claim a cash prize of $1 million.

The "Sandstorm" vehicle, designed by a team from Carnegie-Mellon University (CMU), was one of the favorites in the race (Figure 5.1). It started off well, but at mile 7.4 on a series of switchbacks in a mountainous section of the course, the vehicle went off course, got caught on the side of the road, and destroyed its front tires as it tried unsuccessfully to free itself and get back on the road.

Evan Tahler

Figure 5.1 ▮ "Sandstorm" vehicle that was entered in the DARPA challenge race.
Red Team/Carnegie-Mellon University

No vehicle claimed the prize because the Sandstorm's 7.4 miles was the farthest traveled by any of the vehicles. The vehicles' on-board computer perception systems were unable to accurately perceive turns and obstacles, and their navigation systems were unable to deal with the terrain and obstacles the vehicles encountered. However, just as this book was going to press, on October 8, 2005, 5 of the 23 vehicles entered in the second DARPA race finished the 132-mile course, with a vehicle from Stanford narrowly edging out CMU's Sandstorm and another CMU vehicle.

The result of the second DARPA race testifies to the progress that has been made in designing computer perception systems. However, there are still challenges ahead. Identifying objects is very difficult for computers—for example, being able to indicate "that's a rock" or "that's a dog." The difficulty of this task is illustrated by the fact that systems designed to recognize faces at airport security checkpoints can accurately identify less than half of a group of specially selected faces (Sinha, 2002; also see Chella et al., 2000 and "If You Want to Know More" (page 118) for more on computer perception).

Why is it so difficult for computers to carry out object-recognition tasks that humans can perform easily? The answer to this question relates to our discussion at the beginning of the book about how although most perception is almost effortless, it involves complex "behind the scenes" processes (see page 5). In the first four chapters, we focused on "behind the scenes" activity in the nervous system. This chapter focuses on both behavioral and neural processes that make it possible for people to perceive objects.

We begin by considering some of the problems both humans and computers face in perceiving objects and scenes. We will then describe how psychologists have approached two questions that have been central to the study of object perception since early in the history of research on object perception: (1) How is the environment perceptually organized into objects? and (2) What determines which parts of a scene are perceived as figure and which are seen as background? We will then consider a number of the basic questions about object perception that especially concern perceptual psychologists today, and finally return to robots as we consider why human perception is intelligent (and perhaps why robot perception isn't).

THE CHALLENGE OF OBJECT PERCEPTION

We can appreciate why it has been so difficult to program computers to perceive by considering the following perceptual problems that people usually solve easily, but which have proven to be difficult for even the most powerful computers.

The Stimulus on the Receptors Is Ambiguous

Objects seen from just one viewpoint result in ambiguous information on the receptors. For example, you might think that the scene in Figure 5.2a is a circle of rocks, but viewing it from another angle reveals its true configuration (Figure 5.2b). This ambiguity occurs because a particular image on the retina can be caused by an infinite number of different objects. This fact, which is called the **inverse projection problem**, is illustrated by Figure 5.3. This figure shows a square stimulus (solid lines) that creates a square image on the retina. It also shows that there are a number of other stimuli (dashed lines) that could create exactly the same image on the retina. A larger square that is farther away, a trapezoid that is tilted, as well as an infinite number of other objects, can create the same retinal image as the square. Thus, any image on the retina can be created by an infinite number of objects. Nonetheless, people usually don't have a problem telling the difference between a small square that is close, a large square that is far away, and a tilted trapezoid, even if each of these stimuli creates the same image on the retina.

Objects Can Be Hidden or Blurred

Can you find the pencil and eye glasses in Figure 5.4? Although it might take a little searching, people can find the pencil in the foreground, and the glasses frame next to the scissors, even though only a small portion of these objects are visible. People also easily perceive the book, scissors, and paper as single objects, even though they are partially hidden by other objects.

Ian Macaulay

Figure 5.2 ▮ An environmental sculpture by Thomas Macaulay. (a) When viewed from exactly the right vantage point (the second-floor balcony of the Blackhawk Mountain School of Art, Black Hawk, Colorado), the stones appear to be arranged in a circle. (b) Viewing the stones from the ground floor reveals a truer indication of their configuration.

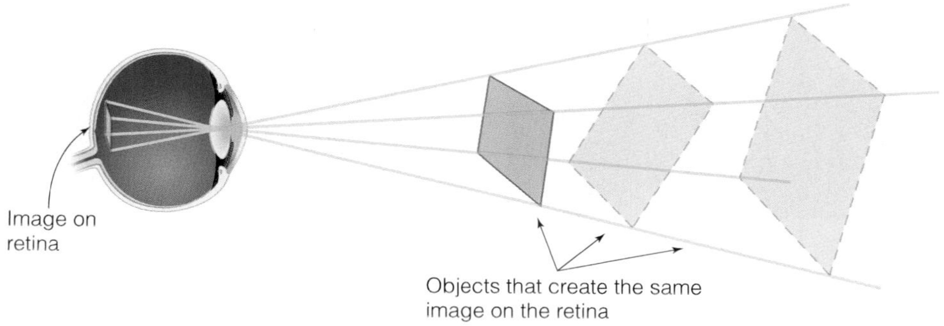

Figure 5.3 ▮ The principle behind the inverse projection problem. The small square stimulus creates a square image on the retina. However, this image could also have been created by the other two shapes and many other stimuli. This is why we say that the image on the retina is ambiguous.

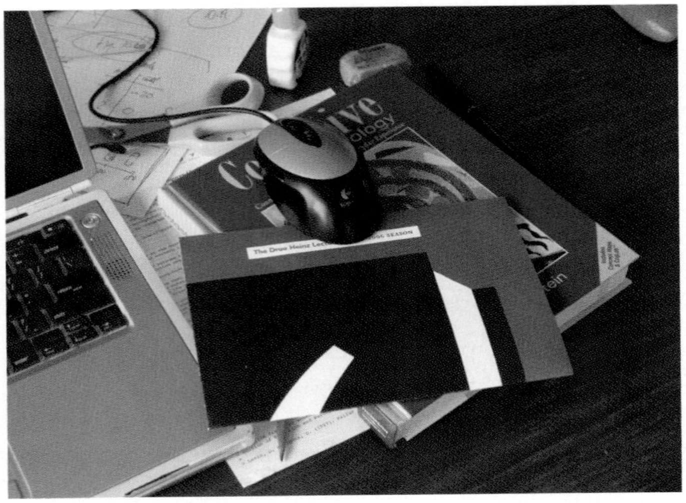

Figure 5.4 ▮ A portion of the mess on the author's desk. Can you locate the hidden pencil (easy) and the author's glasses (hard)?

This problem of hidden objects occurs any time one object obscures part of another object. These occlusions of one object by another are extremely common in the environment, but people easily understand that the object that is covered continues to exist, and they are able to use their knowledge of the environment to determine what is likely to be present.

People are also able to recognize objects that are not in sharp focus, such as the faces in Figure 5.5. See how many of these people you can identify, and then consult the answers on page 98. Despite the degraded nature of these images, people can often identify most of them, whereas computers perform poorly on this task (Sinha, 2002).

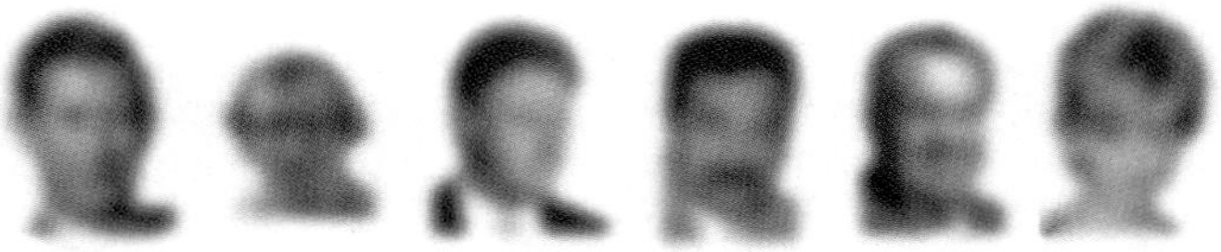

Figure 5.5 ▮ Who are these people? See bottom of page 98 for the answers.
(From Sinha, P. (2002). Recognizing complex patterns. Nature Neuroscience, *5, 1093–1097.)*

Objects Look Different From Different Viewpoints

The images of objects are continually changing, depending on the angle from which they are viewed. Although humans continue to perceive the object in Figure 5.6 as the same chair presented from different angles, this isn't so obvious to a computer. The ability of humans to recognize an object seen from different viewpoints is called **viewpoint invariance.** People's ability to achieve viewpoint invariance enables them to identify the images in Figure 5.7a and c as being the same person, but a computer face-recognition system would rate faces a and b as being more similar (Sinha, 2002).

Bruce Goldstein

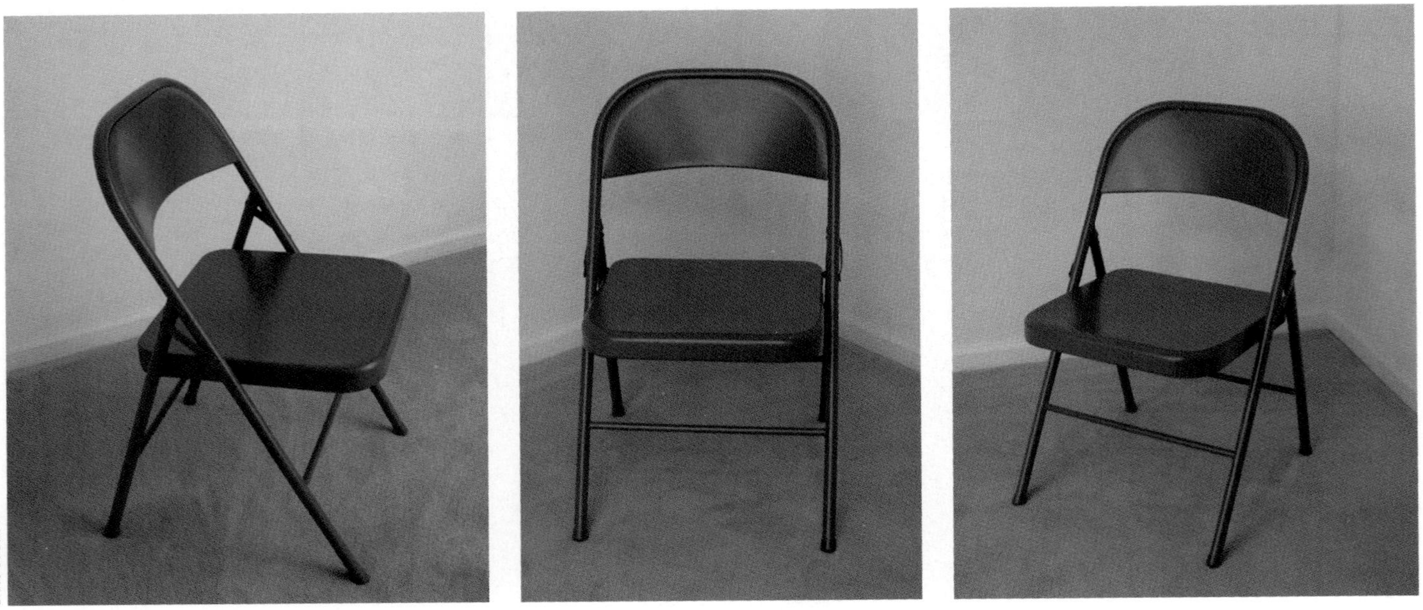

Figure 5.6 ▮ Your ability to recognize each of these views as being of the same chair is an example of viewpoint invariance.

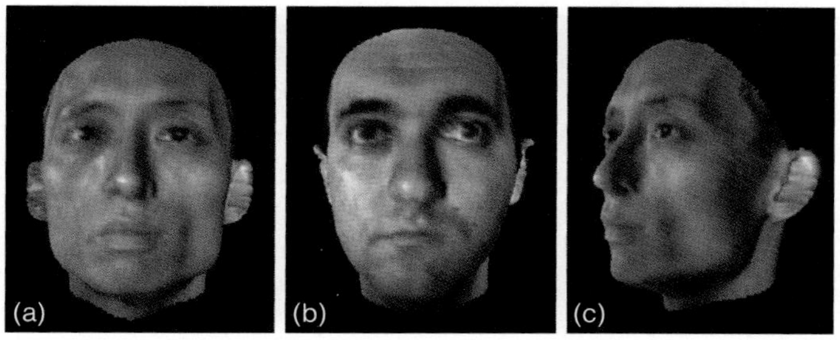

Figure 5.7 ▮ Which photographs are of the same person? *(From Sinha, P. (2002). Recognizing complex patterns.* Nature Neuroscience, *5, 1093–1097.)*

The Reasons for Changes in Lightness and Darkness Can Be Unclear

In a scene such as the one in Figure 5.8, it is necessary to determine which changes in lightness and darkness are due to properties of objects in the scene and which are due to changes in the illumination. It is easy for us to tell that the border between area (a) and area (b) is due to a change in the illumination, caused by the shadow. We can also tell that the border between (a) and (c) occurs because the panel at (a) is made of lighter material than the one at (c). These judgments, which we make with ease, would be difficult for a computer because it has to determine which dark areas are caused by shadows and which are caused by the color of different sections of the wall.

Given the computational powers of even a laptop computer—which can execute hundreds of millions of commands per second—the degree to which humans outperform computers is amazing. How do humans do it? An early attempt at answering this question occurred in Wilhelm Wundt's laboratory at the University of Leipzig.

THE GESTALT APPROACH TO OBJECT PERCEPTION

Wilhelm Wundt founded the first laboratory of scientific psychology in 1879. Wundt and his followers established an approach to psychology called **structuralism**. The basic idea behind structuralism was that perceptions are created by combining elements called **sensations**, just as each of the dots in the face in Figure 5.9 add together to

Figure 5.9 ▮ According to structuralism, a number of sensations (represented by the dots) adds up to create our perception of the face.

Figure 5.8 ▮ It is difficult for a computer to determine which changes in the lightness and colors in this scene are due to properties of different parts of the scene, and which are due to changes in illumination.

create our perception of a face. This approach, which dominated psychology until the 1920s, is important because it stimulated the founding of **Gestalt psychology**, which has made important contributions to our understanding of object perception.

The dominance of structuralism as an explanation for perception set the stage for the founding of Gestalt psychology. In 1911 the psychologist Max Wertheimer was on a train ride through Germany. He got off at Frankfurt and bought a toy stroboscope on the train platform (Boring, 1942). The stroboscope, a mechanical device that created an illusion of movement by rapidly alternating two slightly different pictures, caused Wertheimer to wonder how the structuralist idea that experience is created from sensations could explain the illusion of movement he observed. We can understand why this question arose by looking at Figure 5.10a, which diagrams the principle behind the illusion of movement created by the stroboscope.

(a)

Bruce Goldstein

(b)

Figure 5.10 ▮ (a) Wertheimer's demonstration of movement perception. (b) Moving electronic signs (such as this one) create the perception of movement by applying the same principles studied by Wertheimer.

When two stimuli that are in slightly different positions are flashed one after another with the correct timing, movement is perceived between the two stimuli. This is an illusion called **apparent movement** because there is actually no movement in the display, just two stationary stimuli flashing on and off. How, wondered Wertheimer, can the movement that appears to occur between the two flashing stimuli be caused by sensations? After all, there is no stimulation in the space between the two stimuli, and therefore there are no sensations to provide an explanation for the movement.

Names of faces in Figure 5.5, from left to right: Prince Charles, Woody Allen, Bill Clinton, Saddam Hussein, Richard Nixon, and Princess Diana.

With this question as his inspiration, Wertheimer and two colleagues, Kurt Koffka and Ivo Kohler, set up a laboratory at the University of Frankfurt, called themselves the Gestalt psychologists, and proceeded to do research and publish papers that posed serious problems for the structuralist idea that perceptions are created from sensations (Wertheimer, 1912). The following demonstration illustrates another phenomenon that is difficult to explain on the basis of sensations.

DEMONSTRATION

Making Illusory Contours Vanish

Consider the picture in Figure 5.11. If you see this as a cube floating in space in front of black circles, you probably perceive faint **illusory contours** that represent the edges of the cube (Bradley & Petry, 1977). These contours are called illusory because they aren't actually present in the physical stimulus. You can prove this to yourself by (1) placing your finger over one of the black circles or (2) imagining that the black circles are holes and that you are looking at the cube through these holes. Notice how the illusory contours vanish in both situations. **VIRTUAL LAB 1, 2, 3**

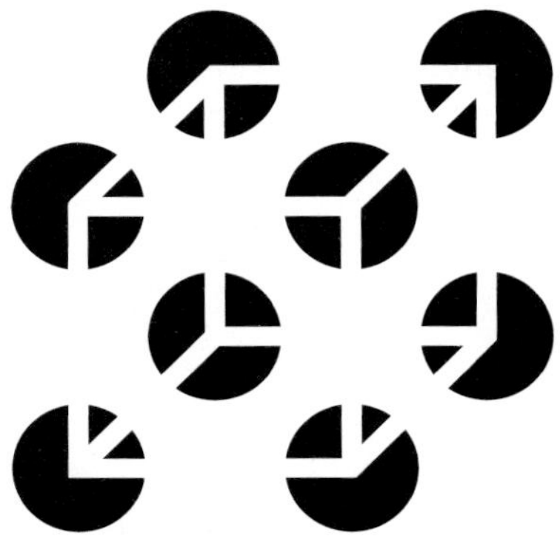

Figure 5.11 ▮ This can be seen as a cube floating in front of eight discs or as a cube seen through eight holes. In the first case, the edges of the cube appear as illusory contours. *(Based on "Organizational Determinants of Subjective Contour: The Subjective Necker Cube," by D. R. Bradley and H. M. Petry, 1977,* American Journal of Psychology, 90, *253–262. American Psychological Association.)* ▮

When you made the contours vanish by placing your finger over a black circle, you showed that the contour was illusory and that our perception of one part of the display (the contours) is affected by the presence of another part (the black circle). The structuralists would have a hard time explaining illusory contours because, just as for the example of apparent movement, they would not be able to identify any sensations along the contours that could lead to our perception of the contour. Additional displays that are difficult to explain in terms of sensations are bistable figures, which switch back and forth as they are viewed, and illusions, in which perceptions of one part of a display are affected by another part. (See Virtual Lab at the end of this chapter for examples.) VL 4–10

Making the contours vanish by imagining that you are looking through black holes poses a similar problem for the structuralists. It is difficult to explain a perception that is present one moment and gone the next in terms of sensations, especially since the stimulus on your retina never changes. Having rejected the idea that perception is built up of sensations, the Gestalt psychologists, proposed the basic principle that *the whole differs from the sum of its parts.*

The idea of the whole differing from the sum of the parts can be understood by returning to the procedure for creating apparent movement, which is illustrated in Figure 5.10a. The *parts* of this display are two stationary flashing lights. But these parts, when presented with the correct timing, create a perception of movement between the two lights. On a more complex level, consider electronic signs, like the one in Figure 5.10b, which display moving advertisements or news headlines. The perception of movement in these displays is so compelling that it is difficult to imagine that the parts that make up this display are stationary lights that are flashing on and off.

This emphasis on "wholes" led the Gestalt psychologists to focus on determining principles to explain **perceptual organization**—how small elements become grouped into larger objects, as when some of the dark areas in Figure 5.12 group to form a Dalmatian, and others are seen as shadows in the background. Proponents of the Gestalt approach to perceptual organization proposed a number of rules that they called the "laws of perceptual organization."

R. C. James

Figure 5.12 ▌ Some black-and-white shapes that become perceptually organized into a dalmatian.

The Gestalt Laws of Perceptual Organization

The **laws of perceptual organization** are a series of rules that specify how we organize small parts into wholes. Here are six of the Gestalt laws.

Pragnanz *Pragnanz,* roughly translated from the German, means "good figure." The **law of pragnanz**, the central law of Gestalt psychology, also called the **law of good figure**, or the **law of simplicity**, states: *Every stimulus pattern is seen in such a way that the resulting structure is as simple as possible.* The familiar Olympic symbol in Figure 5.13a is an example of the law of simplicity at work. We see this display as five circles and not as a larger number of more complicated shapes such as the ones in Figure 5.13b. VL 11

Figure 5.13 ▌ (a) This is usually perceived as five circles, not as the nine shapes in (b).

Similarity Most people perceive Figure 5.14a as either horizontal rows of circles, vertical columns of circles, or both. But when we change the color of some of the columns, as in Figure 5.14b, most people perceive vertical columns of circles. This perception illustrates the **law of similarity**: *Similar things appear to be grouped together.* This law causes circles of the same color to be grouped together.

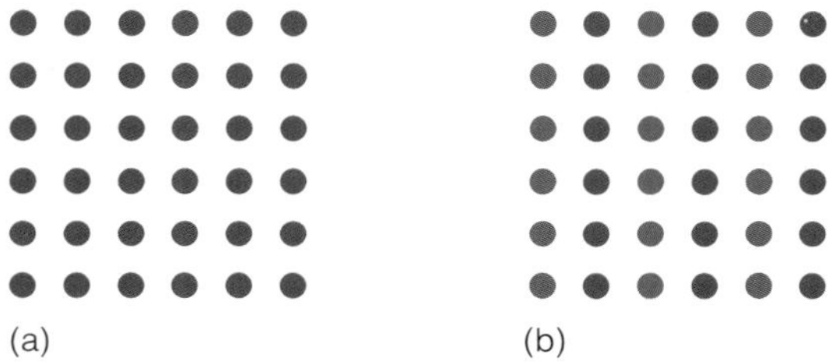

Figure 5.14 ▌ (a) Perceived as horizontal rows or vertical columns or both. (b) Perceived as vertical columns.

Grouping can also occur because of similarity of shape, size, or orientation (Figure 5.15). VL 12

Grouping also occurs for auditory stimuli. For example, notes that have similar pitches and that follow each other closely in time can become perceptually grouped to form a melody. We will consider this and other auditory grouping effects when we describe organizational processes in hearing in Chapter 12.

James A. Finely, AP/Wide World Photos

Figure 5.15 ▌ Ballet anyone? As the Pittsburgh Pirates' Humberto Cota takes a lead off first base, he becomes perceptually linked to the St. Louis Cardinals' Albert Pujols because of the similar orientations of their arms, legs, and bodies.

Good Continuation In Figure 5.16 we see the wire starting at A as flowing smoothly to B. It does not go to C or D because those paths would involve making sharp turns and would violate **the law of good continuation**, which states: *Points that, when connected, result in straight or smoothly curving lines are seen as belonging together, and the lines tend to be seen in such a way as to follow the smoothest path.* Another effect of good continuation is shown in the Celtic knot pattern in Figure 5.17. In this case, good continuation assures that we see a continuous interweaved pattern that does not appear to be broken into little pieces every time one strand overlaps another strand. Good continuation also helped us to perceive the smoothly curving circles in Figure 5.13a. VL 13

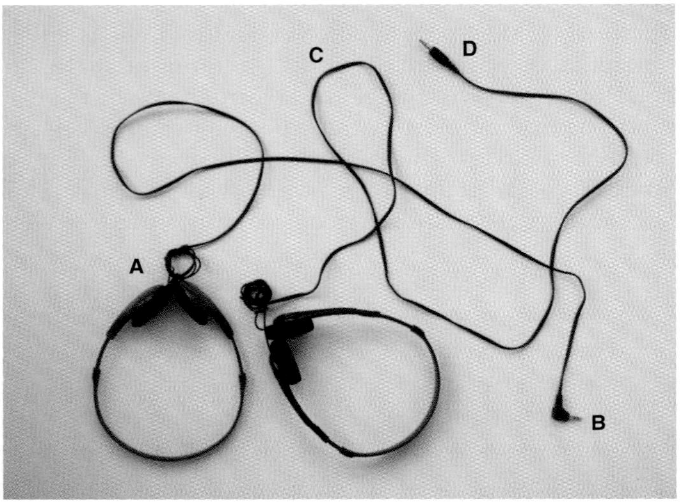

Bruce Goldstein

Figure 5.16 ▌ Good continuation helps us perceive two separate wires, even though they overlap.

Figure 5.17 ▌ We perceive this pattern as continuous interwoven strands because of good continuation.

Proximity, or Nearness Our perception of Figure 5.18b as horizontal rows of circles illustrates **the law of proximity, or nearness**: *Things that are near to each other appear to be grouped together.* We perceive Figure 5.18a as horizontal rows of circles, and although every other circle is changed to a square in Figure 5.19b, we still perceive horizontal rows. In this case the law of proximity overpowers the law of similarity. VL 14

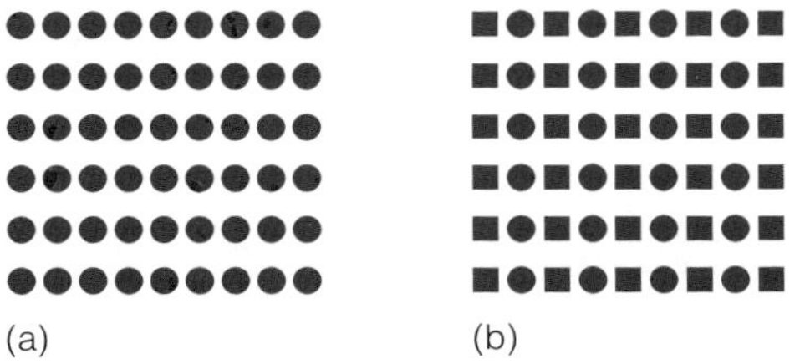

Figure 5.18 ▌ Grouping by nearness. (a) perceived as horizontal rows of circles; (b) still perceived as horizontal rows, even when half of the circles are changed into squares.

Common Fate The **law of common fate** states: *Things that are moving in the same direction appear to be grouped together.* Thus, when you see a flock of hundreds of birds all flying together, you tend to see the flock as a unit, and if some birds start flying in another direction, this creates a new unit (Figure 5.19). VL 15

Meaningfulness or Familiarity According to **the law of familiarity**, *things are more likely to form groups if the groups appear familiar or meaningful* (Helson, 1933; Hochberg, 1971). You can appreciate how meaningfulness influences perceptual organization by doing the following demonstration.

Figure 5.19 ▮ A flock of birds that are moving in the same direction are seen as grouped together. When a portion of the flock changes direction, their movement creates a new group. This illustrates the law of common fate.

DEMONSTRATION

Finding Faces in a Landscape

Consider the picture in Figure 5.20. At first glance this scene appears to contain mainly trees, rocks, and water. But on closer inspection you can see some faces in the trees in the background, and if you look more closely, you can see that a number of faces are formed by various groups of rocks. See if you can find all 12 faces hidden in this picture. ■

Some people find it difficult to perceive the faces at first, but then suddenly they succeed. The change in perception from "rocks in a stream" or "trees in a forest" into "faces" is a change in the perceptual organization of the rocks and the trees. The two shapes that you at first perceive as two separate rocks in the stream become perceptually grouped together when they become the left and right eyes of a face. In fact, once you perceive a particular grouping of rocks as a face, it is often difficult *not* to perceive them in this way—they have become permanently organized into a face. This is similar to the process we observed for the Dalmatian. Once we see the Dalmatian, it is difficult not to perceive it.

The above laws of organization were proposed by the Gestalt psychologists in the early 1900s. Stephen Palmer (1992, 1999) and Palmer and Irvin Rock (1994) have proposed three new grouping principles: the principle of common region, the principle of uniform connectedness, and the principle of synchrony.

Common Region Figure 5.21a illustrates the **principle of common region**: *Elements that are within the same region of space appear to be grouped together.* Even though the dots inside the ovals are farther apart than the dots that are next to each other in neighboring ovals, we see the dots inside the ovals as belonging together. This occurs be-

Figure 5.20 ▮ *The Forest Has Eyes* by Bev Doolittle (1985). Can you find 12 faces in this picture?

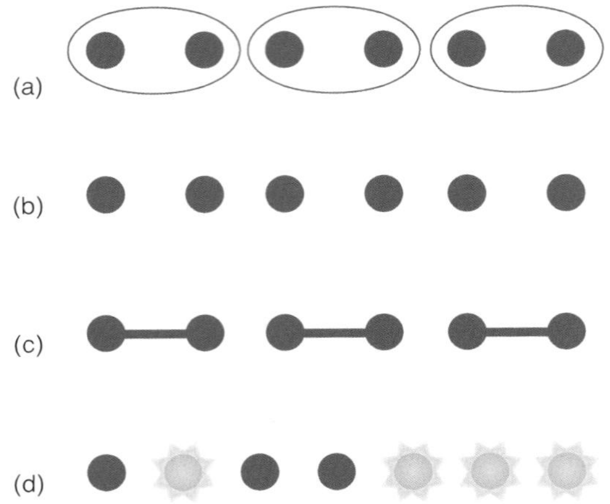

Figure 5.21 ▮ Grouping by (a) common region; (b) proximity; (c) connectedness; and (d) synchrony. The yellow lights blink on and off together.

cause each oval is seen as a separate region of space. VL 16

Uniform Connectedness The **principle of uniform connectedness** states that *a connected region of visual properties, such as lightness, color, texture, or motion, are perceived as a single unit.* For example, consider the display in Figure 5.22b, in which circles form groups of two based on proximity. However, connecting the circles, as in Figure 5.22c, shifts our perception so that the connected dots are perceived as being part of the same object.

Synchrony The **principle of synchrony** states that *visual events that occur at the same time will be perceived as belonging together.* For example, in the display in Figure 5.22d, the lights that blink together are seen as belonging together. Notice that synchrony is like common fate because both principles are dynamic, but synchrony can occur without movement, and the elements don't have to change in the same direction. Thus, one light can go on, and another can go off, but if they change together, they tend to be perceived as belonging together.

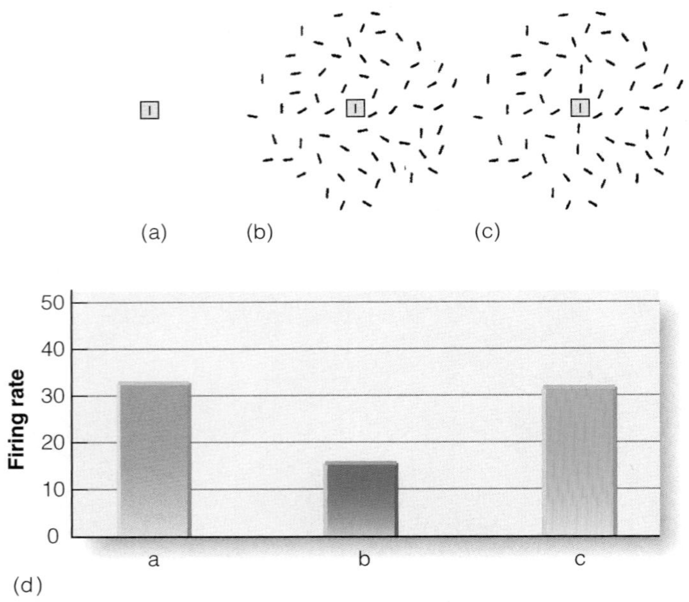

Figure 5.22 ▮ How a neuron in V1 responds to: (a) an oriented bar inside the neuron's receptive field (the square); (b) the same bar surrounded by randomly oriented bars; (c) the bar when it becomes part of a group of vertical bars, due to the principles of similarity and good continuation.
(Reprinted with permission from Neuron, *15, M. K. Zapadia, et al., "Improvement in visual sensitivity by changes in local context: Parallel studies in human observers and in V1 of alert monkey," p. 843–856. Copyright ©1995 Elsevier Science.)*

Neurons That Respond to Grouping

Many years after the Gestalt psychologists proposed the laws of good continuation and similarity, researchers discovered neurons in the visual cortex that respond best to displays that reflect these principles of grouping. For example, Figure 5.22a shows a vertical bar in the receptive field (indicated by the square) of a neuron in area V1 of a monkey's cortex. The neuron responds well to this single bar. When the vertical bar is surrounded with randomly oriented bars (Figure 5.22b), the neuron's response decreases. But when the orientations of some of the previously random bars are changed to a vertical orientation so they form a group with the vertical bar because of similarity and good continuation (Figure 5.22c), the response increases (Zapadia et al., 1995).

The Gestalt "Laws" Are More Accurately Described as "Heuristics"

Although the Gestalt psychologists called the foregoing principles "laws," most perceptual psychologists call them the Gestalt "principles" or "heuristics." The reason for rejecting the term *laws* is that the rules proposed by the Gestalt psychologists don't make strong enough predictions to qualify as laws. Instead, the Gestalt principles are most accurately described as being **heuristics**—rules of thumb that provide a best-guess solution to a problem. We can understand what heuristics are by comparing them to another way of solving a problem, called algorithms.

An **algorithm** is a procedure that is guaranteed to solve a problem. An example of an algorithm is the procedures we learn for addition, subtraction, and long division. If we apply these procedures correctly, we get the right answer every time. In contrast, a heuristic may not result in a correct solution every time. For example, suppose that you want to find a cat that is hiding somewhere in the house. An algorithm for doing this would be to systematically search every room in the house (being careful not to let the cat sneak past you!). If you do this, you will eventually find the cat, although it may take a while. A heuristic for finding the cat would be to first look in the places where the cat likes to hide. So you check under the bed and in the hall closet. This may not always lead to finding the cat, but, if it does, it has the advantage of usually being faster than the algorithm.

We say the Gestalt principles are heuristics because, like heuristics, they are best-guess rules that work most of the time, but not necessarily all of the time. For example, consider the following situation in which the Gestalt laws might cause an incorrect perception: As you are hiking in the woods, you stop cold in your tracks because not too far ahead, you see what appears to be an animal lurking behind a tree (Figure 5.23a). The Gestalt laws of organization play a role in creating this perception. You see the two shapes to the left and right of the tree as a single object because of the Gestalt law of similarity (because both shapes are the same color, it is likely that they are part of the same object). Also, good continuation links these two parts into one because the line along the top of the object extends smoothly from one side of the tree to another. Finally, the image resembles animals you've seen before. For all of these reasons, it is not surprising that you perceive the two objects as part of one animal.

Because you fear that the animal might be dangerous, you take a different path. As your detour takes you around the tree, you notice that the dark shapes aren't an animal after all, but are two oddly shaped tree stumps (Figure 5.23b). So in this case, the Gestalt laws have misled you.

The fact that heuristics are usually faster than algorithms helps explain why the perceptual system is designed to operate in a way that sometimes produces errors. Consider, for example, what the algorithm would be for determining what the shape in Figure 5.23a really is. It would involve walking around the tree so you can see it from different angles and perhaps taking a closer look at the objects behind the tree. Although this may result in an accurate perception, it is potentially risky (what if the shape actually *is* a dangerous animal?) and slow. The advantage of our Gestalt-based heuristics is that they are fast—and correct most of the time.

PERCEPTUAL SEGREGATION: HOW OBJECTS ARE SEPARATED

The idea behind each of the principles of grouping is to describe how portions of a stimulus become grouped to form larger objects. But the Gestalt psychologists were well aware that the problem of perception goes beyond simply deciding how elements group to form objects. They knew that it is also necessary to explain how the opposite occurs—when objects are seen as separated from the rest of the scene in which they appear. This is the problem of **perceptual segregation**.

The question of what causes perceptual segregation is often referred to as the problem of **figure–ground segregation**. When we see a separate object, it is usually seen as a **figure** that stands out from its background, which is called the **ground**. For example, you would probably see a book or papers on your desk as figure and the surface of your desk as ground. The Gestalt psychologists were interested in determining the properties of the figure and the ground and what causes us to perceive one area as figure and the other as ground.

What Are the Properties of Figure and Ground?

One way the Gestalt psychologists studied the properties of figure and ground was by considering patterns like the one in Figure 5.24, which was introduced by Danish psychologist Edgar Rubin in 1915. This pattern is an example of **reversible figure–ground** because it can be perceived alternately either as two blue faces looking at each other, in front of a white background, or as a white vase on a blue background. Some of the properties of the figure and ground are:

- The figure is more "thinglike" and more memorable than the ground. Thus, when you see the vase as fig-

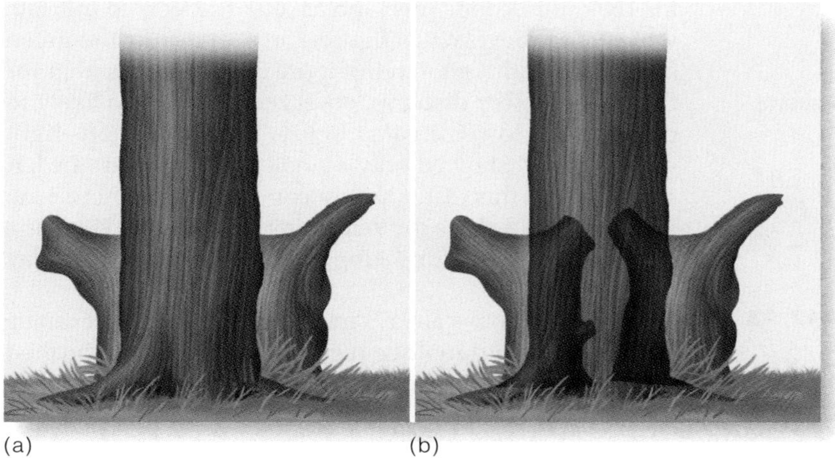

(a) (b)

Figure 5.23 ▮ (a) What lurks behind the tree? (b) It is two strangely shaped tree trunks, not an animal!

Figure 5.24 ▮ A version of Rubin's reversible face–vase figure.

ure, it appears as an object that can be remembered later. However, when you see the same white area as ground, it does not appear to be an object and is therefore not particularly memorable.

- The figure is seen as being in front of the ground. Thus, when the vase is seen as figure, it appears to be in front of the dark background (Figure 5.25a), and when the faces are seen as figure, they are on top of the light background (Figure 5.25b).

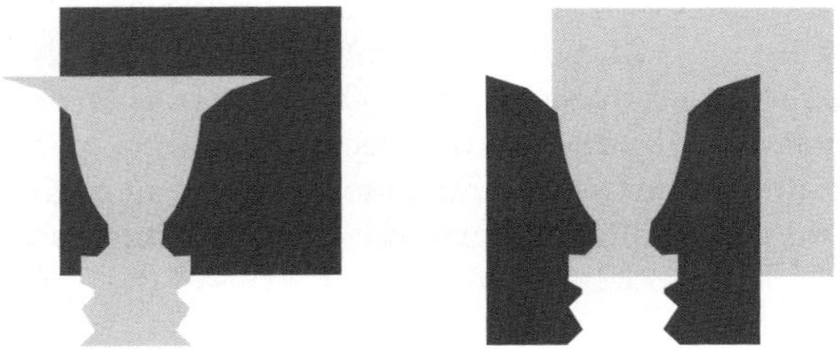

(a) (b)

Figure 5.25 ▮ (a) When the vase is perceived as figure, it is seen in front of a homogeneous dark background. (b) When the faces are seen as figure, they are seen in front of a homogeneous light background.

- The ground is seen as unformed material and seems to extend behind the figure.
- The contour separating the figure from the ground appears to belong to the figure. This property of figure, which is called **border ownership**, means that although figure and ground share a contour, the border is associated with the figure. VL **17, 18**

The following demonstration illustrates the "thingness" property of the figure.

DEMONSTRATION

Judging Similarity

Look at Figure 5.26a, focusing on the black shape that is sitting on a white background. Then look at the two white figures on the black background in (b) and (c) and decide, as quickly as possible, which of the white figures is more similar to (a).

(a) (b) (c)

Figure 5.26 ▮ Look at the black shape in (a), and then quickly decide whether (b) or (c) is more similar to it. (Adapted from Baylis & Driver, 2001.) ■

In controlled experiments, observers were twice as likely to judge (b) as being more similar to (a) (Baylis & Driver, 2001). This result occurs even though shape (c) is actually part of Figure 5.26a because it is the contour of the ground on which the black shape is resting. Shape (b) is not even present in Figure 5.26, but because it is the mirror image of (a), it is perceived as being similar to it. Because shape (a) is perceived as figure, it is memorable, and so is its mirror image. In contrast, shape (c), is not remembered because the ground is "unformed material" that is not memorable.

What Factors Determine Which Area Is Figure?

What factors determine whether an area is perceived as figure or ground? We will illustrate how Shaun Vecera and coworkers (2002) used the phenomenological method to study this question. They showed that regions in the lower part of a display are more likely to be perceived as figure than regions in the upper part. They demonstrated this by flashing stimuli like the ones in Figure 5.27a and b for 150 milliseconds (ms) and asked observers to indicate which area they saw as figure, the red area or the green area. The results, shown in Figure 5.27c, indicate that for the upper–lower displays, observers were more likely to perceive the lower area as figure, but for the left–right displays, they showed only a small preference for the left region. From this result Vecera concluded that there is no left–right preference for determining figure, but there is a definite preference for seeing objects lower in the display as figure.

A conclusion is always more powerful when it can be confirmed using another method. Vecera accomplished by using the phenomenon of figure–ground reversal, like the one Rubin illustrated using the face–vase stimulus in

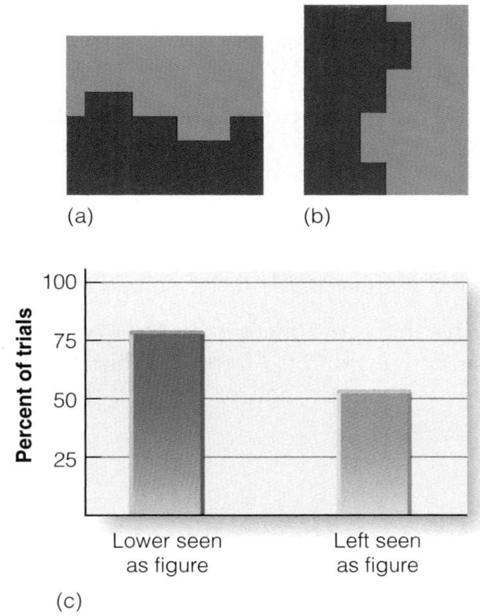

Figure 5.27 ▮ (a) Stimuli from Vecera et al. (2002). (b) Percentage of trials on which lower or left areas were seen as figure.

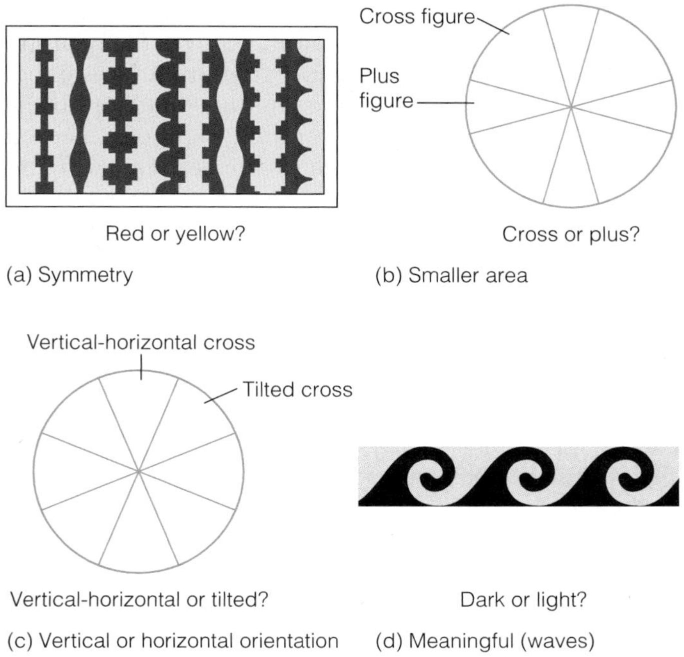

Figure 5.28 ▮ Examples of how displays that are (a) symmetrical; (b) small in size; (c) oriented vertically or horizontally; or (d) meaningful and more likely to be seen as figure.

Figure 5.24. Vecera presented stimuli like the shapes in Figure 5.27 for 30 seconds and asked observers to indicate which area was seen as figure by pressing one button when the green area was figure and another button when the red area was figure. The perception of figure and ground switched back and forth during the 30 seconds, but for the upper–lower stimulus the lower region was seen as figure 84 percent of the time. As in the previous experiment, there was only a small difference between the tendency to perceive the left and right sides as figure.

The conclusion from both of these experiments was that the lower region of a display tends to be seen as figure. Figure 5.28 illustrates four other factors—symmetry, size, orientation, and meaning—that increase the chances that an area will be seen as figure. VL 19

How Do Neurons Respond to Figure and Ground?

How is the property of "figure" coded in neurons? Neurons have been found in various areas of the cortex that respond to characteristics of figure and ground (Zhou et al., 2000). Figure 5.29 shows the stimulus and results for an experiment that shows how a neuron in area V1 of the monkey cortex responds to an area of a display that is perceived as figure but does not respond to an identical area that is not perceived as figure (Lamme, 1995). In (a), the leftward-slanting lines in the square on the right stand out as figure against the rightward-slanting lines of the background. When this *figure* area is positioned over the neuron's receptive field (which is indicated by the green rectangle), the neuron fires, as shown to the right of the

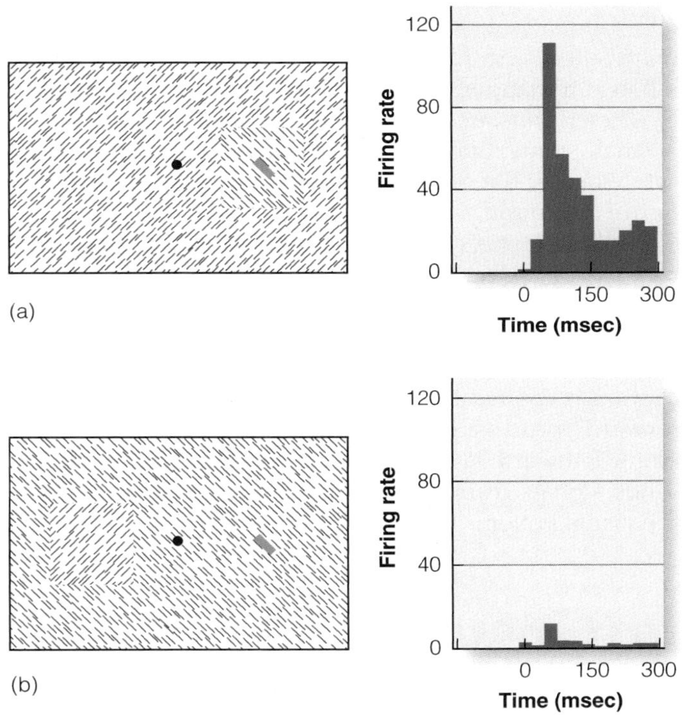

Figure 5.29 ▮ How a neuron in V1 responds to stimuli presented to its receptive field (green rectangle). (a) The neuron responded when the stimulus on the receptive field is figure. (b) There is no response when the same pattern on the receptive field is not figure. (Adapted from Lamme et al., 1995.)

display. However, when the display is changed, as shown in (b), so now the *ground* is positioned over the neuron's receptive field, the neuron hardly fires at all. Notice that exactly the same slanted-line stimulus is falling on the neuron's receptive field in (a) and in (b), but the neuron is activated only when the slanted lines create a figure against a background.

This result is significant because it demonstrates a neural response that corresponds to perception. But it is also significant because this neuron is located early in visual system—in area V1. Remember our description, in Chapter 3, of simple and complex cells in area V1 (see page 60). Because these neurons respond only to simple stimuli such as oriented lines, and are located at such an early stage in the visual system, it had been assumed that they would not be involved in complex perceptions such as the segregation of figure and ground.

Another characteristic of V1 neurons that made them unlikely candidates for differentiating between figure and ground is that they have small receptive fields. Thus, V1 neurons were thought to "look at" only a small portion of a stimulus and so would be poorly suited to detect figure–ground stimuli, which often extend over large portions of the visual field.

But despite these reasons that V1 neurons should not be able to differentiate between figure and ground, they accomplish this feat because of an effect called **contextual modulation**. Contextual modulation occurs when stimulation outside of a neuron's receptive field (which normally causes no response) affects the firing that occurs when stimulation is presented within the neuron's receptive field. Thus, even though the neuron's receptive field is small, contextual modulation comes into play to indicate whether the stimulus falling on the receptive field is figure or ground.

What causes contextual modulation for these neurons? They probably receive signals from higher areas of the visual cortex. This situation, in which signals travel "backward" to "lower" areas in the nervous system, is called **feedback** (Lamme & Roelfsema, 2000). Thus, perception is created by the nervous system both by "feedforward" processing that sends signals from lower areas like V1 toward higher areas and also by feedback that sends signals from higher-level areas to earlier areas in the visual system.

TEST YOURSELF 5.1

1. What are some of the problems that make object perception difficult for computers but not for humans?
2. What is structuralism, and why did the Gestalt psychologists propose an alternative to this way of looking at perception?
3. How did the Gestalt psychologists explain perceptual organization?
4. How did the Gestalt psychologists describe figure–ground segregation?
5. What properties of a stimulus tend to favor perceiving an area as "figure"? Be sure you understand Vecera's experiment that showed that the lower region of a display tends to be perceived as figure.
6. Describe the experiment that showed that a V1 neuron can respond to "figure." What does this result tell us about the nature of processing in the visual system?

MODERN RESEARCH ON OBJECT PERCEPTION

The Gestalt psychologists' ideas about object perception dominated psychology for over 60 years. This approach did an excellent job of describing a number of basic perceptual phenomena such as perceptual organization and figure–ground segregation. Modern perceptual psychologists have taken many of these descriptions as their starting point but have gone beyond the Gestalt psychologist's approach in two ways: (1) They have emphasized *measurement* over description; and (2) they have focused on determining the *mechanisms* responsible for object perception.

We have already considered some of this modern research by describing how Vecera used measurement to determine that lower regions of a display tend to be seen as figure (page 104), and by describing physiological research on neurons that respond to characteristics of figure and ground (page 105). We will now consider additional modern research that has asked the following questions:

1. Why does the visual system respond best to specific types of stimuli?
2. Must a figure be separated from ground before we can recognize objects?
3. How do we recognize objects from different viewpoints?
4. How does the brain process information about objects?

Why Does the Visual System Respond Best to Specific Types of Stimuli?

We began our discussion of perception in Chapter 1 by posing a hypothetical "science project," in which the task was to design a device that can identify objects in the environment. A logical way to get started on this project would be to survey the environment and determine the nature of the objects that your device would have to detect. Then you could design a device that was tuned to detect these particular kinds of objects. As you may have guessed, this is one of the principles behind the design of the human perceptual system, which is, in fact, tuned to match the characteristics of the environment.

Researchers have studied the connection between characteristics of the perceptual system and characteristics of the environment by determining **regularities in the environment**—characteristics of the environment that occur regularly and in many different situations. You can see some of these regularities yourself by looking around. When you do this, you will probably see many straight contours, with a preponderance of verticals and horizontals. You might also notice that curved contours tend to curve smoothly and that when one object partially covers another one, the contour of the object in back "comes out the other side" so when its contour is extended behind the covering object, it forms a straight or smoothly curving line. Many of these contours may be associated with human-made objects, but if you look outside, you may also notice similar situations in nature.

These regularities in the environment are reflected by the Gestalt heuristics. For example, the principle of good continuation reflects the straight and smoothly curving contours that often occur in the environment. Or consider the idea of uniform connectedness. Objects often are defined by areas of the same color or texture, so when an area of the image on the retina has the property of uniform connectedness, it is likely that this area arises from a single environmental shape (Palmer & Rock, 1994). Thus, uniformly connected regions are regularities in the environment, and the perceptual system is designed to interpret these regions so that the environment will be perceived correctly.

One environmental regularity that has been extensively studied is the preponderance of verticals and horizontals in the environment. This property was studied systematically by David Copolla and coworkers (1998) by giving two people digital cameras and having them walk through three different environments: (1) inside buildings on the Duke University campus; (2) outside, on the campus; and (3) in the Duke Forest, a densely wooded area near the campus. Both people carried a device that beeped every 2 minutes, and when they heard the beep, they took a picture of whatever they were observing at the time. When Coppola analyzed the pictures for each environment, he obtained the results shown in Figure 5.30. There was a preponderance of vertical and horizontal orientations, even for the scenes from the forest.

If the perceptual system is tuned to detect horizontals and verticals, we might expect that observers might be more sensitive to horizontals and verticals, and this is exactly what occurs. The fact that people are more sensitive to horizontals and verticals than to other orientations is called the **oblique effect** (Appelle, 1972; Campbell et al., 1966; Orban et al., 1984).

The oblique effect appears to be linked to the activity of orientation-selective neurons because recordings from these neurons in animals reveals that there are more neurons that respond to horizontals and verticals (R. L. DeValois et al., 1982) and that these neurons are allotted proportionally more space in the visual cortex (Coppola et al., 1998; also see Furmanski & Engel, 2000, for evidence that V1 in humans responds better to verticals and horizontals than other orientations).

How are these relationships between environmental regularities, physiology, and perception established? The answer takes us back to our discussion of "Evolution and Plasticity: How Do Neurons Become Specialized?" on page 84 of Chapter 4. It is likely that these relationships are created by two mechanisms: (1) the biological process of evolution, which has, over many thousands of years, shaped our perceptual system so it functions efficiently in the environment; and (2) experience-dependent plasticity, which shapes properties of neurons through our day-to-day contact with the environment. (Remember the Greeble experiments, which showed that learning about Greebles caused neurons to become tuned to respond better to Greebles.)

Must a Figure Be Separated From Ground Before We Can Recognize Objects?

The Gestalt psychologists proposed that one of the first things that occurs in the perceptual process is the segregation of figure from ground. They contended that the figure must stand out from the ground before it can be recognized.

But Bradley Gibson and Mary Peterson (1994) showed that this cannot be the case because figure–ground formation can be affected by the meaningfulness of a stimulus. They demonstrated this by presenting a display like the one in Figure 5.31, which can be perceived in two ways: (1) a standing woman (the black part of the display) or (2) a less meaningful shape (the white part of the display). When they presented stimuli such as this for a fraction of a second and asked observers which region seemed to be the figure, they found that observers were more likely to say that the meaningful part of the display (the woman, in this example) was the figure.

Why were the observers more likely to perceive the woman? One possibility is that they must have recognized that the black area was a familiar object. In fact, when Peterson turned the display upside down, so that it was more difficult to recognize the black area as a woman, observers were less likely to see that area as being the figure. The fact that meaningfulness can influence the assignment of an area as figure means that the process of recognition must be occurring either before or at the same time as the figure is being separated from the ground (Peterson, 1994, 2001).

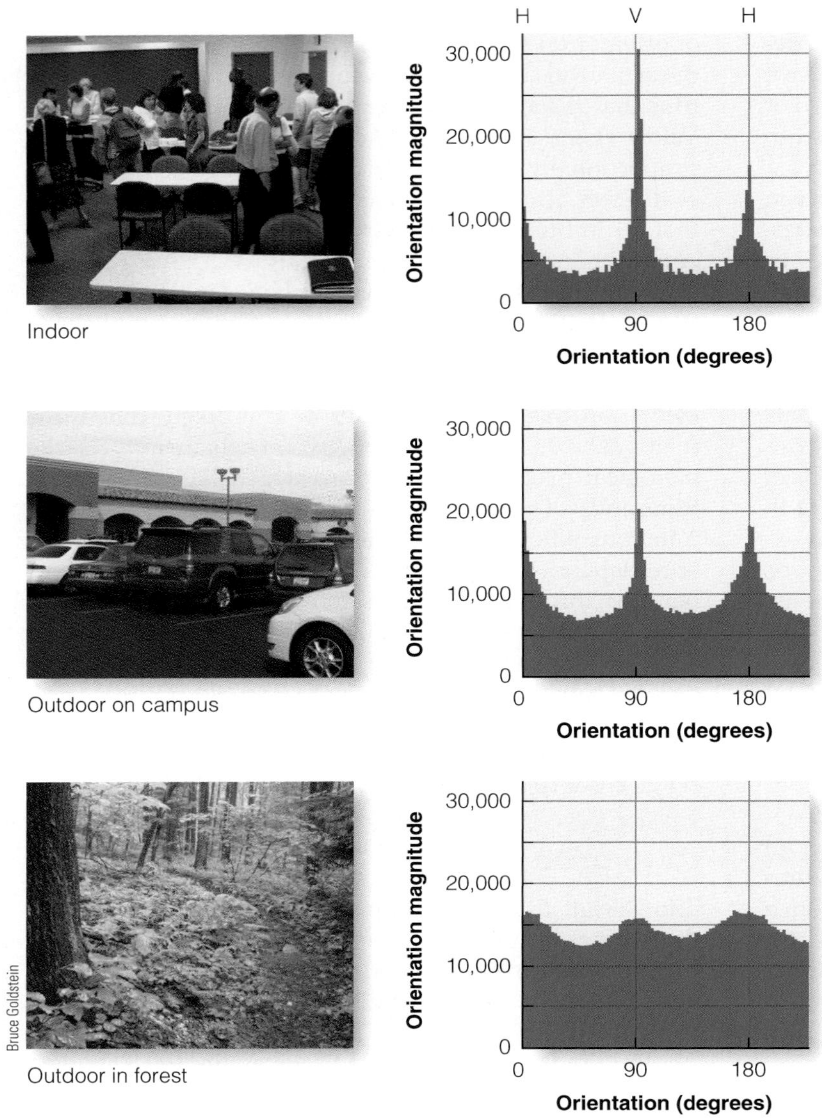

Figure 5.30 ■ Left: Photographs like the ones taken by the participants in Coppola et al.'s (1998) experiment as they walked around the Duke University campus. Right: The results of a computer analysis of the orientations in each type of scene (indoor campus, outdoor campus, and in the forest). The peaks at 0, 90, and 180 degrees indicate that horizontal (H) and vertical (V) are the most common orientations. Similar peaks also occurred at the other horizontal and vertical orientations (270 and 360 degrees).

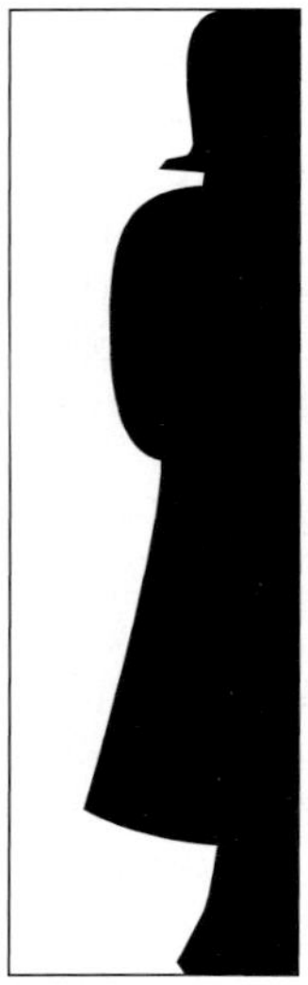

Figure 5.31 ■ Stimulus for Gibson and Peterson's (1994) experiment.

How Do We Recognize Objects From Different Viewpoints?

Many perception researchers have focused on the question, "How do we see three-dimensional objects?" At the beginning of the chapter, we saw that one of the problems facing the perceptual system is the problem of achieving view invariance—being able to recognize an object from a number of different viewpoints (Figure 5.6). Two models of object perception have been proposed that offer different solutions to this problem: (1) structural-description models; and (2) image-description models.

Structural-Description Models **Structural-description models** of object recognition propose that our ability to recognize three-dimensional objects is based on three-dimensional volumes that can be combined to create the overall shape of an object. These volumes are called **volumetric features**. One of the first structural-description models was proposed by David Marr (1982), who described object recognition as involving a sequence of steps that begin with detecting and object's edges and end with the perception of the three-dimensional object. During this process, the visual system represents an object as a group of volumetric features, which, for Marr, were simple geometrical solids such as cylinders. For example, during the process of object perception, a person would be represented by the arrangement of cylindrical volumetric features as shown in Figure 5.32 (Tarr & Vuong, 2002).

This idea of volumetric features was taken a step further by Irving Biederman (1987), who proposed a number of different volumetric features with different shapes as part of his **recognition-by-components (RBC) theory.** Biederman called his volumetric features **geons,** a term that stands for "geometric ions," because just as ions are basic units of molecules (see page 25), these geons are basic units of objects. Figure 5.33a shows a number of geons, which are shapes such as cylinders, rectangular solids, and pyramids. Biederman proposed 36 different geons and suggested that this number of geons is enough to enable us to construct a large proportion of the objects that exist in the environment. Figure 5.33b shows a few objects that have been constructed from geons.

One property of geons, which was proposed to provide a solution to the view invariance problem, is that they have **view-invariant properties**—properties that remain visible even when the geon is viewed from many different angles. An example of a view-invariant property of the rectangular solid in Figure 5.33a is its three parallel edges because these edges remain visible and parallel when viewed from most viewing angles.

You can test the view-invariant properties of the rectangular solid for yourself by picking up a book and moving it around so you are looking at it from many different viewpoints. As you do this, notice what percentage of the time you are seeing three parallel edges. Only occasionally, when viewing the book end-on, do you not see three parallel edges. Biederman called this occurrence an **accidental property** of geons because it occurs rarely and only from certain viewpoints. When accidental properties do occur, it becomes more difficult to recognize the object. For example, when we view the object in Figure 5.34a from the unusual perspective in Figure 5.34b, we can't see

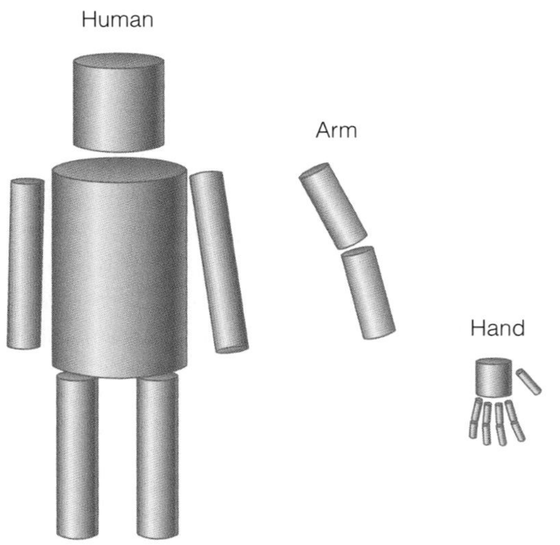

Figure 5.32 ▮ According to the structural-description model proposed by David Marr (1982), a person could be represented by a number of cylindrical volumetric features.

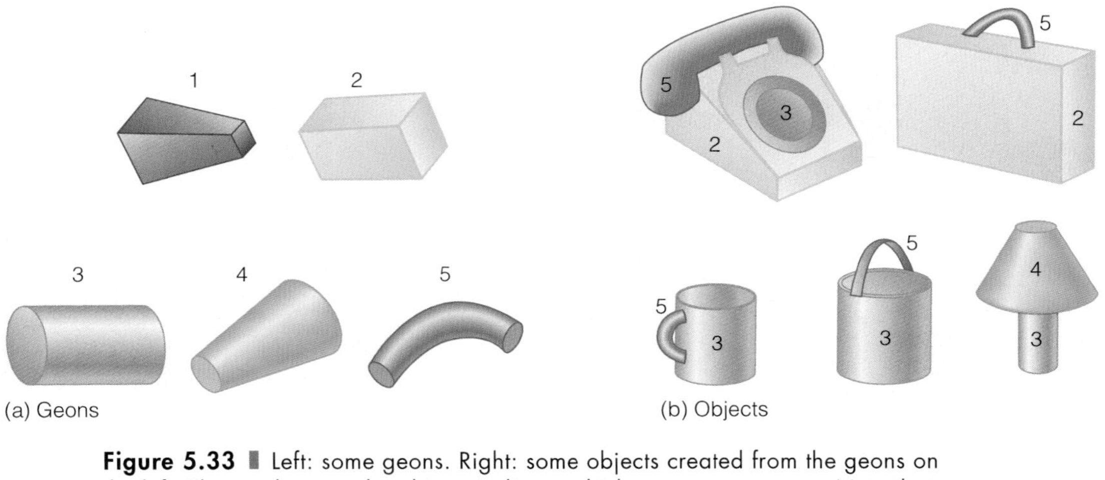

Figure 5.33 ▮ Left: some geons. Right: some objects created from the geons on the left. The numbers on the objects indicate which geons are present. Note that recognizable objects can be formed by combining just two or three geons. Also note that the relations between the geons matter, as illustrated by the cup and the pail. *(Adapted from "Recognition-by-Components: A Theory of Human Image Understanding," by I. Biederman, 1987,* Psychological Review, *94 (2), pp. 115–147 (figures 3, 6, 7, and 11), Copyright © 1987 with permission from the author and the American Psychological Association.)*

Bruce Goldstein

(a) (b)

Figure 5.34 ▮ (a) A familiar object. (b) The same object seen from a viewpoint that obscures most of its geons. This makes it harder to recognize the object.

some of its basic geons and therefore have difficulty identifying it. Another property of geons is **discriminability**, the ability to distinguish each geon from the others from almost all viewpoints.

The main principle of recognition-by-components theory is that if we can perceive an object's geons, we can identify the object (also see Biederman & Cooper, 1991; Biederman et al., 1993). The ability to identify an object if we can identify its geons is called the **principle of componential recovery**. This principle is what is behind our ability to identify objects in the natural environment even when parts of the objects are hidden by other objects. Figure 5.35a shows a situation in which componential recovery can't occur because the visual noise is arranged so the geons cannot be identified. Luckily, parts of objects are rarely obscured in this way in the natural environment, so, as we see in Figure 5.35b, we can usually identify geons and, therefore, can identify the object.

A strength of Biederman's theory is that it shows that we can recognize objects based on a relatively small number of basic shapes. For example, it isn't hard to recognize Figure 5.36a as an airplane, even though it contains only three geons. However, some researchers have criticized recognition-by-components theory on the grounds that although geons may enable us to distinguish between classes of objects (airplanes vs. toasters, for example), they do not always provide enough information to enable us to distinguish between different objects that have the same basic components like, say, horses and zebras. It is likely that volumetric features may be important for perceiving objects, but many other features, such as color, texture, movement, and depth, are probably involved as well.

Image-Description Models **Image-description models** of object recognition propose that our ability to recognize objects from different viewpoints is based on stored two-dimensional views of the object as it would appear from different viewpoints. According to this idea, you recognize the chair in Figure 5.6 from different viewpoints by

(a) (b)

Figure 5.35 ▮ (a) It is difficult to identify the object behind the mask because its geons have been obscured. (b) Now that it is possible to identify geons, the object can be identified as a flashlight.

(From "Recognition-by-Components: A Theory of Human Image Understanding," by I. Biederman, 1985, Computer Vision, Graphics and Image Processing, 32, *29–73. Copyright © 1985 Academic Press. Reprinted by permission.)*

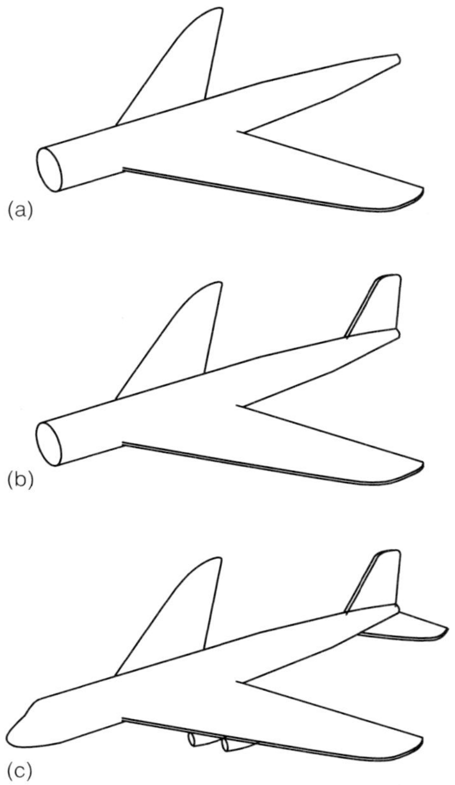

Figure 5.36 ▮ An airplane, as represented (a) by three geons, (b) by four geons, and (c) by nine geons.
(From "Recognition-by-Components: A Theory of Human Image Understanding," by I. Biederman, 1985, Computer Vision, Graphics and Image Processing, *32, 29–73. Copyright © 1985 Academic Press. Reprinted by permission.)*

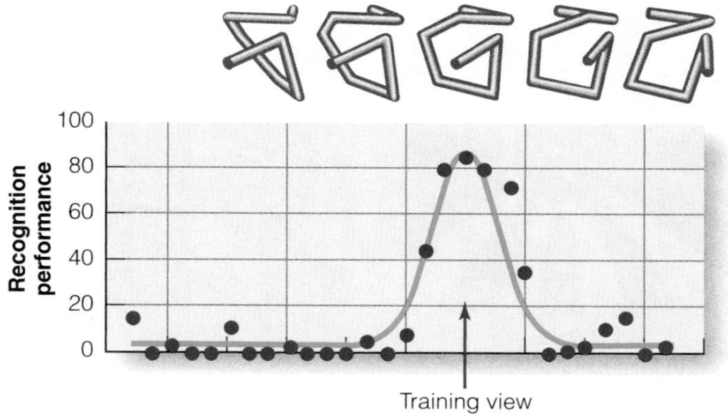

Figure 5.37 ▮ Psychophysical curve showing that a monkey is better at identifying the view of the object that was presented during training (arrow). The drop-off in performance for other viewpoints is an example of a lack of view invariance.

comparing your perception to different representations of the chair that are stored in your memory (Riesenhuber & Poggio, 1999; Tarr, 1995; Ullman, 1989).

This approach to object recognition takes into account the finding that view invariance does not always occur. For example, consider the results in Figure 5.37, which were previously presented in Figure 4.23 (see page 85). This curve shows that when a monkey is trained to recognize a specific view of an object, like the one indicated by the arrow, it can recognize it when tested later. However, recognition is not as good for other views of the object. The fact that the monkey's performance becomes poorer when different views of the object are presented means that view invariance is not occurring.

According to the image-description model, when the object is familiar, such as the chair in Figure 5.6, representations exist and view invariance occurs. However, when the object is novel, such as the one in Figure 5.37, representations do not exist and viewpoint invariance does not occur.

Which Model Is Correct? As with most situations in which competing explanations have been proposed, the actual mechanism for object recognition probably involves elements of both the structural-description and image-description models (Palmeri & Gauthier, 2004). It is likely that we make use of both the volumetric features proposed by structural-description models and stored representations proposed by image-description models as we perceive objects in our environment.

How Does the Brain Process Information About Objects?

If we were to consider all of the neurons in the brain that are activated during the process of object perception, we would see that there is a large amount of activity in the interotemporal (IT) cortex and that other areas are activated as well (Freedman et al., 2003; Hinkle & Connor, 2002; Kourtzi et al., 2003). But researchers who study how the brain processes information about objects have gone beyond simply identifying which areas of the brain are activated by pictures of objects. They are doing experiments to determine what is happening in the brain as people actually perceive and identify objects. We will now describe three of these experiments.

Perceiving an Object: Sunburst or Butterfly? D. L. Sheinberg and Nikos Logothetis (1997) presented a sunburst pattern to a monkey's left eye and a picture such as the butterfly or other animal or object to the right eye (Figure 5.38). This situation, when two very different images are presented to the same places on the left and right eyes, causes **binocular rivalry**—the monkey's perception alternates back and forth between the two images. It sees the sunburst pattern and then, a few seconds later, the butterfly, and then back to the sunburst, and so on.

Sheinberg and Logothetis's goal was to tell when the monkey was perceiving the butterfly and when it was perceiving the sunburst and to see whether there was a connection between the monkey's perceptions and the firing of single neurons in its IT cortex. They accom-

Figure 5.38 ▮ Stimuli similar to those used by Sheinberg and Logothetis (1997). The "sunburst" stimulus was presented to the monkey's left eye and the butterfly to the right eye.

plished this by training a monkey to pull the left lever when it perceived the sunburst pattern and the right lever when it perceived the butterfly. As the monkey was reporting what it was perceiving, they recorded the activity of a neuron in area IT that had previously been shown to respond to the butterfly but not the sunburst. The result of this experiment was straightforward: The cell fired vigorously when the monkey was perceiving the butterfly and ceased firing when the monkey was perceiving the sunburst.

Consider what happened in this experiment. The images on the monkey's retina remained the same throughout the experiment—the sunburst was always positioned on the left retina, and the butterfly was always positioned on the right. The change in the monkey's perception from "sunburst" to "butterfly" must therefore have been happening in the brain, and this experiment showed that these changes in perception are linked to changes in the firing of a neuron in the brain. Similar results have been obtained in humans using fMRI (Lumer, Friston, & Rees, 1998; Lumer & Rees, 1999).

Identifying an Object: Is That Harrison Ford? We know from our discussion of modularity in Chapter 4 that there are many neurons in the fusiform face areas (FFA), in the IT cortex, that respond preferentially to *perceiving* faces. But what happens in the brain when we ask observers to *identify* a face?

Kalanit Grill-Spector and coworkers (2004) studied this question by measuring brain activation in humans as the participants identified pictures of the face of a well-known person—Harrison Ford. Because the researchers were particularly interested in how neurons in the FFA would respond during this task, they focused on the FFA by using a method called the region-of-interest (ROI) approach.

METHOD ▪ Region-of-Interest Approach

One of the challenges of brain imaging research is that although maps have been published indicating the location of different areas of the brain, there is a great deal of variation from person to person in the exact location of a particular area. The **region-of-interest (ROI) approach** deals with this problem by pretesting people on the stimuli to be studied before running an experiment. For example, in the study we are going to describe, Grill-Spector located the FFA in each observer by presenting pictures of faces and nonfaces and noting the area that was preferentially activated by faces. By locating this ROI before doing the experiment, it was possible to focus on the exact area of the brain, which, *for each individual person,* was specialized to process information about faces.

▪ ▪ ▪

Once Grill-Spector determined the location of the FFA for each observer, she presented stimuli as shown in Figure 5.39. On each trial observers saw either (a) a picture of Harrison Ford, (b) a picture of another person's face, or (c) a random texture. Each of these stimuli was presented briefly (about 50 ms) followed immediately by a random-pattern mask, which limited the visibility of each stimulus to just 50 ms.

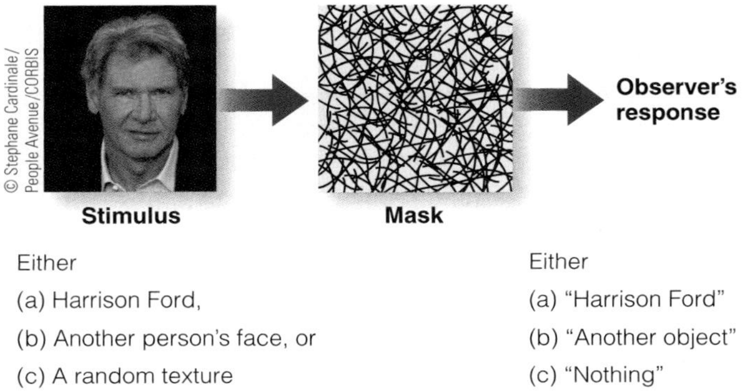

Figure 5.39 ▮ Procedure for the Grill-Spector et al.'s (2004) experiment. See text for details.

METHOD ▪ How to Present a Stimulus Briefly

To present a stimulus, such as a picture, for just 50 ms, we need to do more than just flash the picture for 50 ms because the perception of any stimulus persists for about 250 ms after the stimulus is extinguished—a phenomenon called **persistence of vision**. Thus, a picture that is presented for 50 ms will be *perceived* as lasting 300 ms. To eliminate the persistence of vision it is therefore necessary to flash a **masking stimulus**, which is usually a pattern of randomly oriented lines, immediately after presentation of the picture. This stops the persistence of vision and limits the time that the picture is perceived to 50 ms.

▪ ▪ ▪

The observer's task in this experiment was to indicate, after presentation of the mask, whether the picture was "Harrison Ford," "another object," or "nothing." This is the "observer's response" in Figure 5.39. The results, based on presentation of 60 different pictures of Harrison Ford, 60 pictures of other faces, and 60 random textures, are shown in Figure 5.40. This figure shows the course of brain activation only for the trials in which Harrison Ford's face was presented. The top curve (red) shows that activation was greatest when observers correctly identified the stimulus as Harrison Ford's face. The next curve shows that activation was less when they responded "other object" to Harrison Ford's face. In this case they detected the stimulus as a face but were not able to identify it as Harrison Ford's face. The lowest curve indicates that there was little activation when observers could not even tell that a face was presented.

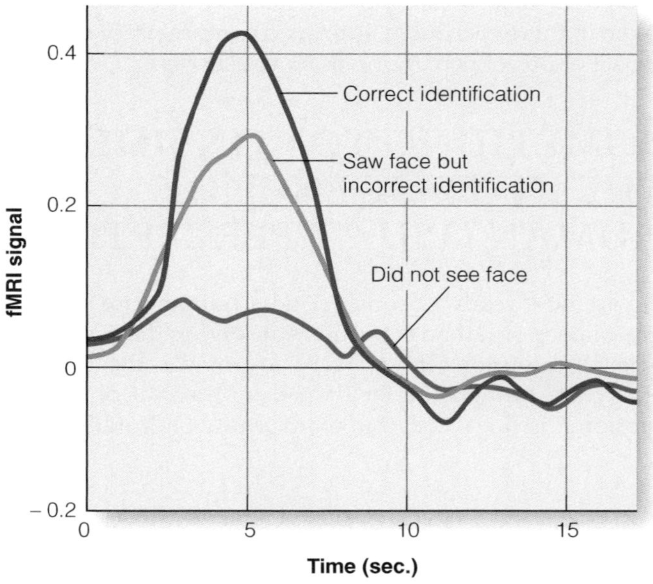

Figure 5.40 ▌ Time-course of brain activation for trials in which Harrison Ford's face was presented.
(Grill-Spector et al., 2004)

This experiment is important because it shows that neural responding is associated not only with the stimulus that is presented, but with the observer's response to the stimulus—in this case, his or her ability to identify or detect the stimulus. *Identifying* the object is associated with a large response, *detecting* an object with a smaller response, and missing the stimulus altogether with the absence of a response.

Identifying an Object: Is That a Cat or a Dog? David Freedman and coworkers (2003) compared the response of the monkey's inferotemporal (IT) and prefrontal (PF) areas. Remember that the IT cortex is concerned with form perception, located in the temporal lobe in the *what* processing stream (Figure 4.13). From the IT cortex, signals travel to the prefrontal (PF) area of the frontal lobe. Freedman's goal was to study how neurons in both the IT and PF areas respond as the monkey recognizes stimuli. To do this, he created two categories of stimuli, "cat" and "dog," using a procedure called morphing.

METHOD ▪ Preparing Stimuli by Morphing

Morphing is a computerized method of combining two stimuli. The basic procedure involves locating corresponding points on two "prototype" stimuli and combining the features that exist at these points in different amounts. You can see the results for a cat prototype and a dog prototype in Figure 5.41, which shows what happens as more and more *dog* is added to *cat*. The stimulus, which starts as 100 percent *cat* on the left, morphs in 5 steps into 100 percent *dog* on the right. The boundary between cat and dog is taken to be the place at which the stimulus becomes more dog than cat. Thus, the left three stimuli in this figure are in the *cat* category, and the right three are in the *dog* category.

▪ ▪ ▪

Freedman used stimuli like the ones in Figure 5.41 to train monkeys to distinguish between the *cat* and *dog* categories using a method called delayed-matching-to-sample.

METHOD ▪ Delayed-Matching-to-Sample

The **delayed-matching-to-sample procedure** is shown in Figure 5.42. The procedure consists of three parts: (1) *The sample period:* Presentation of the "sample" stimulus. In Freedman's experiment this would be either a "dog" or a "cat." (2) *The delay period:* A short delay during which no stimulus is present. In Freedman's experiment the delay was one second long; (3) *The test period:*

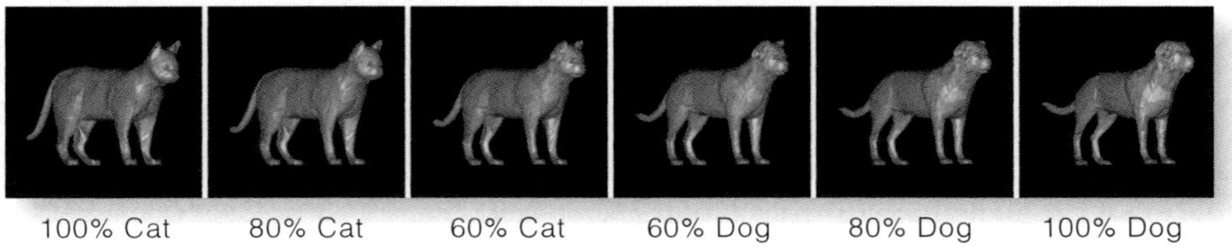

Figure 5.41 ▌ Stimuli for Freedman et al.'s (2003) experiment that were created by morphing an image of a cat and an image of a dog in different proportions.
(From Freedman, D. J. et al., (2003). A comparison of primate prefrontal and inferior temporal cortices during visual categorization. Journal of Neuroscience, 23, *5235–5246.)*

Presentation of a "test" stimulus. This was either a dog or a cat. The monkey's task is to indicate whether or not the test stimulus is in the same category as the sample stimulus.

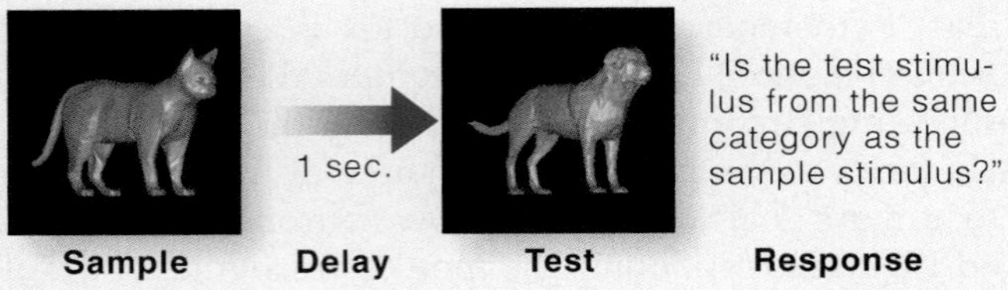

Figure 5.42 ▌ Delayed-matching-to-sample procedure.

■ ■ ■

Freedman applied the delayed-matching-to-sample procedure to his monkeys by training them to release a lever when they judged the test stimulus to be in the same category (either *dog* or *cat*) as the sample stimulus. As the monkeys carried out this task, Freedman recorded the activity of neurons in both IT and PF cortex.

Figure 5.43a shows the results for an IT neuron. The IT neuron responds best when the category *dog* is presented during the sample period, but responds similarly to *dog* and *cat* presented during the test period. Figure 5.43b shows the results for a PF neuron. The PF neuron responds equally to *cat* and *dog* during the sample period, but has a larger response to *dog* during the delay and test periods.

Thus, IT and PF neurons both differentiate between dogs and cats, but under different conditions. The IT neuron responds differently to the *presentation* of cat and dog stimuli (during the sample period), a result we would expect because other research on IT cortex has identified this area as being a module for form perception. However, the PF neuron responds differently when the monkey *remembers* dog and cat stimuli (during the delay) and as the monkey makes a *decision* about the stimuli (during the test period). Thus, the IT neurons are "visual"—they respond to the *perception* of a stimulus, but the PF neurons are "behavioral"—they guide the behavior involved in the matching-to-sample task.

This result therefore demonstrates that saying that a particular area is involved in object perception is just a first step in specifying the physiological processes involved in object perception. The next step, which was taken in this experiment, is to specify more precisely what aspect of object perception that area serves.

SOMETHING TO CONSIDER: THE INTELLIGENCE OF HUMAN OBJECT PERCEPTION

We are now ready to consider why humans are so much more successful than computers at solving the problem of object perception. If we were to answer the question "Why are humans better than computers at object perception?" in one word, that word would be "intelligence."

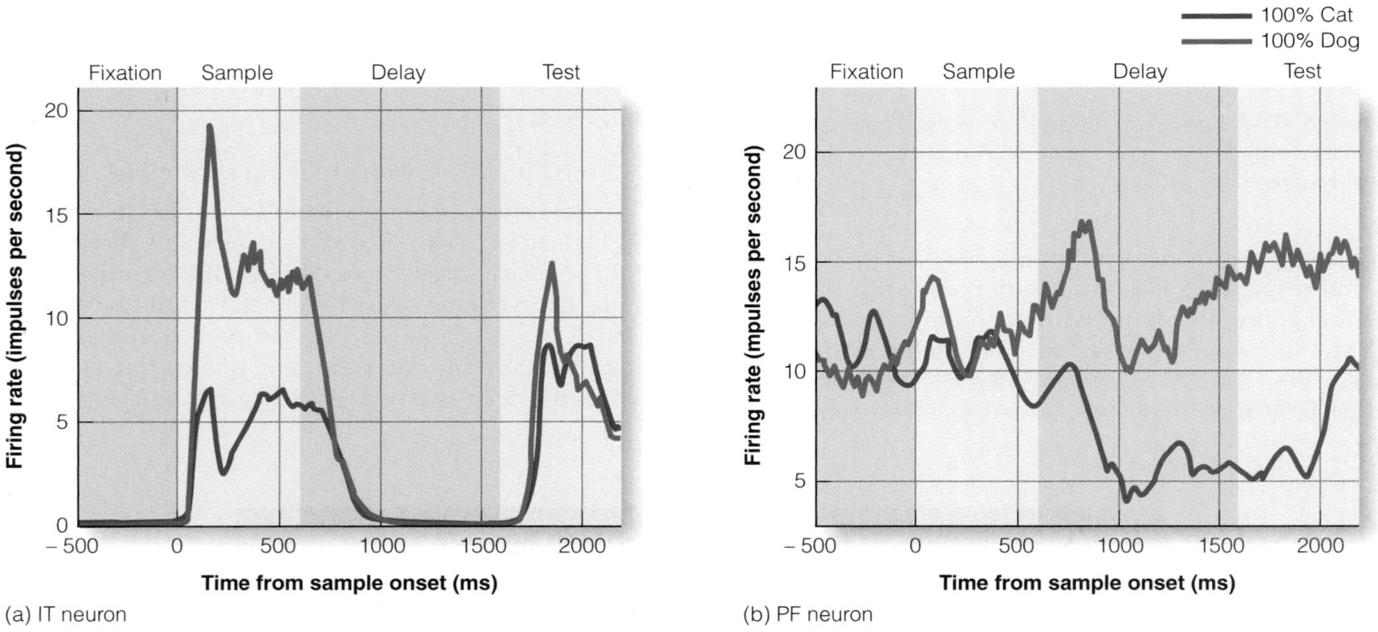

Figure 5.43 ▌ (a) Response of a monkey IT neuron that responds better to a 100-percent dog stimulus (red line) than to a 100-percent cat stimulus (blue) during the "sample" period of the delayed-matching-to-sample task. Other combinations of dog and cat fell between these two extremes. (b) Response of PF neurons to the same stimuli. For this neuron, the response to dog is greater during the delay and test periods.

The process of human perception includes not only the automatic functioning of receptors and neural circuits, but it also involves a "behavioral intelligence," based on our knowledge of the characteristics of the environment, and a "physiological intelligence," based on how our perceptual system is physiologically tuned to our environment.

Early Ideas About Perceptual Intelligence

The idea that human perception is intelligent is not new. We can trace its origins back to Hermann von Helmholtz (1866/1911) who, as professor of physiology at the University of Heidelberg (1858) and professor of physics at the University of Berlin (1871), was one of the preeminent physiologists and physicists of his day. He made many basic discoveries in physiology and physics. In addition, he developed the ophthalmoscope (the device that an optometrist or ophthalmologist uses to look into your eye) and proposed theories of object perception, color vision, and hearing. One of his proposals about perception is a principle called the **theory of unconscious inference**, which states that some of our perceptions are the result of unconscious assumptions that we make about the environment.

The theory of unconscious inference was proposed to account for our ability to create perceptions from stimulus information that can be seen in more than one way. For example, what do you see in the display in Figure 5.44a? Most people perceive a blue rectangle in front of a red rectangle, as shown in Figure 5.44b. But as Figure 5.44c indicates, this display could have been caused by a 6-sided red shape positioned either in front of or behind the blue rectangle. According to the theory of unconscious inference, we infer that Figure 5.44a is a rectangle covering another rectangle because of experiences we have had with similar situations in the past. A corollary of the theory of unconscious inference is the **likelihood principle**, which states that we perceive the object that is *most likely* to have caused the pattern of stimuli we have received.

One reason Helmholtz proposed the likelihood principle is to deal with the ambiguity of the perceptual stimulus that we described at the beginning of the chapter. Helmholtz therefore viewed the process of perception as being similar to the process involved in solving a problem. For perception, the task is to determine which object caused a particular pattern of stimulation, and this problem is solved by a process in which the observer brings his or her knowledge of the environment to bear in order to infer what the object might be. This process is unconscious, hence the term "unconscious inference." According to this idea, we automatically use intelligence to perceive because it is built into our perceptual system (see Rock, 1983, for a modern version of this idea).

This idea of behavioral intelligence is related to the Gestalt heuristics because these "best guess" rules for perception are part of the intelligent "toolbox" that our perceptual system uses to infer what is in the environment.

Modern Ideas About Perceptual Intelligence

We will now present a few examples of how the perceptual system behaves intelligently that are based on modern research on perception. First, let's consider an experiment by Steven Palmer (1975), which used the stimuli in Figure 5.45. Palmer first presented a context scene such as the one on the left and then briefly flashed one of the target pictures on the right. When Palmer asked observers to identify the object in the target picture, they correctly identified an object like the loaf of bread (which is appropriate to the kitchen scene) 80 percent of the time, but correctly identified the mailbox or the drum (two objects that don't fit into the scene) only 40 percent of the time. This experiment shows how people's knowledge of the context provided by a particular scene can influence perception.

An illustration of perceptual intelligence that involves the way illumination affects our perception of objects is illustrated by the following demonstration.

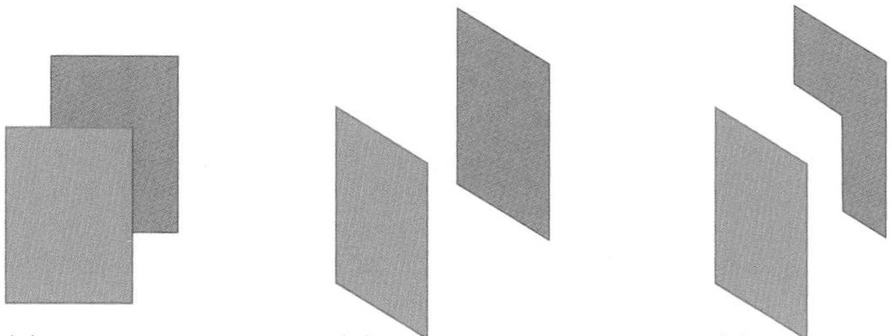

Figure 5.44 ▌ The display in (a) looks like (b)—a blue rectangle in front of a red rectangle—but it could be (c), a blue rectangle and an appropriately positioned 6-sided red figure. *(From Freedman, D. J. et al., (2003). A comparison of primate prefrontal and inferior temporal cortices during visual categorization.* Journal of Neuroscience, 23, *5235–5246.)*

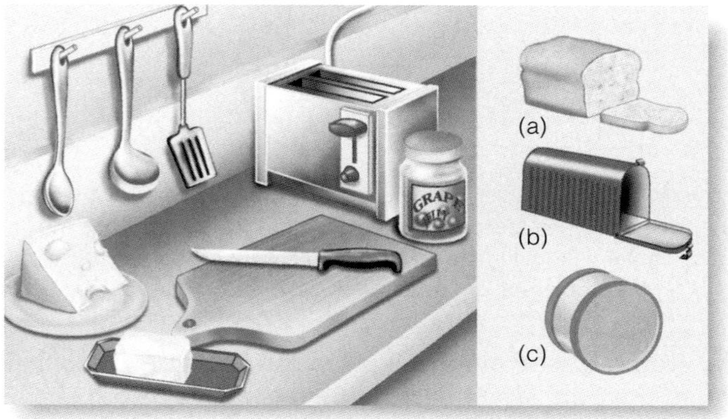

Figure 5.45 ▌ Stimuli used in Palmer's (1975) experiment. The scene at the left is presented first, and the observer is then asked to identify one of the objects on the right.

DEMONSTRATION

Shape From Shading

What do you perceive in Figure 5.46a? Do some of the discs look like they are sticking out, like parts of three-dimensional spheres, and others appear to be indentations? If you do see the discs in this way, notice that the ones that appear to be sticking out are arranged in a square. After observing this, turn the page over so the dot is on the bottom. Does this change your perception?

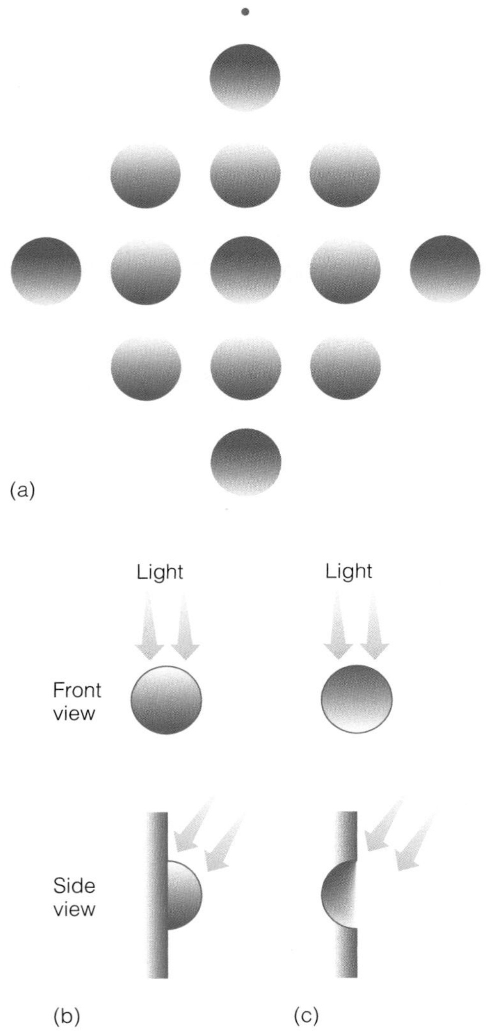

Figure 5.46 ▮ (a) Some of these discs are perceived as jutting out, and some are perceived as indentations. (b) Light coming from above will illuminate the top of a shape that is jutting out, and (c) the bottom of an indentation. ■

You can see from the explanation in Figure 5.46b and c that if we are assuming that light is coming from above (which is usually the case in the environment), then patterns like the circles that are light on the top would be created by an object that bulges out (Figure 5.46b), but a pattern like the circles that are light on the bottom would be created by an indentation in a surface (Figure 5.46c).

The assumption that light is coming from above has been called the **light-from-above heuristic** (Kleffner & Ramachandran, 1992). Apparently, people make the light-from-above assumption because most light in our environment comes from above. This includes the sun, as well as most artificial light sources.

Another example of the light-from-above heuristic at work is provided by the two pictures in Figure 5.47. Figure 5.47a shows indentations created by people walking in the sand. But when we turn this picture upside down, as shown in Figure 5.47b, then the indentations in the sand become mounds of sand. VL 20

The idea that human perception is intelligent brings us back to the race across the desert we described at the beginning of the chapter. One of the reasons that so many of the vehicles failed to finish the race was that they lacked the intelligence that humans automatically bring to the process of perception. The recent success of four vehicles in the second race indicates that computer-guided robots can be programmed to stay on course and avoid obstacles. Robots that can do other things that humans accomplish easily, such as indentifying faces from different angles and identifying objects in cluttered scenes, will need to somehow duplicate the perceptual intelligence that enables humans to perceive, recognize, and act on objects in the environment.

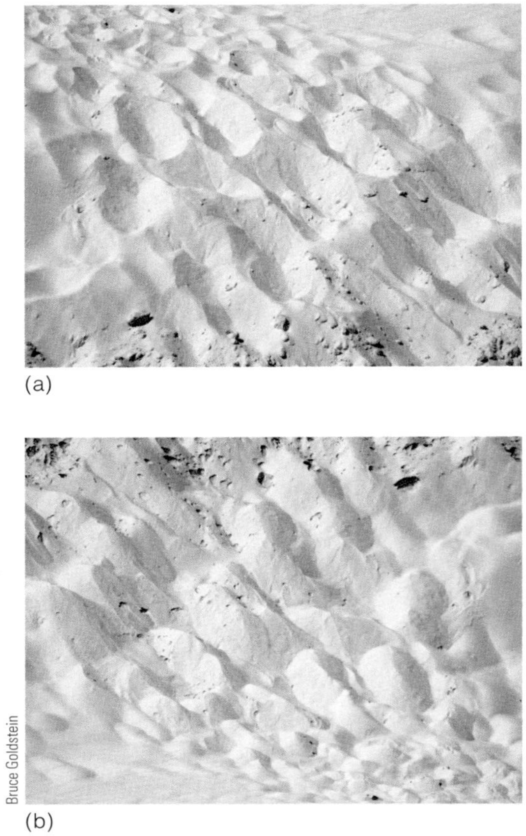

Figure 5.47 ▮ Why does (a) look like indentations in the sand and (b) look like mounds of sand? See text for explanation.

TEST YOURSELF 5.2

1. What does it mean to say that our perceptual system has been shaped by properties of the environment? In answering this question, consider how the Gestalt heuristics reflect regularities of the environment and how these regularities have been studied both behaviorally and physiologically by modern researchers.
2. Why would it be incorrect to state that figure–ground segregation must occur before an object can be recognized?
3. How do volumetric features deal with the viewpoint invariance problem according to RBC theory? How do structural-description and image-description theories deal with this problem?
4. Describe the physiological research that demonstrated a connection between the response of neurons in the FFA and identifying and detecting an object, and research that compared the responding of neurons in IT and PF areas of the monkey's cortex.
5. What does it mean to say that perception is "intelligent"? Describe how the idea of perceptual intelligence is related to Helmholtz's principle of unconscious inference, the Gestalt heuristics, and some modern demonstrations of perceptual intelligence.

THINK ABOUT IT

1. This chapter describes a number of perceptual heuristics, including the Gestalt "laws" and the light-from-above heuristic. Think of some other heuristics—either perceptual or from some other area—that help you solve problems quickly using "best guess" rules.
2. Consider this situation: We saw in Chapter 1 that top-down processing occurs when perception is affected by the observer's knowledge and expectations. Of course, this knowledge is stored in neurons and groups of neurons in the brain. In this chapter, we saw that there are neurons that have become tuned to respond to specific characteristics of the environment. We could therefore say that some knowledge of the environment is built into these neurons. Thus, if a particular perception occurs because of the firing of these tuned neurons, does this qualify as top-down processing?
3. Reacting to the results of the recent DARPA race, Harry says, "Well, we've finally shown that computers can perceive as well as people." How would you respond to this statement?
4. Biological evolution caused our perceptual system to be tuned to the Stone Age world in which we evolved. Given this fact, how do we handle activities like downhill skiing or driving, which are very recent additions to our behavioral repertoire?
5. Vecera showed that regions in the lower part of a stimulus are more likely to be perceived as figure. How does this result relate to the idea that our visual system is tuned to regularities in the environment?
6. The sky is an excellent source of displays that illustrate perceptual organization and figure–ground segregation. For example, when you look at Figure 5.48, you may see the mountains and clouds as figure. But can you identify a "bird" shape in the blue area between the clouds and the mountains? When you do this, the blue area becomes figure. See if you can identify meaningful patterns in the clouds and sky and relate them to familiarity and other laws of organization.

Bruce Goldstein

Figure 5.48 ▌ Which areas do you see as figure and which as ground in this scene? Does this situation change if you perceive the area of sky between the clouds and the mountain as the profile of a bird?

7. What is the picture in Figure 5.49? What does the process you go through as you answer this question tell you about "perceptual intelligence" in general? What

D. W. Gates

Figure 5.49 ▌ What is this?

perceptual assumptions influenced your response to this picture? How is top-down processing involved in your interpretation of this picture?

IF YOU WANT TO KNOW MORE

1. ***Robotic Vehicles.*** To find out more about the vehicles that were entered in the second DARPA race, go to http://www.grandchallenge.org or search for DARPA on the internet.

2. ***Perceiving Figure and Ground.*** When you look at the vase–face pattern in Figure 5.24, you can perceive two blue faces on a white background or a white vase on a blue background, but it is difficult to see the faces and the vase simultaneously. It has been suggested that this occurs because of a heuristic built into the visual system that takes into account the unlikelihood that two adjacent objects would have the same contours and would line up perfectly.

Baylis, G. C., & Driver, J. (1995). One-sided edge assignment in vision: I. Figure-ground segmentation and attention to objects. *Current Directions in Psychological Science 4,* 140–146.

3. ***Global Precedence.*** When a display consists of a large object that is made up of smaller elements, what is processed first by the nervous system, the large object or the smaller elements? An effect called the global precedence effect suggests that the larger object is processed first. An experiment illustrating this effect is included in the Virtual Lab.

Navon, D. (1977). Forest before trees: The precedence of global features in visual perception. *Cognitive Psychology, 9,* 353–383. VL 21

KEY TERMS

Accidental property (p. 109)
Algorithm (p. 102)
Apparent movement (p. 98)
Binocular rivalry (p. 111)
Border ownership (p. 104)
Contextual modulation (p. 106)
Delayed-matching-to-sample procedure (p. 113)
Discriminability (p. 110)
Feedback (p. 106)
Figure (p. 103)
Figure–ground segregation (p. 103)
Geons (p. 109)
Gestalt psychology (p. 97)
Ground (p. 103)
Heuristic (p. 102)
Illusory contour (p. 98)
Image-description model (p. 110)
Inverse projection problem (p. 95)
Law of common fate (p. 100)
Law of familiarity (p. 100)
Law of good continuation (p. 100)
Law of good figure (p. 99)
Law of pragnanz (p. 99)
Law of proximity, or nearness (p. 100)
Law of similarity (p. 99)
Law of simplicity (p. 99)
Laws of perceptual organization (p. 99)
Light-from-above heuristic (p. 116)
Likelihood principle (p. 115)
Masking stimulus (p. 112)
Morphing (p. 113)
Oblique effect (p. 107)
Perceptual organization (p. 99)
Perceptual segregation (p. 103)
Persistence of vision (p. 112)
Principle of common region (p. 101)
Principle of componential recovery (p. 110)
Principle of synchrony (p. 102)
Principle of uniform connectedness (p. 102)
Recognition-by-components theory (p. 109)
Region-of-interest (ROI) approach (p. 112)
Regularities in the environment (p. 107)
Reversible figure–ground (p. 103)
Sensation (p. 97)
Structural-description model (p. 108)
Structuralism (p. 97)
Theory of unconscious inference (p. 115)
View-invariant properties (p. 109)
Viewpoint invariance (p. 96)
Volumetric feature (p. 108)

VISIT YOUR COMPANION WEBSITE FOR THIS BOOK

http://psychology.wadsworth.com/goldstein7e

Check out this companion website where you'll find online resources—glossary, flashcards, web links, multiple-choice and essay questions, and much more!

VIRTUAL LAB

Your Virtual Lab is designed to help you get the most out of this course. The Virtual Lab icons direct you to specific media demonstrations and experiments designed to help you visualize what you are reading about. The number beside each icon indicates the number of the media element you can access through your CD-ROM, Perception PsychologyNow, or WebTutor resource at http:now.ilrn.com/goldstein_7e.

The following lab exercises cover what you've just learned in this chapter:

1 *Linear and Curved Illusory Contours* Examples of how characteristics of illusory contour display affects contours.

2 *Enhancing Illusory Contours* How adding components to a display can enhance illusory contours.

3 *Illusory Contours* Illusory contours that create a square, a triangle, and a cube.

4 *Necker Cube* A solid figure that appears in two different ways as you continue to view it.

5 *Schröder Stairs* A picture of a staircase that can be perceived in two different ways.

6 *Rabbit–Duck Demonstration* A demonstration that can be perceived either as a rabbit or a duck.

7 *Young Woman–Old Woman* A picture that can be perceived as a young woman or an old woman.

8 *Hering Illusion* How background lines can make straight parallel lines appear two curve outward.

9 *Converse Hering Illusion* How background lines can make straight parallel lines appear to curve inward.

10 *Poggendorf Illusion* An illusion in which interrupting a straight line makes the segments of the look like they don't line up.

11 *Law of Simplicity or Good Figure* A situation in which the law of good figure results in an error of perception.

12 *Law of Similarity* How characteristics of a display cause grouping due to similarity.

13 *Law of Good Continuation* How good continuation influences perceptual organization.

14 *Law of Proximity* How varying the distance between elements influences grouping.

15 *Law of Common Fate* Grouping that occurs due to common movement of stimulus elements.

16 *Law of Closure* The effect of adding small gaps to an object.

17 *Faces–Goblet* A display like the one in Figure 5.24 that can be perceived as either a face or a vase.

18 *Real-World Figure–Ground Ambiguity* A reversible figure–ground display using a real vase.

19 *Figure–Ground Ambiguity* How changing the contrast of a painting influences figure–ground segregation.

20 *Shape From Shading 3D Face* A video that shows a situation in which our assumption about the three-dimensional shape of a face can create an error of perception.

21 *Global Precedence* An experiment to determine reaction times in response to large patterns and smaller elements that make up the large patterns.

HIGHMARK
Heinz
NATIONAL LEAGUE
AMERICAN LEAGUE
FedEx
FedEx
FedEx

CHAPTER

6

VISUAL ATTENTION

Chapter Contents

This photo of PNC Park shows a Pittsburgh Pirate game in progress and the city in the background. The yellow fixation dots and red lines indicate eye movements that show where one person looked in the first three seconds of viewing this picture. The eye-movement record indicates that this person first looked just above the right field bleachers and then scanned the ball game. Another person might have looked somewhere else, depending on his or her interests and what attracted his or her attention.

(Eye movement record courtesy of John Henderson.)

Photo by Bruce Goldstein

VL *The Virtual Lab icons direct you to specific animations and videos designed to help you visualize what you are reading about. The number beside each icon indicates the number of the clip you can access through your CD-ROM or your student website.*

Some Questions We Will Consider:

- *Why do we pay attention to some parts of a scene but not to others? (p. 122)*
- *Do we have to pay attention to something to perceive it? (p. 125)*
- *Does paying attention to an object make the object "stand out"? (p. 129)*

Look at the picture on the left, below (Figure 6.1). Count the number of trees, and then immediately read the caption below the picture.

It is likely that you could describe the picture on the left so much more accurately and in greater detail than the one on the right (Figure 6.2). This isn't surprising because you were looking directly at the trees, and not at the hikers. The point of this exercise is that in our everyday perception of our environment, we pay attention to some things and ignore others. We decide that it would be interesting or necessary to look here but not there. And as we shift our gaze from one place to another, we are doing more than just "looking," we are directing our **attention** on specific features of the environment in a way that causes these features to become more deeply processed than those features that are not receiving our attention.

To understand perception as it happens in the real world, we need to go beyond just considering how we perceive isolated objects. We need to consider how observers seek out stimuli, how they perceive some things and not others, and how these active processes shape our perception of these objects and things around them.

We begin by considering the selective nature of attention—the way we attend to some things and ignore others. We then consider two questions: (1) Is attention necessary for perception? and (2) Does attention enhance perception? After describing how researchers have tried to answer these questions, we will consider the idea that attention provides the "glue" that enables us to perceive a coherent, meaningful visual world. Finally, we will describe the connection between attention and neural firing.

ATTENTION AND PERCEIVING THE ENVIRONMENT

In everyday life we often have to pay attention to a number of things at once, a situation called **divided attention.** For example, as you drive down the road, you need to simultaneously attend to the other cars around you, traffic signals, and perhaps what the person in the passenger seat is saying, while occasionally glancing up at the rearview mirror. But there are limits to our ability to divide our attention. For example, reading your textbook while driving would most likely end in disaster. Although divided attention is something that does occur in our everyday experience, our main interest in this chapter will be **selective attention**—focusing on specific objects and ignoring others.

Why Is Selective Attention Necessary?

Why do we selectively focus on some things and ignore others? One possible answer is that we look at things that are interesting. Although that may be true, there is another, more basic, answer. You selectively focus on certain things in your environment because your visual system has been constructed to operate in that way.

Bruce Goldstein

Figure 6.1 ▮ How many trees are there? After counting the trees, and without moving your eyes from the picture, indicate how many of the first four hikers in the picture on the right are males.

Bruce Goldstein

Figure 6.2 ▮ Although you may have noticed that this is an outdoor scene with people walking on a road, it is necessary to focus your attention on the lead hikers to determine if they are males or females.

We can appreciate why attending to only a portion of the environment is necessary by returning to Ellen as she is walking in the woods (see Figure 1.2). As she looks out at the scene before her, millions of her receptors are stimulated, and these receptors send signals out of her eyes and toward the LGN and cortex. The problem the visual system faces is that there is so much information leaving Ellen's retina that if the visual system had to deal with all of it, it would rapidly become overloaded. To deal with this problem, the visual system is designed to select only a small part of this information to process and analyze.

One of the mechanisms that helps achieve this selection is the structure of the retina, which contains the all-cone fovea (see page 32). This area supports detail vision, so we must aim the fovea directly at objects we want to see clearly. In addition, remember that information imaged on the fovea receives a disproportionate amount of processing compared to information that falls outside of the fovea because of the magnification factor in the cortex (see page 73).

How Is Selective Attention Achieved?

One mechanism of selective attention is eye movements —scanning a scene to aim the fovea at places we want to process more deeply. As we will see below, the eye is moving constantly to take in information from different parts of a scene. But even though eye movements are an important mechanism of selective attention, it is also important to acknowledge that there is more to attention than just moving the eyes to look at objects. We can pay attention to things that are not directly on our line of vision, as evidenced by the basketball player who dribbles down court while paying attention to a teammate off to the side, just before she throws a dead-on pass without looking. In addition, we can look directly at something without paying attention to it. You may have had this experience: While reading a book, you become aware that although you were moving your eyes across the page and "reading" the words, you had no idea what you had just read. Even though you were looking at the words, you apparently were not paying attention.

What the examples of the basketball player and reader are telling us is that there is a *mental* aspect of attention that occurs in addition to eye movements. This connection between attention and what is happening in the mind was described over 100 years ago by William James (1890), in his textbook *Principles of Psychology:*

> Millions of items . . . are present to my senses which never properly enter my experience. Why? Because they have no interest for me. My experience is what I agree to attend to. . . . Everyone knows what attention is. It is the taking possession by the mind, in clear and vivid form, of one out of what seem several simultaneously possible objects or trains of thought. . . . It implies withdrawal from some things in order to deal effectively with others.

Thus, according to James, we focus on some things to the exclusion of others. As you walk down the street, the things that you pay attention to—a classmate that you recognize, the "Don't Walk" sign at a busy intersection, and the fact that just about everyone, except you, seems to be carrying an umbrella—stand out more than many other things in the environment. One of our concerns in this chapter is to explain why attention causes some things to stand out more than others. The first step in doing this is to describe the eye movements that guide our eyes to different parts of a scene.

Scanning a Scene

The first task in the study of eye movements is to devise a way to measure them. Early researchers measured eye movements using devices such as small mirrors and lenses that were attached to the eyes, so the cornea had to be anesthetized (Yarbus, 1967). However, modern researchers use camera-based eye trackers, like the one in Figure 6.3, that track the position of the eye without attaching anything to the eye (Henderson, 2003; Morimoto & Mimica, 2005).

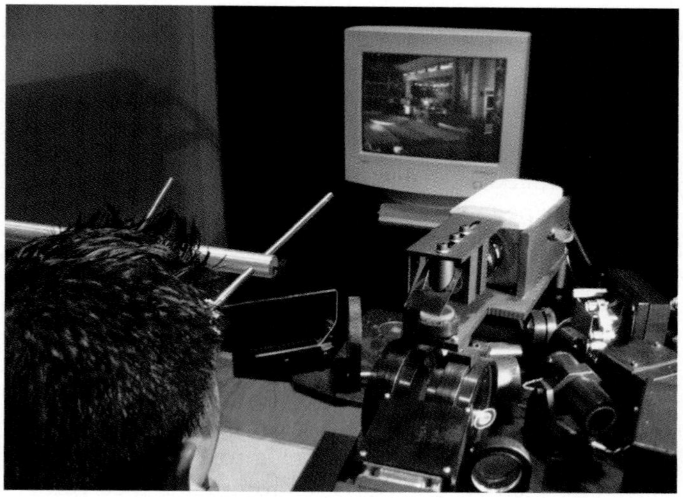

Figure 6.3 ■ A person looking at a stimulus-picture in a camera-based eye tracker.
(Reprinted from Trends in Cognitive Sciences, *7, Henderson, J. M., Human gaze control during real-world scene perception, 498–503, (2003), with permission from Elsevier.)*

The eye movements shown in Figure 6.4 and the chapter-opening picture on page 120 are called **saccades**. The saccades are punctuated by pauses, indicated by the dots, where the eye stops momentarily to take in information about a specific part of the scene. These pauses, which are called **fixations**, indicate where the person is attending. When a person is asked to simply view a scene, he or she typically makes about three fixations per second.

What determines where we fixate in a scene? The answer to this question is complicated because our looking behavior depends on a number of factors, including char-

Figure 6.4 ▮ Scan path of a person viewing a picture of a fountain in Bordeaux, France. Fixations are indicated by the yellow dots and eye movements by the red lines. This person looked at high-interest areas of the picture such as the statues and lights but ignored areas such as the fence and the sky. *(Reprinted with permission from John M. Henderson. Scan path for person viewing fountain in Bordeaux, France.)*

(a) Visual scene

(b) Saliency map

Figure 6.5 ▮ (a) A visual scene. (b) Salience map of the scene determined by analyzing the color, contrast, and orientations in the scene. Lighter areas indicate greater salience. *(Reprinted from* Vision Research, 42, *Parkhurst, D., Law, K., & Niebur, E., Modeling the Role of Salience in the Allocation of Overt Visual Attention, 107–123 (2002) with permission from Elsevier.)*

acteristics of the scene and the knowledge and goals of the observer.

Characteristics of the Scene In Figure 6.5a, certain areas stand out because they are brightly colored, have high contrast, or have highly visible orientations. These areas are described as having high **stimulus salience**—they are conspicuous and therefore attract attention based on their stimulus properties.

Capturing attention by stimulus salience is a bottom-up process—it depends solely on the pattern of stimulation falling on the receptors as opposed to the meaningfulness of the images. By taking into account three characteristics of the displays in Figure 6.5a—color, contrast, and orientation—Derrick Parkhurst and coworkers (2002) created the **saliency map** in Figure 6.5b. To determine whether observers' fixations were controlled by stimulus saliency as indicated by the map, Parkhurst measured where people fixated when presented with various pictures. He found that the initial fixations were closely associated with the saliency map, with fixations being more likely on high-saliency areas. As people continued to view the pictures, other factors—such as the meanings of the objects in the pictures—apparently begin influencing scanning, especially for meaningful pictures such as the one in Figure 6.5a.

Picture Meaning and Observer Knowledge Once an observer understands the meaning of a scene, then his or her knowledge of characteristics of a specific type of scene can influence the observer's eye movements. This knowledge can take the form of a **scene schema**—knowledge about what is contained in typical scenes. An example of a scene schema is an "office schema," which includes the knowledge that an office usually contains a computer, books, and a desk. This knowledge can help guide fixations from one area of a scene to another. In addition, people fixate more often on particularly meaningful areas of pictures, such as human faces, than empty areas.

The Observer's Task A recent advance in eye-tracker technology is the development of lightweight, head-mounted eye trackers, which make it possible to determine a person's fixations and eye movements as they perform tasks in the environment. This device has enabled researchers to show that when a person is carrying out a task, the demands of the task override factors such as stimulus saliency. Figure 6.6 shows the fixations and eye movements that occurred as a person was making a peanut butter sandwich. The process of making the sandwich begins with the transfer of a slice of bread from the bag to the plate. Notice that this operation is accompanied by an eye movement. The peanut butter jar is then fixated, and it is then lifted and moved to the front as its lid is removed. The knife is then fixated just before it is picked up to scoop the peanut butter and spread it on the bread (M. F. Land & Hayhoe, 2001).

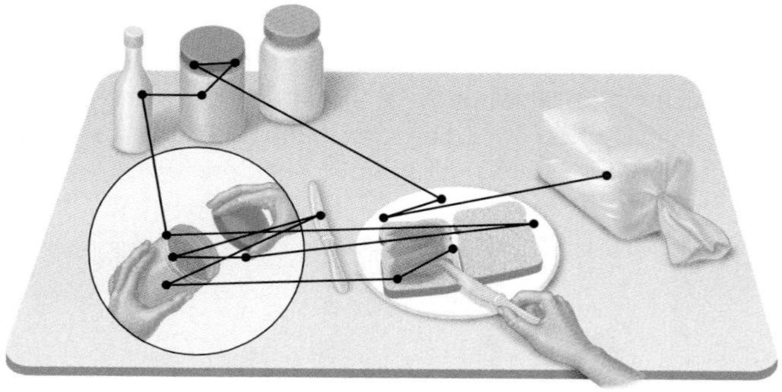

Figure 6.6 ▌ Sequence of fixations of a person making a peanut butter sandwich. The first fixation is on the loaf of bread. (From Land & Hayhoe, 2001.)

The key finding of these measurements, and also of another experiment in which eye movements were measured as a person prepared tea (M. F. Land et al., 1999), was that the person's eye movements were driven primarily by the task. The person did not fixate on objects or areas that were irrelevant to the task. Furthermore, the eye movement usually preceded a motor action by a fraction of a second. For example, the person first fixated the peanut butter jar and then reached over to pick it up.

Because a number of factors are involved in determining where a person looks, it isn't surprising that there is a good deal of individual variation in the way pictures are scanned. Although it is often possible to predict *where* in a particular picture people will fixate, it is more difficult to predict the *order* in which things will be fixated because of this variability from person to person.

IS ATTENTION NECESSARY FOR PERCEPTION?

Although there is no question that attention is a major mechanism of perception, many researchers have gone beyond saying that attention is *important* for perception, and make the assertion that attention is *necessary* for perception. We will see that there is evidence that supports this idea, but before we describe it, let's consider evidence indicating that we can take in some information even from scenes we don't attend to or attend to only slightly.

When Can Perception Occur Without Attention?

When observers are shown a scene for just a fraction of a second—so they are essentially perceiving the scene as a whole, without having time to make any eye movements—they can perceive the "gist" of the scene. Thus, when pictures such as a kitchen scene or a landscape are presented for 100 ms, followed by a mask (see Method, p. 112), observers can identify the scenes as "a kitchen" or "a farm," although they cannot identify small details within the scene (Biederman, 1981; Schyns & Oliva, 1994).

A recent demonstration of perception without focused attention has been provided by Fei Fei Li and coworkers (2002), who showed that we can take in information from a rapidly presented photograph that is located off to the side from where we are attending. Li's observers were asked to focus their attention at the center of a display where five letters would be flashed (Figure 6.7).

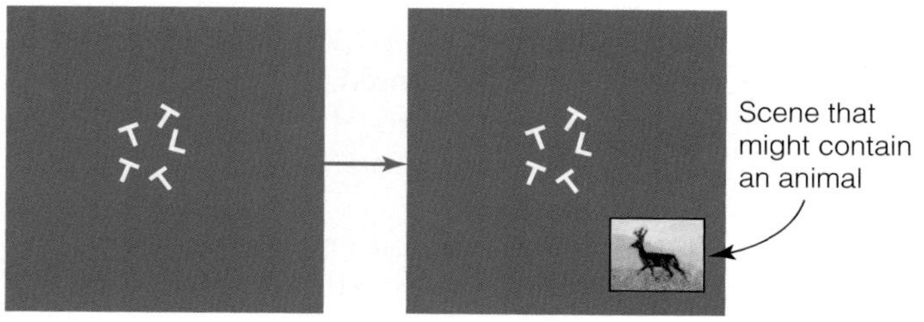

Figure 6.7 ▌ Stimulus similar to those used by Li et al. (2002). See text for procedure.

Their task was to decide, as quickly as possible, whether all five letters were the same or whether one of the letters was different. Almost immediately after the letters appeared, a photograph of an environmental scene was flashed off to the side for 27 ms, followed by a mask, at a different position on each trial. Even though the observers' attention was directed away from the photograph by the letter task, and even though the photograph was flashed so briefly that eye movements were not possible, observers were able to correctly indicate whether an animal was present in the photograph in 76 percent of the trials (50 percent would be chance performance, because animals were present in half of the pictures). Another experiment using a similar procedure has shown that it is possible to identify photographs of faces as male or female when they are presented for only 150 ms (Reddy et al., 2004).

You could argue that it might be possible to pay attention even when images are presented briefly and off to the side. However, because observers were required to focus attention on the letter-discrimination task and did not know where the pictures would be flashed, it is likely that attention was nearly absent in these experiments, and that observers were not able to *focus* their attention on the environmental scenes or faces. Thus, it is safe to conclude that some perception is possible even in the absence of focused attention.

When Is Attention Necessary for Perception?

Our ability to see the "gist" of a scene even when it is presented briefly or off to the side, is an important skill, but there is a great deal of evidence that when it comes to determining specific details, focused attention is necessary. This has been illustrated in a number of ways.

Inattentional Blindness **Inattentional blindness** occurs when a stimulus that is not attended is not perceived, even though a person is looking directly at it. Arien Mack and Irvin Rock (1998) demonstrated this effect using the procedure shown in Figure 6.8. The observer's task is to indicate which arm of the cross is longer, the horizontal or the vertical. Then, on the inattention trial of the series, a small test object, which is within the observer's field of clear vision, is added to the display. When observers are then given a recognition test in which they are asked to pick the object that was presented, they are unable to do so. Paying attention to the vertical and horizontal arms apparently made observers "blind" to the unattended test object.

VIRTUAL LAB 1

Mack demonstrated inattentional blindness using rapidly flashed geometrical test stimuli. But other research has shown that similar effects can be achieved using more naturalistic stimuli that are presented for longer periods of time.

Imagine looking at a display in a department store window. When you focus your attention on the display, you will probably fail to notice the reflections on the surface of the window. Shift your attention to the reflections, and you become unaware of the display inside the window. Daniel Simons and Christopher Chabris (1999) created a situation in which one part of a scene is attended and the other is not. They created a 75-second film that showed two teams of three players each, one team that was passing a basketball around, and the other that was "guarding" that team by following them around as in a basketball game. Observers were told to count the number of passes, a task that focused their attention on one of the teams. After about 45 seconds, one of two events occurred. Either a woman carrying an umbrella or a person in a gorilla suit walked through the "game," an event that took 5 seconds.

After seeing the video, observers were asked whether they saw anything unusual happen or whether they saw anything other than the six players. Nearly half—46 percent—of the observers failed to report that they saw the woman or the gorilla. In another experiment, when the gorilla stopped in the middle of the action, turned to face the camera, and thumped its chest, half of the observers still failed to notice the gorilla (Figure 6.9). These experiments demonstrate that when observers are attending to one sequence of events, they can fail to notice another event, even when it is right in front of them (also see Goldstein & Fink, 1981; Neisser & Becklen, 1975).

Figure 6.9 ▮ Frame from the "gorilla" film.
(Figure provided by Daniel Simons. Simons, D. J., & Chabris, C. F. (1999). Gorillas in our midst: sustained inattentional blindness for dynamic events. Perception, *28, 1059–1074.)*

Change Detection Following in the footsteps of the superimposed image experiments, researchers developed another way of studying the link between attention and perception. Instead of presenting several stimuli at the

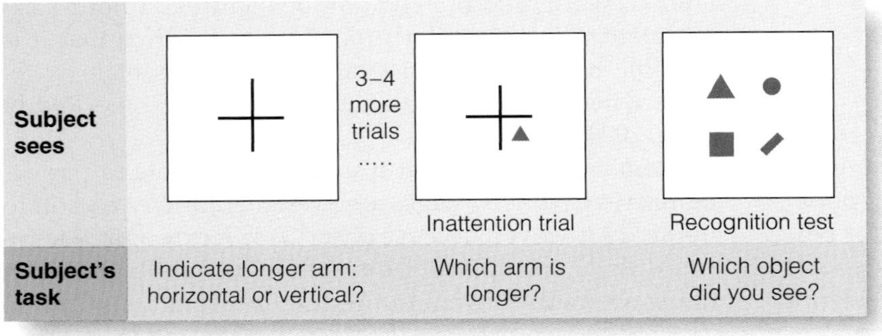

Figure 6.8 ▮ Inattentional blindness experiment. (a) Participants judge whether the horizontal or vertical arm is larger on each trial. (b) After a few trials, a geometrical object is flashed, along with the arms. (c) Then the participant is asked to pick which geometrical stimulus was presented.

same time, they presented stimuli one after another. To appreciate how this works, try the following demonstration.

DEMONSTRATION

Change Detection

When you are finished reading these instructions, look at the picture in Figure 6.10 for just a moment, and then turn the page and see whether you can determine what is different in Figure 6.11. Do this now.

Bruce Goldstein

Figure 6.10 ▮ Stimulus for change-blindness demonstration. See text. ■

Were you able to see what was different in the second picture? People often have trouble detecting the change even though it is obvious when you know where to look. (Try again, paying attention to the lower left portion of the picture.) Ronald Rensink and coworkers (1997) did a similar experiment in which they presented one picture, followed by a blank field, followed by the same picture but with an item missing, followed by the blank field, and so on. The pictures were alternated in this way until observers were able to determine what was different about the two pictures. Rensink found that the pictures had to be alternated back and forth a number of times before the difference was detected. VL 2

This difficulty in detecting changes in scenes is called **change blindness** (Rensink, 2002). The importance of attention (or lack of it) in determining change blindness is demonstrated by the fact that when Rensink added a cue indicating which part of a scene had been changed, participants detected the changes much more quickly (also see Henderson & Hollingworth, 2003; Rensink, 2002).

The change-blindness effect also occurs when the scene changes in different shots of a film. Figure 6.12 shows successive frames from a video of a brief conversation between two women. The noteworthy aspect of this video is that changes take place in each new shot. In Shot B, the woman's scarf has disappeared; in Shot C, the other woman's hand is on her chin, although moments later, in Shot D, both arms are on the table. Also, the plates change color from red in the initial views to white in Shot D.

Although participants who viewed this video were told to pay close attention to the film, only 1 of 10 participants claimed to notice any changes. Even when the participants were shown the video again and were warned that there would be changes in "objects, body position, or clothing," they noticed fewer than a quarter of the changes that occurred (Levin & Simons, 1997).

Change blindness is interesting not only because it illustrates the importance of attention for perception, but also because it is a counterintuitive result. When David Levin (2000) told a group of observers about the changes that occurred in film sequences like the ones in Figure 6.12, and also showed them still shots from the film, 83 percent of the observers predicted that they would notice the changes. However, in experiments in which observers did not know which changes were going to occur, only 11 percent noticed the changes. Thus, even though people *feel* that they would detect such obvious changes, they fail to do so when actually tested. Levin coined the term **change blindness blindness** to describe the fact that people are "blind" to the fact that change blindness will occur.

One reason people think they would see the changes might be that from past experience they know that abrupt changes rarely occur in real life, and when they do occur, they are usually noticed. However, changes that occur in real life are often accompanied by motion, which creates a signal that attracts our attention and provides a cue as to where the change will occur. But in change blindness experiments, the change signal is eliminated by presenting a blank field, or a different film shot, between the two almost-identical stimuli. Thus, attention is not directed to the change, and we miss it (Rensink, 2000).

So these experiments show that by disrupting attention, we miss changes. It also provides another insight about the visual process that is not obvious from our experience. One of the paradoxes of vision is that although you can't make out the details of objects that are off to the side of where you are looking (see Chapter 3, p. 48), the overall scene nonetheless appears to be "sharp" and in focus (Figure 6.13). (If this isn't obvious, look out at an object in your environment and notice how things off to the side appear. Do parts of the scene that are off to the side appear "fuzzy" or "sharp"?)

The observation that the entire scene appears sharp might lead to the impression that the visual system creates a clear representation of the whole scene, however, the results of the change blindness experiments show that this isn't so. The fact that we miss seeing changes that we aren't cued to look for shows that only a small part of the environment is encoded in detail (Noe, 2000).

This lack of a detailed representation of a scene may

seem like a bad thing, but we apparently function quite well without being aware of every detail in our environment. One reason is that we are so familiar with our environment that if we "fill in the blanks" based on our past experiences, we can predict approximately what will be in a particular scene. One of the things that helps us accomplish this "filling in" are the scene schemas we mentioned earlier (office containing a computer, books, and a desk). For example, if we briefly see a scene that includes a gas station, we know, from our schema for "gas station," that there are probably gas pumps in front of the station.

To summarize this section, the answer to the question, "Is attention necessary for perception?" is "No" if we just want to be able to achieve a general awareness of the "gist" of a scene. However, the answer is "Yes" if we need to detect the details within a scene and the details of specific objects in the scene.

Bruce Goldstein

Figure 6.11 ▮ Stimulus for change-blindness demonstration.

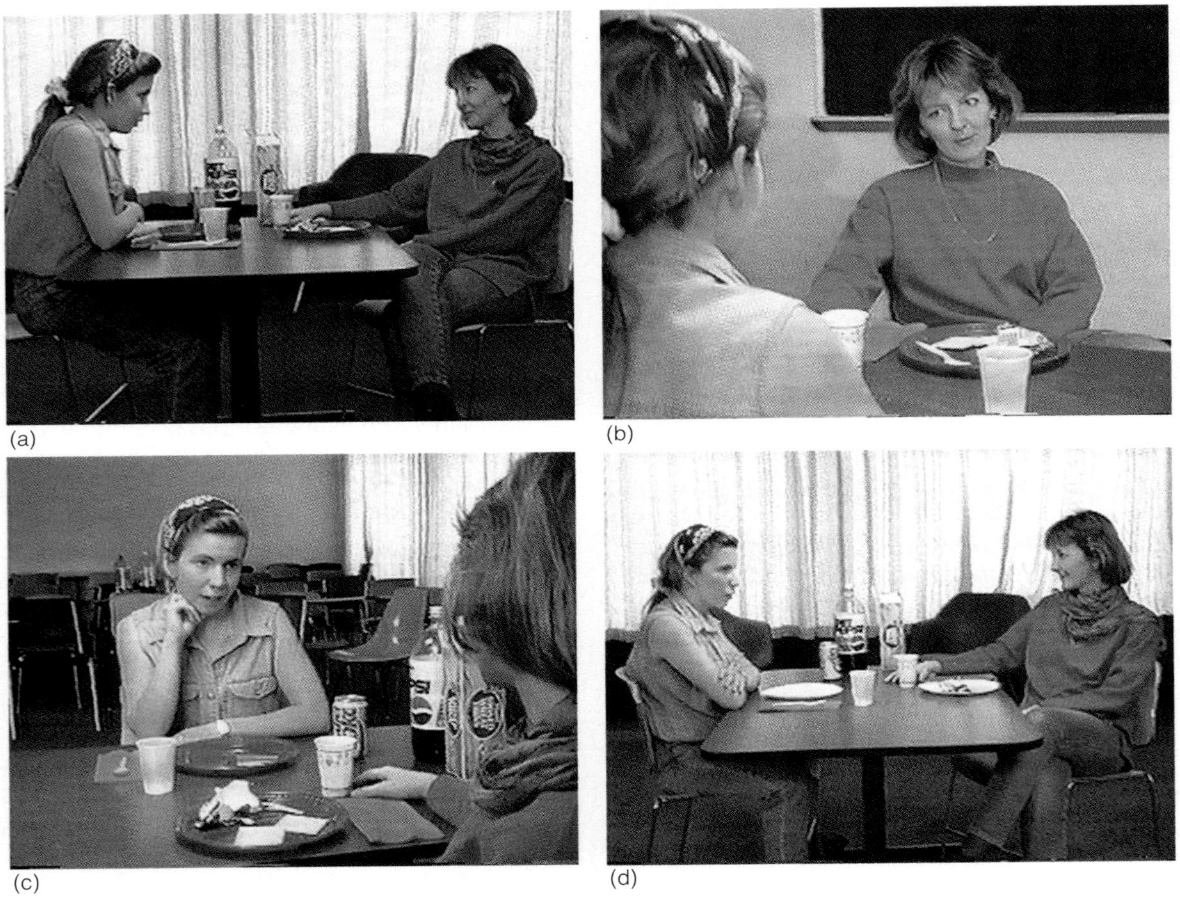

Figure 6.12 ▮ Frames from a video that demonstrates change blindness. The woman on the right is wearing a scarf around her neck in shots A, C, and D, but not in shot B. Also, the color of the plates changes from red in frame C to white in frame D, and the hand position of the woman on the left changes between shots C and D.
(Levin, D. & Simons, D. (1997). Failure to detect changes in attended objects in motion pictures. Psychonomic Bulletin and Review, 4, *501–506.)*

(a)

Bruce Goldstein

(b)

Figure 6.13 ▮ (a) Scene with blur added to simulate the decrease in visual acuity that occurs in the periphery of the visual field. The fixation point is on the woman's face. (b) The same scene without blur. Even though our ability to see details is poor in the periphery, we generally experience the world as being "sharp" rather than blurry. (Blurring courtesy of Stuart Anstis.)

TEST YOURSELF 6.1

1. What are two reasons that we focus on some things and ignore others? Relate your answer to the structure and function of the visual system.
2. What is selective attention? Divided attention?
3. What are the general characteristics of eye movements and fixations?
4. Describe the factors that influence how we direct our attention in a scene.
5. What does it mean to say that perception can occur without focused attention?
6. Describe the following two situations that illustrate that attention is necessary for perception: (1) inattentional blindness; (2) change detection.
7. What is the reasoning behind the idea that change blindness occurs because of a lack of attention? In your answer, indicate how the situation in change blindness experiments differs from the situation in which change occurs in real life.
8. What do the results of change blindness experiments tell us about the nature of the visual system's representation of the environment?

DOES ATTENTION ENHANCE PERCEPTION?

William James, whose statement at the beginning of this chapter described attention as withdrawing from some things in order to deal effectively with others, did no experiments. Thus, many of the statements he made in his book *Principles of Psychology* were based purely on James's psychological insights. What is amazing about these insights is that many of them were correct. This is the case for James's idea that attending to a stimulus makes it more "clear and vivid." However, only recently have we been able to confirm this idea based on experimental evidence. We will consider this evidence by first describing some experiments showing that paying attention increases our ability to react rapidly to a stimulus.

Effects of Attention on Information Processing

Michael Posner and coworkers (1980) developed a procedure called **precueing** to answer the question: Does attention to a specific location improve processing of a stimulus presented at that location? Figure 6.14 shows the stimulus display used for the precueing procedure. Observers looked at a small square flanked by two lights on each side. Initially none of the lights were turned on, but at the beginning of a trial, a *cueing* signal was flashed inside the square that indicated which light was going to be turned on (Figure 6.14a). One second later, one of the lights off to the side was illuminated (usually the one that was indicated by the cueing signal, but occasionally a light at another position was illuminated) (Figure 6.14b). The observers' task was to push a button as soon as they saw the light.

The result of this experiment was that observers responded faster when the light appeared at the location indicated by the cueing signal than when it appeared at the

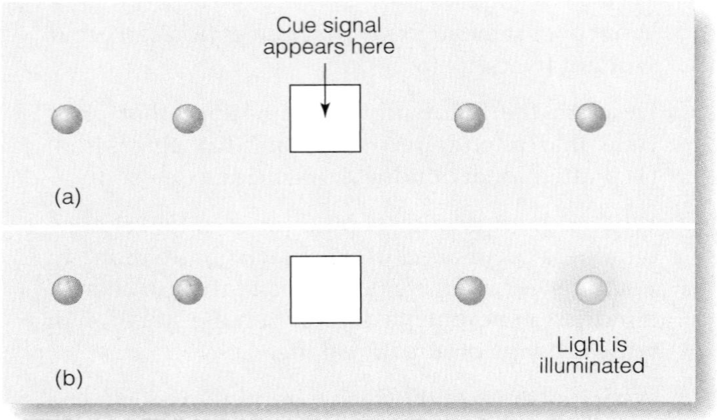

Figure 6.14 ▮ (a) In Posner et al.'s (1980) precueing procedure, a cue signal inside the square indicates where the light will be flashed. (b) Then one of the lights is illuminated.

different locations, even though they had kept their eyes fixed steadily on the small box. Posner interpreted this result not in terms of perception, but in terms of information processing. The precueing result, according to Posner, shows that information processing is more efficient at the place where attention is directed.

There is additional evidence that attention enhances information processing. When attention is directed to one place on an object, the enhancing effect of this attention spreads throughout the object. This idea was demonstrated in an experiment by Robert Egly and coworkers (1994), in which the observer first saw two side-by-side rectangles followed by a cue signal indicating where the target would probably appear (Figure 6.15a). After the cue, the observer pressed a button when the target appeared anywhere in the display (Figure 6.15b). Reaction time was fastest when the target appeared at A, where the cue signal predicted it would appear. However, the most important result of this experiment is that observers responded faster when the target appeared at B, which is in the same rectangle as A, than when it appeared at C, which is in the neighboring rectangle. Notice that B's advantage occurs even though B and C are the same distance from A. Apparently, the enhancing effect of attention had spread within the rectangle on the right so even though the cue was at A, some enhancement occurred at B as well.

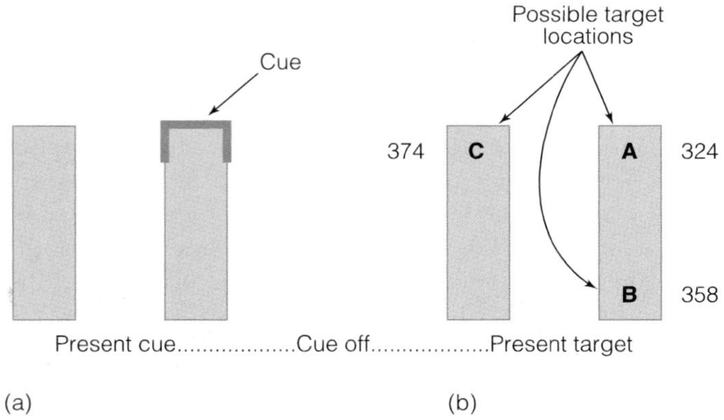

Figure 6.15 ▮ In Egly et al.'s (1994) experiment, (a) a cue signal appears at one place on the display, then (b) a target is flashed. Numbers are reaction times in ms for targets presented at A, B, and C, when the cue appeared at position A.

The same result occurs even when the rectangles are occluded by a horizontal bar, as shown in Figure 6.16a (Moore et al., 1998). This "spreading enhancement" may help us perceive occluded objects, such as our "animal" lurking behind the tree from Chapter 5 (Figure 6.16b). Because the effects of attention spread behind the tree, our awareness spreads throughout the object, thereby enhancing the chances we will interpret the interrupted shape as being a single object. (Also see Baylis & Driver, 1993; Driver & Baylis, 1989, 1998; and Lavie & Driver, 1996, for more demonstrations of how attention spreads throughout objects.)

The above results, which show that attention can enhance information processing, may have implications for perception. However, the experiments we have described do not necessarily support James's suggestion that paying attention to one object alters the *appearance* of the object. We can appreciate this by noting that in these reaction-time tasks, the observer sees the stimulus and then responds by pressing a button. It is possible, therefore, that the stimulus could *appear* identical with or without atten-

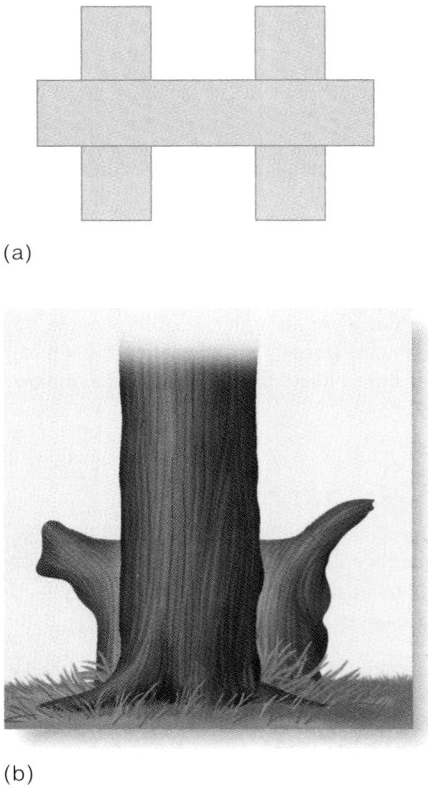

Figure 6.16 ▮ (a) Stimulus in Figure 6.15 but with a horizontal bar added (Moore et al., 1998). (b) Possible animal lurking behind a tree (see Figure 5.23, p. 103).

tion, but that attention could be enhancing the observer's ability to *press the button* quickly. Thus, to answer the question of whether attention affects an object's *appearance,* we need to do an experiment that measures the perceptual response to a stimulus rather than the speed of responding to the stimulus.

Effects of Attention on Perception

One possible way to measure the *perceptual response* to seeing a stimulus is shown in Figure 6.17a. An observer views two stimuli and is instructed to pay attention to one of them and decide whether it is brighter than the other, unattended, stimulus. The stimuli could be presented at different intensities from trial to trial, and the goal would be to determine whether observers report that the attended stimulus appears brighter on trials when the two stimuli have the same intensity.

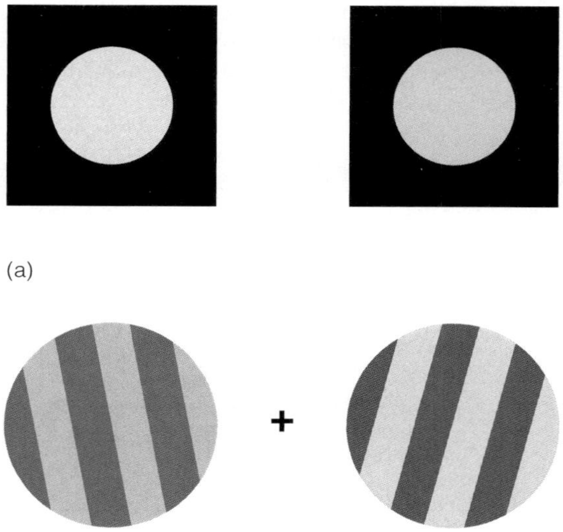

(a)

(b)

Figure 6.17 ▌ (a) Stimuli to measure how attention might affect perception. (b) Stimuli used by Carrasco et al. (2004).

This procedure is a step in the right direction because it focuses on what the observer is seeing rather than on how fast the observer can react to the stimulus. However, can we be sure that the observer is accurately reporting his or her perceptions? If the observer has a preconception that paying attention to a stimulus should make it stand out more, this might influence the observer to report that the attended stimulus appears brighter, when, in reality, the two stimuli may appear equally bright (Luck, 2004).

A recent study by Marissa Carrasco and coworkers (2004) has eliminated this possible source of bias by devising a clever procedure that avoids directly asking the observer to judge the object's appearance. Carrasco used grating stimuli with alternating light and dark bars, like the one in Figure 6.17b. She was interested in determining whether attention enhanced the *perceived contrast* between the bars. Higher perceived contrast would mean that there would appear to be an enhanced difference between the light and dark bars. However, instead of asking observers to judge the contrast of the stimuli, she instructed observers to look at the fixation mark between the two gratings and to indicate the *orientation* of the grating that had the higher contrast. For the stimuli shown in the illustration, the correct response would be the grating on the right, because it has a slightly higher contrast than the one on the left. Thus, the observer had to first decide which grating had higher contrast and then indicate the orientation of that grating.

The question Carrasco was interested in answering was whether paying attention to one of the gratings would make it *appear* to have more contrast. To answer this question, she flashed a small dot over one of the gratings just before the bars appeared. This dot caused the observers to shift their *attention* to that side, even though they were keeping their eyes fixed on the center dot. (To prevent the possibility of eye movements, the small dot was presented just 160 ms before the grating, which is not enough time for an eye movement to occur.)

Carrasco found that when there was a large difference in contrast between the two gratings, the attention-capturing dot had no effect. However, when two gratings had the same contrast, observers were more likely to report the orientation of the one that was preceded by the dot. Thus, when two gratings were actually the same, the one that received attention appeared to have more contrast. Over 100 years after William James suggested that attention makes an object "clear and vivid," we can now say that we have good experimental evidence that attention does, in fact, enhance the appearance of an object.

ATTENTION AND EXPERIENCING A COHERENT WORLD

We have seen that attention is one of the primary mechanisms we use to focus on important things in the environment, that attending to an object brings it to the forefront of our consciousness and may even alter its appearance. Furthermore, not attending to an object can cause us to miss it altogether. We now consider yet another function of attention, one that is not obvious from our everyday experience. This function of attention is to help create **binding**, which is the process by which features—such as color, form, motion, and location—are combined to create our perception of a coherent object.

Why Is Binding Necessary?

We can appreciate why binding is necessary by remembering our discussion of modularity in Chapter 4, when we learned that separated areas of the brain are special-

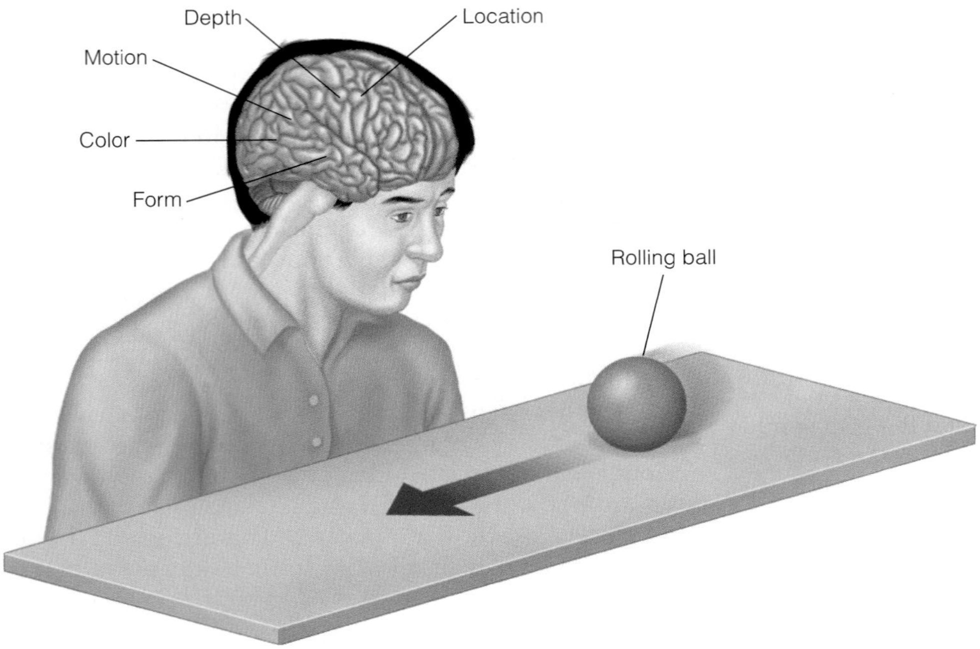

Figure 6.18 ▮ Any stimulus, even one as simple as a rolling ball, activates a number of different areas of the cortex. Binding is the process by which these separated signals are combined to create a unified percept.

ized for the perception of different qualities. In Chapter 4 we focused on the inferotemporal (IT) cortex, which is associated with perceiving forms. But there are also areas associated with motion, location, and possibly color (the exact location of a color area, if it exists, is still being researched) located at different places in the cortex.

Thus, when you see a red ball roll by, cells sensitive to forms fire in the IT cortex, cells sensitive to movement fire in the medal temporal (MT) cortex, and cells sensitive to color fire in other areas as well (Figure 6.18). But even though the ball's shape, movement, and color cause firing in different areas of the cortex, you don't perceive the ball as separated shape, movement, and color perceptions. You experience an integrated perception of a ball, with all of these components occurring together.

This raises an important question: How do we combine all of these physically separate neural signals to achieve a unified perception of the ball? This question, which is called the **binding problem**, has been answered both at the behavioral and physiological levels. We begin at the behavioral level by describing feature integration theory, which assigns a central role to attention in the solution of the binding problem.

Feature Integration Theory

According to **feature integration theory**, which was proposed by Anne Treisman and G. Gelade (1980; also see Treisman, 1988, 1999), attention plays a central role in solving the binding problem. Feature integration theory states that initially, in the **preattentive stage** of the perceptual processing, the features of an object (color, orientation, location, etc.) are separated (Figure 6.19). Focusing attention on the object triggers the **focused attention stage**, and this focused attention combines, or "binds," the object's features into a coherent perception of the object.[1]

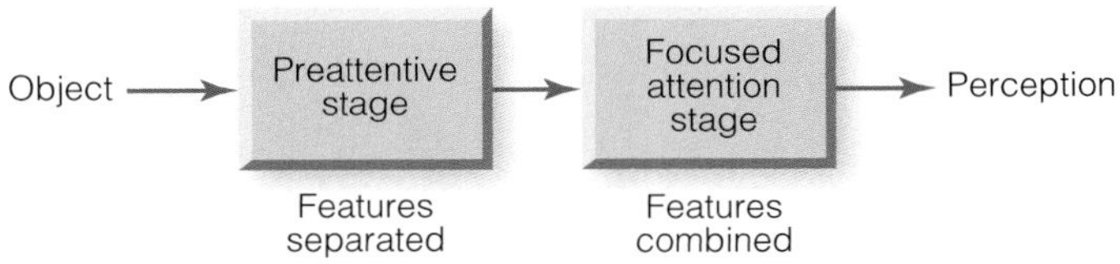

Figure 6.19 ▮ Flow diagram of Treisman's (1988) feature integration theory.

Treisman links the process of binding to physiology by noting that an object causes activity in both the *what* and *where* streams of the cortex (see page 77). Activity in the *what* stream would include information about features such as color and form. Activity in the *where* stream would include information about location and motion. According to Treisman, attention is the "glue" that combines the information from the *what* and *where* streams. Thus, we perceive all of the features of an object as being combined at a specific location.

Let's consider how this might work for the object in Figure 6.20a. All of this object's features are registered as being located in the same area because this is the only object present. When we pay attention to the object, its features are all combined at that location, and we perceive the object. This process is simple because we are dealing

[1] This is a simplified version of feature integration theory. For a more detailed description of the model, which also includes "feature maps" that code the location of each of an object's features, see Treisman (1999).

Figure 6.20 ▮ (a) A single object. Binding features is simple in this case because all of the features are at one location. (b) When multiple objects with many features are present, binding becomes more complicated.

with a single object at a fixed location. However, things become more complicated when we introduce multiple objects, as normally occurs in the environment.

When we consider multiple objects, numerous features are involved, and these features exist at many different locations (Figure 6.20b). The perceptual system's task is to associate each of these features with the object to which it belongs. Feature integration theory proposes that in order for this to occur, we need to focus our attention on each object in turn. Once we attend to a particular location, the features at that location are bound together and are associated with the object at that location.

What evidence supports the idea that focused attention is necessary for binding? One line of evidence, **illusory conjunctions**, is based on the finding that under some conditions, features associated with one object can become incorrectly associated with another object.

Illusory Conjunctions Illusory conjunctions were first demonstrated in an experiment by Treisman and H. Schmidt (1982), which used a stimulus display of four objects flanked by two black numbers, as shown in Figure 6.21. They flashed this display onto a screen for one-fifth of a second, followed by a random-dot masking field designed to eliminate any residual perception that may remain after the stimuli were turned off. Observers were told to report the black numbers first and then to report what they saw at each of the four locations where the shapes had been. Under these conditions, observers reported seeing illusory conjunctions on 18 percent of the trials. For example, after seeing the display in Figure 6.21, in which the small triangle was red and the small circle was green, they might report seeing a small red circle and a small green triangle.

Figure 6.21 ▮ Stimuli for Treisman and Schmidt's (1982) illusory conjunction experiment.

Although illusory conjunctions may seem like a phenomenon that would occur only in the laboratory, Treisman (2005) relates a situation in which she perceived illusory conjunctions in the environment. After thinking she'd seen a bald-headed man with a beard, she looked again and realized that she had actually seen two men—one bald and one with a beard—and had combined their features to create an illusory bald, bearded man.

The reason illusory conjunctions occurred for the stimuli in Figure 6.21 is that these stimuli were presented rapidly and the observer's attention was distracted from the target object by having them focus on the black numbers. Treisman and Schmidt found, however, that asking their observers to attend to the target objects eliminated the illusory conjunctions.

More evidence that supports the idea that illusory conjunctions are caused by a failure of attention is provided by studies of patient R.M., who had parietal lobe damage that resulted in a condition called **Balint's syndrome**. The crucial characteristic of this syndrome is an inability to focus attention on individual objects. According to feature detection theory, lack of focused attention would make it difficult for R.M. to combine features correctly, and this is exactly what happened. When R.M. was presented with two different letters of different colors, such as a red T and a blue O, he reported illusory conjunctions such as "blue T" on 23 percent of the trials, even when he was able to view the letters for as long as 10 seconds (Friedman-Hill et al., 1995; Robertson et al., 1997).

Visual Search Another approach to studying the role of attention in binding has used a task called visual search. **Visual search** is something we do any time we look for an object among a number of other objects, like looking for a friend in a crowd or trying to find Waldo in a "Where's Waldo?" picture (Handford, 1997). A type of visual search called conjunction search has been particularly useful in studying binding.

METHOD ■ Searching for Conjunctions

We can understand what a conjunction search is by first describing another type of search called a feature search. Before reading further, look at Figure 6.22, and find the horizontal green line in (a) and then in (b). The search you carried out in Figure 6.22a was a **feature search** because the target can be found by looking for a single feature—"horizontal." In contrast, the search you carried out in Figure 6.22b was a **conjunction search** because it was necessary to search for a combination (or conjunction) of two or more features on the same stimulus. In Figure 6.22b, you couldn't focus just on green because there are vertical green lines, and you couldn't focus just on horizontal because there are horizontal red lines. You had to look for the *conjunction* of horizontal and green. VL 3

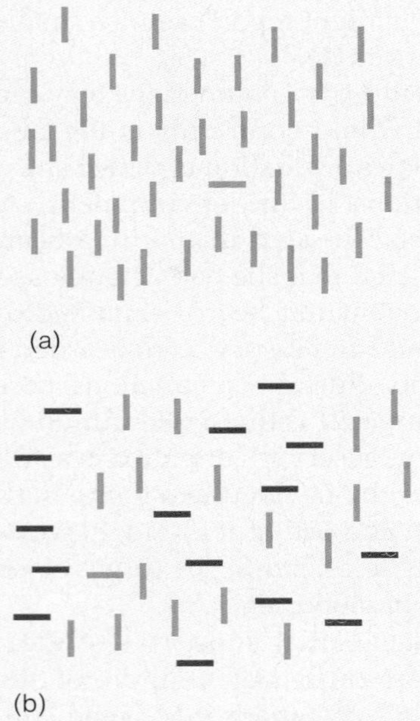

Figure 6.22 ■ Find the horizontal green line in (a) and then in (b).

Conjunction searches are useful for studying binding because finding the target in a conjunction search involves focusing attention at a specific location. To test the idea that attention to a location is required for a conjunction search, a number of researchers have tested Balint's patient R.M. and have found that he cannot find the target when a conjunction search is required (Robertson et al., 1997). Patients with damage to the parietal lobe also have difficulty with conjunction searches (Ambridge et al., 1999), and when observers without brain damage carry out a conjunction search, their parietal lobe is activated (Shafritz et al., 2002). This connection between the parietal lobe and conjunction searches makes sense when we remember that the parietal lobe is the destination of the *where* stream, which is involved in determining the locations of objects.

Table 6.1 summarizes the link between attention and good binding (as indicated by few illusory conjunctions or successful conjunction search) and lack of attention and poor binding (more illusory conjunctions or failed conjunction search.)

Table 6.1

	Good Binding	Poor Binding
Illusory Conjunctions	Focus attention: No illusory conjunctions	Distract attention: Some illusory conjunctions Balint's syndrome: More illusory conjunctions
Conjunction Search	Target located Parietal lobe activated	Balint's syndrome: Target not located

The Physiological Approach to Binding

One of the notable things about our description of binding, above, is that we introduced the problem physiologically by noting how different qualities are processed in different places in the brain. But we then described a behavioral explanation of the problem based on how observers focus attention on objects. We will now return to physiology by considering an idea about how the brain might go about solving the binding problem. Although attention is not central to this explanation, we will see that attention may be involved.

To solve the binding problem, the brain must combine information contained in neurons that are located in different places. For example, in the case of our red ball, the brain must combine information from separated areas that are activated by form, color, and motion. There are anatomical connections between these different areas so neurons in these areas can communicate with one another (Gilbert & Wiesel, 1989; Lamme & Roelfesma, 2000). But what is it that they communicate?

One physiological solution to the binding problem, the **synchrony hypothesis**, states that when neurons in different parts of the cortex are firing to the same object, the pattern of nerve impulses in these neurons will be synchronized with each other. To simplify our explanation of how this works, let's consider what might happen just for neurons that signal orientation (we'll come back to color and movement in a moment). Remember, from Chapter 4, that neurons are organized into orientation columns in the brain (see page 75). This means that an object that contains a number of orientations will be represented by the firing of neurons located in different orientation columns. So, even when we are considering just orientation, there is a binding problem because the brain needs to be able to determine that the activity in these separate orientation columns all comes from the same object.

According to the synchrony hypothesis, this is accomplished as shown in Figure 6.23. Here we see that the various orientations that form the woman stimulate a group of neurons, and that these neurons all fire in synchrony with each other. In contrast, the orientations from another object—the dog—stimulate a different group of neurons. These neurons have a different firing pattern than the neurons representing the woman, but they fire in synchrony with each other. It is important to note that "synchrony" does not simply mean that neurons fire at the same time but that they fire with the same *pattern* of nerve impulses. Notice how this occurs for the woman and for the dog. This situation lets the brain know which neurons represent the woman and which ones represent the dog. Thus, synchrony binds together responses that are generated by the same object but that occur in different places in the cortex.

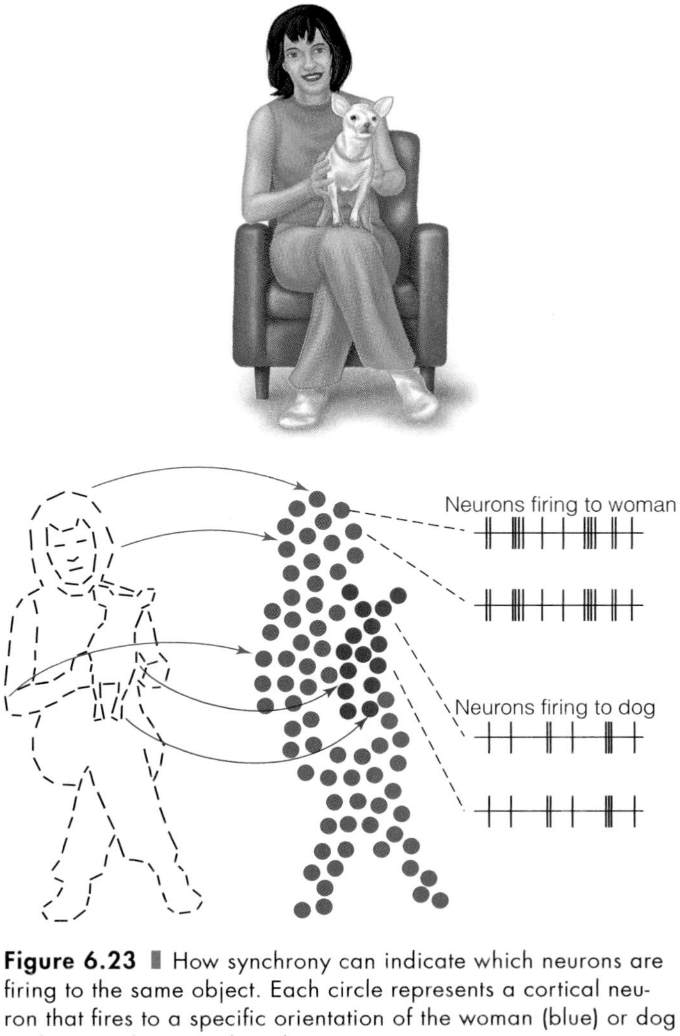

Figure 6.23 ▌ How synchrony can indicate which neurons are firing to the same object. Each circle represents a cortical neuron that fires to a specific orientation of the woman (blue) or dog (red). (Based on Engel et al., 1999.)

Carrying the idea one step further, it has been proposed that synchrony may occur between neurons representing different qualities of an object. According to this idea, when the red ball rolls by, it will cause neurons in different parts of the cortex that respond to color, movement, and shape to fire in synchrony with each other, and this synchronized firing will indicate that these three qualities all belong to the ball (Stryker, 1989).

Note that although attention is not a central part of the synchrony hypothesis, there is evidence that attention may increase synchrony (Engel, 1999). Thus, perhaps further research will enable us to draw connections between the behavioral explanation of binding, which emphasizes the role of attention, and the physiological explanation, which emphasizes synchrony of neural firing. Also, even though there is a great deal of physiological evidence that synchrony does occur in neurons that are associated with the same object (Brosch, Bauer, & Eckhorn, 1997; Engel, 1999; Neuenschwander & Singer, 1996; Roskies, 1999), the synchrony hypothesis is not accepted by all researchers. More research is necessary to determine whether synchrony is, in fact, the signal that causes binding to occur.

THE PHYSIOLOGY OF ATTENTION

How does attention affect neurons in the visual system? This question has attracted a great deal of research, which has determined that attention affects the firing of neurons throughout the visual system. We will focus here on one of the main conclusions from this research—that is, that attention enhances the firing of neurons. The results of a typical experiment are shown in Figure 6.24. Carol Colby and coworkers (1995) trained a monkey to keep its eyes fixated on a dot marked *Fix* (see Figure 6.24a) while a peripheral light was flashed at a location off to the right. In the "fixation only" condition (Figure 6.24a), the monkey's task was to look at the fixation light and to release its hand from a bar when the fixation light was dimmed. In the "fixation and attention" condition (Figure 6.24b), the monkey still kept its eyes fixed on the fixation light but had to release the bar when the peripheral light was dimmed. Thus, in this condition, the monkey had to pay attention to what was happening to the peripheral light, off to the side of where it was looking.

As the monkey was performing these tasks, Colby recorded from a neuron in the parietal cortex that fired to the peripheral light. The records in Figure 6.24 show that this neuron responded poorly to the peripheral light when the monkey was not paying attention to it, but responded well when the monkey was paying attention to

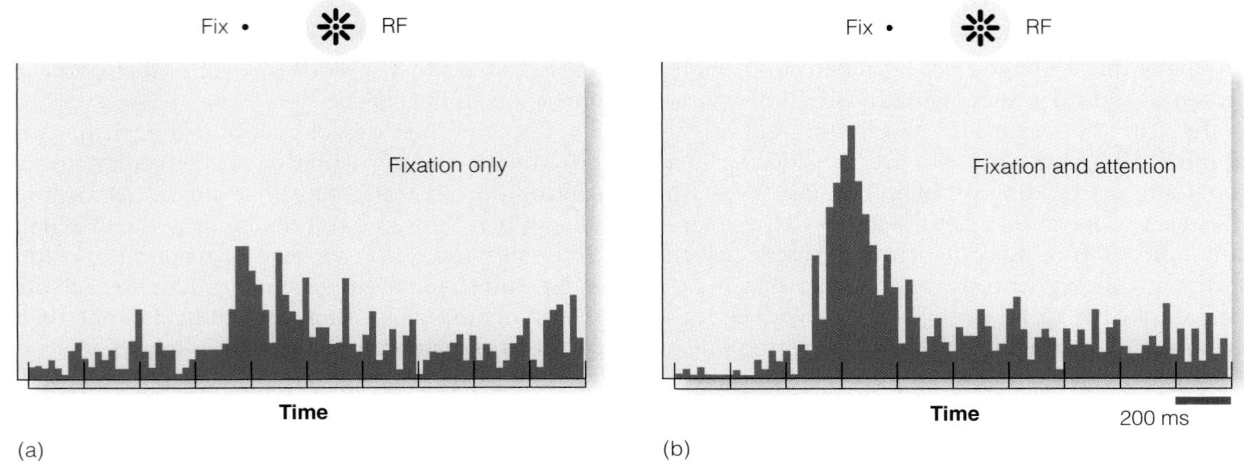

Figure 6.24 ▮ The results of Colby et al.'s (1995) experiment showing how attention affects the responding of a neuron in a monkey's parietal cortex. The monkey always looked at the dot marked FIX. A light was flashed within the circle marked RF. (a) Nerve firing when the monkey was not paying attention to the light. (b) Nerve firing when the monkey was paying attention to the light.
(Reprinted from C. L. Colby, J. R. Duhamel, and M. E. Goldberg. From "Oculocentric Spatial Representation in Parietal Cortex." From Cerebral Cortex, *5, 1995, 470–481. Copyright © 1995, with permission from Oxford University Press.)*

it. Remember that the image on the monkey's retina was always the same because the monkey was always looking directly at the fixation point. Thus, the greater response when the monkey was paying attention to the peripheral light must be caused not by any change of the stimulus on the monkey's retina, but by the monkey's attention to the light. This means that the firing of a neuron depends on more than just the shape or size or orientation of a stimulus. It also depends on how important the stimulus is for behavior.

This enhancement of responding by attention has been demonstrated in many single-unit recording experiments on animals (Bisley & Goldberg, 2003; Moran & Desimone, 1985; Reynolds & Desimone, 2003) and also in brain imaging experiments in humans (Behrmann et al., 2004; Downar et al., 2001; Kastner et al., 1999). The single-unit experiments show that although the enhancement effect occurs as early in the visual system as V1, the effect becomes stronger at higher areas in the visual system (Figure 6.25). This makes sense because higher areas are more likely to reflect an observer's knowledge or characteristics of an object such as its meaning or behavioral significance (see Gottleib et al., 2002).

This enhancement of neural responding may have many effects on perception, but one effect seems particularly clear—the enhancement of neural responding caused by attention creates a signal that is equivalent to the signal that would be created by increasing the contrast of the stimulus. Thus, it is likely that this enhancement is what is behind the results of Carrasco's behavioral experiment we described on page 131, which showed that paying attention to a grating stimulus made it appear to have more contrast.

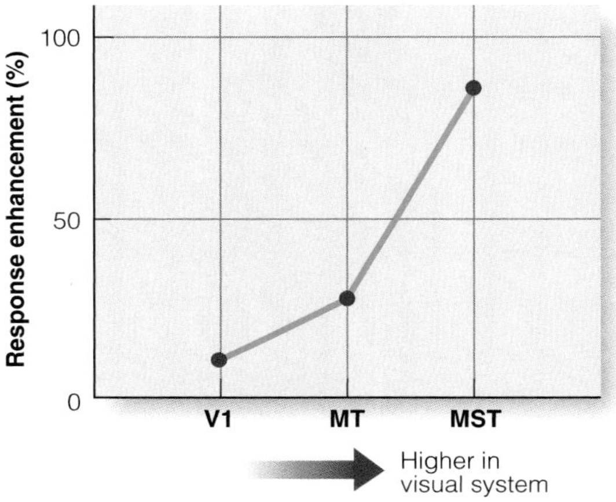

Figure 6.25 ▮ Enhancement of the rate of nerve firing caused by attention for neurons in areas V1, MT, and MST. Area MT is in the dorsal stream, and MST is further "downstream." (Based on Maunsell, 2003.)

SOMETHING TO CONSIDER: DO NEURONS NOTICE STIMULI?

We began this chapter by describing how people shift their attention from place to place by scanning a scene. To end the chapter, we consider an experiment that asks the question: How do neurons respond as we encounter objects while we scan a scene? David Sheinberg and Nikos Logothetis (2001) answered this question by recording from IT neurons as a monkey was scanning a scene. In the first part of their experiment, the monkeys were trained to move a lever to the left in response to pictures of some objects and to the right to pictures of other objects. These objects included people, animals, and views of human-made objects such as toys and drinking cups.

After the monkeys had learned the correct response to each object, Sheinberg and Logothetis found IT neurons that responded to specific objects. They found that if a neuron responded to a picture when the picture was presented alone, on a blank field, it also responded to the object when it was placed in an environmental scene. An example can be seen in Figure 6.26, in which a parrot has been placed on the roof of a church.

Having shown that the parrot on the roof causes an IT neuron to fire when the parrot is flashed within the neuron's receptive field, the next task was to determine whether the cell would fire to the parrot when the monkey came upon it while freely scanning the picture. The data below the picture in Figure 6.26 shows neural firing when the monkey fixated on the parrot and when the monkey moved the lever. Immediately after the monkey fixated the parrot, the neuron fired, and shortly after the neuron fired, the monkey moved the lever, indicating that it had identified the parrot. Sheinberg and Logothetis found that even when a monkey's gaze came very close to an object, the neurons didn't fire unless the monkey *noticed* the object, as indicated by moving the lever.

Figure 6.26 ▌ Top: scan path as a monkey looked for a target (the parrot on the roof). Just below picture: firing of an IT neuron as the monkey was looking. Bottom: graph showing how far the monkey's gaze was from the parrot. Notice that the neuron begins firing just after the monkey has fixated on the parrot and shortly after this the monkey pulls the lever.
(Sheinberg, D. L., & Logothetis, N. K. (2001). Noticing familiar objects in real world scenes: The role of temporal cortical neurons in natural vision. Journal of Neuroscience, 21, *1340–1350.)*

What this experiment shows is that some neurons fire only after the monkey looked at *and* noticed the parrot. Think about what this tells us about the connection between neural firing and perception. A particular scene may contain many different objects, and the brain contains many neurons that respond to those objects. But even though the retina is bombarded with stimuli that could, potentially, cause these neurons to fire, it appears that the stimuli that count the most are the ones that are being looked at *and* noticed. What's important is not the image on the retina, but whether the image is behaviorally significant to the observer.

TEST YOURSELF 6.2

1. What evidence is there that attention enhances visual information processing? Why can't we use this evidence to draw conclusions about the connection between attention and perception?
2. Describe the experiment that shows an object's appearance can be changed by attention. What clever feature of this experiment was used to avoid the effect of bias?
3. What is the binding problem? Describe the physiological processes that create this problem.
4. What are the two stages in feature integration theory? What does feature integration theory propose about the role of attention in perception and binding?
5. What evidence links attention and binding? Describe evidence that involves both illusory conjunctions and conjunction search.
6. What is the "synchrony" explanation for the physiological basis of binding? Has any connection been demonstrated between this explanation and attention?
7. Describe physiological experiments that show that attention enhances neural firing.
8. Describe the experiment that showed that neurons fire when the monkey notices an object.

THINK ABOUT IT

1. If salience is determined by characteristics of a scene such as contrast, color, and orientation, why might it be correct to say that paying attention to an object can increase its salience?
2. Can you think of situations from your experience that are similar to the change blindness experiments in

Figure 6.27 ▮ Leon Kroll, *Morning on the Cape*. Try showing this picture to a number of people for 1–2 seconds, and ask them what they notice first and what else they see. You can't determine eye-scan patterns using this method, but you may gain some insight into differences in the way different people look at pictures.

that you missed seeing an object that was easy to see once you knew it was there? What do you think was behind your failure to see this object?

3. Art composition books often state that it is possible to arrange elements in a painting in a way that controls both what a person looks at in a picture and the order in which the person looks at things. An example of this would be the statement that when viewing Kroll's *Morning on the Cape* (Figure 6.27), the eye is drawn first to the woman with the books in the foreground, and then to the pregnant woman. But measurements of eye movements show that there are individual differences in the way people look at pictures. For example, E. H. Hess (1965) reported large differences between how men and women looked at the Kroll picture. Try showing this picture, and others, to people as suggested in the figure caption to see if you can observe these individual differences in picture viewing. (Hess, E. H., 1965. Attitude and pupil size. *Scientific American, 212,* 46–54.)

IF YOU WANT TO KNOW MORE

1. ***Eye Movements.*** The role of eye movements in determining attention is often studied by measuring the sequence of fixations that a person makes when freely viewing a picture. However, another important variable is how long a person looks at particular areas of a picture. Factors that determine the length of fixation may not be the same as factors that determine the sequence of fixations.

   Henderson, J. M. (2003). Human gaze control during real-world scene perception. *Trends in Cognitive Sciences, 7,* 498–503.

2. ***When Does Selection Occur in Selective Attention?*** A classic controversy in the field of attention is whether selective attention involves "early selection" or "late selection." Researchers in the "early selection" camp state that when there are many messages present, people select one to attend to based on physical characteristics of the message, such as a person's voice. Researchers in the "late selection" camp state that people don't select which message to attend until they have analyzed the meaning of the various messages that are present.

   Broadbent, D. E. (1958). *Perception and communication.* London: Pergamon.

   Luck, S. J., & Vecera, S. P. (2002). Attention. In H. Pashler & S. Yantis (Eds.), *Stevens' handbook of experimental psychology* (3rd ed., pp. 235–286). New York: Wiley.

   Treisman, A. M. (1964). Selective attention in man. *British Medical Bulletin, 20,* 12–16.

3. ***Dividing Attention.*** Our ability to divide our attention among different tasks depends on the nature of the task and also on how well we have practiced specific tasks. The following two references describe (1) the idea that task difficulty determines our ability to divide our attention, and (2) the finding that when people play video games, they may increase their ability to divide their attention among different tasks.

   Green, G. S., & Bavelier, D. (2003). Action video game modifies visual selective attention. *Nature, 423,* 534–537.

   Lavie, N. (1995). Perceptual load as a necessary condition for selective attention. *Journal of Experimen-*

tal Psychology: Human Perception and Performance, 21, 451–486.

4. ***Features and Visual Search.*** Visual search has been used not only to study binding, as described in this chapter, but also to study how the match or mismatch between features in the target and the distractors can influence the ability to find the target. When a target has features that differ from the distractors, the target "pops out" and so is perceived immediately. However, when the target shares features with the distractors, search takes longer. You can demonstrate this for yourself in Virtual Lab 3: Feature Analysis.

Treisman, A. (1986). Features and objects in visual processing. *Scientific American, 255,* 114B–125B.

Treisman, A. (1998). The perception of features and objects. In R. D. Wright (Ed.), *Visual attention* (pp. 26–54). New York: Oxford University Press.

KEY TERMS

VISIT YOUR COMPANION WEBSITE FOR THIS BOOK

http://psychology.wadsworth.com/goldstein7e

Check out this companion website where you'll find online resources—glossary, flashcards, web links, multiple-choice and essay questions, and much more!

VIRTUAL LAB

Your Virtual Lab is designed to help you get the most out of this course. The Virtual Lab icons direct you to specific media demonstrations and experiments designed to help you visualize what you are reading about. The number beside each icon indicates the number of the media element you can access through your CD-ROM, Perception PsychologyNow, or WebTutor resource at http:now.ilrn.com/goldstein_7e.

The following are the lab exercises covering what you've just learned in this chapter:

1 *Inattentional Blindness Stimuli* The sequence of stimuli presented in an inattentional blindness experiment.

2 *Change Blindness* A test of your ability to detect changes that happen slowly.

3 *Feature Analysis* A number of visual search experiments in which you can determine the function relating reaction time and number of distractors for a number of different types of targets and distractors.

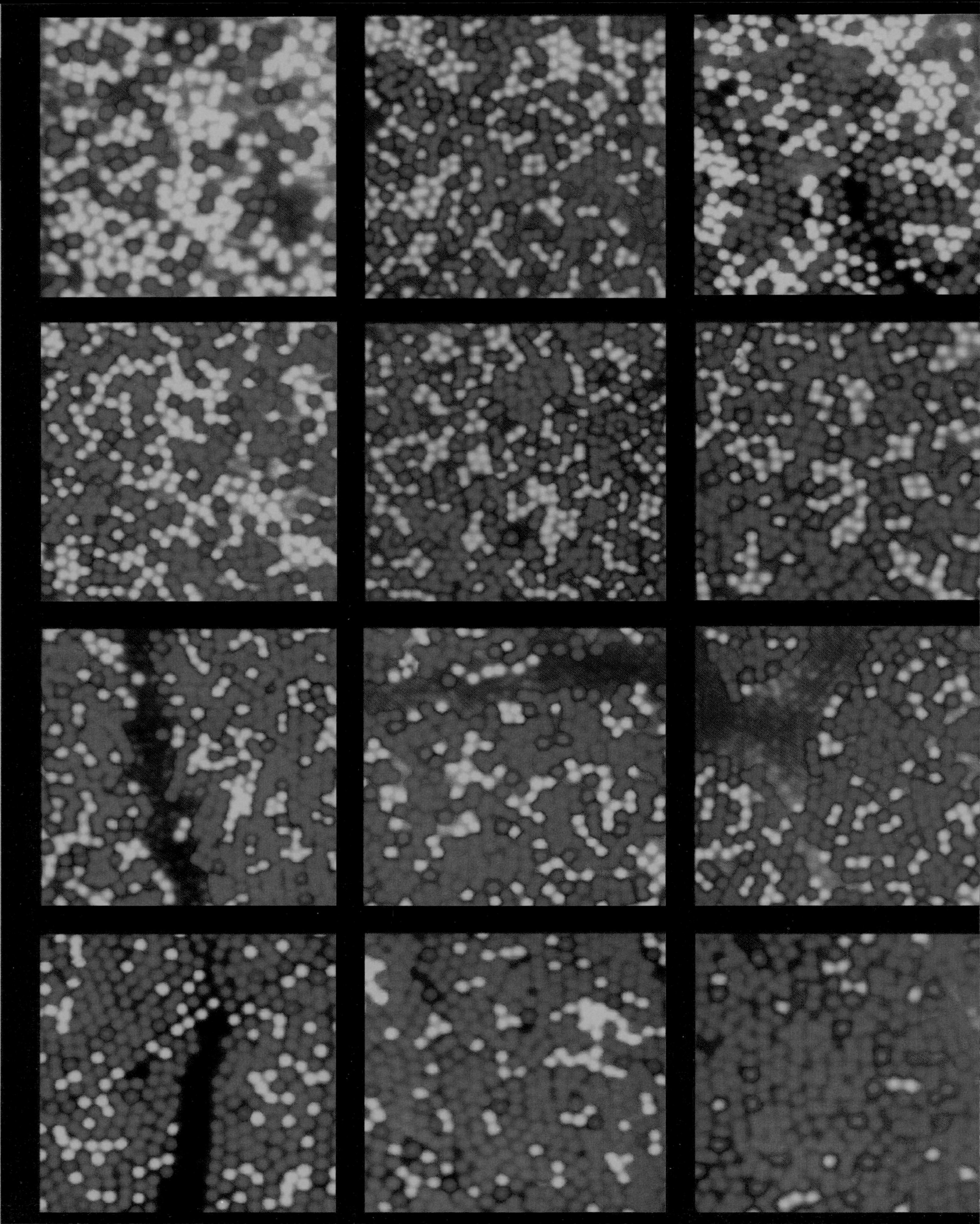

CHAPTER

7

PERCEIVING COLOR

Chapter Contents

These mosaics show cones in an area on the edge of the fovea from twelve different people with normal color vision. The images are false colored so blue, green, and red represent the short-, medium-, and long-wavelength cones, respectively. (The true colors are yellow, purple, and bluish-purple.) Notice the enormous variability in the relative proportions of medium- and long-wavelength cones, even in these "normal" observers.
(From "Formation and acquisition of the retinal image," by D. R. Williams & H. Hofer, 2003. In L. M. Chalupa and J. S. Werner *The Visual Neurosciences,* MIT Press, Cambridge, MA, pp. 795–810.)

VL *The Virtual Lab icons direct you to specific animations and videos designed to help you visualize what you are reading about. The number beside each icon indicates the number of the clip you can access through your CD-ROM or your student website.*

Some Questions We Will Consider:

- *What does someone who is "color-blind" see? (p. 151)*
- *Why do we perceive blue dots when a yellow flash bulb goes off? (p. 153)*
- *How is our perception of a color affected by its surroundings? (p. 158)*

Color is one of the most obvious and pervasive qualities in our environment. We interact with it every time we note the color of a traffic light, choose clothes that are color coordinated, or appreciate the colors of a painting. We pick favorite colors (blue is the most favored; Terwogt & Hoeksma, 1994), we react emotionally to colors (we turn purple with rage, green with envy, or feel blue); Terwogt & Hoeksma, 1994; Valdez & Mehribian, 1994), and we imbue colors with special meanings (for example, red signifies danger; purple, royalty; green, ecology). But for all of our involvement with color, we sometimes take it for granted, and—just as with our other perceptual abilities—we may not fully appreciate color until we lose our ability to experience it. The depth of this loss is illustrated by the case of Mr. I, a painter who became color-blind at the age of 65 after suffering a concussion in an automobile accident:

> In March of 1986, the neurologist Oliver Sacks[1] received an anguished letter from Mr. I, who, identifying himself as a "rather successful artist," described how ever since he had been involved in an automobile accident, he had lost his ability to experience colors, and he exclaimed with some anguish, that "My dog is gray. Tomato juice is black. Color TV is a hodge-podge. . . ."
>
> In the days following his accident, Mr. I had become more and more depressed. His studio, normally awash with the brilliant colors of his abstract paintings, appeared drab to him, and his paintings, meaningless. Food, now gray, became difficult for him to look at while eating; and sunsets, once seen as rays of red, had become streaks of black against the sky.

Mr. I's color blindness was caused by cortical injury experienced after a lifetime of experiencing color, whereas most cases of total color blindness or of color deficiency (partial color blindness, which we'll discuss in more detail later in this chapter) occur at birth because of the genetic absence of one or more types of cone receptors. Most people who are born color-blind are not disturbed by their lack of color perception—because they have never experienced color. However, some of their reports, such as the darkening of reds, are similar to Mr. I's. People with total color blindness often echo Mr. I's complaint that it is sometimes difficult to distinguish one object from another, as when his brown dog, which he could easily see silhouetted against a light-colored road, became very difficult to perceive when seen against irregular foliage.

Eventually, Mr. I overcame his strong psychological reaction and began creating striking black-and-white pictures. But his account of his color-blind experiences provides an impressive testament to the central place of color in his life. (See Heywood, Cowey, & Newcombe, 1991; Nordby, 1990; R. S. L. Young, Fishman, & Chen, 1980; and Zeki, 1990, for additional descriptions of cases of complete color blindness.)

In this chapter, we consider color perception in two parts. In the first part, we answer the question: What is the connection between color perception and the firing of neurons? In the second part, we consider another question: How do we perceive the colors and lightness of objects in the environment under changing illumination?

INTRODUCTION TO COLOR

Why do we perceive different colors? We will begin answering this question by first speculating about some of the functions color serves in our lives and in the lives of monkeys. We will then look at how we describe our experience of color and how this experience is linked to the properties of light.

What Are Some Functions of Color Vision?

Color adds beauty to our lives, but it is more than that. Color serves important signaling functions, both natural and contrived by humans. The natural and human-made world has provided many color-signals that help us identify and classify things. I know the rock on my desk contains copper by the rich vein of blue that runs through it. I know a banana is ripe when it has turned yellow, and I know to stop when the traffic light turns red.

In addition to its signaling function, color helps facilitate perceptual organization, the process we discussed in Chapter 5 (p. 99) by which small elements become grouped perceptually into larger objects. Color perception greatly facilitates the ability to tell one object from another and especially to see objects against a varied background, such as flowers in a field or individual people in a crowd. In fact, this ability is crucial to the survival of many species. Consider, for example, a monkey foraging for fruit in the forest or jungle. A monkey with good color vision easily detects red fruit against a green background (Figure 7.1a), but a color-blind monkey would find it more difficult to find the fruit (Figure 7.1b).

This link between good color vision and the ability to detect colored food has led to the proposal that monkey and human color vision may have evolved for the express purpose of detecting fruit (Mollon, 1989, 1997; Sumner & Mollon, 2000; Walls, 1942). This suggestion sounds rea-

[1]Dr. Sacks, well known for his elegant writings describing interesting neurological cases, came to public attention when he was played by Robin Williams in the 1995 film *Awakenings.*

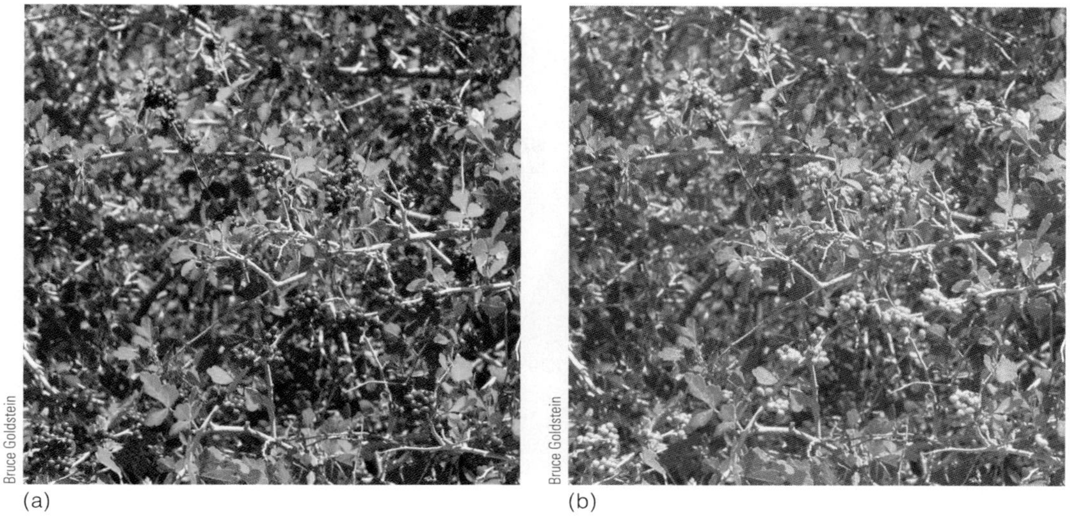

Figure 7.1 ■ (a) Red berries in green foliage. (b) These berries become more difficult to detect without color vision.

sonable when we consider the difficulty color-blind human observers have when confronted with the seemingly simple task of picking berries. Knut Nordby (1990), a totally color-blind visual scientist who sees the world in shades of gray, described his experience as follows: "Picking berries has always been a big problem. I often have to grope around among the leaves with my fingers, feeling for the berries by their shape" (p. 308). If Nordby's experience, which is similar to Mr. I's difficulty in seeing his dog against foliage, is any indication, a color-blind monkey would have difficulty finding berries or fruit and might be less likely to survive than monkeys with color vision.

Our ability to perceive color not only helps us detect objects that might otherwise be obscured by its surroundings, but it also helps us recognize and identify things we can see easily. James W. Tanaka and L. M. Presnell (1999) demonstrated this by asking observers to identify objects like the ones in Figure 7.2, which either appeared in their normal colors, like the yellow bananas, or in inappropriate colors, like the purple bananas. The result was that observers recognized the appropriately colored objects more rapidly and accurately. Thus, knowing the colors of familiar objects helps us to recognize these objects (Tanaka et al., 2001).

Figure 7.2 ■ Normally colored fruit and inappropriately colored fruit.

(Reprinted from, Trends in Cognitive Sciences, 5, *Tanaka, J., Weiskopf, D., & Williams, P., The role of color in high-level vision, 211–215, (2001) with permission from Elsevier.)*

How Can We Describe Color Experience?

We can describe all the colors we can discriminate by using the terms red, yellow, green, blue, and their combinations (Abramov & Gordon, 1994; Hurvich, 1981). When people are presented with many different colors and are asked to describe them, they can describe all of them when they are allowed to use all four terms, but they can't when one of these terms is omitted. Furthermore, other colors, such as orange, violet, purple, and brown, are not needed to achieve these descriptions (Fuld, Wooten, & Whalen, 1981; Quinn, Rosano, & Wooten, 1988). Red, yellow, green, and blue are therefore considered to be basic colors by color researchers.

Figure 7.3 shows the four basic colors arranged in a circle, so that each is perceptually similar to the one next to it. The order of the four basic colors in the color circle—blue, green, yellow, and red—matches the order of the colors in the visible spectrum, in which the short-wavelength end of the spectrum is blue, green is in the middle of the spectrum, and yellow and red are at the long-wavelength end of the spectrum.

Although the color circle is based on four colors, there are more than four colors in the circle. In fact, people can discriminate about 200 different colors across the length of the visible spectrum (Figure 7.4; Gouras, 1991). Furthermore, we can create even more colors by changing the intensity to make colors brighter or dimmer, or by adding white to change a color's **saturation**. White is equal amounts of all wavelengths across the spectrum, and adding white decreases a color's saturation. For example, adding white to the deep red at the top of the color circle makes it become pink, which is a less saturated (or **desaturated**) form of red.

By changing the wavelength, the intensity, and the saturation, we can create about a million or more different discriminable colors (Backhaus, 1998; Gouras, 1991). Of

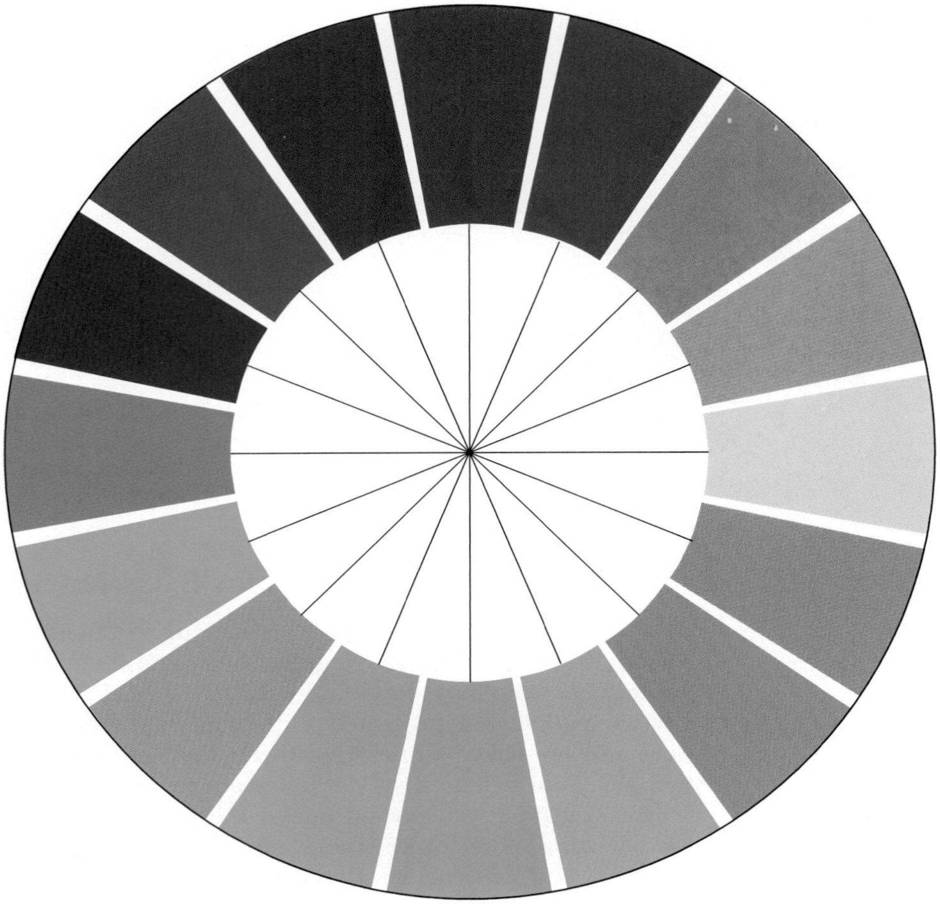

Figure 7.3 ▮ The color circle. Colors are arranged by placing perceptually similar colors next to each other, so the four basic colors are positioned at 12, 3, 6, and 9 o'clock on the circle.
(From Color Vision, *by Leo M. Hurvich, 1981. Reprinted by permission of Dr. Leo M. Hurvich.)*

course, the differences between some of these colors are extremely small, as you can demonstrate by changing the color palette on your computer from "hundreds of colors" to "thousands of colors" to "millions of colors." When you do this, you will notice that the screen doesn't change much from "hundreds of colors" to "millions of colors." Although we may be able to discriminate millions of colors, we encounter only a fraction of that number in everyday experience. The paint chips at the paint store total less than a thousand, and the *Munsell Book of Colors,* once the color "bible" for designers, contained 1,225 color samples (Wysecki & Stiles, 1965). The Pantone Matching System in current use by graphic artists has about 1,200 color choices.

What Is the Relationship Between Wavelength and Color Perception?

The first step in understanding how our nervous system creates our perception of color is to determine how our perception is related to a specific physical property of light. Figure 7.4 shows that the spectrum stretches from short wavelengths (400 nm) to long wavelengths (700 nm), and bands of wavelengths within this range are associated with different colors. Wavelengths from about 400 to 450 nm appear violet; 450 to 490 nm, blue; 500 to 575 nm, green; 575 to 590 nm, yellow; 590 to 620, orange; and 620 to 700, red.

The colors we perceive in the spectrum are related

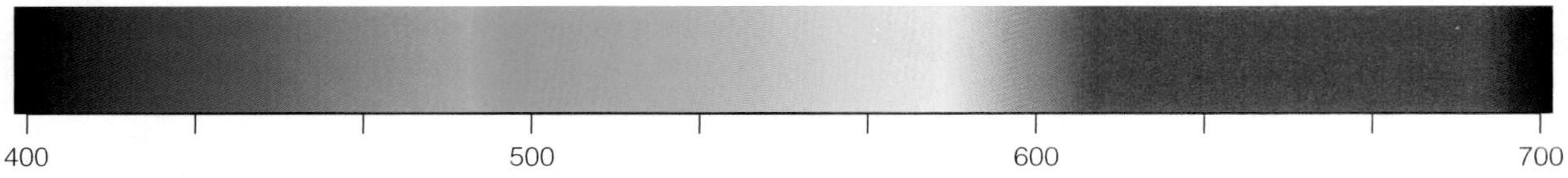

Figure 7.4 ▮ The visible spectrum.

to their wavelengths, but what about the colors of objects? The colors of objects are largely determined by the wavelengths of light that are *reflected* from the objects. This is illustrated in Figure 7.5, which shows **reflectance curves**—plots of the percentage of light reflected versus wavelength—for a number of objects. Notice that black paper and white paper both reflect all wavelengths equally across the spectrum, but blue and green pigments, and the tomato reflect some wavelengths but not others.

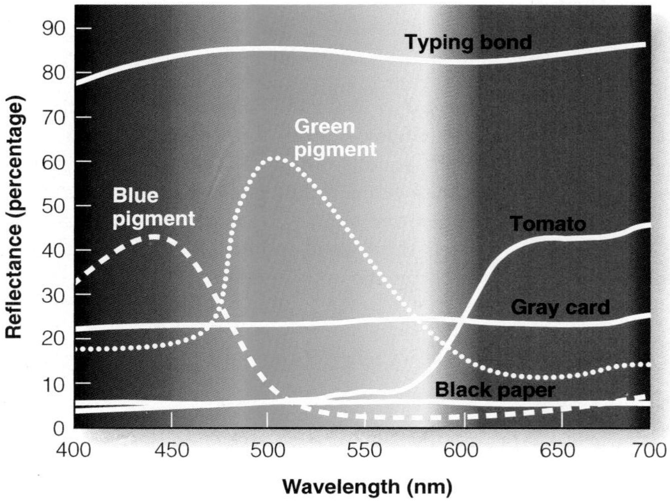

Figure 7.5 ▮ Reflectance curves for surfaces that appear white, gray, and black, and for blue and green pigments, and a tomato.
(Adapted from Color: Its Principles and Their Applications, *by F. W. Clulow, 1972, Morgan and Morgan. Copyright © 1972 by F. W. Clulow. Used by permission of the author.)*

When some wavelengths are reflected more than others—as for the blue paint, green paint, or red tomato—we call these **chromatic colors**, or **hues**.[2] This property of reflecting some wavelengths more than others, which is a characteristic of chromatic colors, is called **selective reflection**. Table 7.1 indicates the relationship between the wavelengths reflected and the color perceived. When light reflection is flat across the spectrum—that is, contains no hue, such as white, black, and all the grays between these two extremes—we call these colors **achromatic colors**.

An excellent example of the difference between chromatic and achromatic color is provided by the colors of some glaciers (Figure 7.6). The snow on top of glaciers appears white because it reflects all wavelengths equally. But inside the glacier, crystalline structures are formed that do not reflect all wavelengths equally. This ice selectively reflects the short wavelengths, which causes the ice to appear deep blue.

Table 7.1 ▮ *Relationship between predominant wavelengths reflected and color perceived*

Wavelengths Reflected	Perceived Color
Short	Blue
Medium	Green
Long	Red
Long and medium	Yellow
Long and a little medium	Orange
Long and short	Purple
Long, medium, and short	White

Most colors in the environment are created by the way objects selectively reflect some wavelengths. But in the case of things that are transparent, such as liquids, plastics, and glass, chromatic color is created by **selective transmission**, so only some wavelengths pass through the object or substance. For example, cranberry juice selectively transmits long-wavelength light and appears red, whereas limeade selectively transmits medium-wavelength light and appears green.

Other things can influence color perception. For example, our perception of an object's color can be influenced by the background on which an object is seen. Thus a blue bird flying to its nighttime perch against a red-tinged sunset will appear different than when it is perched amongst the green foliage of a tree. We will discuss this effect, called simultaneous color contrast, later in the chapter. For now, we will focus on the link between wavelength and color. We will do this by considering how wavelengths are represented by signals in the nervous system.

Historically, the problem of relating wavelength and activity in the nervous system has been approached in two different ways that have led to two different theories of color vision. Both of these theories were proposed in the 1800s based on behavioral data, and remarkably, both were basically correct. As we will see, the physiological evidence to support them didn't become available until over 70 years after they were originally proposed.

We will consider each of the theories in turn by first describing the behavioral evidence on which the theory was based and then describing the physiological evidence that became available later.

[2]The term "hue" is rarely used in everyday language. We usually say, "The color of the fire engine is red" rather than "The hue (or chromatic color) of the fire engine is red." Therefore, throughout the rest of this book, we will use the word *color* to mean "chromatic color" or "hue," and we will use the term *achromatic color* to refer to white, gray, or black.

Figure 7.6 ▮ Glacier showing achromatic color (white) in areas that reflect all wavelengths equally. Inside the crevice, the crystal structure of the tightly packed ice absorbs the medium and short wavelengths and selectively reflects short wavelengths. This area therefore has chromatic color (blue).

TRICHROMATIC THEORY OF COLOR VISION

The **trichromatic theory of color vision**, which stated that color vision depends on the activity of three different receptor mechanisms, was proposed by two eminent 19th-century researchers, Thomas Young (1773–1829) and Hermann von Helmholtz (1821–1894). They based their theory on the results of a psychophysical procedure called color matching.

Behavioral Evidence for the Theory

In the **color-matching experiments**, observers adjusted the amounts of three different wavelengths of light mixed together in a "comparison field," until the color of this mixture matched the color of a single wavelength in a "test field." For example, the observer might be asked to mix together 420-nm, 560-nm, and 640-nm lights in a comparison field until the color of this field matched the color of a 500-nm light presented in the test field (Figure 7.7). The key findings of these color-matching experiments were that:

1. By correctly adjusting the proportions of three wavelengths, it was possible to make the comparison and test fields match.
2. A person with normal color vision needed to use at least three wavelengths in order to match all wavelengths in the spectrum. (Any three wavelengths can be used, as long as any one of them can't be matched by mixing the other two.) People with normal color vision could not, however, match all wavelengths in

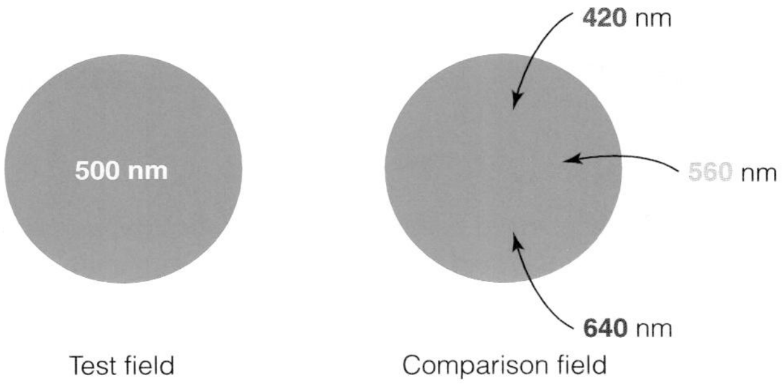

Figure 7.7 ▮ In a color-matching experiment, the observer adjusts the amount of three wavelengths in one field (right) so it matches the color of the single wavelength in other field (left).

the spectrum with only two wavelengths. For example, if they were given only the 420-nm and 640-nm lights to mix, they would be unable to match certain colors. As we will see later, people who are color deficient, and therefore can't perceive all colors in the spectrum, can match the colors of all wavelengths in the spectrum by mixing only two other wavelengths. VIRTUAL LAB 1

The Theory: Vision Is Trichromatic

Based on the finding that people with normal color vision need at least three wavelengths to match any wavelength in the test field, Thomas Young (1802) proposed the trichromatic theory of color vision. This theory was later championed by Helmholtz (1852) and is therefore also called the **Young-Helmholtz theory of color vision**. The central idea of the theory is that color vision depends on three receptor mechanisms, each with different spectral sensitivities. (Remember from Chapter 2 that spectral sensitivity indicates the sensitivity to wavelengths across the visible spectrum, as shown in Figure 2.26).

According to this theory, light of a particular wavelength stimulates the three receptor mechanisms to different degrees, and the pattern of activity in the three mechanisms results in the perception of a color. Each wavelength is therefore coded in the nervous system by its own pattern of activity in the three receptor mechanisms.

Physiology of Trichromatic Theory

Over 70 years after the trichromatic theory was first proposed, physiological research identified the three receptor mechanisms proposed by the theory.

Cone Pigments Physiological researchers who were working to identify the receptor mechanisms proposed by trichromatic theory asked the following question: Are there three mechanisms, and, if so, what are their physiological properties? This question was answered in the 1960s, when researchers were able to measure the absorption spectra of three different cone visual pigments, with maximum absorption in the short- (419-nm), middle- (531-nm), and long-wavelength (558-nm) regions of the spectrum (S, M, and L in Figure 7.8; P. K. Brown & Wald, 1964; Dartnall et al., 1983; Schnapf, Kraft, & Baylor, 1987).

Another important advance in our understanding of the physiology of color vision came in the 1980s, when Nathans, Thomas, and Hogness (1986) isolated and sequenced the genes encoding the protein parts of the three different cone pigments (called opsins, see Figure 2.19). This enabled Nathans and coworkers to show that different types of pigments have different sequences of the small molecular groups called amino acids that make up the opsin molecule (see Mollon, 1989, 1993).

These differences in the opsin's amino acids are what cause different pigments to have different absorption spectra. Thus, the short- and middle-wavelength cones, which have only 44 percent of their amino acid sequences in common, have peak absorptions that are separated by 112 nm. In contrast, the middle- and long-wavelength cones, which have about 96 percent identical amino acid sequences, have peak absorptions that are separated by only 27 nm.

Cone Responding and Color Perception If color perception is based on the pattern of activity of these three receptor mechanisms, we should be able to determine which colors will be perceived if we know the response of each of the receptor mechanisms. Figure 7.9 shows the relationship between the responses of the three kinds of receptors and our perception of color. In this figure, the responses in the S, M, and L receptors are indicated by the size of the receptors. For example, blue is signaled by a large response in the S receptor, a smaller response in the M receptor, and an even smaller response in the L receptor. Yellow is signaled by a very small response in the S receptor and large, approximately equal responses in the M and L receptors. **VL 2, 3**

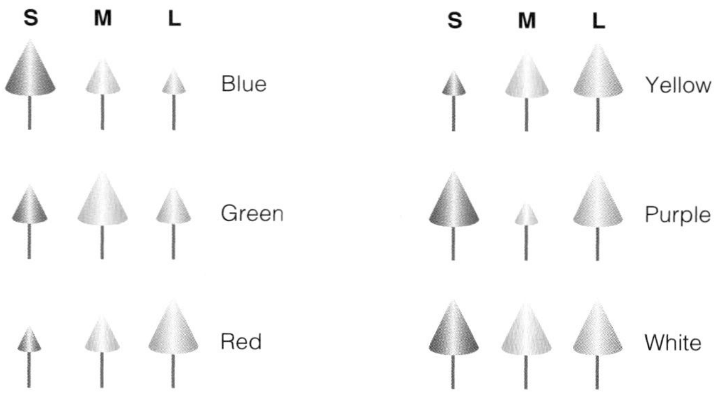

Figure 7.9 Patterns of firing of the three types of cones to different colors. The size of the cone symbolizes the size of the receptor's response.

Thinking of wavelengths as causing certain patterns of receptor responding helps us to predict which colors should result when we combine lights of different colors. For example, what color should result if we project a spot of blue light onto a spot of yellow light? The patterns of receptor activity in Figure 7.9 show that blue light causes high activity in the S receptors and that yellow light

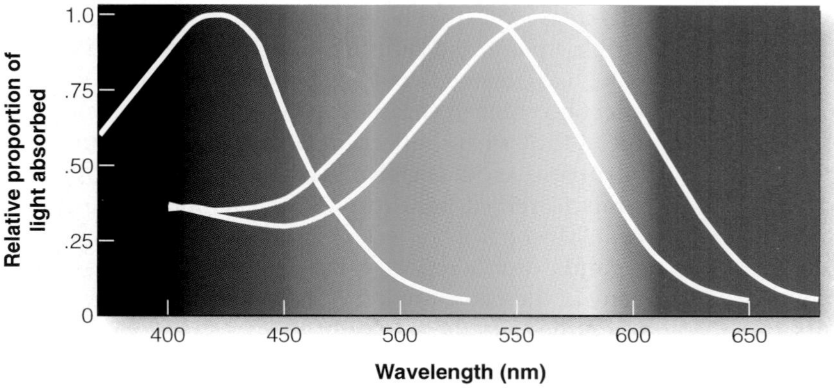

Figure 7.8 Absorption spectra of the three cone pigments.
(From Dartnall, Bowmaker, & Mollon, 1983.)

causes high activity in the M and L receptors. Thus, combining both lights should stimulate all three receptors equally, and we should perceive white because white light contains an equal distribution of wavelengths across the spectrum. This is exactly the result we achieve if we mix blue and yellow lights. (This result surprises some people, because mixing blue and yellow *paints* results in green. The reason we achieve different results from lights and paints is explained in the box "Mixing Colored Paints.")

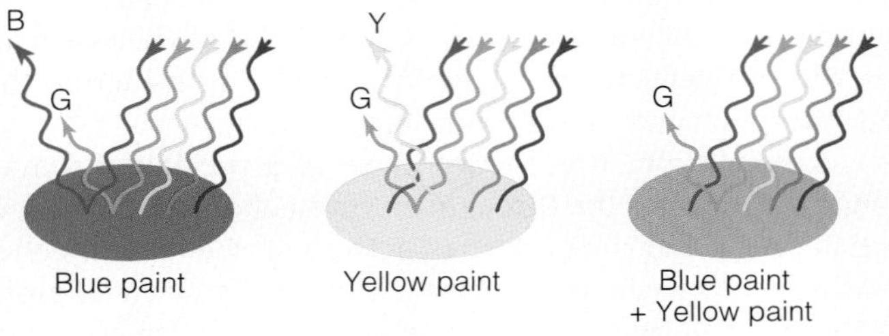

Figure 7.11 ▌ Mixing blue paint and yellow paint creates a paint that appears green. This is subtractive color mixture.

MIXING COLORED PAINTS

Mixing *lights,* as when we superimpose a blue light and a yellow light to result in white (Figure 7.10), is called **additive color mixture** because all of the wavelengths in each light reach the eye and stimulate the cone receptors. Mixing blue and yellow *paints* to create green is called **subtractive color mixture** because each paint in the mixture subtracts wavelengths and decreases the light reaching the cone receptors. We can understand how this works by considering the wavelengths that are subtracted from white light by the blue paint and by the yellow paint (see Figure 7.11 and Table 7.2).

Table 7.2 ▌ *Parts of the spectrum that are absorbed and reflected by blue and yellow paint.*

Note: The colors that are totally absorbed are indicated by shaded squares for each paint. Light that is usually seen as green is the only light that is reflected in common by both paints.

Parts of spectrum

	Blue	Green	Yellow	Orange	Red
Blue paint	Reflects all	Reflects some Absorbs some	Absorbs all	Absorbs all	Absorbs all
Yellow paint	Absorbs all	Reflects some Absorbs some	Reflects all	Absorbs all	Absorbs all

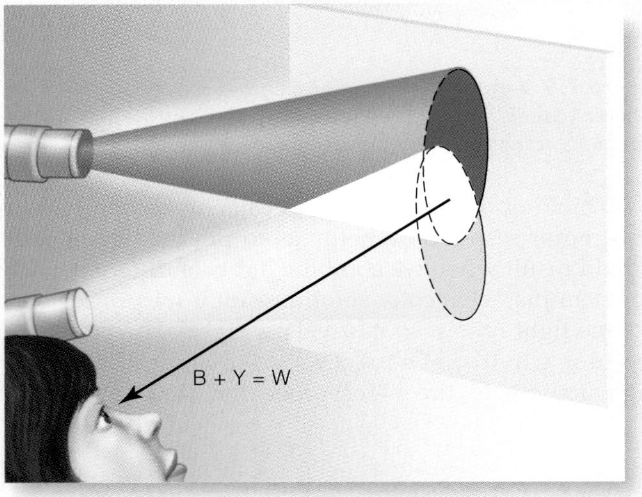

Figure 7.10 ▌ Superimposing a blue light and a yellow light creates the perception of white in the area of overlap. This is additive color mixing.

Blue paint absorbs wavelengths associated with yellow, orange, red, and some of the green, and reflects blue and a little green. Yellow paint absorbs blue, orange, red, and some of the green, and reflects yellow and a little green. When we mix the two paints together, both paints still absorb the same colors they absorbed when alone. From Table 7.2, we can see that the mixture of blue and yellow will therefore absorb all of the blue, yellow, orange, and red. What we perceive is the color that is reflected by both paints in common. Because green is the only color reflected by both paints, mixing blue paint and yellow paint results in green.

The reason that our blue and yellow mixture results in green is that both paints reflect a little green. If our blue paint had reflected only blue and our yellow paint had reflected only yellow, these paints would reflect no color in common, so mixing them would result in little or no reflection across the spectrum, and the mixture would appear black. It is rare, however, for paints to reflect light in only one region of the spectrum. Most paints reflect a broad band of wavelengths. If paints didn't reflect a range of wavelengths, then many of the color-mixing effects of paints that we take for granted would not occur. ▪

Now that we know that our perception of colors is determined by the pattern of activity in different kinds of receptors, we can explain the physiological basis behind the color-matching results that led to the proposal of trichromatic theory. Remember that in a color-matching experiment, a wavelength in one field is matched by adjusting the proportions of three different wavelengths in another field (Figure 7.7). This result is interesting because the lights in the two fields are physically different (they contain different wavelengths) but they are perceptually identical (they look the same). This situation, in which two physically different stimuli are perceptually identical, is called **metamerism**, and the two identical fields in a color-matching experiment are called **metamers**.

The reason metamers look alike is that they both result in the same pattern of response in the three cone receptors. For example, when the proportions of a 620-nm red light and a 530-nm green light are adjusted so the mixture matches the color of a 580-nm light, which looks yellow, the two mixed wavelengths create the same pattern of activity in the cone receptors as the single 580-nm light (Figure 7.12). The 530-nm green light causes a large response in the M receptor, and the 620-nm red light causes a large response in the L receptor. Together, they result in a large response in the M and L receptors and a much smaller response in the S receptor. This is the pattern for yellow and is the same as the pattern generated by the 580-nm light. Thus, as far as the visual system is concerned, these lights are identical.

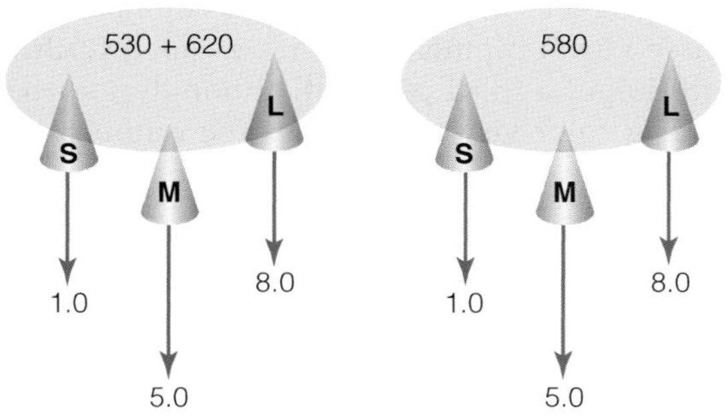

Figure 7.12 ■ The proportions of 530- and 620-nm lights in the field on the left have been adjusted so that the mixtures appear identical to the 580-nm light in the field on the right. The numbers indicate the responses of the short-, medium-, and long-wavelength receptors. There is no difference in the responses of the two sets of receptors so the two fields are perceptually indistinguishable.

Are Three Receptor Mechanisms Necessary for Color Vision? According to trichromatic theory, a light's wavelength is signaled by the pattern of activity of three receptor mechanisms. But do we need three different mechanisms to see colors? The answer to this question is that color vision is possible with two receptor types but not with one. Let's first consider why color vision cannot occur with just one receptor type.

Remember from our discussion of visual transduction in Chapter 2 (see page 33) that a visual pigment molecule is activated when it absorbs one quantum (or photon) of light. This absorption changes the shape of the molecule—a process called isomerization—and triggers a sequence of reactions that eventually generates an electrical signal in the receptor. The reason one receptor type won't work is that absorption of a photon causes the same effect no matter what the wavelength. This is called the **principle of univariance**.

Figure 7.13a indicates what the principle of univariance means when a person has only one visual pigment, which we will call pigment 1. Presenting 1,000 photons of a 550-nm light to this person's eye will isomerize 100 molecules of pigment 1 because the pigment absorbs 10 percent of the light at 550 nm. Presenting 1,000 photons of 590-nm light isomerizes 50 pigment molecules because the pigment absorbs 5 percent of the light at 590 nm. The response to the 590-nm light will, therefore, be smaller than the response to the 550-nm light.

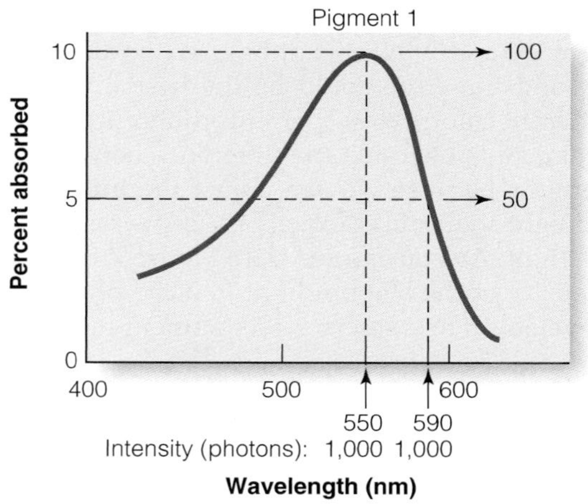

Wavelength	Photons	Isomerized
550	1,000	100
590	1,000	50

(a)

Figure 7.13 ■ (a) Absorption spectrum for pigment 1, showing how to determine the number of molecules isomerized by 1,000 photons of 550- and 590-nm light. The number on the left axis is the percentage of light absorbed. The numbers indicated by the arrows on the right are this percentage multiplied by the intensity of each wavelength. The table shows the result as the number of pigment molecules isomerized by each wavelength.

(continued)

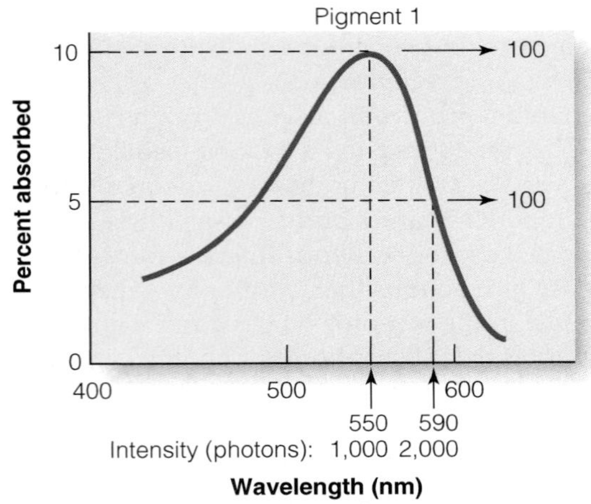

Wavelength	Photons	Isomerized
550	1,000	100
590	2,000	100

(b)

Figure 7.13 (*continued*) ▮ (b) When the intensity of the 590-nm light is increased to 2,000 photons, both wavelengths isomerize 100 pigment molecules.

You might think that this difference between the response to 550 and 590 nm would signal two different wavelengths and therefore could be the basis for perceiving two different colors. However, this difference in response does not enable us to tell the difference between the two wavelengths because we can adjust the intensity of the 590-nm light so it causes exactly the same response as the 550-nm light. As you can see from Figure 7.13b, doubling the intensity of the 590-nm light to 2,000 photons causes this wavelength to isomerize 100 pigment molecules, just like the 550-nm light. Thus, when there is just one visual pigment, we can make any two wavelengths cause the same response by adjusting the *intensity* of one of them. Because of this, one pigment does not provide the information needed to tell one wavelength from another and cannot, therefore, serve as the basis for color vision. This is why we see in shades of gray when the single rod visual pigment controls our vision under dim illuminations.

Adding a second pigment solves the problem created by univariance because although we can still adjust the intensity of two wavelengths to cause the same response in one of the pigments, it is not possible to adjust the intensities to cause the same responses in two pigments simultaneously. An example is shown in Figure 7.14. We saw from Figure 7.13b that 1,000 photons of 550-nm light and 2,000 photons of 590-nm light both isomerize 100 molecules of pigment 1. But from Figure 7.14 we can see that these two stimuli do not isomerize the same number of molecules in pigment 2. The 1,000-photon 550-nm light isomerizes 50 molecules and the 2,000-photon 590-nm light isomerizes 20 molecules.

We could try many other intensities of these wavelengths, but we would always find that the responses to different wavelengths are always different when we take the response of both pigments into account. Because this gives the visual system a way to tell the difference between different wavelengths, no matter what the intensities, color vision becomes possible. As we will see when we consider color deficiency later in this chapter, there are people with just two types of cone pigment. These people, who are called dichromats, do see colors, just as our calculations predict, but they see fewer colors than people with three visual pigments, who are called **trichromats**. The addition of a third pigment, although not necessary for creating color vision, increases the number of colors that can be seen across the visual spectrum.

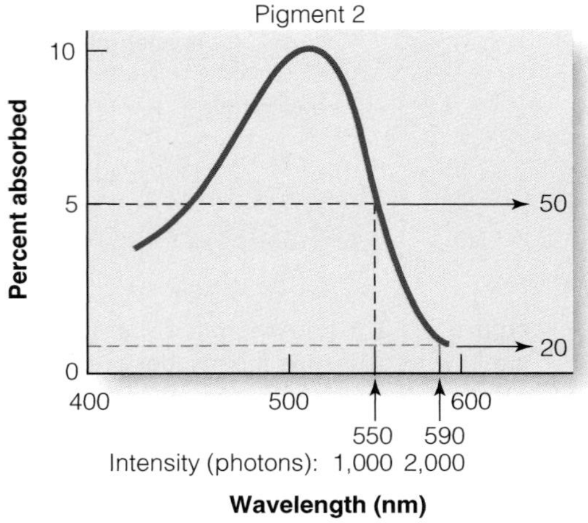

Wavelength	Photons	Isomerized
550	1,000	50
590	2,000	20

Figure 7.14 ▮ Same as Figure 7.13 but for pigment 2, which absorbs light at shorter wavelengths than pigment 1. The table shows that the same intensities and wavelengths that had identical effects for pigment 1 have different effects for pigment 2.

TEST YOURSELF 7.1

1. What are the various functions of color vision?
2. What physical property is most closely associated with color perception? How is this demonstrated by differences in reflection of different objects?
3. Describe trichromatic theory and the experiments on which it was based. How does this theory explain the results of color-matching experiments?
4. Describe how trichromatic theory is based on cone pigments and how the code for color can be determined by the activity of the cones.
5. What are metamers, and how can our perception of metamers be explained by the code for color described above? Why is color vision possible when there are only two different cone pigments but not possible when there is just one pigment? What is the effect of having three pigments rather than just two?
6. Why does mixing blue and yellow lights result in white, but mixing blue and yellow paints result in green?

COLOR DEFICIENCY

It has long been known that some people have difficulty perceiving certain colors. We have described the case of Mr. I, who lost his ability to see color due to brain damage. However, most problems with color vision involve just a partial loss of color perception, called **color deficiency**, which is associated with problems with the receptors in the retina.

In a famous early report of color deficiency, well-known 18th-century chemist John Dalton (1798/1948) described his own color perceptions as follows: "All crimsons appear to me to consist chiefly of dark blue: but many of them seem to have a tinge of dark brown. I have seen specimens of crimson, claret, and mud, which were very nearly alike" (p. 102).

Dalton's descriptions of his abnormal color perceptions led to the early use of the term *Daltonism* to describe color deficiency. We now know that there are a number of different types of color deficiency. This has been determined by a color vision test like the one shown in Figure 7.15, which is called an **Ishihara plate**. In this example, people with normal color vision see a "74"; people with a form of red-green color deficiency do not see this. Another way to determine the presence of color deficiency is by using the color-matching procedure to determine the minimum number of wavelengths needed to match any other wavelength in the spectrum. This procedure has revealed the following three types of color deficiency: VL 4

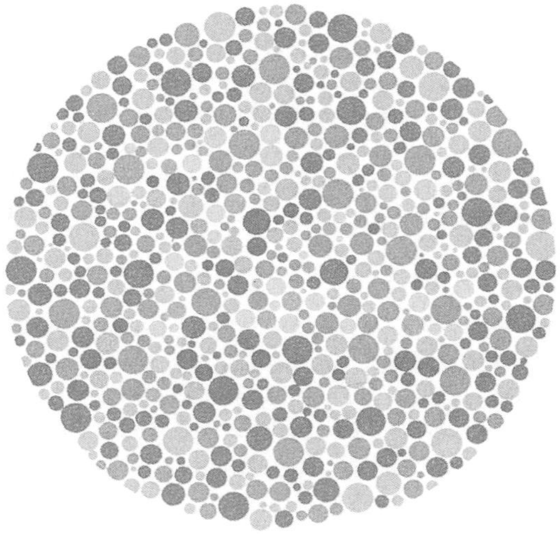

Figure 7.15 ▮ Ishihara plate for testing for color deficiency.

1. A **monochromat** can match any wavelength in the spectrum by adjusting the intensity of any other wavelength. Thus, a monochromat needs only one wavelength to match any color in the spectrum (see Figure 7.7).
2. A **dichromat** needs only two wavelengths to match all other wavelengths in the spectrum.
3. An **anomalous trichromat** needs three wavelengths to match any wavelength, just as a normal trichromat does. However, the anomalous trichromat mixes these wavelengths in different proportions from a trichromat, and an anomalous trichromat is not as good at discriminating between wavelengths that are close together.

Once we have determined whether a person's vision is color deficient, we are still left with the question: What colors does a person with color deficiency see? When I pose this question in my class, a few students suggest that we can answer this question by pointing to objects of various colors and asking a color-deficient person what he sees. (Most color deficient people are male as we will see.) This method does not, however, really tell us what the person perceives because a color-deficient person may say "red" when we point to a strawberry simply because he has learned that people call strawberries "red." It is quite likely that the color-deficient person's experience of "red" is very different from the experience of the person without color defieiency. For all we know, he may be having an experience similar to what a person without deficient color vision would call "yellow."

To determine what a dichromat perceives, we need to locate a **unilateral dichromat**—a person with trichromatic vision in one eye and dichromatic vision in the other eye. Both of the unilateral dichromat's eyes are connected to the same brain, so this person can look at a color with his dichromatic eye and then determine which color it corresponds to in his trichromatic eye. Although unilateral dichromats are extremely rare, the few who have been tested have helped us determine the nature of a dichromat's color experience (Alpern, Kitahara, & Krantz, 1983; Graham et al., 1961; Sloan & Wollach, 1948). Let's now look at the nature of the color experience of both monochromats and dichromats.

Monochromatism

Monochromatism is a rare form of color blindness that is usually hereditary and occurs in only about 10 people out of 1 million (LeGrand, 1957). Monochromats usually have no functioning cones; therefore, their vision has the characteristics of rod vision in both dim and bright lights. Monochromats see everything in shades of lightness (white, gray, and black) and can therefore be called **color-blind** (as opposed to dichromats, who see some chromatic colors and therefore should be called color-deficient).

In addition to a loss of color vision, people with hereditary monochromatism have poor visual acuity and are so sensitive to bright lights that they often must protect their eyes with dark glasses during the day. The reason for this sensitivity is that the rod system is not designed to function in bright light and so becomes overloaded in strong illumination, creating a perception of glare.

Dichromatism

Dichromats experience some colors, though a lesser range than trichromats. There are three major forms of dichromatism: protanopia, deuteranopia, and tritanopia. The two most common kinds, protanopia and deuteranopia, are inherited through a gene located on the X chromosome (Nathans et al., 1986).

Males (XY) have only one X chromosome, so a defect in the visual pigment gene on this chromosome causes color deficiency. Females (XX), on the other hand, with their two X chromosomes, are less likely to become color deficient, because only one normal gene is required for normal color vision. These forms of color vision are therefore called sex-linked because women can carry the gene for color deficiency without being color-deficient themselves, and they can pass the condition to their male offspring. Thus, many more men than women are dichromats.

- **Protanopia** affects 1 percent of males and 0.02 percent of females and results in the perception of colors across the spectrum indicated in Figure 7.16a. A protanope perceives short-wavelength light as blue, and as wavelength is increased, the blue becomes less and less saturated until, at 492 nm, the protanope perceives gray. The wavelength at which the protanope perceives gray is called the **neutral point**. At wavelengths above the neutral point, the protanope perceives yellow, which becomes more saturated as wavelength is increased.
- **Deuteranopia** affects about 1 percent of males and 0.01 percent of females and results in the perception of colors across the spectrum as shown in Figure 7.16b. A deuteranope perceives blue at short wavelengths, sees yellow at long wavelengths, and has a neutral point at about 498 nm (Boynton, 1979).

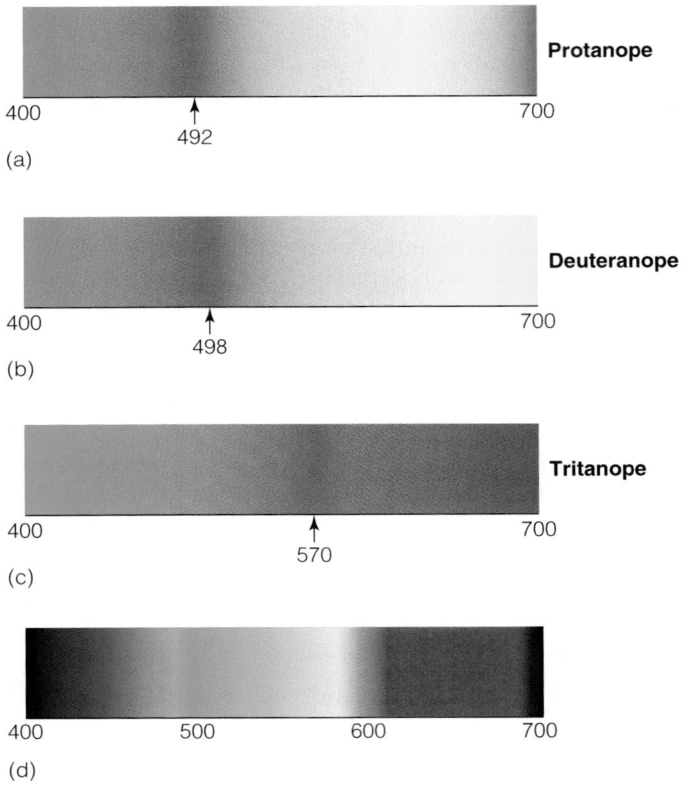

Figure 7.16 ▮ (a–c) The color perceptions of the three kinds of dichromats. The number at the arrow indicates the wavelength of the neutral point, the wavelength at which gray is perceived. (d) Color perception of a trechromat.
(Spectra courtesy of Jay Neitz)

- **Tritanopia** is very rare, affecting only about 0.002 percent of males and 0.001 percent of females. A tritanope sees blue at short wavelengths, sees red at long wavelengths, and has a neutral point at 570 nm (Alpern et al., 1983). VL 5-8

Physiological Mechanisms of Receptor-Based Color Deficiency

What are the physiological mechanisms of color deficiency? Most monochromats have no color vision because they have just one type of cone or no cones. (Review Figure 7.13 to be sure you understand why color vision does not occur if there is just one pigment.) Dichromats are missing one visual pigment, with the protanope missing the long-wavelength pigment and the deuteranope missing the medium-wavelength pigment (W. A. H. Rushton, 1964). Because of the tritanope's rarity and because of the low number of short-wavelength cones, even in normal retinas, it has been difficult to determine which pigment tritanopes are missing, but they are probably missing the short-wavelength pigment.

More recent research has identified differences in the genes that determine visual pigment structure in trichromats and dichromats (Nathans et al., 1986). Based on this gene research, it has also been suggested that anomalous trichromats probably match colors differently from normal trichromats and have more difficulty discriminating between some wavelengths because their M and L pigment spectra have been shifted so they are closer together (Neitz, Neitz, & Jacobs, 1991).

OPPONENT-PROCESS THEORY OF COLOR VISION

Although trichromatic theory explains a number of color vision phenomena, including color matching and color mixing, and some facts about color deficiency, there are some color perceptions it cannot explain. These color perceptions were demonstrated by Ewald Hering (1834–1918), another eminent physiologist who was working at about the same time as Helmholtz. Hering used the results of phenomenological observations, in which stimuli were presented and observers described what they perceived, to propose the **opponent-process theory of color vision.** This theory stated that color vision was caused by opposing responses generated by blue and yellow and by red and green.

Behavioral Evidence for the Theory

You can make some phenomenological observations similar to Hering's by doing the following demonstrations.

DEMONSTRATION

"Opposing" Afterimages

Cover the blue and yellow squares in Figure 7.17 with a piece of white paper and illuminate the red and green squares with your desk lamp. Pick a spot on the border between the two squares and look at it for about 30 seconds. If you then look at a piece of white paper and blink, the image you see, which is called an *afterimage,* is colored. Notice the position of the red and green areas in the afterimage. Then repeat this procedure for the blue and yellow squares. ■

Figure 7.17 ▮ Color matrix for afterimage and simultaneous contrast demonstrations.

Hering's observation that viewing a red field generates a green afterimage, that viewing a green field generates a red afterimage, and that analogous results occur for blue and yellow, led him to propose that red and green are paired and blue and yellow are paired. VL 9–12

DEMONSTRATION

Afterimages and Simultaneous Contrast

Cut out a ½-inch square of white paper and place it in the center of the green square in Figure 7.17. Cover the other squares with white paper and stare at the center of the white square for about 30 seconds. Then look at a white background and blink to observe the afterimage. What color is the outside area of the afterimage? What color is the small square in the center? Repeat your observations on the red, blue, and yellow squares in Figure 7.17. ■

When you made your observations using the green square, you probably confirmed your previous observation that green and red are paired because the afterimage corresponding to the green area of the original square is red. But the color of the small square in the center also shows that green and red are paired: Most people see a green square inside the red afterimage. This green afterimage is due to **simultaneous color contrast**, an effect that occurs when surrounding an area with a color changes the appearance of the surrounded area. In this case, the red afterimage surrounds a white area and causes the white area to appear green. Table 7.3 indicates this result and the results that occur when we repeat this demonstration on the other squares. All of these results show a clear pairing of red and green and of blue and yellow. VL 13–17

Table 7.3 ▮ *Results of afterimage and simultaneous contrast demonstration*

Original Square	Color of Outside Afterimage	Color of Inside Afterimage
Green	Red	Green
Red	Green	Red
Blue	Yellow	Blue
Yellow	Blue	Yellow

DEMONSTRATION

Visualization and Color Scaling

The first part of this demonstration involves visualizing colors. Start by visualizing the color red. Attach this color to a specific object such as a fire engine, if that makes your visualizing easier. Now visualize a reddish-yellow and then a reddish-green. Which of these two combinations is easiest to visualize? Now do the same thing for blue. Visualize a pure blue, then a bluish-green and a bluish-yellow. Again, which of the combinations is easiest to visualize?

Most people find it easy to visualize a bluish-green or a reddish-yellow but find it difficult (or impossible) to visualize a reddish-green or a bluish-yellow. The idea that it is difficult to see blue and yellow or red and green together brings us to the second part of the demonstration.

For the color scaling part of the demonstration, refer to the color patches in Figure 7.18. Your task is to estimate the percentages of blue, green, yellow, and red in each patch, and enter your estimates in the table below. For example, an estimate for the 450 nm patch might be 90 percent blue and 10 percent red.

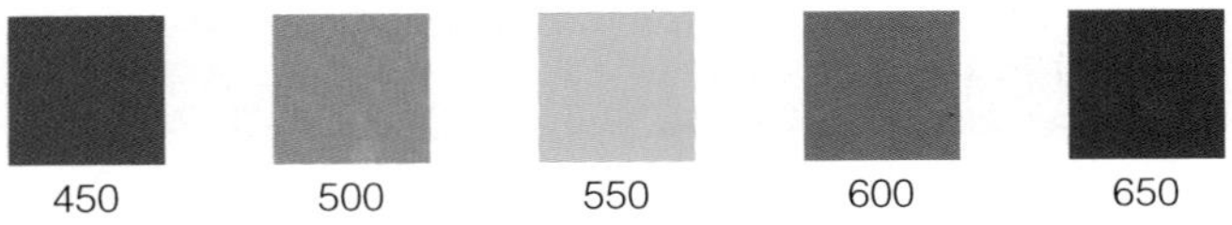

Figure 7.18 ▮ Estimate the percentage of blue, green, yellow, and red in each patch, and enter your estimates in the table for each wavelength.

	% Blue	% Green	% Yellow	% Red
450				
500				
550				
600				
650				

Once you have done this, notice whether you judged any of the patches as containing both blue and yellow or both red and green. When a large number of observers carried out this task, they rarely reported seeing blue and yellow or red and green at the same time (Abramov & Gordon, 1994), just as the results of the visualization demonstration would predict. ■

The above observations, plus Hering's observation that people who are color-blind to red are also color-blind to green, and that people who can't see blue also can't see yellow, led to the conclusion that red and green are paired and that blue and yellow are paired. Based on this conclusion, Hering proposed the opponent-process theory of color vision (Hering, 1878, 1905, 1964).

The Theory: Vision Is an "Opponent" Process

The basic idea underlying Hering's theory is shown in Figure 7.19. He proposed three mechanisms, each of which responds in opposite ways to different intensities or wavelengths of light. The Black (−) White (+) mechanism responds positively to white light and negatively to the absence of light. Red (+) Green (−) responds positively to red and negatively to green, and Blue (−) Yellow (+) responds negatively to blue and positively to yellow.

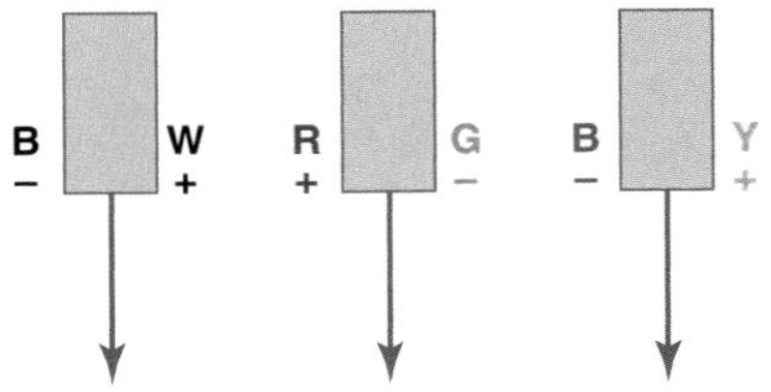

Figure 7.19 ▮ The three opponent mechanisms proposed by Hering.

Hering thought that these positive and negative responses were caused by the buildup and breakdown of chemicals in the retina. He believed that white, yellow, and red causes a reaction that results in a buildup of the chemicals, and black, green, and blue causes a reaction that results in a breakdown of the chemicals. Although this part of Hering's theory was not correct, modern physiological research showed that these colors do cause physiologically opposite responses.

The Physiology of Opponent-Process Vision

Although Hering's phenomenological observations supported his theory, opponent-process theory was not initially taken as seriously as trichromatic theory. This is because the phenomenological nature of the after image and visualization evidence was not as easy to verify as the more objective color-matching results that supported trichromatic theory. In addition, people found it difficult to imagine a physiological process that resulted in opposite responses to different wavelengths. However, modern research, which has measured the response of single neurons to different wavelengths, has provided physiological evidence for neurons that respond in opposite ways to blue and yellow and to red and green.

Opponent Neurons In the 1950s and 60s researchers began finding **opponent neurons** in the retina and lateral geniculate nucleus that responded with an excitatory response to light from one part of the spectrum and with an inhibitory response to light from another part (R. L. De-Valois, 1960; Svaetichin, 1956). For example, Figure 7.20 shows records from four neurons in the lateral geniculate nucleus that respond to light at one end of the spectrum with an increase in nerve firing and to light at the other end of the spectrum with an inhibition of spontaneous ac-

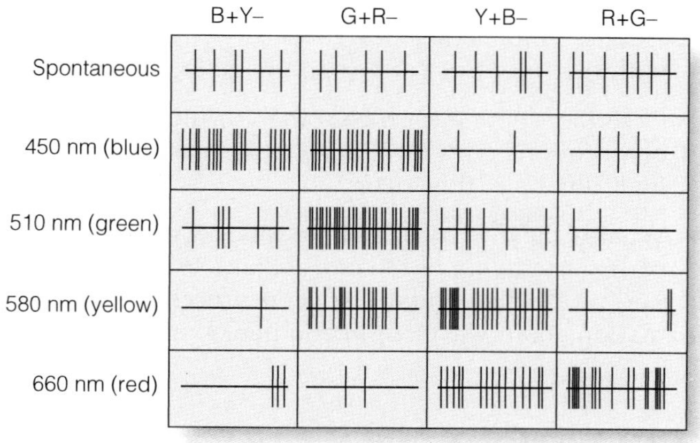

Figure 7.20 ▌ Responses of opponent cells in the monkey's lateral geniculate nucleus. These cells respond in opposite ways to blue and yellow (B+Y– or Y+B–) and to red and green (G+R– or R+G–).
(From "Primate Color Vision," by R. L. DeValois and G. H. Jacobs, 1968, Science, 162, *533–540, figure 5. Copyright © 1968 by the American Association for the Advancement of Science. Reprinted by permission.)*

tivity. For each cell, spontaneous activity is indicated in the top record, and the responses to 450-nm (blue), 510-nm (green), 580-nm (yellow), and 660-nm (red) lights are shown in the other records.

The B+Y– cell responds to the 450-nm light with an increase in firing and to the 580-nm light with an inhibition of spontaneous activity. The G+R– cell increases its firing to the 510-nm light and decreases its firing to the 660-nm light. The Y+B– and R+G– cells also show opponent responses, but they are inhibited by short wavelengths and are excited by long wavelengths (see also R. L. DeValois et al., 1966). **VL 18–23**

How Opponent Responding Can Be Created by Three Receptors The discovery of opponent neurons provided physiological evidence for opponent process theory to go with the three different cone pigments of trichromatic theory. In the 1800s it was thought that only one of these theories could be correct. But now we know that both theories are correct and that each one describes physiological mechanisms at different places in the visual system. Figure 7.21 shows how this works.

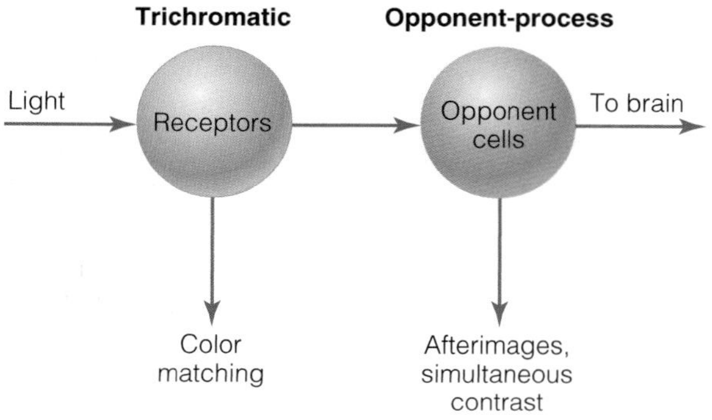

Figure 7.21 ▌ Our experience of color is shaped by physiological mechanisms, both in the receptors and in opponent neurons.

Trichromatic theory describes what is happening right at the beginning of the visual system, in the receptors of the retina. The existence of three different kinds of cone receptors is why it takes a minimum of three wavelengths to match any wavelength in the spectrum. Opponent-process theory describes events later in the visual system. Opponent cells are responsible for perceptual experiences such as afterimages and simultaneous contrast.

Figure 7.22 shows two neural circuits in which three types of cones are wired in a way that creates two kinds of opponent neurons. In Circuit 1 the short-wavelength cone sends an excitatory signal to the ganglion cell, and the medium- and long-wavelength cones pool their activity and then send inhibitory signals to this cell. (The bipolar cells have been omitted to simplify the circuits.) This creates a B+Y– opponent neuron. In Circuit 2, the medium-wavelength cone sends excitatory signals and the long-wavelength cone sends inhibitory signals to the ganglion cell. This creates a G+R– opponent neuron.

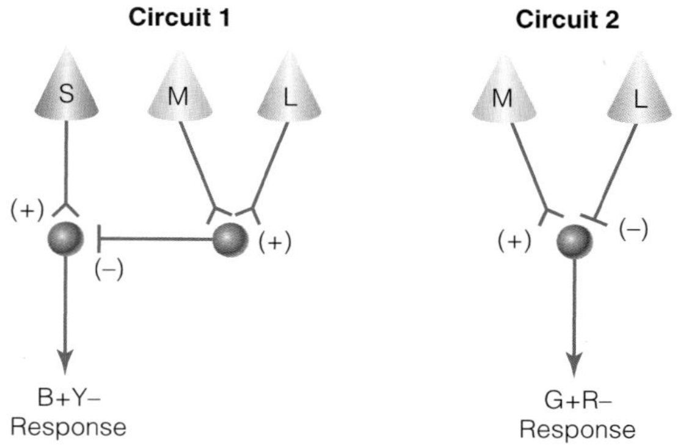

Figure 7.22 ▌ Neural circuit showing how the blue–yellow and red–green mechanisms can be created by excitatory and inhibitory inputs from the three types of cone receptors.

The important thing about these two circuits is that their responses are determined both by the wavelengths to which the receptors respond best and by the arrangement of inhibitory and excitatory synapses. Processing for color vision therefore takes place in two stages: First, the receptors respond with different patterns to different wavelengths (trichromatic theory), and then later neurons integrate the inhibitory and excitatory signals from the receptors (opponent-process theory).

COLOR IN THE CORTEX

How is color represented in the cortex? One possible answer is that there is a specific area in the cortex that is a specialized "color center" that processes information about color (Livingstone & Hubel, 1988; Zeki, 1983a, 1983b). **Cerebral achromatopsia**, color blindness due to damage to the cortex, supports this idea. Although Mr. I's cerebral achromatopsia meant that he could no longer see color, he still had excellent visual acuity and could still see form and movement. This absence of color perception, while other visual functions remained relatively normal, supports the idea that an area specialized for color perception has been damaged.

However, when researchers record from neurons in the cortex, a different picture emerges. They find cortical neurons that respond to just some wavelengths in the spectrum, or have opponent responses, in many areas of the cortex, including the striate cortex (V1) and areas V2 and V4 in the ventral processing stream (see Figure 4.18). But these neurons that respond to color also usually respond to specific forms and orientations (Lennie et al., 1990; Leventhal et al., 1995; Shein & Desimone, 1990). Also, many of the wavelength-selective neurons in the area that was originally designated as the "color module" respond to white, leading some researchers to question the idea that these neurons determine our perception of color (Gordon & Abramov, 2001; also see Girard et al., 2002; Heywood & Cowey, 1998; Hinkle & Connor, 2002). Taken together, the evidence seems to show that there may not be a single "module" for color vision (Engel et al., 1997; Gegenfurtner, 2001; Zeki & Marini, 1998). Thus, color vision presents an example of distributed processing in the cortex (see Chapter 4, page 88).

Discovering the cortical mechanism for color perception is complicated because there are two issues involved in determining how the cortex processes color information: (1) Where is information about wavelength processed? and (2) Where is the perception of color determined? You might think these are equivalent questions because color is determined largely by wavelength. However, there are people who can't see colors but who can use information about wavelength. An example is M.S., who suffered from cerebral achromatopsia due to an illness that left his cone pigments intact but damaged his cortex (Stoerig, 1998). Although he could not see color, he was able to use wavelength information being sent to the brain by the cones. For example, he could detect the border between two adjacent fields with different wavelengths even though they both appeared the same shade of gray.

This result and others show that wavelength information is being processed by the undamaged area of M.S.'s brain but that this information is not being transformed into the experience of color due to damage to another area. Understanding how color perception occurs in the brain, therefore, involves determining both how wavelength information is processed and how further processing of this information creates the experience of color.

TEST YOURSELF 7.2

1. What is color deficiency? How can it be detected using the procedure of color mixing? How can we determine how a color-deficient person perceives different wavelengths?
2. How is color deficiency caused by (a) problems with the receptors? and (b) damage to the cortex?
3. Describe opponent-process theory, including the observations on which it is based and the physiological basis of this theory.
4. What is the evidence that a number of areas in the cortex are involved in color vision? Why is it important to distinguish between processing information about wavelength and perceiving color?

PERCEIVING COLORS UNDER CHANGING ILLUMINATION

It is midday, with the sun high in the sky, and as you are walking to class you notice a classmate who is wearing a particularly attractive green sweater. Then, a few minutes later, as you are sitting in class, you again notice the same green sweater. The fact that the sweater appears green both outside under sunlight and inside under the artificial illumination of lightbulbs may not seem particularly remarkable. After all, the sweater *is* green, isn't it? However, when we consider the interaction between the illumination and the properties of the sweater, we can appreciate that your perception of the sweater as green, both outside and inside, represents a remarkable achievement of the visual system. This achievement is called **color constancy**—we perceive the colors of objects as being relatively constant even under changing illumination.

We can appreciate why color constancy is an impressive achievement by considering the interaction between illumination, such as sunlight or lightbulbs, and the reflection properties of an object, such as the green sweater. First, let's consider the illumination. Figure 7.23 shows

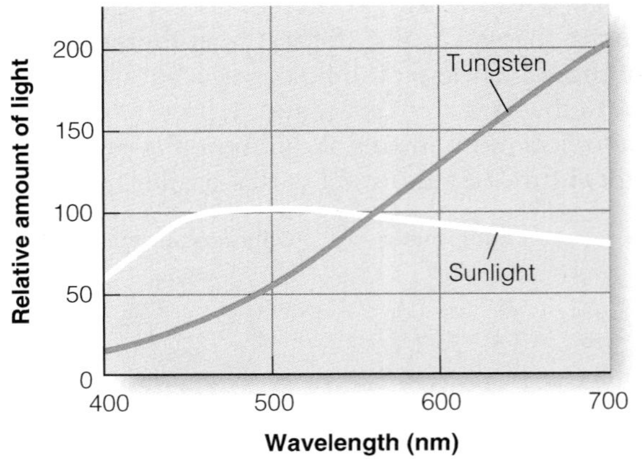

Figure 7.23 ▌ The wavelength distribution of sunlight and of light from a tungsten light bulb.
(Based on data from "Spectral Distribution of Typical Daylight as a Function of Correlated Color Temperature," by D. B. Judd, D. L. MacAdam & G. Wyszecki, 1964. Journal of the Optical Society of America, *54, 1031–1040.)*

the wavelengths that are contained in sunlight and the wavelengths that are contained in light from a lightbulb. The sunlight contains approximately equal amounts of energy at all wavelengths, which is a characteristic of white light. The bulb contains much more energy at long wavelengths. This wavelength distribution is sometimes called "tungsten" light because it is produced by the tungsten filament inside the lightbulb. This large amount of long-wavelength light is why the tungsten bulb looks slightly yellow. (Note that lightbulb manufacturers now make a "daylight" bulb that simulates natural light.)

Now consider the interaction between the wavelengths produced by the illumination and the wavelengths reflected from the green sweater. The reflectance curve of the sweater is indicated by the green line in Figure 7.24. It reflects mostly medium-wavelength light, as we would expect of something that is green. To determine the wavelengths actually reflected from the sweater, we multiply this curve by the amount of light at each wavelength for the sunlight and for the tungsten light. The result indicates that the sweater reflects more long-wavelength light into the eye when it is seen under tungsten illumination (gold curve) than when it is seen under sunlight (white curve). Nonetheless, we still see the sweater as green.

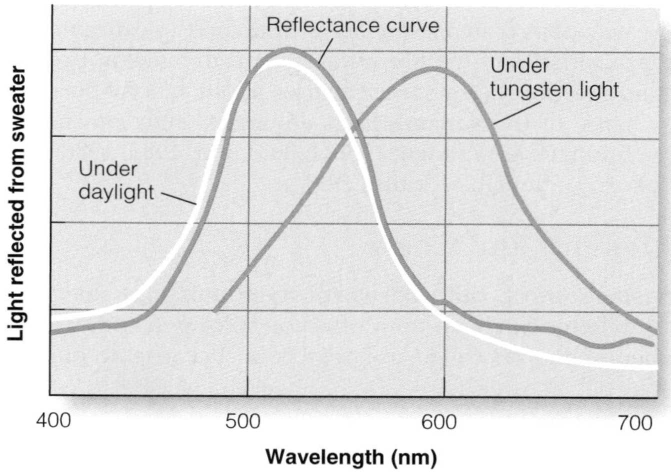

Figure 7.24 ▌ The reflectance curve of a sweater (green curve) and the wavelengths reflected from the sweater when it is illuminated by daylight (white) and by tungsten light (gold).

DEMONSTRATION

Color Perception Under Changing Illumination

View the color circle of Figure 7.3 so it is illuminated by natural light by taking it outdoors or illuminating it with light from a window. Then illuminate it with the tungsten lightbulb of your desk lamp. Notice whether the colors change and, if so, how much they change. ■

In this demonstration you may have noticed some change in color as you changed the illumination, but the change was probably much less than we would predict based on the change in the wavelength distribution of the light. Even though the wavelengths reflected from a blue object illuminated by long-wavelength-rich tungsten light can match the wavelengths reflected by a yellow object illuminated by sunlight (Jameson, 1985), our perception of color remains relatively constant with changing illumination. As color-vision researcher Dorthea Jameson puts it, "A blue bird would not be mistaken for a goldfinch if it were brought indoors" (1985, p. 84).

Researchers still do not completely understand why color constancy occurs, however it is likely that it is caused by a number of things working together. We will consider some of these things, beginning with chromatic adaptation.

Chromatic Adaptation

One reason why color constancy occurs lies in the results of the following demonstration.

DEMONSTRATION

Adapting to Red

Illuminate Figure 7.25 with a bright light from your desk lamp; then, with your left eye near the page and your right eye closed, look at the field with your left eye for about 30 to 45 seconds. Then look at various colored objects in your environment, first with your left eye and then with your right.

Figure 7.25 ▌ Adapting field for chromatic adaptation demonstration. ■

This demonstration shows that color perception can be changed by **chromatic adaptation**—prolonged exposure to chromatic color. Adaptation to the red light selectively bleaches your long-wavelength cone pigment, which decreases your sensitivity to red light and causes you to see the reds and oranges viewed with your left (adapted) eye as less saturated and bright than those viewed with the right eye.

We can understand how chromatic adaptation contributes to color constancy by realizing that when you walk into a room illuminated with tungsten light, the eye adapts to the long-wavelength-rich light, which decreases your eye's sensitivity to long wavelengths. This decreased sensitivity causes the long-wavelength light reflected from objects to have less effect than before adaptation, and this compensates for the greater amount of long-wavelength "tungsten" light that is reflected from everything in the room. Because of this adaptation, the tungsten illumination has only a small effect on your perception of color.

This idea that chromatic adaptation is responsible for color constancy has been tested in an experiment by Keiji Uchikawa and coworkers (1989). Observers viewed isolated patches of colored paper under three different conditions (Figure 7.26): (a) *baseline:* paper and observer illuminated by white light; (b) *observer not adapted:* paper illuminated by red light, observer by white (the illumination of the object is changed, but the observer is not chromatically adapted); and (c) *observer adapted to red:* both paper and observer illuminated by red light (the illumination of the object is changed, and the observer is chromatically adapted).

The results from these three conditions are shown above each condition. For the *baseline condition,* a green patch is perceived as green. For the *observer not adapted condition,* the observer perceives the patches of color as being shifted toward the red. Thus, color constancy did not occur in this condition. But in the *observer adapted to red condition,* perception was shifted only slightly to the red. Thus, the chromatic adaptation has created **partial color constancy**—the perception of the object is shifted but not as much as when there was no chromatic adaptation. The eye adjusts its sensitivity to different wavelengths in order to keep color perception approximately constant under different illuminations.

The Effect of the Surroundings

An object's perceived color is affected not only by the observer's state of adaptation, but also by the object's surroundings, as shown by the following demonstration.

DEMONSTRATION

Color and the Surroundings

Illuminate the green quadrant of Figure 7.17 with tungsten light, and then look at the square through a small hole punched in a piece of paper so that all you see through the hole is part of the green area. Now repeat this observation while illuminating the same area with daylight from your window. ■

When the surroundings are masked, most people perceive the green area to be slightly more yellow under the tungsten light than in daylight, which shows that color constancy works less well when the surroundings are masked. A number of investigators have shown that color constancy works best when an object is surrounded by objects of many different colors, a situation that often occurs when viewing objects in the environment (E. H. Land, 1983, 1986; E. H. Land & McCann, 1971).

The surroundings help us achieve color constancy because the visual system—in ways that are still not completely understood—uses the information provided by the way objects in a scene are illuminated to estimate the characteristics of the illumination and to make appropriate corrections. (For some theories about exactly how the presence of the surroundings enhances color constancy, see Brainard & Wandell, 1986; E. H. Land, 1983, 1986; and Pokorny, Shevell, & Smith, 1991.)

Memory and Color

A small effect, but one worth mentioning, is that past knowledge can have some effect on color perception. This phenomenon is called **memory color** because an object's

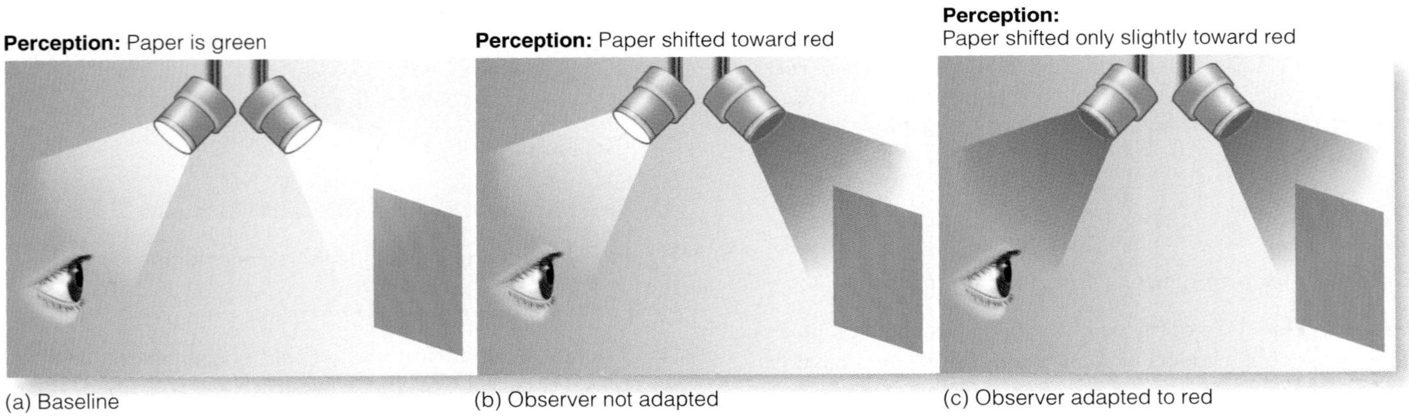

Figure 7.26 ■ The three conditions in Uchikawa et al.'s (1989) experiment. See text for details.

characteristic color influences our perception of its color. Research has shown that because people know the colors of familiar objects, like a red stop sign, or a green tree, they judge these familiar objects as having richer, more saturated colors than unfamiliar objects that reflect the same wavelengths (Jin & Shevell, 1996; Ratner & McCarthy, 1990). Thus, our ability to remember the colors of familiar objects may help us perceive these colors under different illuminations.

Another effect of memory on color perception occurs not because we remember the colors of familiar objects, but because we often don't accurately remember the colors we have seen in the past. Thus, when we see a red stop sign that is illuminated by a street light at night, we may not notice that it appears a slightly different shade of red than when we saw it illuminated by sunlight earlier in the day. Remembering that stop signs are red helps us perceive them as red, however, we don't remember the exact shade of red, and we don't notice the slight shifts that occur in our perception when we view objects under different illuminations at different times (Jin & Shevell, 1996).

Although we don't totally understand why color constancy occurs, it is a good thing it does. Without color constancy, it would be meaningless to say "the sweater is green" or "the car is red" (Delahunt & Brainard, 2004). Without color constancy, the color we see would depend on how the sweater or car was being illuminated. Luckily, color constancy works, so we can refer to objects as having a particular well-defined color.

LIGHTNESS CONSTANCY

We not only perceive chromatic colors like red and green as remaining relatively constant, even when the illumination changes, but we also perceive achromatic colors, like white, gray, and black, as remaining fairly constant as well. Thus, we perceive a Labrador retriever as black when it is inside under dim illumination, and it remains black even when it runs out of the house into bright sunlight.

Consider the problem facing the visual system in this situation. The Labrador retriever lying on the rug in the living room is illuminated by a 100-watt lightbulb in the overhead light fixture. Some of the light that hits the retriever's black coat is reflected, and we see the coat as black. When the dog goes outside, so its coat is illuminated by bright sunlight, much more light hits its coat, compared to inside, and therefore much more light is also reflected. But the dog still appears black. Even though more light is reflected, the perception of the shade of achromatic color (white, gray, and black), which we call **lightness**, remains the same. This constancy of achromatic color in the face of changes in the amount of light reflected into the eyes is called **lightness constancy**.

The visual system's problem is that the amount of light reaching the eye from an object depends on two things: (1) illumination—how much light is striking the object's surface—and (2) the object's **reflectance**—the proportion of this light that the object reflects into our eyes. When lightness constancy occurs, our perception of lightness is determined not by the illumination hitting an object, but by the object's reflectance. Objects that look black reflect about 5 percent of the light. Objects that look gray reflect about 10 to 70 percent of the light (depending on the shade of gray); and objects that look white, like the paper in this book, reflect 80 to 90 percent of the light. Thus, our perception of an object's lightness is related not to the *amount* of light that is reflected from the object, which can change depending on the illumination, but on the *percentage* of light reflected from the object, which remains the same no matter what the illumination.

You can appreciate the existence of lightness constancy by imagining a checkerboard illuminated by room light, like the one in Figure 7.27. In this checkerboard, the white squares have a reflectance of 90 percent, and the black squares have a reflectance of 5 percent. Because the intensity inside the room is 100 units, the white squares reflect 90 units and the black squares reflect 5 units. Now, when we take the checkerboard outside into bright sunlight, where the intensity is 10,000, the white squares reflect 9,000 units of light, and the black squares reflect 500 units. But even though the black squares now reflect much more light than the white squares did when the checkerboard was inside, they still look black. Your perception is determined by the reflectance, not the amount of light reflected.

What is responsible for lightness constancy? There are a number of possible causes.

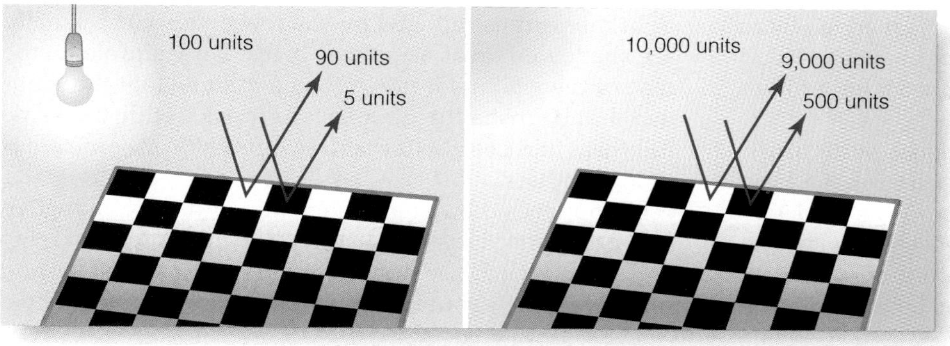

Figure 7.27 ▌ A black-and-white checkerboard illuminated by tungsten light and by sunlight.

Intensity Relationships: The Ratio Principle

One observation about our perception of lightness is that when an object is illuminated evenly—that is, when the illumination is the same over the whole object, as in our checkerboard example—then the ratio principle determines lightness. The **ratio principle** states that two areas that reflect different amounts of light look the same if the *ratios* of their intensities to the intensities of the surrounding areas are the same (Jacobson & Gilchrist, 1988; Wallach, 1963). Thus, even though the amount of light reflected from our checkerboard is increased by a factor of 100 when we move it outside, the ratio of the intensity reflected from the white square to the intensity reflected from the black square remains the same. Because the ratio is 90 to 5 in both cases, our perception of the white and black squares remains the same. But although the ratio principle works well for flat, evenly-illuminated objects like our checkerboard, things get more complicated for objects in three-dimensional scenes, which may be illuminated unevenly.

Lightness Perception Under Uneven Illumination

If you look around, you will probably notice that the illumination is not even over the entire scene, as was the case for our two-dimensional checkerboard. The illumination in three-dimensional scenes is usually uneven because of shadows cast by one object onto another or because one part of an object faces the light and another part faces away from the light. For example, in Figure 7.28, in which a shadow is cast across a wall, it is necessary to determine whether the changes in appearance we see across the wall are due to differences in the lightness or color of different parts of the wall or to differences in the way the wall is illuminated.

The problem for the perceptual system is that it has to somehow take the uneven illumination into account. One way to state this problem is that the perceptual system needs to distinguish between reflectance edges and illumination edges. A **reflectance edge** is an edge where the reflectance of two surfaces changes. Thus, the border between areas *a* and *b* in Figure 7.28 is a reflectance edge. An **illumination edge** is an edge where the illumination changes. Thus, the border between *b* and *c* is an illumination edge. (Also see Figure 5.8 for another example.)

Some explanations for how the visual system distinguishes between these two types of edges have been proposed (see Adelson, 1999; Gilchrist, 1994; and Gilchrist et al., 1999, for details). The basic idea behind these explanations is that the perceptual system uses a number of sources of information to take the illumination into account. Let's look at a few of these sources of information.

Figure 7.28 ▌ This unevenly illuminated wall contains both reflectance edges and illumination edges. The perceptual system must distinguish between these two types of edges to accurately perceive the actual properties of the wall and other parts of the scene, as well.

The Information in Shadows In order for lightness constancy to work, the visual system needs to be able to take the uneven illumination created by shadows into account. It must determine that this change in illumination caused by a shadow is due to an illumination edge and not due to a reflectance edge. Obviously, the visual system usually succeeds in doing this because although the light intensity is reduced by shadows, you don't usually see shadowed areas as gray or black. For example, in the case of the wall in Figure 7.29, you assume that the shadowed and unshadowed areas are bricks with the same lightness and color, but that less light falls on some areas than on others.

How does the visual system know that the change in intensity caused by the shadow is an illumination edge and not a reflectance edge? One thing the visual system may take into account is the shadow's meaningful shape.

Bruce Goldstein

Figure 7.29 ▮ The pattern created by shadows on a surface is usually interpreted as a change in the pattern of illumination, not as a change in the material making up the surface. The fact that we see all of the bricks on this wall as made of the same material, despite the illumination changes, is an example of lightness constancy.

In this particular example, we know that the shadow was cast by a tree, so we know it is the illumination that is changing, not the color of the bricks on the wall. Another clue is provided by the nature of the shadow's contour, as illustrated by the following demonstration.

DEMONSTRATION

The Penumbra and Lightness Perception

Place an object, such as a cup, on a white piece of paper on your desk. Then illuminate the cup at an angle with your desk lamp and adjust the lamp's position to produce a shadow with a slightly fuzzy border, as in Figure 7.30a. (Generally, moving the lamp closer to the cup makes the border get fuzzier.) The fuzzy border of a shadow is called the shadow's **penumbra**. Now take your marker and draw a thick line, as shown in Figure 7.30b, so you can no longer see the penumbra. What happens to your perception of the shadowed area inside the black line?

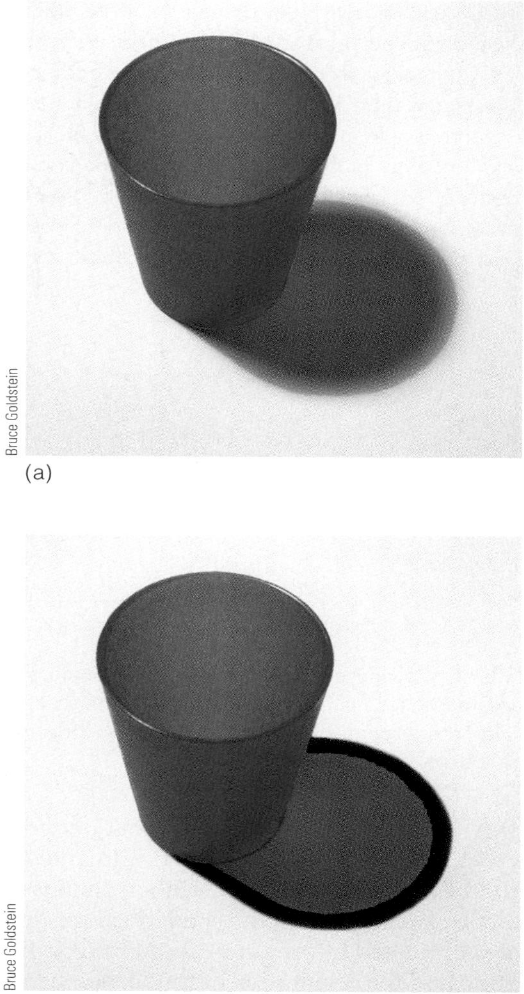

(b)

Figure 7.30 ▮ (a) A cup and its shadow. (b) The same cup and shadow with the penumbra covered by a black border. ■

Covering the penumbra causes most people to perceive a change in the appearance of the shadowed area. Instead of looking like a shadow on a piece of white paper, it looks like a dark spot on the paper. In other words, the shadow and its penumbra are initially perceived as an illumination edge, but masking off the penumbra changes the perception to a reflectance edge.

The Orientation of Surfaces The following demonstration provides an example of how information about the orientation of a surface affects our perception of lightness.

DEMONSTRATION

Perceiving Lightness at a Corner

Stand a folded index card on end so that it resembles the outside corner of a room, and illuminate it so that one side is illuminated and the other is in shadow. When you look at the corner, you can easily tell that both sides of the corner are made of the same white material but that the nonilluminated side is shadowed (Figure 7.31a). In other words, you perceive the edge between the illuminated and shadowed "walls" as an illumination edge.

Now create a hole in another card and, with the hole a few inches from the corner of the folded card, view the corner with one eye about a foot from the hole (Figure 7.31b). If, when viewing the corner through the hole, you perceive the corner as a flat surface, your perception of the left and right surfaces will change.

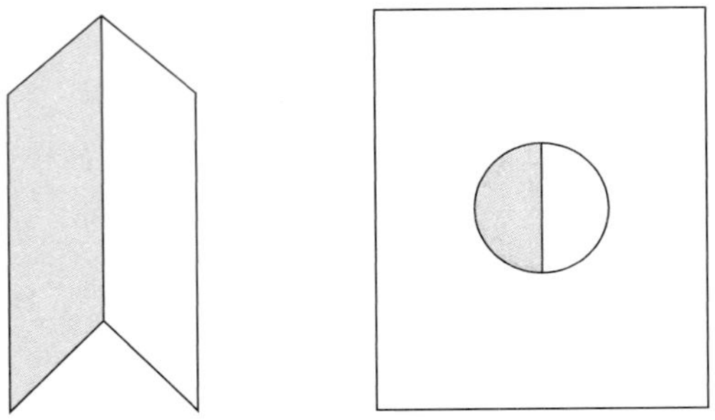

(a) (b)

Figure 7.31 ▮ Viewing a shaded corner. (a) Illuminate the folded card so one side is illuminated and the other is in shadow. (b) View the card through a small hole so the two sides of the corner are visible, as shown. ■

In this demonstration the illumination edge you perceived at first became transformed into an erroneous perception of a reflectance edge. The erroneous perception occurs because viewing the shaded corner through a small hole eliminated information about the conditions of illumination and the orientation of the corner. In order for lightness constancy to occur, it is important that the visual system have adequate information about the conditions of illumination. Without this information, lightness constancy can break down.

How Images Are Perceptually Organized Figure 7.32 provides an example of how lightness perception can be affected by the way elements are perceptually organized (Anderson & Winawer, 2005). The four disks on the left are identical to the four disks on the right in terms of the pattern and intensity of light reflected from the disks. To prove this to yourself, mask the surroundings by viewing each disk through a hole punched in a piece of paper.

Despite being *physically* identical, the disks on the left appear dark and the ones on the right appear light. This is because the visual system organizes the dark areas differently in the two displays. In the display on the left, the dark areas are seen as belonging to dark disks that are partially obscured by a light "mist." In the display on the right, the dark areas are seen as belonging to dark "mist" that is partially obscuring white disks. Thus, the way the various parts of the display are perceptually organized influences our perception of lightness. (See "If You Want to Know More" at the end of the chapter for some additional examples of how our perception of lightness can be affected by characteristics of a display.)

Jon Winawer

(a) (b)

Figure 7.32 ▮ Perceptual: (a) 4 dark discs partially covered by a white mist; (b) 4 light discs partially covered by a dark mist. Physical: the discs are identical in (a) and (b).
(Anderson, B. L., & Winawer, J. (2005). Image segmentation and lightness perception. Nature, *434, 79–83.)*

SOMETHING TO CONSIDER: CREATING COLOR EXPERIENCE

We know that our experience of color, like all of our sensory experiences, is created by the nervous system. Information about the wavelengths that are reflected from objects is coded in neural impulses, which are then transformed into the experience of color somewhere in the cortex.

But there is something special about the creation of color experience. Unlike some visual qualities like shape, depth, location, and movement, the connection between the physical stimulus (the wavelength of light) and the experience of color ("I see blue") is arbitrary. To understand what this means, let's consider Figure 7.33a, which shows an observer saying that he sees a blue square that is about 4 feet away. We can check the observer's perception of "squareness" by measuring the sides of the object with a ruler; and, when we do this, we confirm that this object is, in fact, a square. We can also check the observer's perception of distance by measuring the actual distance with a tape measure. In this case, we find that the object is actually 3.5 feet away, which tells us that the observer's estimate does not exactly match the actual distance of the object.

Although we can check the correctness of the experiences of shape and distance with a physical measuring device like a ruler or tape measure, what about our observer's pronouncement that the object is "blue"? We can measure the object's reflectance curve and find that it reflects a band of short-wavelength light (Figure 7.33b). But is there any reason that we should think that these particular wavelengths should result in "blue," other than

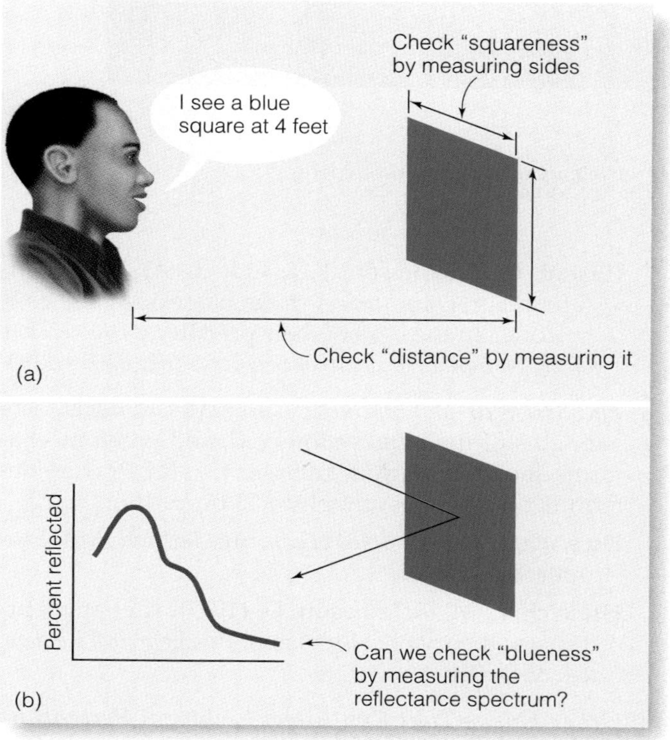

Figure 7.33 ▮ (a) We can check perception of shapes and distance with measuring instruments, but (b) we can't check color perception by measuring reflectance. See text for details.

because we have learned that short wavelengths are usually associated with "blue"? Isaac Newton didn't think so, as indicated by this statement in his book *Optiks* (1704):

> The Rays to speak properly are not coloured. In them there is nothing else than a certain Power and Disposition to stir up a Sensation of this or that Colour. . . . So Colours in the Object are nothing but a Disposition to reflect this or that sort of Rays more copiously than the rest. . . .

Newton's idea is that the colors that we see in response to different wavelengths are not contained in the rays of light themselves. Instead, *colors are created by our perceptual system,* and, although specific colors are related to specific wavelengths, the connection between wavelength and the experience we call "color" is an arbitrary one. There is nothing intrinsically "blue" about short wavelengths or "red" about long wavelengths. In fact, light rays are simply energy that has no color at all. Looking at it this way, color is not a property of wavelength but is the brain's way of letting us know what wavelengths are present.

We can find similar examples in the other senses. We will see in Chapter 11 that our experience of hearing is caused by pressure changes in the air. But why do we perceive rapid pressure changes as high pitches and slow pressure changes as low pitches? Is there anything intrinsically "high-pitched" about rapid pressure changes? Or consider the sense of smell. We perceive some substances as "sweet" and others as "rancid," but where is the "sweetness" or "rancidity" in the molecular structure of the substances that enter the nose? Again, the answer is that these perceptions are not in the molecular structures. They are created by the action of the molecular structures on our nervous system.

We can better understand the idea that some perceptual qualities—like color, or pitch, or smell—are literally created by our nervous system, by considering animals that can perceive energy that humans can't perceive at all. For example, in Chapter 2 we noted that honeybees are sensitive to light in the ultraviolet region of the spectrum (very short wavelengths) that humans can't see because one of the honeybee's receptors absorbs maximally at 335 nm (Menzel & Backhaus, 1989; Menzel et al., 1986; see Figure 2.30). What "color" do you think bees perceive at these short wavelengths? You are free to guess, but you really have no way of knowing because, as Newton stated, "The Rays . . . are not coloured." There is no color in the wavelengths, so the bee's nervous system creates its experience of color. For all we know, the honeybee's experience of color is quite different from ours, even for wavelengths in the middle of the spectrum that both humans and honeybees perceive.

The idea that the experience of color is a creation of the nervous system adds another dimension to the idea that our experience is shaped by physiology. Experience is not only *shaped* by physiology, but—in cases such as color vision, and hearing, taste, and smell—the very nature of our experience is *created* by physiology.

TEST YOURSELF 7.3

1. What is color constancy? Describe three factors that help achieve color constancy.
2. What is lightness constancy? Describe the factors that are responsible for lightness constancy.
3. What does it mean to say that color is created by the nervous system?

THINK ABOUT IT

1. A person with normal color vision is called a trichromat. This person needs to mix three wavelengths to match all other wavelengths and has three cone pigments. A person who is color deficient is called a dichromat. This person needs only two wavelengths to match all other wavelengths and has only two operational cone pigments. A hypothetical tetrachromat would need four wavelengths to match all other

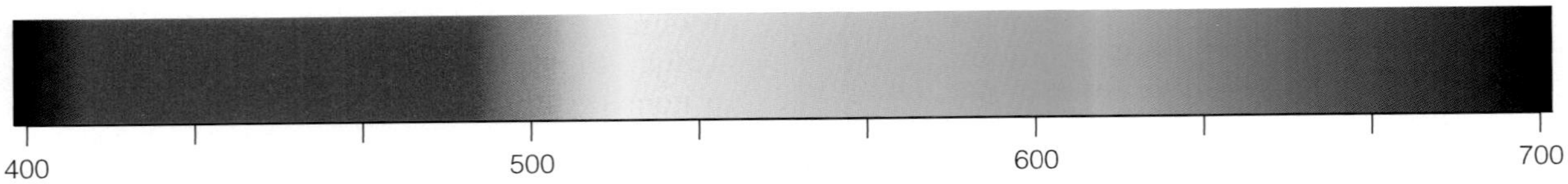

Figure 7.34 ▌ In this "inverted" spectrum, short wavelengths appear red and long wavelengths appear blue.

wavelengths and would have four cone pigments. If a trichromat were to meet a tetrachromat, would the tetrachromat think that the trichromat was color deficient? How would the tetrachromat's color vision be "better than" the trichromat's?

2. When you walk from outside, which is illuminated by sunlight, to inside, which is illuminated by "tungsten" illumination, your perception of colors remains fairly constant. But under some illuminations, such as streetlights called "sodium-vapor" lights that sometimes illuminate highways or parking lots, colors do seem to change. Why do you think color constancy would hold under some illuminations, but not others?

3. In the "Something to Consider" section, we argued that the connection between *wavelength* and *color experience* is arbitrary. What if you met a person who experienced the entire spectrum as "inverted," as shown in Figure 7.34, so the person perceives short wavelengths as red and long wavelengths as blue? Can you think of a way to determine whether this person's perception of color is different from yours?

IF YOU WANT TO KNOW MORE

1. ***Color Vision in Animals.*** What does your cat or dog see? Are there animals other than humans who have trichromatic vision? Are there animals who have better color vision than humans?

   Jacobs, G. H. (1993). The distribution and nature of colour vision among the mammals. *Biological Review, 68,* 413–471.

   Neitz, J., Geist, T., & Jacobs, G. H. (1989). Color vision in the dog. *Visual Neuroscience, 3,* 119–125.

   Varela, F. J., Palacios, A. G., & Goldsmith, T. H. (1993). Color vision of birds. In H. P. Zeigler & H-J. Bishof (Eds.), *Vision, brain and behavior in birds* (pp. 77–98). Cambridge: MIT Press.

2. ***The Adaptive Nature of Animal Coloration.*** Some birds have bright plumage to attract mates. This could be dangerous if these colors also made these birds more obvious to predators. It has been shown that Swedish songbirds reflect light in the ultraviolet area of the spectrum, which other songbirds can see. However, these wavelengths are not very conspicuous to potential predators.

   Hastad, O., Victorsson, J., & Odeen, A. (2005). Differences in color vision make passerines less conspicuous in the eyes of their predators. *Proceedings of the National Academy of Sciences, 102,* 6391–6394.

3. ***The Strength of Opponent Color Mechanisms.*** The strengths of the blue, yellow, red, and green mechanisms shown in Virtual Labs 14, 15, and 16 were determined using a psychophysical procedure.

   Hurvich, L. (1981). *Color vision.* Sunderland, MA: Sinauer Associates.

   Hurvich, L. M., & Jameson, D. (1957). An opponent-process theory of color vision. *Psychological Review, 64,* 384–404.

4. ***Other Things That Can Affect Lightness Perception.*** At the end of the chapter, we saw that our perception of lightness depends on a number of things in addition to the amount of light reflected from objects. Figure 7.35 is another example of this because the intensity distributions are identical in both displays. This display shows that surface curvature can affect lightness displays. Other displays have been created that show how lightness depends on the perception of surface layout. Also see Virtual Lab 24, the Troxler Effect, which shows that perception of lightness can be affected by the sharpness of an object's border. VL 24

   Knill, D. C., & Kersten, D. (1991). Apparent surface curvature affects lightness perception. *Nature, 351,* 228–230.

   Adelson, E. H. (1999). Light perception and lightness illusions. In M. Gazzaniga (Ed.), *The new cognitive neurosciences* (pp. 339–351). Cambridge, MA: MIT Press.

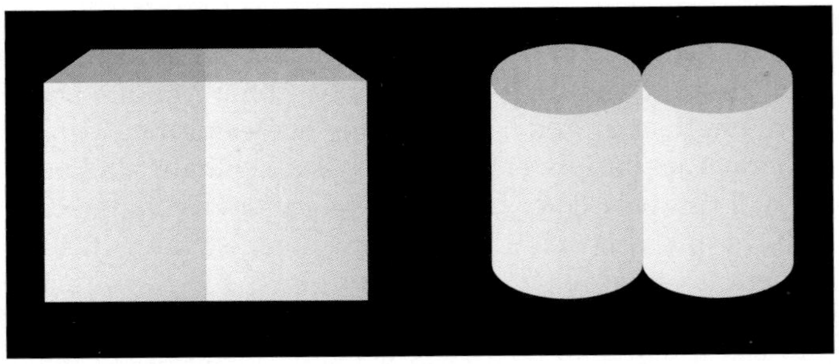

(a) (b)

Figure 7.35 ▌ The light distribution is identical for (a) and (b), though it appears to be different.
(Figure courtesy of David Knill and Daniel Kersten.)

KEY TERMS

Achromatic color (p. 145)
Additive color mixture (p. 148)
Anomalous trichromat (p. 151)
Cerebral achromatopsia (p. 155)
Chromatic adaptation (p. 157)
Chromatic color (p. 145)
Color-blind (p. 152)
Color constancy (p. 156)
Color deficiency (p. 151)
Color-matching experiment (p. 146)
Desaturated (p. 143)
Deuteranopia (p. 152)
Dichromat (p. 151)
Hue (p. 145)
Illumination edge (p. 160)
Ishihara plates (p. 151)
Lightness (p. 159)
Lightness constancy (p. 159)
Memory color (p. 158)
Metamer (p. 148)
Metamerism (p. 148)
Monochromat (p. 151)
Neutral point (p. 152)
Opponent neurons (p. 154)
Opponent-process theory of color vision (p. 153)
Partial color constancy (p. 158)
Penumbra (p. 161)
Principle of univariance (p. 149)
Protanopia (p. 152)
Ratio principle (p. 160)
Reflectance (p. 159)
Reflectance curves (p. 145)
Reflectance edge (p. 160)
Saturation (p. 143)
Selective transmission (p. 145)
Selective reflection (p. 145)
Simultaneous color contrast (p. 153)
Subtractive color mixture (p. 148)
Trichromat (p. 150)
Trichromatic theory of color vision (p. 146)
Tritanopia (p. 152)
Unilateral dichromat (p. 151)
Young-Helmholtz theory of color vision (p. 146)

VISIT YOUR COMPANION WEBSITE FOR THIS BOOK

http://psychology.wadsworth.com/goldstein7e

Check out this companion website where you'll find online resources—glossary, flashcards, web links, multiple-choice and essay questions, and much more!

VIRTUAL LAB

Your Virtual Lab is designed to help you get the most out of this course. The Virtual Lab icons direct you to specific media demonstrations and experiments designed to help you visualize what you are reading about. The number beside each icon indicates the number of the media element you can access through your CD-ROM, Perception PsychologyNow, or WebTutor resource at http:now.ilrn.com/goldstein_7e.

The following are the lab exercises covering what you've just learned in this chapter:

1 *Color Mixing*
2 *Cone Response Profiles and Hue* How the relative response of each type of cone changes across the visible spectrum.
3 *Cone Response Profiles and Perceived Color* Relative cone responses for colors arranged in the color circle.
4 *Color Arrangement Test*
5 *Rod Monochromacy* How the spectrum appears to a rod monochromat.
6 *Dichromacy* How removing one type of cone affects color perception.
7 *Dichromats and Monochromats* How a scene is perceived by dichromats and a monochromat.
8 *Neutral Points in Dichromats* Location of the neutral point for each type of dichromat.
9 *"Oh Say Can You See" Afterimage Demonstration* An American flag afterimage that illustrates the opponent nature of afterimages.
10 *Color Contingent Motion* How viewing differently colored gratings causes an aftereffect.
11 *Motion Contingent Color* How viewing red and green gratings creates an aftereffect.
12 *McCollough Effect* How viewing a vertical red grating and a horizontal green grating can cause aftereffects in correspondingly oriented black and white gratings.
13 *Simultaneous Color Contrast* How the perception of a gray dot is affected as it moves across a blue–yellow background.
14 *Color Assimilation* How bars moving across a colored display take on the color of the background.
15 *Measuring Illusions* Measure the size of the simultaneous contrast effect.
16 *Simultaneous Contrast: Dynamic* How perception of a gray dot changes as it moves across a background that is graded from white to black.
17 *Simultaneous Contrast: Static* A simultaneous contrast display like the one in Figure 3.12.
18 *Red–Green Opponent Cells* How the response of a red–green opponent cell changes when stimulated with different wavelengths.
19 *Missing Blue–Yellow Channel* Which colors are most likely to be confused by a tritanope?
20 *Mixing Complementary Colors* How mixing blue and yellow, and red and green results in gray when mixed in the correct proportions.
21 *Strength of Blue–Yellow Mechanisms* The strength of blue and yellow components of the blue–yellow opponent mechanism across the spectrum.
22 *Strength of Red–Green Mechanism* The strength of the red and green components of the red–green opponent mechanism across the spectrum.
23 *Opponent-Process Coding of Hue* The strengths of opponent mechanisms across the spectrum (combining the blue–yellow and red–green demonstrations).
24 *Troxler Effect* How vision fades when contours are blurred.

CHAPTER

8

PERCEIVING DEPTH AND SIZE

Chapter Contents

This scene near the California coast illustrates how the sizes of objects relative to one another can provide information about an object's size. The size of the house in the lower part of the picture indicates that the surrounding trees are extremely tall. The sizes of objects in the field of view can also provide information about depth. The smallness of the trees on the top of the hill suggests that the hill is far away. Bruce Goldstein

VL *The Virtual Lab icons direct you to specific animations and videos designed to help you visualize what you are reading about. The number beside each icon indicates the number of the clip you can access through your CD-ROM or your student website.*

Some Questions We Will Consider:

- *How can we see far into the distance based on the flat image on the retina? (p. 168)*
- *Why do we see depth better with two eyes than with one eye? (p. 173)*
- *Why don't people appear to shrink in size when they walk away? (p. 182)*

You can easily tell that this book is about 18 inches away and, when you look up at the scene around you, that other objects are located at distances ranging from the nose on your face (very close!) to across the room, down the street, or even as far as the horizon, depending on where you are. What's amazing about this ability to see the distances of objects in your environment is that these objects, and the scene as a whole, is based on a two-dimensional image on your retina.

We can begin to appreciate the problem of perceiving depth based on two-dimensional information on the retina by focusing on two points on the retina, N and F, shown in Figure 8.1. These points represent where rays of light have been reflected onto the retina from the tree, which is near (N) and the house, which is farther away (F). If we look just at these places on the retina, we have no way of knowing how far the light has traveled to reach points N and F. For all we know, the light stimulating either point on the retina could have come from 1 foot away or from a distant star. Clearly, we need to expand our view beyond single points on the retina to determine where objects are located in space.

When we expand our view from two isolated points to the entire retinal image, we increase the amount of information available to us because now we can see the images of the house and the tree. However, because this image is two-dimensional, we still need to explain how we get from the flat image on the retina to the three-dimensional perception of the scene. One way researchers have approached this problem is to ask what information is contained in this two-dimensional image that enables us to perceive depth in the scene. This is called the **cue approach to depth perception**.

The cue approach to depth perception focuses on identifying information in the retinal image that is correlated with depth in the scene. For example, when one object partially covers another object, as the tree in the foreground in Figure 8.1 covers part of the house, the object that is partially covered must be at a greater distance than the object that is covering it. This situation, which is called **occlusion**, is a signal, or cue, that one object is in front of another. According to cue theory, we learn the connection between this cue and depth through our previous experience with the environment. After this learning has occurred, the association between particular cues and depth becomes automatic, and when these depth cues are present, we experience the world in three dimensions. A number of different types of cues that signal depth in a scene have been identified. We can divide these cues into three major groups:

1. *Oculomotor.* Cues based on our ability to sense the position of our eyes and the tension in our eye muscles.
2. *Monocular.* Cues that work with one eye.
3. *Binocular.* Cues that depend on two eyes.

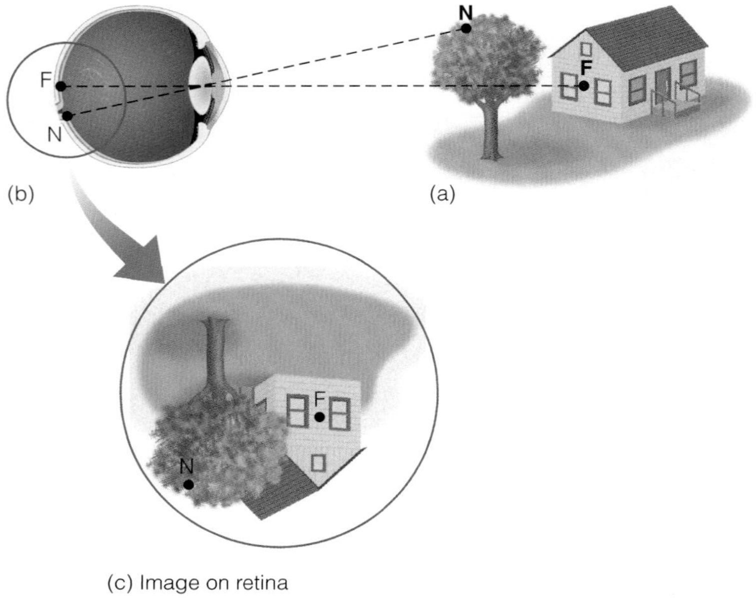

Figure 8.1 ▮ (a) The house is farther away than the tree, but (b) the images of points F on the house and N on the tree both fall on the two-dimensional surface of the retina, so (c) these two points, considered by themselves, do not tell us the distances of the house and the tree.

OCULOMOTOR CUES

The **oculomotor cues** are created by (1) convergence, the inward movement of the eyes that occurs when we look at nearby objects, and (2) accommodation, the change in the shape of the lens that occurs when we focus on objects at various distances. The idea behind these cues is that we can *feel* the inward movement of the eyes that occurs when the eyes converge to look at nearby objects, and we feel the tightening of eye muscles that change the shape of the lens to focus on a nearby object. You can experience the feelings in your eyes associated with convergence and accommodation by doing the following demonstration.

DEMONSTRATION

Feelings in Your Eyes

Look at your finger as you hold it at arm's length. Then, as you slowly move your finger toward your nose, notice how you feel your eyes looking inward and become aware of the increasing tension inside your eyes. ■

VIRTUAL LAB 1,2

The feelings you experience as you move your finger closer are caused by (1) the change in convergence angle as your eye muscles cause your eyes to look inward, as in Figure 8.2a, and (2) the change in the shape of the lens as the eye accommodates to focus on a near object (see Figure 2.11). If you move your finger farther away, the lens flattens, and your eyes move away from the nose until they are both looking straight ahead, as in Figure 8.2b. Convergence and accommodation indicate when an object is close and are useful up to a distance of about arm's length, with convergence being the more effective of the two (Cutting & Vishton, 1995; Mon-Williams & Tresilian, 1999; Tresilian et al., 1999).

MONOCULAR CUES

Monocular cues work with only one eye. They include accommodation, which we have described under oculomotor cues; pictorial cues, which is depth information that can be depicted in a two-dimensional picture; and movement-based cues, which are based on depth information created by movement.

Pictorial Cues

Pictorial cues are sources of depth information that can be depicted in a picture, such as the illustrations in this book or the image on the retina (Goldstein, 2001b).

Occlusion We have already described the depth cue of occlusion. Occlusion occurs when one object hides or partially hides another from view. The partially hidden object is seen as being farther away, so the mountains in Figure 8.3 are perceived as being farther away than the hill. Note that occlusion does not provide information about an object's absolute distance; it indicates relative distance—we know that the object that is partially covered is farther away than another object, but from occlusion alone we can't tell how much farther.

Relative Height According to the cue of **relative height**, objects with their bases higher in the field of view are usually seen as being more distant. Notice how this applies to the two motorcycles in Figure 8.3. There is also a connection between an observer's gaze and distance. Looking straight out at an object high in the visual field, near the horizon, indicates greater depth than looking down, as you would for an object lower in the visual field (Ooi et al., 2001). When objects are *above* the horizon like the clouds, being *lower* in the field of view indicates more depth.

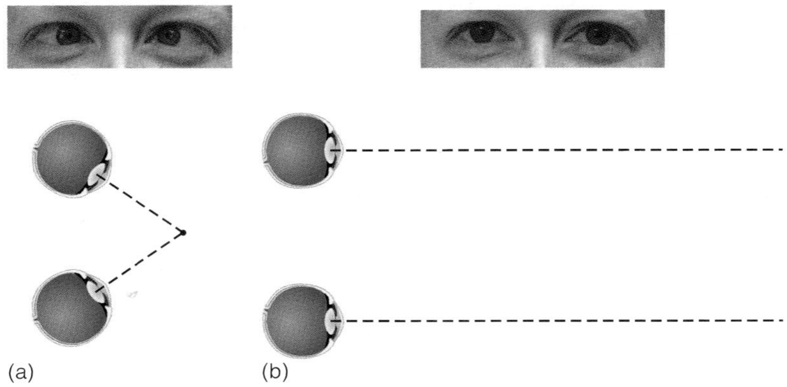

Figure 8.2 ■ (a) Convergence of the eyes occurs when a person looks at something that is very close. (b) The eyes look straight ahead when the person observes something that is far away.

Figure 8.3 ▌ A scene in Tucson, Arizona, containing a number of depth cues: occlusion (the cactus occludes the hill, which occludes the mountain); perspective convergence (the sides of the road converge in the distance); relative size (the far motorcycle is smaller than the near one); and relative height (the far motorcycle is higher in the field of view; the far cloud is lower).

Relative Size According to the cue of **relative size**, when two objects are of equal size, the one that is farther away will take up less of your field of view than the one that is closer. Notice how this applies to the motorcycles and telephone poles in Figure 8.3.

Perspective Convergence When parallel lines extend out from an observer, they are perceived as converging—becoming closer together—as distance increases. This perceptual coming-together of parallel lines, which is illustrated by the road in Figure 8.3, is called **perspective convergence**.

Familiar Size We use the cue of **familiar size** when we judge distance based on our prior knowledge of the sizes of objects. We can apply this idea to the coins in Figure 8.4. If you are influenced by your knowledge of the actual size of dimes, quarters, and half-dollars, you would probably say that the dime is closer than the quarter. An experiment by William Epstein (1965) shows that under certain conditions, our knowledge of an object's size influences our perception of that object's distance. The stimuli in Epstein's experiment were equal-sized photographs of a dime, a quarter, and a half-dollar, which were positioned the same distance from an observer. By placing these photographs in a darkened room, illuminating them with a spot of light, and having observers view them with one eye, Epstein created the illusion that these pictures were real coins.

When the observers judged the distance of each of the coin photographs, they estimated that the dime was closest, the quarter was farther than the dime, and the half-dollar was the farthest of them all. The observers' judgments were influenced by their knowledge of the sizes of real dimes, quarters, and half-dollars. This result did not occur, however, when the observers viewed the scene with both eyes, because the use of two eyes provided information indicating the coins were at the same distance. The cue of familiar size is therefore most effective when other information about depth is absent (see also Coltheart, 1970; Schiffman, 1967).

Figure 8.4 ▌ Drawings of the stimuli used in Epstein's (1965) familiar-size experiment. The actual stimuli were photographs that were all the same size as a real quarter.

Atmospheric Perspective **Atmospheric perspective** occurs when more distant objects appear less sharp and often have a slight blue tint. The farther away an object is, the more air and particles (dust, water droplets, airborne pollution) we have to look through, making objects that are farther away look less sharp and bluer than close objects. Figure 8.5 illustrates atmospheric perspective. The details of the nearby hills are sharp and well defined, but as we look across the hills toward the other side of the bay, details become hazier and the hills appear bluer, until the color of the farthest hill almost matches the color of the water.

If, instead of viewing these hills, you were standing on the moon, where there is no atmosphere, and hence no atmospheric perspective, far craters would look just as

Bruce Goldstein

Figure 8.5 ▮ A scene along the coast of California that illustrates atmospheric perspective.

clear as near ones. But on Earth, there is atmospheric perspective, with the exact amount depending on the nature of the atmosphere.

Texture Gradient Another source of depth information is the **texture gradient**: Elements that are equally spaced in a scene appear to be more closely packed as distance increases, such as the textured ground in the scene in Figure 8.6. Remember that according to the cue of relative size, more distant objects appear smaller. This is exactly what happens to the far-away elements in the texture gradient.

Bruce Goldstein

Figure 8.6 ▮ A texture gradient in Death Valley, California.

Shadows Shadows that are associated with objects can provide information regarding the locations of these objects. Consider, for example, Figure 8.7. In Figure 8.7a, occlusion provides straightforward information indicating that the wine glass is in front of the vase. However, changing the occlusion, as in Figure 8.7b, creates a confusing display because although relative height seems to indicate that the vase is farther away than the wine glass, occlusion now indicates that the vase is closer than the wine glass. But perhaps the vase is in front of the glass, floating

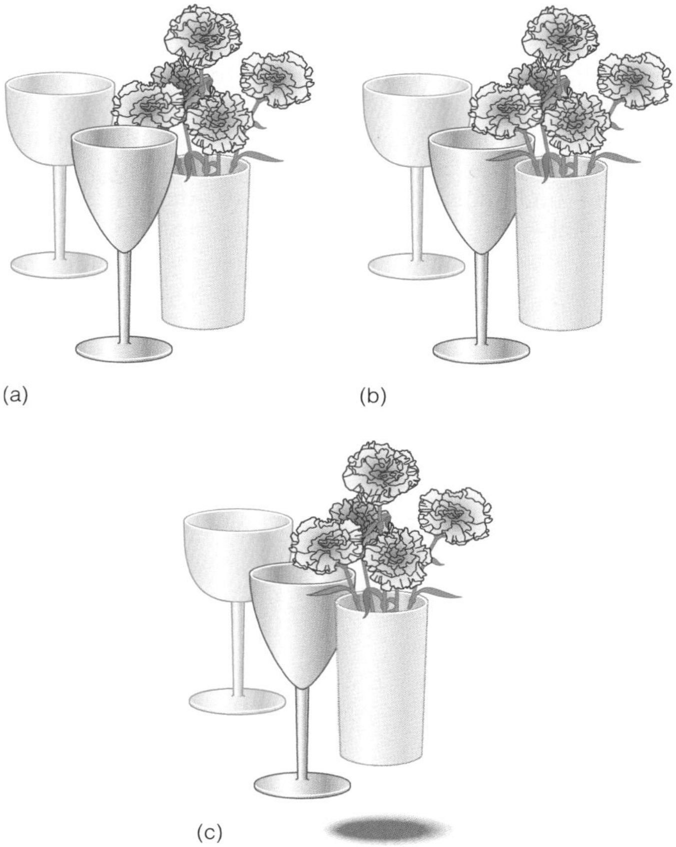

(a) (b) (c)

Figure 8.7 ▮ (a) Occlusion indicates that the tapered glass is in front of the round glass and vase. (b) Overlap now indicates that the vase is in front of the tapered glass, but there is something strange about this picture. (c) The cast shadow under the vase provides additional information about its position in space, which helps clear up the confusion.

in the air. Adding the shadow in Figure 8.7c indicates that this is, in fact, the case. The shadow indicates where in space the vase is hovering and, in doing this, helps locate the object in depth (Mamassian, Knill, & Kersten, 1998).

Shadows also enhance the three-dimensionality of objects. This occurs for the mountains in Figure 8.3, but later in the day, when the sun is directly overhead and there are no shadows, the mountains appear almost flat. VL 3

Movement-Produced Cues

All of the cues we have described so far work if the observer is stationary. If, however, we decide to take a walk, new cues emerge that further enhance our perception of depth. We will describe two different movement-produced cues: (1) movement parallax and (2) deletion and accretion.

Movement Parallax **Movement parallax** occurs when as we move, nearby objects off to the side of our direction of movement appear to glide rapidly past us, but more distant objects appear to move more slowly. Thus, when you look out the side window of a moving car or train, nearby objects appear to speed by in a blur, whereas objects on the horizon may appear to be moving only slightly.

We can understand why movement parallax occurs by noting how the image of a near object—the tree in Figure 8.8—and a far object—the house—move across the retina as the eye moves from position 1 to position 2. At position 1 the tree's image is at T1 and the house's image is at H1. When the eye moves to position 2, the tree's image moves all the way across the retina to T2, as indicated by the dashed line. However, the house's image moves only from H1 to H2. Thus, the image of a near object travels a large distance across the retina and therefore appears to move rapidly as the observer moves, but the image of a far object travels a much smaller distance across the retina and therefore appears to move more slowly as the observer moves.

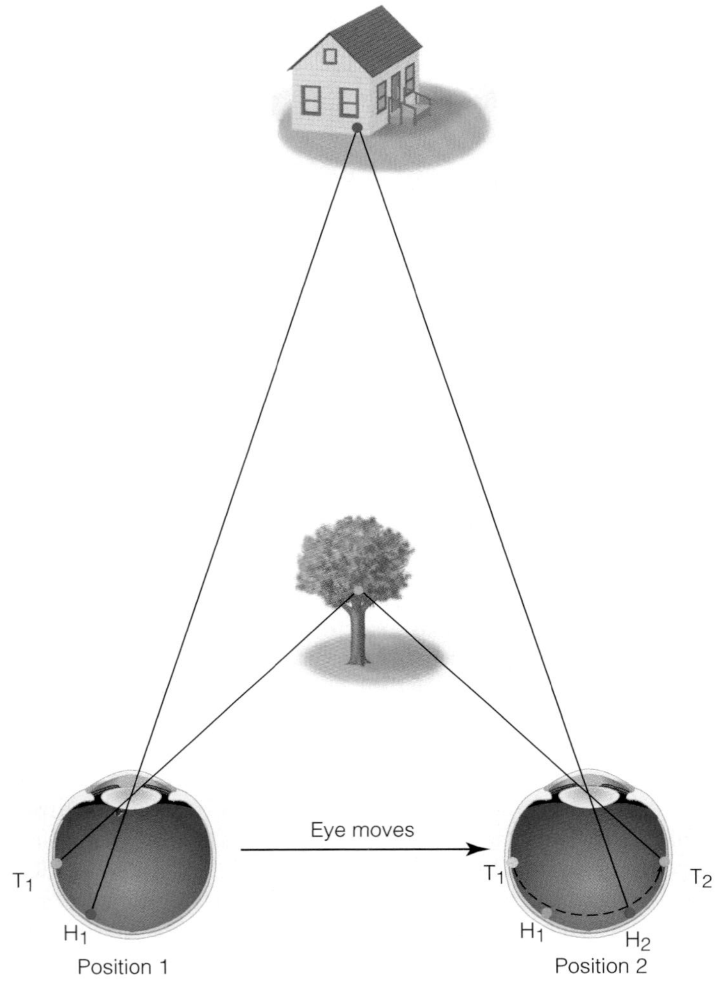

Figure 8.8 ▮ One eye, moving from left to right, showing how the images of a nearby tree and a faraway house change their position on the retina because of this movement. The image of the tree moves farther on the retina than the image of the house.

Movement parallax is one of the most important sources of depth information for many animals, and the information provided by movement parallax has also been used to enable human-designed mechanical robots to determine how far they are from obstacles as they navigate through the environment (Srivinisan et al., 1997). Movement parallax is also widely used to create an impression of depth in cartoons and video games. **VL 4**

Deletion and Accretion The depth cue of **deletion** occurs when a farther object is covered by a nearer object due to sideways movement of an observer relative to the objects (compare Figure 8.9b to 8.9a). Another way of describing deletion would be *occlusion-in-motion* because the amount of occlusion, or covering up, changes as the person moves. The opposite effect, **accretion**, occurs when the observer moves in the other direction, so the farther object is uncovered (Compare Figure 8.9c to Figure 8.9a). These cues, which are related both to movement parallax and overlap because they occur when overlapping surfaces appear to move relative to one another, are especially effective for detecting depth at an edge (Kaplan, 1969).

Our discussion so far has described a number of the cues that contribute to our perception of depth. As shown in Table 8.1, these cues work over different distances, some only at close range (convergence and accommodation), some at close and medium ranges (relative height, movement parallax), some at long range (atmospheric perspective), and some at the whole range of depth perception (occlusion and relative size; Cutting & Vishton, 1995). For example, we can appreciate how occlusion operates over a wide range of distances by noticing how this cue works over a distance of a few inches for the cactus flower in Figure 8.10a, and over a distance of many miles for the scene in Figure 8.10b.

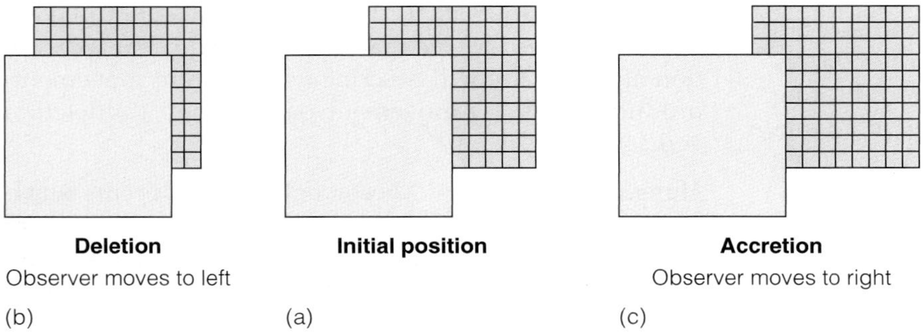

Figure 8.9 ▮ Starting with the view in the center (a), moving to the left causes deletion (covering) of the rear object (b). Moving to the right causes accretion (uncovering) of the rear object (c).

Table 8.1 ▮ *Range of effectiveness of different depth cues*

Depth Information	0–2 Meters	2–20 Meters	Above 30 Meters
Occlusion	✓	✓	✓
Relative size	✓	✓	✓
Accommodation and convergence	✓		
Movement	✓	✓	
Relative height		✓	✓
Atmospheric perspective			✓

Source: Based on Cutting & Vishton, 1995.

Bruce Goldstein

(a)

Bruce Goldstein

(b)

Figure 8.10 ▮ (a) Occlusion operating on a small scale: The flower near the center occludes the cactus, so appears closer. (b) Occlusion operating on a larger scale: The green shrubbery occludes the river; the buildings in Pittsburgh occlude one another; the city occludes the hills in the far distance. Occlusion indicates only that one object is closer than another object. What other depth cues make us aware of the actual distances in this scene?

BINOCULAR DEPTH INFORMATION

In addition to the cues we have described so far, there is one other important source of depth information—the differences in the images received by our two eyes. Because our eyes view the world from positions that are about 6 cm apart in the average adult, this difference in the viewpoint of the two eyes creates the cue of binocular disparity.

Binocular Disparity

Binocular disparity is the difference in the images in the left and right eyes. The following demonstration illustrates this difference.

DEMONSTRATION

Two Eyes: Two Viewpoints

Close your right eye. Hold your finger vertically about 6 inches in front of you and position it so it is partially covering an object in the distance. Look directly at the distant object, then switch eyes, so your left eye is closed and you are looking directly at the distant object with your right eye. When you switch eyes, how does the position of your finger change relative to the far object? ■

When you switched from looking with your left eye to your right, you probably noticed that your finger appeared to move to the left relative to the far object. Figure 8.11 diagrams what happened on your retinas. The green line in Figure 8.11a shows that when the left eye was open, the images of the finger and far object both fell on the same place on the retina. This occurred because you were looking right at both objects, so their images would fall on the fovea. The green lines in Figure 8.11b show that when the right eye was open, the image of the far object still fell on the fovea because you were looking at it, but the image of the finger was now off to the side.

The difference between the images in the left and right eyes shown in Figure 8.11 creates binocular disparity. To describe how disparity works, we need to introduce the idea of corresponding retinal points. **Corresponding retinal points** are the places on each retina that would overlap if one retina could be slid on top of the other. In Figure 8.12, we see that the two foveas, marked F, fall on corresponding points, and that the two A's and the two B's also fall on corresponding points. VL 5

To take the idea of corresponding points into the real world, let's consider the lifeguard in Figure 8.13a, who is looking directly at Frieda. Frieda's image falls on the lifeguard's foveas (F in Figure 8.13b), which are corresponding points. Harry's and Susan's images also fall on corresponding points, H and S, on the two eyes. The dashed line that passes through Harry, Frieda, and Susan is called

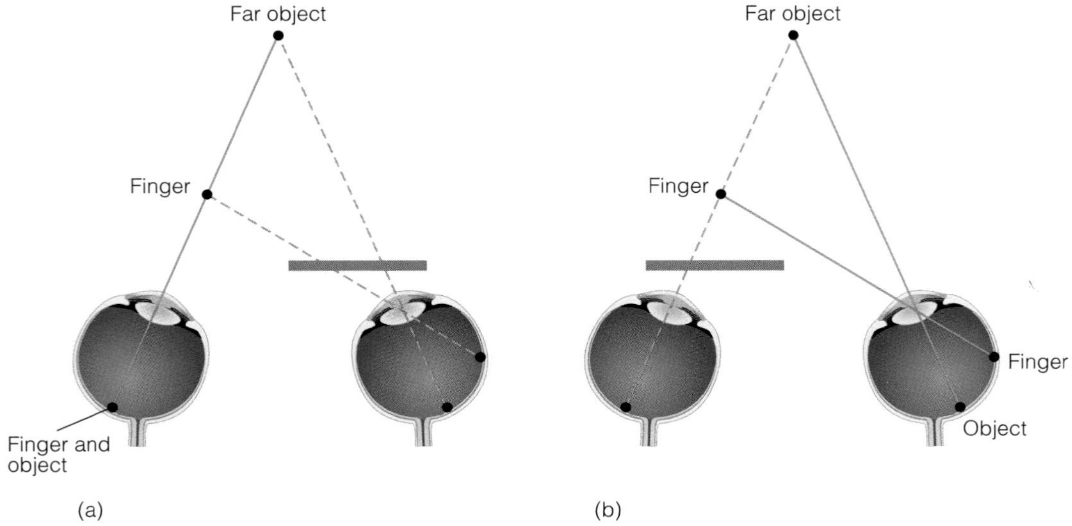

Figure 8.11 ▮ Location of images on the retina for the "Two Eyes: Two Viewpoints" demonstration. (a) Both images are on the fovea when the left eye is open. (b) The images are on different places on the retina when the right eye is open.

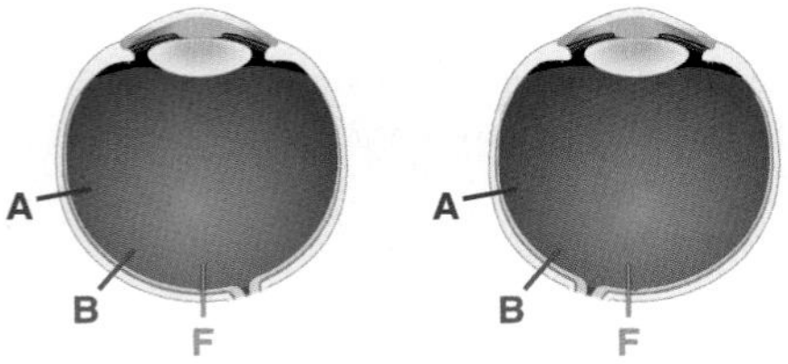

Figure 8.12 ▮ Corresponding points on the two retinas. To determine corresponding points, imagine that one eye is slid on top of the other one.

the **horopter**, which is an imaginary circle that passes through the point of fixation (where the lifeguard is looking, which would be Frieda) and indicates the location of objects that fall on corresponding points on the two retinas.

Now let's consider where Carol's and Lee's images fall on the lifeguard's retinas. Because their heads are not located on the horopter, their images fall on **noncorresponding (or disparate) points**, as indicated in Figure 8.14. Carol's image falls on noncorresponding points C in the left eye and X in the right eye. (Note that if you slid the retinas on top of each other, points C and X would

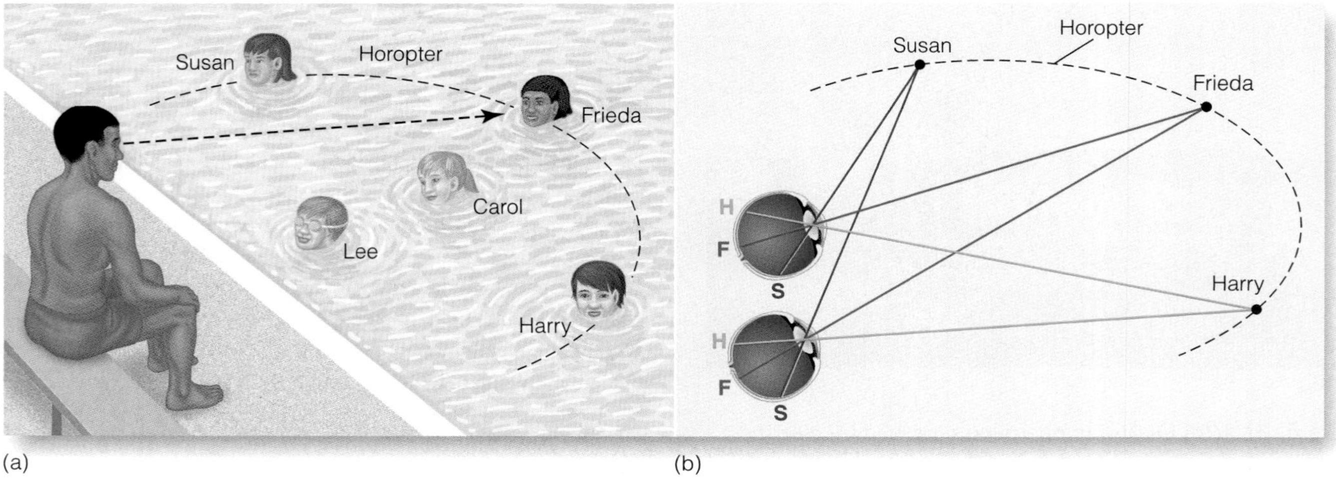

Figure 8.13 ▮ (a) When the lifeguard looks at Frieda, the images of Frieda, Susan, and Harry fall on corresponding points on the lifeguard's retinas, and the images of the other swimmers fall on noncorresponding points. (b) The locations of the images of Susan, Frieda, and Harry on the lifeguard's retina.

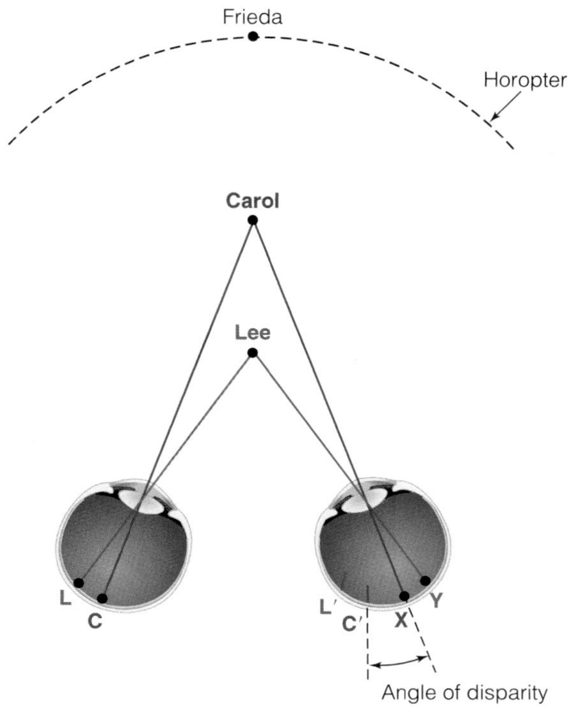

Figure 8.14 ▮ The location of the images of Carol and Lee in the lifeguard's eyes. Because Carol and Lee are not located on the horopter, their images fall on noncorresponding points.

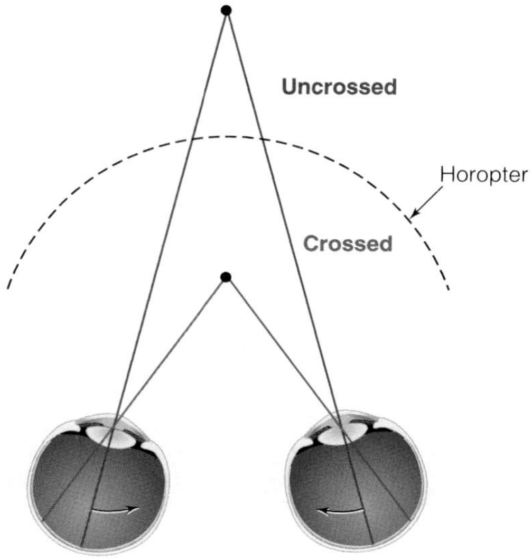

Figure 8.15 ▮ Crossed disparity occurs for objects in front of the horopter; uncrossed disparity occurs for objects behind the horopter. The arrows indicate that the retinal images move inward, toward the nose, as the object moves farther away.

not overlap.) The corresponding point to C in the left eye, indicated by C′ in the right eye, is far from point X. Also note that a similar situation exists for Lee, whose images fall on L in the left eye and Y in the right eye.

The images at C and X are called disparate images because they do not fall on corresponding points. The angle between C′ and X is called the **angle of disparity**. The key to binocular depth perception is that the farther the object is from the horopter, the greater the angle of disparity. Notice, for example, that Lee's images, on L and Y, are more disparate than Carol's images. Thus, the amount of disparity indicates how far Lee and Carol are from where the lifeguard is looking. Because Lee's angle of disparity is greater than Carol's, he must be located farther from the horopter and is therefore closer to the lifeguard.

When objects are located in front of the horopter, as Carol and Lee are, their images move out to the sides of the retinas, and the resulting disparity is called **crossed disparity**. Notice that this is what happened to the image of the finger in the earlier demonstration (Figure 8.11), which was located in front of the far object. VL 6

When objects are located beyond the horopter, as in Figure 8.15, their images move inward on the retinas, creating a condition called **uncrossed disparity**. The farther behind the horopter an object is, the more its images move inward on the retinas, and the greater its disparity. Thus, crossed disparity indicates that an object is nearer than the horopter, and uncrossed disparity indicates that an object is farther than the horopter. (To remember which disparity is crossed and which is uncrossed, just remember that you have to cross your eyes to fixate on objects as they get nearer. Near objects create crossed disparity.)

We have seen that the disparity information contained in the images on the retinas provides information indicating an object's distance from where we are looking. However, just because this information exists on the retina doesn't guarantee that it is being used by the brain to create an impression of depth.

The impression of depth that results from information provided by binocular disparity is called **stereopsis**. An example of stereopsis is provided by the depth effect achieved by the **stereoscope**, a device introduced by the physicist Charles Wheatstone (1802–1875), which produces a convincing illusion of depth by using two slightly different pictures. This device, extremely popular in the 1800s and reinvented as the View Master in the 1940s, presents two photographs that are made with a camera with two lenses separated by the same distance as the eyes. The result is two slightly different views, like those shown in Figure 8.16. The stereoscope presents the left picture to the left eye and the right picture to the right eye. This creates the same binocular disparity that occurs when a person views the scene naturally, so that slightly different images appear in the left and right eyes. In this next demonstration, the binocular disparity created by two pictures creates a perception of depth.

Bruce Goldstein

(a) Left eye image

(b) Right eye image

Figure 8.16 ▮ The two images of a stereoscopic photograph. The difference between the two images, such as the distances between the front cactus and the window in the two views, creates retinal disparity. This creates a perception of depth when (a) the left image is viewed by the left eye and (b) the right image is viewed by the right eye.

DEMONSTRATION

Binocular Depth From a Picture, Without a Stereoscope

Place a 4 × 6 card vertically, long side up, between the stairs in Figure 8.17, and place your nose against the card so that you are seeing the left-hand drawing with just your left eye and the right-hand drawing with just your right eye. (Blink back and forth to confirm this separation.) Then relax and wait for the two drawings to merge. When the drawings form a single image, you should see the stairs in depth, just as you would if you looked at them through a stereoscope. VL 7, 8, 9

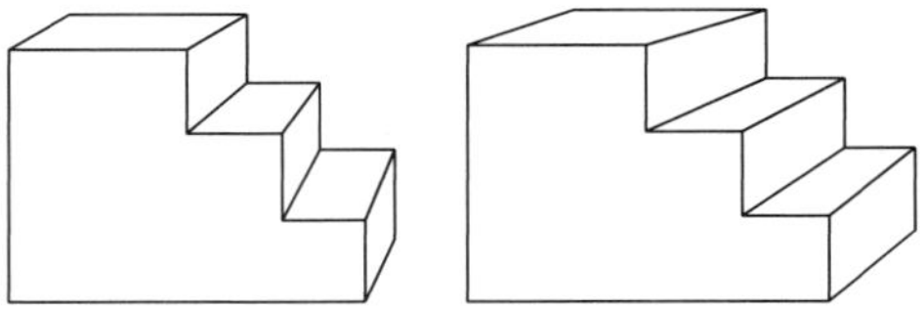

Figure 8.17 ▪

UPI/Corbis–Bettmann

Figure 8.18 ▮ A scene in a movie theater in the 1950s, when three-dimensional movies were first introduced. The glasses create different images in the left and right eyes, and the resulting disparity leads to a convincing impression of depth.

The principle behind the stereoscope is also used in 3-D movies. The left-eye and right-eye images are presented simultaneously on the screen, slightly displaced from one another, to create disparity. These images can be presented separately to the left and right eyes by coloring one red and the other green and viewing the film through glasses with a red filter for one eye and a green filter for the other eye (Figure 8.18). Another way to separate the images is to create the left and right images from polarized light—light waves that vibrate in only one direction. One image is polarized so its vibration is vertical, and the other is polarized so its vibration is horizontal. Viewing the film through polarizing lenses, which let vertically polarized light into one eye and horizontally polarized light into the other eye, creates the disparity that results in three-dimensional perception.

Our conclusion that disparity creates stereopsis seems to be supported by the demonstration above, which shows that we perceive depth when two slightly displaced views are presented to the left and right eyes. However, this demonstration alone doesn't prove that disparity creates a perception of depth because images such as those in Figure 8.16 also contain potential depth cues, such as occlusion and relative height, that could contribute to our perception of depth. In order to show that disparity alone can result in depth perception, Bela

Julesz (1971) created a stimulus called the random-dot stereogram, which contained no pictorial cues.

By creating stereoscopic images of random-dot patterns, Julesz showed that subjects can perceive depth in displays that contain no depth information other than disparity. Two such random-dot patterns, which constitute a **random-dot stereogram**, are shown in Figure 8.19. These patterns were constructed by first generating two identical random-dot patterns on a computer and then shifting a square-shaped section of the dots to the right, in the pattern on the right. This shift is too subtle to be seen in these dot patterns, but we can understand how it is accomplished by looking at the diagrams below the dot patterns. In these diagrams, the black dots are indicated by 0's, A's, and X's and the white dots by 1's, B's, and Y's. The A's and B's indicate the square-shaped section where the shift is made in the pattern. Notice that the A's and B's are shifted one unit to the right in the right-hand pattern. The X's and Y's indicate areas uncovered by the shift that must be filled in with new black dots and white dots to complete the pattern. VL 10

The effect of shifting one section of the pattern in this way is to create disparity. When the two patterns are presented simultaneously to the left and the right eyes in a stereoscope, we perceive a small square floating above the background. Because binocular disparity is the only depth information present in these stereograms, disparity alone must be causing the perception of depth that we perceive.

Psychophysical experiments, particularly those using Julesz's random-dot stereograms, show that retinal disparity creates a perception of depth. But before we can fully understand the mechanisms responsible for depth perception, we must answer one more question: How does the visual system match the parts of the images in the left and right eyes that correspond to one another? This is the **correspondence problem,** and as we will see, it has still not been fully explained.

The Correspondence Problem

Let's return to the stereoscopic images of Figure 8.16. When we view this image in a stereoscope, we see different parts of the image at different depths because of the disparity between images on the left and right retinas. Thus, the cactus and the window appear to be at different distances when viewed through the stereoscope because they create different amounts of disparity. But in order for the visual system to calculate this disparity, it must compare the images of the cactus on the left and right retinas and the images of the window on the left and right retinas. This is the correspondence problem. How does the visual system match up the images in the two eyes?

A possible answer to this question is that the visual system may match the images on the left and right retinas on the basis of the specific features of the objects. For example, the upper-right window pane on the left could be matched with the upper-right pane on the right, and so on. Explained in this way, the solution seems simple: Most things in the world are quite discriminable from one another, so it is easy to match an image on the left retina with the image of the same thing on the right retina. But

1	0	1	0	1	0	0	1	0	1
1	0	0	1	0	1	0	1	0	0
0	0	1	1	0	1	1	0	1	0
0	1	0	A	A	B	B	1	0	1
1	1	1	B	A	B	A	0	0	1
0	0	1	A	A	B	A	0	1	0
1	1	1	B	B	A	B	1	0	1
1	0	0	1	1	0	1	1	0	1
1	1	0	0	1	1	0	1	1	1
0	1	0	0	0	1	1	1	1	0

1	0	1	0	1	0	0	1	0	1
1	0	0	1	0	1	0	1	0	0
0	0	1	1	0	1	1	0	1	0
0	1	0	Y	A	A	B	B	0	1
1	1	1	X	B	A	B	A	0	1
0	0	1	X	A	A	B	A	1	0
1	1	1	Y	B	B	A	B	0	1
1	0	0	1	1	0	1	1	0	1
1	1	0	0	1	1	0	1	1	1
0	1	0	0	0	1	1	1	1	0

Figure 8.19 ▮ Top: a random-dot stereogram. Bottom: the principle for constructing the stereogram. See text for an explanation.

what about images in which matching similar points would be extremely difficult, as with Julesz's random-dot stereogram?

You can appreciate the problem involved in matching similar parts of a stereogram by trying to match up the points in the left and right images of the stereogram in Figure 8.19. Most people find this to be an extremely difficult task, involving switching their gaze back and forth between the two pictures and comparing small areas of the pictures one after another. But even though matching similar features on a random-dot stereogram is much more difficult and time consuming than matching features in the real world, the visual system somehow matches similar parts of the two stereogram images, calculates their disparities, and creates a perception of depth. A number of proposals, all too complex to describe here, have been put forth to explain how the visual system solves the correspondence problem, but a totally satisfactory answer has yet to be proposed (see Blake & Wilson, 1991; Menz & Freeman, 2003; Ohzawa, 1998; Ringbach, 2003).

THE PHYSIOLOGY OF DEPTH PERCEPTION

Most of the research on the physiology of depth perception has concentrated on looking for neurons that signal information about binocular disparity. But neurons have also been found that signal the depth indicated by pictorial depth cues.

Neurons That Respond to Pictorial Depth

Ken-Ichino Tsutsui and coworkers (2002, 2005) studied the physiology of neurons that respond to the depth indicated by texture gradients by showing monkeys stimuli like the ones in Figure 8.20. Monkeys perceive the pattern in Figure 8.20a as slanting to the right, 8.20b as flat, and 8.20c as slanting to the left. The records below the texture gradient patterns are the responses of a neuron in an area in the parietal cortex that had been associated with depth perception in other studies. This neuron does not fire to

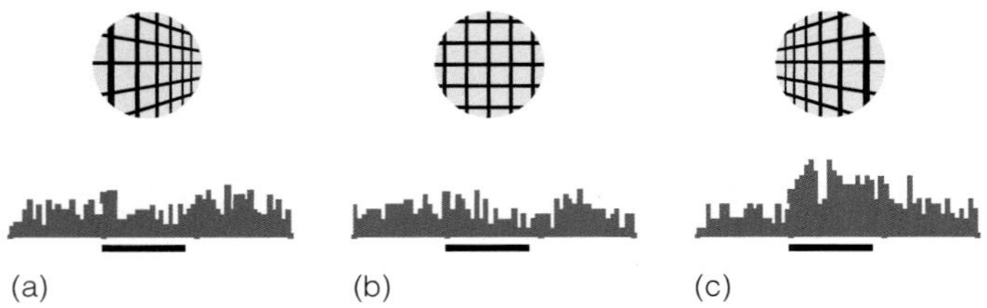

Figure 8.20 ▌ Top: gradient stimuli. Bottom: response of neurons in the parietal cortex to each gradient. This neuron fires to the pattern in (c), which the monkey perceives as slanting to the left.
(From Tsutsui et al., 2002, 2005.)

the right-slanting gradient, or to a flat pattern, but does fire to the left-slanting gradient. Thus, this neuron fires to a display in which depth is indicated by the pictorial depth cues of texture gradients. This neuron also responds when depth is indicated by disparity, so it is tuned to respond to depth whether it is determined by pictorial depth cues or by binocular disparity. (Also see Sereno et al., 2002, for a description of a neuron that responds to the depth cue of movement parallax.)

Neurons That Respond to Binocular Disparity

One of the most important discoveries about the physiology of depth perception was the finding that there are neurons that are tuned to respond to specific amounts of disparity (Barlow et al., 1967; Hubel & Weisel, 1970). These neurons are called **binocular depth cells** or **disparity-selective cells.** A given cell responds best when stimuli presented to the left and right eyes create a specific amount of disparity. Figure 8.21 shows a disparity-tuning curve for one of these neurons (Uka & DeAngelis, 2003). This particular neuron responds best when the left and right eyes are stimulated to create a disparity of about 1 degree.

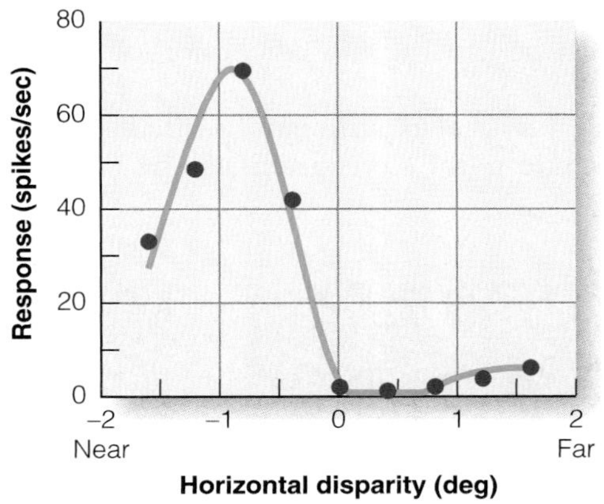

Figure 8.21 ▌ Disparity tuning curve for a disparity-sensitive neuron. This curve indicates the neural response that occurs when stimuli presented to the left and right eyes create different amounts of disparity.
(From Uka & DeAngelis, 2003.)

Figure 8.22 applies this idea of disparity detectors to our lifeguard from Figure 8.13. Remember that the lifeguard was looking at Frieda, so Frieda's images were on the lifeguard's fovea at F in both eyes. Because the foveas are corresponding points, these images had zero disparity and therefore activated disparity-selective neurons in the lifeguard's brain that were tuned to zero-disparity. However, Lee's images fell on noncorresponding points L and Y, which resulted in the angle of disparity shown in the diagram. Therefore, stimulation of points L and Y activated disparity-selective neurons that were tuned to this

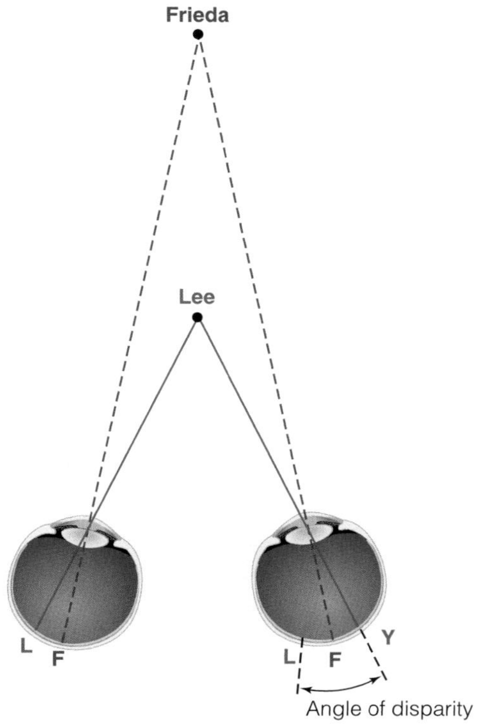

Figure 8.22 ▌ Where images of Frieda and Lee fall on the retina. See text for explanation.

angle of disparity. The firing of these disparity-selective neurons provides information in the lifeguard's brain that locates Lee relative to Frieda.

Connecting Binocular Disparity and Depth Perception

Just because disparity-selective neurons fire best to a specific angle of disparity doesn't prove that these neurons have anything to do with depth perception. To show that disparity-selective neurons are actually involved in depth perception, we need to demonstrate a connection between disparity and behavior.

Randolph Blake and Helmut Hirsch (1975) demonstrated this connection by showing that eliminating binocular neurons eliminates depth perception. They eliminated binocular neurons by rearing cats so their vision was alternated between the left and right eyes every other day during the first 6 months of their lives. After this 6-month period of presenting stimuli to just one eye at a time, Blake and Hirsch recorded from neurons in the cat's cortex and found that (1) these cats had few binocular neurons, and (2) they were not able to use binocular disparity to perceive depth. Thus, eliminating binocular neurons eliminates stereopsis and confirms what everyone suspected all along—that disparity-selective neurons are responsible for stereopsis.

Another technique that has been used to demonstrate a link between neural responding and depth perception is **microstimulation**. Microstimulation is achieved by inserting a small electrode into the cortex and passing an electrical charge through the electrode to activate the neurons near the electrode (Cohen & Newsome, 2004). Neurons that are sensitive to the same disparities tend to be organized in clusters, so stimulating one of these clusters activates a group of neurons that respond best to a specific disparity.

Gregory DeAngelis and coworkers (1998) trained a monkey to indicate the depth created by presenting disparate images to the left and right eyes. Presumably, the monkey perceived depth because the disparate images on the monkey's retina activated disparity-selective neurons in the cortex. But what would happen if microstimulation were used to activate a different group of disparity-selective neurons? DeAngelis and coworkers stimulated disparity-selective neurons that were tuned to a disparity different from what was indicated by the images on the retina. When they did this, the monkey shifted its depth judgment toward the disparity signaled by the stimulated neurons. This experiment provides another demonstration of a connection between disparity-selective neurons and depth perception. In addition, brain-imaging experiments on humans show that a number of different areas are activated by stimuli that create binocular disparity (Backus et al., 2001; Kwee et al., 1999; Ts'o et al., 2001).

TEST YOURSELF 8.1

1. What is the basic problem of depth perception, and how does the cue approach deal with this problem?
2. What monocular cues provide information about depth in the environment?
3. What is binocular disparity? How is it related to the depths of objects in a scene? How is it related to stereopsis?
4. What does perception of depth from a random-dot stereogram demonstrate?
5. What is the correspondence problem? Has this problem been solved?
6. What is the relationship between the firing of neurons in the cortex and depth perception? Be sure to distinguish between (a) experiments that demonstrated a connection between neurons that respond to *depth information* and (b) experiments that demonstrate a connection between neural responding and *depth perception*.

PERCEIVING SIZE

We discuss size perception next because our perception of size can be affected by our perception of depth. This link between size perception and depth perception is graphically illustrated by the following example:

Whiteout—one of the most treacherous weather conditions possible for flying—can arise quickly and unexpectedly. As Frank pilots his helicopter across the Antarctic wastes, blinding light, reflected down from thick cloud cover above and up from the pure white blanket of snow below, makes it difficult to see the horizon, details on the surface of the snow, or even up from down. He is aware of the danger because he has known pilots dealing with similar conditions who had flown at full power directly into the ice. He thinks he can make out a vehicle on the snow far below, and he drops a smoke grenade to check his altitude. To his horror, the grenade falls only three feet before hitting the ground. Realizing that what he thought was a truck was actually a discarded box, Frank pulls back on the controls and soars up, his face drenched in sweat, as he comprehends how close he just came to becoming another whiteout fatality.

This fictional account is based on descriptions of actual flying conditions at an Antarctic research base. It illustrates that our ability to perceive an object's size can sometimes be drastically affected by our ability to perceive the object's distance. A small box seen close up can, in the absence of accurate information about its distance, be misperceived as a large truck seen from far away (Figure 8.23). The idea that we can misperceive size when accurate depth information is not present was demonstrated in a classic experiment by A. H. Holway and Edwin Boring (1941).

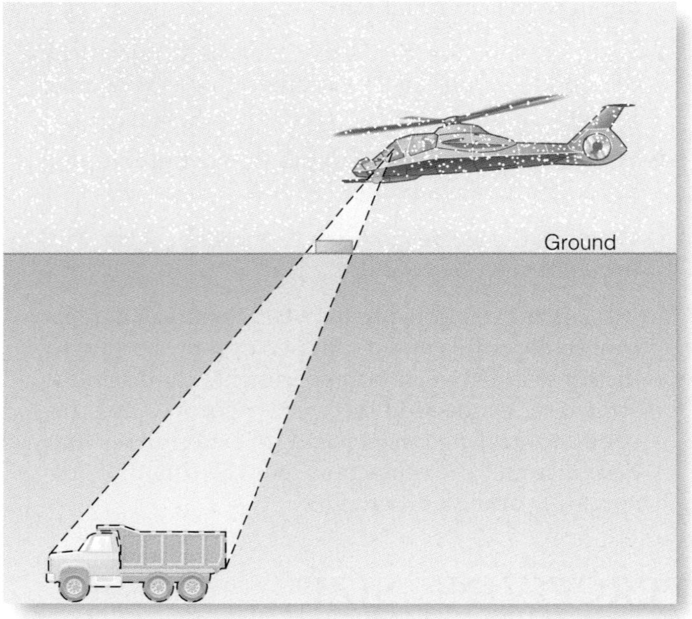

Figure 8.23 ■ When the helicopter pilot loses the ability to perceive distance, due to "whiteout," a small box that is close can be mistaken for a truck that is far away.

The Holway and Boring Experiment

Observers in Holway and Boring's experiment sat at the intersection of two hallways and saw a luminous test circle when looking down the right hallway and a luminous comparison circle when looking down the left hallway (Figure 8.24). The comparison circle was always 10 feet from the observer, but the test circles were presented at distances ranging from 10 feet to 120 feet. The observer's task on each trial was to adjust the diameter of the comparison circle to match that of the test circle.

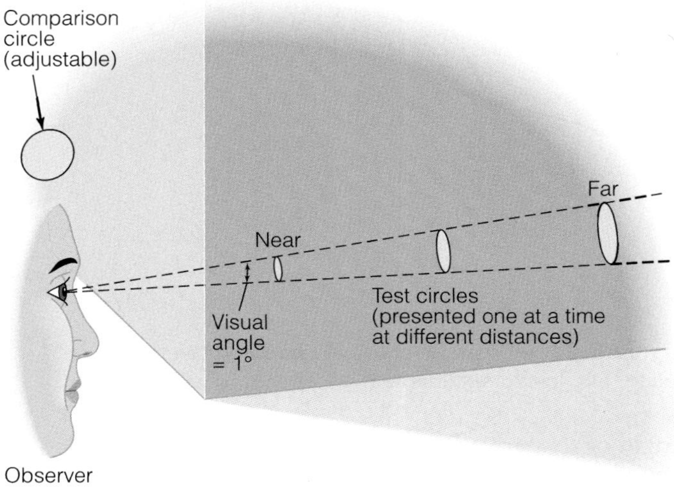

Figure 8.24 ■ Setup of Holway and Boring's (1941) experiment. The observer changes the diameter of the comparison circle to match his or her perception of the size of the test circle. Each of the test circles has a visual angle of 1 degree. This diagram is not drawn to scale. The actual distance of the far test circle was 120 feet.

An important feature of the test stimuli was that they all cast exactly the same-sized image on the retina. We can understand how this was accomplished by introducing the concept of visual angle.

What Is Visual Angle? **Visual angle** is the angle of an object relative to the observer's eye. For example, Figure 8.25a shows how we determine the visual angle of a stimulus (a person, in this example) by extending lines from the person to the lens of the observer's eye. The angle between the lines is the visual angle. Notice that the visual angle depends on both the size of the stimulus and on its distance from the observer, so when the person moves closer, as in Figure 8.25b, his or her visual angle becomes larger.

The visual angle tells us how large the object will be on the back of the eye. There are 360 degrees around the entire circumference of the eyeball, and an object with a visual angle of 1 degree would take up 1/360 of this circum-

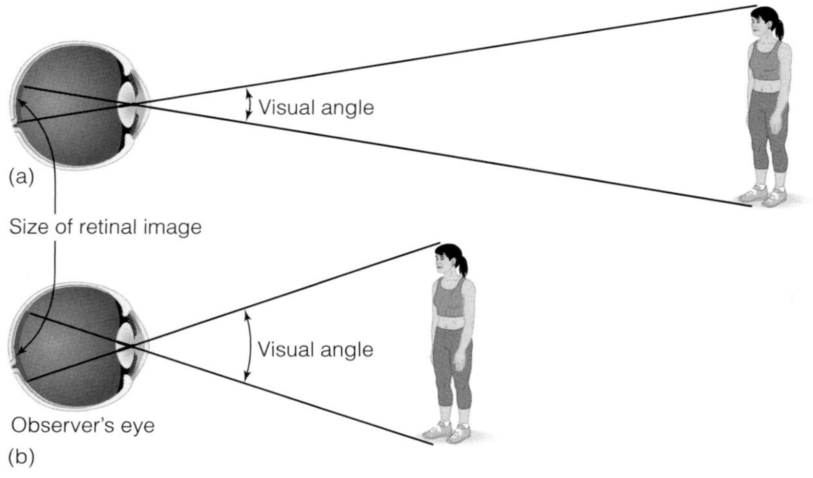

Figure 8.25 ▮ (a) The visual angle depends on the size of the stimulus (the woman in this example) and its distance from the observer. (b) When the woman moves closer to the observer, the visual angle and the size of the image on the retina increases. This example shows how halving the distance between the stimulus and observer doubles the size of the image on the retina.

ference—about 0.3 mm on an average-sized adult eye. One way to get a feel for visual angle is to fully extend your arm and look at your thumb, as the woman in Figure 8.26 is doing. The approximate visual angle of the thumb at arm's length is 2 degrees. Thus, an object that is exactly covered by the thumb held at arm's length, such as part of the iPod® in Figure 8.26, has a visual angle of approximately 2 degrees.

This "thumb technique" provides a way to determine the approximate visual angle of any object in the environment. It also illustrates an important property of visual angle: A small object that is near (like the thumb) and a larger object that is far (like the iPod) can have the same visual angle. This is illustrated in Figure 8.27, which shows a nearby flower urn that has the same visual angle as a skyscraper that is miles away.

How Holway and Boring Tested Size Perception in a Hallway The idea that objects with different sizes can have the same visual angle was used in the creation of the test circles in Holway and Boring's experiment. You can see from Figure 8.24 that small circles were positioned close to the observer, and larger circles were positioned farther away, so that all of the circles had a visual angle of 1 degree. Objects with the same visual angle have the same size on the retina, so all of the test circles had the same-sized image on the observers' retinas, no matter where in the hallway they were located.

In the first part of Holway and Boring's experiment, many depth cues were available, so the observer could easily judge the distance of the test circles. The results, indicated by line 1 in Figure 8.28, show that even though all of the retinal images were the same size, observers

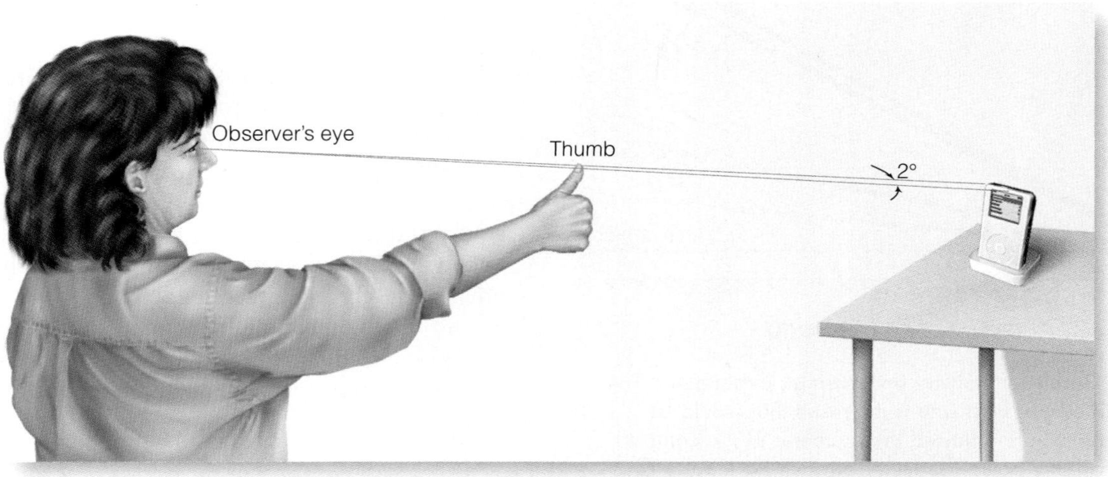

Figure 8.26 ▮ The "thumb" method of determining the visual angle of an object. When the thumb is at arm's length, whatever it covers has a visual angle of about 2 degrees. The woman's thumb covers half the width of her iPod, so we can determine that the visual angle of the iPod's total width is about 4 degrees.

Bruce Goldstein

Figure 8.27 ▮ Both of these objects have the same visual angle, even though there is a huge difference in their physical sizes.

based their judgments on the physical sizes of the circles. When they viewed a large test circle that was located far away (far circle in Figure 8.24), they made the comparison circle large (point F in Figure 8.28). However, when they viewed a small test circle that was located nearby (near circle in Figure 8.24), they made the comparison circle small (point N in Figure 8.28). The observers' adjustment of the comparison circle to match the physical size of the test circles means that they were accurately judging the physical sizes of the circles.

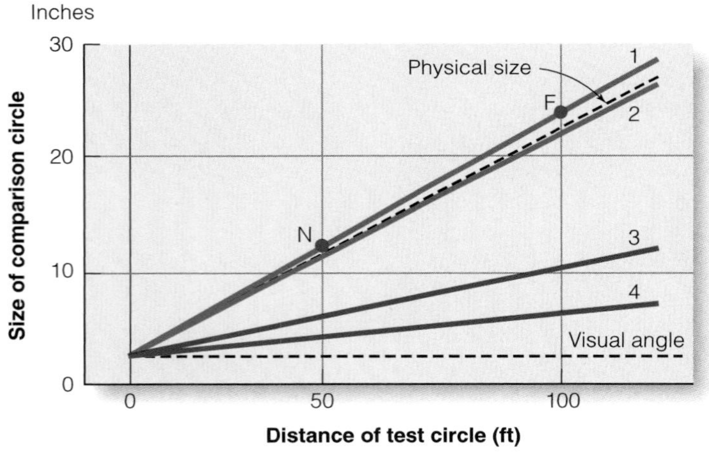

Figure 8.28 ▮ Results of Holway and Boring's experiment. The dashed line marked *physical size* is the result that would be expected if the observers adjusted the diameter of the comparison circle to match the actual diameter of each test circle. The line marked *visual angle* is the result that would be expected if the observers adjusted the diameter of the comparison circle to match the visual angle of each test circle.
(From "Determinants of Apparent Visual Size with Distance Variant," by A. H. Holway and E. G. Boring, 1941, American Journal of Psychology, *54, 21–34, figure 2. University of Illinois Press.)*

Holway and Boring then determined how accurate the observers' judgments would be when there was less depth information. They did this by having the observer view the test circles with one eye (line 2 in Figure 8.28), then by having the observer view the test circles through a peephole (line 3), and finally by adding drapes to the hallway to eliminate reflections (line 4). The results of these experiments indicate that as it became harder to determine the distance of the test circles, the observer's perception of the sizes of the circles became inaccurate.

Eliminating depth information made it more difficult to judge the physical sizes of the circles, and the observers' perception of size was determined not by the actual sizes of objects but by the size of the objects' retinal images. Because all of the test circles in Holway and Boring's experiment had the same retinal size, they were judged to be about the same size once depth information was eliminated. Thus, the results of this experiment indicate that size estimation is based on the actual sizes of objects when there is good depth information, and that size estimation is strongly influenced by the object's visual angle when depth information is eliminated.

An example of size perception that is determined by visual angle is our perception of the sizes of the sun and the moon, which, due to a cosmic coincidence, have the same visual angle. The fact that they have identical visual angles becomes most obvious during an eclipse of the sun. Although we can see the flaming corona of the sun surrounding the moon, as shown in Figure 8.29, the moon's disk almost exactly covers the disk of the sun.

If we calculate the visual angles of the sun and the moon, the result is 0.5 degrees for both. As you can see in Figure 8.29, the moon is small (diameter 2,200 miles) but close (245,000 miles from Earth), whereas the sun is large (diameter 865,400 miles) but far away (93 million miles from Earth). Even though these two celestial bodies are vastly different in size, we perceive them to be the same size because, as we are unable to perceive their distance, we base our judgment on their visual angles.

In yet another example, we perceive objects viewed from a high-flying airplane as very small. Because we have no way of accurately estimating the distance from the airplane to the ground, we perceive size based on objects' visual angles, which are very small because we are so high up.

Size Constancy

The examples just described all demonstrate a link between our perception of size and our perception of depth, with good depth perception favoring accurate size perception. And even though our perception of size is not al-

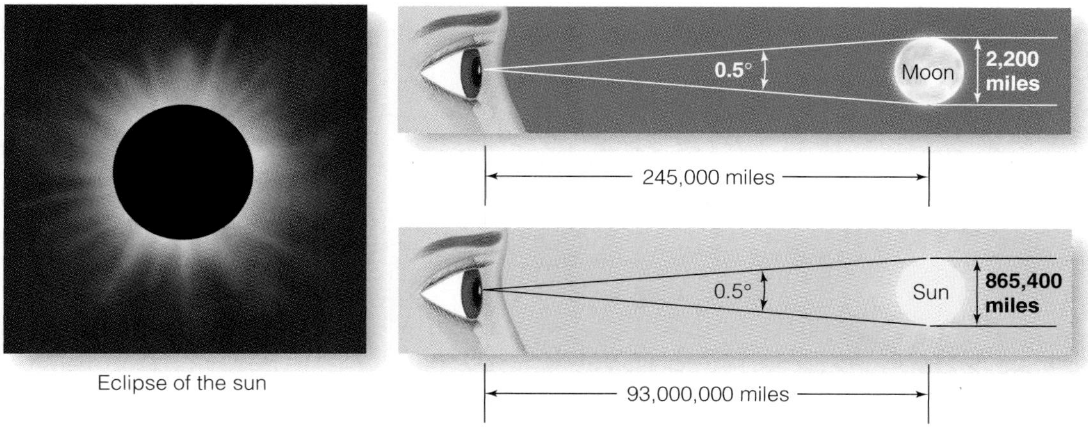

Figure 8.29 ▌ The moon's disk almost exactly covers the sun during an eclipse because the sun and the moon have the same visual angles.

ways totally accurate (Gilinsky, 1951), it is good enough to cause psychologists to propose the principle of size constancy. The principle of **size constancy** states that our perception of an object's size remains relatively constant, even when we view an object from different distances, which changes the size of the object's image on the retina.

To introduce the idea of size constancy to my perception class, I ask for a volunteer from the front row. I stand about 3 feet away and ask the person to estimate my height. Their guess is usually accurate, around 5 feet 10 inches. I then take one large step back so I am now 6 feet away and ask the person to estimate my height again. It probably doesn't surprise you that their new estimate of my height remains about the same. The point of this demonstration is that even though the size of my image on the person's retina is halved when I step back to 6 feet (see Figure 8.25), the person senses my size as remaining about the same. This is size constancy. The following demonstration illustrates size constancy in another way.

DEMONSTRATION

Perceiving Size at a Distance

Hold a quarter between the fingertips of each hand so you can see the faces of both coins. Hold one coin about a foot from you and the other at arm's length. Observe the coins with both of your eyes open and note their sizes. Under these conditions, most people perceive the near and far coins as being approximately the same size. Now close one eye, and holding the coins so they appear side-by-side, notice how your perception of the size of the far coin changes so that it now appears smaller than the near coin. This demonstrates how size constancy is decreased under conditions of poor depth information. ■

Size Constancy as a Calculation The link between size constancy and depth perception has led to the proposal that size constancy is based on a constancy-scaling mechanism that takes an object's distance into account (Gregory, 1966). This constancy-scaling mechanism, which we will call **size-distance scaling**, operates according to the equation $S = K (R \times D)$, where S is the object's perceived size, K is a constant, R is the size of the retinal image, and D is the perceived distance of the object. According to this equation, as a person walks away from you, the size of the person's image on your retina, R, gets smaller, but your perception of the person's distance, D, gets larger. These two changes balance each other, and the net result is that you perceive the person's size, S, as remaining constant.

DEMONSTRATION

Size-Distance Scaling and Emmert's Law

You can demonstrate size-distance scaling to yourself by looking at the center of the circle in Figure 8.30 for about 60 seconds. Then look at the white space to the side of the circle and blink to see the circle's afterimage. Before the afterimage fades, also look at a wall far across the room. You should see that the size of the afterimage depends on where you look. If you look at a distant surface, such as the far wall of the room, you see a large afterimage that appears to be far away. If you look at a near surface, such as the page of this book, you see a small afterimage that appears to be close.

Figure 8.30 ▌ Afterimage stimulus. ■

Figure 8.31 illustrates the principle underlying the effect you just experienced, which was first described by Emmert in 1881. Staring at the circle in Figure 8.30 bleached a small circular area of visual pigment on your

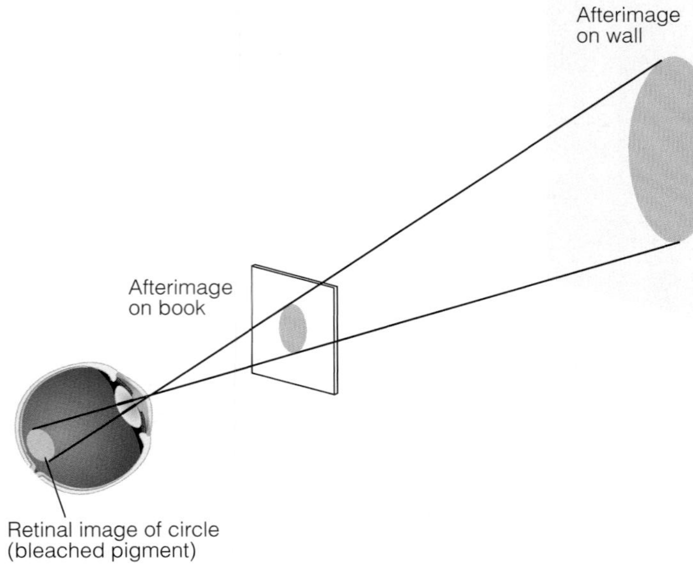

Figure 8.31 ▮ The principle behind the observation that the size of an afterimage increases as the afterimage is viewed against more distant surfaces.

retina. This bleached area of the retina determines the retinal size of the after-image and remained constant no matter where you were looking.

The perceived size of the afterimage, as shown in Figure 8.31, is determined by the distance of the surface against which the afterimage is viewed. This relationship between the apparent distance of an afterimage and its perceived size is known as **Emmert's law**: The farther away an afterimage appears, the larger it will seem. This result follows from our size-distance scaling equation, $S = R \times D$. The size of the bleached area of pigment on the retina, R, always stays the same, increasing the afterimage's distance, D, which increases the magnitude of $R \times D$. We therefore perceive the size of the afterimage, S, as larger when it is viewed against the far wall.

Other Information for Size Perception Although we have been stressing the link between size constancy and depth perception, there are other sources of information in the environment that also help achieve size constancy. One source of information for size perception is relative size. We often use the sizes of familiar objects in our environment as a yardstick to judge the size of other objects, as in Figure 8.32, in which the size of the woman indicates that the wheel is very large. (Also see the chapter-opening picture, facing page 167, in which the size of the house indicates that the trees are very tall.) This idea that our perception of the sizes of objects can be influenced by the sizes of nearby objects explains why we often fail to appreciate how tall basketball players are, when all we see for comparison are other basketball players. But as soon as a person of average height stands next to one of these players, their true height becomes evident.

Bruce Goldstein

Figure 8.32 ▮ The size of this wheel becomes apparent when it can be compared to an object of known size, such as the person. If the wheel were seen in total isolation, it would be difficult to know that it is so large.

Another source of information for size perception is the relationship between objects and texture information on the ground. Figure 8.33 shows two cylinders sitting on a texture gradient formed by a cobblestone road. Even if we have trouble perceiving the depth of the near and far cylinders, we can tell that they are the same size because both cover the same portion of a paving stone.

Figure 8.33 ▌ Two cylinders resting on a texture gradient. The fact that the bases of both cylinders cover about one unit on the gradient indicates that the bases of the two cylinders are the same size.

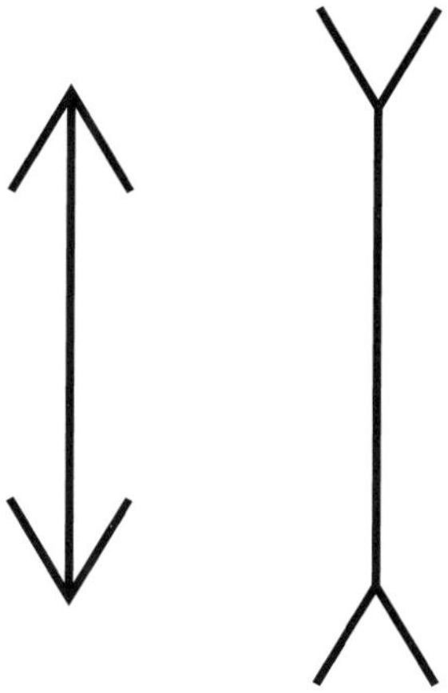

Figure 8.34 ▌ The Müller-Lyer illusion. Both lines are actually the same length.

VISUAL ILLUSIONS

Size constancy contributes to our experience of **veridical perception**—perception that matches the actual physical situation. Veridical perception is most likely to occur in well-lit natural environments in which lots of perceptual information is available. But when conditions are such that we receive inaccurate information, as did our helicopter pilot in whiteout weather conditions, veridical perception breaks down and we experience an illusion—a nonveridical perception such as mistaking a small box for a truck.

The size illusion experienced by our helicopter pilot is an example of an illusion occurring in the natural environment. However, most of the illusions that psychologists have studied are ones that they have devised, like the Müller-Lyer illusion in Figure 8.34. The goal in constructing these illusions is to do experiments that will uncover the mechanism responsible for the illusion.

The Müller-Lyer Illusion

In the **Müller-Lyer illusion**, the right vertical line appears to be longer than the left vertical line, even though they are both exactly the same length (measure them). It is obvious by just looking at these figures that one line appears longer than the other, but you can measure how *much* longer the right line appears by using the simple matching procedure described in the following demonstration. VL 11, 12, 13

DEMONSTRATION

Measuring the Müller-Lyer Illusion

The first step in measuring the Müller-Lyer illusion is to create a "standard stimulus" by drawing a line 30 millimeters long on an index card and adding outward-going fins, as in the right figure in Figure 8.34. Then, on separate cards, create "comparison stimuli" by drawing lines that are 28, 30, 32, 34, 36, 38, and 40 millimeters long with inward-going fins, as in the left figure. Then, ask your observer to pick the comparison stimulus that most closely matches the length of the standard stimulus. The difference in length between the standard stimulus and the comparison stimulus chosen by your observer (typically between 10 percent and 30 percent) defines the size of the illusion. Try this procedure on a number of people to see how variable it is. ■

Misapplied Size-Constancy Scaling Why does the Müller-Lyer display cause a misperception of size? Richard Gregory (1966) explains the illusion on the basis of a mechanism he calls **misapplied size constancy scaling**. He points out that size constancy normally helps us maintain a stable perception of objects by taking distance into account. Thus, size constancy scaling causes a 6-foot-tall person to appear 6 feet tall, no matter what his distance. Gregory proposes, however, that the very mechanisms that help us maintain stable perceptions in the three-dimensional world sometimes create illusions when applied to objects drawn on a two-dimensional surface.

We can see how misapplied size-constancy scaling works by comparing the left and right lines in Figure 8.34 to the left and right lines that have been superimposed on the corners of the building in Figure 8.35. Gregory suggests that the fins on the right line in Figure 8.35 make this line look like part of an inside corner, and that the fins on the left line make this line look like part of an outside cor-

Figure 8.35 ▮ According to Gregory (1973), the Müller-Lyer line on the left corresponds to an outside corner, and the line on the right corresponds to an inside corner. Note that the two vertical lines are the same length (measure them!).

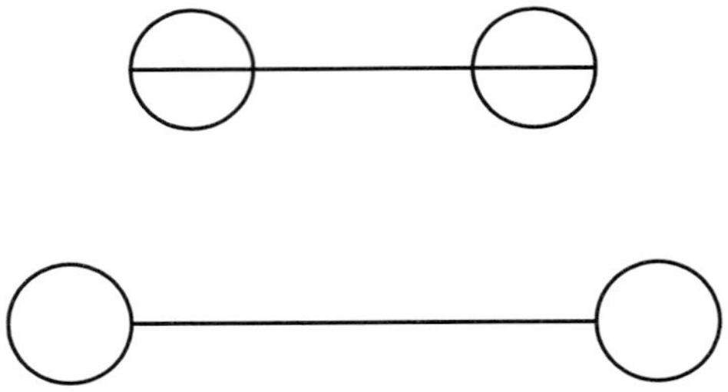

Figure 8.36 ▮ The "dumbbell" version of the Müller-Lyer illusion. As in the original Müller-Lyer illusion, the two lines are actually the same length.

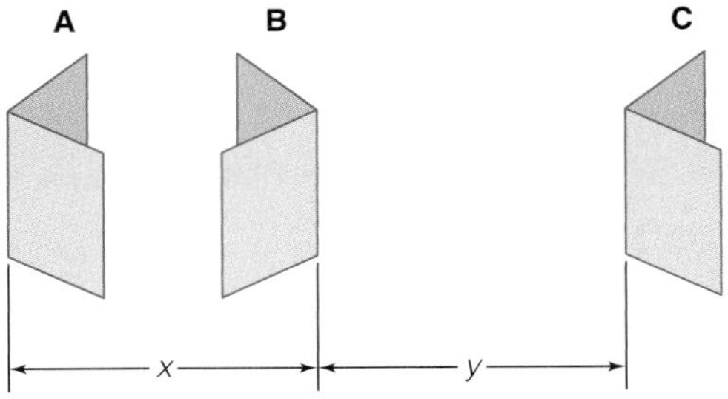

Figure 8.37 ▮ A three-dimensional Müller-Lyer illusion. Although the distances *x* and *y* are the same, distance *y* appears larger, just as in the two-dimensional Müller-Lyer illusion.

ner. Because inside corners are usually farther away than outside corners (as in this example), we see the right line as being farther away, and our size-distance scaling mechanism causes this line to appear longer. (Remember that $S = R \times D$. The retinal sizes, *R*, of the two lines are the same, so the perceived size, *S*, is determined by the perceived distance, *D*.)

At this point, you may say that although the Müller-Lyer figures may remind Gregory of inside and outside corners, they don't look that way to you (or at least they didn't until Gregory told you to see them that way). But according to Gregory, it is not necessary that you be consciously aware that these lines can represent three-dimensional structures; your perceptual system unconsciously takes the depth information contained in the Müller-Lyer figures into account, and your size-distance scaling mechanism adjusts the perceived sizes of the lines accordingly.

Gregory's theory of visual illusions has not, however, gone unchallenged. For example, figures like the dumbbell in Figure 8.36, which contain no obvious perspective or depth, still result in an illusion. And Patricia DeLucia and Julian Hochberg (1985, 1986, 1991; Hochberg, 1987) have shown that the Müller-Lyer illusion occurs for a display like the one in Figure 8.37, in which it is obvious that the spaces between the two sets of fins are not at different depths. (Measure distances *x* and *y* to convince yourself that they are the same.) You can experience this effect for yourself by doing the following demonstration.

DEMONSTRATION

The Müller-Lyer Illusion With Books

Pick three books that are the same size and arrange two of them with their corners making a 90-degree angle and standing in positions A and B, as shown in Figure 8.37. Then, without using a ruler, position the third book at position C, so that distance *y* appears to be equal to distance *x*. Check your placement, looking down at the books from the top and from other angles as well. When you are satisfied that distances *x* and *y* appear about equal, measure the distances with a ruler. How do they compare? ■

If you set distance *y* so that it was smaller than distance *x*, this is exactly the result you would expect from the two-dimensional Müller-Lyer illusion, in which the distance between the outward-going fins appears enlarged compared to the distance between the inward-going fins. You can also duplicate the illusion shown in Figure 8.37 with your books by using your ruler to make distances *x* and *y* equal. Then, notice how the distances actually appear. The fact that we can create the Müller-Lyer illusion by using three-dimensional stimuli such as these, as well as demonstrations like the dumbbell in Figure 8.36, is difficult for Gregory's theory to explain.

Conflicting Cues Theory R. H. Day (1989, 1990) has proposed the **conflicting cues theory**, which states that our perception of line length depends on two cues: (1) the actual length of the vertical lines, and (2) the overall length of the figure. According to Day, these two conflicting cues are integrated to form a compromise perception of length. Because the overall length of the right figure in Figure 8.34 is larger due to its outward-oriented fins, this length causes the vertical line to appear larger.

Another version of the Müller-Lyer illusion, shown in Figure 8.38, results in the perception that the space between the dots is greater in the lower figure than in the upper figure, even though the distances are actually the same. According to Day's conflicting cues theory, the space in the lower figure appears greater because the overall extent of the figure is greater. Thus, although Gregory feels that depth information is involved in determining illusions, Day rejects this idea and says that cues for length are what is important. Let's now look at some more examples of illusions and the mechanisms that have been proposed to explain them.

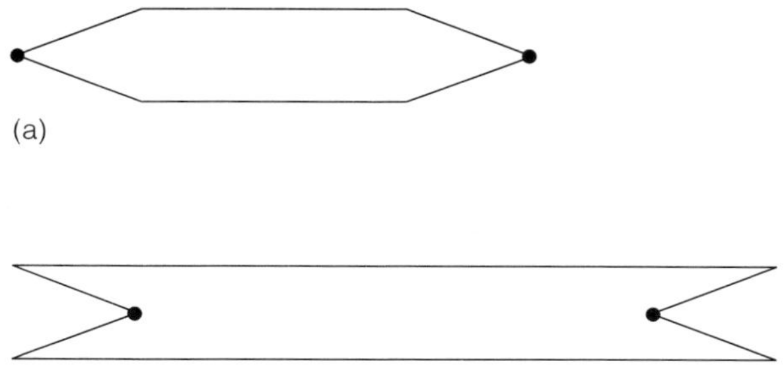

Figure 8.38 ▮ An alternate version of the Müller-Lyer illusion. We perceive that the distance between the dots in (a) is less than the distance in (b), even though the distances are the same.
(From Day, 1989.)

The Ponzo Illusion

In the **Ponzo** (or railroad track) **illusion**, shown in Figure 8.39, both horizontal rectangles are the same length and have the same visual angle, but the one on top appears longer. According to Gregory's misapplied scaling explanation, the top line appears longer because of depth information that makes it appear farther away. Thus, just as for the Müller-Lyer illusion, the scaling mechanism corrects for this apparently increased depth (even though there really isn't any, because the illusion is on a flat page), and we perceive the top line to be larger. (Also see Prinzmetal et al., 2001; Shimamura & Prinzmetal, 1999, for another explanation of the Ponzo illusion.) VL 14, 15

Bruce Goldstein

Figure 8.39 ▮ The Ponzo (or railroad track) illusion. The two horizontal rectangles are the same length on the page (measure them), but the far one appears larger.

The Ames Room

The **Ames room** causes two people of equal size to appear very different in size (Ittleson, 1952). In Figure 8.40, you can see that the woman on the right looks much taller

© The Exploratorium/S. Schwartzenberg

Figure 8.40 ▮ The Ames room. Both women are actually the same height, but the woman on the right appears taller because of the distorted shape of the room.

than the woman on the left. This perception occurs even though both women are actually about the same height. The reason for this erroneous perception of size lies in the construction of the room. The shapes of the wall and the windows at the rear of the room make it look like a normal rectangular room when viewed from a particular observation point; however, as shown in the diagram in Figure 8.41, the Ames room is shaped so that the left corner of the room is almost twice as far away from the observer as the right corner.

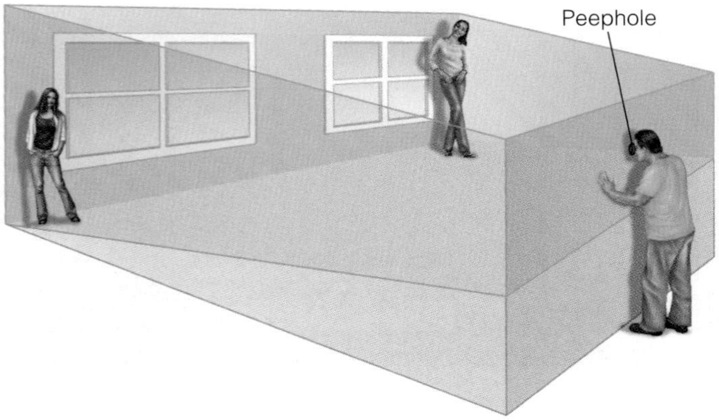

Figure 8.41 ▌ The Ames room, showing its true shape. The woman on the left is actually almost twice as far away from the observer as the woman on the right; however, when the room is viewed through the peephole, this difference in distance is not seen. In order for the room to look normal when viewed through the peephole, it is necessary to enlarge the left side of the room.

What's happening in the Ames room? The construction of the room causes the woman on the left to have a much smaller visual angle than the one on the right. We think that we are looking into a normal rectangular room at two women who appear to be at the same distance, so we perceive the one with the smaller visual angle as shorter. We can understand why this occurs by returning to our size-distance scaling equation, $S = R \times D$. Because the perceived distance, *D,* is the same for the two women, but the size of the retinal image, *R,* is smaller for the woman on the left, her perceived size, *S,* is smaller.

Another explanation for the Ames room is based not on size-distance scaling, but on relative size. The relative size explanation states that our perception of the size of the two people is determined by how they fill the distance between the bottom and top of the room. Because the woman on the right fills the entire space and the woman on the left occupies only a little of it, we perceive the woman on the right as taller (Sedgwick, 2001).

The Moon Illusion

You may have noticed that when the moon is on the horizon, it appears much larger than when it is higher in the sky. This enlargement of the horizon moon compared to the elevated moon, shown in Figure 8.42, is called the **moon illusion**. An explanation of the moon illusion that involves depth perception is called the **apparent-distance theory**, which is based on the idea that the horizon moon is viewed across the filled space of the terrain, which contains depth information, but when the moon is higher in the sky it is viewed through empty space, which contains little depth information.

Figure 8.42 ▌ An artist's conception of the moon illusion showing the moon on the horizon and high in the sky simultaneously.

The idea that the horizon is perceived as farther away than the sky overhead is supported by the fact that when people estimate the distance to the horizon and the distance to the sky directly overhead, they report that the horizon appears to be farther away. That is, the heavens appear "flattened" (Figure 8.43). The key to the moon illusion, according to apparent-distance theory, is that both the horizon and the elevated moons have the same visual angle, and because the horizon moon is seen against the horizon, it will appear to be farther away than the elevated moon, and so it will appear larger.

The moon illusion is so striking that people often doubt that the horizon and elevated moons have the same visual angle. But because the moon's physical size (2,200 miles in diameter) and distance from Earth (245,000 miles) are constant throughout the night, the moon's visual angle must be constant. If you are still skeptical, photograph the horizon and the elevated moons

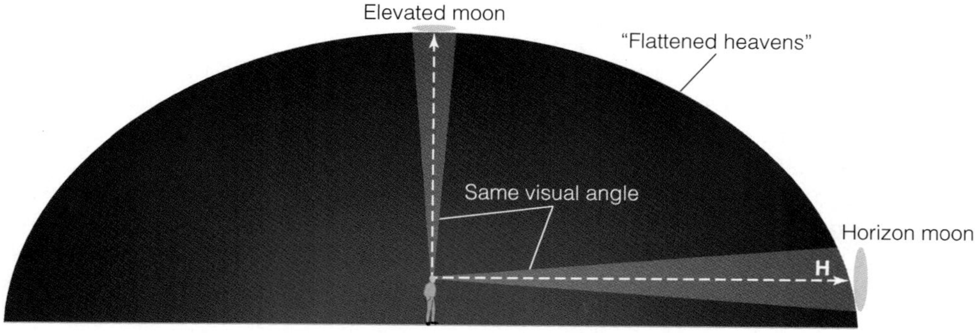

Figure 8.43 ▌ When observers are asked to consider that the sky is a surface and are asked to compare the distance to the horizon (H) and the distance to the top of the sky on a clear moonless night, they usually say that the horizon appears farther away. This results in the "flattened heavens" shown above.

with a digital camera. When you compare the two images, you will find that the diameters in the resulting two pictures are identical. Or you can view the moon through a quarter-inch-diameter hole (the size produced by most standard hole punches) held at about arm's length. For most people, the moon just fits inside this hole, wherever it is in the sky.

Lloyd Kaufman and Irvin Rock have done a number of experiments that support the apparent-distance theory. In one of their experiments, they showed that when the horizon moon was viewed over the terrain, which made it seem farther away, it appeared 1.3 times larger than the elevated moon; however, when the terrain was masked off so that the horizon moon was viewed through a hole in a sheet of cardboard, the illusion vanished (Kaufman & Rock, 1962a, 1962b; Rock & Kaufman, 1962).

The principle involved in the apparent-distance explanation of the moon illusion is the same one that causes an afterimage to appear larger if it is viewed against a faraway surface in the Emmert's law demonstration (Figure 8.31). Just as the near and far afterimages have the same visual angles, so do the horizon and the elevated moons. The afterimage that appears on the wall across the room simulates the horizon moon; the circle appears farther away, so your size-distance scaling mechanism makes it appear larger. The afterimage that appears on the page of the book simulates the elevated moon; the circle appears closer, so your scaling mechanism makes it appear smaller (King & Gruber, 1962).

Some researchers, however, are skeptical of the apparent-distance theory. They question the idea that the horizon moon appears farther away, as shown in the flattened heavens effect in Figure 8.43, because some observers see the horizon moon as floating in space in front of the sky (Plug & Ross, 1994).

Another theory of the moon illusion is the **angular size-contrast theory**, which states that the moon appears smaller when it is surrounded by larger objects. Thus, when the moon is elevated, the large expanse of sky surrounding it makes it appear smaller. However, when the moon is on the horizon, less sky surrounds it, so it appears larger (Baird, Wagner, & Fuld, 1990).

Even though scientists have been proposing theories to explain the moon illusion for hundreds of years, there is still no agreement on an explanation (Hershenson, 1989). Apparently a number of factors are involved (in addition to the ones we have considered here), including: atmospheric perspective (looking through haze on the horizon can increase size perception), color (redness increases perceived size), and oculomotor factors (convergence of the eyes, which tends to occur when we look toward the horizon and can cause an increase in perceived size; Plug & Ross, 1994). Just as many different sources of depth information work together to create our impression of depth, many different factors may work together to create the moon illusion and perhaps the other illusions as well.

SOMETHING TO CONSIDER: DISTANCE PERCEPTION DEPENDS ON THE ENVIRONMENT AND ON THE SELF!

Our discussion of depth perception has focused on identifying information in the environment or on the image on the retina that is related to distances of objects. But recent research shows that perceiving distance may also be determined by more "personal" factors—specifically, by a particular person's ability to take "action" within the environment.

One example of this is an experiment in which people

who wore a heavy backpack while making distance judgments increased their estimates of distance (Figure 8.44a; Proffitt et al., 2003). Note that the people in this experiment did not have to walk the distances wearing the backpack; they just wore the backpack while making their distance estimates. Could it be that judging distance depends on the effort that people believe will be involved if they have to carry out an action associated with the distance estimate?

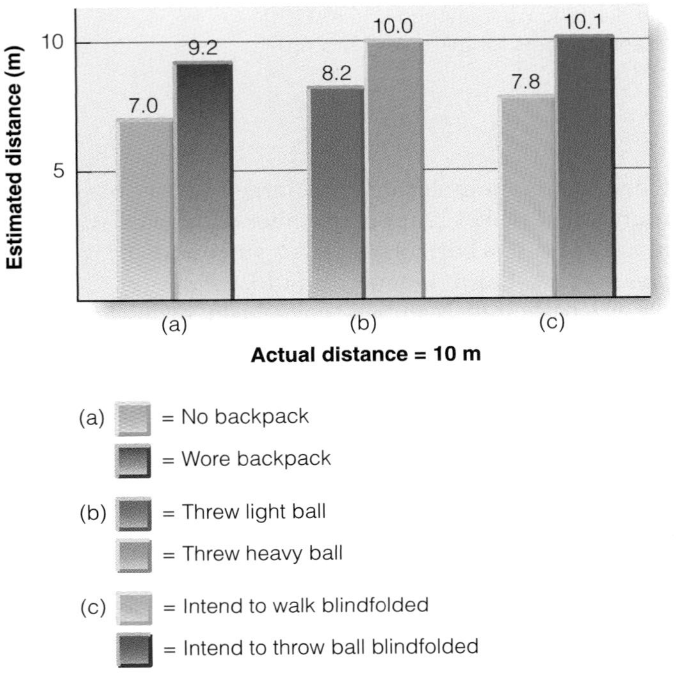

Figure 8.44 ▌ Results of experiments by Proffitt et al. (2003) and Witt et al. (2004). For each of the conditions, larger distance estimates were associated with greater effort.

An experiment by Janice Witt and coworkers (2004) indicates that the answer to this question is "yes." They had participants throw balls to targets ranging from 4 to 10 meters away. After they had thrown either a light ball or a heavy ball, participants estimated the distances to the targets. The results for the 10-meter target, shown in Figure 8.44b, indicate that distance estimates were larger after throwing the heavy ball.

Finally, here's an additional twist to these findings: Apparently, distance judgments are determined not only by the amount of effort people associate with a distance but with whether or not they think they will actually have to exert that effort. This was demonstrated by dividing participants who had thrown heavy balls into two groups. One group was told that they were going to have to throw balls at the targets while blindfolded, and the other group was told that they were going to have to walk to the targets while blindfolded. The results, shown in Figure 8.44c, show that the group that was told they would be throwing estimated the distance as greater than those who were told they would be walking.

What all of this adds up to is that distance perception depends both on optical information, such as monocular and binocular depth cues, and also on actions we intend to perform and the effort associated with these actions. Perception, therefore, is about both the environment we perceive and the person who is doing the perceiving.

TEST YOURSELF 8.2

1. Describe the Holway and Boring experiment. What do the results of this experiment tell us about how size perception is influenced by depth perception?
2. What are some examples of situations in which our perception of an object's size is determined by the object's visual angle? Under what conditions does this occur?
3. What is size constancy, and under what conditions does it occur?
4. What is size-distance scaling? How does it explain size constancy?
5. Describe information (other than depth) that can influence our perception of size.
6. Describe how illusions of size, such as the Müller-Lyer illusion, the Ponzo illusion, the Ames room, and the moon illusion, can be explained in terms of size-distance scaling.
7. What are some problems with the size-distance scaling explanation of (a) the Müller-Lyer illusion and (b) the moon illusion? What alternative explanations have been proposed?
8. What does it mean to say that the perception of distance depends not only on optical information but also on the "self"?

VL **16–18**

THINK ABOUT IT

1. Texture gradients are said to provide information for depth perception because elements in a scene become more densely packed as distance increases.

The classic example of a texture gradient is a tiled floor, like the one in Figure 10.5, which has regularly-spaced elements. But regularly spaced elements are more the exception than the rule in the environment. For example, consider the hillside in Figure 8.45, in which the rocks and weeds are irregularly spaced. (1) Do you think texture gradients could play a role in determining the perception of depth in this scene? (2) Make an informal survey of your environment, both inside and outside, and decide whether texture gradients could play a role in determining depth in these environments.

Bruce Goldstein

Figure 8.45 ▮ An irregular texture on a hillside.

2. How could you determine the contribution of binocular vision to depth perception? One way would be to close one eye and notice how this affects your perception. Try this, and describe any changes you notice. Then devise a way to quantitatively measure the accuracy of depth perception that is possible with two-eyed and one-eyed vision.

3. One of the triumphs of art is creating the impression of depth on a two-dimensional canvas. Go to a museum or look at pictures in an art book, and identify the depth information that helps increase the perception of depth in these pictures. You may also notice that you perceive less depth in some pictures, especially abstract ones. In fact, some artists purposely create pictures that are perceived as "flat." What steps do these artists have to take to accomplish this?

IF YOU WANT TO KNOW MORE

1. ***Depth Perception in Animals.*** Most animals have some kind of depth perception because it is essential for an animal's ability to navigate through the environment. But there are differences in the types of depth information different animals use.

Collett, T. S., & Harkness, L. I. K. (1982). Depth vision in animals. In D. J. Ingle, M. A.Goodale, & R. J. W. Mansfield (Eds.), *Analysis of visual behavior* (pp. 111–176). Cambridge, MA: MIT Press.

McFadden, S. A. (1987). The binocular depth stereoacuity of the pigeon and its relation to the anatomical resolving power of the eye. *Vision Research, 27,* 1967–1980.

Srinivasan, M. V., & Ventatesh, S. (Eds.). (1997). *From living eyes to seeing machines.* New York: Oxford.

2. ***Echolocation in Bats.*** Bats are able to sense the depths and positions of objects in the dark because they use a system called echolocation, which involves sending out high-frequency pulses. Some of these pulses bounce off objects, and the bat notes how long it takes for the pulse to return.

Griffin, D. R. (1944). Echolocation by blind men and bats. *Science, 100,* 589–590.

Suga, N. (1990, June). Biosonar and neural computation in bats. *Scientific American,* pp. 60–68.

3. ***Effect of Early Experience on the Development of Binocular Neurons.*** Experiments in which animals are reared with vision restricted to one eye at a time show that early experience perceiving with two eyes is necessary in order for binocular neurons to develop normally.

Blake, R., & Hirsch, H. V. B. (1975). Deficits in binocular depth perception in cats after alternating monocular deprivation. *Science, 190,* 1114–1116.

Olson, C. R., & Freeman, R. D. (1980). Profile of the sensitive period for monocular deprivation in kittens. *Experimental Brain Research, 39,* 17–21.

4. ***How Depth Cues Are Combined in the Brain.*** Our perception of depth is determined by a combination of different cues working together. The experiments described in the following article shows which brain structures may be involved in combining these cues.

Welchman, A. E., Deubelius, A., Conrad, V., Bülthoff, H. H., & Kourtzi, Z. (2005). 3D shape perception from combined depth cues in human visual cortex. *Nature Neuroscience, 8,* 820–827.

KEY TERMS

Accretion (p. 172)
Ames room (p. 187)
Angle of disparity (p. 175)
Angular size-contrast theory (p. 189)
Apparent-distance theory (p. 188)
Atmospheric perspective (p. 170)
Binocular depth cell (p. 178)
Binocular disparity (p. 173)
Conflicting cues theory (p. 187)
Correspondence problem (p. 177)
Corresponding retinal points (p. 173)
Crossed disparity (p. 175)
Cue approach to depth perception (p. 168)
Deletion (p. 172)
Disparity-selective cell (p. 178)
Emmert's law (p. 184)
Familiar size (p. 170)
Horopter (p. 174)
Microstimulation (p. 179)
Misapplied size constancy scaling (p. 185)
Monocular cue (p. 169)
Moon illusion (p. 188)
Movement parallax (p. 171)
Müller-Lyer illusion (p. 185)
Noncorresponding (disparate) points (p. 174)
Occlusion (p. 168)
Oculomotor cue (p. 169)
Perspective convergence (p. 170)
Pictorial cue (p. 169)
Ponzo illusion (p. 187)
Random-dot stereogram (p. 177)
Relative height (p. 169)
Relative size (p. 170)
Size constancy (p. 183)
Size-distance scaling (p. 183)
Stereopsis (p. 175)
Stereoscope (p. 175)
Texture gradient (p. 171)
Uncrossed disparity (p. 175)
Veridical perception (p. 185)
Visual angle (p. 180)

VISIT YOUR COMPANION WEBSITE FOR THIS BOOK

http://psychology.wadsworth.com/goldstein7e

Check out this companion website where you'll find online resources—glossary, flashcards, web links, multiple-choice and essay questions, and much more!

VIRTUAL LAB

Your Virtual Lab is designed to help you get the most out of this course. The Virtual Lab icons direct you to specific media demonstrations and experiments designed to help you visualize what you are reading about. The number beside each icon indicates the number of the media element you can access through your CD-ROM, Perception PsychologyNow, or WebTutor resource at http:now.ilrn.com/goldstein_7e.

The following are the lab exercises covering what you've just learned in this chapter:

1 *Convergence as a Depth Cue* How the convergence angle changes as a function of an object's distance.

2 *Convergence* A video showing how convergence of the eyes depends on an object's distance.

3 *Shape from Shading* How the shadows that result from illumination can help define the shape of a rotating three-dimensional object.

4 *Motion Parallax* Demonstration of how objects change their relative position in response to observer movement.

5 *The Horopter and Corresponding Points* How corresponding points on the two eyes can be determined by sliding one eye over the other. How the angle of convergence changes with different distances of fixation.

6 *Disparity and Retinal Location* How disparity changes as one object is moved closer to the eye as a person fixates on another object.

7 *Pictures* Some "classic" stereograms of photographs. Red-green glasses required.

8 *Outlines* Stereogram of a Necker cube. Red-green glasses required.

9 *Depth Perception* An experiment in which you can determine how your perception of depth changes with the amount of binocular disparity. Red-green glasses required.

10 *Random-Dot Stereogram* How the perception of depth can be created by random-dot stereograms. Red-green glasses required.

11 *The Müller-Lyer Illusion* Measure the effect of the Müller-Lyer illusion with both inward and outward fins.

12 *Müller-Lyer Illusion 2* How the fins of the Müller-Lyer illusion affect the perception of the sizes of two lines.

13 *Müller-Lyer Variations* Variations of the Müller-Lyer illusion, including the dumbbell version.

14 *The Ponzo Illusion* Measure the size of the Ponzo (railroad track) illusion.

15 *Size Perception and Depth* How perspective cues can cause two "monsters" to appear different in size.

16 *Horizontal–Vertical Illusion* Measure the size of the horizontal–vertical illusion.

17 *Poggendorf Illusion* Measure the size of the Poggendorf illusion.

18 *Zollner Illusion* How context can affect the perceived orientation of parallel lines.

CHAPTER

9

PERCEIVING MOVEMENT

Chapter Contents

The blur of traffic moving past Westminster Abby in London. We perceive motion both when objects move across our field of view, as in this scene, and when we follow moving objects with our eyes, as when we track the flight of a passing bird.

VL *The Virtual Lab icons direct you to specific animations and videos designed to help you visualize what you are reading about. The number beside each icon indicates the number of the clip you can access through your CD-ROM or your student website.*

Some Questions We Will Consider:

- *Why do some animals freeze in place when they sense danger? (p. 198)*
- *When we scan a room, the image of the room moves across the retina, but we perceive the room as remaining stationary. Why does this occur? (p. 200)*
- *How does our perception of movement depend on past experiences? (p. 208)*

Many animals become totally still when they sense danger. They do this for survival because as long as they remain still, they may be unseen by a potential predator, but as soon as they move, they become instantly visible. For the predator seeking prey, and the potential prey on the lookout for predators to avoid, the perception of movement is crucial for survival. Although some animals may have poor depth perception or rudimentary color vision, none lack the ability to perceive motion.

We will begin this chapter by describing some of the ways that motion perception is achieved and studied, and then we will see that motion perception has functions other than being essential for survival. We will then show how perceiving movement is not quite as simple as it might at first seem because although we perceive motion in the environment, we, ourselves, are usually moving.

STUDYING MOVEMENT PERCEPTION

Before we start considering some of the problems involved in understanding movement perception, it is important to understand that there are a number of different ways to achieve the perception of motion.

1. *Real movement.* Movement occurs when an object moves across an observer's field of view (Figure 9.1a). This situation is called **real movement** because the object is physically moving.
2. *Apparent movement.* We introduced apparent movement in Chapter 5, when we told the story of how Max Wertheimer observed that presenting two stationary stimuli, one after another, in slightly different locations, can cause the perception of movement between these stimuli. This perception is called **apparent movement** because there is no actual (or real) movement between the stimuli. This is the basis for the movement we perceive in movies, television, and in moving signs that are used for advertising and entertainment (Figure 9.1b). **VIRTUAL LAB 1–4**
3. *Induced movement.* Apparent movement is an illusion because we perceive movement even though

Bruce Goldstein (photos)

Figure 9.1 ▌ Four ways to create the perception of movement: (a) real movement—the object moves; (b) apparent movement—dots blinking on and off create a moving message (see Figure 5.10 for the beginning of this message); (c) induced movement—the moon appears to race through the clouds; (d) movement aftereffects.

the stimuli are not moving. **Induced movement** is an illusion that occurs when movement of one object induces the perception of movement in another object. You've experienced induced movement if you've seen the moon racing through the clouds on a windy night. The moon is actually stationary, but the moving clouds make it appear to be moving (Figure 9.1c). VL 5

4. *Movement aftereffect.* **Movement aftereffects** occur after viewing a moving stimulus for 30 to 60 seconds and then seeing movement in the opposite direction when viewing a stationary stimulus. One example of a movement aftereffect is the **waterfall illusion**: If you look at a waterfall for 30 to 60 seconds (be sure it fills up only part of your field of view) and then look at part of the scene that is stationary, you will see movement in a direction opposite to the waterfall's movement. Movement aftereffects can also occur after viewing other kinds of motion. For example, viewing a rotating spiral that appears to move inward causes the apparent expansion of a stationary object. VL 6–9

Researchers studying movement perception have investigated all of the types of perceived movement described above—and some others as well. Our purpose, however, is not to understand every type of movement perception but to understand some of the principles governing movement perception in general. To do this, we will focus on real movement and apparent movement.

For many years, researchers treated the apparent movement created by flashing stationary pictures and the real movement created by actual movement through space as though they were separate phenomena, governed by different mechanisms. However, there is ample evidence that these two types of movement have much in common, including activating the same area of the brain (J. A. Stevens et al., 2000). Today's researchers therefore study both types of movement together and concentrate on discovering general mechanisms that apply to both. In this chapter, we will follow this approach as we look for general mechanisms of movement perception.

THE FUNCTIONS OF MOTION PERCEPTION

Motion perception provides information that is important both for survival and for determining the true shapes of objects.

Surviving to Perceive Another Day

Motion perception is universal not just because of predator–prey relationships. The ability to perceive movement is such a basic mechanism for interacting with the world that its loss can become a crippling disability. For example, a 43-year-old woman lost the ability to perceive movement when she suffered a stroke that damaged an area of her cortex that corresponds to the monkey's medial temporal cortex (area MT), which we will see is an important center for the perception of movement. Her condition, which is called **motion agnosia**, made it difficult for her to pour tea or coffee into a cup because the liquid appeared frozen, so she couldn't perceive the fluid rising in the cup and had trouble knowing when to stop pouring (Zihl et al., 1983, 1991). It was also difficult for her to follow dialogue because she couldn't see movements of a speaker's face and mouth.

But the most disturbing effect of her brain damage was the sudden appearance or disappearance of people or objects: People sometimes suddenly appeared or disappeared from rooms because she couldn't see them walking, and crossing the street presented serious problems because at first a car might seem far away, but then suddenly, without warning, it would appear very near. This disability was, therefore, not just a social inconvenience but enough of a threat to the woman's well-being that she rarely ventured outside into the world of moving—and sometimes dangerous—objects.

Perceiving Objects

Hermann von Helmholtz, the 19th-century physicist who is associated with the trichromatic theory of color vision (see page 146) was also interested in other aspects of perception. Here is what he has to say about how movement can play a role in perceiving objects.

> Suppose, for instance, that a person is standing still in a thick woods, where it is impossible for him to distinguish, except vaguely and roughly, in the mass of foliage and branches all around him what belongs to one tree and what to another. But the moment he begins to move forward, everything disentangles itself, and immediately he gets an apperception of the material contents of the woods and their relations to each other in space. (1866/1911, p. 296)

Helmholtz is saying that movement of the observer causes a previously confusing scene to become meaningful. Movement accomplishes this in Helmholtz's example by perceptually organizing elements that had previously not been associated with each other, so it becomes possible to tell which branches belong to one tree and which belong to another one. You can experience something similar to what Helmholtz describes by doing the following demonstration.

DEMONSTRATION

Perceiving a Camouflaged Bird

For this demonstration, you will need to prepare stimuli by photocopying the bird and the hatched-line pattern in Figure 9.2. Then cut out the bird and the hatched pattern so they are separated. Hold the picture of the bird up against a window during the day. Turn the copy of the hatched pattern over so the pattern is facing out the window (the white side of the paper should be facing you) and place it over the bird. If the window is adequately illuminated by daylight, you should be able to see the hatched pattern. Notice how the presence of the hatched pattern makes it more difficult to see the bird. Then, slide the bird back and forth under the pattern, and notice what happens to your perception of the bird (from D. Regan, 1986).

Figure 9.2 ▌ The bird becomes camouflaged when a transparency of the random lines is superimposed on a transparency of the bird. When the bird is moved relative to the lines, it becomes visible, an example of how movement enhances the perception of form.
(From Form in Motion Parallax; and from "Luminance Contrast: Vernier Discrimination," Spatial Vision, 1, *305–318. Reprinted by permission of David Regan.)* ■

The stationary bird is difficult to see when covered by the pattern because the bird and the pattern are made up of similar lines. But as soon as all of the elements of the bird begin moving in the same direction, the bird becomes visible. This is what Helmholtz described, except in his example, the observer was moving rather than the object. Either way, movement helps organize perception to make confusing or hidden objects visible. This is why a mouse might freeze in place when it is being stalked by a cat. It wants to avoid becoming perceptually organized in the cat's mind!

Your response to the camouflaged bird demonstration might be that although movement does make the bird easy to perceive amid the tangle of obscuring lines, this seems like a special case because most of the objects we see are not camouflaged. But if you remember our discussion of the "inverse projection problem" in Chapter 5, which showed that all objects in the environment cast ambiguous images on the retina, you can appreciate that moving relative to an object can help determine its true shape. For example, moving around the "horse" in Figure 9.3 reveals that its shape is not exactly what you may have expected based on your initial view. Thus, our movement relative to objects is constantly adding to the accuracy of our perception of these objects. A great deal of research has shown that observers can perceive shapes more rapidly and accurately when the shape is moving relative to the observer (Wexler et al., 2001).

Figure 9.3 ▌ Three views of a "horse." Moving around an object can reveal its true shape.

Another example of how movement perception can provide information about objects is provided by the **kinetic depth effect**, in which movement of an object's two-dimensional shadow can change the perception of the shadow into the perception of a three-dimensional object, such as the wire cube in Figure 9.4. When the cube's shadow is stationary, it looks flat, but when the cube is rotated, as indicated by the arrow, the moving shadow takes on a three-dimensional appearance, even though it is seen on a two-dimensional surface. You can demonstrate this

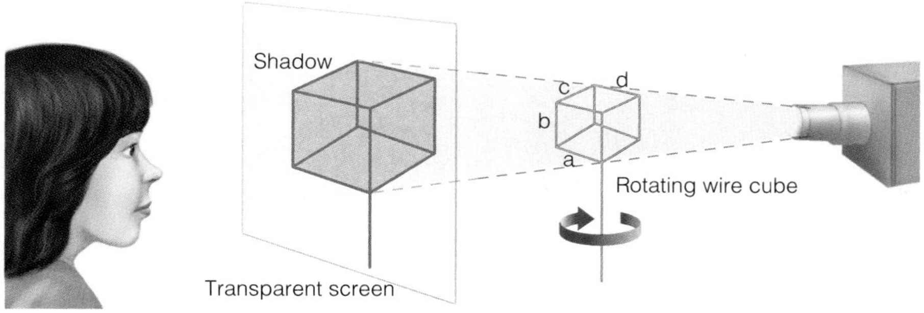

Figure 9.4 ▌ Setup similar to the one used by Wallach and O'Connell (1953) to demonstrate the kinetic depth effect.

effect for yourself by doing the following demonstration with a paper clip.

VL 10-14

DEMONSTRATION

The Kinetic Depth Effect With a Paper Clip

Bend a paper clip so that it reproduces sides a, b, c, and d of the shape in Figure 9.4. Then, cast a shadow of the paper clip on a piece of paper, as shown in Figure 9.5, and while viewing the shadow from the other side of the paper, rotate the paper clip. The result should be a perception that is more three-dimensional than when the shadow was stationary. ■

The kinetic depth effect is an example of **structure-from-motion**—how movement can create perceptual structure. In fact, our example of the camouflaged bird is also an example of structure-from-motion because motion results in perception of an organized structure. Later in the chapter, when we discuss biological motion, we will return to the idea that movement can create structure.

THE MOVING OBSERVER

Now that we have considered some of the functions of motion perception, we are ready to consider the central question of this chapter: What mechanisms are responsible for our perception of motion? As we mentioned at the beginning of the chapter, this question is complicated by the fact that not only do objects in the environment move, but observers move as well, which creates the following three situations:

1. An object moves, and the observer remains stationary. In the example in Figure 9.6a, Jeremy walks past Maria as Maria looks straight ahead. This is the "simple" case of movement perception because Jeremy's movement creates an image that moves across Maria's retina.
2. An object moves, and the observer follows the object with his or her eyes. In the example in Figure 9.6b, Jeremy walks past Maria, and Maria follows him with her eyes. Now things become more interesting because Maria is keeping her fovea aimed at Jeremy, so Jeremy's image on her retina remains stationary. Despite the fact that the image remains stationary, Maria still perceives Jeremy as moving.
3. An observer moves through a stationary environment. In the example in Figure 9.6c, Maria walks through the environment. This creates a situation that is the opposite of situation 2 because as Maria moves, an image of the environment moves across her retina. Nonetheless, she perceives the environment as remaining stationary.

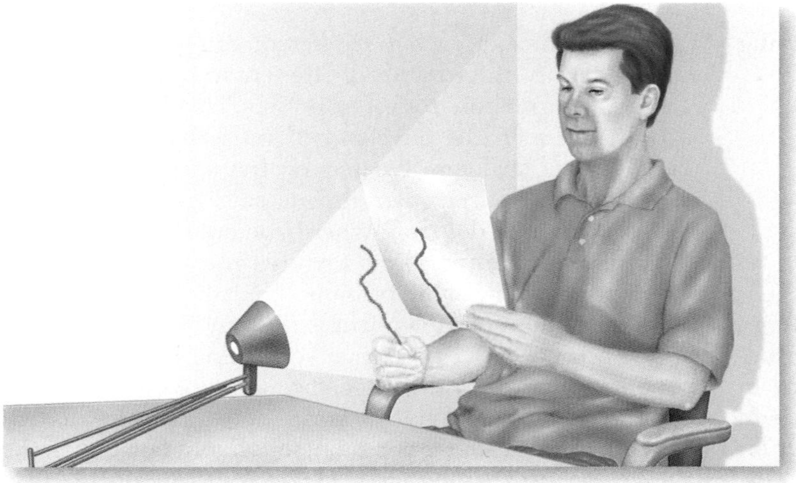

Figure 9.5 ▌ Shadow-casting by a bent paper clip. To achieve a sharp shadow, position the paper clip about 2 feet from your desk lamp. (If it is too close to the lamp, the shadow will be fuzzy.) To perceive the kinetic depth effect, rotate the paper clip between your fingers while observing the shadow from the other side of the paper.

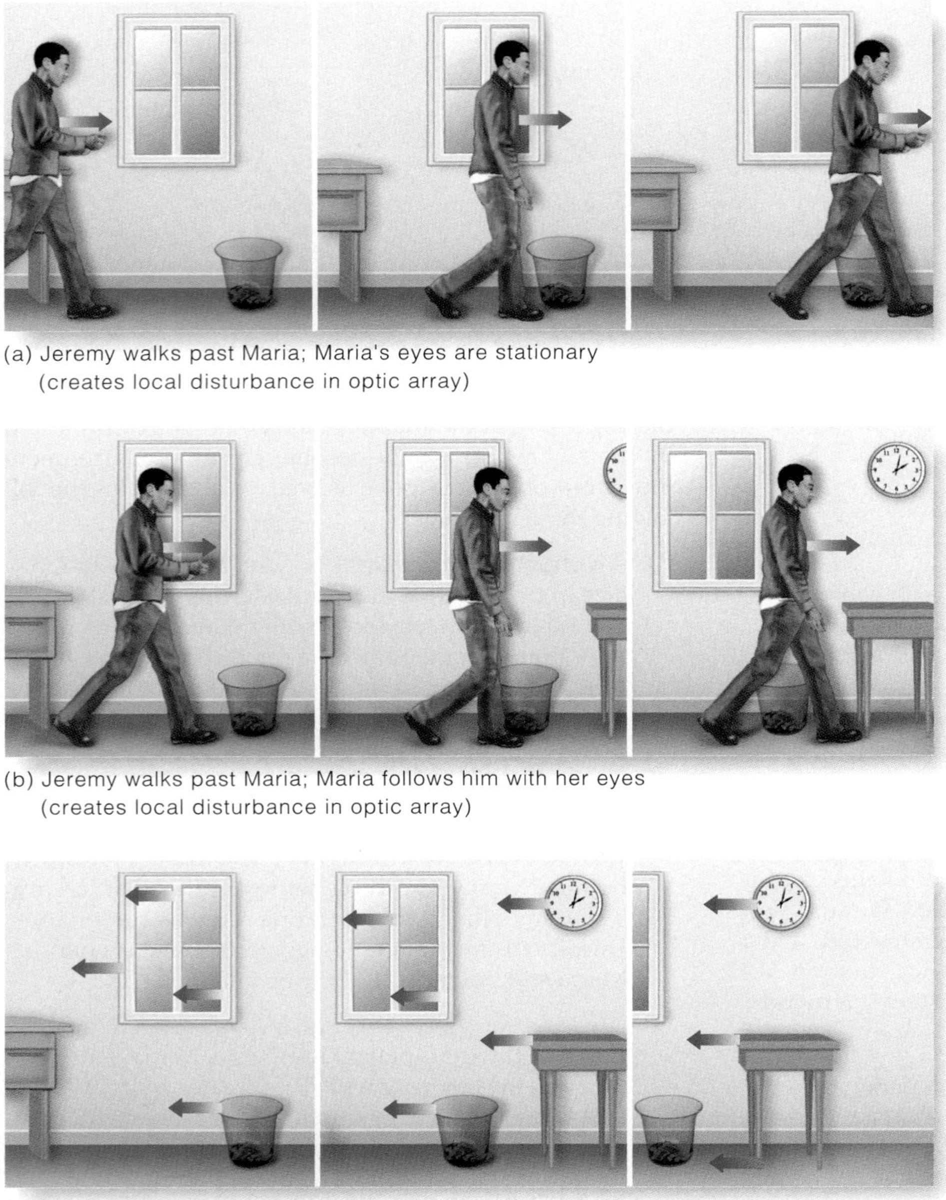

(a) Jeremy walks past Maria; Maria's eyes are stationary
(creates local disturbance in optic array)

(b) Jeremy walks past Maria; Maria follows him with her eyes
(creates local disturbance in optic array)

(c) Maria walks through the scene
(creates global optic flow)

Figure 9.6 ■ In (a) and (b), Jeremy walks past as Maria observes him. Maria perceives him as moving in (a), when his image moves across her retina, and in (b), when his image stays fixed on her fovea. In (c), when Maria walks through the environment, she perceives the environment as stationary, even though its image is moving across her retina. The text describes how the stimulus information provided by the optic array and global flow helps determine these perceptions.

We will now describe two approaches to explaining the three situations in Figure 9.6.

The Behavioral Approach: Taking Environmental Information Into Account

The approach to movement perception we will describe in this section was pioneered by J. J. Gibson, who spent most of his career describing a way of thinking about perception called the ecological approach. We will describe the reasoning behind the ecological approach in Chapter 10, "Perception and Action." For now, we will focus on how Gibson dealt with the moving observer problem.

Gibson's approach to perception can be stated simply as, "Identify information in the environment that provides information for perception." He thought about information in the environment in terms of the **optic array**—the structure created by the surfaces, textures, and contours of the environment (see Figure 2.10). Thus, when you look out from where you are right now, all of the surfaces, contours, and textures you see make up the optic array. What is important about the optic array for the perception of movement is the way it changes when the observer moves or when something in the environment moves. As we will see, the nature of the changes in the optic array provides information that helps us tell whether the observer is moving or whether objects in the environment are moving.

Gibson focused on the information provided by changes in the optic array. He describes the situation in Figure 9.6a, in which Jeremy walks across Maria's field of view, as Maria looks straight ahead, as a **local disturbance in the optic array**. A local disturbance in the optic array occurs when one object moves relative to the environment, covering and uncovering the stationary background. This local disturbance signals that Jeremy is moving relative to the environment.

The beauty of considering movement perception in terms of information in the optic array is that this approach also explains the situation in Figure 9.6b, in which Maria perceives Jeremy as moving, even if she follows him with her eyes. This sequence of views shows that when Maria is following Jeremy with her eyes so he remains centered in the scene, he still covers and uncovers the background, as in Figure 9.6a. Thus, this situation also creates a local disturbance in the optic array, and Maria perceives Jeremy as moving.

Finally, consider the sequence of views in Figure 9.6c, when Maria decides to walk through the environment. The key feature of these views is that entire optic array is moving. This overall movement of the optic array, called **global optic flow**, indicates that it is the observer that is moving and not the environment. Thus, Maria perceives the environment as remaining stationary as she walks through it.

Gibson's approach succeeds in explaining, in a fairly simple way, the problem of the moving observer, by considering the nature of information provided by the environment. As we will see in Chapter 10, he used this approach to explain other perceptual phenomenon as well.

The Physiological Approach: The Corollary Discharge

We will now describe a way that movement perception can be explained physiologically by considering the connection between the firing of neurons and perception. This approach, called the **corollary discharge theory**, proposes that movement perception depends on the following three types of signals (Figure 9.7; Gyr, 1972; Teuber, 1960; von Holst, 1954).

1. A **motor signal (MS)**, which is sent to the eye muscles when the observer moves or tries to move her eyes.
2. A **corollary discharge signal (CDS)**, which is a copy of the motor signal.
3. An **image movement signal (IMS)**, which occurs when an image stimulates the receptors as it moves across the retina.

According to corollary discharge theory, our perception of movement is determined by whether the corollary discharge signal, the image movement signal, or both reach a structure called the **comparator**, which receives inputs from neurons that carry these signals. Movement is perceived when the comparator receives either the image movement signal alone or the corollary discharge signal alone (Figures 9.8a and 9.8b), but movement is not perceived when both signals reach the comparator simultaneously (Figure 9.8c). VL 15

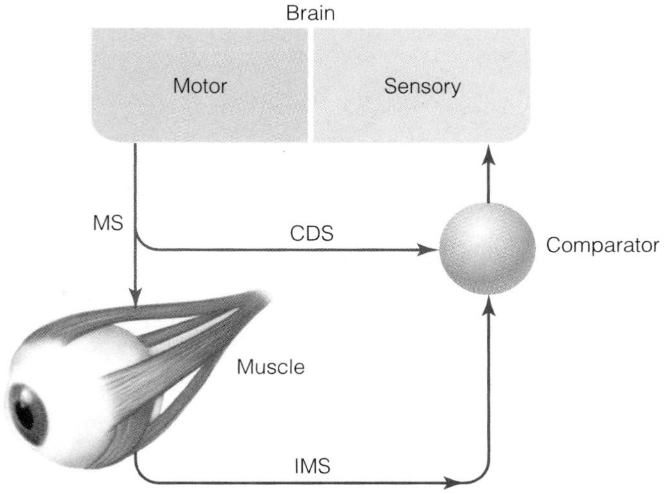

Figure 9.7 The corollary discharge model. The motor area sends the motor signal (MS) to move the eyes to the eye muscles and sends the corollary discharge signal (CDS) to a structure called the comparator. Movement of a stimulus across the retina generates an image movement signal (IMS), which also goes to the comparator. The comparator sends its output to the visual cortex. See text for details.
(From "Perception," by H. L. Teuber, 1960. In J. Field, H. W. Magoun & V. E. Hall (Eds.) Handbook of Physiology, *Section 1,* Neurophysiology, *Vol. 3, pp. 1595–1668, figure 31. Copyright © 1960 by the American Physiological Society. Reprinted by permission.)*

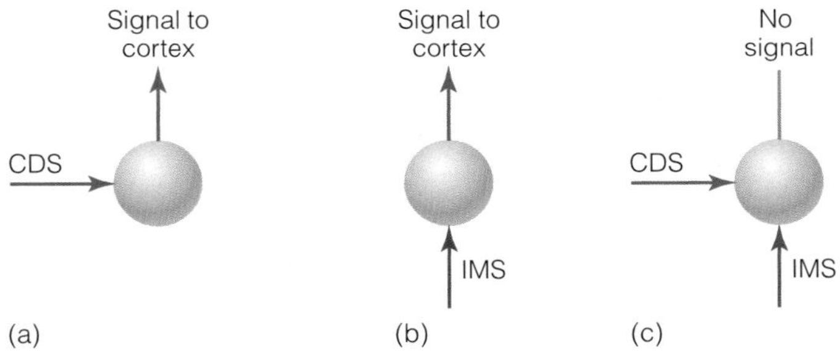

Figure 9.8 How inputs to the comparator (circle) affect movement perception. When the comparator receives either the corollary discharge signal (CDS) alone, as in (a), or the image movement signal (IMS) alone, as in (b), it sends a movement signal to the cortex, and movement is perceived. When the comparator receives both the CDS and IMS signals, a movement signal is not sent to the cortex, and no movement is perceived.

Behavioral Demonstrations of Corollary Discharge Theory The corollary discharge model has been tested behaviorally by determining whether movement perception does, in fact, occur when only the corollary discharge reaches the comparator. This has been accomplished in the following four ways, three of which you can experience for yourself.

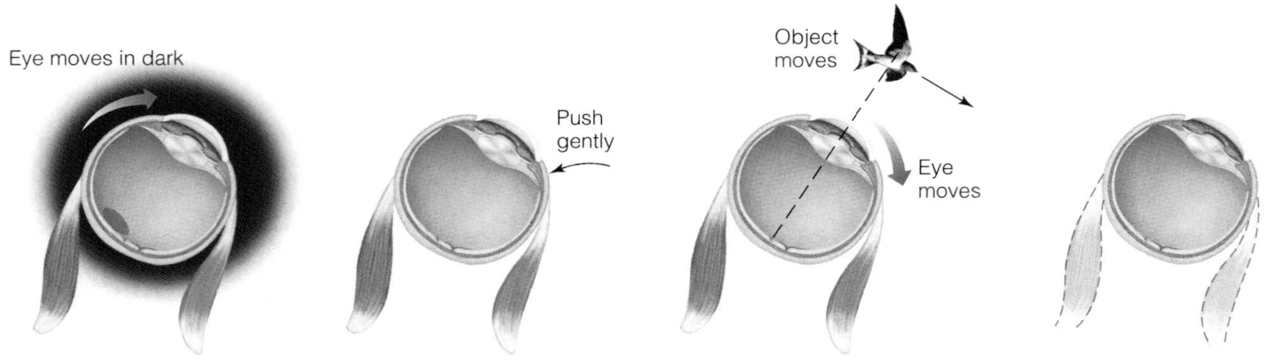

(a) Bleached patch stays stationary on retina as eye moves
(b) Push on eyeball; eye stationary
(c) Eye moves to follow target
(d) Eye muscles paralyzed; eye remains stationary when observer tries to move eye

Figure 9.9 ▮ In all four examples shown in the figure, a signal is sent to the eye muscles, and a corollary discharge is generated. However, no image movement signal is generated, so movement is perceived. See text for details.

1. By observing an afterimage as you move your eyes in a dark room (Figure 9.9a).

DEMONSTRATION

Eliminating the Image Movement Signal With an Afterimage

Illuminate the circle in Figure 8.30 (p. 183) with your desk lamp and look at it for about 60 seconds. Then, go into your closet (or a completely dark room) and observe what happens to the circle's afterimage (blink to make it come back if it fades) as you look around. Notice that the afterimage moves in synchrony with your eye movements. ■

Why does the afterimage appear to move when you move your eyes? The answer cannot be that an image is moving across your retina because the circle's image always remains at the same place on the retina. (Remember that the circle's image is actually a bleached-out patch of visual pigment.) Without movement of the stimulus across the retina, there is no image movement signal. However, a corollary discharge signal accompanies the motor signals sent to your eye muscles as you move your eyes. Thus, only the corollary discharge reaches the comparator, and you see the afterimage move. This condition, and the others described below, is summarized in Table 9.1.

2. By pushing on your eyeball while keeping your eye steady (Figure 9.9b).

Table 9.1 ▮ *Four ways corollary discharge can cause the perception of movement when there is no movement on the retina*

Condition	Image Movement Signal?	Corollary Discharge Signal?	Perceive Movement?
1. Move eyes while viewing afterimage in the dark (Figure 9.9a).	NO, afterimage always stays on same place in retina.	YES, signal is sent to the eye muscles to move eyes.	YES
2. Push on eyeball while looking at a spot to keep eyes stationary (Figure 9.9b).	NO, the eye remains stationary because observer is holding fixation on a spot.	YES, signal is sent to muscles to keep eye stationary.	YES
3. Move eyes to follow a target (Figure 9.9c).	NO, the target stays on fovea at all times.	YES, signal sent to eye muscles to move eye.	YES
4. Paralyze eye muscles and try to move eye (Figure 9.9d).	NO, the eye doesn't move because it is paralyzed.	YES, signal sent to eye muscles to attempt to move eye.	YES

DEMONSTRATION

Seeing Movement by Pushing on Your Eyeball

While looking steadily with one eye at a point in the environment, gently push back and forth on the side of your eyelid, as shown in Figure 9.10. As you do this, you will see the scene move.

Bruce Goldstein

Figure 9.10 ▌ Every time this person pushes on her eyelid she sees the world jiggle. ■

Why do you see movement when you push on your eyeball? According to Lawrence Stark and Bruce Bridgeman (1983), when you push on your eyeball while keeping your eye fixed on a particular point, your eyes remain stationary because your eye muscles are pushing against the force of the finger so you can maintain steady fixation on the point. The motor signal sent to the eye muscles to hold the eye in place creates a corollary discharge, which occurs alone because there is no image movement signal. We therefore see the scene move (also see Bridgeman & Stark, 1991; Ilg, Bridgeman, & Hoffmann, 1989).

3. By following a moving object such as a flying bird with your eyes (Figure 9.9c).

In this situation the eyes move to follow the bird, so the bird's image remains stationary on the observer's retina and there is no image movement signal. But because the eyes are moving, a corollary discharge occurs and the observer perceives the bird's movement.

4. By paralyzing an observer's eye muscles and having the observer try to move his or her eyes (Figure 9.9d).

In this situation, when the observer tries to move his or her eyes, a motor signal is sent to the eye muscles and causes a corollary discharge. But the paralyzed eye remains stationary, so there is no image movement signal. Only the corollary discharge reaches the comparator, so movement should be perceived. John Stevens showed that this occurs by volunteering to be temporarily immobilized by a paralytic drug (Stevens et al., 1976). When he tried to move his eyes, the scene in front of him appeared to jump to a new position, just as predicted by the corollary discharge model. (See also Matin et al., 1982, for another paralysis experiment.)

These four behavioral demonstrations support the central idea proposed by corollary discharge theory that there is a signal (the corollary discharge) that indicates when the observer moves, or tries to move, his or her eyes. When the theory was first proposed, there was little physiological evidence to support it, but now there is a great deal of physiological evidence for the theory.

Physiological Evidence for Corollary Discharge Theory

In all of the examples summarized in Table 9.1, there is a corollary discharge but no image movement signal. What would happen if there was no corollary discharge but there *was* a movement image signal? That is apparently what happened to R.W., a 35-year-old male who complained that he experienced vertigo (dizziness) anytime he moved his eyes or experienced movement when he looked out the window of a moving car.

A brain scan revealed that R.W. had lesions in an area of his cortex called the medial superior temporal area (MST), which is known to be important for movement perception. Behavioral testing of R.W. also revealed that as he moved his eyes, the stationary environment appeared to move with a velocity that matched the velocity with which he was moving his eyes (Haarmeier et al., 1997). Apparently, the damage to his brain had eliminated the corollary discharge signal that normally corrects for eye movements.

Research on monkeys has provided evidence that there are neurons in the visual system that take eye movements into account. Figure 9.11 shows the response recorded from a motion-sensitive neuron in the monkey's extrastriate cortex. This neuron responds strongly when the monkey holds its eyes stationary and a bar is swept across the cell's receptive field (Figure 9.11a), but does not respond when the bar is held stationary and the monkey moves its eyes so the cell's receptive field sweeps across the bar (Figure 9.11b; Galletti & Fattori, 2003). This is called a **real-movement neuron** because it responds only when the stimulus moves and doesn't respond when the eye moves, even though the stimulus on the retina—a bar sweeping across the cell's receptive field—is the same in both situations. This real movement neuron must be receiving information like the corollary discharge, which tells the neuron when the eye is moving. Real movement neurons also have been observed in many areas of the cortex (Battaglini, Galletti, & Fattori, 1990, 1996; Robinson & Wurtz, 1976).

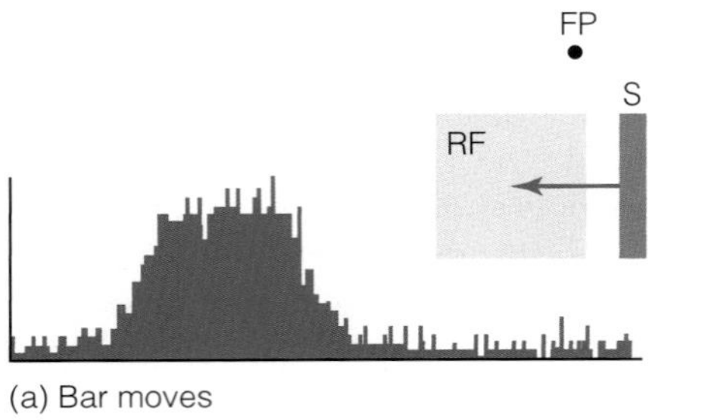

Figure 9.11 ▮ Responses of a neuron in a monkey's cortex. In (a) the neuron fires when a bar moves to the left across the neuron's receptive field (RF) as the monkey looks at the fixation point (FP); In (b) the neuron does not fire when the monkey moves its eye to the right, even though this also causes the bar to move to the left across the receptive field.
(Adapted from Galletti & Fattori, 2003).

TEST YOURSELF 9.1

1. Describe four different situations that can result in movement perception. Which of these situations results in real movement, and which results in illusions of movement?
2. What are some of the functions of movement? What are some examples of the link between movement and perceiving objects?
3. What is the moving observer problem, and how has it been solved by considering the nature of stimuli in the environment that are associated with movement?
4. How has the moving observer problem been explained by the corollary discharge? Describe both behavioral and physiological evidence for operation of the corollary discharge.

HOW NEURONS SIGNAL THE DIRECTION OF MOVEMENT

In describing the physiological approach to the moving observer problem, we were concerned with how the visual system determines whether movement of a stimulus across the retina is caused by movement of the stimulus or by movement of the observer. We are now going to consider a different question: If the eye remains stationary, how do neurons determine the direction in which a stimulus moves across the retina? At the beginning of our discussion of the moving observer problem, we described this situation as the "simple" case of movement perception. However, we will now see that explaining how the firing of neurons signals movement across a stationary retina is not so simple after all.

Researchers have used two kinds of stimuli to study the neural response to movement. They have used moving bars, like the ones in Figure 9.12a, and they have used moving dots like those in Figure 9.12b. Research with each of these types of stimuli has made important contributions to our understanding of the physiology of movement perception. We begin by considering moving bars.

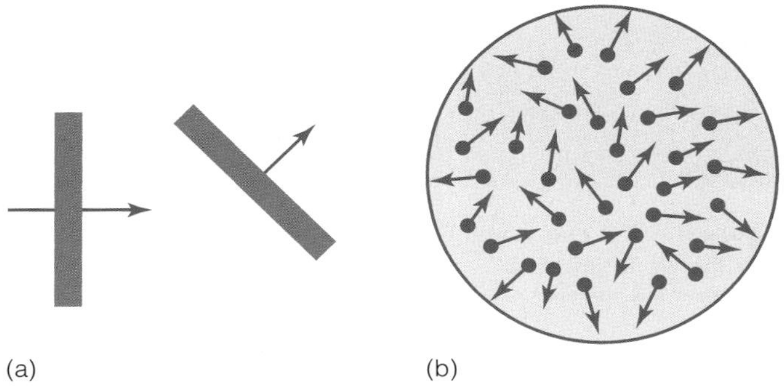

Figure 9.12 ▮ Stimuli used to study the neural response to movement: (a) oriented moving bars; (b) fields of moving dots.

Determining the Direction in Which Oriented Bars Are Moving

In Chapter 3, we described complex cortical cells that respond when an appropriately oriented bar moves in a specific direction (Figure 9.12a). When these neurons were first discovered, they were seen as providing a way for the visual system to determine the direction in which a stimulus was moving. However, it soon became clear that even though these neurons fire to the movement of oriented bars, the firing of these neurons does not provide adequate information about the direction in which a stimulus is moving. We can understand why this is so by considering the aperture problem.

The Aperture Problem The **aperture problem** occurs when observation of a small portion of a larger stimulus results in misleading information about the direction in which the larger stimulus is moving. To appreciate what this means, do the following demonstration.

DEMONSTRATION

Movement of a Bar Across an Aperture

Make a small aperture, about 1 inch in diameter, by creating a circle with the figures of your left hand, as shown in Figure 9.13 (alternatively, you can create a circle by cutting a hole in a piece of paper). Then orient a pencil vertically, and move the pencil from left to right behind the circle, as in (a). As you do this focus on the direction the pencil appears to be moving *inside the aperture.* Now, again holding the pencil vertically, position the pencil below the circle, as shown in (b) and move it up behind the aperture, at a 45-degree angle. Again, notice the direction in which the pencil appears to be moving *as seen through the aperture.*

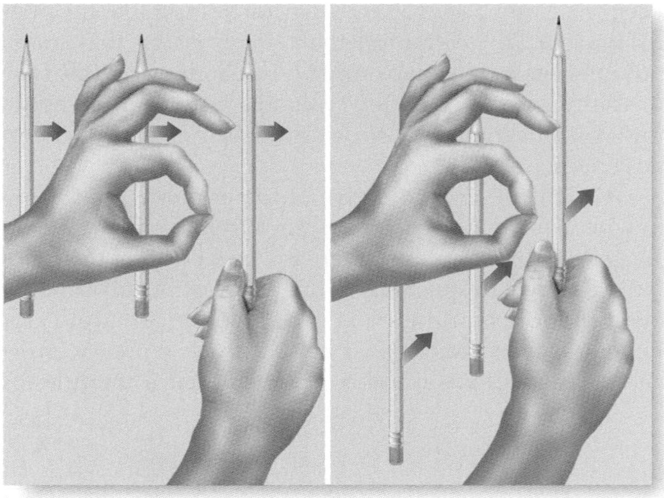

(a) (b)

Figure 9.13 ■ "Movement of a Bar Across an Aperture" demonstration. See text for details. ■

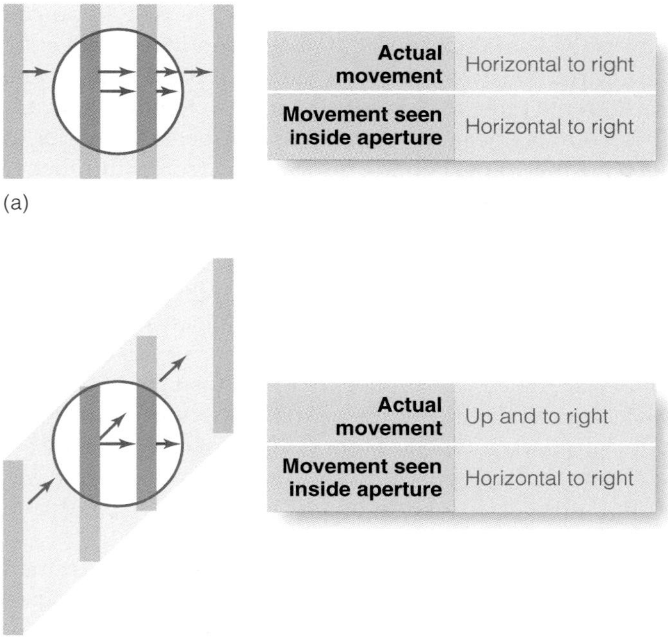

Figure 9.14 ■ Actual movement and movement seen through the aperture in the demonstration pictured in Figure 9.13. A bar moves behind a surface and becomes visible as it passes behind a circular opening (the aperture). (a) Vertical bar moves horizontally. (b) Vertical bar moves up at a 45-degree angle. Blue arrows = actual direction of movement. Red arrows = perceived direction of movement through the aperture.

Let's consider each situation in turn. In Figure 9.13a the pencil was moved horizontally from left to right, so it is not surprising that you would perceive the pencil as moving horizontally within the aperture. This situation is diagrammed in Figure 9.14a, which indicates that your perception of the pencil's movement (red arrows) matches the direction in which it was actually moving (blue arrows).

However, in Figure 9.13b, when the pencil was moved up and to the right, something different happened. Even though the pencil was no longer moving horizontally (blue arrows in Figure 9.14b), you probably still perceived the edge of the pencil as moving horizontally across the aperture (red arrows). (If you didn't perceive it that way, try the demonstration again, being sure to narrow your focus on how the pencil is moving within the aperture.)

This demonstration shows that movement of an edge seen through a small aperture can appear the same for different directions of movement. Movement of an edge viewed through an aperture is perceived to occur *perpendicularly to the orientation of the edge,* even when the actual movement may be in another direction. Because the edge is oriented vertically in our example, the edge appears to be moving horizontally when viewed through the aperture.

The situation we have described poses a problem for the visual system because most neurons in the primary visual receiving area, V1, which respond to bars that move in a specific direction, have small receptive fields. Imagine, for example, that instead of being a viewing aperture, the circle in Figure 9.14b is the receptive field of one of these neurons. Remember that a neuron's receptive field is the area on the retina which, when stimulated, influences the firing rate of the neuron. This means that the receptive field is essentially the "viewing aperture" through which the neuron views stimuli moving across the retina. As far as this neuron is concerned, movement up-and-to-the-right and movement horizontally-to-the-right stimulate its receptive field in the same way. Thus, the activity of this single neuron would not provide accurate information about the direction in which the bar is moving.

Solving the Aperture Problem We can compare the problem facing the visual system to the problem you might have if you tried to perceive a scene by viewing it through a small hole in a piece of paper held at arm's length. It is difficult to perceive the scene when you can view only a small part of it at once, even if you move the paper around so you can view different parts of the scene through the hole. If, however, you were to add a few additional holes near the original one, it becomes easier to perceive the scene. Pooling information from a number of different areas of the scene increases your ability to perceive it.

Apparently, the visual system solves the aperture problem in a similar way, by pooling information from a number of cortical neurons with small receptive fields. The idea is that signals from a number of V1 cells may converge on neurons higher-up in the visual system. One place this might occur is the medial temporal cortex (MT), a nucleus that contains a large number of directionally selective neurons. Figure 9.15 shows the location of the MT cortex in the brain and where it is located in the dorsal processing stream.

Christopher Pack and Richard Born (2001) determined how neurons in the monkey's MT cortex responded to moving bars like the ones shown in Figure 9.14. Pack and Born found that when the monkey's MT neurons first began responding, the neuron's response—about 70 msec after the bars were presented—was determined by the *orientation* of the bar. Thus the first response of these neurons would be the same for the two situations in Figure 9.14. However, later in the response—140 ms after the bars were presented—these neurons began responding to the *actual directions* in which the bars were moving. What this may mean is that it took time for the MT neurons to receive and process information from a number of V1 neurons. Once this happened, the MT neurons were able to use this pooled information to determine the direction in which the bars were moving.

Determining the Direction in Which Fields of Dots Are Moving

So far, we have been focusing on how neurons might signal the direction in which a bar is moving. We considered bars because of the early research of David Hubel and Thorsten Wiesel (1965) which showed that there are complex and end-stopped neurons in the cortex that respond to moving bars (see pages 60–61), and because there are many moving edges in the environment. However, more recent research has used moving dot stimuli like the ones in Figure 9.12b. Although there may not be that many moving dots in the environment, research using this type of stimulus has provided valuable information about how neurons in the MT cortex process information about movement.

We will describe a series of experiments that show how neurons in MT cortex respond to movement. We focus on MT cortex because there is a great deal of evidence that this area is specialized for processing information about motion, and therefore qualifies as a "module" for movement perception (just as IT cortex, which we discussed in Chapters 4 and 5, is considered a module for

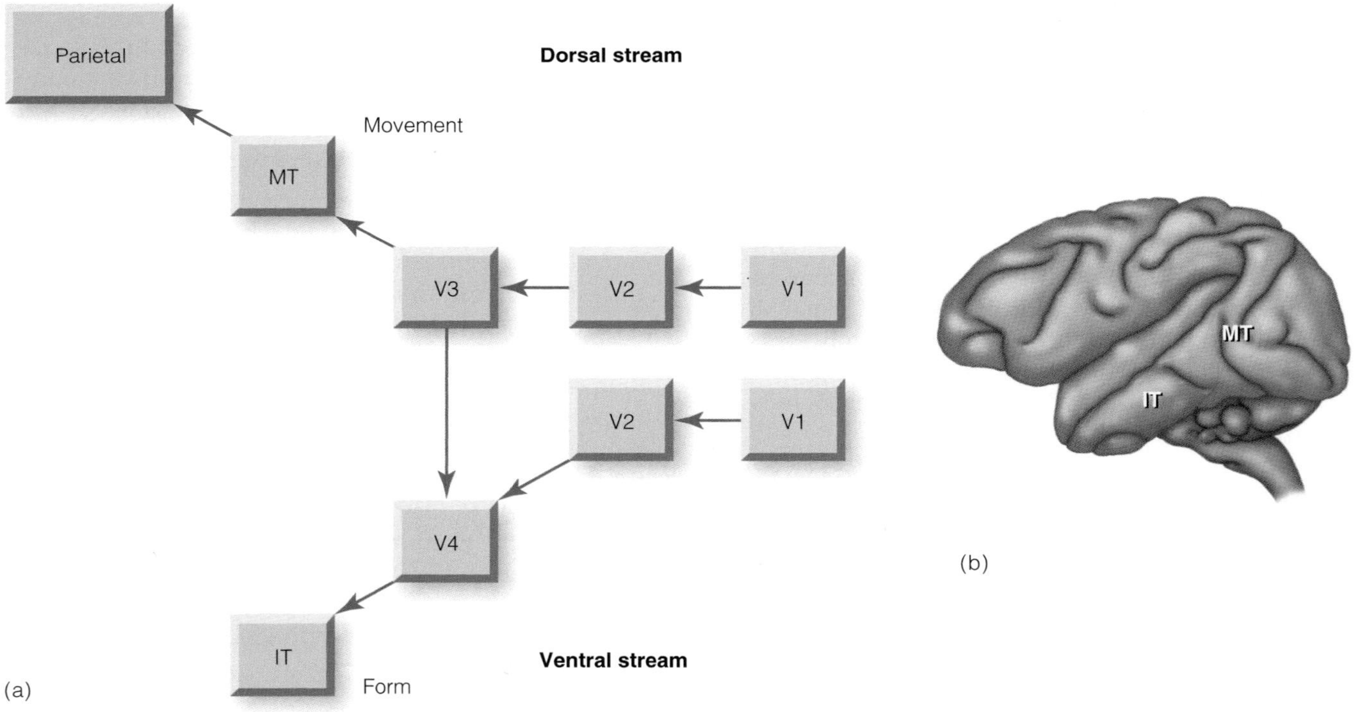

Figure 9.15 ▌ (a) Some of the nuclei in the dorsal and ventral streams. The MT cortex, which is a module for movement perception, is in the dorsal stream, and the IT cortex, which is a module for form perception, is in the ventral stream. (b) The location of the MT and IT cortex in the brain.

form perception). The research we will describe used moving dots as stimuli, which has the advantage of providing a way to vary how difficult it is to detect the direction of movement.

Firing and Coherence Figure 9.16 illustrates moving dot stimuli. Actual moving dot stimuli are created by a computer, which varies the **coherence**, or the degree to which the dots move in the same direction. For example, Figure 9.16a represents zero correlation of the directions of the dots' movements, so that all of the dots are moving randomly, much like the "snow" you see when your TV set is tuned between channels. In this case, the coherence is zero percent. Figure 9.16b represents a coherence of 50 percent, which means that at any point in time half of the dots are moving in the same direction. Figure 9.16c represents 100 percent coherence, so all of the dots are moving in the same direction.

William Newsome and coworkers (1989) did an experiment in which they determined the relationship between a monkey's ability to detect motion of moving dot stimuli with different amounts of coherence and the firing of MT neurons. They determined this relationship by simultaneously measuring (1) a monkey's ability to judge the direction in which dots were moving, and (2) the response of a neuron in the monkey's MT cortex.

They found that as the dots' coherence increased, two things happened: (1) the MT neuron fired more rapidly, and (2) the monkey judged the direction of movement more accurately. In fact, the firing of the MT neuron and the monkey's behavior were so closely related that the researchers could predict one from the other. For example, when the dots' coherence was 0.8 percent, the neuron's response did not differ appreciably from the baseline firing rate on each trial, and the monkey was able to judge the direction of the dots' movement with only chance accuracy. But at a coherence of 12.8 percent, the MT neuron always fired faster than its baseline rate, and the monkey judged the direction of movement correctly on virtually every trial.

These experiments are notable because they measure neural responding and behavior simultaneously in the same animal. This procedure is extremely challenging because before the recording experiments can begin, monkeys must be trained for months so they can indicate the direction in which they perceive the dots moving. However, the payoff for all this effort is that the experimenter can measure behavior and neural responding simultaneously, which is the most powerful way to demonstrate connections between physiology and behavior. The use of this technique made it possible for Newsome to demonstrate that the connection between neural firing and behavior is so close that it is possible to predict the monkey's ability to judge the direction of movement by monitoring the firing of only a few MT neurons.

Effect of Lesioning The connection between MT neurons and movement perception has also been demonstrated by lesioning MT cortex. Newsome and Edward Paré (1988) found that monkeys could just begin to detect the direction of motion in patterns with coherence as low as 1 or 2 percent. However, after area MT was lesioned, the monkey could not begin detecting the direction of motion until coherence was increased to 10–20 percent (see also Movshon & Newsome, 1992; Pasternack & Merigan, 1994). Remember, from the experiments described above, that normal, nonlesioned monkeys can correctly determine the direction of movement almost 100 percent of the time when the coherence is 12.8 percent.

Microstimulation Another procedure that can alter movement perception is **microstimulation** (Cohen & Newsome, 2004). In Chapter 8 (page 179), when we described how microstimulation was used to study depth perception, we saw that an electrical charge passed through an electrode activates neurons that are near the

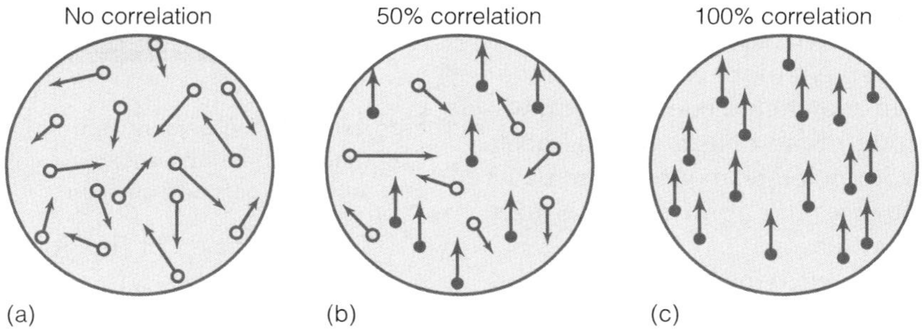

Figure 9.16 ▌ Moving-dot displays. These pictures represent moving-dot displays that were created by a computer. Each dot survives for a brief interval (20–30 microseconds), after which it disappears and is replaced by another randomly placed dot.
(From "A Selective Impairment of Motion Perception Following Lesions of the Middle Temporal Visual Area (MT)," by W. T. Newsome and E. B. Pare, 1988, Journal of Neuroscience, *8 (6), 2201–2211, figure 1. Copyright © 1988 by Society for Neuroscience. Reprinted by permission of Oxford University Press.)*

electrode. Anthony Movshon and Newsome (1992) took advantage of the fact that neurons that prefer specific directions are arranged in columns in the MT cortex (Albright, Desimone, & Gross, 1984), so by electrically stimulating one column, they could activate a group of neurons that responded best to a particular direction of movement.

They determined whether activating these neurons affected the monkey's movement perception by stimulating neurons that responded best to a particular direction of movement while a monkey was judging the direction of dots that were moving in another direction. When they applied the stimulation, the monkey suddenly shifted its judgment toward the direction signaled by the stimulated neurons. For example, when the monkey was judging movement of dots that were moving horizontally to the right, and a column of MT neurons that preferred downward movement was stimulated, the monkey began responding as though the dots were moving downward and to the right. This is the result we would expect if MT neurons are involved in determining the perception of the direction of movement.

MOTION PERCEPTION AND EXPERIENCE

So far, we have described movement perception as an automatic outcome of processing that is triggered by stimulation of the retina or stimulation of the retina combined with signals indicating the eyes are moving. But movement perception also involves processes that depend on the observers' past experiences.

In previous chapters, we described situations in which a person's past experience can affect perception. For example, in Chapter 1 we saw that presenting a picture of a rat or a man's face can influence our perception of an ambiguous figure immediately afterward (page 8). This rat–man demonstration is an example of an effect of short-term experience on perception.

We have also seen that longer-term experiences can affect perception. For example, in Chapter 5 we described an experiment in which observers more easily identify a drawing of a loaf of bread in a kitchen scene than a drawing of a mailbox, even though both objects have almost the same shape. Thus, our knowledge about objects usually found in kitchens influences our ability to recognize objects that are placed in that setting.

Just as our experience with kitchens can influence object perception, our experience with motion that occurs in our everyday environment can influence motion perception. We will see from the following examples that we can demonstrate these effects of experience behaviorally by investigating how people perceive real-world stimuli. We will also see that experience can be reflected in neural responding, so that neurons become tuned to respond best to stimuli that we have often experienced (see page 84 Chapter 4, where we introduced this idea). We begin by describing research on a very familiar type of movement called biological motion.

Biological Motion

What would you see if you placed small lights on a person's body, as in Figure 9.17, and viewed the lights in a dark room? The answer depends on whether the person is moving or stationary. When the person is stationary, the lights look like a meaningless pattern. However, as soon as the person starts walking, with arms and legs swinging back and forth and feet moving in flattened arcs, first one leaving the ground and touching down, and then the other, the lights are immediately perceived as being caused by a walking person. This movement of a person or other living organism is called **biological motion.** The biological motion stimulus created by placing lights on a person is called a **point-light walker** stimulus (Johansson, 1975). VL 16

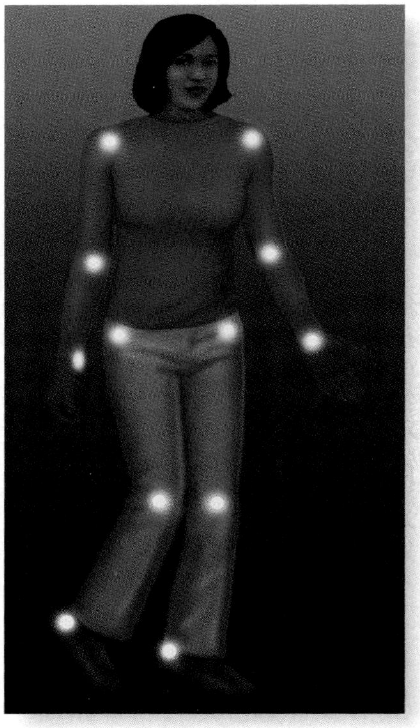

Figure 9.17 ▌ A person wearing lights for a biological motion experiment. In the actual experiment, the room is totally dark, and only the lights can be seen.

The perception of the point-light walker stimulus as a person walking is an example of *structure-from-motion* that we introduced at the beginning of the chapter. One reason we are particularly good at perceptually organizing the complex movement of an array of moving dots into the perception of a walking person is that we see biological motion all the time. Every time you see a person walking, running, or behaving in any way that involves movement, you are seeing biological motion. Our ability to easily organize biological movements into meaningful perceptions led some researchers to suspect that there may be an area in the brain that responds to biological movement, just as there is an area that is specialized to perceive faces.

E. D. Grossman and Randolph Blake (2001) provided evidence supporting this idea by measuring observers' brain activity as they viewed the moving dots created by a point-light walker (Figure 9.18a) and as they viewed dots that moved similarly to the point-light walker dots, but were scrambled so they did not result in the impression of a person walking (Figure 9.18b). They found that activity in an area in the temporal cortex called the superior temporal sulcus (STS) was greater for biological motion than for scrambled motion in all eight of their observers.

The STS receives signals from both the ventral (*what*) and dorsal (*where/how*) streams. It makes senses that the area associated with biological motion would receive signals from both the ventral and dorsal streams because perceiving biological motion involves both creating a meaningful structure (a *what* function) and perceiving movement (a *where/how* function).

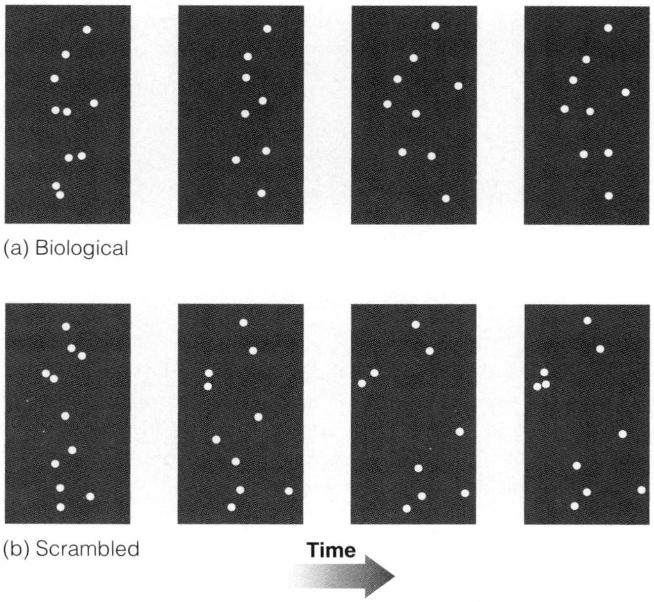

Figure 9.18 ▮ Frames from the stimuli used by Grossman and Blake (2001). (a) Sequence from the point-light walker stimulus. (b) Sequence from the scrambled point-light stimulus.

From results such as these, plus many other experiments that have recorded both brain activity in humans and the responding of single neurons in animals (S. J. Blakemore & Decety, 2001; Oram & Perrett, 1994; Servos et al., 2002), it has been established that an area in the STS is activated by biological motion. Most of these studies show that the area activated by biological motion is different from the areas activated by other kinds of motion, such as the MT cortex. This finding is supported by the behavior of patients like the woman we described at the beginning of the chapter, who have become "motion blind" due to damage of the MT cortex. Even though these people can't perceive the movement of objects, they can still recognize human actions from point-light displays (McLeod et al., 1996; Viana et al., 1990). This supports the idea that the perception of biological motion is served by a different cortical area than the perception of other motion stimuli.

Apparent Motion: The Occlusion Heuristic

Consider the display in Figure 9.19a. To create a stimulus that would result in apparent movement, Vilayanur Ramachandran and Stuart Anstis (1986) first presented the triangle and square on the left together and then the square on the right. Figures 9.19b and 9.19c show two possible ways that apparent movement could be perceived: The triangle and square could move to the right and fuse into a square (Figure 9.19b), or the square could move diagonally to the right while the triangle blinks on and off (Figure 9.19c).

But observers saw neither of those perceptions. Instead, they saw the lower square move up and to the right, while the triangle moved to the right and appeared to slide under the square so it was hidden behind it (Figure 9.19d). According to Ramachandran and Anstis, this perception is a reflection of the **occlusion heuristic**, a rule that states that when one object covers another object, the covered object continues to exist. So the triangle and square move to the same position, but the square covers the triangle, which continues to exist, even though it is hidden.

In another experiment, Ramachandran and Anstis flashed the two dots on the left in Figure 9.20, followed by the dot on the right. Observers perceived this as the two

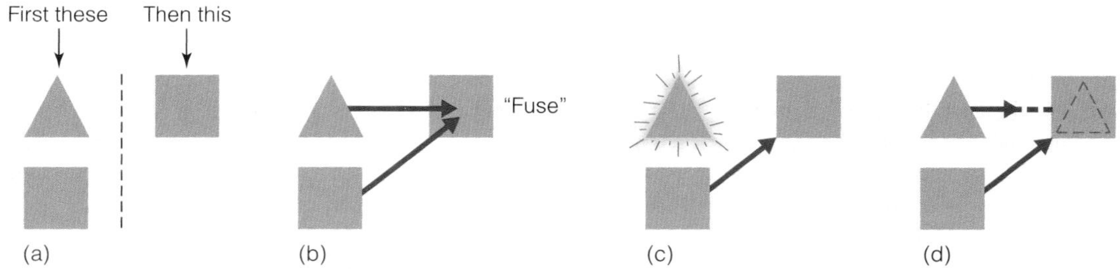

Figure 9.19 ▮ (a) Stimulus presentation in the Ramachandran and Anstis experiment. The triangle and lower square are flashed simultaneously, followed by the top square. Parts (b), (c), and (d) are possible perceptions. See text for details.

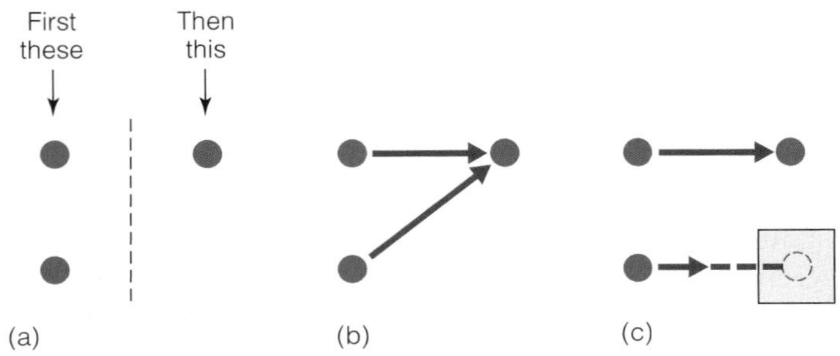

Figure 9.20 ▮ (a) Stimulus presentation in the moving dot experiment. (b) Perception that results from the presentation in (a). Both dots move to the position of the dot on the right. (c) Placing an occluder in the position shown changes the perception of the movement of the lower dot, so it moves to the right and under the occluder.

dots moving to the position on the right (Figure 9.20b). But adding a square, as in Figure 9.20c, caused a change in this perception. Now both dots moved to the right and observers perceived the bottom dot as sliding under the square. Again, in line with the occlusion heuristic, the dot continues to exist, even though it is behind the square.

VL 17, 18

Apparent Motion: Limits Imposed by the Human Body

Another demonstration of how knowledge affects apparent motion perception involves a principle called the **shortest-path constraint**—apparent movement tends to occur along the shortest path between two stimuli, even though many other paths are also possible (Figure 9.21).

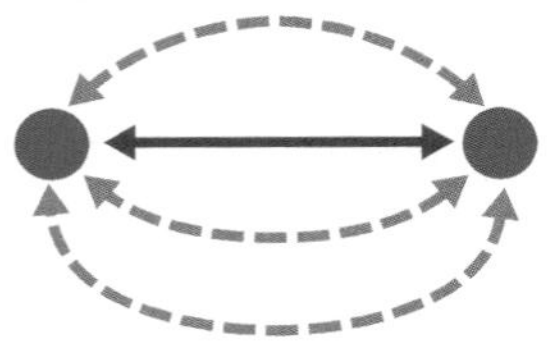

Figure 9.21 ▮ According to the shortest-path constraint, the apparent movement between the two rapidly alternating dots should occur along the shortest pathway (solid arrows) even though many other pathways are possible (dashed arrows).

Maggie Shiffrar and Jennifer Freyd (1990, 1993) used pictures like the ones in Figure 9.22 to determine what would happen when observers are shown two meaningful stimuli that would normally violate this constraint. These two pictures are designed to pose the following question: When these pictures are alternated rapidly, will observers perceive the woman's hand as moving through her head (this impossible movement would follow the shortest-path constraint), or will they perceive her hand as moving around her head (this likely movement would violate the shortest path constraint)?

Shiffrar and Freyd found that the answer to this question depends on the length of time between the onset of

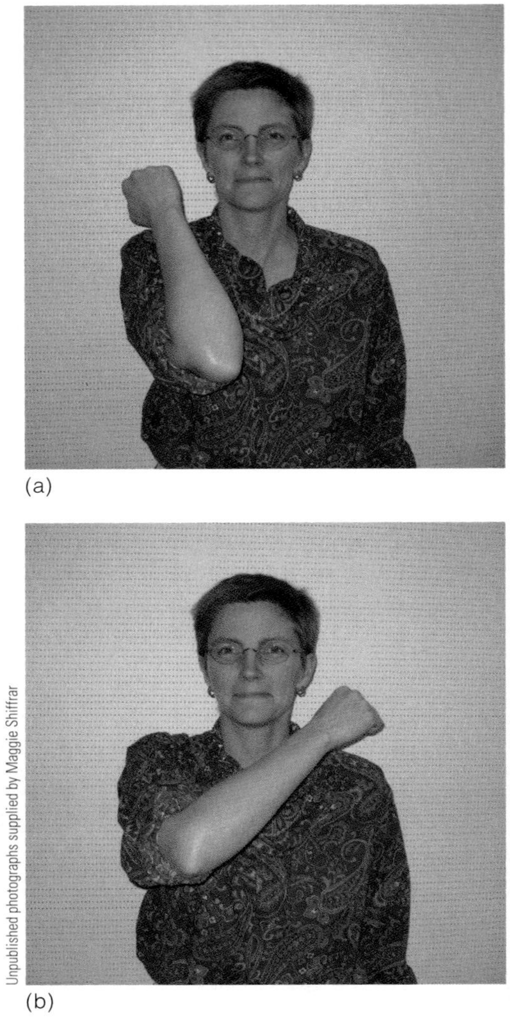

Figure 9.22 ▮ Photographs used as stimuli in the Shiffrar and Freyd (1990) experiment. When these pictures are alternated rapidly, the hand making a fist appears to move from one position to the other. The hand appears to go through the head at short SOAs and around the head at long SOAs.

the first and second pictures, called stimulus onset asynchrony (SOA). At SOAs below about 200 ms, observers were more likely to perceive the hand as moving through the head, thereby following the shortest-path constraint. However, at SOAs longer than 200 ms, the likelihood of perceiving movement around the woman's head increased, which violates the shortest-path constraint.

These results are interesting for two reasons: (1) They show that the visual system needs time to process information in order to perceive the movement of complex meaningful stimuli (although 200 ms may seem like a short period of time, it is a long processing time by the nervous system's standards); and (2) they suggest that there may be something special about the meaning of the stimulus—in this case, the human body—that influences the way movement is perceived. To test the idea that the human body is special, Shiffrar and coworkers showed that when objects, such as boards, are used as stimuli, the likelihood of perceiving movement along the longer path didn't increase with increasing SOA, as it does for pictures of humans (Chatterjee, Freyd, & Shiffrar, 1996).

What is happening in the cortex when observers view apparent motion generated by pictures like the one in Figure 9.22? Jennifer Stevens and coworkers (2000) measured brain activation using the PET scan technique to find out. They found that both types of movement activated areas in the parietal cortex associated with movement, but when the observers saw the likely movement, the motor cortex—which is involved in creating movement—was activated as well. Thus, the motor cortex is activated when the perceived movements are humanly possible but isn't activated when the perceived movements are not possible.

This connection between the brain area associated with perceiving movement and the motor area reflects the close connection between perception and movement. We have already described how perception of an object can be enhanced by movement of the observer or by movement of the object, a situation called structure-from-motion. But the connection extends far beyond enhancing our perception of objects: it plays an important role in enabling us to carry out everyday activities, such as walking toward a goal, catching a ball, and picking up a cup of coffee. In the next chapter, as we describe the perceptual mechanisms involved in carrying out these actions, we will gain an even greater appreciation of the close link between perceiving movement in the environment and physically moving through the environment.

SOMETHING TO CONSIDER: IMPLIED MOTION

Look at the picture in Figure 9.23. Although it is a still picture, it depicts an action that involves motion, a situation called **implied motion**. Jennifer Freyd (1983) showed that when people see pictures like this one, they not only perceive a still picture of an action, but they extend the action in their mind based on what will most likely happen next. She demonstrated this by presenting a picture like the one in Figure 9.23 and then following it with other pictures of the same action, some showing the action an instant earlier than the original picture and some showing the action an instant later. When observers were asked to indicate whether the second picture was the same as or different from the original picture, they often said that the picture that depicted the action *later in time* was identical to the original. This result has been described as showing that the picture "continued on its journey in the person's mind" (David & Senior, 2000), a situation Freyd called **representational momentum**.

Representational momentum is an example of experience influencing perception because it depends on our knowledge of the way situations involving movement typically unfold. The effect of experience on representational momentum was studied by Catherine Reed and Norman Vinson (1996) by presenting a sequence of pictures, as in Figure 9.24. Each picture was seen as a still picture because the sequence was presented slowly enough so no apparent motion occurred. Thus, any motion that did occur was implied by the positions and meanings of the objects in the pictures. After the third picture, which was called the *memory picture,* the observer saw the *test picture.* The test picture could appear in the same position as the memory picture or slightly lower or slightly higher. The observer's task was to indicate as quickly as possible whether the test picture was in the same position as the memory picture.

Bruce Goldstein

Figure 9.23 ▌ Picture that implies motion. See text for details.

Reed and Vinson wanted to determine whether the meaning of a picture had any effect on representational momentum, so they used pictures with different meanings. Figure 9.24a shows the *rocket picture,* and Figure 9.24b shows the *weight picture.* They found that the rocket showed a greater representational momentum effect than the weight. That is, observers were more likely

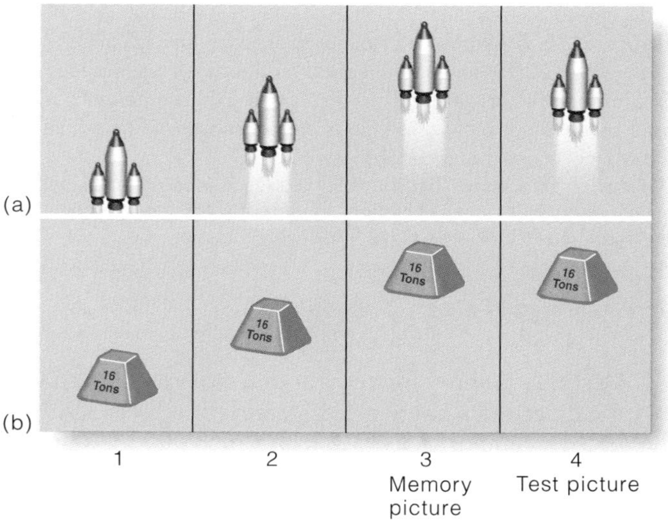

Figure 9.24 ▌ Stimuli used by Reed and Vinson (1996) to demonstrate the effect of experience on representational momentum. See text for details.

to say that the test picture of the rocket that appeared in a position higher than the memory picture, was in the same position as the memory picture. Reed and Vinson therefore concluded that the representational momentum effect is affected by a person's expectations about the motion of an object and that learned properties of objects (that rockets go up, for example) contributes to these expectations. (See "If You Want to Know More," item 3, for further thoughts about representational momentum.)

If implied motion causes an object to continue moving in a person's mind, then it would seem reasonable that this continued motion would be reflected by activity in the brain. When Zoe Kourtzi and Nancy Kanwisher (2000) measured the fMRI response in areas MT and MST to pictures like the ones in Figure 9.25, they found that implied motion pictures (IM) caused a greater response than non-implied motion pictures (No-IM), rest pictures (R), or house pictures (H). Thus, areas of the brain that are involved in our perception of actual motion also fire in response to still images that simply imply motion (also see Senior et al., 1999). **VL 19, 20**[1]

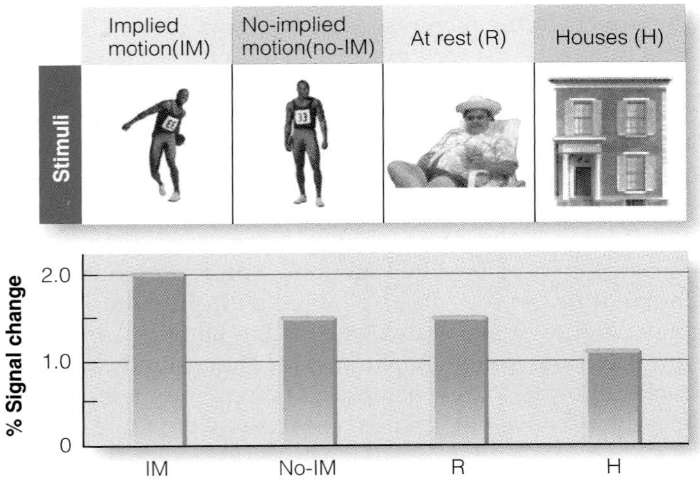

Figure 9.25 ▌ Examples of pictures used by Kourtzi and Kanwisher (2000) to depict implied motion (IM), no implied motion (no-IM), "at rest" (R), and a house (H). The height of the bars below each picture indicates the average fMRI response of the MT cortex to that type of picture.

(Kourtzi, Z. and Kanwisher, N. Activation in human MT/MST by static images with implied motion. Journal of Cognitive Neuroscience, 12, *48–55, MIT Press (2000).)*

TEST YOURSELF 9.2

1. Describe (a) how movement detectors in V1 signal the direction a bar is moving; and (b) why individual movement detectors don't provide adequate information about the direction in which a bar is moving.
2. Describe the physiological experiment that suggests a physiological solution for the aperture problem.
3. Describe the series of experiments that used moving dots as stimuli and recorded from neurons in MT cortex. What do the results of these experiments enable us to conclude about the physiology of movement perception?
4. Describe a number of ways that illustrate the idea that the perception of movement can depend on an observer's experience in the environment. Be sure to consider both behavioral and physiological evidence for this idea.

[1]These "extra" virtual lab items provide demonstrations of principles that are not directly covered in this chapter.

THINK ABOUT IT

1. We perceive real movement when we see things that are physically moving, such as cars on the road and people on the sidewalk. But we also see movement on TV, in movies, on our computer screens, and in electronic displays such as those in Times Square. How are images presented in these situations in order to result in the perception of movement? (This may require some research.)
2. In this Echapter, we described a number of principles that also hold for object perception (Chapter 5) and the perception of depth and size (Chapter 8). Find examples from Chapters 5 and 8 of the following (page numbers are for this chapter).
   - There are neurons that are specialized to respond to specific stimuli (203, 212).
   - A person's experience can affect perception (208).
   - There are parallels between physiology and perception (207).
   - More complex stimuli are processed in higher areas of the cortex (209, 212).
3. In the "Something to Consider" section, we stated that the representational momentum effect shows how knowledge can affect perception. Why could we also say that representational momentum illustrates an interaction between perception and memory?

IF YOU WANT TO KNOW MORE

1. ***Effect of Early Experience on Movement Perception.*** When kittens are raised in an environment that is illuminated by flashing lights, they lose the ability to detect the direction of moving stimuli. Experience in perceiving movement is necessary in order for movement perception to develop.

   Pasternak, T. (1990). Vision following loss of cortical directional selectivity. In M. A. Berkley & W. C. Stebbins (Eds.), *Comparative perception* (Vol. 1, pp. 407–428). New York: Wiley.
2. ***Movement Aftereffects and the Brain.*** After viewing a waterfall, a rotating spiral, or moving stripes, an il-

lusion of movement called a movement aftereffect occurs. These effects have been linked to activity in the brain.

Anstis, S. M., Verstraten, F. A. J., & Mather, G. (1998). The motion aftereffect: A review. *Trends in Cognitive Science, 2,* 111–117.

3. ***Cats Perceive Biological Motion.*** The perception of biological motion is not restricted to humans. There is evidence that cats can perceive it as well.

Blake, R. (1993). Cats perceive biological motion. *Psychological Science, 4,* 54–57.

KEY TERMS

Aperture problem (p. 204)
Apparent movement (p. 196)
Biological motion (p. 208)
Coherence (p. 207)
Comparator (p. 201)
Corollary discharge signal (CDS) (p. 201)
Corollary discharge theory (p. 201)
Global optic flow (p. 201)
Image movement signal (IMS) (p. 201)
Implied motion (p. 211)
Induced movement (p. 197)
Kinetic depth effect (p. 198)
Local disturbance in the optic array (p. 201)
Microstimulation (p. 207)
Motion agnosia (p. 197)
Motor signal (MS) (p. 201)
Movement aftereffect (p. 197)
Occlusion heuristic (p. 209)
Optic array (p. 200)
Point-light walker (p. 208)
Real movement (p. 196)
Real-movement neuron (p. 203)
Representational momentum (p. 211)
Shortest-path constraint (p. 210)
Structure-from-motion (p. 199)
Waterfall illusion (p. 197)

VISIT YOUR COMPANION WEBSITE FOR THIS BOOK

http://psychology.wadsworth.com/goldstein7e

Check out this companion website where you'll find online resources—glossary, flashcards, web links, multiple-choice and essay questions, and much more!

VIRTUAL LAB

Your Virtual Lab is designed to help you get the most out of this course. The Virtual Lab icons direct you to specific media demonstrations and experiments designed to help you visualize what you are reading about. The number beside each icon indicates the number of the media element you can access through your CD-ROM, Perception PsychologyNow, or WebTutor resource at http:now.ilrn.com/goldstein_7e.

The following are the lab exercises covering what you've just learned in this chapter:

1 *The Phi Phenomenon, Space, and Time* How the perception of apparent motion created by flashing two spheres depends on the distance and time interval between the spheres.

2 *Illusory Contour Motion* How alternating two displays that contain illusory contours can result in perception of a moving contour.

3 *Apparent Movement and Figural Selection* How movement is perceived when vertical and horizontal rectangles are flashed in different positions.

4 *Motion Capture* How dots on a surface are "captured" by apparent movement of that surface.

5 *Induced Movement* How the perception of movement can be influenced by movement of the background.

6 *The Waterfall Illusion* How viewing a moving horizontal grating can cause an aftereffect of motion.

7 *The Spiral Motion Aftereffect* How viewing a rotating spiral can cause an aftereffect of motion, which is opposite to the direction of rotation.

8 *Color Contingent Motion* How viewing a moving red-green grating can result in an aftereffect of movement.

9 *Motion Contingent Color* How viewing moving red and green gratings can create an aftereffect of movement.

10 *Motion Parallax and Object Form* How the image of an object changes when it is viewed from different angles.

11 *Kinetic Depth Effect* How rotation of two-dimensional images can provide information about an object's shape.

12 *Shape from Movement* How movement of some dots in a field of dots can create perception of an object.

13 *Form and Motion* How moving dot patterns can create the perception of three-dimensional forms. Click on "parameters" to set up this demonstration.

14 *Motion Reference* How the presence of two moving "reference" dots can influence the perceived movement of another dot that is moving between them.

15 *Corollary Discharge Model* How the corollary discharge model operates for movement of objects and movement of the observer.

16 *Biological Motion* How the movement of point-light walker stimuli can create the perception of walking people.

17 *Motion and Introduced Occlusion* How placing your finger over an apparent movement display can influence the perception of an object's motion.

18 *Field Effects and Apparent Movement* How introducing an occluder in an apparent-movement display can influence the perception of an object's motion.

19 *Context and Apparent Speed* How the perceived speed of a bouncing ball changes when it is near a border.

20 *Motion in Depth* How stereoscopic vision can result in the perception of movement in depth. Red-green glasses required.

CHAPTER

10

PERCEPTION AND ACTION

Chapter Contents

The mechanisms that enable Lance Armstrong to negotiate this bend involve using both perceptual mechanisms that enable him to see what is happening around him, and action mechanisms that help him keep his bike upright and stay on course. These mechanisms work in concert with one another, with perception guiding action and action, in turn, influencing perception.

VL *The Virtual Lab icons direct you to specific animations and videos designed to help you visualize what you are reading about. The number beside each icon indicates the number of the clip you can access through your CD-ROM or your student website.*

Some Questions We Will Consider:

- *How does the way the environment "flows by" a moving car help the driver stay on the road? (p. 217)*
- *How can an outfielder know where to run to get under a fly ball? (p. 225)*
- *How do neurons in the brain respond when a person performs an action and when the person watches someone else perform the same action? (p. 227)*

It is March madness in college basketball, and in a crucial game in the NCAA tournament a player charges toward the basket, stops, twists, takes off on his right foot, and seems to levitate straight up while bringing the ball down through the hoop for a resounding slam dunk. This example of athletic skill illustrates the close link between perception and action. As we will see in this chapter, just about everything we do involves a close coupling of perception and action. Feats in team sports like basketball and baseball, and in individual sports like gymnastics and figure skating, all involve not only strength and athleticism but the ability to coordinate movements of various parts of the body relative to each other and movement of the entire body with the rest of the environment. Athletes achieve this coordination by monitoring the relationship between their actions and their perceptions. Thus, the twist added to the basketball player's jump in midair occurs in response to his perception of the position of his own body relative to the basket and to the defender who is attempting to block his shot.

This coordination between perception and action occurs not only when a basketball player is shooting a basket. It also occurs as you walk down the street or negotiate a turn in your car. In fact, perception and action almost always occur together. Most of our perceptions occur as we are moving within the environment or are acting on the environment in some way. As we noted at the beginning of the book, some researchers see action as the most important outcome of the perceptual process because of its importance for survival. According to this idea, what is most important about perceiving a car approaching, as we cross the street, is the action we take to get out of the car's way. If we consider vision from the point of view of biological evolution, it is accurate to say that vision evolved not just to provide us with a way of seeing a car approaching, but also to help us avoid getting hit by the car (Musseler et al., 2004).

You already know that perception is not a stationary experience. You know from the description of how the visual system is organized that the dorsal (or *where,* or *how*) stream is concerned with movement, location, and how actions are carried out (Chapter 4, p. 77). You know from the chapter on attention that even if you sit still in a chair while perceiving, your eyes are constantly moving in order to extract information from different locations and objects in a scene (Chapter 6, p. 123). You know from the chapter on movement that research on movement has asked both "How do we perceive movement?" and "How do we perceive while we are moving?" (Chapter 9, p. 199).

Given that we have already described these aspects of the active nature of perception, you may wonder why a chapter on this topic is necessary. The answer is that action is such an important aspect of perception that there is still more of the story to tell. One part of the story has to do with ideas of the psychologist J. J. Gibson, who first began focusing on the relationship between perception and action in the late 1950s and over the next three decades laid the foundation for the ecological approach to perception. The other part of the story has occurred more recently, as psychologists and physiologists have begun extending the study of visual perception to places in the brain that are concerned not only with vision but with how the information provided by vision becomes transformed into action.

THE ECOLOGICAL APPROACH TO PERCEPTION

The **ecological approach to perception** focuses on studying perception as it occurs in the natural environment and emphasizes the connection between perception and how a person moves through the environment. We will describe the ecological approach by considering some of the basic principles of this approach as set forth by J. J. Gibson.

The Beginnings of the Ecological Approach

The ecological approach was, to some degree, a reaction to the traditional way of studying perception, especially as practiced in the 1950s and 1960s, when Gibson was beginning his research on perception. Gibson felt that traditional laboratory research, in which observers are often constrained so their heads don't move, was too artificial.

While working on a way to improve a pilot's ability to land an airplane, Gibson realized that the traditional laboratory approach to studying perception might not reflect what observers actually do in the environment. He found that the traditional cues for perceiving depth, such as overlap and relative size (see Figure 8.3), did not adequately explain how a pilot approaching a runway at a high rate of speed could judge his position relative to the runway. For Gibson, the major question of perception became "What information do perceivers use as they move through the environment?" One type of information Gibson identified was optic flow.

Optic Flow

To introduce optic flow, let's consider what you would see while driving across a bridge (Figure 10.1). The bridge's girders zoom by rapidly just outside your car window and more slowly as you look further down the bridge.

Figure 10.1 ▮ The flow of the environment as seen through the front window of a car speeding across a bridge toward the destination indicated by the white dot. (The red object in the foreground is the hood of the car.) The flow is more rapid closer to the car. This is indicated by the increased blur and the longer arrows. This flow occurs everywhere except at the white dot, which is the focus of expansion that is located at the car's destination at the end of the bridge.

This movement of the girders past the car is **optic flow**. The magnitude of this flow is indicated by the blur in the photograph, with more blur indicating greater flow. This difference in flow that occurs as a function of distance from the car is called a **gradient of flow**. VIRTUAL LAB 1

According to Gibson, the gradient of flow provides information about an observer's speed and also about where the observer is heading. This is illustrated in Figure 10.2a, which shows the optic flow experienced by an airplane pilot flying over a runway. The pilot sees a pattern of elements that flow along the ground. The length of the arrows indicates the speed of flow, which is rapid in the foreground and becomes slower toward the horizon, just as for our car traveling across the bridge in Figure 10.1.

An important property of the optic flow is that there is a point in the distance where there is no flow. This point, which is marked with a dot in Figures 10.1 and 10.2, is called the **focus of expansion (FOE)**. It is centered on the observer's destination and therefore provides information indicating where the observer is heading. Figure 10.2b shows what the optic flow would look like for a plane coming in for a landing. The location of the focus of expansion on the runway indicates where the plane will touch down.

Besides identifying optic flow as information that a moving observer can use to determine his or her speed and heading, Gibson identified some important characteristics of this optic flow information. One characteristic of optic flow is that it is **self-produced information**. Flow is created when the observer moves, and then this flow provides perceptual information that helps the observer carry out further movements. Gibson (1979) described this reciprocal relationship between movement and perception by pointing out that we need to perceive to move and that we also need to move to perceive (see Figure 10.3). Movement creates flow, which then provides information that guides further movement.

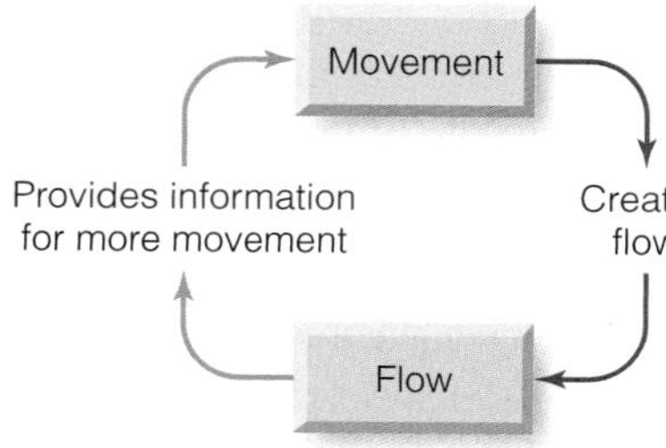

Figure 10.3 ▮ The relationship between movement and flow is reciprocal, with movement causing flow and flow guiding movement. This is the basic principle behind much of our interaction with the environment.

Another characteristic of optic flow is that it produces **invariant information**. We introduced the idea of invariant information in Chapter 5, when we described the recognition-by-components approach to object perception (see page 109). We defined an invariant as a property that remains constant under different conditions. For Gibson, the key invariants are the properties that remain constant as an observer moves through the environment. Optic flow provides invariant information be-

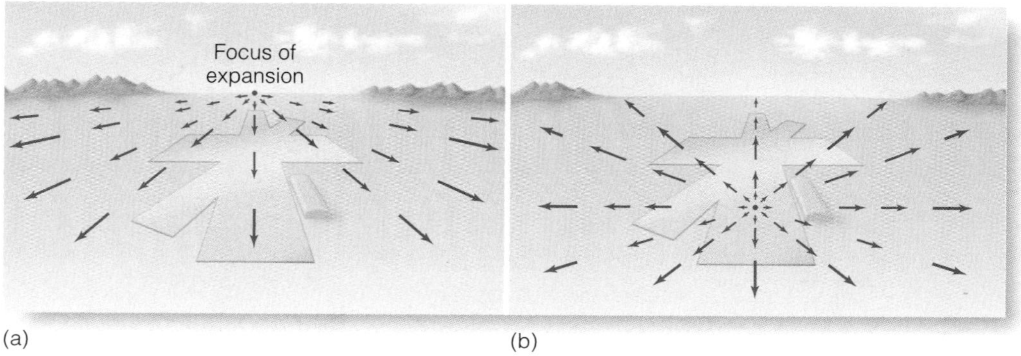

Figure 10.2 ▮ (a) Optic flow for an airplane flying over a runway. The length of the arrows indicates the speed of flow. The focus of expansion is at the dot. (b) Optic flow field for an airplane coming in for a landing.
(From James J. Gibson, The Senses Considered As Perceptual Systems. *Copyright © 1966 by Houghton Mifflin Company. Used with permission.)*

cause it occurs no matter where the observer is, as long as he or she is moving. The focus of expansion is also invariant because it is always centered on where the person is heading. This property of invariance is also illustrated by another source of environmental information, called texture gradients.

Texture Gradients

We introduced the idea of texture gradients as a source of depth information in Chapter 8 (see Figure 8.6). A **texture gradient** occurs when elements that are equally spaced in a scene appear to be more closely packed as distance increases, such as the square tiles in the floor and the pattern on the ceiling and on the wall in Figure 10.4. Texture gradients provide invariant information because no matter where you move, the information provided by the gradient is still there. For example, if you were to walk to the door at the end of the room in Figure 10.4, you would see a different view of the room, but the texture gradients on the floor, ceiling, and wall continue to provide information about the depths and sizes of objects in the scene.

Another example of how texture gradients provide invariant information is provided by the object that is sitting on the gradient in Figure 10.5. We see the object as covering one unit on the gradient when we view it from position 1 and it continues to cover one unit when we walk to another position and view it from position 2. This invariant information contributes to the perception of size constancy (see Chapter 8, p. 182), so we perceive the size of the object as remaining the same when viewed from different distances.

Figure 10.4 ▮ A hallway with texture gradients on the floor, ceiling, and walls.

Figure 10.5 ▮ A cylinder on a texture gradient that is viewed from two different positions.

Affordances

One of Gibson's most radical proposals, which he introduced in his last book, *The Ecological Approach to Visual Perception* (1979), was affordances. **Affordances** are the information specified by a stimulus pattern that indicates how the stimulus can be used. An example is seeing a chair as something to sit on or a flight of stairs as something to climb. Gibson would call this the "sit-on-able" property of the chair and the "climb-able" property of the stairs. Thus, Gibson believed that we perceive not just objects, but what an object does for us—its use. This idea of affordances fits with Gibson's ecological approach, with its emphasis on studying the active observer, because affordances provide possibilities for action (Jones, 2003).

NAVIGATING THROUGH THE ENVIRONMENT

Although only a small fraction of present-day perception researchers identify themselves as "ecological psychologists," perception research today routinely considers the role of action and movement in perception, and how perception occurs in naturalistic scenes. For example, Gibson's proposal that people use optic flow to determine their heading as they move through the environment has stimulated a great deal of research investigating whether people use flow information to determine their direction of movement.

Do People Use Flow Information?

Research on whether people use flow information has asked observers to make judgments regarding their heading, based on computer-generated displays of moving dots that create optic flow stimuli. When observers view flow stimuli like the one in Figure 10.6a, which indicates flow for moving straight ahead, and 10.6b, which indicates the flow created by traveling in a curved path, they can judge where they are heading relative to the vertical line to within about 0.5 to 1 degree (W. Warren, 1995, 2003). VL 2

To study whether people use flow in an actual environmental situation, Michael Land and David Lee (1994) fitted an automobile with instruments to record the angle of the steering wheel and the speed, and measured where the driver was looking with a video eye tracker. According to Gibson, the focus of expansion indicates the place toward which a moving observer is headed. However, Land and Lee found that when driving straight ahead, the driver does look straight ahead but not directly at the focus of expansion (Figure 10.7a).

What happens as the driver negotiates a curve? This task poses a problem for the idea of focus of expansion because the driver's destination keeps changing as the car negotiates the curve. Land and Lee found that when going around a curve, drivers don't look directly at the road,

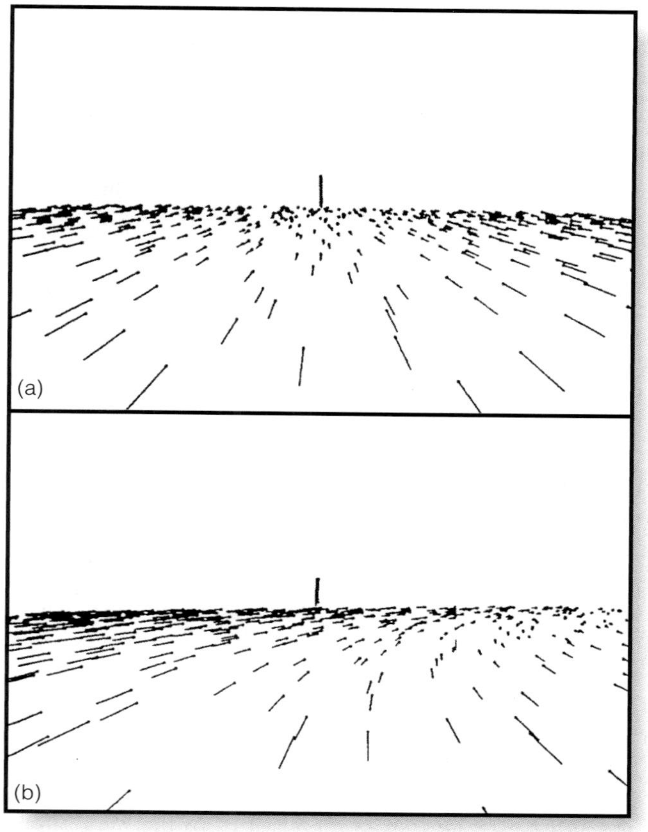

Figure 10.6 ▌ (a) Optic flow generated by a person moving straight ahead toward the vertical line on the horizon. The lengths of the lines indicate the person's speed. (b) Optic flow generated by a person moving in a curved path that is headed to the right of the vertical line.
(From W. H. Warren (1995). Self-motion: Visual perception and visual control. In Perception of Space and Motion, a volume in the series of Handbook of Perception and Cognition, *Second Edition, ed. William Epstein and Sheena J. Rogers, copyright ©1995 by Academic Press, reproduced by permission of the publisher.)*

but look at the tangent point of the curve on the side of the road, as shown in Figure 10.7b. Based on these results, Land and Lee suggested that drivers probably use information in addition to optic flow to determine their heading (see also Land & Horwood, 1995; S. K. Rushton & Salvucci, 2001; Wann & Land, 2000; Wilke & Wann, 2003, for more research on the information drivers use to stay on the road).

Flow Is Not Always Necessary for Determining Heading

Apparently, an important strategy used by walkers (and perhaps drivers as well) is the **visual direction strategy** in which observers keep their body pointed toward a target. If they go off course, the target will drift to the left or right, and the walker corrects course to recenter the target (Fajen & Warren, 2002; Rushton et al., 1998).

Another indication that flow information is not always necessary for navigation is that we can find our way

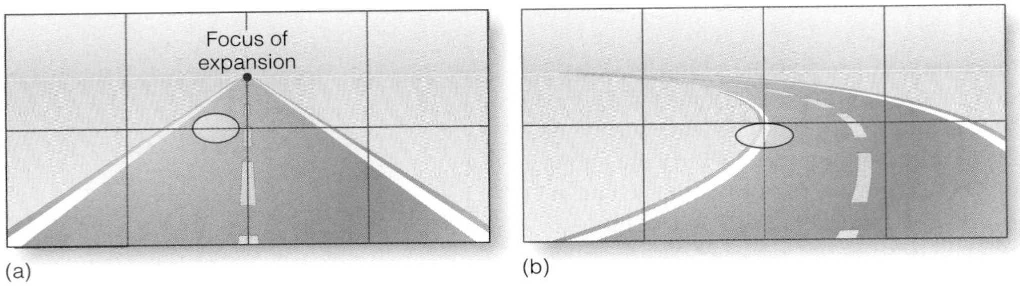

Figure 10.7 ▌ Results of Land and Lee's (1994) experiment. The ellipses indicate the place where the drivers were most likely to look while driving down (a) a straight road and (b) a curve to the left.
(Land, M. F., & Lee, D. N., 1994. Where we look when we steer. Nature, 369, *742–744.)*

even when flow information is minimal, such as at night or in a snowstorm (Harris & Rogers, 1999). Jack Loomis and coworkers (Loomis et al., 1992, 1996; Philbeck, Loomis, & Beall, 1997) have demonstrated this by using a "blind walking" procedure to show that observers can locate nearby targets with their eyes closed.

In blind-walking experiments, people observe a target object located up to 12 meters away, then walk to the target with their eyes closed. These experiments show that people are able to walk directly toward the target and stop within a fraction of a meter of it. In fact, people can do this even when they are asked to walk off to the side first and then make a turn and walk to the target, while keeping their eyes closed. Some records from these "angled" walks are shown in Figure 10.8, which depicts the paths taken when a person first walked to the left from the "start" position and then was told to turn either at turn point 1 or 2 and walk to a target that was 6.0 meters away. The fact that the person stopped close to the target shows that we are able to accurately navigate short distances in the absence of any visual stimulation at all (also see Sun et al., 2004).

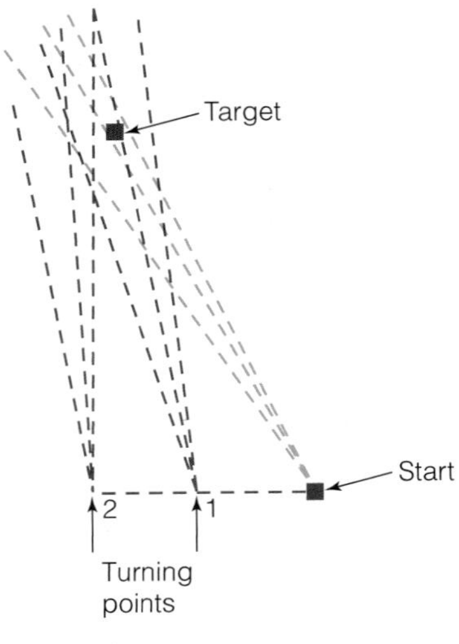

Figure 10.8 ▌ The results of a "blind walking" experiment (Philbeck et al., 1997). Participants looked at the target, which was 6 meters from the starting point, then closed their eyes and began walking to the left. They turned either at point 1 or 2, keeping their eyes closed the whole time, and continued walking until they thought they had reached the target.
(From J. W. Philbeck, J. M. Loomis, and A. C. Beall (1997). Visually perceived location is an invariant in the control of action. Perception and Psychophysics 59, *601–612. Adapted with permission.)*

Flow, Posture, and Balance

Although it makes sense that flow provides information for heading, especially when the scene is moving rapidly as when you drive down the road, it is not so obvious that flow would have anything to do with an activity such as standing in one place, which seems to involve little movement at all. But ecological researchers realized that vision is involved in helping us to maintain our balance or posture. You can see this yourself by doing the following demonstration.

DEMONSTRATION

Keeping Your Balance

Keeping your balance is something you probably take for granted. Stand up. Raise one foot from the ground and stay balanced on the other. Then close your eyes and observe what happens. ■

Did staying balanced become more difficult when you closed your eyes? Vision provides a frame of reference that helps the muscles constantly make adjustments to help maintain balance. Although the vestibular system of the inner ear and the receptors in our muscles and joints, which help us sense the positions of our limbs, are generally considered the major mechanisms of balance, a number of experiments have demonstrated a direct connection between vision and our ability to maintain our balance.

The importance of vision in maintaining balance was demonstrated by David Lee and Eric Aronson (1974). Lee and Aronson placed 13- to 16-month-old toddlers in a "swinging room" (Figure 10.9). In this room, the floor is

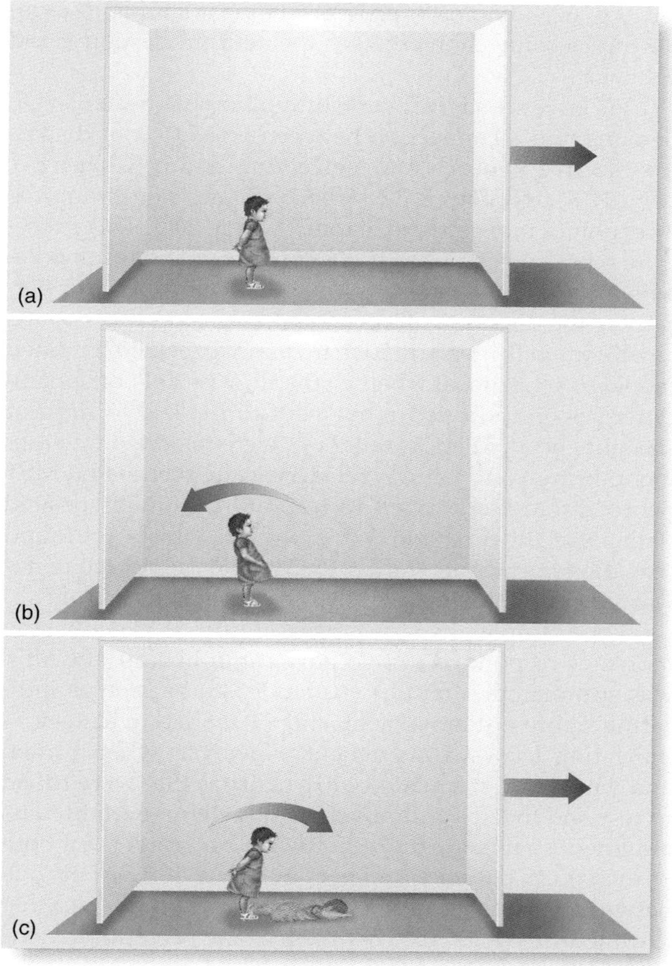

Figure 10.9 ▌ Lee and Aronson's swinging room. (a) Moving the room forward creates the same optic flow pattern (shown in Figure 10.10b) that occurs when a person sways backward, as in (b). To compensate for this apparent sway, subjects sway forward, as in (c), and often lose their balance and fall down. *(Based on figure from "Visual Proprioceptive Control of Standing in Human Infants," by D. N. Lee and E. Aronson, 1974,* Perception and Psychophysics, *15, 529–532, figure 2. Psychonomics Society Publications.)*

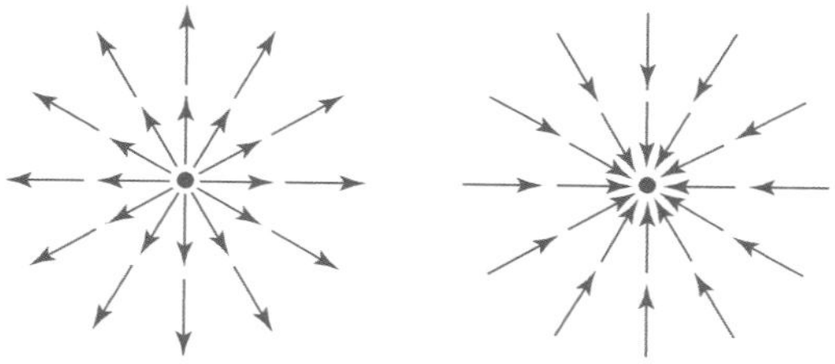

Figure 10.10 ▌ Flow patterns that occur (a) when we move forward and (b) when we move backward.

stationary, but the walls and ceiling can swing forward and backward. The idea behind the swinging room was to duplicate the visual stimulation that normally occurs as our bodies sway forward and backward, creating visual optic flow patterns as we see elements of the environment move relative to us. Swaying forward creates an expanding optic flow pattern (Figure 10.10a), and swaying backward creates a contracting optic flow pattern (Figure 10.10b).

These flow patterns provide information about body sway. Without realizing it, we are constantly using this information to make corrections for this sway so that we can stand upright. Lee and Aronson reasoned that if they created a flow pattern that made people think they were leaning forward or backward, they could cause them to lean in the opposite direction to compensate. They accomplished this by moving the room either toward or away from the standing children, and the children responded as predicted. When the room moved toward them (creating the flow pattern for swaying forward), they leaned back, and when it moved away (creating the flow pattern for swaying backward), they leaned forward. In fact, many of the children did more than just lean: 26 percent swayed, 23 percent staggered, and 33 percent fell down!

Adults were also affected by the swinging room. If they braced themselves, "oscillating the experimental room through as little as 6 mm caused adult subjects to sway approximately in phase with this movement. The subjects were like puppets visually hooked to their surroundings and were unaware of the real cause of their disturbance" (Lee, 1980, p. 173). Adults who didn't brace themselves could, like the toddlers, be knocked over by their perception of the moving room.

The swinging room experiments show that vision is such a powerful determinant of balance that it can override the traditional sources of balance information provided by the inner ear and the receptors in the muscles and joints (see also C. R. Fox, 1990). In a developmental study, Bennett Berthenthal and coworkers (1997) showed that infants as young as 4 months old sway back and forth in response to movements of a room, and that the coupling of the room's movement and the swaying becomes better with age. (See also Stoffregen et al., 1999, for more evidence that flow information can influence posture while standing still and W. H. Warren et al., 1996, for evidence that flow is involved in maintaining posture while walking.)

The Physiology of Navigation: Neurons in the Brain

As we move through the environment, using flow and other information to guide us, neurons in the brain are responding to this information. Researchers have shown that there are neurons in the monkey's brain that respond to optic flow and that there are areas in the human brain that are activated as people navigate through the environment.

Optic Flow Neurons Where would we expect to find neurons that respond to optic flow? A logical place to start would be the medial temporal (MT) area in the monkey's dorsal stream because we know that neurons in this area respond to the direction of movement (see Chapter 9, p. 206). As it turns out, neurons in MT do not respond to flow patterns, but neurons in the *medial superior temporal area* (MST), which receives signals from MT (Figure 10.11), do respond to flow patterns.

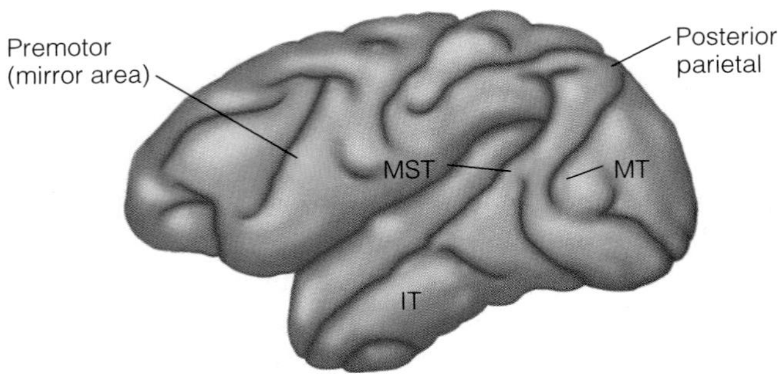

Figure 10.11 ▮ Monkey brain, showing key areas for movement perception and visual-motor interaction. IT = infero temporal cortex; MT = medial temporal area; MST = medial superior temporal area.

Figure 10.12 shows the response of neurons in MST that respond best to patterns of dots that are expanding outward (Figure 10.12a) and also neurons that respond best to circular motions (Figure 10.12b; see also Duffy & Wurtz, 1991; Orban et al., 1992; Regan & Cynader, 1979). What does the existence of these optic flow neurons mean? We know from previous discussions that finding a neuron that responds to a specific stimulus is only the first step in determining whether this neuron has anything to do with perceiving that stimulus (see Chapter 3, p. 62; Chapter 8, p. 179). The next step is to demonstrate a connection between the neuron's response and behavior.

We have seen how microstimulation has been used to demonstrate a connection between activation of disparity-selective neurons and perceiving depth (Chapter 8, page 179), and between MT neurons and perceiving the direction of movement (Chapter 9, page 208). This procedure has also been used to demonstrate a connection between activation of optic flow neurons in MST and perceiving the direction of movement.

Kenneth Britten and Richard van Wezel (2002) trained monkeys to indicate whether the flow of dots on a computer screen indicated movement to the left or right or straight ahead. Then, as monkeys were making that judgment, Britten and van Wezel electrically stimulated MST neurons that were tuned to respond to flow associated with a specific direction. When they did this, they found that the stimulation shifted the monkey's judgments toward the direction favored by the stimulated neuron.

For example, the blue bars in Figure 10.13 show how monkeys responded to two flow stimuli before the MST was stimulated. Stimulus (A) tended to be seen as indicating rightward movement, and (B) tended to be seen as indicating leftward movement. However, when Britten and van Wezel stimulated MST neurons that were tuned to respond to leftward movement, the monkey shifted its judgment so it made more "leftward" judgments for both of these flow patterns (red bars in Figure 10.13). This link between MST firing and perception supports the idea that flow neurons do, in fact, help determine perception of the direction of movement.

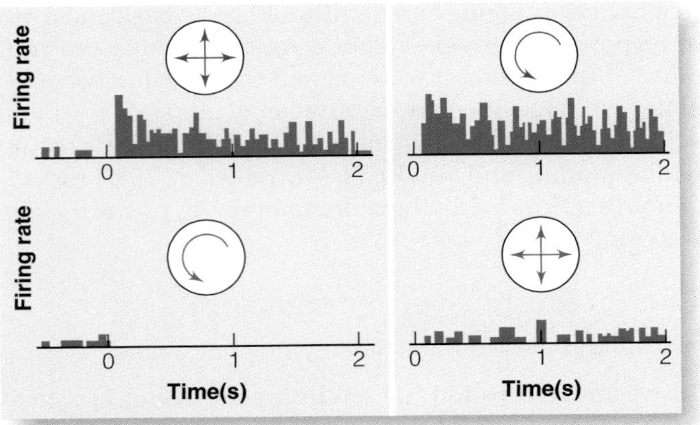

(a) Neuron 1 (b) Neuron 2

Figure 10.12 ▮ (a) Response of a neuron in the monkey's MST that responds with a high rate of firing to an expanding stimulus (top record) but that hardly fires to a stimulus that moves with a circular motion (bottom record) or with other types of motion (not shown). (b) Another neuron that responds best to circular movement (top) but does not respond well to an expanding pattern or other types of movement (bottom).
(From Graziano, Andersen, & Snowden, 1994.)

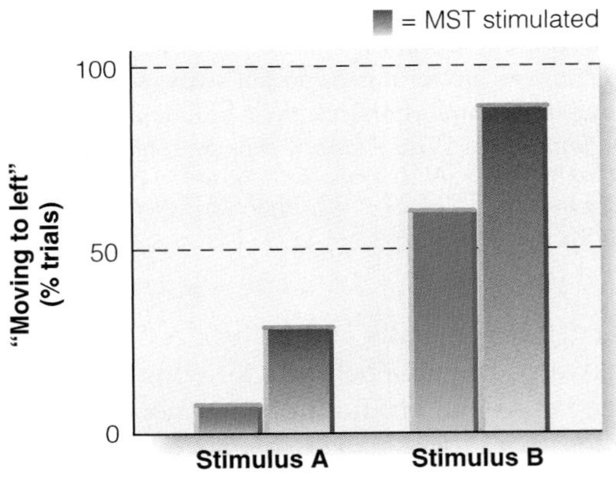

Figure 10.13 ▮ How microstimulation of MST neurons that were tuned to respond to leftward movement affected a monkey's judgment of the direction in which two flow stimuli were moving. Blue bars: judgment before microstimulation. Red bars: judgment during microstimulation.

Brain Areas for Navigation There is more to navigating through the environment than perceiving the direction of movement. An essential part of navigation is knowing what path to take to reach your destination. People often use landmarks to help them find their way. For example, although you may not remember the name of a specific street, you might remember that you need to turn right at the gas station on the corner.

In Chapter 4 we saw that there are neurons in the parahippocampal place area (PPA) that respond to buildings, the interiors of rooms, and other things associated with locations (see Chapter 4, page 84). We now return to the PPA, but instead of just describing neurons that respond to pictures of houses or rooms, we will describe some experiments that have looked at the connection between activity in the PPA and using landmarks to navigate through the environment.

First, let's consider an experiment by Eleanor Maguire and coworkers (1998) in which observers viewed a computer screen to see a tour through a "virtual town" (Figure 10.14a). Observers first learned the town's layout and then, as they were being scanned in a PET scanner, they were given the task of navigating from one point to another in the town (Figure 10.14b).

(a)

(b)

Figure 10.14 ▌ (a) Scene from the "virtual town" viewed by Maguire et al.'s (1998) observers. (b) Plan view of the town showing three of the paths observers took between locations A and B. Activity in the hippocampus and parietal lobe was greater for the accurate path (1) than for the inaccurate paths (2 and 3). *(Reprinted with permission from Maguire, E. A., Burgess, N., Donnett, J. G., Frackowiak, R. S. J., Frith, C. D., O'Keefe, J., Knowing where, and getting there: A human navigation network,* Science, *vol. 280, 921–924, (1998).)*

Maguire and coworkers found that navigating activated the right hippocampus and part of the parietal cortex. They also found that activation was greater when navigation between two locations, A and B, was accurate (path 1 in Figure 10.14b) compared to when it was inaccurate (paths 2 and 3). Based on these results, Maguire concluded that the hippocampus and portions of the parietal lobe form a "navigation network" in the human cortex.

But what about landmarks that people use to find their way through environments? Gabriele Janzen and Miranda van Turennout (2004) investigated the role of landmarks in navigation by having observers first study a film sequence that moved through a "virtual museum" (Figure 10.15). Observers were told that they needed to learn their way around the museum well enough to be able to guide a tour through it. Objects ("exhibits") were located along the hallway of this museum, some at "decision points," like the object at (a), which marks a place where it is necessary to make a left turn, and some at "nondecision points" like the one at (b).

After studying the museum's layout in the film, observers were given a recognition test while in an fMRI scanner. They saw objects that had been in the hallway and objects they had never seen. Their brain activation was measured in the scanner as they indicated whether they remembered seeing each object. The results, displayed in Figure 10.15c, show that activity in the right parahippocampal gyrus was greater for remembered objects that were located at decision points than for objects that were not at decision points (left pair of bars). Furthermore, this advantage for "decision-point objects" occurred even for objects that were not remembered during the recognition test (right pair of bars).

Janzen and van Turennout concluded that the brain automatically distinguishes objects that are used as landmarks to guide navigation. Thus, the brain responds not just to the object but to how relevant that object is for guiding navigation. This means that the next time you are trying to find your way along a route that you have traveled before but aren't totally confident about, activity in your parahippocampal gyrus may automatically be "highlighting" landmarks that indicate where you should make that right turn, even though you may not remember having seen that object before.

TEST YOURSELF 10.1

1. What are some examples of the connection between action and perception that were described in earlier chapters?
2. Why did J. J. Gibson propose the ecological approach to perception?

(continued)

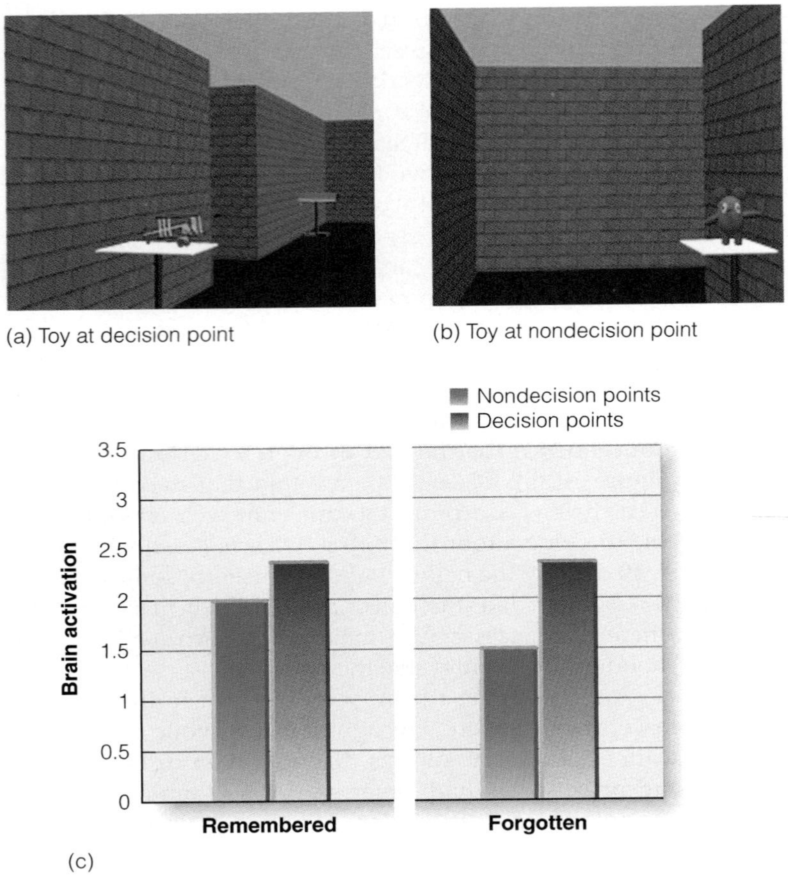

Figure 10.15 ▮ (a & b) Two locations in the "virtual museum" viewed by Janzen and van Turennout's (2004) observers. (c) Brain activation during the recognition test for objects that had been located at decision points (red bars) and nondecision points (blue bars).
(Janzen, G., & van Turennout, M. (2004). Selective neural representation of objects relevant for navigation. Nature Neuroscience, *7, 673–677.)*

3. Describe the following aspects of Gibson's approach: optic flow, self-produced information, invariance, texture gradients, affordances.
4. What kinds of information do people use to navigate through the environment? Consider the evidence for flow and for other information.
5. Describe optic flow neurons in MST and how the connection between their reponse and perception was established by microstimulation.
6. Describe Maguire's and Janzen and van Turennout's experiments, which show that the parahippocampal gyrus is involved in navigation through the environment.

SKILLED ACTIONS

We've seen that moving through the environment by walking or driving is guided by both optic flow and other information. But what about the movements involved in athletic feats, such as dunking a basketball or running to catch a fly ball hit to the outfield? What environmental information do athletes use to carry out the skilled actions required by their sports? To begin answering this question, we will consider research on two actions, somersaulting and catching a fly ball.

Somersaulting

Gymnastics involves split-second timing and balance. We can appreciate the problem facing a gymnast who wants to execute an airborne backward somersault by realizing that, within 600 ms, the gymnast must execute the somersault and then end in exactly the correct body configuration precisely at the moment that he or she hits the ground (Figure 10.16).

Figure 10.16 ▮ "Snapshots" of a somersault, starting on the left and finishing on the right.
(From Bardy & Laurent, 1998)

One way this could be accomplished is to learn to run off a predetermined sequence of motions within a specific period of time. In this case, performance should be the same with eyes opened and eyes closed. However, Benoit Bardy and Makel Laurent (1998) found that expert gymnasts performed somersaults more poorly with their eyes closed. Films showed that when their eyes were opened, the gymnasts appeared to be making in-the-air corrections to their trajectory. For example, a gymnast who initiated the extension of his or her body a little too late compensated by performing the rest of the movement more rapidly.

Another interesting result was that closing the eyes did not affect the performance of novice somersaulters as much as it affected the performance of experts. Apparently, experts learn to coordinate their movements with their perceptions, but the novices have not yet learned to do this. Thus, somersaulting, like other forms of actions, involves the regulation of action during the continuous flow of perceptual information as depicted in Figure 10.16.

Catching a Fly Ball

An outfielder's ability to catch a fly ball on the run is amazing when we consider that although the outfielder may be over 300 feet from home plate, he or she usually starts running almost immediately and then ends up at the ball's landing place, often just before the ball gets there.

How does the outfielder determine where the ball is going to land? One way would be to determine the ball's speed and the angle at which it is rising, and then calculate the parabolic arc that the ball will follow to its destination. The problem with this tactic is not only that it involves a complex calculation, but that it would be difficult for an outfielder located 300 feet away from home plate to accurately estimate speed and angle.

Michael McBeath and coworkers (1995) proposed a strategy for catching a fly ball called the **linear optical trajectory (LOT) strategy** (Figure 10.17). The basis of the LOT strategy is that if the ballplayer runs so the view of the ball overhead follows a straight-line path, the ball will always be directly above, so when the ball reaches the ground, the outfielder will be there to catch it.

As you can see from the diagram in Figure 10.17, the LOT strategy predicts that the ball player will run in a slightly curved path. When Michael McBeath and coworkers (1995; also see Shaffer et al., 2002) filmed outfielders as they chased fly balls, they found that they did follow curved paths, as the theory predicts. When they had outfielders view the ball through a viewfinder of a mini–video camera, their view of the ball, as recorded by the video camera, matched the view predicted by LOT.

To see whether this result also holds for dogs chasing Frisbees, Dennis Shaffer and coworkers (2004) outfitted Romeo, a Frisbee-catching springer spaniel, with a micro–video camera that indicated where he was looking. As predicted by LOT, Romeo ran along a curved path that kept the Frisbee directly overhead.

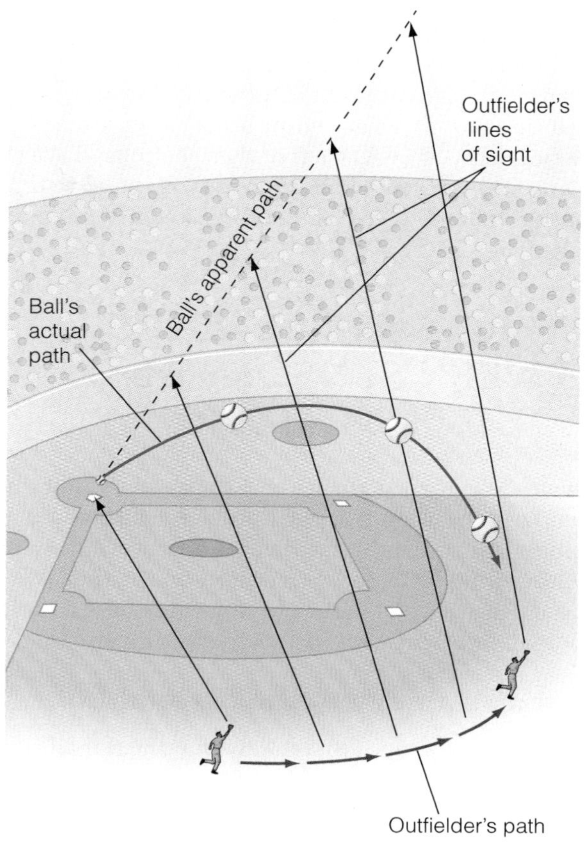

Figure 10.17 ▮ A fly ball travels along the path shown by the baseball. An outfielder who runs so the ball appears to follow a straight-line path (dashed line) will eventually intersect with the ball's position.
(Reprinted with permission from "How Baseball Outfielders Determine Where to Run to Catch Fly Balls," by M. K. McBeath, D. M. Shaffer, and M. K. Kaiser, 1995, Science*, 268, 569–573, figure 3b. Copyright © 1995 by the American Association for the Advancement of Science.)*

Although following the LOT strategy would enable an outfielder to arrive at the place where the ball lands, other researchers have questioned this strategy, based on the fact that outfielders often arrive at the ball's landing spot well before the ball gets there (Chodosh et al., 1995; Jacobs et al., 1996). Apparently the LOT may not be the only information that ballplayers take into account when catching fly balls (see McLeod et al., 2002). However, the important point for our purposes is that whether outfielders use the LOT strategy, another strategy, or a combination of strategies, the way they catch fly balls is based on a continuous interaction, like the one diagrammed in Figure 10.3, in which perception guides actions, which create new information for perception, which guides further action, and so on.

Although we may still have a lot to learn about how athletes carry out skilled actions, it is clear that the perceptions needed to achieve these actions are closely linked to movements that are synchronized with the ongoing flow of their perceptions. The ability to move through the environment, to maintain our posture, and to catch a fly ball all depend on visual stimuli that are created by the movements involved in each of these actions. If we stand perfectly still, not only do our movements stop, but the information that we were using to guide these movements vanishes.

PHYSIOLOGICAL LINKS BETWEEN SENSORY AND MOTOR FUNCTIONS

We have described neurons and brain areas that are involved in navigation. We will now consider some more physiological research that has been concerned with establishing links between perception and action. We will start with the parietal cortex, because it is the endpoint of the dorsal, or *where/how,* visual processing stream.

Effect of Damage to the Parietal Lobe

In Chapter 4 (see page 78), we saw that the dorsal stream, which travels from the visual cortex to the parietal lobe, is responsible for locating objects and taking action with regard to objects. When we described the case of D.F., we saw that she had damage to her temporal lobe, which made it difficult for her to recognize objects. However, her parietal lobe was intact, so she had no difficulty placing a card through an oriented "mail slot." But patients with parietal lobe damage have **optic ataxia**, a condition in which they reach for objects slowly and inaccurately and often also have trouble forming their hands to match the shape of the object they are trying to grasp.

A recent study of two patients with parietal lobe damage shows that the parietal lobe may also be important for avoiding obstacles while reaching. Igor Schindler and coworkers (2004) studied two patients with optic ataxia to test the idea that the parietal lobe is involved in avoiding obstacles. Observers viewed a display consisting of two vertical cylinders that were shifted to different positions on each trial. Figure 10.18 shows the position of the two cylinders on two different trials. The blue pair is shifted to the right compared to the red pair. Observers were given two tasks: for the *bisection task,* they had to point to a place exactly midway between the cylinders; for the *reaching task,* they had to reach between the cylinders to touch a gray strip that was 20 cm behind the cylinders.

The results for the bisection task are shown above the horizontal line in Figure 10.18. The red A (ataxia observers) and red C (control observers) indicate where the observers pointed for the red pair of cylinders. The blue A and blue C indicate where the observers pointed for the blue pair of cylinders. The results for the ataxia and control observers were the same: They both shifted their

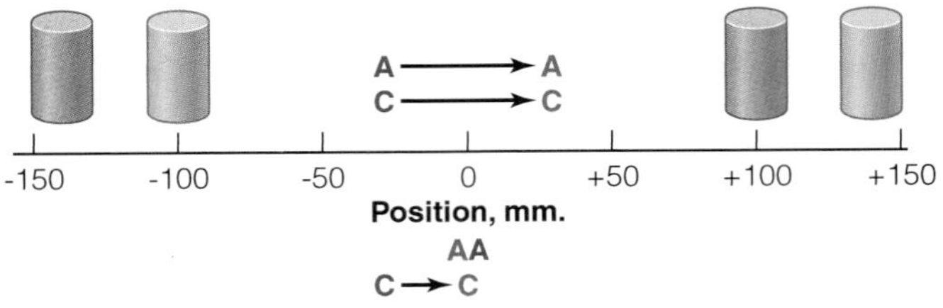

Figure 10.18 ▮ Results of Schindler et al.'s (2004) experiment that tested the behavior of patients with optic ataxia on a bisection task (results indicated by letters above the line; A = ataxia patients; C = control participants) and a reaching task (results below the line). See text for details.
(From I. Schindler et al. (2004). Automatic avoidance of obstacles is a dorsal stream function: Evidence from optic ataxia. Nature Neuroscience, *7, 779–784.)*

pointing to the right when the cylinders were positioned to the right.

The results for the reaching task are shown below the line. The red and blue C's indicate that the control observers adjusted their reach when the cylinders were moved to the right by reaching more to the right as though they were avoiding a potential obstacle. However, the red and blue A's indicate that the ataxia observers made no adjustment when the cylinders were shifted. They just kept reaching straight ahead.

Schindler concluded that the dorsal stream (which is affected by the parietal lobe damage) provides guidance that we automatically build into our movements in order to avoid obstacles. This mechanism appears to operate unconsciously when we reach for something in an environment that may contain other close-by objects as well. Although this experiment was concerned only with reaching, perhaps the dorsal stream also helps us automatically avoid obstacles when we are walking through a cluttered environment. Further research is needed to determine whether this is the case.

Properties of Neurons in the Parietal Lobe

Some neurons in the monkey's parietal lobe respond best to visual stimuli and others respond best to reaching for stimuli (Murata et al., 1996; Sakada et al., 1997). Figure 10.19a illustrates the response of a **visual-dominant neuron.** This neuron responds when the monkey looks at a button or presses the button in the light, but does not respond to pushing the button in the dark. Figure 10.19b shows the response of a **motor-dominant neuron.** This neuron responds well to pushing the button both in the light and in the dark, but doesn't respond well to just looking at the button. Thus, some neurons in the parietal lobe respond best to looking at objects (vision-dominant), and others respond best to manipulating objects (motor-dominant). There are also some neurons that respond to both looking at objects and manipulating them. This mixture of neurons reflects the parietal lobe's role in the interaction between perception and action.

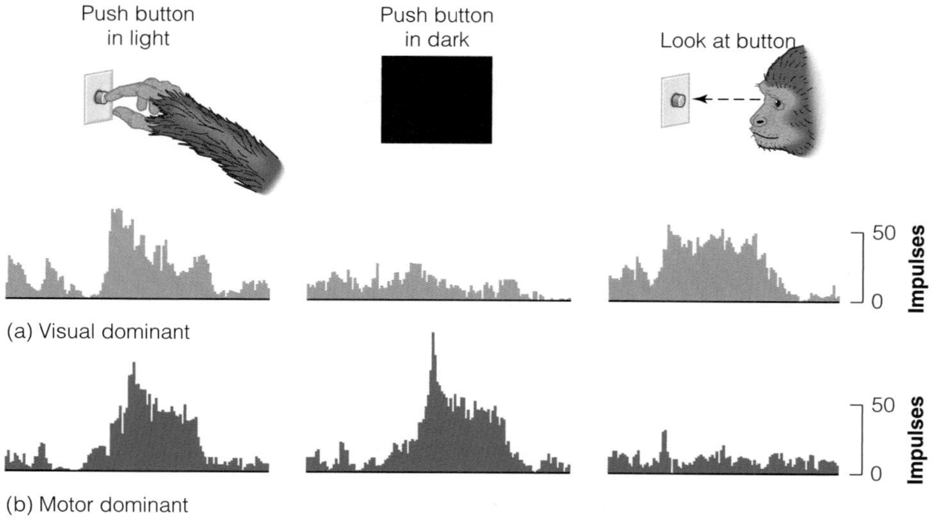

Figure 10.19 ▌ Two types of parietal neurons that respond to visual and motor tasks. See text for details. *(From H. Sakata, M. Taira, M. Kusunoki, A. Murata, and Y. Tanaka (1977). The parietal association cortex in depth perception and visual control of hand action.* Trends in Neurosciences, 20, *p. 350–356. Adapted with permission.)*

Other research has found neurons in the parietal cortex that respond before a monkey actually grasps an object (Calton et al., 2002). This kind of neuron responds after a monkey receives a cue signal to move its hand to grab an object that is about to appear. Because this type of neuron fires even before the object appears, it signals the monkey's *intention* to grasp an object (Calton et al., 2002; Gold & Mazurek, 2002; Snyder et al., 2000). The neurons we have described have been found in a number of subareas in the parietal cortex, mostly in the posterior parietal cortex (see Figure 10.11). Because so many of these neurons are involved with reaching behavior, they together make up a network called the **parietal reach region** (PRR; Snyder et al., 2000). The parietal reach region sends signals to the premotor area (see Figure 10.11), which contains neurons that respond not only to carrying out actions, but to observing these same actions being performed by others.

Mirror Neurons in Premotor Cortex

Neurons in the premotor area called **mirror neurons** respond both when a monkey grasps an object and when the monkey observes someone else (usually the experimenter) grasping an object. These neurons are called mirror neurons because the neuron's response to watching the experimenter grasp an object, the neuron's response mirrors the response that would occur if the monkey were performing the action.

Figure 10.20 shows a mirror neuron that fires (a) as the monkey watches the experimenter grasp a piece of food on a tray and (b) also as the monkey grasps the food. Just looking at the food causes no response, and watching the experimenter grasp the food with a pair of pliers, as in (c), causes only a small response (Gallese et al., 1996; Rizzolatti, Forgassi, & Gallese, 2000).

Most mirror neurons are specialized to respond to only one type of action, such as grasping or placing an object somewhere. Although you might think that the monkey may have been responding to the anticipation of receiving food, the type of object made little difference. The neurons responded just as well when the monkey observed the experimenter pick up a three-dimensional object that was not food.

Mirror neurons, like other neurons in the parietal and premotor areas, are concerned with action. But mirror neurons are special because they respond both when a monkey performs an action and when the monkey sees

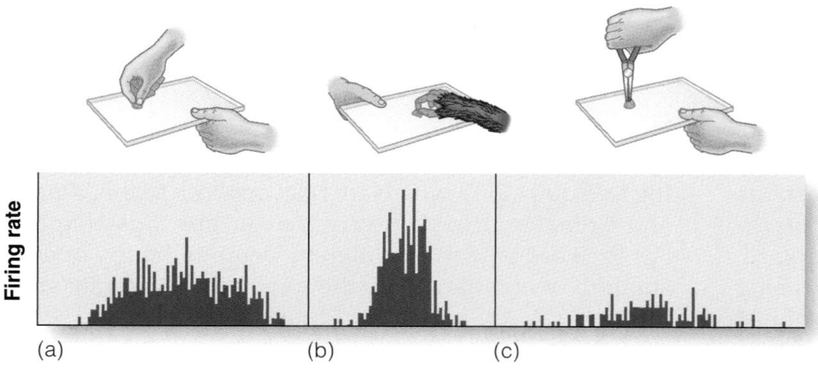

Figure 10.20 ▌ Response of a mirror neuron. (a) Response to watching the experimenter grasp food on the tray. (b) Response when the monkey grasps the food. (c) Response to watching the experimenter pick up food with a pair of pliers. *(From G. Rizzolatti et al. (2000).* Cognitive Brain Research, 3, *p. 131–141. Adapted with permission from Elsevier Science.)*

another animal perform the same action. Consider what is happening when a mirror neuron fires in response to seeing someone else perform an action. This firing not only indicates what the other person (or monkey) is doing but provides information about the characteristics of the action because the neuron's response to watching an action is the same as the neuron's response to actually performing the action. This means that one function of the mirror neurons might therefore be to help understand another person's (or monkey's) actions and react appropriately to them (Rizzolatti & Arbib, 1998; Rizzolatti et al., 2000).

Another function of mirror neurons may be to help imitate the observed action. The idea that there are neurons involved in imitation may even have something to do with an incident involving the golfer Tiger Woods, when he was an infant. The incident, as related by Woods's father, Earl Woods, can be traced to his practice of placing Tiger in a high chair to watch him practice his golf swing by hitting balls into a net in his garage. One day, Tiger, who was still young enough to be an unsteady walker, climbed down from his high chair, picked up a club, and executed a golf swing that was a passable imitation of his father's swing. It was at that point that Earl realized that his son might have a very strong aptitude for golf (Owen, 2000).

Of course, we have no way of knowing what was happening in baby Tiger's brain as he watched his father swing at all of those golf balls. But we can speculate that perhaps he was experiencing his father's swing through the activity of his own mirror neurons, and that this experience enabled him to fashion a good imitation of the swing—even though he may never have practiced it. This is not that unlikely a guess, especially because fMRI measurements of brain activity in humans as they imitate another person's actions show that there may be mirror neurons in the human brain (Fadiga et al., 1995; Hari et al., 1998; Iacobini et al., 1999).

In addition to mirror neurons for vision, the premotor area also contains **audiovisual mirror neurons** that respond to actions that produce sounds. These neurons respond when a monkey performs a hand-action *and* also when it hears the sound associated with this action (Kohler et al., 2002). For example, the results in Figure 10.21 show the response of a neuron that fires (a) when the monkey sees and hears the experimenter break a peanut, (b) when the monkey just sees the experimenter break the peanut, (c) when the monkey just hears the sound of the breaking peanut, and (d) when the *monkey* breaks the peanut.

What's important about these neurons is that many of them are *selective*—they respond only to specific actions and the sounds associated with these actions. For example, a neuron that responds to a peanut breaking responds weakly, or not at all, to sounds of paper being ripped or a stick dropping. What this means is that just *hearing* a peanut breaking or just *seeing* a peanut being broken causes activity that is also associated with the perceiver's *action* of breaking a peanut. Thus, mirror neurons may be involved not only in understanding what is going on in the environment, but also with helping link sensory perceptions and motor actions in a way that helps us act within and on our environment.

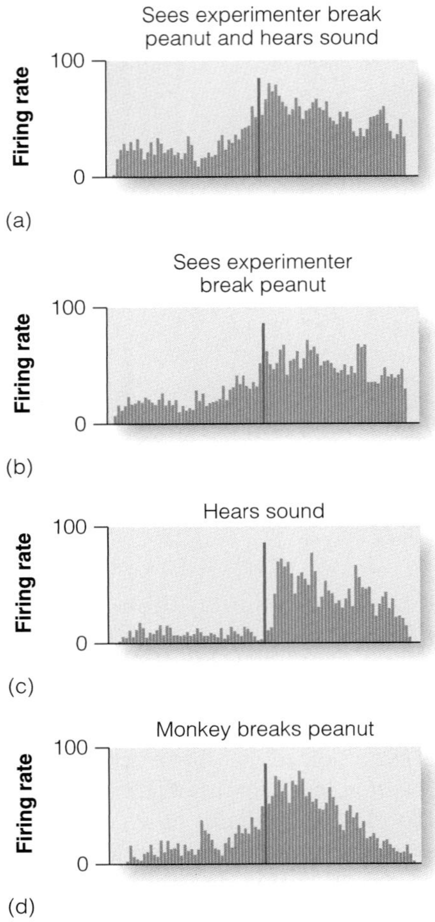

Figure 10.21 ▮ Response of an audiovisual mirror neuron to four different stimuli.
(From E. Kohler et al. (2002). Hearing sounds, understanding actions: Action representation in mirror neurons. Science, 297, *846–848.)*

SOMETHING TO CONSIDER: ARE WE WATCHING THE SAME MOVIE?

Now that we have reached the end of the section of the book dedicated mainly to vision, let's consider the following two questions, which are relevant both to this chapter and to material we have covered in previous chapters: (1) To what extent do different people's brains operate similarly when they view the same environmental stimuli? and (2) Are specialized brain areas activated when stimuli appear in naturalistic scenes?

Uri Hasson and coworkers (2004) explored these questions by showing observers a 30-minute excerpt from the Clint Eastwood film *The Good, the Bad, and the Ugly,* while measuring their brain activation using fMRI (Pessoa, 2004) . Because the observers' only task was to report the plot at the end of the experiment, they freely viewed the movie much as they would if they were watching it in a theater or at home. Hasson reasoned that the images and plot of a film created a situation that was much more ecologically valid than the single stimuli used in most other experiments.

By comparing the activation patterns of the different observers' brains, Hasson found that roughly 30 percent of the activation in one person's brain could be predicted by the signals from another person's brain (Figure 10.22). Hasson concluded from this match between people's brain activity that individual brains "tick collectively" during natural vision.

The correlation of brain activity that Hasson observed is remarkable for a few reasons. First, it is difficult to exactly align equivalent areas in people's brains due to normal variations in the location of brain areas in different people. Second, different people can experience the same movie in different ways. Of course, a 30-percent correlation leaves ample room for individuality, so although your brain may be "ticking" in synchrony with the brain of the person who is sitting next to you in the movie theater, your brain is also doing its own thing, based on your unique individual responses to the film.

Hasson also found that brain areas associated with faces (the FFA) and places (the PPA) were more highly activated when these stimuli appeared on the screen (Figure 10.23). Thus, faces activated the FFA and buildings and places activated the PPA, even while observers freely viewed a film in which these stimuli appeared in the course of telling a story. This kind of experiment, and the many others that have used naturalistic stimuli such as pictures of scenes, show that we have come a long way from the early days of visual neurophysiology in which the connection between brain activity and perception was explored with stimuli such as small spots and oriented lines.

Figure 10.22 ▮ Hasson et al. (2004) observed a correlation between the brain responses of people watching the same movie. The records shown here are not actual brain recordings but are presented to illustrate the correspondence between brain signals in different observers as they viewed the film.
(Based on Hasson, U., Nir, Y., Levy, I., Fuhrmann, G., & Malach, R. (2004). Intersubject synchronization of cortical activity during natural vision. Science, 303, *1634–1640.)*

TEST YOURSELF 10.2

1. What is the evidence that skilled gymnasts take perceptual information into account as they perform?
2. Describe the LOT strategy that has been proposed to explain how an outfielder catches a fly ball. Also, describe the evidence for this theory from experiments on both humans and dogs.
3. Why is it accurate to say that the parietal cortex is an area in which interactions between perception and action occur? Describe (a) the experiment on patients with optic ataxia, and (b) neurons in the parietal cortex that respond to both perception and action.
4. What are mirror neurons, and what is their possible functional significance? Describe both visual and audiovisual mirror neurons.
5. How did the experiment in which observers watched a Clint Eastwood film show that (a) brain activity is partially synchronized for different observers, and (b) specialized neurons respond when their preferred stimuli are presented in naturalistic contexts?

THINK ABOUT IT

1. We have seen that gymnasts appear to take visual information into account as they are in the act of executing a somersault. In the sport of synchronized diving, two people execute a dive simultaneously from two side-by-side diving boards. They are judged

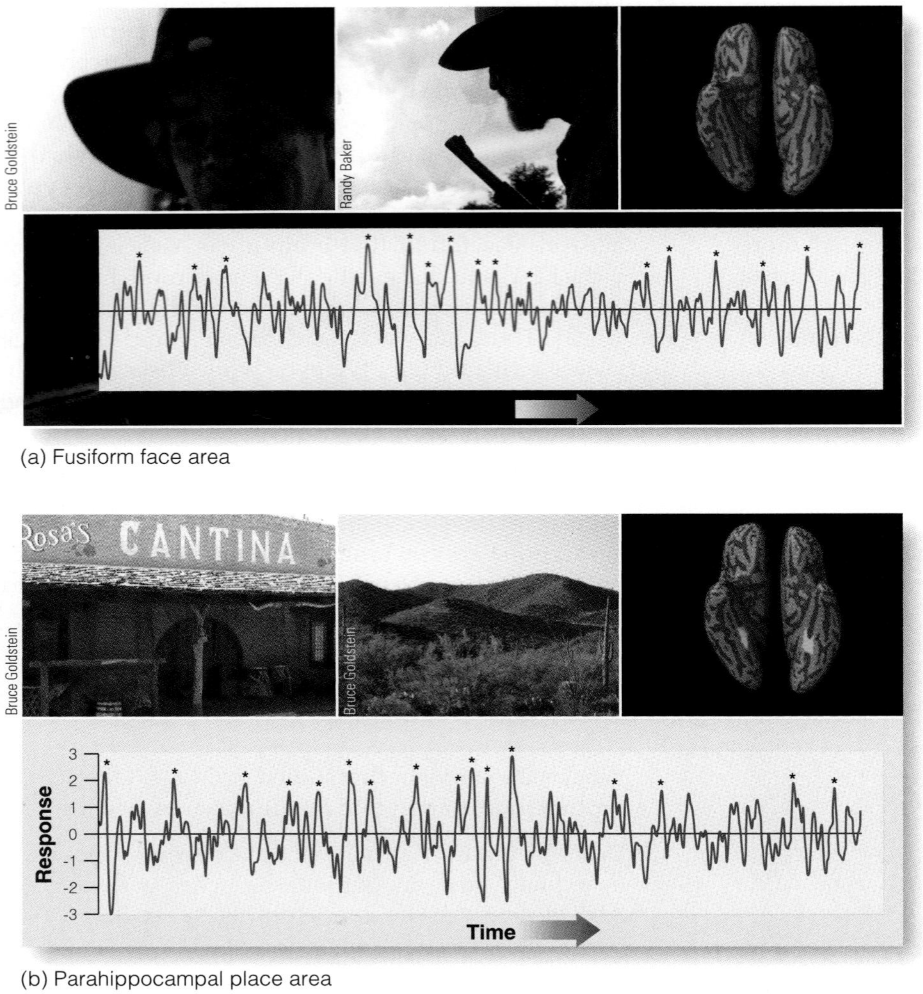

Figure 10.23 ▮ Averaged responses recorded during viewing of the movie *The Good, the Bad, and the Ugly* to screen images similar to those shown above each record. The top record is from the fusiform face area (shown in red on the brain). Peaks marked with asterisks (*) coincided with the presence of faces on the screen. The bottom record is from the parahippocampal place area (shown in green on the brain). Marked peaks coincided with the presence of outdoor scenes, indoor scenes, or buildings.
(Hasson, et al., 2004.)

based on how well they execute the dive and how well the two divers are synchronized with each other. What environmental stimuli do you think synchronized divers need to take into account in order to be successful?

2. Can you identify specific environmental information that you use to help you carry out actions in the environment? This question is often particularly relevant to athletes.

3. It is a common observation that people tend to slow down as they are driving through long tunnels. Explain the possible role of optic flow in this situation.

IF YOU WANT TO KNOW MORE

1. ***Ecological Psychology.*** Ecological psychologists have studied many behaviors that occur in the natural environment. Here are a few papers that are associated with the ecological approach. Also, looking at recent issues of the journal *Ecological Psychology* will give you a feel for modern research by psychologists who identify themselves with the ecological approach.

Lee, D. N., & Reddish, P. E. (1976). Plummeting gannets: A paradigm of ecological optics. *Nature, 293,* 293–294.

Rind, F. C., & Simmons, P. J. (1999). Seeing what is coming: Building collision-sensitive neurons. *Trends in Neurosciences, 22,* 215–220.

Schiff, W., & Detwiler, M. L. (1979). Information used in judging impending collision. *Perception, 8,* 647–658.

Shaw, R. E. (2003). The agent-environment interface: Simon's indirect or Gibson's direct coupling? *Ecological Psychology, 15,* 37–106.

Turvey, M. T. (2004). Space (and its perception): The first and final frontier. *Ecological Psychology, 16,* 25–29.

2. ***Gibson's Books.*** J. J. Gibson described his approach in three books that explain his philosophy and approach in detail.

Gibson, J. J. (1950). *The perception of the visual world.* Boston: Houghton Mifflin.

Gibson, J. J. (1966). *The senses considered as perceptual systems.* Boston: Houghton Mifflin.

Gibson, J. J. (1979). *The ecological approach to visual perception.* Boston: Houghton Mifflin.

3. ***Motor Area of Brain Activated When Sounds Are Associated With Actions.*** Research has shown that the motor area of the cortex is activated when trained pianists hear music. This does not occur in nonpianists, presumably because the link between finger movements and sound is not present in these people.

Haueisen, J., & Knosche, T. R. (2001). Involuntary motor activity in pianists evoked by music perception. *Journal of Cognitive Neuroscience, 136,* 786–792.

KEY TERMS

Affordance (p. 219)
Audiovisual mirror neuron (p. 227)
Ecological approach to perception (p. 216)
Focus of expansion (FOE) (p. 217)
Gradient of flow (p. 217)
Invariant information (p. 217)
Linear optical trajectory (LOT) strategy (p. 225)
Mirror neuron (p. 227)
Motor-dominant neuron (p. 226)
Optic ataxia (p. 226)
Optic flow (p. 217)
Parietal reach region (p. 227)
Self-produced information (p. 217)
Texture gradient (p. 218)
Visual direction strategy (p. 219)
Visual-dominant neuron (p. 226)

VISIT YOUR COMPANION WEBSITE FOR THIS BOOK

http://psychology.wadsworth.com/goldstein7e

Check out this companion website where you'll find online resources—glossary, flashcards, web links, multiple-choice and essay questions, and much more!

VIRTUAL LAB

Your Virtual Lab is designed to help you get the most out of this course. The Virtual Lab icons direct you to specific media demonstrations and experiments designed to help you visualize what you are reading about. The number beside each icon indicates the number of the media element you can access through your CD-ROM, Perception PsychologyNow, or WebTutor resource at http:now.ilrn.com/goldstein_7e.

The following are the lab exercises covering what you've just learned in this chapter:

1 *Flow From Walking Down a Hallway* A computer-generated program showing the optic flow that occurs when moving through a patterned hallway.

2 *Stimuli Used in Warren Experiment* Moving stimulus pattern seen by observers in William Warren's experiment.

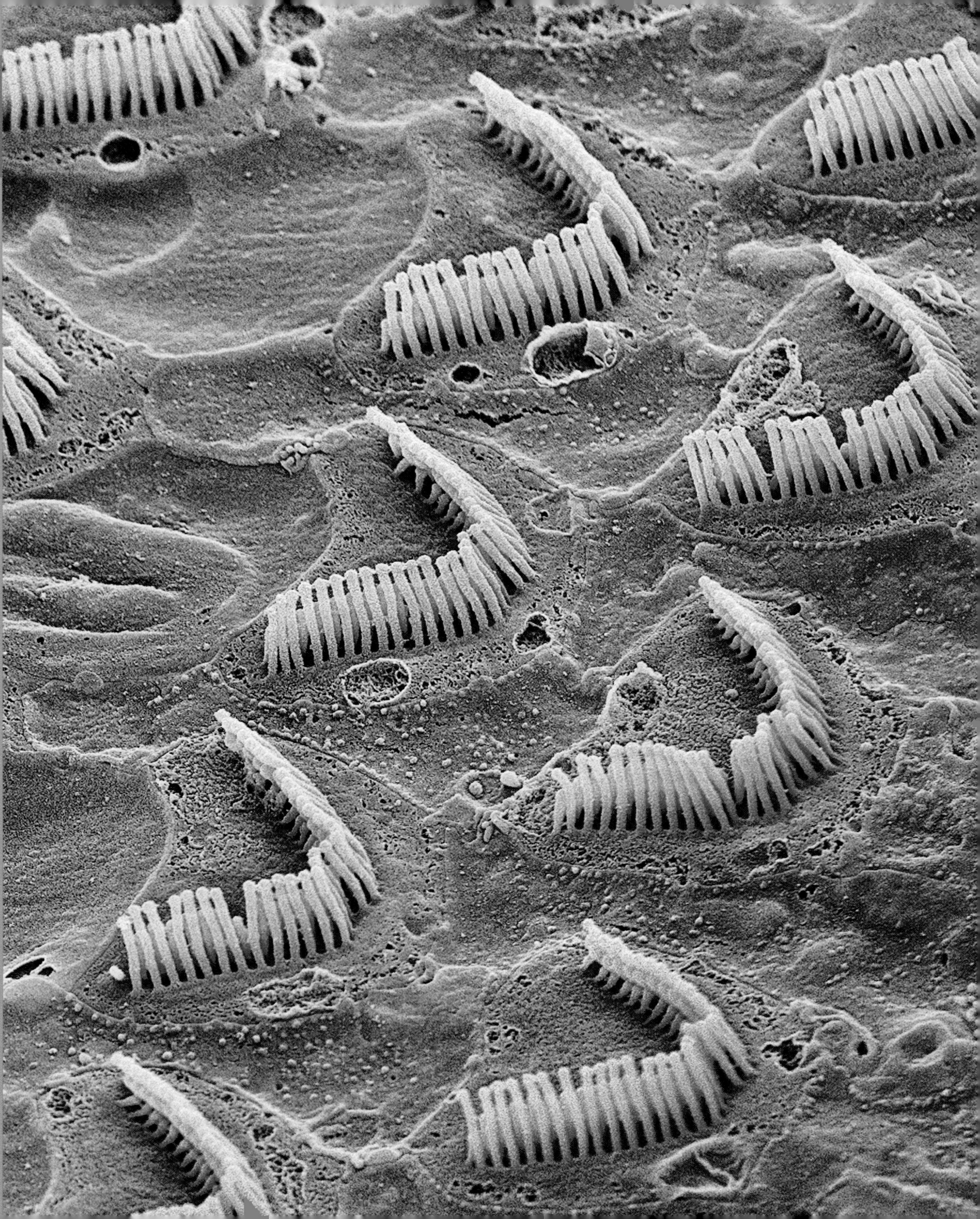

SOUND, THE AUDITORY SYSTEM, AND PITCH PERCEPTION

CHAPTER 11

Chapter Contents

A scanning electron micrograph of hair cell receptors in the cochlea of the inner ear. Color has been added to differentiate the receptors from surrounding structures. © SPL/Photo Researchers, Inc.

VL *The Virtual Lab icons direct you to specific animations and videos designed to help you visualize what you are reading about. The number beside each icon indicates the number of the clip you can access through your CD-ROM or your student website.*

Some Questions We Will Consider:

- *If a tree falls in the forest and no one is there to hear it, is there a sound? (p. 235)*
- *What is it that makes sounds high pitched or low pitched? (p. 235)*
- *How do sound vibrations inside the ear lead to the perception of different pitches? (p. 245)*
- *How are sounds represented in the auditory cortex? (p. 254)*

> Hearing has an extremely important function in my life. I was born legally blind, so although I can see, my vision is highly impaired and is not correctable. Even though I am not usually shy or embarrassed, sometimes I do not want to call attention to myself and my disability. . . . There are many methods that I can use to improve my sight in class, like sitting close to the board or copying from a friend, but sometimes these things are impossible. Then I use my hearing to take notes. . . . My hearing is very strong. While I do not need my hearing to identify people who are very close to me, it is definitely necessary when someone is calling my name from a distance. I can recognize their voice, even if I cannot see them.

This statement, written by one of my students, Jill Robbins, illustrates a special effect hearing has had on her life. The next statement, by student Eileen Lusk, illustrates her reaction to temporarily losing her ability to hear.

> In an experiment I did for my sign language class, I bandaged up my ears so I couldn't hear a sound. I had a signing interpreter with me to translate spoken language. The two hours that I was "deaf" gave me a great appreciation for deaf people and their culture. I found it extremely difficult to communicate, because even though I could read the signing, I couldn't keep up with the pace of the conversation. . . . Also, it was uncomfortable for me to be in that much silence. Knowing what a crowded cafeteria sounds like and not being able to hear the background noise was an uncomfortable feeling. I couldn't hear the buzzing of the fluorescent light, the murmur of the crowd, or the slurping of my friend's Coke (which I usually object to, but which I missed when I couldn't hear it). I saw a man drop his tray, and I heard nothing. I could handle the signing, but not the silence.

You don't have to bandage up your ears for 2 hours to appreciate what hearing adds to your life. Just close your eyes for a few minutes, observe the sounds you hear, and notice what they tell you about your environment. What most people experience is that by listening closely they become aware of many events in the environment that without hearing they would not be aware of at all.

For example, as I sit here in my office in the psychology department, I hear the *whooshing* sound of the air conditioning system, and other things as well that I would be unaware of if I had to rely only on my sense of vision: people talking in the hall; a car passing by on the street below; and an ambulance, siren blaring, making its way up the hill toward the hospital. If it weren't for hearing, my world at this particular moment would be limited to what I can see in my office and the scene directly outside my window. Although the silence might make it easier to concentrate on writing this book or studying my lecture notes, without hearing I would be unaware of many of the events in my environment.

Our ability to hear events that we can't see serves an important signaling function for both animals and humans. For an animal living in the forest, the rustle of leaves or the snap of a twig may signal the approach of a predator. For humans living in the city, hearing provides signals such as the warning sound of a smoke alarm or an ambulance siren, the distinctive high-pitched cry of a baby who is distressed, or telltale noises that signal problems in a car engine.

But hearing has other functions, too. On the first day of my perception class, I ask my students which sense they would choose to keep if they had to pick between hearing and vision. Two of the strongest arguments for keeping hearing instead of vision are music and speech. Many of my students wouldn't want to give up hearing because of the pleasure they derive from listening to music, and they also realize that speech is important because it facilitates communication between people.

Helen Keller, who was both deaf and blind, stated that she felt being deaf was worse than being blind because blindness isolated her from things, but deafness isolated her from people. Being unable to hear people talking creates an isolation that makes it difficult to relate to hearing people and sometimes makes it difficult even to know what is going on. To appreciate this last point, try watching a dramatic program on television with the sound turned off. You may be surprised at how little, beyond physical actions and perhaps some intense emotions, you can understand about the story.

Our goal in this chapter is to describe the basic mechanisms responsible for our ability to hear. We will begin by describing the nature of sound and how we experience both laboratory-produced sounds and naturally occurring sounds in the environment. We then consider the physiology behind our perception of pitch, starting with how structures in the ear respond to sound and then how different parts of the brain respond to sound.

As you read this chapter, you will see that there are important differences between vision and hearing, especially when we consider the complex path that the sound stimulus must negotiate in order to reach the receptors. You will also see that there are similarities, especially in the cortex, where there is evidence that there are *what* and *where* streams in the auditory system that are similar to the *what* and *where* streams we have described for vision.

PRESSURE WAVES AND PERCEPTUAL EXPERIENCE

The first step in understanding hearing is to define what we mean by *sound* and to show how we measure the characteristics of sound. One way to answer the question, "what is sound" is to consider the following question: *If a tree falls in the forest and no one is there to hear it, would there be a sound?*

This question is useful because it shows that we can use the word **sound** in two different ways. Sometimes *sound* refers to a physical stimulus, and sometimes it refers to a perceptual response. The answer to the question about the tree depends on which of the following definitions of sound we use.

- *Physical definition:* Sound is *pressure changes* in the air or other medium.

Answer to the question: "Yes," because the falling tree causes pressure changes whether or not someone is there to hear them.

- *Perceptual definition:* Sound is the *experience* we have when we hear.

Answer to the question: "No," because if no one is in the forest, there would be no experience.

This difference between physical and perceptual is important to be aware of as we discuss hearing in this chapter and the next two. Luckily, it is usually easy to tell from the context in which the terms are used whether "sound" refers to the physical stimulus or to the experience of hearing. For example "the sound of the trumpet pierced the air" refers to the experience of sound, but "the sound's level was 10 decibels" refers to sound as a physical stimulus. We will first describe sound as a physical stimulus and will then describe sound as a perceptual experience.

The Sound Stimulus Produced by a Loudspeaker

A sound stimulus occurs when the movements or vibrations of an object cause pressure changes in air, water, or any other elastic medium that surrounds the object. Let's begin by considering your radio or stereo system's loudspeaker, which is really a device for producing vibrations to be transmitted to the surrounding air. People have been known to turn up the volume control on their stereos high enough so vibrations can be felt through a neighbor's wall, but even at lower levels the vibrations are there.

The speaker's vibrations affect the surrounding air, as shown in Figure 11.1. When the diaphragm of the speaker moves out, it pushes the surrounding air molecules together, increasing the density of molecules near the diaphragm. This increased density increases the air pressure. When the speaker diaphragm moves back in, it decreases the density of molecules near the diaphragm, decreasing the air pressure. By repeating this process many hundreds or thousands of times a second, the speaker creates a pattern of alternating high- and low-pressure regions in the air as neighboring air molecules affect each other. This pattern of air pressure changes, which travels through air at 340 meters per second (and through water at 1,500 meters per second), is called a **sound wave.**

You might get the impression from Figure 11.1a that this traveling sound wave causes air to move outward from the speaker into the environment. What is actually happening is analogous to the ripples created by a pebble dropped into a still pool of water (Figure 11.1b). As the ripples move outward from the pebble, the water at a particular place moves up and down. This becomes obvious when you realize that the ripples would cause a toy boat

(a) (b)

Figure 11.1 ▮ (a) The effect of a vibrating speaker diaphragm on the surrounding air. Dark areas represent regions of high air pressure, and light areas represent areas of low air pressure. (b) When a pebble is dropped into still water, the resulting ripples appear to move outward. However, the water is actually moving up and down, as indicated by movement of the boat. A similar situation exists for the sound waves produced by the speaker in (a).

to bob up and down—not to move outward. Similarly, although *air pressure changes* move outward from the speaker, the *air* at each location remains in approximately the same place.

So far we have been describing pressure changes in the air but have mentioned nothing about hearing. Returning to our example of the tree falling in the forest, we have been describing sound as a physical stimulus. But the question that is important for perception is: What is the *perceptual experience* that is associated with these pressure changes?

Sound waves are invisible to our eyes, but they can sometimes be felt as tactile perceptions through the skin. Perhaps you have felt the pulsations of bass notes at a loud concert, especially if you happened to be sitting near the speakers. Or you may have felt pulsations as a car drives by with its stereo turned way up. These tactile perceptions of sound wave are usually limited to very intense bass notes.

Hearing is the predominant experience caused by sound waves. The specific perceptual experiences caused by sound waves are determined by the nature of the pressure changes. We will now consider how two characteristics these pressure changes—amplitude and frequency—are related to the experience of hearing.

We introduce amplitude and frequency by focusing on a simple kind of sound wave, called a **pure tone**, in which pressure changes occur in a pattern described by a mathematical function called a sine wave, as shown in Figure 11.2. Tones with this pattern of pressure changes are occasionally found in the environment. A person whistling or the high-pitched notes produced by a flute are close to pure tones. Tuning forks, which are designed to vibrate with a sine-wave motion, also produce pure tones, and pure tones for laboratory studies of hearing are generated by computers, which can cause a speaker diaphragm to vibrate in and out with a sine-wave motion. This vibration can be described by noting its **amplitude**—the size of the pressure change and its **frequency**—the number of times per second that the pressure changes repeat. We will first consider the physical characteristic of amplitude, and the experience associated with it—loudness.

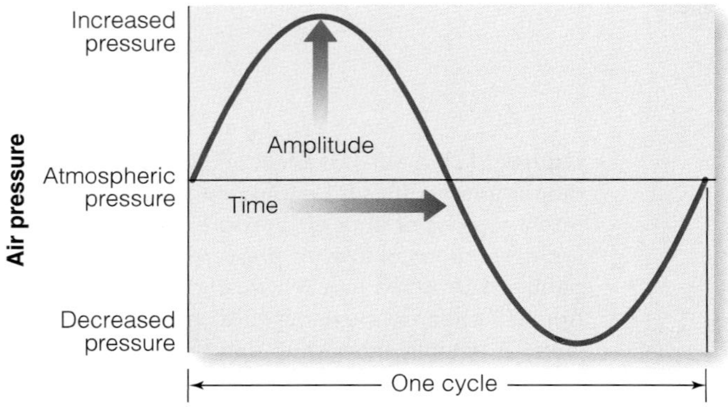

Figure 11.2 ▮ Sine-wave pressure changes for a pure tone.

Amplitude and Loudness

One way to specify a sound's amplitude would be to indicate the difference in pressure between the high and low peaks of the sound wave. Figure 11.3 shows three pure tones with different amplitudes. Larger amplitudes are associated with an increase in the *perceptual* experience of **loudness**—the magnitude of auditory sensation (Plack & Carlyon, 1995). Table 11.1 lists some environmental sounds, ranging from ones that aren't very loud, such as a barely audible whisper or leaves rustling, to those

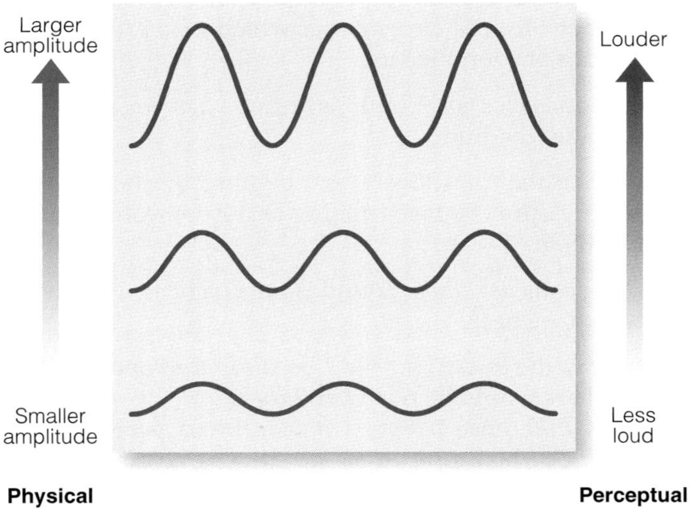

Figure 11.3 ▮ Increases of the physical property of *amplitude* from small to large (blue arrow) are associated with increases in the perceptual experience of *loudness* (red arrow).

Table 11.1 ▮ *Relative amplitudes and decibels for environmental sounds*

Sound	Relative amplitude	Decibels (dB)
Barely audible (threshold)	1	0
Leaves rustling	10	20
Quiet residential community	100	40
Average speaking voice	1,000	60
Express subway train	100,000	100
Propeller plane at takeoff	1,000,000	120
Jet engine at takeoff (pain threshold)	10,000,000	140
Spacecraft launch at close range	100,000,000	160

that are extremely loud, such as a jet engine at takeoff. The amplitudes listed in the second column indicate that (1) increases in amplitude are associated with increases in loudness, and (2) the sound waves created by events in the environment have an extremely large range of amplitudes.

To compress this large range into a more manageable scale, auditory researchers use a unit of sound called the **decibel**, which is named after Alexander Graham Bell, the inventor of the telephone. The following equation is used to convert sound pressure into decibels:

$$\text{Number of dB} = 20\ \text{logarithm}(p/p_o)$$

where dB stands for decibels, *p* is the sound pressure of the stimulus, and p_o is a standard sound pressure, which is usually set at 20 micropascals, where a pascal is a unit of pressure and a micropascal is one millionth of a pascal. We can use the equation above to calculate the decibels for this tone as follows:

If pressure = 20 micropascals (mp),

$$\text{dB} = 20\log(20/20) = 20(\log 1.0)$$
$$= 20(0)\ (\text{the log of } 1.0 = 0) = 0\ \text{db SPL}$$

Adding the notation for **sound pressure level, SPL,** indicates that we have used the standard pressure of 20 micropascals as p_o in our calculation. In referring to the decibels or sound pressure of a sound stimulus, the term **level** or **sound level** is usually used.

Let's now continue our calculation of dB for two higher pressure levels:

If pressure = 200 mp: $20\log(200/20) = 20(\log 10)$
$= 20(1) = 20$ db SPL

If pressure = 2,000 mp: $20\log(2000/20)$
$= 20(\log 100) = 20(2) = 40$ db SPL

Notice that *multiplying* sound pressure by 10 *adds* 20 dB. As you can see from the right-hand column in Table 11.1, continuing this process all the way up to a sound pressure of 100 million increases the decibels to only 160. The dB scale is useful because it compresses the large range of sound pressures into a more manageable range. In addition, decibels, which are a *physical* measure, are related to the *psychological experience* of loudness. This relationship is illustrated in Figure 11.4, which shows the relationship between decibels and loudness for a pure tone, determined by S. S. Stevens's magnitude estimation procedure (see Chapter 1, page 15). In this experiment, loudness was judged relative to a standard of a 1,000-Hz tone at 40 dB, which was assigned a value of 1. Thus, a tone that sounds 10 times louder than this standard would be judged to have a loudness of 10. This curve indicates that increasing the sound level by 10 dB almost (but not quite) doubles the sound's loudness. **VIRTUAL LAB 1,2**

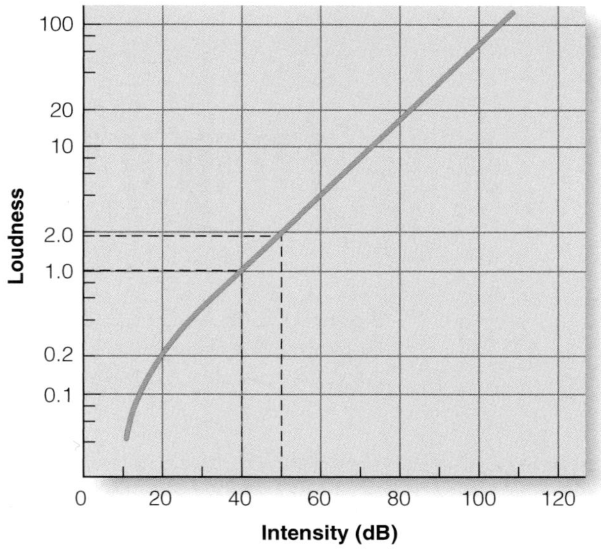

Figure 11.4 ▌ Loudness of a 100-Hz tone as a function of intensity, determined using magnitude estimation. The dashed lines show that increasing intensity from 40 to 50 dB causes approximately a doubling of loudness.
(Adapted from Gulick, Gescheider, & Frisina, 1989.)

Frequency and Pitch

Frequency, the other characteristic of a pure tone, is illustrated in Figure 11.5, which shows three different frequencies. Frequency is indicated in units called **Hertz (Hz)**, in which 1 Hertz is 1 cycle per second. Frequency is linked to the experience of **pitch**—the psychological quality of a tone that we describe as "high" or "low." Low

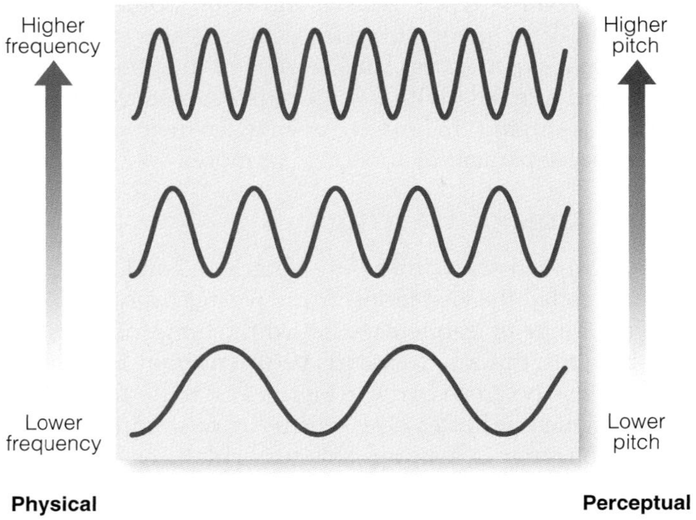

Figure 11.5 ▌ Increases of the physical property of *frequency* from low to high (blue arrow) are associated with increases in the perceptual experience of *pitch* (red arrow).

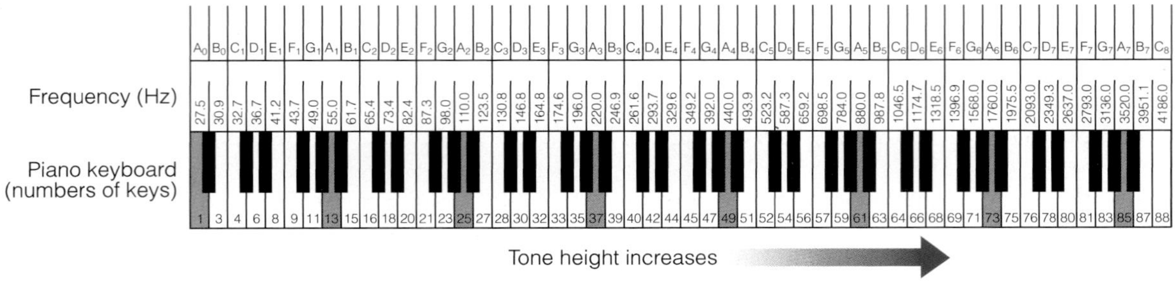

Figure 11.6 ▌ A piano keyboard, indicating the frequency associated with each key. Notes with the same letter, like the A's (in orange) are separated by octaves and have the same tone chroma. Moving up the keyboard increases frequency and tone height.

frequencies cause the experience of low pitches, and high frequencies cause high pitches. **Tone height** is the perceptual experience of increasing pitch that accompanies increases in a tone's frequency. Thus, if we start at the left, or bass, end of a piano keyboard, the lowest note has a frequency of 27.5 Hz. As we move up the keyboard, tone height increases and we eventually reach the highest note, at the far right end of the keyboard, which has a frequency of 4,186 Hz (Figure 11.6).

In addition to the increase in tone height that occurs as we move from the bass to the treble end of the piano keyboard, something else happens: The letters of the notes A, B, C, D, E, F, and G repeat, and we notice that notes with the same letter sound similar. Because of this similarity, we say that notes with the same letter have the same **tone chroma**. Every time we pass the same letter on the keyboard, we have gone up an interval called an **octave**. Tones separated by octaves have the same tone chroma. Interestingly, notes with the same chroma have frequencies that are multiples of one another. Thus, A_1, the lowest note on the piano, has a frequency of 27.5 Hz; A_2's frequency is 55 Hz; A_3's is 110 Hz, and so on. Somehow this doubling of frequency for each octave results in similar perceptual experiences. Thus, a male with a low-pitched voice and a female with a high-pitched voice can be regarded as singing "in unison," even when their voices are separated by an octave or more. VL 3

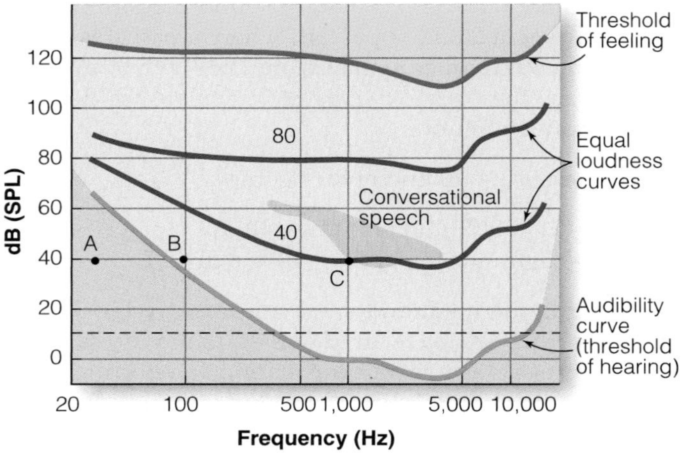

Figure 11.7 ▌ The audibility curve and the auditory response area. Hearing occurs in the light green area between the audibility curve (the threshold for hearing) and the upper curve (the threshold for feeling). Tones with combinations of dB and frequency that place them in the light red area below the audibility curve cannot be heard. Tones above the threshold of feeling (yellow area) result in pain. The places where the dashed line at 10 dB crosses the audibility function indicate which frequencies can be heard at 10 dB SPL.

(From "Loudness: Its Definition, Measurement, and Calculation," by H. Fletcher and W. A. Munson, 1933, Journal of the Acoustical Society of America*, 5, 82–108, figure 4. Copyright © 1993 by the American Institute of Physics. Reprinted by permission.)*

The Range of Hearing

Just as we can see within only a narrow band of wavelengths called the visible spectrum, we hear only within a specific range of frequencies, called the range of hearing. For humans, this range extends between about 20 Hz and 20,000 Hz. The green curve in Figure 11.7 is the **audibility curve**, which indicates how sensitivity to sound changes across the range of hearing. This curve plots the threshold for hearing determined by free-field presentation (listening to a loudspeaker) versus frequency. From this curve, we can see that we are most sensitive (the threshold for hearing is lowest) at frequencies between 2,000 and 4,000 Hz, the range of frequencies that is most important for understanding speech. VL 4

Although the useful range of human hearing extends between about 20 and 20,000 Hz, other animals have different "windows" on the auditory world. Below the low end of the human's hearing range, elephants can hear stimuli below 20 Hz. Above the high end of the human range, dogs can hear frequencies above 40,000 Hz, cats can hear above 50,000 Hz, and the upper range for dolphins extends as high as 150,000 Hz.

The light green area above the audibility curve is called the **auditory response area** because we can hear tones that fall within this area. At intensities below the audibility curve (light red), we can't hear a tone. For example, we wouldn't be able to hear a 30-Hz tone at 40 dB SPL (point A). The upper boundary of the auditory response area is the curve marked "threshold for feeling." Tones with these high amplitudes are the ones we can "feel" and also can become painful and can cause damage to the auditory system. In fact, damage can occur at levels below the threshold for feeling if the duration of the exposure is long enough. That is why OSHA, which sets government standards for occupational safety, mandates that workers should not be exposed to levels greater than 90 dB for an 8-hour workday.

The audibility curve and auditory response area indicate that the loudness of pure tones depends not only on sound pressure but also on frequency. We can appreciate how loudness depends on frequency by comparing the loudness of two tones that have the same level but different frequencies. For example, point B in Figure 11.7 indicates where a 40-dB SPL 100-Hz tone is located in the response area, and point C indicates where a 40-dB SPL 1000-Hz tone is located. The locations of these two points indicate that these two tones would have very different loudnesses. Because the 100-Hz tone is located just above the audibility curve, it is just above threshold, so it would be just barely heard. However, the 1,000-Hz tone is far above threshold, well into the auditory response area, so it would be much louder than the 100-Hz tone. Thus, saying that a pure tone has a level of 40-dB SPL tells us nothing about its loudness unless we know its frequency.

Another way to understand the relationship between loudness and frequency is by looking at the **equal loudness curves** in Figure 11.7. These curves indicate the number of decibels that create the same perception of loudness at different frequencies. We measure an equal loudness curve by designating one tone as a standard and matching the loudness of all other tones to it. For example, the curve marked 40 in Figure 11.7 was determined by matching the loudness of frequencies across the range of hearing to a 1,000-Hz 40-dB SPL tone. Similarly, the curve marked 80 was determined by matching the loudness of different frequencies to a 1,000-Hz 80-dB SPL tone.

Notice that the audibility curve and the equal loudness curve marked 40 bend up at high and low frequencies, but the equal loudness curve marked 80 is flatter, curving up only at frequencies above about 5,000 Hz. This means that at 80-dB SPL, all tones from 30 to 5,000 Hz have about the same loudness. The difference between the relatively flat 80 curve and the upward-bending curves at lower decibel levels explains something that happens as you adjust the volume control on your stereo system. If you are playing music at a fairly high level—say, 80-dB SPL—you should be able to easily hear each of the frequencies in the music because, as the equal loudness curve for 80 indicates, all frequencies between about 20 Hz and 5,000 Hz sound equally loud at this intensity.

However, when you turn the intensity down to 10-dB SPL, all frequencies don't sound equally loud. In fact, from the audibility curve in Figure 11.7 we can see that frequencies below about 400 Hz (the bass notes) and above about 12,000 Hz (the treble notes) are inaudible at 10 dB. (To determine the frequencies below and above which a 10-dB tone is inaudible, notice that the dashed 10-dB line crosses the audibility curve at about 400 Hz and 12,000 Hz. This means that frequencies lower than 400 Hz and higher than 12,000 Hz are not audible at 10 dB.)

Being unable to hear very low and very high frequencies creates a bad situation because it means that when you play music softly you won't hear the very low or very high frequencies. To compensate for this, some stereo receivers have a button labeled "loudness" that boosts the level of very high and very low frequencies, when the volume control is turned down. This enables you to hear these frequencies, even when you are playing your stereo very softly.

Sound Quality: Timbre

We have been focusing on two basic characteristics of our perceptual experience of sound—loudness and pitch. But two tones can have the same loudness and pitch and sound different. For example, when a flute and a bassoon play the same note with the same loudness, we can still tell the difference between these two instruments. We might describe the sound of the flute as *clear* or *mellow* and the sound of the bassoon as *nasal* or *reedy*. When two tones have the same loudness, pitch and duration, but sound different, this difference is a difference in **timbre** (pronounced tim'-ber or tam'-bre).

To understand how timbre is related to the physical properties of sound, we need to broaden our perspective beyond pure tones. A pure tone, by definition, has a single frequency. We have seen that we can specify the frequency of a pure tone stimulus by indicating how many times per second the sine wave repeats itself. Our auditory experience is dominated, however, not by pure tones, but by more complex sounds created by musical instruments, people speaking, and the various sounds produced by nature and machines. These complex stimuli contain many frequencies, and it is those additional frequencies that help create different timbres.

We can understand how complex stimuli are made up of many frequencies by considering a technique called **additive synthesis**, which can be used to produce complex sounds by adding simple components. The starting point for creating a complex tone by additive synthesis is a single pure tone, like the one in Figure 11.8a, which is called the **fundamental frequency**, or first harmonic, of the complex tone. We will assume that the frequency of this fundamental is 440 Hz. We then add additional pure tones to the fundamental, each of which has a frequency that is a multiple of the fundamental. For the 440-Hz fundamental, the frequency of the second tone is 880 Hz (Figure 11.8b) and the frequency of the third tone is 1,320 Hz (Figure 11.8c). These additional tones are higher **harmonics** of the tone. The 800-Hz tone is the second harmonic and the 1,320-Hz tone is the third harmonic.

VL 5, 6

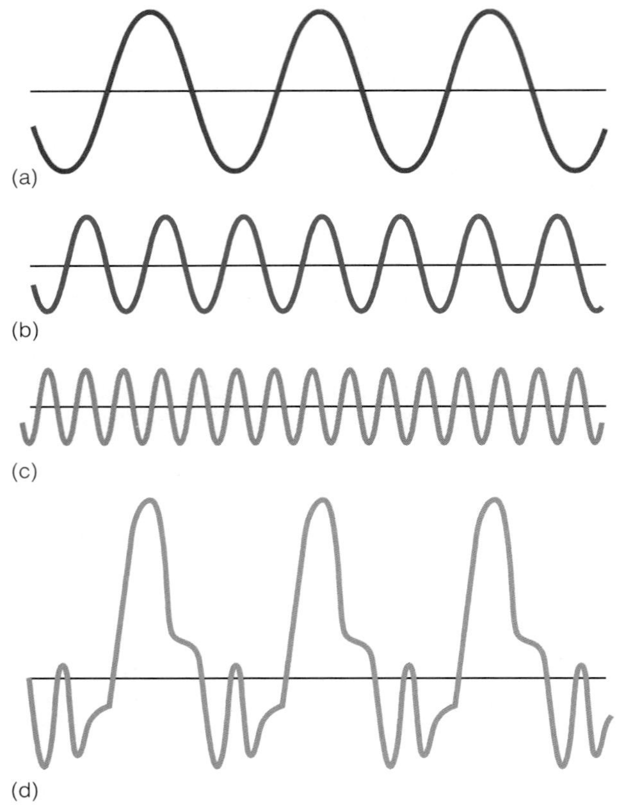

Figure 11.8 ▮ Additive synthesis. (a) Pressure changes for a pure tone with frequency = 440 Hz. (b) The second harmonic of this tone, with a frequency of 880 Hz. (c) The third harmonic, with a frequency of 1,320 Hz. (d) The sum of the three harmonics creates the waveform for a complex tone.

Adding these harmonics to the fundamental creates a sound that can resemble a musical instrument because the sounds produced by most musical instruments have many harmonics, with the amplitudes of the various harmonics giving each instrument its distinctive sound. The pattern of pressure changes for a complex musical tone consists of the sum of these components, as shown in Figure 11.8d. Most musical tones have many more harmonics than this one, so the pattern of pressure changes is even more complex than the one in Figure 11.8d.

A way to indicate the harmonic components of a complex wave that we have created by addititive synthesis is shown in Figure 11.9, which is called a **frequency spectrum**. The position of each line on the horizontal axis indicates the harmonic's frequency and the height of the line indicates the harmonic's amplitude. The three lines (a), (b), and (c) in Figure 11.9 correspond to the three harmonics (a), (b), and (c) in Figure 11.8.

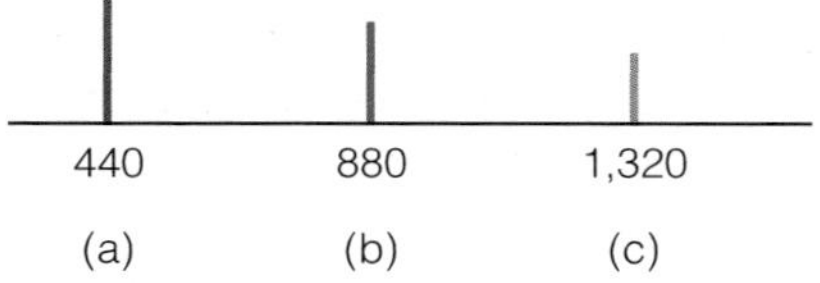

Figure 11.9 ▮ The frequency spectrum for the tone in Figure 11.8d. The heights of the lines indicate the amplitude of each of the frequencies that make up the tone.

Figure 11.10 uses frequency spectra to compare the harmonics of a guitar, a bassoon, and an alto saxophone playing the note G3 with a fundamental frequency of 196 Hz. Both the relative strengths of the harmonics and the number of harmonics are different in these instruments. For example, the guitar has more high-frequency harmonics than either the bassoon or the alto saxophone. Although the frequencies of the harmonics are always multiples of the fundamental frequency, harmonics may be absent, as is true of some of the high-frequency harmonics of the bassoon and the alto saxophone.

The difference in the harmonics of different instruments is one factor that causes musical instruments to have different timbres. Timbre also depends on the time course of the tone's **attack** (the buildup of sound at the beginning of the tone) and on the time course of the tone's

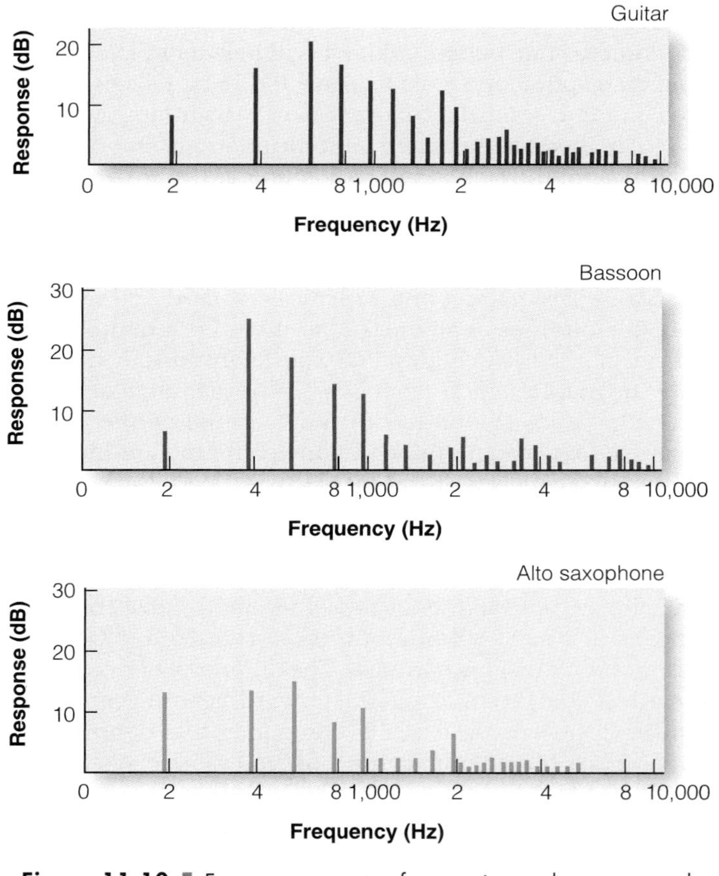

Figure 11.10 ▮ Frequency spectra for a guitar, a bassoon, and an alto saxophone playing a tone with a fundamental frequency of 196 Hz. The position of the lines on the horizontal axis indicates the frequencies of the harmonics and their height indicates their intensities.

(From Music, Physics, and Engineering, 2nd ed. by H. F. Olson, 1967. Copyright © 1967 by Dover Publications, Inc. Reprinted by permission.)

decay (the decrease in sound at the end of the tone). Thus, it is easy to tell the difference between a tape recording of a high note played on the clarinet and a recording of the same note played on the flute when the attack, the decay, and the sustained portion of the tone are heard. It is, however, difficult to distinguish between the same instruments when the tone's attack and decay are eliminated by erasing the first and last 1/2-second of the recording (Berger, 1964; also see Risset & Mathews, 1969).

Another way to make it difficult to distinguish one instrument from another is to play an instrument's tone backward. Even though this does not affect the tone's harmonic structure, a piano tone played backward sounds more like an organ than a piano because the tone's original decay has become the attack and the attack has become the decay (Berger, 1964; Erickson, 1975). Thus, timbre depends both on the tone's steady-state harmonic structure and on the time course of the attack and decay of the tone's harmonics. VL 7

The sounds we have been considering so far—pure tones and the tones produced by musical instruments—are all periodic sounds. That is, the pattern of pressure changes repeats, as in the tone in Figure 11.8d. There are also aperiodic sounds, which have sound waves that do not repeat. Examples of aperiodic sounds would be a cash register drawer slamming shut, people talking, and noises such as the static on a radio not tuned to a station. The sounds produced by these events are more complex than musical tones, but many of these sound stimuli can also be analyzed into a number of simpler frequency components. We will describe how we perceive speech stimuli in Chapter 13. We will focus on pure tones and musical tones in this chapter because these sounds are the ones that have been used in most of the basic research on the operation of the auditory system. In the next section we will begin considering how the sound stimuli we have been describing are processed by the auditory system so that we can experience sound.

TEST YOURSELF 11.1

1. What are some of the functions of sound? Especially note what information sound provides that is not provided by vision.
2. What are two possible definitions of sound? (Remember the tree falling in the forest.)
3. What are the physical characteristics of sound, amplitude, and frequency? Why was the decibel scale developed to measure amplitude? Is decibel "perceptual" or "physical"?
4. What is the relationship between amplitude and loudness? Which one is "physical" and which one is "perceptual"?
5. How is frequency related to pitch, tone height, and tone chroma? Which of these is physical, and which is perceptual?
6. What is the audibility curve, and what does it tell us about what tones we can experience and about the relationship between a tone's frequency and its loudness?
7. What is timbre? Describe the characteristics of complex tones and how these characteristics determine timbre.

THE EAR

The auditory system must accomplish three basic tasks before we can hear. First, it must deliver the sound stimulus to the receptors. Second, it must transduce this stimulus from pressure changes into electrical signals, and third, it must process these electrical signals so they can indicate qualities of the sound source such as pitch, loudness, timbre, and location.

We begin our description of how the auditory system accomplishes these tasks by focusing on the ear, at the beginning of the auditory system. Our first question, "How does energy from the environment reach the receptors?" takes us on a journey through what Diane Ackerman (1990) has described as a device that resembles "a contraption some ingenious plumber has put together from spare parts." An overall view of this "contraption" is shown in Figure 11.11. The ear is divided into three divisions: outer, middle, and inner. We begin with the outer ear.

The Outer Ear

When we talk about ears in everyday conversation, we are usually referring to the **pinnae**, the structures that stick out from the sides of the head. Although this most obvious part of the ear is of some importance in helping us determine the location of sounds and is of great importance for those who wear eyeglasses, it is the part of the ear we could most easily do without. The major workings of the ear are found within the head, hidden from view.

Sound waves first pass through the **outer ear**, which consists of the pinna and the **auditory canal** (Figure 11.11). The auditory canal is a tubelike structure about 3 cm long in adults that protects the delicate structures of the middle ear from the hazards of the outside world. The auditory canal's 3-cm recess, along with its wax, which has an unpleasant effect on curious insects (Schubert, 1980), protects the delicate **tympanic membrane**, or **eardrum**, at the end of the canal and helps keep this membrane and the structures in the middle ear at a relatively constant temperature.

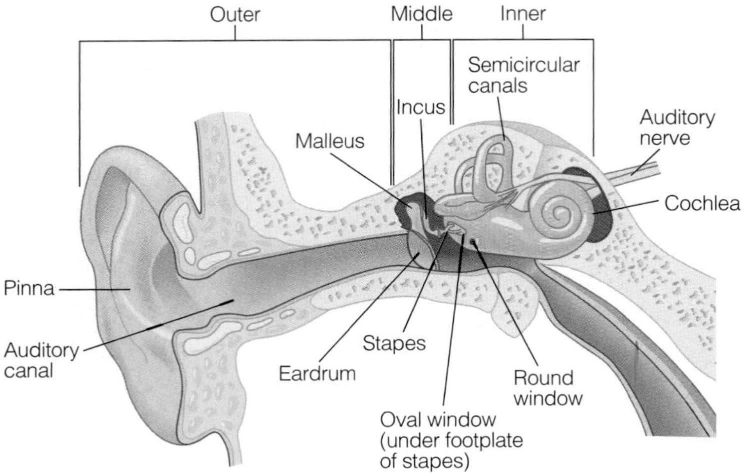

Figure 11.11 ▌ The ear, showing its three subdivisions—outer, middle, and inner.
(Redrawn by permission from Human Information Processing, *by P. H. Lindsay and D. A. Norman, 2nd ed. 1977, p. 229. Copyright © 1977 by Academic Press, Inc.)*

In addition to its protective function, the outer ear has another role: to enhance the intensities of some sounds by means of the physical principle of resonance. **Resonance** occurs when sound waves that are reflected back from the closed end of the auditory canal interact with sound waves that are entering the auditory canal. This interaction reinforces some of the sound's frequencies, with the frequency that is reinforced the most being determined by the length of the canal. The frequency reinforced the most is called the **resonant frequency** of the canal.

We can appreciate how the resonant frequency depends on the length of the canal by noting how the tone produced by blowing across the top of a soda bottle changes as we drink more soda. Drinking more soda increases the length of the air path inside the bottle, which decreases the resonant frequency, and this creates a lower-pitched tone. Measurements of the sound pressures inside the ear indicate that the resonance that occurs in the auditory canal has a slight amplifying effect on frequencies between about 2,000 and 5,000 Hz.

The Middle Ear

When airborne sound waves reach the tympanic membrane at the end of the auditory canal, they set it into vibration, and this vibration is transmitted to structures in the middle ear, on the other side of the tympanic membrane. The **middle ear** is a small cavity, about 2 cubic centimeters in volume, which separates the outer and inner ears (Figure 11.12). This cavity contains the **ossicles**, the three smallest bones in the body. The first of these bones, the **malleus** (also known as the *hammer*), is set into vibration by the tympanic membrane, to which it is attached, and transmits its vibrations to the **incus** (or *anvil*), which, in turn, transmits its vibrations to the **stapes** (or *stirrup*). The stapes then transmits its vibrations to the inner ear by pushing on the membrane covering the **oval window**.

Why are the ossicles necessary? We can answer this question by noting that both the outer ear and middle ear are filled with air, but the inner ear contains a watery liquid that is much denser than the air (Figure 11.13). The mismatch between the low density of the air and the high density of this liquid creates a problem: pressure changes in the air are transmitted poorly to the much denser liquid. If these vibrations had to pass directly from the air to the liquid, only about 3 percent of the vibrations would be transmitted (Durrant & Lovrinic, 1977). The ossicles help solve this problem by amplifying the vibration in two ways: (1) concentrating the vibration of the large tympanic membrane onto the much smaller stapes (Figure 11.14a), and (2) being hinged to create a lever action

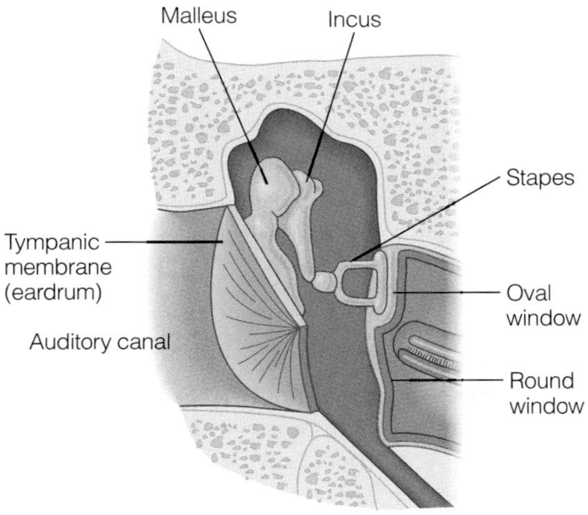

Figure 11.12 ▌ The middle ear. The three bones of the middle ear transmit the vibrations of the tympanic membrane to the inner ear.

Figure 11.13 ▌ Environments inside the outer, middle, and inner ears. The fact that liquid fills the inner ear poses a problem for the transmission of sound vibrations from the air of the middle ear.

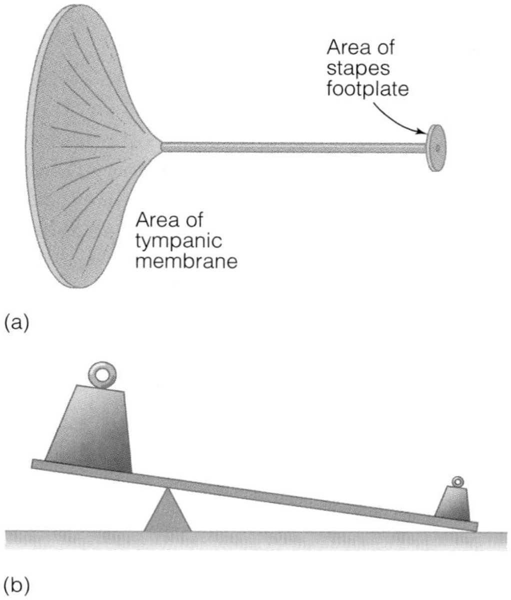

Figure 11.14 ▌ (a) A diagrammatic representation of the tympanic membrane and the stapes, showing the difference in size between the two. (b) How lever action can amplify the effect of a small weight. The lever action of the ossicles amplifies the sound vibrations reaching the tympanic inner ear.

((a) From "Hearing: Its Function and Dysfunction," by E. D. Schubert, 1980, Disorders of Human Communication, Vol. 1. *pg. 15 and 18. Copyright © 1980 Springer-Verlag Wien-New York. Reprinted by permission.)*

similar to what enables a small weight on the long end of a board balanced on a fulcrum to overcome a larger weight on the short end of the board (Figure 11.14b; Schubert, 1980). We can appreciate the amplifying effect of the ossicles by noting that in patients whose ossicles have been damaged beyond surgical repair, it is necessary to increase the sound by a factor of 10 to 50 to achieve the same hearing as when the ossicles were functioning.

Not all animals require this amplification provided by the ossicles in the human. For example, fish need no amplification because there is only a small mismatch between the density of water, which transmits sound in the fish's environment, and the liquid inside the fish's ear. Thus, fish have no outer or middle ear.

The middle ear also contains the **middle-ear muscles**, the smallest skeletal muscles in the body. These muscles are attached to the ossicles, and at very high sound intensities they contract to dampen the ossicle's vibration, thereby protecting the structures of the inner ear against potentially painful and damaging stimuli.

The Inner Ear

The main structure of the **inner ear** is the liquid-filled **cochlea** (Figure 11.15a). The liquid is set into vibration by the movement of the stapes against the oval window. The cochlea, which is a bony snaillike structure, is difficult to visualize because it is rolled into 2-¾ turns. But we can see the structure inside more clearly by imagining how the

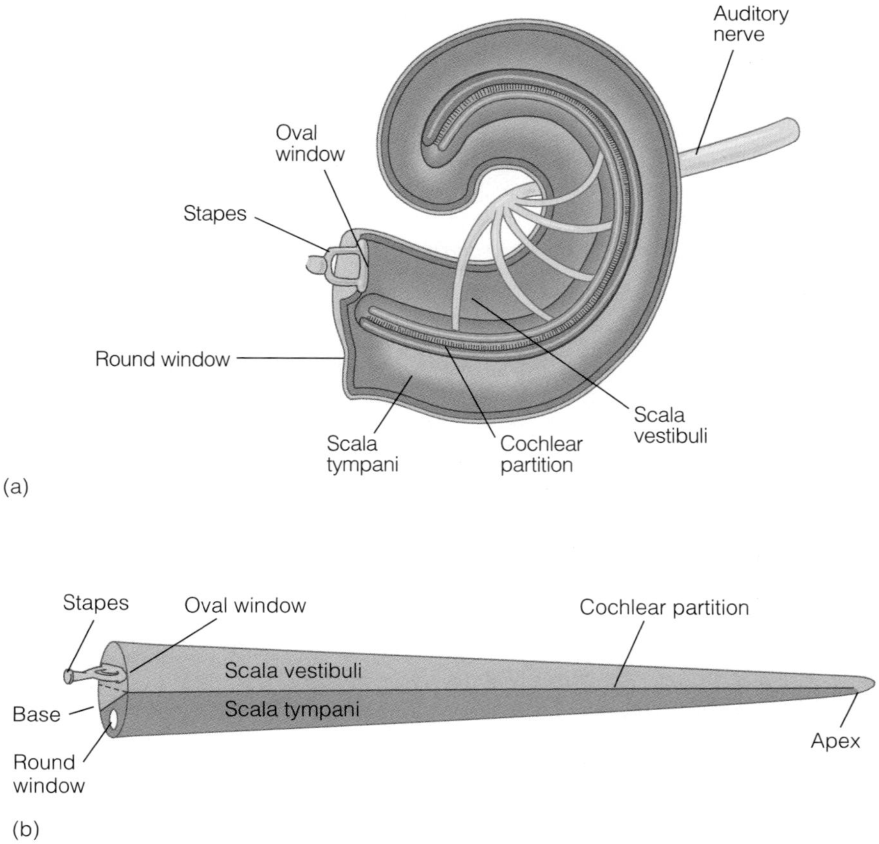

Figure 11.15 ▌ (a) A partially uncoiled cochlea. (b) A fully uncoiled cochlea. The cochlear partition, which is indicated here by a line, actually contains the basilar membrane and the organ of Corti, which are shown in Figure 11.16.

cochlea would appear if uncoiled to form a long straight tube (Figure 11.15b). The most obvious feature of the uncoiled cochlea is that the upper half, called the scala vestibuli, and the lower half, called the scala tympani, are separated by a structure called the **cochlear partition**. This partition extends almost the entire length of the cochlea, from its **base** near the stapes to its **apex** at the far end. Note that this diagram is not drawn to scale and so doesn't show the cochlea's true proportions. In reality, the uncoiled cochlea would be a cylinder 2 mm in diameter and 35 mm long.

We can best see the structures within the cochlear partition by looking at the cochlea end-on and in cross section, as in Figure 11.16a. When we look at the cochlea in this way, we see that the cochlear partition contains a large structure called the **organ of Corti**. Figure 11.16b shows the key structures of the organ of Corti.

- The **hair cells**, shown in red in Figure 11.16b, are the receptors for hearing. The **cilia**, which protrude from the tops of the cells, are where the sound acts to produce electrical signals. There are two types of hair cells, the **inner hair cells** and the **outer hair cells**.
- The **basilar membrane** supports the Organ of Corti and vibrates in response to sound.
- The **tectorial membrane** extends over the hair cells.

One of the most important events in the auditory process is the bending of the cilia. This bending transduces the vibrations caused by the sound stimulus into electrical signals. The cilia bend because the in-and-out movement of the stapes creates pressure changes in the liquid inside the cochlea that sets the cochlear partition into an up-and-down motion, as indicated by the blue arrow in Figure 11.16b.

This up-and-down motion of the cochlear partition causes two effects: (1) it sets the organ of Corti into an up-and-down vibration, and (2) it causes the tectorial membrane to move back-and-forth, as shown by the red arrow. These two motions cause the cilia of the inner hair cells to bend because of their movement against the surrounding liquid and because they are in contact with the tectorial membrane (Dallos, 1996).

The bending of the cilia of the inner hair cells generates the electrical signal that is transmitted to fibers in the auditory nerve. (We will describe the function of the outer hair cells later in the chapter.) The amount the cilia must bend to cause an electrical signal is extremely small. At the threshold for hearing, cilia movements as small as 100 trillionths of a meter (100 picometers) can generate a response in the hair cell. To give you an idea of just how small a movement this is, consider that if we were to increase the size of a cilium so it was as big as the Eiffel Tower, the movement of the cilia would translate into a movement of the pinnacle of the Eiffel Tower of only 10 mm (Figure 11.17; Hudspeth, 1983, 1989).

Given the small amount of movement needed to hear a sound, it isn't surprising that the auditory system can detect extremely small pressure changes. In fact, the auditory system can detect pressure changes so small that they cause the eardrum to move only 10^{-11} cm, a dimension that is less than the diameter of a hydrogen atom (Tonndorf & Khanna, 1968), and the auditory system is so sensitive that the air pressure at threshold in the most sensitive range of hearing is only 10 to 15 dB above the air pressure generated by the random movement of air mol-

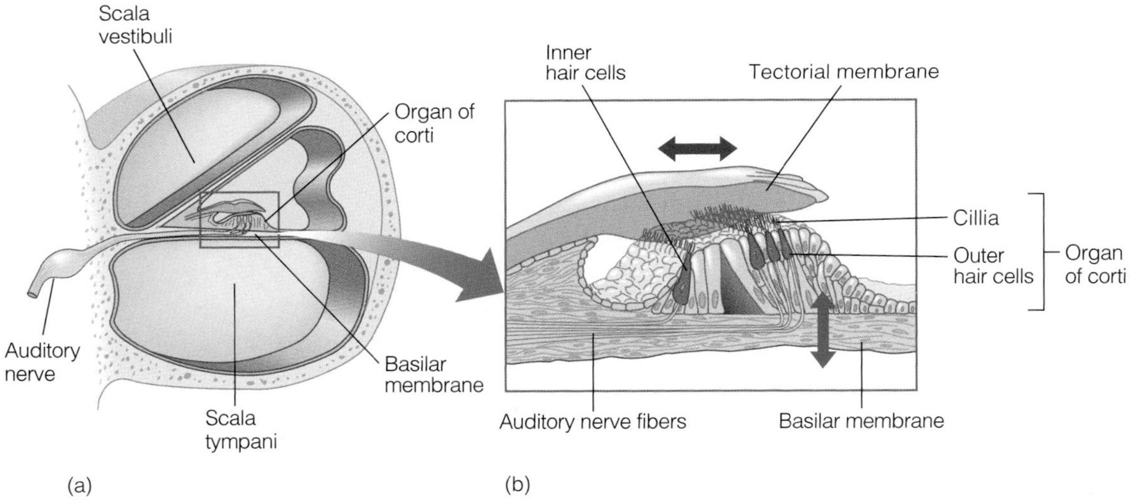

Figure 11.16 (a) Cross-section of the cochlea. (b) Close-up of the organ of Corti, showing how it rests on the basilar membrane. Arrows indicate the motions of the basilar membrane and tectorial membrane that are caused by vibration of the cochlear partition.
(b) (Adapted from Denes and Pinson.)

Figure 11.17 ▮ The distance the cilia of a hair cell moves at the threshold for hearing is so small that if the volume of an individual cilium is scaled up to that of the Eiffel Tower, the equivalent movement of the Eiffel Tower would be about 10 mm.

ecules. This means that if our hearing were much more sensitive than it is now, we would hear the background hiss of colliding air molecules!

THE COCHLEA

We have seen that the ear is a sophisticated system for receiving and transmitting sound vibrations to the auditory receptors. Our goal is to understand how these vibrations are represented in the auditory system by the firing of neurons. Most of the early research on this problem used pure tones. Later in the chapter we will look at some recent research that has used more complex sound stimuli.

We will consider two possible ways neurons might signal the frequency of a pure tone by referring to Figure 11.18, which is a schematic view of the cochlear partition, showing the nerve fibers that come from hair cells all along the length of the partition. Each of these fibers signals the hair cell activity at a particular place along the cochlear partition.

Two ways these fibers can signal the frequency of a tone are by:

1. *Which* of the fibers are firing. Figure 11.18a illustrates a situation in which activation of hair cells on a specific place on the basilar membrane activates a specific group of nerve fibers, indicated in red.

2. *How* these fibers are firing. Figure 11.18b represents the idea that information can be carried in the rate of nerve firing or the pattern of nerve impulses.

We will see that the auditory system uses both of these types of information to indicate frequency. We will first describe research that showed that frequency is coded by *which* fibers are firing. This idea, which is associated with a series of studies begun by Georg von Békésy in 1928, culminated in his being awarded the Nobel Prize in physiology and medicine in 1961.

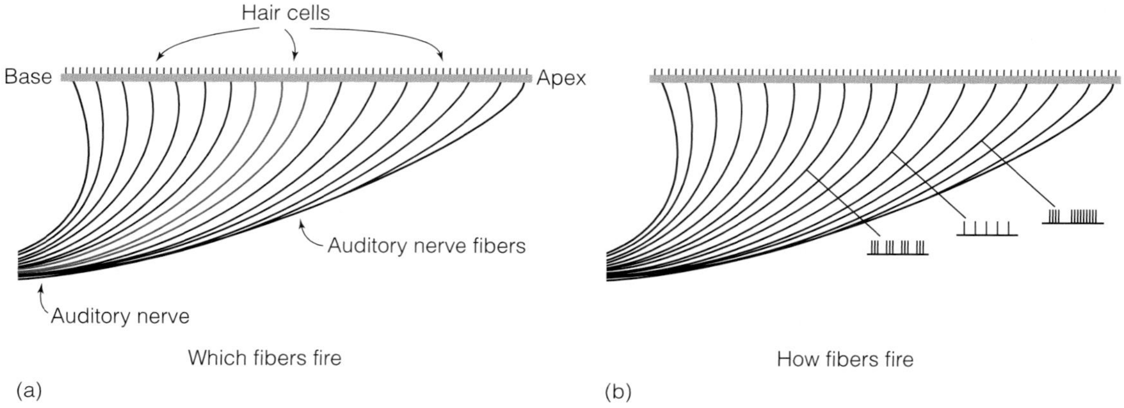

Figure 11.18 ▮ Hair cells all along the cochlea send signals to nerve fibers that combine to form the auditory nerve. This figure indicates that these fibers can signal a tone's frequency: (a) by which fibers fire in response to the tone; and (b) by the pattern of nerve impulses in response to the tone. See text for details.

Békésy's Place Theory of Hearing

Békésy proposed the **place theory of hearing**, which states that the frequency of a sound is indicated by the place along the organ of Corti at which nerve firing is highest. Thus, place theory states that frequency is indicated by which fibers are firing.

Békésy approached the problem of determining the code for frequency by determining how the basilar membrane vibrated in response to different frequencies. He determined this in two ways: (1) by actually observing the vibration of the basilar membrane and (2) by building a model of the cochlea that took into account the physical properties of the basilar membrane.

Békésy observed the vibration of the basilar membrane by boring a hole in the ear of a human cadaver, stimulating it with sound, and observing the membrane's vibration by using a rapidly flashing light to "freeze" the motion of the membrane and a microscope to enable him to see the tiny movements (Békésy, 1960). He found that the vibrating motion of the basilar membrane is similar to the motion that occurs when one person holds the end of a rope and "snaps" it, sending a wave traveling down the rope. This **traveling wave** motion of the basilar membrane is shown in Figure 11.19.

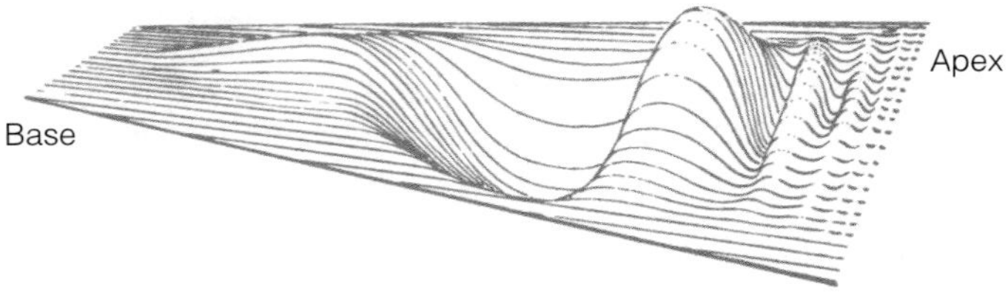

Figure 11.19 ▌ A perspective view showing the traveling wave motion of the basilar membrane. This picture shows what the membrane looks like when the vibration is "frozen," with the wave about ⅔ of the way down the membrane.

(From "Shearing Motion in Scala Media of Cochlear Models," by J. Tonndorf, 1960, Journal of the Acoustical Society of America, 32, *238–244, figure 7b. Copyright © 1960 by the American Institute of Physics. Reprinted by permission.)*

Békésy also determined how the basilar membrane vibrates by analyzing its structure. In this analysis he took note of two important facts: (1) the base of the basilar membrane (the end located nearest the stapes) is three or four times narrower than the apex of the basilar membrane (the end of the membrane located at the far end of the cochlea; Figure 11.20), and (2) the base of the membrane is about 100 times stiffer than the apex. Using this information, Békésy constructed models of the cochlea that revealed that the pressure changes in the cochlea cause the basilar membrane to vibrate in a traveling wave.

Figure 11.21 shows the traveling wave at three successive moments in time. The solid horizontal line represents the basilar membrane at rest. Curve 1 shows the position of the basilar membrane at one moment during its

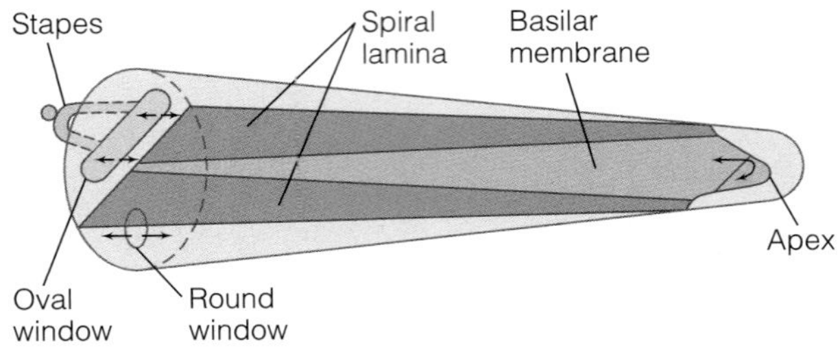

Figure 11.20 ▌ A perspective view of an uncoiled cochlea, showing how the basilar membrane gets wider at the apex end of the cochlea. The spiral lamina is a supporting structure that makes up for the basilar membrane's difference in width at the stapes and the apex ends of the cochlea.

(From "Hearing: Its Function and Dysfunction," by E. D. Schubert, 1980, Disorders of Human Communication, Vol. 1. *pg. 15 and 18. Copyright © 1980 Springer-Verlag Wien-New York. Reprinted by permission.)*

vibration, and curves 2 and 3 show the positions of the membrane at two later moments. From these curves we can see that most of the membrane vibrates, but that some parts vibrate more than others. The **envelope of the traveling wave**, which is indicated by the dashed line, indicates the maximum displacement that the wave causes at each point along the membrane. This maximum displacement is important because it tells us which hair cells and nerve fibers along the basilar membrane will be affected the most by the membrane's vibration. The amount that the cilia move depends on the amount that the basilar membrane is displaced. Therefore, hair cells located near the place where the basilar membrane vibrates the most will be stimulated the most strongly, and the nerve fibers associated with these hair cells will therefore fire the most strongly.

Békésy's (1960) observations of the basilar membrane's vibrations led him to conclude that the envelope of the traveling wave of the basilar membrane has two important properties:

1. The envelope has a peak amplitude at one point on the basilar membrane. The envelope of Figure 11.21

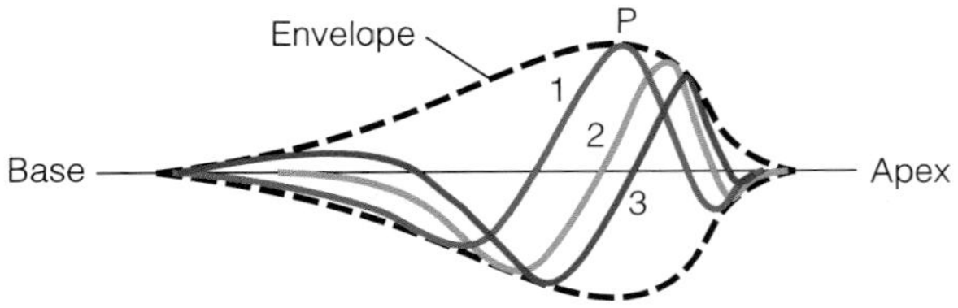

Figure 11.21 ▌ Vibration of the basilar membrane, showing the position of the membrane at three instants in time, indicated by the blue, green, and red lines, and the envelope of the vibration, indicated by the black dashed line. P indicates the peak of the basilar membrane vibration.

(From Experiments in Hearing, *by G. von Bekesy, 1960, figures 11.43. Copyright © 1960 by Mc-Graw-Hill Book Company, New York. Reprinted by permission.)*

indicates that point P on the basilar membrane is displaced the most by the traveling wave. Thus, the hair cells near point P will send out stronger signals than those near other parts of the membrane.

2. The position of this peak on the basilar membrane is a function of the frequency of the sound. We can see in Figure 11.22, which shows the envelopes of vibration for stimuli ranging from 25 to 1,600 Hz, that low frequencies cause maximum vibration near the apex. High frequencies cause less of the membrane to vibrate, and the maximum vibration is near the base. (One way to remember this relationship is to imagine low-frequency waves as being long waves that reach farther.)

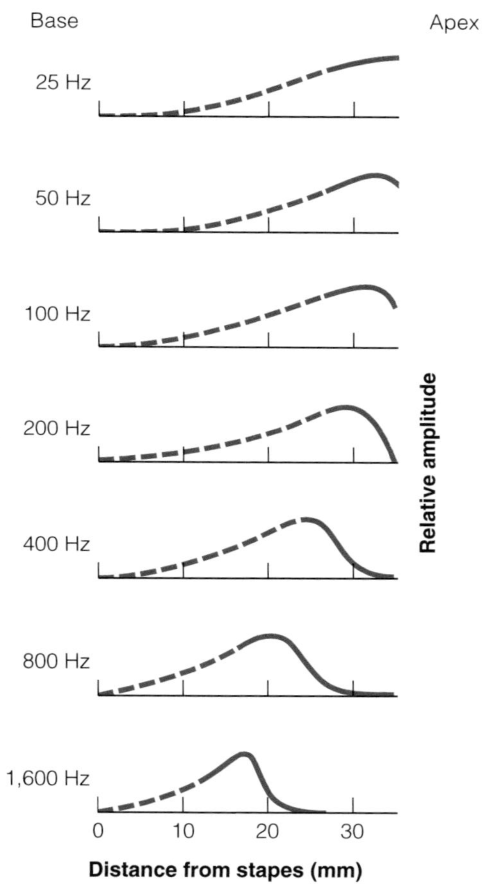

Figure 11.22 The envelope of the basilar membrane's vibration at frequencies ranging from 25 to 1,600 Hz, as measured by Békésy (1960). These envelopes were based on measurements of damaged cochleas. The envelopes are more sharply peaked in healthy cochleas.

Evidence for Place Theory

Békésy's linking of the place on the cochlea with the frequency of the tone has been confirmed by measuring the electrical response of the cochlea and of individual hair cells and auditory nerve fibers. For example, placing disc electrodes at different places along the length of the cochlea and measuring the electrical response to different frequencies results in a **tonotopic map**—an orderly map of frequencies along the length of the cochlea (Culler et al., 1943). This result, shown in Figure 11.23, confirms the idea that the apex of the cochlea responds best to low frequencies and the base responds best to high frequencies. More precise electrophysiological evidence for place coding is provided by determining that auditory nerve fibers that signal activity at different places on the cochlea respond to different frequencies.

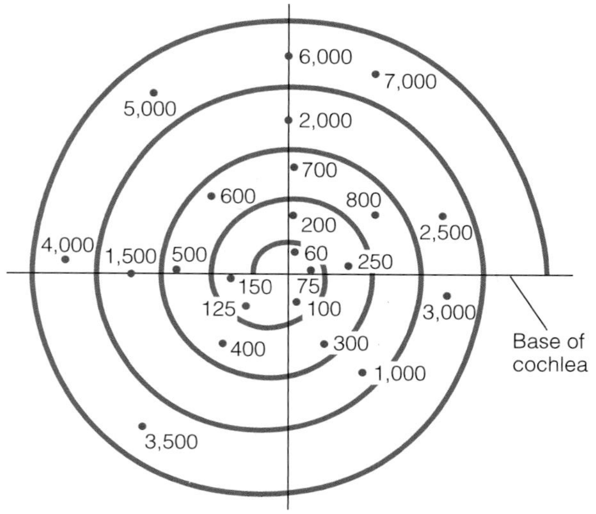

Figure 11.23 Tonotopic map of the guinea pig cochlea. Numbers indicate the location of the maximum electrical response for each frequency.
(From "A Revised Frequency Map of the Guinea Pig Cochlea," by E. A. Culler, J. D. Coakley, K. Lowy. & N. Gross, 1943, American Journal of Psychology, *56, 475–500, figure 11. Copyright © 1943 by the Board of Trustees of the University of Illinois. Used with the permission of the University of Illinois Press.)*

METHOD ■ Neural Frequency Tuning Curves

Each neuron in the cochlea and in the auditory nerve respond to a narrow range of frequencies. This range is indicated by each neuron's **frequency tuning curve**. This curve is determined by presenting pure tones of different frequencies, and measuring how many decibels are necessary to cause the neuron to fire. This decibel level is the threshold for that frequency. Plotting the threshold for each frequency results in frequency tuning curves like the ones in Figure 11.24. The arrow under each curve indicates the frequency to which the neuron is most sensitive. This frequency is called the **characteristic frequency** of the particular auditory nerve fiber.

■ ■ ■

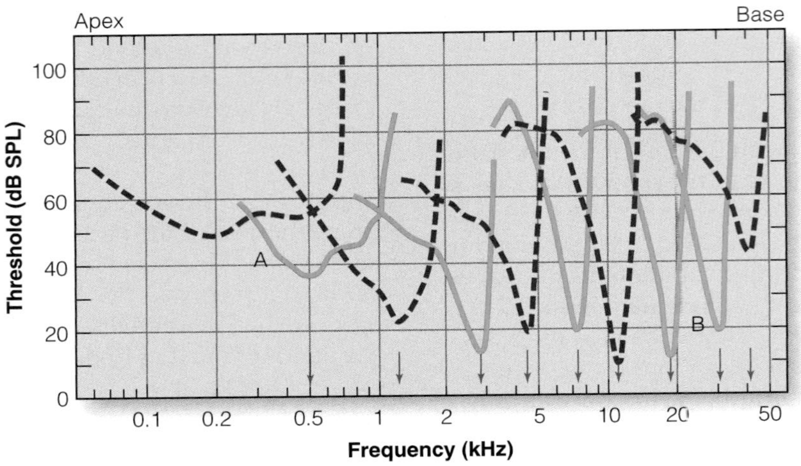

Figure 11.24 ▮ Frequency tuning curves of cat auditory nerve fibers. The characteristic frequency of each fiber is indicated by the arrows along the frequency axis. The frequency scale is in kilohertz (kHz), where one kHz = 1,000 Hz.
(A. R. Palmer (1987). Physiology of the cochlear nerve and cochlear nucleus. In M. P. Haggard and E. F. Evans (Eds.), Hearing. *Edinburgh: Churchill Livingstone, p. 838–855.)*

The frequency tuning curves in Figure 11.24 were recorded from auditory nerve fibers that originated at different places along the cochlea. As we would expect from Békésy's place theory, the fibers originating near the base of the cochlea have high characteristic frequencies, and those originating near the apex have low characteristic frequencies.

The idea that the frequency of a tone is represented by the firing of fibers located at specific places along the cochlea has also been supported by the results of psychophysical experiments using a procedure called **auditory masking**.

METHOD ▪ Auditory Masking

The basic principle behind auditory masking is that one tone can mask or decrease our perception of another tone that is occurring at the same time. The procedure for an auditory masking experiment is shown in Figure 11.25. First, the threshold for hearing is determined at a number of frequencies (blue arrows), by determining the lowest intensity at each frequency that can just be heard (Figure 11.25a). Then, an intense masking stimulus (red arrow) is presented at one frequency and, while the masking stimulus is sounding, the thresholds for all frequencies are redetermined (Figure 11.25b). What typically happens in a masking experiment is that the masking tone causes the largest increase in threshold for test tones at the masking tone's frequency, and causes less of an increase in the threshold of test tones that are above and below the masking tone's frequency. VL 8

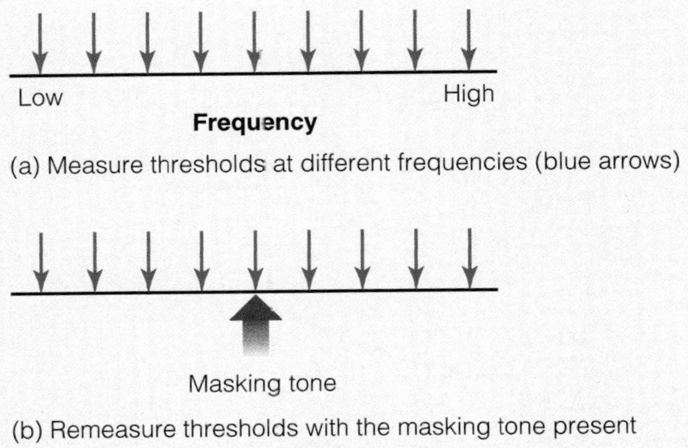

Figure 11.25 ▮ The procedure for a masking experiment. (a) Threshold is determined across a range of frequencies. Each blue arrow indicates a frequency where the threshold is measured. (b) The threshold is redetermined at each frequency (blue arrows) in the presence of a masking stimulus (red arrow).

Figure 11.26 shows the results of a masking experiment in which the masking tone was a noise that contained frequencies between 365 and 455 Hz (Egan & Hake, 1950). Notice that the thresholds for frequencies near the masking tone are raised the most. Also notice that this curve is not symmetrical. That is, the masking effect spreads more to high frequencies than to low frequencies.

We can relate the larger effect of masking on high-frequency tones to the vibration of the basilar membrane by looking at Figure 11.27, which reproduces the vibration patterns caused by 200- and 800-Hz test tones and a

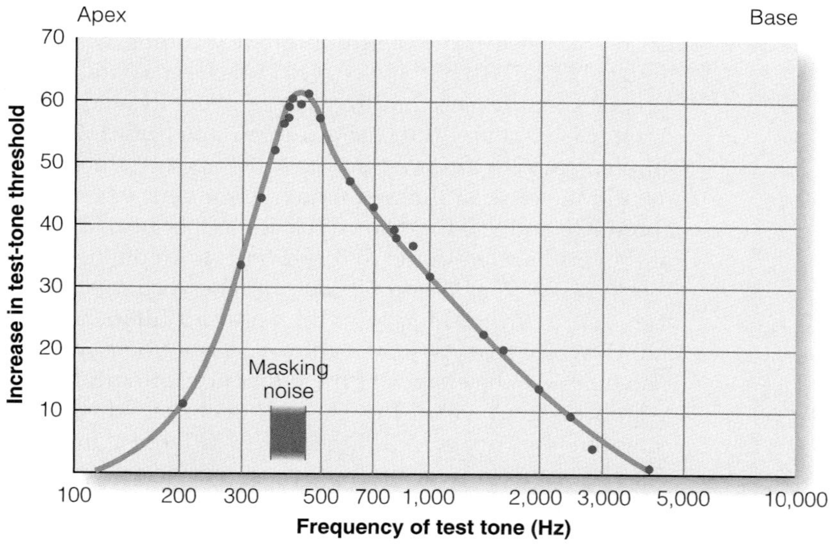

Figure 11.26 ▌ Results of Egan and Hake's (1950) masking experiment. The threshold increases the most near the frequencies of the masking noise and the masking effect spreads more to high frequencies than to low frequencies.
(Adapted from "On the Masking Pattern of a Simple Auditory Stimulus," by J. P. Egan and H. W. Hake, 1950, Journal of the Acoustical Society of America, 22, *622–630. Copyright © 1950 by the American Institute of Physics. Adapted by permission.)*

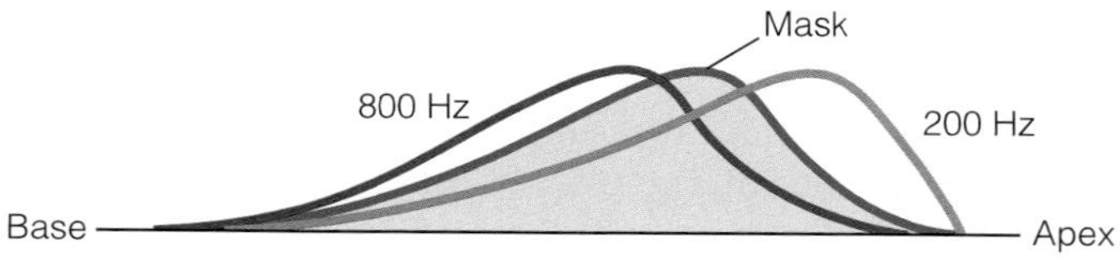

Figure 11.27 ▌ Vibration patterns caused by 200- and 800-Hz test tones, and the 400-Hz mask (shaded), taken from basilar membrane vibration patterns in Figure 11.22. Notice that the vibration caused by the masking tone overlaps the 800-Hz vibration more than the 200-Hz vibration.

400-Hz masking tone. We can see how a 400-Hz masking tone would affect the 200- and 800- Hz tones by noting how their vibration patterns overlap. Notice that the pattern for the 400-Hz tone, which is shaded, almost totally overlaps the pattern for the higher-frequency 800-Hz tone, but that it does not overlap the peak vibration of the lower-frequency 200-Hz tone. We would therefore expect the masking tone to have a large effect on the 800-Hz tone but a smaller effect on the 200-Hz tone, and this is exactly what happens. Thus, Békésy's description of the way the basilar membrane vibrates predicts the masking function in Figure 11.26.

Updating Békésy

Békésy's place theory has been confirmed by many experiments over the years. Some of these experiments have also improved our knowledge of the way the basilar membrane vibrates and have strengthened the link between this vibration and what we perceive. Consider, for example, Békésy's picture of how the basilar membrane vibrates in Figure 11.22. A problem with these curves is that two nearby frequencies would cause overlapping and almost identical patterns of vibration. Yet psychophysical experiments show that we can distinguish small differences in frequency. For example, Békésy's vibration patterns for 400 and 405 Hz are almost identical, but we can distinguish between these two frequencies.

To deal with this problem, researchers measured the basilar membrane's vibration using healthier cochleas and techniques more sensitive than the ones available to Békésy (Johnstone & Boyle, 1967; Khanna & Leonard, 1982; Narayan et al., 1998). These observations showed that the peak vibration for a particular frequency is even more sharply localized than Békésy had observed, so there is less overlap between the curves for nearby frequencies.

These new measurements explained our ability to distinguish between small differences in frequency, but they also posed a new question: Why does the basilar membrane vibrate more sharply in healthier cochleas? The answer to this question appears to be that the entire outer hair cells (not just the cilia) of live animals respond to sound by moving, and this movement affects the vibration of the basilar membrane. This outer hair cell movement, called the **motile response**, is a slight tilting and a change of length.

An important property of this motile response is that it is tuned to frequency. Thus, high-frequency sounds cause motile responses in the outer hair cells near the base of the basilar membrane, and low-frequency sounds cause motile responses in outer cells near the apex of the basilar membrane (Brownell et al., 1985; Dallos, 1996; Patuzzi, 1996; Zenner, 1986). Apparently, the motile response causes the outer hair cells to push on the basilar membrane, as shown by the arrows in Figure 11.28, and this pushing amplifies the motion of the basilar mem-

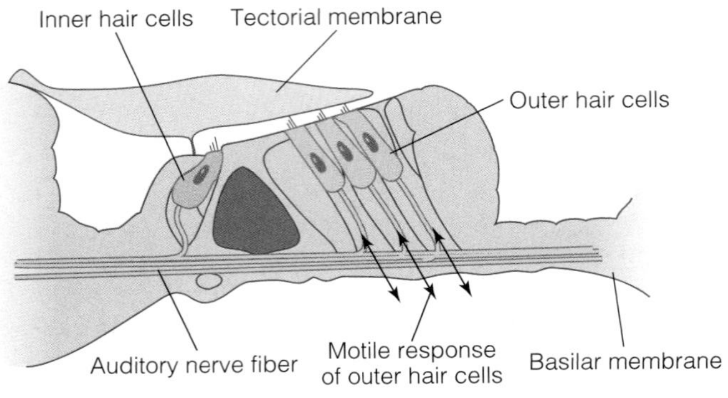

Figure 11.28 ▮ A cross-section of the organ of Corti, showing the outer hair cells on the right. The arrows at the base of the outer hair cells indicate how movement of the hair cells (the motile response) exerts pressure on the basilar membrane.

brane and sharpens its response to specific frequencies. Thus, the outer hair cells and the basilar membrane work together to create maximum vibration at a specific place along the cochlea for each frequency, and this vibration is translated into firing of the inner hair cells. Figure 11.29 summarizes the way the inner and outer hair cells and basilar membrane work together to accomplish this.

The Basilar Membrane as a Frequency Analyzer

Starting with the idea that a particular frequency causes maximum activation at a specific place along the basilar membrane, auditory researchers have proposed that the cochlea operates as though it consists of a bank of filters, each of which processes a limited band of frequencies. This idea is supported by both physiological and psychophysical evidence.

Tuning Curves One way to visualize this bank of filters is to look back at the neural frequency tuning curves in Figure 11.24. Each of these curves indicate the band of frequencies that causes auditory nerve fibers located at different places along the basilar membrane to fire. For example, Curve A is for a fiber near the apex of the basilar membrane of a cat that responds to frequencies between about 300 and 900 Hz. Curve B is for a fiber near the base of the basilar membrane that responds to frequencies between about 20,000 and 30,000 Hz. These curves, therefore, represent the shapes of the auditory filters as measured by the responses of auditory nerve fibers. We can also measure the shapes of the filters perceptually by determining the **psychophysical tuning curve**, which indicates the intensity of masking tones of difference frequencies that cause a low-intensity pure tone to become just barely detectable.

METHOD ▪ Psychophysical Tuning Curves

The procedure for measuring the psychophysical tuning curve is diagrammed in Figure 11.30. First, a test tone is presented, as indicated by the blue arrow in Figure 11.30a. This test tone has a low level, usually around 10 dB, so it causes activity on only a small area along the basilar membrane. To determine which other frequencies also cause activity at this location, we present masking tones, indicated by the red arrows in Figure 11.30b. These tones have frequencies below, at, and above the frequency of the test tone. We measure the level of each masking tone that eliminates perception of the test tone. The assumption behind this procedure is that if the masking tone eliminates perception of the test tone, it must be causing activity at the location on the basilar membrane that is activated by the test tone.

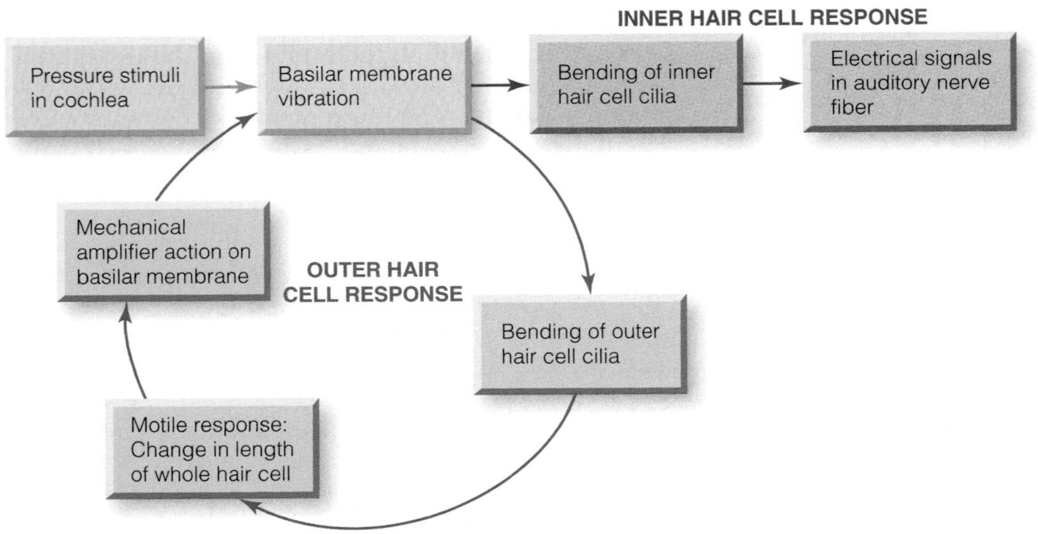

Figure 11.29 ▮ Cooperation between the inner and outer hair cells: The basilar membrane's vibration is sharpened by the motile response of the outer hair cells and this vibration, in turn, stimulates the inner hair cells, which send their signals to fibers in the auditory nerve.

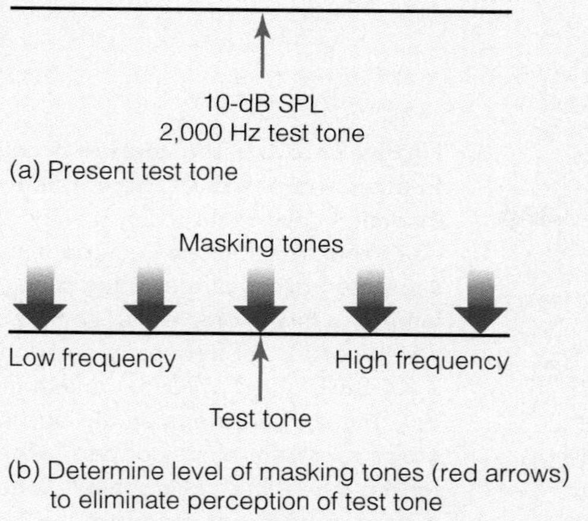

Figure 11.30 ▮ The procedure for measuring a psychophysical tuning curve. (a) A 10-dB SPL test tone (blue arrow) is presented; (b) then a series of masking tones (red arrows) are presented at each frequency. The psychophysical tuning curve is determined by measuring the sound pressure of each masking tone that reduces the perception of the test tone to threshold.

▪ ▪ ▪

Figure 11.31 shows psychophysical tuning curves determined using test tones at a number of test frequencies (indicated by the blue dots). These curves indicate that each test tone is affected by a narrow range of masking tone frequencies. Notice that these psychophysical tuning curves, which were determined by measuring *perception,* look very much like the neural curves in Figure 11.24, which were determined by measuring *the firing of auditory nerve fibers.* The fact that the perceptual and neural curves are very similar suggests a close connection between our perception of different frequencies and the firing of these auditory nerve fibers (B. C. J. Moore, 2001).

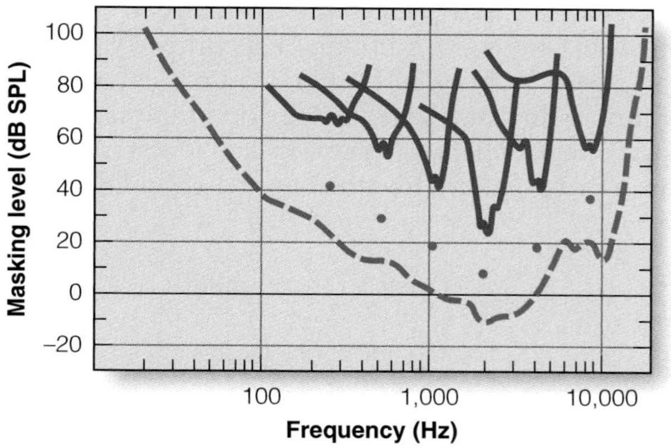

Figure 11.31 ▮ Psychophysical tuning curves for a number of test-tone frequencies (dots). Notice how the minimum masking intensities for the curves match the shape of the audibility curve (dashed line).
(Based on Vogten, 1974).

The Basilar Membrane's Response to Complex Tones

We have seen that a pure tone causes maximal stimulation at a specific location on the basilar membrane. But what about more complex sounds such as musical tones or speech? To answer this question, let's return to our discussion of musical tones from page 240. Remember that musical tones consist of a number of frequencies—a fundamental frequency and harmonics that are multiples of the fundamental.

We have seen how a musical tone can be created by the process of additive synthesis (Figure 11.8). But what if we reverse this process by starting with the musical tone and determining the pure-tone components of this tone? This can be accomplished by using a mathematical procedure developed by the French mathematician Jean Baptiste Fourier in 1811. Fourier's procedure, which is called **Fourier analysis,** is based on his insight that a complex waveform can be broken down into a number of sine-wave components. By applying the equations of Fourier analysis to sound waves like the one in Figure 11.32a, it is possible to "work backward" and determine that this

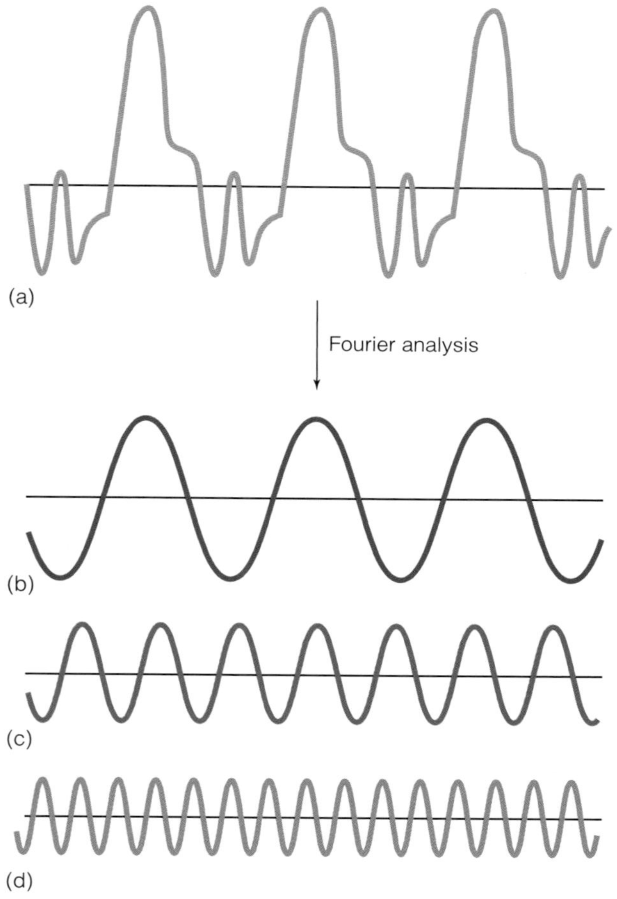

Figure 11.32 ▮ A complex sound wave. Applying Fourier analysis to this wave indicates that it is made up of the three components in (b), (c), and (d).

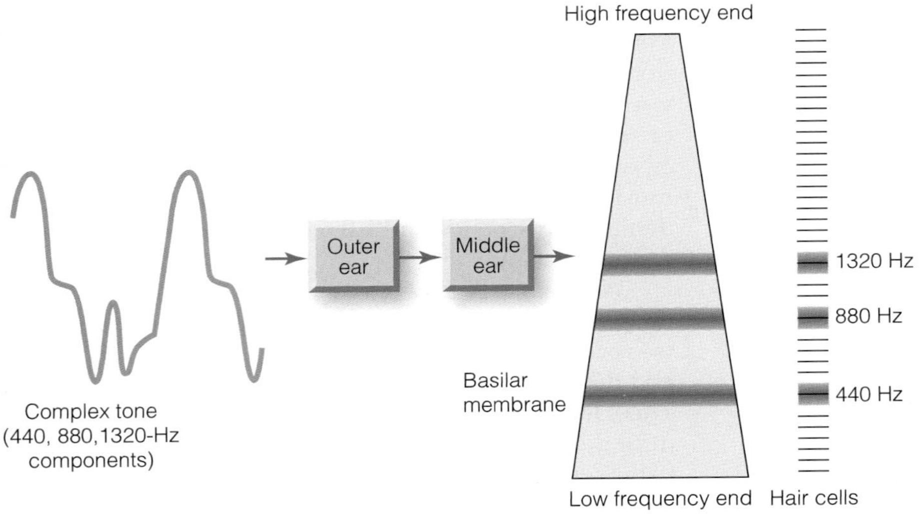

Figure 11.33 ▮ The cochlea is called a frequency analyzer because it analyzes incoming sound into its frequency components and translates the components into separated areas of excitation along its length. In this example, the complex tone, which consists of frequency components at 440, 880, and 1,320 Hz, enters the outer ear. The shaded areas on the basilar membrane represent places of peak vibration for the tone's three components, and the darkened hair cells represent the hair cells that will be most active in response to this tone.

complex tone is made up of sine-wave components with frequencies of 440, 880, and 1,320 Hz.

Now that we know that it is possible to use a mathematical formula to separate a complex wave into its sine-wave components, we consider the question of how the basilar membrane responds to a complex tone such as the one in Figure 11.32. We know that different places along the basilar membrane respond to narrow bands of frequencies. Thus, it seems reasonable to suggest that each of the components of a complex tone might activate a different area of the membrane. Stating this in terms of filters, we can suggest that each component of a complex tone would activate the filter that is tuned to respond best to the frequencies of that component.

Research that has measured how the basilar membrane responds to complex tones confirms these ideas. Thus, a complex tone, like the one in Figure 11.32, will cause the most neural activity in auditory nerve fibers with characteristic frequencies of 440, 880, and 1,320 Hz, as shown in Figure 11.33 (Hudspeth, 1989). By responding to the individual components of a complex tone, the basilar membrane is essentially performing its own Fourier analysis on the tone. We can, therefore, think of the cochlea as a frequency analyzer that breaks a complex tone into its harmonics and responds to each harmonic.

How the Timing of Neural Firing Can Signal Frequency

We have been focusing on the idea that frequency is signaled by *which* fibers in the cochlea fire to a tone. However, remember from Figure 11.18b that frequency can also be signaled by *how* the fibers fire. This idea is supported by measurements of auditory nerve firing that show that fibers fire in bursts and that the timing of these bursts corresponds to the frequency of the sound stimulus. The way this works is illustrated in Figure 11.34, which shows the pressure changes of a pure tone stimulus and the firing of three auditory nerve fibers.

We can see that each of the fibers fire at or near the peak of the sine-wave stimulus. This property of firing is called **phase locking** because the neurons always fire at the same point, or phase, of the sound stimulus. When large groups of fibers are phase-locked to a stimulus, they create a firing pattern like the one shown in Figure 11.35.

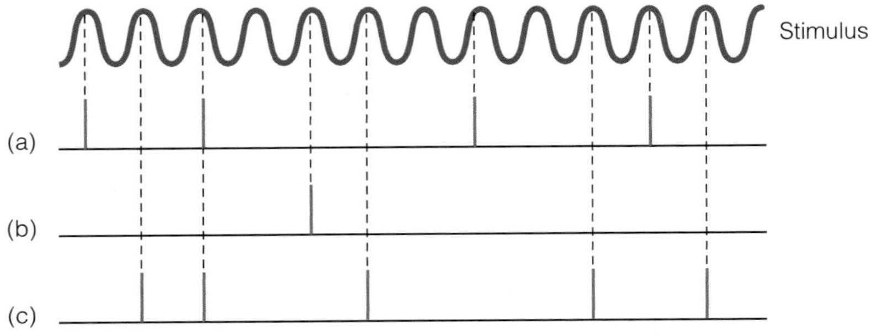

Figure 11.34 ▮ The response of three nerve fibers (a, b, and c) that are phase-locked to the stimulus. Notice that the fibers don't fire on every cycle of the stimulus, but when they do fire, they fire only when the stimulus is at or near its peak.

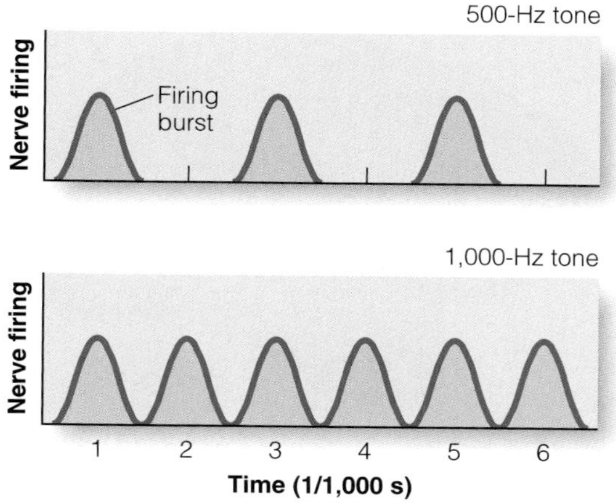

Figure 11.35 ▮ Phase locking causes large numbers of nerve fibers to fire in bursts separated by silent intervals.

The group of fibers fires in bursts separated by silent intervals, with the timing of these bursts depending on the frequency of the stimulus. Thus, the rate of bursting of a group of fibers provides information about the frequency of the sound stimulus.

From the research we have described, we can conclude that frequency is coded in the cochlea and auditory nerve based both on which fibers are firing (place theory) and on the timing of nerve impulses in auditory nerve fibers (phase locking). This information for frequency, which is contained in the auditory nerve fibers, is then transmitted through a series of structures and eventually arrives at the cortex.

TEST YOURSELF 11.2

1. Describe the structure of ear, focusing on the role that each component plays in transmitting the vibrations that enter the outer ear to the auditory receptors in the inner ear.
2. Describe Békésy's place theory of hearing and the physiological and psychophysical evidence that supports his theory.
3. What does it mean to say that the basilar membrane performs a Fourier analysis on a complex tone?
4. How can the frequency of a sound be signaled by the *rate* of nerve firing?

CENTRAL AUDITORY PROCESSING

So far we have been focusing on how the ear creates electrical signals in hair cells and fibers of the auditory nerve. But, of course, perception does not occur in the ear or in the auditory nerve. Just as for vision, we need to follow signals from the receptors to more central structures in order to understand perception.

Pathway From the Cochlea to the Cortex

The auditory nerve carries the signals generated by the inner hair cells away from the cochlea and toward the auditory receiving area in the cortex. Figure 11.36 shows the

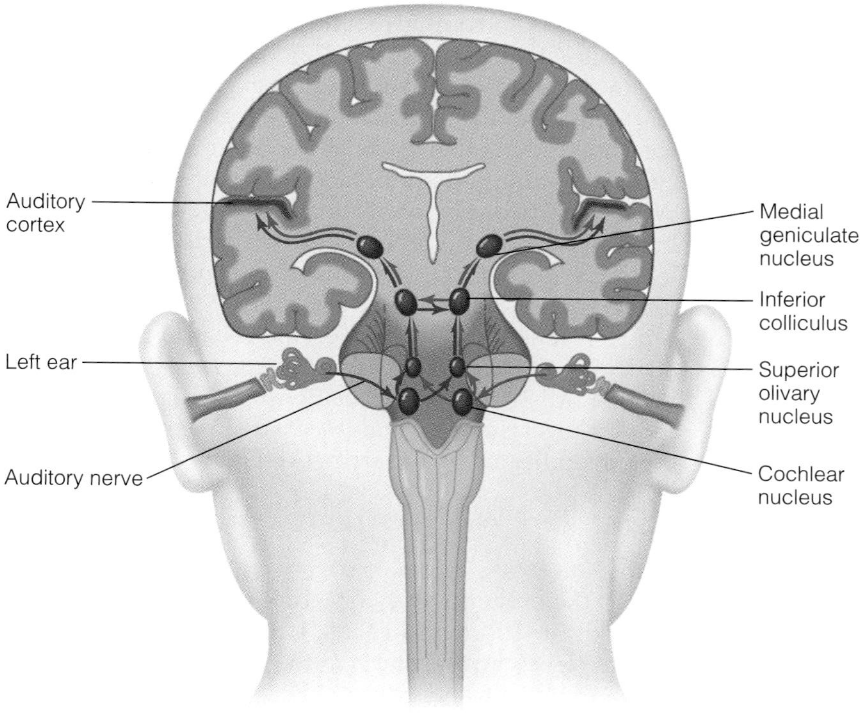

Figure 11.36 ▮ Diagram of the auditory pathways. This diagram is greatly simplified, as numerous connections between the structures are not shown. Note that auditory structures are bilateral—they exist on both the left and right sides of the body—and that messages can cross over between the two sides.
(Adapted from Wever, 1949.)

pathway the auditory signals follow from the cochlea to the auditory cortex. Auditory nerve fibers from the cochlea synapse in a sequence of **subcortical structures**—structures below the cerebral cortex. This sequence begins with the **cochlear nucleus** and continues to the **superior olivary nucleus** in the brain stem, the **inferior colliculus** in the midbrain, and the **medial geniculate nucleus** in the thalamus. (Signals from the retina synapse in the nearby lateral geniculate nucleus in the thalamus.)

From the medial geniculate nucleus, fibers continue to the primary **auditory receiving area (A1)**, in the temporal lobe of the cortex. If you have trouble remembering this sequence of structures, remember the acronym SONIC MG (a very fast sports car), which represents the three structures between the cochlear nucleus and the auditory cortex, as follows: SON = Superior Olivary Nucleus; IC = Inferior Colliculus; MG = Medial Geniculate Nucleus.

A great deal of processing occurs as signals travel through the subcortical structures that form the pathway between the cochlea and cortex. Some of this processing can be related to perception. For example, processing in the inferior colliculus is important for determining auditory localization—where a sound appears to originate in space (Litovsky et al., 2002)—and it has been suggested that one of the functions of subcortical structures in general is to respond to individual features of complex stimuli (Frisna, 2001; Nelken, 2004). There has been a tremendous amount of research on these subcortical structures, but we will focus on what happens once the signals reach the cortex.

Auditory Areas in the Cortex

As we begin discussing the auditory areas of the cortex, some of the principles we will describe may seem familiar because many of them are similar to principles we introduced in our description of the visual system in Chapters 3 and 4. Most of the discoveries about the auditory areas of the cortex are fairly recent compared to discoveries about the visual areas, so in some cases discoveries about the auditory cortex that are being made today are similar to discoveries that were made about the visual system 10 or 20 years earlier. For example, you may remember that it was initially thought that most visual processing occurred in the primary visual receiving area (V1), but beginning in the 1970s, it became obvious that other areas were also important for visual processing.

Recently it has been discovered that a similar situation occurs for hearing. At first most research focused on the primary auditory receiving area (A1) in the temporal lobe (Figure 11.37). But recently additional areas have been discovered that extend auditory areas in the cortex beyond A1. Research on the monkey describes cortical processing as starting with a **core area**, which includes the primary auditory cortex (A1) and some nearby areas. Signals then travel to an area surrounding the core, called the **belt area**, and then to the **parabelt area** (Kaas, Hackett, & Tramo, 1999; Rauschecker, 1997, 1998).

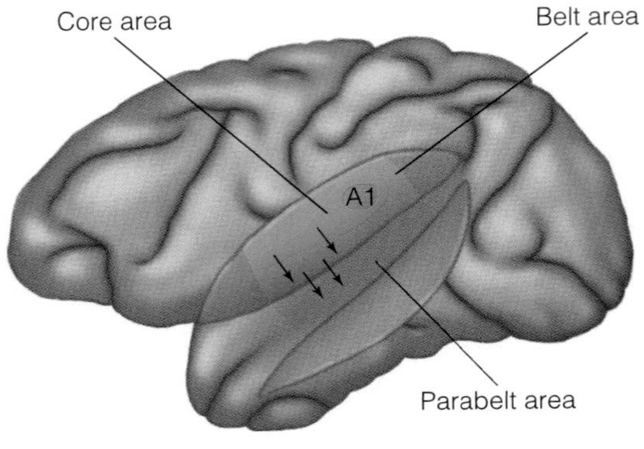

Figure 11.37 ▮ The three main auditory areas in the cortex are the core area, which contains the primary auditory receiving area (A1), the belt area, and the parabelt area. Signals, indicated by the arrows, travel from core, to belt, to parabelt. The temporal lobe is pulled back to show areas that would not be visible from the surface.
(Adapted from J. H. Kaas, T. A. Hackett, and M. J. Tramo, (1999). "Auditory processing in primate cerebral cortex," Current Opinion in Neurobiology, *9, 164–170.)*

One of the properties of these auditory areas is **hierarchical processing**—signals are first processed in the core and then travel to the belt and then to the parabelt. One finding that supports this idea is that the core area can be activated by simple sounds, such as pure tones, but areas outside the core require more complex sounds, such as auditory noise that contains many frequencies, human vocalizations, and monkey "calls" (Wissinger et al., 2001).

The fact that areas outside the auditory core require complex stimuli is similar to the situation in the visual system in which neurons in the visual cortex (V1) respond to spots or oriented lines, but neurons in the temporal lobe respond to complex stimuli such as faces and landmarks (see Figures 4.18 and 4.22).

In addition to discovering an expanded area in the temporal lobe that is devoted to hearing, recent research has shown that other parts of the cortex also respond to auditory stimuli (Figure 11.38; Poremba et al., 2003). What is particularly interesting about this picture of the brain is that there are areas in the parietal and frontal lobes that are activated by both visual and auditory stimuli. What is significant about this overlay of the two senses is that some of the overlap occurs in areas associated with the *what* and *where* streams for vision (Ungerleider & Mishkin, 1982). This finding is related to the recent discovery of *what* and *where* streams in the auditory system, indicated by the arrows in Figure 11.38.

What and *Where* Streams for Hearing

In the late 1990s, evidence began accumulating that suggested the existence of two streams for hearing (Kaas & Hackett, 1999; Romanski et al., 1999). The *what,* or *ventral,* stream (green arrow) starts in the anterior (front) part of the core and belt, and extends to the prefrontal cortex. The *where,* or *dorsal,* stream (red arrow) starts in the posterior

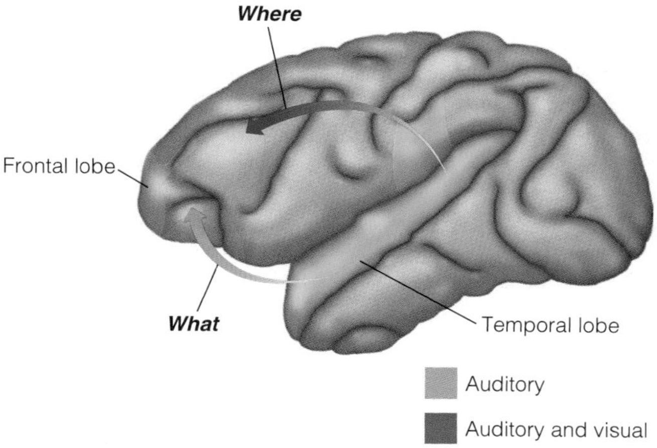

Figure 11.38 ▮ Areas in the monkey cortex that respond to auditory stimuli. The green areas respond to auditory stimuli, the purple areas to both auditory and visual stimuli. The arrows from the temporal lobe to the frontal lobe represent the *what* and *where* streams in the auditory system.
(Adapted from Poremba, et al., 2003.)

(rear) part of the core and belt, and extends to the parietal cortex and the prefrontal cortex. The *what* stream is responsible for identifying sounds, and the *where* stream for locating sounds.

Some of the first evidence supporting the idea of *what* and *where* streams for hearing came from experiments that showed that neurons in the *anterior* of the core and belt responded to the sound pattern of a stimulus, and neurons in the *posterior* of the core and belt responded to the location of the stimulus (Rauschecker & Tian, 2000; Tian et al., 2001).

Cases of human brain damage also support the *what/where* idea (Clarke et al., 2002). For example, Figure 11.39a shows the areas of the cortex that are damaged in J.G, a 45-year-old man with temporal lobe damage caused by a head injury, and E.S., a 64-year-old woman with parietal and frontal lobe damage caused by a stroke. Figure 11.39b shows that J.G. can locate sounds but his recognition is poor, whereas E.S. can recognize sounds but her ability to locate them is poor. Thus, J.G.'s *what* stream is damaged and E.S's *where* stream is damaged.

The *what/where* division is also supported by brain scan experiments. Figure 11.40 shows areas of cortex that are more strongly activated by recognizing pitch (a *what* task) in yellow and areas that are more strongly activated by detecting a location (a *where* task) in blue (Alain et al., 2001). Notice that pitch processing causes greater activation in ventral parts of the brain (anterior temporal cortex), and sound localization causes greater activity in dorsal regions (parietal cortex and frontal cortex). (Also see Meader et al., 2001; Wissinger et al., 2001.) Thus, there is evidence from animal recording, the effects of brain damage, and brain scanning that supports the idea that different areas of the brain area activated by identifying sounds and by localizing sounds.

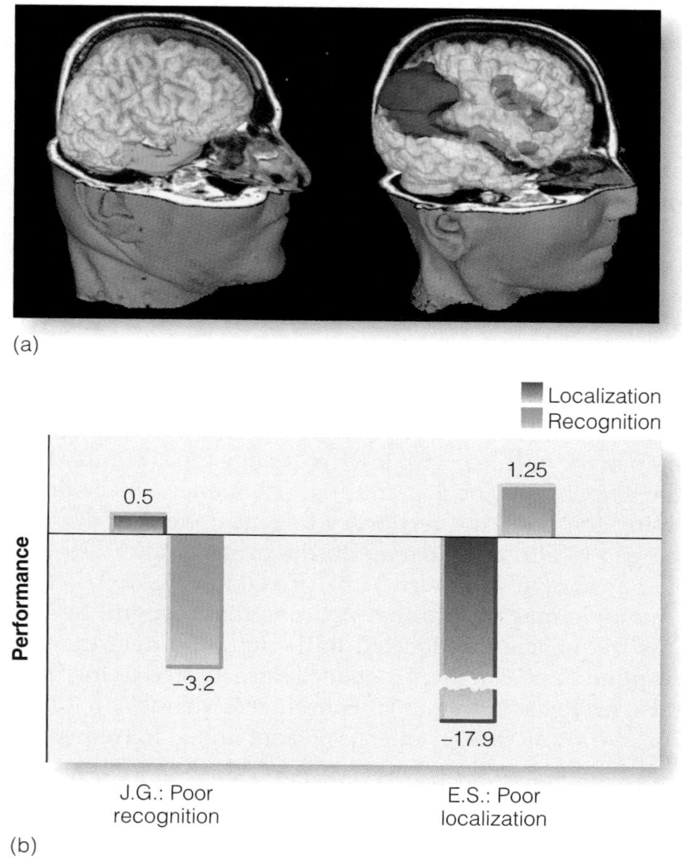

Figure 11.39 ▮ (a) Colored areas indicate brain damage for J.G. (left) and E.S. (right). (b) Performance on recognition test (green bar) and localization test (red bar). The horizontal line indicates normal performance.
(Clarke, S., Thiran, A. B., Maeder, P., Adriani, M., Vernet, O., Regli, L., Cuisenaire, O., & Thiran, J-P. (2002). What and where in human auditory: Selective deficits following focal hemispheric lesions. Experimental Brain Research, *147, 8–15.)*

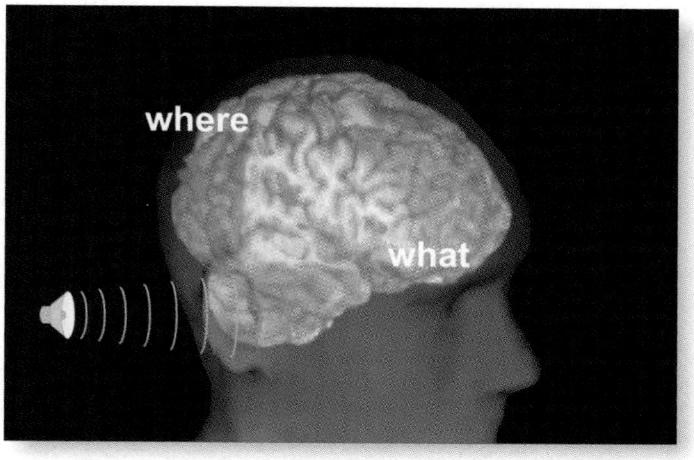

Figure 11.40 ▮ Areas associated with *what* (yellow) and *where* (blue) auditory functions as determined by brain imaging.
(Alain, C., Arnott, S. R., Hevenor, S., Graham, S., & Grady, C. L. (2001). "What" and "where" in the human auditory system. Proceedings of the National Academy of Sciences, 98, *12301–12306.)*

THE AUDITORY CORTEX AND PERCEPTION

What is the function of the primary auditory receiving area (A1)? As we will see in the next chapter, there is a great deal of evidence that A1 is necessary for localizing sounds. However, the situation for pitch perception has not been so straightforward.

Perceiving Pitch and Complex Sounds

One finding that seems to indicate that A1 would be important for perceiving pitch is the presence of tonotopic maps in A1. Just as pure tones are arranged in a tonotopic map in the cochlea, with low-frequency tones stimulating the apex of the cochlea and high-frequency tones stimulating the base, the responses to pure tones are also arranged in a tonotopic map on the primary auditory cortex, as shown in Figure 11.41 (Kosaki et al., 1997). This tonotopic map shows that neurons that respond best to low frequencies are located to the left, and neurons that respond best to higher frequencies are located to the right (also see Reale & Imig, 1980; Schreiner & Mendelson, 1990).

We know that (1) pitch is closely linked to frequency, and (2) there are tonotopic maps in A1, so it would seem reasonable to conclude that A1 would be important for perceiving pitch. However, the results of early research suggest that this is not the case because removal of A1 had little or no effect on a monkey's ability to learn to discriminate between different frequencies (Neff et al., 1975). These results puzzled researchers for years. However, advances in technology, better behavioral testing, and the use of more complex stimuli have recently led to the conclusion that A1 is, in fact, involved in perceiving pitch, especially for complex sound stimuli. Here is some of the evidence:

Effect of Training on Tonotopic Maps Training that involves a particular frequency increases the space devoted to that frequency in A1. Gregg Recanzone and coworkers (1993) demonstrated this by training owl monkeys to discriminate between two frequencies near 2,500 Hz. After the training had caused a large improvement in the monkey's ability to tell the difference between frequencies, a tonotopic map of A1 was determined (Recanzone et al., 1993). The results indicate that compared to a monkey that had no discrimination training (Figure 11.42a), the trained monkey (Figure 11.42b) had much more space devoted to neurons that respond best to 2,500 Hz.

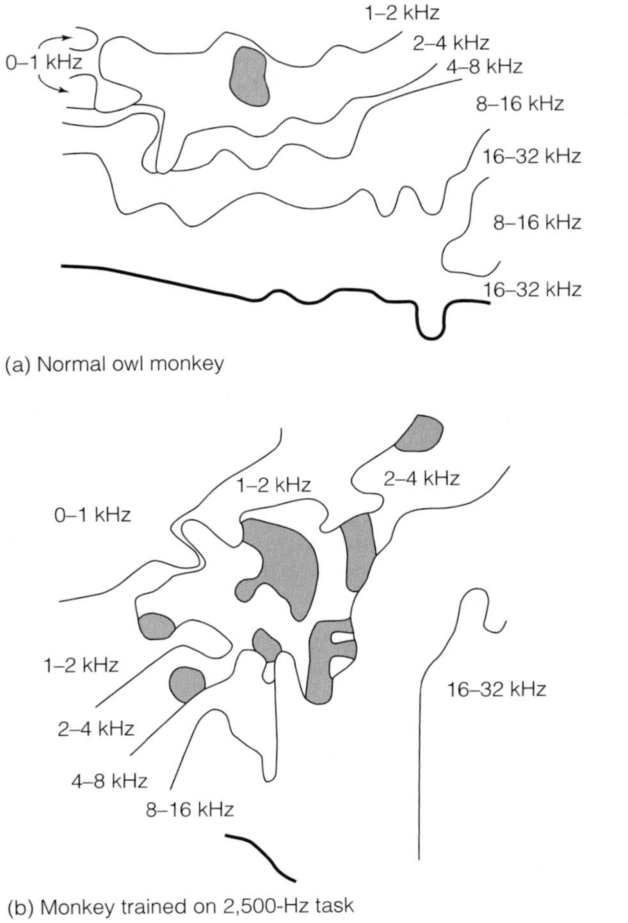

Figure 11.42 (a) Tonotopic map of the owl monkey's primary auditory receiving area (A1), showing areas that contain neurons with the characteristic frequencies indicated. The blue area contains neurons with CF = 2,500 Hz. (b) Tonotopic map of an owl monkey that was trained to discriminate between frequencies near 2,500 Hz. The blue areas indicate that after training more of the cortex responds best to 2,500 Hz. *(From Recanzone et al., 1993.)*

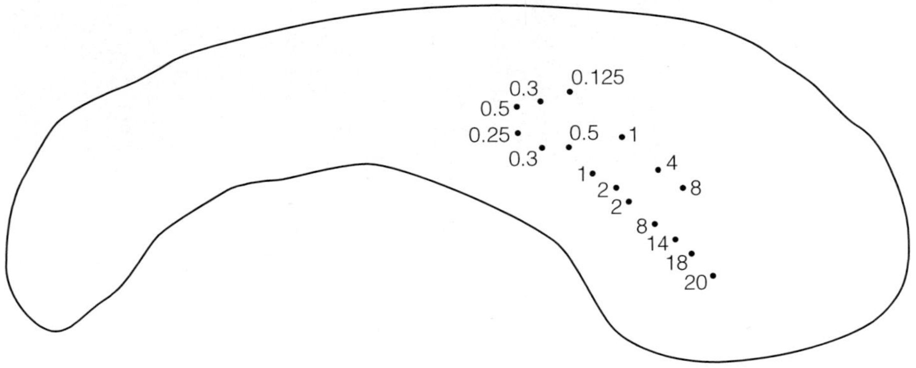

Figure 11.41 The outline of the core area of the monkey auditory cortex, showing the tonotopic map on the primary auditory receiving area, A1, which is located within the core. The numbers represent the characteristic frequencies (CF) of neurons in thousands of Hz. Low CF's are on the left, and high CF's are on the right. *(Adapted from Kosaki et al., 1997).*

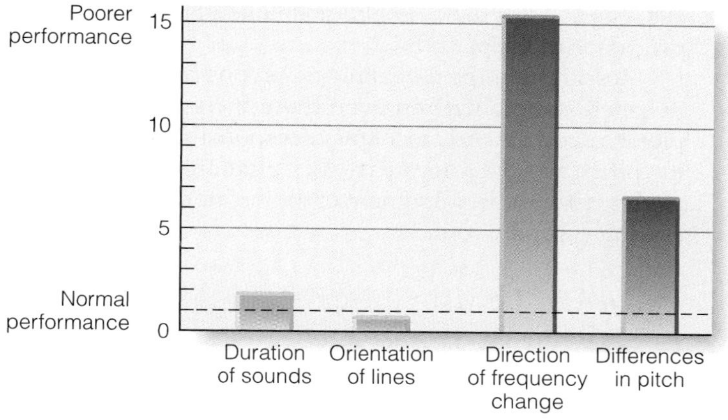

Figure 11.43 ▮ Performance of patient A, with auditory cortex damage, on 4 tasks. See text for details.
(Based on data from Tramo et al., 2002.)

Effect of Brain Damage in Humans Mark Tramo and coworkers (2002) studied a patient they called *A*, who had suffered extensive damage to his auditory cortex on both sides of the brain due to two successive strokes. The green bars in Figure 11.43 show that *A's* ability to judge the duration of sounds and the orientation of lines was normal, but the red bars show that his ability to judge the direction of frequency change (high to low or low to high) and to detect differences in pitch were much worse than normal. This result, which shows that damage to the auditory cortex affects the ability to discriminate between frequencies, led Tramo to conclude that the auditory cortex is important for frequency discrimination.

Brain Scans in Humans The results of brain scan experiments reveal a very important property of the auditory areas of the cortex: Tasks that require the recognition of pitch tend to activate areas that are equivalent to the core area in monkeys, whereas tasks that require the recognition of more complex stimuli, like melodies, activate areas outside the core that are equivalent to the monkey's parabelt area (Patterson et al., 2002; also see Griffiths et al., 1996; Warren et al., 2003).

This finding fits with a result from monkey research that we mentioned earlier, when we introduced the idea of hierarchical processing on page 254: The core area can be activated by pure tones, but outside the core, complex auditory stimuli are more effective. Thus, results from both monkeys and humans demonstrate that similar principles hold for the visual and auditory systems: early cortical areas, such as A1 and V1, can be activated by simple stimuli (spots and lines for vision; pure tones for hearing), but later areas that are farther "downstream" need more complex stimuli to become activated (faces and buildings for vision; band-passed noise, communication sounds, and melodies for hearing).

The Effect of the Missing Fundamental

To end our discussion of the function of the auditory cortex, we will consider a perceptual effect that has intrigued and puzzled auditory researchers for years. This is the phenomenon called the **effect of the missing fundamental**—removing the fundamental frequency and other lower harmonics from a musical tone does not change the tone's pitch.

We can understand this effect by considering the frequency spectra in Figure 11.44. (Remember from Figure 11.9 that each line represents the harmonic with frequency indicated under the line, and the height of the line indicates the amount of energy in that harmonic.) The spectrum in Figure 11.44a is for a tone with a fundamental frequency of 400 Hz. Figure 11.44b shows the same spectrum, but with the fundamental removed, and Figure 11.44c, with the fundamental and two additional harmonics removed. If you were to listen to the sounds produced by these three stimuli, you would notice that their timbre has changed, so tones (b) and (c) sound different from the tone that contains the fundamental and all the harmonics. However, you would also notice that even though the *timbres* of the tones are different, the *pitches* of all three are the same. Thus, based on pitch, a person could match all three sounds to a 400-Hz pure tone. This constancy of pitch, even when lower harmonics

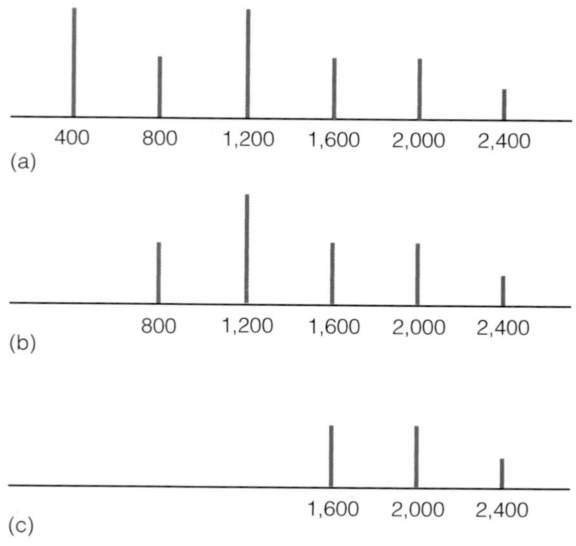

Figure 11.44 ▮ (a) Frequency spectra for a tone with a fundamental frequency of 400 Hz. (b) First harmonic (the fundamental) removed. (c) First three harmonics removed. All three of these tones are perceived to have the same pitch.

are removed, is the effect of the missing fundamental, and the pitch that we perceive in tones that have had harmonics removed is called **periodicity pitch**. VL 9, 10

The phenomenon of periodicity pitch has a number of practical consequences. Consider, for example, what happens as you listen to music on a cheap radio that can't reproduce frequencies below 300 Hz. If the music contains a tone with a fundamental frequency of 100 Hz, your radio can't reproduce the fundamental frequency of the 100-Hz tone or of the 200-Hz second harmonic of that tone. Even though the radio reproduces only the third (300-Hz) and higher (400, 500, 600, and so on) harmonics of this tone, periodicity pitch comes to the rescue and causes you to perceive a pitch equivalent to that produced by a 100-Hz tone. Similarly, even though the telephone doesn't reproduce the fundamental frequency of the human voice, we are usually able to recognize familiar voices on the phone (Truax, 1984).

Our experience of periodicity pitch means that the perception of the pitch of complex tones can't be explained by considering only the basilar membrane's pattern of vibration. We say this because all of the sound stimuli in Figures 11.44 have the same pitch, even though they cause different patterns of vibration on the basilar membrane. This means that our perception of pitch must be determined not just by the activity in the cochlea but by the way structures past the cochlea analyze the information that originates in the cochlea.

One piece of evidence that supports this is the finding that periodicity pitch is perceived even when two tones are presented to different ears. For example, presenting a 400-Hz tone to the left ear and a 500-Hz tone to the right ear would result in a perception of pitch that corresponds to 100 Hz (see Houtsma & Goldstein, 1972). (Remember that harmonics are always multiples of the fundamental frequency. This means that the difference between two adjacent harmonics corresponds to the fundamental frequency, so in this example, the fundamental frequency associated with these two tones would be 100 Hz.) The fact that periodicity pitch is perceived when the tones are presented to separate ears means that pitch perception must be determined somewhere in the auditory system where signals from both ears are combined. The first place this occurs is the superior olivary nucleus (see Figure 11.36).

Further evidence that pitch is determined centrally is the finding that patients with damage to a specific area of the auditory cortex in the right hemisphere are unable to hear periodicity pitch (Zatorre, 1988). These results and others have led to the proposal that our perception of the pitch of complex tones is the result of a **central pitch processor** in the cortex—a central mechanism that analyzes the pattern of harmonics and selects the fundamental frequency that is most likely to have been part of that pattern (see Evans, 1978; Getty & Howard, 1981; J. L. Goldstein, 1978; Meddis & Hewitt, 1991; Srulovicz & Goldstein, 1983; and Wightman, 1973, for details of various central processor models).

Research on the mechanism responsible for periodicity pitch is ongoing. But even though we still can't completely describe the mechanism responsible for periodicity pitch, we do know that this phenomenon provides evidence for the involvement of the auditory cortex in processing complex sounds.

How the Auditory Cortex Is Shaped by Experience

In Chapter 4 we described how the phenomenon of experience-dependent plasticity operates in the visual system. An example we cited is the Greeble experiments, which showed that training people to recognize Greebles increased the neural response to Greebles in the fusiform face area (FFA; see page 86). An example of experience-dependent plasticity in the auditory system is the experiment we described on page 256, in which training owl monkeys to discriminate between frequencies near 2,500 Hz increased the amount of space on the cortex devoted to this frequency (Figure 11.42).

Experience-dependent plasticity for hearing has also been demonstrated for humans. Christo Pantev and coworkers (1998) showed that musical training enlarges the area of auditory cortex that responds to piano tones. They compared the cortical response to piano tones of musicians who had been playing their instruments from 12 to 28 years to the response of people who had never played an instrument. The results indicated that 25 percent more cortex was activated for the musicians compared to the nonmusicians. Another study has shown that electrical activity elicited from the auditory areas of professional musicians is twice as strong as the activity elicited from the auditory areas of nonmusicians (Schneider et al., 2002).

Thus, just as visual areas of the brain are shaped by training with visual stimuli, auditory areas are shaped by training with auditory stimuli. Perhaps the most striking demonstration of shaping-by-training is an experiment by Jonathan Fritz and coworkers (2003), which showed how rapidly experience-dependent plasticity can occur for hearing. He demonstrated this by recording from neurons in the marmoset while they were involved in an auditory task.

Figure 11.45a is a plot that shows how a neuron in the marmoset's auditory cortex responds to different frequencies before training. In this plot, red and yellow indicates increased firing in response to sound, green indicates an average level of firing, and blue indicates decreased firing in response to sound. Thus, this plot indicates how the neuron responds to frequencies between 2,000 and 16,000 Hz (vertical axis) at various times after the tone is presented (horizontal axis). For example, look at the dashed line labeled A in Figure 11.45a. Looking at the far left, we can see that just after an 8,000-Hz tone is presented, firing rate increases and then continues at a high

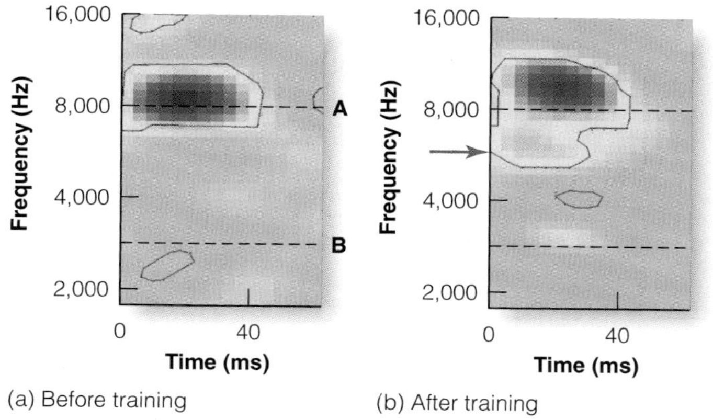

Figure 11.45 ▌ Response of a neuron in the marmoset auditory cortex: (a) before training; (b) after training. See text for details. *(Fritz, J., Shamma, S., Elhilali, M., & Klein, D. (2003). Rapid task-related plasticity of spectrotemporal receptive fields in primary auditory cortex.* Nature Neuroscience, *6, 1216–1223.)*

rate for 40 ms. In contrast, the dashed line labeled B indicates that this neuron's firing rate remains about the same when a 3,000-Hz tone is presented.

Once Fritz determined the characteristics of a particular neuron, he then trained the marmoset to lick a water spout as it was hearing a series of complex sounds and to stop licking when it heard a pure tone. Thus, in a particular block of trials the marmoset was learning to be ready to respond to a particular frequency of pure tone.

After just a few trials in which the marmoset responded to the pure tone, Fritz remeasured the neuron's response function and obtained the plot in Figure 11.45b. The frequency of the training tone is indicated by the arrow, and if we look directly to the right of this arrow, we can see that the neuron's response profile has changed so its firing rate now increases to this frequency (indicated by yellow), whereas before training it remained about the same (indicated by green). Thus, just a small amount of training caused the neuron to become tuned to respond better to this frequency. What is amazing about this result is not only how rapidly it occurred, but that in many neurons the effect lasted for hours after the training. The auditory system, therefore, shapes its neurons to respond better to environmental stimuli that are behaviorally important to the animal. If this sounds familiar, it is because the same thing happens in the visual system (see pages 85–86; 106–107).

SOMETHING TO CONSIDER: COCHLEAR IMPLANTS—WHERE SCIENCE AND CULTURE MEET

One cause of deafness is damage to the hair cells in the cochlea. When this occurs, hearing aids are ineffective because the damaged hair cells cannot convert the amplified sound provided by the hearing aid into electrical signals. A solution to this problem has been provided by a device called a **cochlear implant** in which electrodes are inserted in the cochlea to create hearing by electrically stimulating the auditory nerve fibers.

The Technology

The cochlear implant bypasses the damaged hair cells and stimulates auditory nerve fibers directly. The following are the basic components of a cochlear implant (Figure 11.46):

- The microphone (1), which is worn behind the person's ear, receives the sound signal, transforms it into electrical signals, and sends these signals to the sound processor.
- The sound processor (2), which looks like a small transistor radio, shapes the signal generated by the microphone to emphasize the information needed for the perception of speech by splitting the range of frequencies received by the microphone into a number of frequency bands. These signals are sent, in the form of an electrical code, from the processor to the transmitter. Newer versions of cochlear implants now package the entire sound processor in what looks like a behind-the-ear hearing aid.
- The transmitter (3), mounted on the mastoid bone, just behind the ear, transmits the coded signals received from the processor through the skin to the receiver.
- The receiver (4) is surgically mounted on the mastoid bone, beneath the skin. It picks up the coded signals from the transmitter and converts the code into signals that are sent to electrodes implanted inside the cochlea (5).

The implant makes use of Békésy's observation that there is a tonotopic map of frequencies on the cochlea, in which high frequencies are represented by activity near the base of the cochlea and low frequencies are represented by activity at the apex of the cochlea. The most widely used implants therefore have a multichannel design that uses a number of electrodes to stimulate the cochlea at different places along its length, depending on the frequencies in the stimuli received by the microphone. Stimulation of the cochlea causes signals to be sent the auditory area of the cortex, and hearing results.

What does a person using this system hear? The answer to this question depends on the person. Most people are able to recognize a few everyday sounds, such as horns honking, doors closing, and water running. In addition, many people are able to perceive speech. In the best cases, people can perceive speech on the telephone, but it is more common for cochlear-implant recipients to use the sounds perceived from their implant in conjunction with speech reading. In one test, 24 people scored

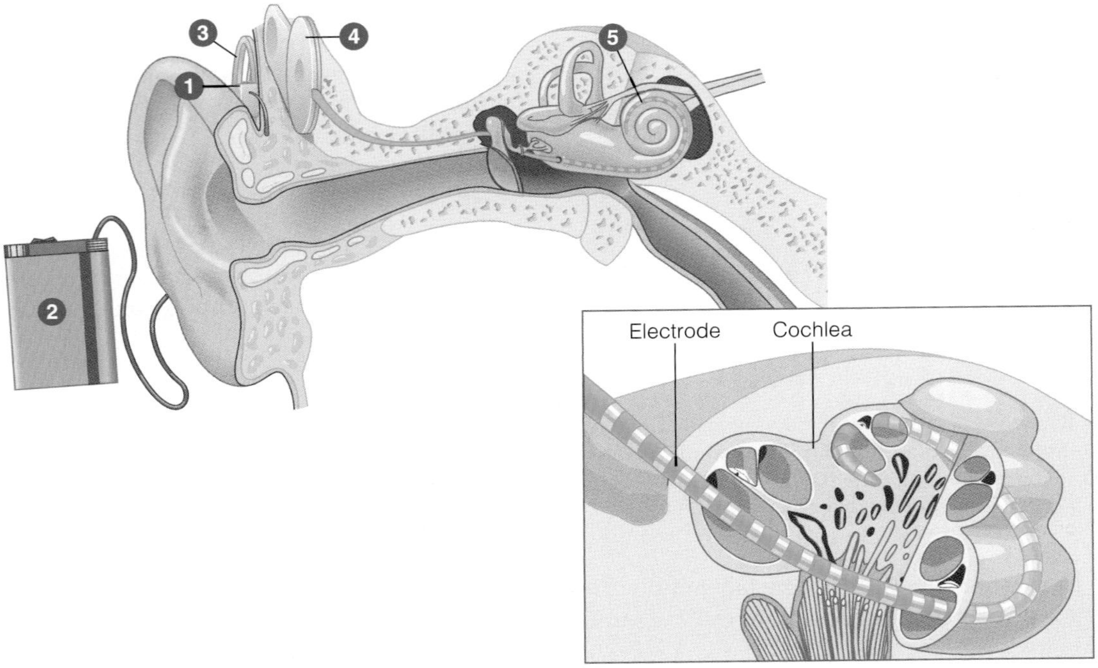

Figure 11.46 ▮ Cochlear implant device. See text for details.

54 percent on a test of speech reading alone and 83 percent when speech reading was combined with sound from the implant. In addition, the implant enabled people to track speech much more rapidly—16 words per minute using speech reading alone and 44 words per minute with speech reading plus the implant (Brown, Dowell, & Clark, 1987; Owens, 1989). In another test it was found that deaf children who received a cochlear implant before the age of 5 years were able to learn to produce speech more easily than children who received the implant when they were older (Tye-Murray, Spencer, & Woodworth, 1995).

As of 2002, over 40,000 people had received cochlear implants (Rauschecker & Shannon, 2002). The best results occur for people who were able to perceive speech before they became deaf. These people are most likely to understand speech with the aid of the implant because they already know how to connect the sounds of speech with specific meanings. Thus, these people's ability to perceive speech often improves with time, as they again learn to link sounds with meanings.

The development of cochlear implants is an impressive demonstration of how basic research yields practical benefits. The technology of cochlear implants, which has made it possible to bring deaf adults and children into the world of hearing (Kiefer et al., 1996; Tye-Murray et al., 1995), is the end result of discoveries that began in perception or physiology laboratories many years earlier. In this case, it was George von Békésy's research on how the vibration of the basilar membrane depends on the frequency of the sound that provided the knowledge about the operation of the ear that made implants possible.

The Controversy

Many deaf people have had strong negative reactions to cochlear implants. It might be hard for a hearing person to understand why. "After all," a hearing person might say, "don't cochlear implants offer an opportunity for deaf people to enter the world of the hearing?" But many deaf people see statements like this as part of the problem. To people in the deaf community, the cochlear implant is a symbol of the hearing world's desire to "fix" deaf people, even though deaf people can communicate perfectly well with American Sign Language (ASL) and have a rich and functioning culture that is every bit as vibrant and fulfilling as other cultures that are based on ethnicity or nationality. Thus, many in the deaf community see the widespread use of cochlear implants, particularly in young children, as a threat to the existence of their culture (CBS News, 2001; Scientific American Frontiers, 2001).

In addition to the cultural issue, there is also the fear that a young child receiving an implant will be handicapped in terms of language development if receiving the implant causes him or her to avoid learning American Sign Language. The problem is that the sounds provided by the implant generally do not replace the richness of language that is available to someone who is fluent in ASL, and early experience with language is important not only for communication, but for cognitive development in general.

This controversy about cochlear implants was highlighted in 2001 by an award-winning documentary called *The Sound and the Fury*. The controversy still continues, however it may be cooling somewhat. The National Association of the Deaf, which had opposed cochlear implants for years, recently decided not to take sides on the issue. Reasons for this shift include improvements in cochlear implant technology and an increased awareness that a child who is exposed to both oral English and American Sign Language may be able to function in both hearing and deaf worlds without changing the child's positive identification as a deaf person.

TEST YOURSELF 11.3

1. What is the pathway from the cochlea to the auditory cortex, and what functions might it serve, over and above simply transmitting signals to the brain?
2. What areas of the brain, in addition to the primary auditory receiving area (A1), respond to auditory stimuli?
3. What is the evidence for *what* and *where* streams for hearing?
4. What is the evidence that the auditory cortex is important for perceiving pitch? What are some parallels between auditory research on this problem and research we have described earlier on the visual system?
5. What is the evidence that the auditory cortex is "plastic"?
6. How does a cochlear implant work? How successful has this technology been at providing hearing to deaf individuals? Why is this procedure controversial in the deaf community?

THINK ABOUT IT

1. In the effect of the missing fundamental, the brain somehow creates a perception of pitch that is usually associated with the fundamental frequency of a complex tone, even though the fundamental frequency is absent. What information about the fundamental frequency might the brain use to achieve this?
2. One of the principles that we introduced in studying vision is how perception can be determined by activity at all levels in the visual system, from receptors to the brain. What are some examples of this principle for the sense of hearing?
3. Which auditory streams, *what*, *where*, or a combination of the two, would be involved in the following: (1) finding an object dropped in the dark based on hearing it roll across the rug and onto the floor; (2) recognizing a friend's voice on the telephone; (3) listening to music through headphones; (4) following the sound of an ambulance as it speeds down the street with its siren blaring.

IF YOU WANT TO KNOW MORE

1. ***Activation of Auditory Cortex by Vision*** Deaf people use the visual sense to help them understand speech, by "speech reading" (reading lip and face movements). It has been shown that speech reading activates the auditory cortex. Another example of one sense being activated by stimulation usually associated with another sense is that the visual cortex is activated when blind people use touch to read Braille.

   Calvert, G. A., et al. (1997). Activation of auditory cortex during silent lipreading. *Science, 276,* 593–596.

   Sadato, N., et al. (1996). Activation of the primary visual cortex by Braille reading blind subjects. *Nature, 380,* 526–528.

2. ***Cross-Modal Experience: Synaesthesia*** One of the most intriguing connections between the senses is a phenomenon called synaesthesia, in which presentation of stimuli from one sense can cause an experience associated with another sense. An example of this would be seeing light in response to sound.

   Marks, L. (1975). On colored-hearing synaesthesia: Cross-modal translations of sensory dimensions. *Psychological Bulletin, 82,* 303–331.

   Paulesu, E., et al. (1995). The physiology of colored hearing. *Brain, 118,* 661–676.

3. ***Losing One Sense Can Hurt Another One*** There is evidence that deafness reduces performance on visual attention tasks and that a cochlear implant can improve both hearing and visual attention.

   Quittner, A. L., et al. (1994). The impact of audition on the development of visual attention. *Psychological Science, 5,* 347–353.

4. ***The Cochlear Implant Controversy*** The controversy over the use of cochlear implants that is discussed at the end of this chapter is a fascinating one that touches many people's lives. To find out more, go to Google or another search engine, and type in "cochlear implant controversy."

KEY TERMS

Additive synthesis (p. 239)
Amplitude (p. 236)
Apex of the cochlea (p. 244)
Attack (p. 240)
Audibility curve (p. 238)
Auditory canal (p. 241)
Auditory masking (p. 248)
Auditory receiving area (A1) (p. 254)
Auditory response area (p. 238)
Base of the cochlea (p. 244)
Basilar membrane (p. 244)
Belt area (p. 254)
Central pitch processor (p. 258)
Characteristic frequency (p. 247)
Cilia (p. 244)
Cochlea (p. 243)
Cochlear implant (p. 259)
Cochlear nucleus (p. 254)
Cochlear partition (p. 244)
Core area (p. 254)
Decay (p. 241)
Decibel (p. 237)
Eardrum (p. 241)
Effect of the missing fundamental (p. 257)
Envelope of the traveling wave (p. 246)
Equal loudness curve (p. 239)
Fourier analysis (p. 251)
Frequency (p. 236)
Frequency spectrum (p. 240)
Frequency tuning curve (p. 247)
Fundamental frequency (p. 239)
Hair cells (p. 244)
Harmonics (p. 239)
Hearing (p. 236)
Hertz (Hz) (p. 237)
Hierarchical processing (p. 254)
Incus (p. 242)
Inferior colliculus (p. 254)
Inner ear (p. 243)
Inner hair cells (p. 244)
Level (p. 237)
Loudness (p. 236)
Malleus (p. 242)
Medial geniculate nucleus (p. 254)
Middle ear (p. 242)
Middle-ear muscles (p. 243)
Motile response (p. 249)
Octave (p. 238)
Organ of Corti (p. 244)
Ossicles (p. 242)
Outer ear (p. 241)
Outer hair cells (p. 244)
Oval window (p. 242)
Parabelt area (p. 254)
Periodicity pitch (p. 258)
Phase locking (p. 252)
Pinna (p. 241)
Pitch (p. 237)
Place theory of hearing (p. 246)
Psychophysical tuning curve (p. 250)
Pure tone (p. 236)
Resonance (p. 242)
Resonant frequency (p. 242)
Sound (p. 235)
Sound level (p. 237)
Sound pressure level (SPL) (p. 237)
Sound wave (p. 235)
Stapes (p. 242)
Subcortical structure (p. 254)
Superior olivary nucleus (p. 254)
Tectorial membrane (p. 244)
Timbre (p. 239)
Tone chroma (p. 238)
Tone height (p. 238)
Tonotopic map (p. 247)
Traveling wave (p. 246)
Tympanic membrane (p. 241)

VISIT YOUR COMPANION WEBSITE FOR THIS BOOK

http://psychology.wadsworth.com/goldstein7e

Check out this companion website where you'll find online resources—glossary, flashcards, web links, multiple-choice and essay questions, and much more!

VIRTUAL LAB

Your Virtual Lab is designed to help you get the most out of this course. The Virtual Lab icons direct you to specific media demonstrations and experiments designed to help you visualize what you are reading about. The number beside each icon indicates the number of the media element you can access through your CD-ROM, Perception PsychologyNow, or WebTutor resource http:now.ilrn.com/goldstein_7e.

The following lab exercises cover what you've just learned in this chapter:

1 *Decibel Scale* Demonstrates how loudness increases for a 10-dB increase in decibels.

2 *Loudness Scaling* Do a magnitude estimation experiment to determine the relationship between dB and loudness.

3 *Tone Height and Tone Chroma* A demonstration of tone height and tone chroma.

4 *Frequency Response of the Ear* Shows how our ability to hear a tone that is always at the same dB level depends on its frequency.

5 *Harmonics of a Gong* A demonstration that enables you to hear each of the individual harmonics that make up the sound produced by a gong.

6 *Effect of Harmonics on Timbre* How adding harmonics to a tone changes the quality of the sound.

7 *Timbre of a Piano Tone Played Backward* How changing presenting piano tones backward (so the end of the tone comes first and the beginning come last) affects our perception of the tone's quality.

8 *Masking High and Low Frequencies* How a high-frequency test tone and a low-frequency test tone are affected by a masking tone.

9 *Periodicity Pitch: Eliminating the Fundamental and Lower Harmonics* How your perception of a tone changes as harmonics are removed.

10 *Periodicity Pitch: St. Martin's Chimes With Harmonics Removed* How your perception of a melody changes as harmonics are removed.

CHAPTER 12

SOUND LOCALIZATION AND THE AUDITORY SCENE

Chapter Contents

The band U2 performing at the opening of the 2002 Grammy awards at the Staples Center in Los Angeles. Our perception of music depends on the nature of the sound stimuli produced by musical instruments and the human voice, the acoustics of the venue where the music is being played, and the physiological functioning of the auditory system. © Reuters/CORBIS

VL *The Virtual Lab icons direct you to specific animations and videos designed to help you visualize what you are reading about. The number beside each icon indicates the number of the clip you can access through your CD-ROM or your student website.*

Some Questions We Will Consider:

- *What makes it possible to tell where a sound is coming from in space? (p. 267)*
- *When we are listening to a number of musical instruments playing at the same time, how can we perceptually separate the sounds coming from the different instruments? (p. 274)*
- *Why does music sound better in some concert halls than in others? (p. 280)*

Imagine you are at a concert. The setting is intimate and the music is unamplified, so what you hear is what is coming out of the instruments, not loudspeakers. The vocalist is in front center, and the guitar, drums, and piano are spread out across the stage, with the piano on the left and drums on the right. You note that the sound seems more "spacious" in person than when you listen to it on your iPod, and as you close your eyes you can easily locate the singer directly in front, the piano to the left, and the drums to the right. You also note one of the disadvantages of a live performance as you try to ignore the irritating voice of the person directly behind you, who can't seem to stop talking.

In this chapter, we will consider how you are able to judge where sounds are coming from, even with your eyes closed. We will first describe the auditory stimuli and then how the auditory system processes these stimuli. We will also consider another aspect of your listening experience—your ability to hear the sounds produced by each of the musicians separately, even as they play together. Finally, we will consider how your experience is affected by the fact that you are listening to music inside a small room, as opposed to a larger room, or outside.

AUDITORY LOCALIZATION

When you perceive objects located at different positions based on their sounds, you are experiencing **auditory space**. Auditory space extends around your head in all directions, existing wherever there is a sound. To experience auditory space, close your eyes and notice the sounds around you, paying particular attention to the directions and distances of these sounds. Unless you are in an extremely quiet environment, you will probably be able to perceive objects (a computer humming, for example) and events (people talking, cars driving by) located at various positions in space.

These feats of locating objects in space based on their sound are examples of **auditory localization**. Researchers have studied people's ability to localize sounds by determining how well people can locate the position of the sound along the **azimuth coordinate**, which extends from left to right (Figure 12.1), the **elevation coordinate**, which extends up and down, and the **distance coordinate**, which specifies how far a sound source is from the listener. In this chapter, we will be focusing on the azimuth and elevation coordinates. In the following demonstration, you can determine how well people can localize sounds along these coordinates.

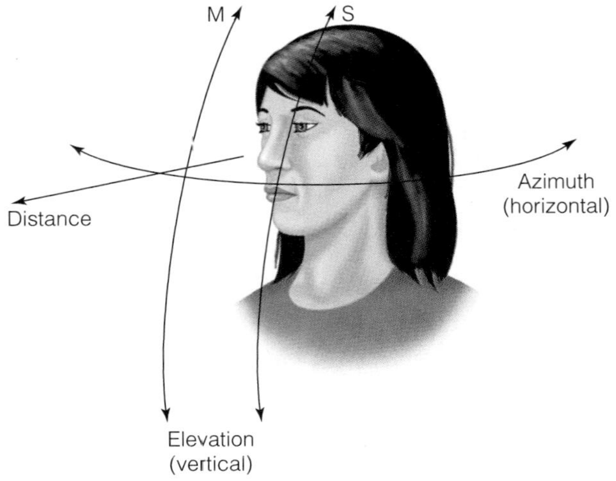

Figure 12.1 ▌ Azimuth, elevation, and distance coordinates for localization. Two elevation coordinates are shown, one (M) in which the vertical coordinate is positioned on the person's midline, and the other (S), which is off to the side.

DEMONSTRATION

Sound Localization

Have a friend close her eyes. Say that you are going to rattle your keys at various places around her head and that she should point to where the sound is coming from. Do this along the person's azimuth (left to right) and elevation (up and down) coordinates, and include some sounds both in front of the person and behind her head. Note how accurate she is for sounds in various locations. After you are through, ask your friend if she found some locations harder to judge than others. ■

There is substantial variability between different listeners' ability to localize sounds (so you might want to try this on a few people), but when measurements from a number of people are averaged, results like those in Figure 12.2 are obtained. This figure indicates, on an imaginary sphere that surrounds a listener's head, how well listeners can localize sounds that are in different positions in space (Makous & Middlebrooks, 1990; Middlebrooks & Green, 1991). Listeners can localize sounds that are directly in front of them most accurately (localization errors average 2 to 3.5 degrees) and sounds that are off to the side and behind their head least accurately (localization errors are as high as 20 degrees).

The problems the auditory system faces in determining locations are formidable. We can appreciate one of the

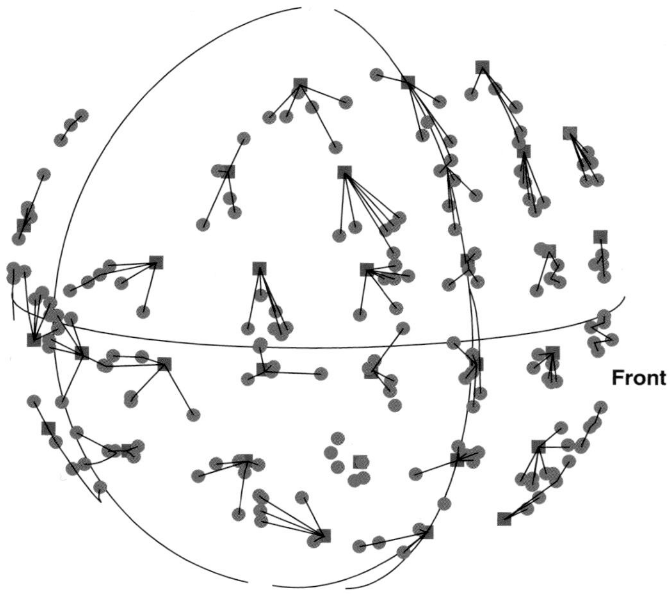

Figure 12.2 ■ Measurements of sound localization ability. Red squares indicate the actual sound locations, and the circles are the listeners' estimates of their location. Longer lines connecting the squares and circles indicate less accurate localization.

(From "Sound Localization by Human Listeners," by J. C. Middlebrooks & David M. Green, 1991, Annual Review of Psychology, *42, 135–159, figure 1. Copyright © 1991 Annual Reviews, Inc. Reprinted by permission.)*

problems by comparing the information available for vision and for hearing in Figure 12.3. Information for the relative locations of the bird and the cat are contained in the image of the bird and the cat on the surface of the retina. But the ear is different—the frequencies of the bird's *tweet* and cat's *meow* are indicated by the place that is stimulated along the cochlea, but there is no information for location. To determine the location of the cat and bird, the auditory system carries out a calculation that makes use of **location cues** created by the way sound interacts with the listener's head and ears.

Cues for Location: Signals Reaching the Ears

There are two types of location cues. **Binaural cues** are based on sound reaching the left and right ears. **Monaural cues** depend on just one ear.

Binaural Cues The two binaural cues—interaural time difference and interaural intensity difference—are based on a comparison of the sound signals reaching the left and right ears. Sounds that are off to the side reach one ear before the other. The difference between the times that the sound reaches the left and right ears is called the **interaural time difference (ITD)**. The basis for the idea that there is a difference in the time that a sound reaches the left and right ears is illustrated in Figure 12.4. When the source is located directly in front of the listener, at A,

Figure 12.3 ■ Comparing location information for vision and hearing. *Vision:* The bird and cat are located at different places and are imaged on different places on the retina. *Hearing:* The frequencies in the sounds from the bird and cat are spread out over the cochlea, with no regard to the locations of the bird and cat.

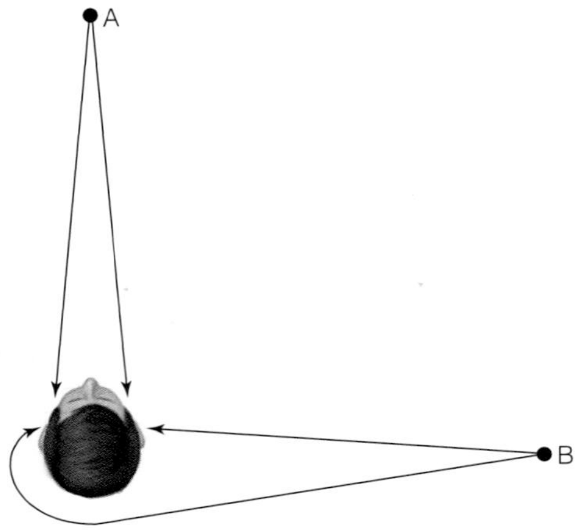

Figure 12.4 ▌ The principle behind interaural time difference (ITD). The tone directly in front of the listener, at A, reaches the left and the right ears at the same time. However, when the tone is off to the side, at B, it reaches the listener's right ear before it reaches the left ear.

the distance to each ear is the same, and the sound reaches the left and right ears simultaneously. However, if a source is located off to the side, at B, the sound reaches the right ear before it reaches the left ear. Because the ITD is larger for sounds that are located more to the side, the magnitude of the ITD can be used as a cue to determine a sound's location (Wightman & Kistler, 1998).

The other binaural cue, **interaural level difference (ILD)**, is based on the difference in the sound pressure level (or just "level") of the sound reaching the two ears. A difference in level between the two ears occurs because the head creates a barrier that reduces the intensity of sounds that reach the far ear. This reduction of intensity at the far ear occurs for high-frequency sounds, but not for low-frequency sounds.

VIRTUAL LAB 1

We can understand why an ILD occurs for high frequencies but not for low frequencies by drawing an analogy between sound waves and water waves. Consider, for example, the small ripples in Figure 12.5a that are ap-

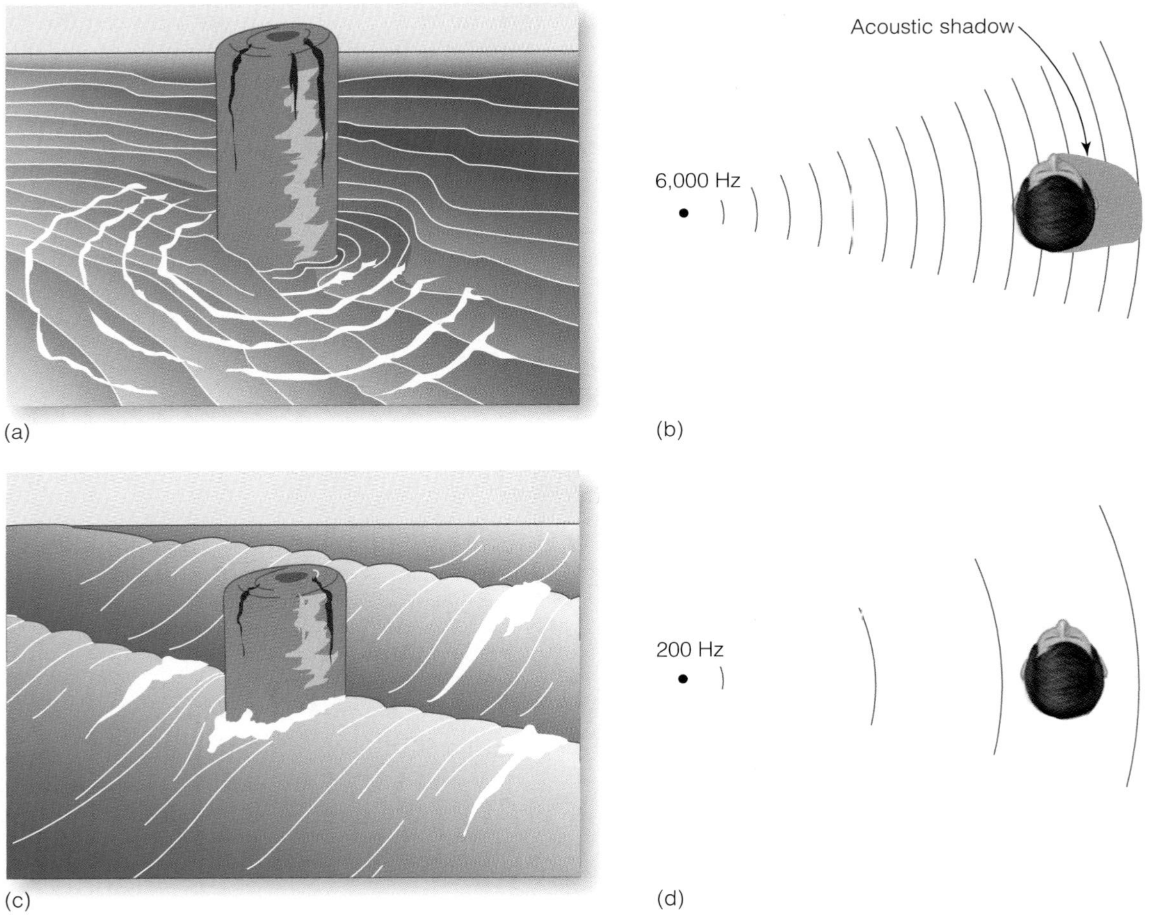

Figure 12.5 ▌ Why interaural level difference (ILD) occurs for high frequencies but not for low frequencies. (a) The pole interferes with small water ripples just as (b) the listener's head interferes with small high-frequency sound waves. (c) The pole does not interfere with large waves, just as (d) the listener's head does not interfere with large low-frequency sound waves.

proaching a pole protruding from the water. Because the spacing of these ripples is smaller than the size of the pole, they hit the front of the pole and bounce off. This changes the motion of the ripples on the other side of the pole. Similarly, the high-frequency sound waves shown in Figure 12.6b are disrupted by the head, which creates a decrease in sound intensity on the far side of the head, called the **acoustic shadow**.

In contrast to what happens for small ripples, the large waves shown in Figure 12.5c proceed uninterrupted past the pole. Similarly, the low-frequency sound waves in Figure 12.5d, which are spaced far apart compared to the size of a person's head, are unaffected by the head. Thus, the cue of ILD is not effective for low-frequency sound stimuli.

This effect of frequency on the interaural level difference has been measured by using small microphones to record the intensity of the sound reaching each ear in response to a sound source located at different positions relative to the head (Figure 12.6). The results show that the level is hardly affected by changes in location for frequencies below about 1,000 Hz, but that the level is greatly affected by locations for higher frequencies.

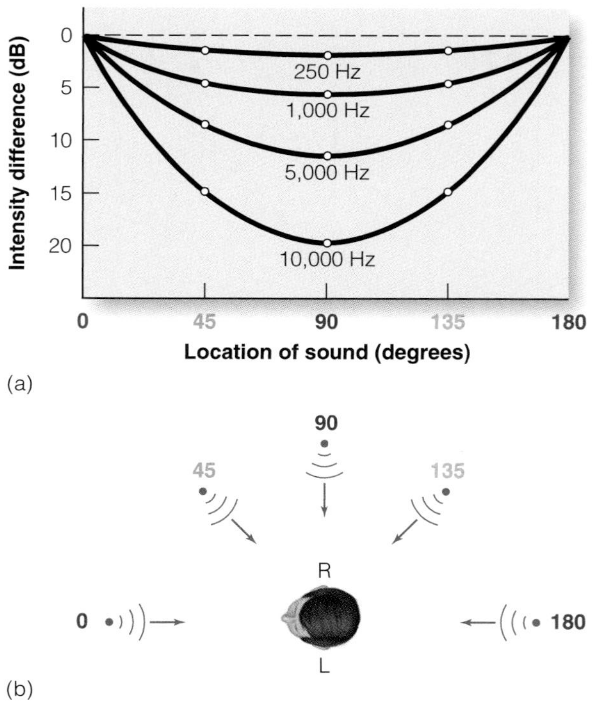

Figure 12.6 ▌ (a) The difference in intensity between the two ears for a 70-dB-SPL tone of different frequencies located at different places around the head. (b) The dots indicate the locations of the tones used for the intensity measurement in the graph in (a). The tones were all located 2 m from the center of the listener's head.

(From Hearing: Physiological Acoustics, Neural Coding and Psychoacoustics, *by W. Lawrence Gulick, G. A. Gescheider, R. D. Frisina, 1989, p. 324. Copyright ©1989 by Oxford University Press, Inc. Reprinted by permission.)*

Monaural Cue Before the sound stimulus enters the auditory canal, it is reflected from the head and back and forth within the various folds of the pinnae. The effect of this interaction with the head and pinnae has been measured by placing small microphones inside a listener's ears and comparing the frequencies picked up by the microphones with the frequencies coming from the sound source. The difference between the sound from the source and the sound actually entering the ears is called the **head-related transfer function (HRTF)** because the head and pinnae decrease the intensity of some frequencies and enhance others (Middlebrooks, 1997; Wightman & Kistler, 1993; Yost, 2001).

The HRTF is called a **spectral cue** because information for location is provided by the spectrum of frequencies that occurs at each location. This is illustrated in Figure 12.7, which shows the HRTFs for sounds coming from different elevations along the midline. For sound coming from below, there are decreases (or notches) in the HRTF at around 6,000 Hz, 11,000 Hz, and 14,000 Hz; but for sound directly in front, there is a notch at 10,000 Hz and a peak at 13,000 Hz, and, for sound from above, there is a large notch between 8,000 and 10,000 Hz (Middlebrooks, 2000). These different patterns of frequencies for different locations are the spectral cues to localization. As we will see below, listeners use the information provided by all three cues—spectral, ITD, and ILD—to determine the locations of sounds.

Cues for Location: Effects on Behavior

So far we have been describing the information for determining location that is provided by binaural and monaural cues. But what is the evidence that this information is actually used? To answer this question, we need to do behavioral experiments. An important technique that has been used in these behavioral experiments is the virtual auditory space technique.

METHOD ▪ Virtual Auditory Space

Sound stimuli can be presented to listeners in two ways. **Free-field presentation** involves presenting sounds at various positions around a listener's head. This is usually accomplished by moving speakers to different positions in space, and testing the listener in the dark. The listener indicates the position of the sound, either by pointing to it or by indicating azimuth and elevation coordinates. **Headphone presentation** involves presenting sounds through headphones. This way of presenting sound has the advantage that the experimenter has precise control over the stimuli. For example, it is possible to vary the timing and intensities of the signals reaching the left and right ears.

However, having the listener wear headphones creates a problem. Wearing the headphones eliminates the spectral cues that are created by sound bouncing

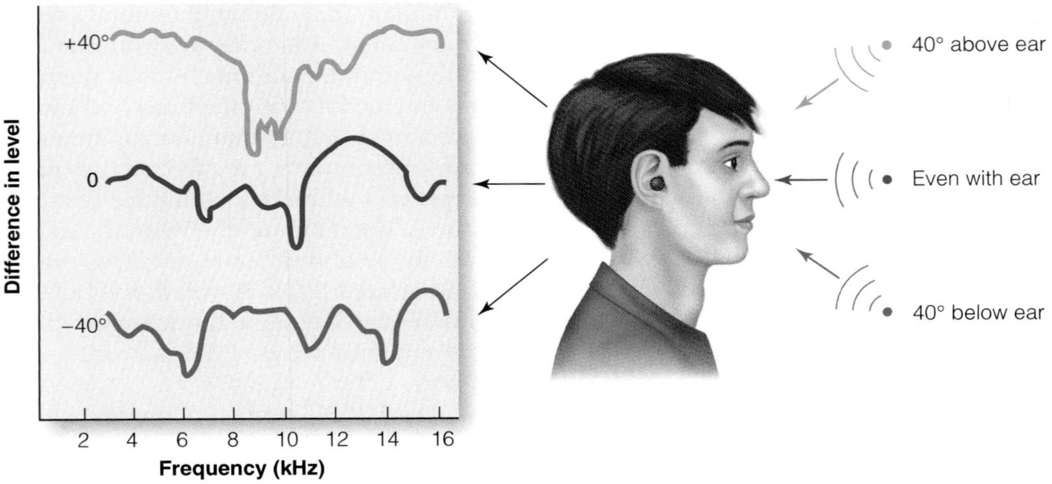

Figure 12.7 ▮ Head-related transfer functions (HRTFs) recorded by a small microphone inside the listener's right ear for sounds at three different locations. These functions indicate how the frequencies of the sound source are affected by interactions of the sound with the head and the pinna. Notches indicate a decrease in level and peaks an increase.

around inside the pinna, and the result is that sounds are perceived to originate inside the head. You can check this out yourself by noting where the sound is coming from as you listen to music through headphones. If you perceive the sound as coming from inside your head, you are experiencing **internalization**.

Internalization can be eliminated by (1) measuring characteristics of a person's HRTF; (2) programming these characteristics into a computer; and (3) having the computer process the sound that is delivered to the ears through headphones. When this is done, the headphone-wearing listener experiences **externalization**—sounds are heard as originating in space, as in the normal listening environment. This creation of the perception of an external sound source when using headphones is called **virtual auditory space (VAS)**.

■ ■ ■

Judging Azimuth Locations Researchers have used the virtual auditory space technique to determine whether interaural time differences (ITDs) cause listeners to perceive sounds as coming from different locations. Using this technique, Fredric Wightman and Doris Kistler (1992) programmed HRTFs, ITDs, and ILDs that corresponded to sounds at different locations along the azimuth. Listeners were fairly accurate at judging the locations of these sounds, as shown by the red points in Figure 12.8.

In this experiment, all three cues—the HRTF, the ITD, and the ILD—were set to indicate a particular location. But how do we know what each of these cues, individually, is contributing to perception? To answer this question, Wightman and Kistler did another experiment in which they kept the ITD constant, at a value that indicated one direction, and varied ILD and HRTF. The result for the value of ITD that indicated a direction of 90 degrees (straight ahead) is shown by the blue points in Figure 12.8. No matter what direction the ILD or spectral cues indicated, judgments were based on ITD. These results occurred only when the sound included low frequencies, so Wightman and Kistler concluded that ITD is the dominant cue for low-frequency sounds.

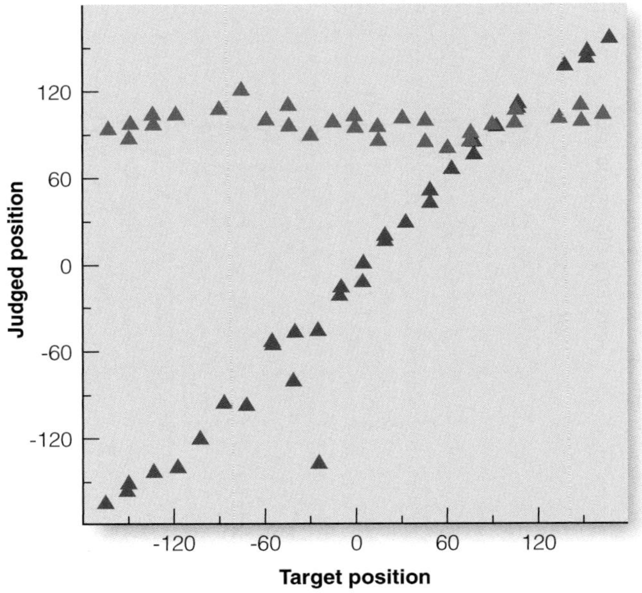

Figure 12.8 ▮ Red points: how a listener judged positions of a low-frequency sound presented through earphones. Sound locations were created by presenting sounds with HRTFs, ITDs, and ILDs that were associated with specific left-right positions relative to the listener. Blue points: judged positions based on the same HRTFs and ITDs as before, but with the ILD kept fixed at the value associated with 90 degrees.

Wightman and Kistler (1997) studied how ILD affects localization in another series of experiments. They found that varying ILD has little effect on the perception of location for low-frequency sounds but is effective at higher frequencies. (Remember the wave pictures in Figure 12.5.) The results of many experiments indicate that ITD and ILD are used for judging location along the azimuth coordinate, with ITD being effective at low-frequencies and ILD being effective at high frequencies.

Judging Elevation and Other "Ambiguous" Locations

Although ITD and ILD provide information that enables people to judge location along the azimuth coordinate, they provide ambiguous information about the elevation of a sound source. Consider, for example, what happens when we position a speaker directly in front of a person, such as at point A in Figure 12.9. At that location, the speaker is the same distance from each ear, so ITD and ILD are zero. However, if we move the speaker along the elevation coordinate to positions B and C, the speaker is still the same distance from both ears, so the ITD and ILD are still zero. Thus, an ITD or ILD of zero can occur when sound is at a number of different locations.

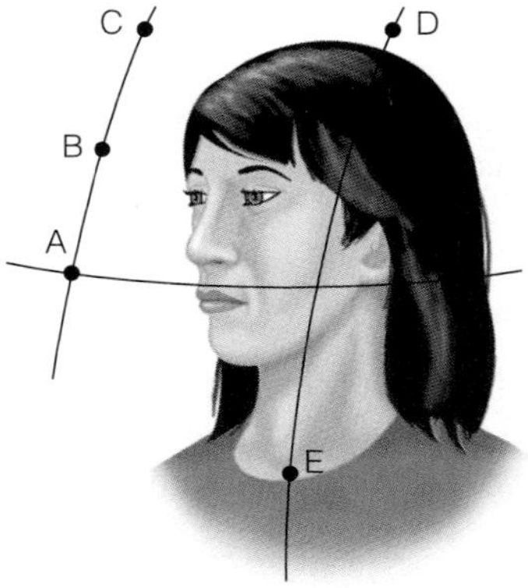

Figure 12.9 ▌ The ILDs and ITDs are zero for sounds originating at positions A, B, and C. The ILDs and ITDs are the same for sounds originating at positions D and E.

Similarly, speakers located at positions D and E, off to the side, are closer to the left ear than to the right ear, but because the distances from the left and right ears are the same in both locations, sounds coming from these locations will have the same ILD and ITD. Because these cues provide ambiguous information about location along the elevation coordinate, they are poorly suited for indicating the elevation of a sound source.

The ambiguous nature of the information provided by ITD and ILD at different elevations, means that another source of information is needed to locate sounds along the elevation coordinate. Luckily, spectral cues come to the rescue because there is convincing evidence that people use these cues to judge elevation. One way this has been demonstrated has been by showing that smoothing out the nooks and crannies of the pinnae with molding compound makes it difficult to locate sounds along the elevation coordinate (Gardner & Gardner, 1973).

The idea that localization can be affected by using a mold to change the inside contours of the pinnae was carried a step further by Paul Hofmann and coworkers (1998). They determined how localization changes when the mold is worn for several weeks, and then what happens when the mold is removed. The results for one listener's localization performance measured before the mold was inserted are shown in Figure 12.10a. Sounds were presented at positions indicated by the intersections of the black grid. Average localization performance is indicated by the blue grid. The overlap between the two grids indicates that localization was accurate.

After measuring initial performance, Hofmann fitted his listeners with molds that altered the shape of the pinnae and therefore changed the person's HRTF. Figure 12.10b shows that localization performance is poor for the elevation coordinate immediately after the mold is inserted, but locations can still be judged at locations along the azimuth coordinate. This is exactly what we would expect if binaural cues are used for judging azimuth location and spectral cues are responsible for judging elevation locations.

Hofmann continued his experiment by retesting localization as his listeners continued to wear the molds. You can see from Figure 12.10c–d that localization performance improved, until by 19 days localization had become reasonably accurate. Apparently, the person had learned, over a period of weeks, to associate new spectral cues to different directions in space.

What do you think happened when the molds were removed? It would be logical to expect that once adapted to the new set of spectral cues created by the molds, localization performance would suffer when the molds were removed. However, as shown in Figure 12.10e, localization remained excellent immediately after removal of the ear molds. Apparently, training with the molds created a new set of correlations between spectral cues and location, but the old correlation was still there, as well. One way this could occur is if different sets of neurons were involved in responding to each set of spectral cues, just as separate brain areas are involved in processing different languages in people who speak more than one language (King et al., 2001; Wightman & Kistler, 1998).

The research we have been describing has all measured localization under laboratory conditions. This enabled researchers to isolate individual cues to study their effect on localization. But in the real world, these cues work together to help us accurately locate sounds. In real-world listening, we also move our heads, which provides additional ITD, ILD, and spectral information, helping us locate continuous sounds. Vision also plays a role in sound localization, as when you hear talking and see a person making gestures and lip movements that match what you are hearing. Thus, although we may sometimes have difficulty determining a sound's location, the richness of the environment and our ability to actively

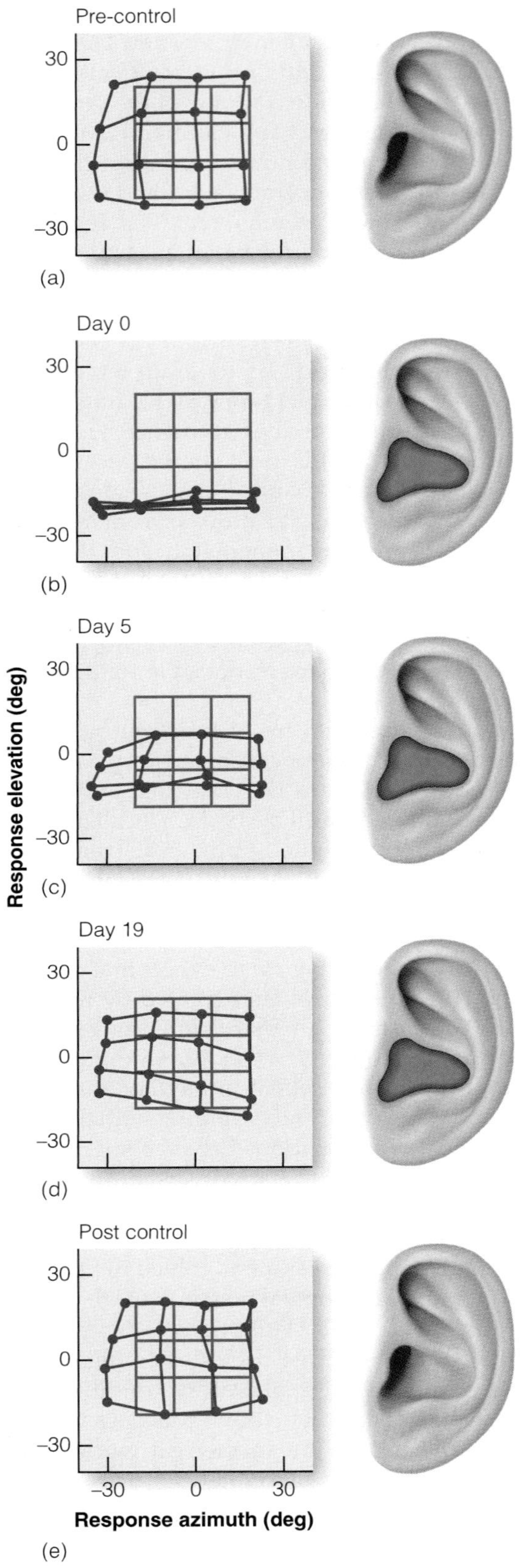

Figure 12.10 ▌ How localization changes when a mold is placed in the ear. See text for explanation.
(Reprinted from Trends in Cognitive Sciences, *5, King, A. J., Schnupp, J. W. H., & Doubell, T. P., The shape of ears to come: dynamic coding of auditory space., 261–270, (2001), with permission from Elsevier.)*

search for information often helps us zero in on a sound's location.

THE PHYSIOLOGICAL REPRESENTATION OF AUDITORY SPACE

How is auditory space represented physiologically? This question has been answered by (1) identifying neurons that respond to specific interaural time differences and (2) showing that there are maps of space, called topographic maps, on the surfaces of structures in the auditory system.

Interaural Time Difference Detectors

Researchers have identified neurons in the monkey's auditory cortex called **interaural time difference detectors** that respond to specific interaural time differences. An example of an interaural time difference detector would be a neuron that responds best when a sound reaches the left ear first and the right ear 500 microseconds (μs) later. Each neuron responds best to a different delay (Brugge & Merzenich, 1973; Litovsky & Yin, 1998). These interaural time difference neurons have been found not only in auditory cortex, but also in nuclei as early in the auditory system as the superior olivary nucleus, the first nucleus in the system to receive inputs from both ears (Hall, 1965).

Topographic Maps

A **topographic map** contains points on a neural structure that correspond in a systematic way to locations in space. (Be sure not to confuse this with *tonotopic* maps, which we described in Chapter 11. A tonotopic map contains points on a neural structure that correspond to *frequencies* of a sound stimulus, whereas for *topographic* maps the points correspond to *locations* of the sound stimulus.)

Figure 12.11 shows the results of experiments in which sounds were presented in the space surrounding a barn owl. Each rectangle indicates an area that caused a single neuron in a structure called the mesencephalicus lateralus dorsalis (MLD) to respond. For example, sounds located in the space outlined by rectangle A caused the neuron at A on the MLD to respond; sounds from area B caused the neuron at B to respond; and sounds from area C caused the neuron at C to respond. Thus, when the neuron at A on the MLD responds, this signals that sound is located within area A, and activity in neurons B and C indicate that the sound is coming from areas B and C, respectively.

The area of space associated with each neuron is the neuron's **receptive field for sound location**. Remember that we defined the receptive field of visual neurons as *the area on the retina that, when stimulated, influences the firing rate of the neuron.* We can define the receptive field for neurons involved in sound localization as *the location in space from which sound influences the firing of the neuron.*

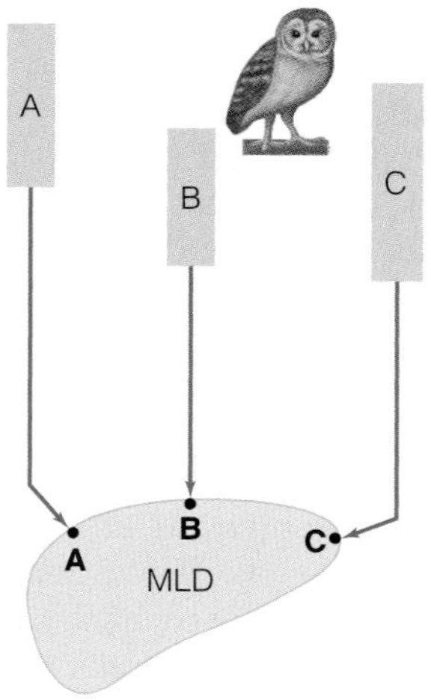

Figure 12.11 ▮ The receptive fields for location (the rectangles) of three neurons in the owl's MLD.
(From "A Neural Map of Auditory Space in the Owl," by E. I. Knudsen and M. Konishi, 1978, Science*, 200, 795–797, figure 1. Copyright © 1978 by the American Association for the Advancement of Science. Reprinted by permission.)*

Notice that the way neurons A, B, and C are positioned relative to each other in the MLD is similar to the way receptive fields A, B, and C are positioned relative to each other in space. This parallel between the locations of neurons in the MLD and locations in space means that there is a topographic map of auditory space in the MLD. Similar maps of auditory space also exist in mammals' subcortical structures, such as the inferior colliculus.

The Cortex

The evidence that the auditory cortex is necessary for localization is straightforward: Removal of all or part of the auditory cortex decreases the accuracy of localization. This has been demonstrated in monkeys, which become very poor at localizing sounds after their auditory cortex has been removed (Heffner & Heffner, 1990). We also saw in Chapter 11 that cortical damage due to a stroke can affect a person's ability to localize sounds.

Given the importance of the auditory cortex for localization, it would seem logical (1) that there would be spatially tuned neurons in the cortex—neurons that are tuned to respond to sounds coming from specific areas in space—and (2) that these spatially tuned neurons would be arranged to form topographic maps. However, in their quest to find spatially tuned neurons and topographic maps in monkeys, researchers have generally come up empty-handed. Most neurons in the monkey's cortex respond to sounds over a wide area and are not arranged in topographic maps. Thus, although there is a topographic map of auditory space in the owl MLD, and some maps in subcortical structures in mammals, a similar topographic map has not been found in the monkey's cortex.

How, then, is space represented in the monkey's cortex? Researchers searching for an answer to this question have made two important discoveries: First, there are cortical neurons called **panoramic neurons** that signal location by their pattern of firing (Middlebrooks et al., 1994, 1998). The way location is signaled by these neurons is illustrated in Figure 12.12, which shows the pattern of firing of one cortical neuron to sounds coming from a number of directions. Notice that the neuron fires to sounds coming from all directions but that the *pattern* of impulses is different for different directions. That's why this neuron is called a panoramic neuron—it fires to sounds originating from all directions and indicates each location by its pattern of firing. Because a large number of neurons fire to a particular tone, information from a number of these neurons could help to precisely locate a sound (Barinaga, 1994).

The other discovery about localization in the cortex is the *where* stream for hearing that we described in Chapter 11 (see page 254). A particularly important thing about the *where* stream is that as we move up this stream, from auditory cortex (A1) to belt, to parabelt areas, neurons become more spatially tuned to location (although the tuning is still wide), and also respond better to the locations of complex sounds, which contain many frequencies. Perhaps the eventual answer to how space is represented in the cortex will be found in higher-level auditory areas in the *where* stream.

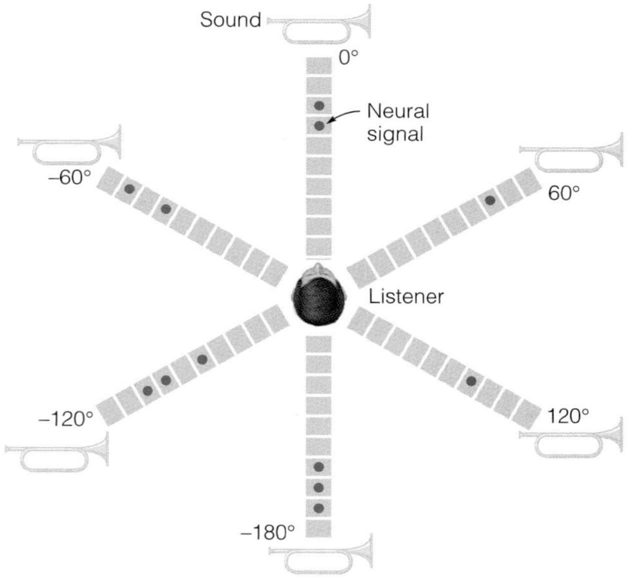

Figure 12.12 ▮ Panoramic neuron. When the sound is directly in front of the listener, at 0 degrees, the neuron fires two impulses in quick succession, as indicated by the dots on the line. However, when the sound is at −60 degrees, there is a slight pause between the two impulses. Other directions cause other patterns of firing. Thus, this neuron has a different timing code for each direction.
(Data from "A Panoramic Code for Sound Location by Cortical Neurons," by J. C. Middlebrooks, A. E. Clock, L. Xu & D. M. Green, 1994, Science*, 264, 842–844. Copyright © 1994 by the American Association for the Advancement of Science. Adapted by permission.)*

TEST YOURSELF 12.1

1. How is auditory space described in terms of three coordinates?
2. How well can people localize sounds that are in front, to the side, and in back?
3. What is the basic difference between determining the location of a sound source and determining the location of a visual object?
4. Describe the different types of information that are *available* for determining a sound's location and the conditions under which each of these types of information are actually *used.*
5. What is virtual auditory space, and how has it been used in auditory research?
6. How is auditory space represented physiologically (a) in subcortical structures, and (b) in the auditory cortex?

IDENTIFYING SOUND SOURCES

We have, up until now, been considering how we perceive sounds produced by a single source. We now consider how we perceive sounds produced by many sources that occur simultaneously or close together in time.

Auditory Scene Analysis

We opened this chapter with the example of a bird chirping in a tree and a cat meowing on the ground below. We can't tell where the bird and cat are located based on which receptors in the listener's cochlea are stimulated because these receptors respond to the frequencies in a sound, not to where the sound is located in space.

We now return to our bird and cat to consider a related problem: How does the auditory system tell that there are two sound sources—a bird and a cat? This may seem like a simple problem. After all, the bird and cat make different sounds that are easy to tell apart. But when we look at the information that these sounds create on the cochlea, we can appreciate that the problem is not so simple.

If the bird and cat are chirping and meowing at exactly the same time, the pressure changes created by each one combine in the ear, as shown in Figure 12.13, and stimulate the receptors in the cochlea. But which hair cells are being stimulated by the cat's meow, and which by the bird's song? The pressure changes from both sounds are mixed together, so there is no way to answer this question just from looking at the physical signal or the pattern of vibration on the cochlea. Just as we can't use place information on the cochlea to determine the locations of the bird and cat, we also can't use this information to determine which sounds are produced by the bird and which are produced by the cat.

Basically, this is the same problem that you face when you are talking to a friend at a noisy party. Even though the sounds produced by your friend's conversation are mixed together on your cochlea with the sounds produced by all of the other people's conversations, plus perhaps music, the sound of the refrigerator door slamming, and glasses tinkling, you are somehow able to separate what your friend is saying from all of the other sounds. The array of sound sources in the environment is called the **auditory scene**, and the process by which you separate the stimuli produced by each of the sources in the scene into separate perceptions is called **auditory scene analysis** (Bregman, 1990, 1993; Darwin, 1997; Yost, 2001).

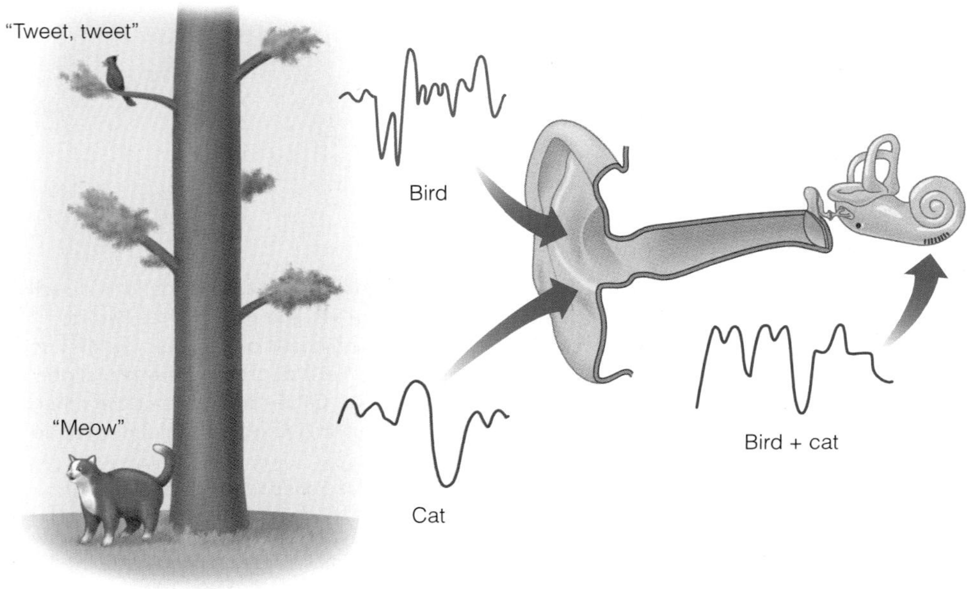

Figure 12.13 ■ The bird and cat from Figure 12.3, but showing the pattern of pressure changes for each one and the combined signal that enters the ear. The problem in identifying which sound comes from the bird and which comes from the cat is that they are mixed together on the cochlea.

It might seem as though one way to analyze an auditory scene into its separate components would be to use information about where each source is coming from. You can separate your friend's voice and the slamming of the refrigerator door because your friend is standing nearby and the sound of the refrigerator door is coming from the next room. Although the sound sources' positions in space can help you separate the sources from one another, this can't be the whole story because even when you listen to a recording played through a single speaker, you can still hear the separate instruments, even though you have no information about where the instruments are located in space (Yost, 1997). There must, therefore, be other information in addition to spatial location that enables you to analyze an auditory scene into separate sound sources. We can describe this information in terms of **principles of auditory grouping**.

Principles of Auditory Grouping

In Chapter 5, we introduced the idea that the visual system uses a number of different heuristics, proposed by the Gestalt psychologists and modern researchers, to determine which elements of a visual scene belong together. We saw that these heuristics are based on properties of visual stimuli that usually occur in the environment (see page 102). Now, as we turn to the sense of hearing, we will see that a similar situation exists for auditory stimuli. There are a number of heuristics that help us perceptually organize elements of an auditory scene, and these heuristics are based on how sounds usually originate in the environment. For example, tones that originate from a single source usually come from one point in space. Thus, one factor that helps us separate one source from another are the locations of the sounds. We will now consider location again, plus some additional principles of auditory grouping.

Location Sounds created by a particular source usually come from one position in space or from a slowly changing location. Anytime two sounds are separated in space, the cue of location helps us separate them perceptually. In addition, when a source moves, it typically follows a continuous path rather than jumping erratically from one place to another. For example, this continuous movement of sound helps us perceive the sound from a passing car as originating from a single source.

Similarity of Timbre and Pitch Sounds that have the same timbre are often produced by the same source. This principle simply means that we tend to group similar-sounding stimuli together. We can illustrate this by considering an effect called the **Wessel effect**, created by David Wessel (1979). Wessel presented listeners with sequences of tones, as shown in Figure 12.14a. In this figure, the green circles are tones with one timbre, and the yellow circles are tones with a different timbre.

When Wessel presented the tones slowly, they sounded like three repeated notes that increased in pitch and changed in timbre, as would occur if a clarinet alter-

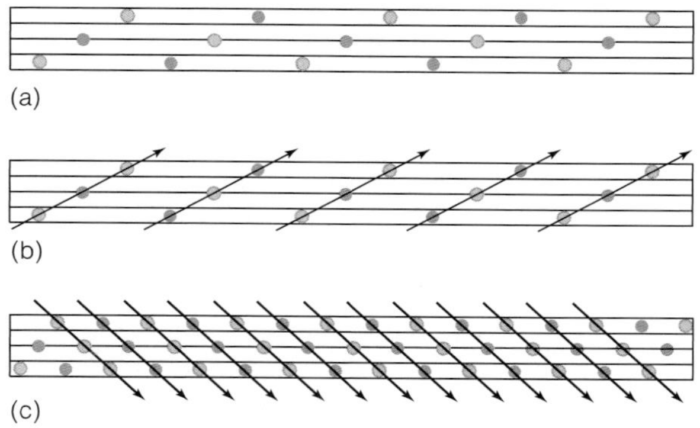

Figure 12.14 ❚ (a) The repeating series of three notes presented by Wessel (1979). The yellow circles stand for a tone with one timbre, and the green circles for a tone with a different timbre. (b) When the tones are presented slowly, they are perceived as ascending sequences of notes that alternate in timbre. (c) When the tones are presented rapidly, they are perceived as descending sequences of notes with the same timbre. This is Wessel's (1979) timbre illusion.

nated notes with a trumpet (Figure 12.14b). However, when they were played rapidly, notes with different timbres were heard as separate descending streams with different timbres, as would occur if the clarinet and trumpet each played separate three-note sequences (Figure 12.14c). This is an example of a phenomenon called **auditory stream segregation**—the separation of the acoustic stimuli entering the ear into different perceptual streams (also see Bregman & Pinker, 1978). VL 2

Auditory stream segregation based on timbre occurs in everyday listening when two people are talking simultaneously and we can separate their conversations based on the fact that one has a raspy voice, and one has a smooth, mellow voice. This ability to separate auditory streams also occurs due to differences in pitch because tones that have similar pitches tend to be perceived as belonging together.

Composers made use of grouping by similarity of pitch long before psychologists began studying it. Composers in the Baroque period (1600–1750) knew that when a single instrument plays notes that alternate rapidly between high and low tones, the listener perceives two separate melodies, with the high notes perceived as being played by one instrument and the low notes as being played by another. An excerpt from a composition by J. S. Bach that uses this device is shown in Figure 12.15. When this passage is played rapidly, the low notes sound as though they are a melody played by one instrument, and the high notes sound like a different melody played by another instrument. This effect, which has been called *implied polyphony,* or *compound melodic line,* by musicians, is an example of auditory stream segregation (see Jones & Yee, 1993; Yost & Sheft, 1993).

Albert Bregman and Jeffrey Campbell (1971) demonstrated auditory stream segregation based on pitch by alternating high and low tones, as shown in the sequence in Figure 12.16. When the high-pitched tones were slowly al-

Figure 12.15 ▌ Four measures of a composition by J. S. Bach (Choral Prelude on *Jesus Christus unser Heiland*, 1739). When played rapidly, the upper notes become perceptually grouped and the lower notes become perceptually grouped, a phenomenon called *auditory stream segregation.*

ternated with the low-pitched tones, as in Figure 12.16a, the tones were heard in one stream, one after another: Hi-Lo-Hi-Lo-Hi-Lo, as indicated by the dashed line. But when the tones were alternated very rapidly, the high and low tones became perceptually grouped into two auditory streams so that the listener perceived two separate streams of sound, one high-pitched and one low-pitched, occurring simultaneously (Figure 12.16b; see Heise & Miller, 1951, and Miller & Heise, 1950, for an early demonstration of auditory stream segregation).

This grouping of tones into streams by similarity of pitch is also demonstrated by an experiment done by Bregman and Alexander Rudnicky (1975). The listener is first presented with two standard tones, X and Y (Figure 12.17a). When these tones are presented alone, it is easy to perceive their order (XY or YX). However, when these tones are sandwiched between two distractor (D) tones (Figure 12.17b), it becomes very hard to judge their order. The name *distractor tones* is well taken: They distract the listener, making it difficult to judge the order of tones X and Y.

But the distracting effect of the D tones can be eliminated by adding a series of "captor" (C) tones (Figure 12.17c). These captor tones have the same pitch as the distractors. Thus, they capture the distractors and form a stream that separates the distractors from tones X and Y. The result is that X and Y are perceived as one stream and the distractors as another stream, so it is much easier to perceive the order of X and Y. VL 3, 4

A final example of how similarity of pitch causes grouping is an effect called the **scale illusion**, or **melodic channeling**. Diana Deutsch (1975, 1996) demonstrated this effect by presenting two sequences of notes simultaneously (Figure 12.18a). These notes were heard through earphones, with successive notes from the two sequences alternating between the left ear (blue notes) and the right ear (red notes). Notice that in the left ear, the notes alternate from low to high to low (blue notes), and in the right ear, the notes alternate from high to low to high (red notes). However, Deutsch's listeners perceived smooth sequences of notes in each ear, with the higher notes in the right ear and the lower ones in the left ear (Figure 12.18b). Even though the ears received both high and low notes, grouping by similarity of pitch caused listeners to group the lower notes in the left ear (which started with a low note) and the higher notes in the right ear (which started with a high note).

The scale illusion highlights an important property of perceptual grouping. Most of the time, the principles of auditory grouping help us to accurately interpret what is happening in the environment. It is most effective to perceive similar sounds as coming from the same source because this is what usually happens in the environment. In Deutsch's experiment, the perceptual system applies the principle of grouping by similarity to the artificial stimuli presented through earphones and makes the mistake of assigning similar pitches to the same ear. But most of the time, when psychologists aren't controlling the stimuli, sounds with similar frequencies are often produced by the same sound source, so the auditory system usually uses pitch to correctly determine where sounds are coming from.

Proximity in Time Sounds that occur in rapid progression tend to be produced by the same source. We can illustrate the importance of timing in stream segregation

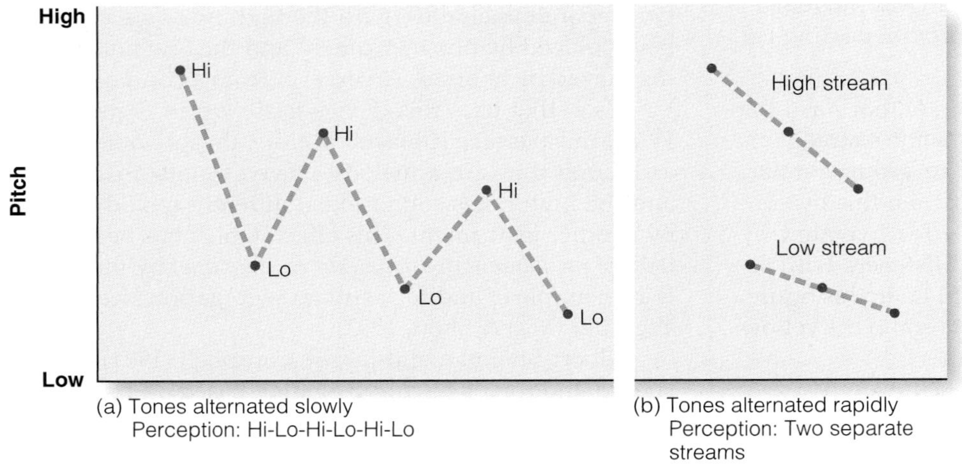

Figure 12.16 ▌ (a) When high and low tones are alternated slowly, auditory stream segregation does not occur, so the listener perceives alternating high and low tones. (b) Faster alternation results in segregation into high and low streams.

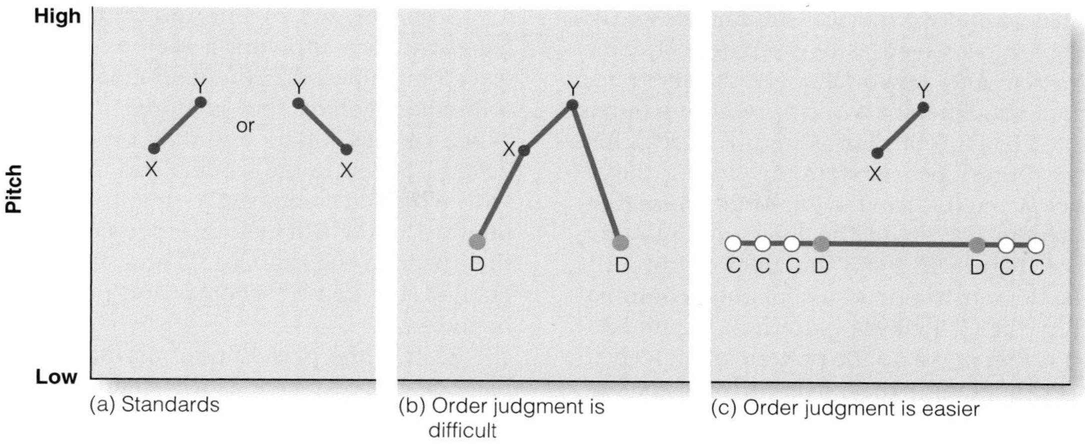

Figure 12.17 ▮ Bregman and Rudnicky's (1975) experiment. (a) The standard tones X and Y have different pitches. (b) Test 1: the distractor (D) tones group with X and Y, making it difficult to judge the order of X and Y. (c) Test 2: the addition of captor (C) tones with the same pitch as the distractor tones causes the distractor tones to form a separate stream (law of similarity) and makes it easier to judge the order of tones X and Y. (Based on Bregman & Rudnicky, 1975.)

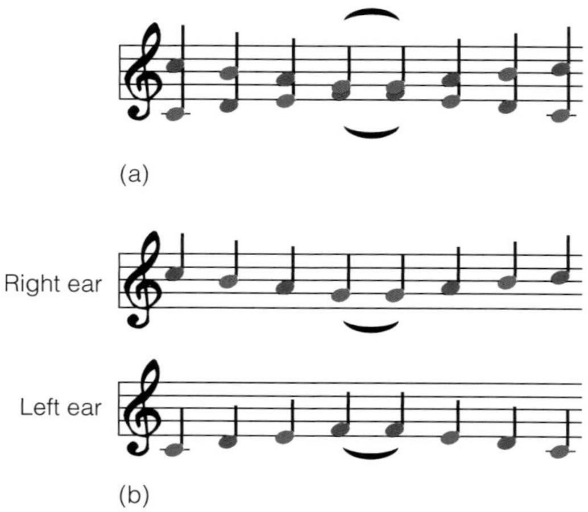

Figure 12.18 ▮ (a) These stimuli were presented to a listener's left ear (blue) and right ear (red) in Deutsch's (1975) scale-illusion experiment. Notice how the notes presented to each ear jump up and down. (b) What the listener hears. Although the notes in each ear jump up and down, the listener perceives smooth sequences of notes. This effect is called the scale illusion, or melodic channeling.

(From "Two-Channel Listening to Musical Scales," by D. Deutsch, 1975, Journal of the Acoustical Society of America, 57. Copyright ©1975 by the American Institute of Physics. Reprinted by permission.)

by returning to our examples of grouping by similarity. Before stream segregation due to similarity of timbre or pitch can occur, tones with similar timbres or frequencies have to occur close together in time. If the tones are too far apart in time, as in Figure 12.16a, segregation will not occur, even when the tones are similar in pitch.

In addition, sounds that stop and start at different times tend to be produced by different sources. If you are listening to one instrument playing and then another one joins in later, you know that two sources are present. VL 5, 6

Good Continuation Sounds that stay constant or that change smoothly are often produced by the same source. This property of sounds leads to a principle analogous to the principle of good continuation for vision. Sound stimuli with the same frequency or smoothly changing frequencies are perceived as continuous even when they are interrupted by another stimulus.

A musical example of this principle is shown in Figure 12.19a (Deutsch, 1996). This musical excerpt consists of one series of identical repeated notes (top) and another sequence that rises and then falls in pitch (bottom). Even

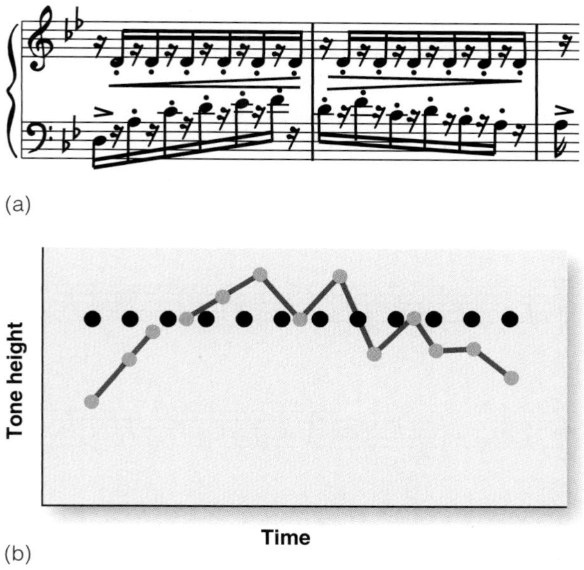

Figure 12.19 ▮ (a) A selection from *Leyenda* by Albinez, showing the two musical lines, one of repeating notes and the other a sequence of changing notes. (b) The listeners perceive the repeating notes as one stream (black circles) and the changing tones as another stream even though the notes overlap. (Adapted from Deutsch, 1996)

though the pitches of the two musical streams cross (Figure 12.19b), they are perceived as two separate streams.

Richard Warren and coworkers (1972) illustrated good continuation in a different way by presenting bursts of tone interrupted by gaps of silence (Figure 12.20a). Listeners perceived these tones as stopping during the silence. But when Warren filled in the gaps with noise (Figure 12.20b), listeners perceived the tone as continuing behind the noise (Figure 12.20c). This demonstration is analogous to the demonstration of visual good continuation illustrated by the Celtic knot pattern in Figure 5.17. Just as the strands that make up the pattern are perceived as continuous even though they overlap one another, a tone can be perceived as continuous even though it is interrupted by bursts of noise. VL 7

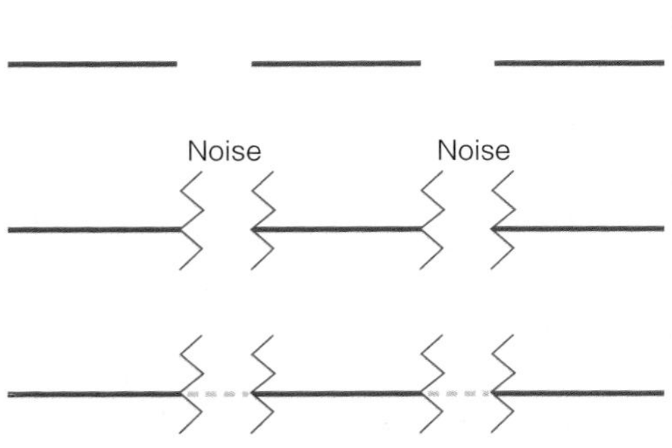

Figure 12.20 ■ A demonstration of good continuation, using tones.

Experience An example of how past experience can affect the perceptual grouping of auditory stimuli is provided by W. Jay Dowling (1973). He had participants listen to two interleaved melodies by alternating notes of "Three Blind Mice" with notes of "Mary Had a Little Lamb" (Figure 12.21). Listeners reported hearing a meaningless jumble of notes. However, when they were told the names of the songs, they were able to hear each song's melody.

Figure 12.21 ■ (a) "Three Blind Mice," (b) "Mary Had a Little Lamb," and (c) the two melodies interleaved ("Three Blind Mice": red notes, stems up; "Mary Had a Little Lamb": blue notes, stems down).

According to Dowling and Dane Harwood (1986), the listeners were applying a **melody schema** to the interleaved melodies. A melody schema is a representation of a familiar melody that is stored in a person's memory. When people don't know that a melody is present, they have no access to the schema and therefore have nothing with which to compare the unknown melody. But when they are told which melody is present, they compare what they hear to their stored "Three Blind Mice" or "Mary Had a Little Lamb" schemas and perceive the melodies. VL 8

Each of the principles of auditory grouping that we have described provides information about the number and identity of sources in the auditory environment. But each principle alone is not foolproof, and basing our perceptions on just one principle can lead to error—as in the case of the scale illusion, which is purposely arranged so similarity of pitch dominates our perception. Thus, in most naturalistic situations, we base our perceptions on a number of these cues working together. This is similar to the situation we described for visual perception in which our perception of objects depends on a number of organizational principles working together, and our perception of depth depends on a number of depth cues working together. VL 9

HEARING INSIDE ROOMS

So far in this chapter and also in Chapter 11, we have seen that our perception of sound depends on various properties of the sound, including its frequency, sound level, location in space, and relation to other sounds. But we have left out the fact that in our normal everyday experience we hear sounds in a specific setting, such as a small room, a large auditorium, or outside. As we consider this aspect of hearing, we will see why we perceive sounds differently when we are outside and inside, and how our perception of sound quality is affected by specific properties of indoor environments.

Figure 12.22 shows how the nature of the sound reaching your ears depends on the environment in which you hear the sound. If you are listening to someone playing a guitar on an outside stage, some of the sound you hear reaches your ears after being reflected from the ground or objects like trees, but most of the sound travels directly from the sound source to your ears (Figure 12.22a). If, however, you are listening to the same guitar in an auditorium, then a large proportion of the sound bounces off the auditorium's walls, ceiling, and floor before reaching your ears (Figure 12.22b). The sound reaching your ears directly, along path a, is called **direct sound**, and the sound reaching your ears later, along paths like b, c, and d, is called **indirect sound**.

The fact that sound can reach our ears directly from where the sound is originating and indirectly from other locations creates a potential problem for accurately localizing the sound. However, even though reflections from

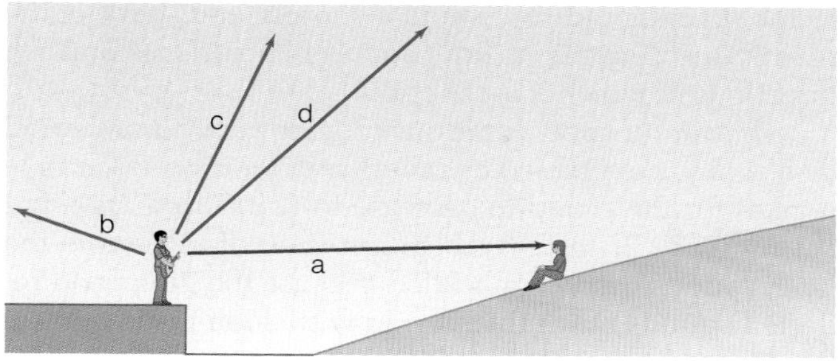

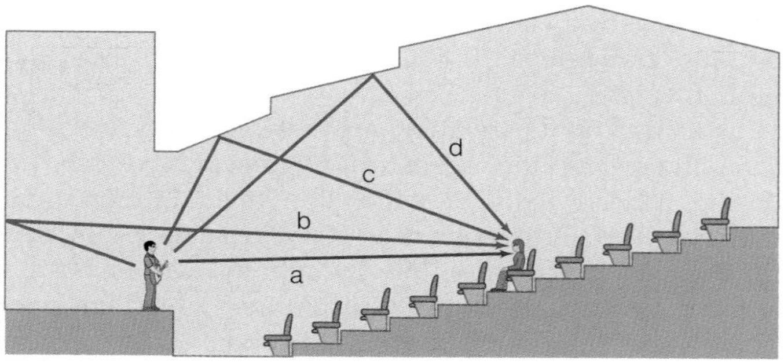

Figure 12.22 ▌ (a) When you hear a sound outside, you hear mainly direct sound (path a). (b) When you hear a sound inside a room, you hear both direct sound (a) and indirect sound (b, c, and d) that is reflected from the walls, floor, and ceiling of the room.

surfaces enable us to receive a sequence of sounds coming from many directions, we generally perceive the sound as coming from only one location. We can understand why this occurs by considering the results of research in which listeners were presented with sounds originating from two different locations.

Perceiving Two Sounds That Reach the Ears at Different Times

Research on sound reflections and the perception of location has usually simplified the problem by having people listen to sounds coming from two speakers separated in space, as shown in Figure 12.23. Ruth Litovsky and coworkers (1997, 1999) designated the speaker on the right as the *lead speaker,* and the one on the left as the *lag speaker.* When they presented sounds simultaneously in the two speakers, listeners heard one sound centered between the two speakers (Figure 12.23a). This perception of two sounds as one is called **fusion.** When the lead sound was presented first, followed by the lag sound with a delay of less than 1 ms, listeners perceived a single sound located nearer the lead speaker (Figure 12.23b). At delays between about 1 and 5 milliseconds, the sound appeared to be coming from the lead speaker alone (Figure 12.23c). This situation, in which the sound appears to originate from the lead speaker, is called the **precedence effect** because we perceive the sound as coming from the source that reaches our ears first (Wallach, Newman, & Rosenzweig, 1949). VL 10

At intervals greater than about 5 milliseconds, Litovsky's listeners began hearing two separate sounds, one after another (Figure 12.23d). The time separation at which the sounds are no longer fused, so two separate sounds are heard, is called the **echo threshold.** The echo threshold was about 5 milliseconds in Litovsky's experiment, in which the stimuli were two identical clicks. However, the echo threshold becomes longer when the lag sound is at a lower level than the lead sound (as occurs for sound that reaches the ears indirectly after being reflected from surfaces in a room) and also for sounds with long durations, such as speech and music.

The precedence effect governs most of our indoor lis-

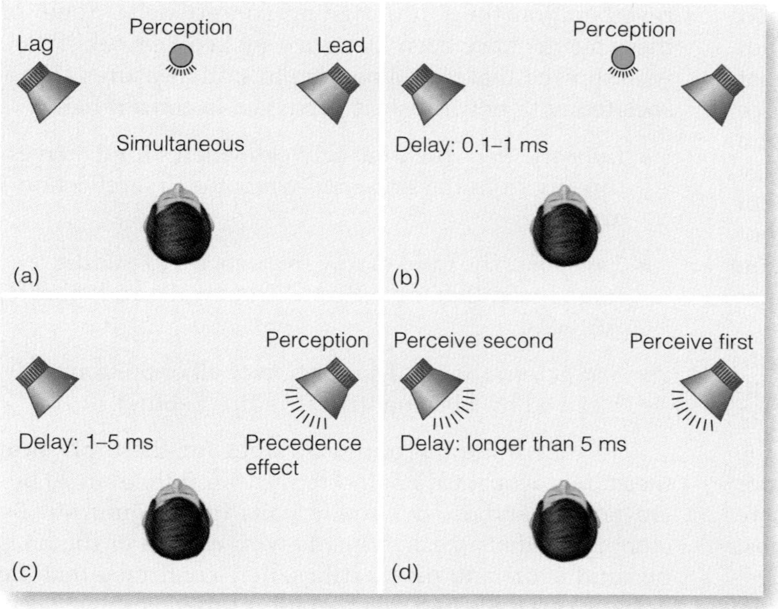

Figure 12.23 ▌ Results of an experiment in which sounds are presented by two speakers. See text for details. (Data from Litovsky et al., 1999.)

tening experience. The indirect sounds reflected from the walls have a lower level than the direct sound and reach our ears with delays of about 5 to 10 ms for small rooms, and with larger delays for larger rooms like concert halls. The operation of the precedence effect means that we generally perceive sound as coming from its source, rather than from many different directions at once. You can demonstrate the precedence effect to yourself by doing the following demonstration.

DEMONSTRATION

The Precedence Effect

To demonstrate the precedence effect, set the controls on your stereo system so that both speakers play the same sounds, and position yourself between the speakers so that you hear the sound coming from a point between both speakers. Then move a small distance to the left or right. When you do this, does the sound appear to be coming from only the nearer speaker? ■

You perceive the sound as coming from the nearer speaker because the sound from the nearer speaker is reaching your ears first, just as in Figure 12.23c, in which there was a delay between the sounds presented by the two speakers. But even though you hear the sound as coming from the near speaker, this doesn't mean that you aren't hearing the far speaker. The sound from the far speaker changes the quality of the sound, giving it a fuller, more expansive quality (Blauert, 1997; Yost & Guzman, 1996). You can demonstrate this by positioning yourself closer to one speaker and having a friend disconnect the other speaker. When this happens, you will notice a difference in the quality of the sound.

Architectural Acoustics

Having solved the location problem for sounds heard in rooms, we now consider how properties of the room can affect the quality of the sound we hear. When we studied vision, we saw that our perception of light depends not only on the nature of the light source but also on what happens to the light between the time it leaves its source and the time it enters our eyes. When light passes through haze on its way from an object to our eyes, the object may seem bluer or fuzzier than it would if the haze were not there. Similarly, our perception of sound also depends not only on the sound produced at the source, but also on how the sounds are reflected from the walls and other surfaces in a room.

Architectural acoustics, the study of how sounds are reflected in rooms, is largely concerned with how indirect sound changes the quality of the sounds we hear in rooms. The major factor affecting indirect sound is the amount of sound absorbed by the walls, ceiling, and floor of the room. If most of the sound is absorbed, then there are few sound reflections and little indirect sound. If most of the sound is reflected, then there are many sound reflections and a large amount of indirect sound. Another factor affecting indirect sound is the size and shape of the room. This determines how sound hits surfaces and the directions in which it is reflected.

The amount and duration of indirect sound produced by a room is expressed as **reverberation time**—the time it takes for the sound to decrease to 1/1000th of its original pressure. If the reverberation time of a room is too long, sounds become muddled because the direct and reflected sounds reach the listener with a long delay. In extreme cases, such as cathedrals with stone walls, these delays are perceived as echoes, and it may be difficult to accurately localize the sound source. If the reverberation time is too short, music will sound "dead," and it becomes difficult to produce sounds of very high intensity.

VL 11

Because of the relationship between reverberation time and perception, acoustical engineers have tried to design concert halls in which the reverberation time matches the reverberation time of halls that are renowned for their good acoustics, like Symphony Hall in Boston and the Concertgebouw in Amsterdam, which have reverberation times of about 2.0 seconds. However, an "ideal" reverberation time does not always predict good acoustics. This is illustrated by the problems associated with the design of New York's Philharmonic Hall. When it opened in 1962, Philharmonic Hall had a reverberation time of close to the ideal of 2.0 seconds. Even so, the hall was criticized for sounding as though it had a short reverberation time, and musicians in the orchestra complained that they could not hear each other. These criticisms resulted in a series of alterations to the hall, made over many years, until eventually, when none of the alterations proved satisfactory, the entire interior of the hall was destroyed and the hall was completely rebuilt in 1992. It is now called Avery Fisher Hall.

The experience with Philharmonic Hall, plus new developments in the field of architectural acoustics, has led architectural engineers to consider factors in addition to reverberation time in designing concert halls. Some of these factors have been identified by Leo Beranek (1996), who showed that the following physical measures are associated with how music is perceived in concert halls:

- *Intimacy time:* The time between when sound arrives directly from the stage and when the first reflection arrives.
- *Bass ratio:* The ratio of low frequencies to middle frequencies that are reflected from walls and other surfaces.
- *Spaciousness factor:* The fraction of all of the sound received by a listener that is indirect sound.

To determine the optimal values for these physical measures, acoustical engineers measured them in 20 opera houses and 25 symphony halls in 14 countries. By comparing their measurements with ratings of the halls by conductors and music critics, they confirmed that the best concert halls had reverberation times of about 2 seconds and also found that 1.5 seconds was better for opera houses, with the shorter time being necessary to enable people to clearly hear the singers' voices. They also found that intimacy times of about 20 ms and high bass ratios and spaciousness factors were associated with good acoustics (Glanz, 2000). When these factors have been taken into account in the design of new concert halls, the result has been acoustics rivaling the best halls in the world.

The problems facing architects in the design of concert halls emphasizes the complexity of the factors determining sound quality. The sound stimulus that actually reaches a listener is far more complex than single pure tones, or even musical tones, because of the way sounds interact with objects in the environment.

SOMETHING TO CONSIDER: INTERACTIONS BETWEEN VISION AND HEARING

The division of this book into separate chapters for each sense might give the impression that the senses operate independently of one another. This impression would, of course, be erroneous because we rarely just hear sound, see visual stimuli, or smell odors, in isolation. Perception, as it occurs in the natural environment, involves interactions among all the senses. We will now look at a few examples of some interactions between hearing and vision.

In general, there is overlap between where a sound seems to be coming from and where we see the source of this sound. You hear the annoying person talking behind you at a concert and turn around to see that the person is, in fact, located just about where you would have predicted. But sometimes vision and hearing provide discrepant information, as when the sound is produced at one place but you see the apparent sound source somewhere else. A familiar example of this phenomenon occurs in movie theaters when an actor's dialogue is produced by a speaker located on the right side of the screen, while the image of the actor who is talking is located in the center of the screen, many feet away. When this happens, we hear the sound coming from its seen location (the image at the center of the screen) rather than from where it is actually produced (the speaker to the right of the screen). This effect is called **visual capture**, or the **ventriloquism effect**. Note that because virtually all theaters have stereophonic sound, the match between sound position and characters on the screen is at least partially caused by the binaural cues we described earlier in the chapter. But before the advent of stereophonic sound, the ventriloquism effect alone caused movie viewers to perceive sound as originating from places on the screen rather than from off to the side.

There are other situations in which sound and visual stimuli appear to have the same location, even though sound is coming from one place and a visual stimulus is located in another place. For example, when a sound that would normally be perceived as moving from left to right is heard while a person is viewing a visual stimulus that is moving from right to left, both sound and visual stimuli appear to be moving from right to left (Soto-Faraco et al., 2002, 2004). This is another example of visual capture.

Visual capture is important because it reflects the way we usually experience stimuli in the environment. Another illustration of this connection is shown in Figure 12.24. Robert Sekuler and coworkers (1997) presented an animated display that showed two identical objects moving diagonally: one from left to right and the other from right to left, and crossing in the middle. Eighty-eight percent of Sekuler's observers perceived these objects as moving past each other and continuing their straight-line motion, as shown in Figure 12.24a. The other 12 percent of observers perceived the objects as contacting each other and bouncing off in opposite directions, as shown in Figure 12.24b. However, when Sekuler added a brief "click" sound just when the objects appeared adjacent to each other, 63 percent perceived them as colliding and bouncing off in opposite directions. As was the case for visual capture, in which vision influenced hearing, this example, in which hearing influences vision, also seems to reflect the way we normally perceive events in the environment. When a sound occurs just as two moving objects become adjacent to one another, this usually means that a collision has occurred to cause the sound.

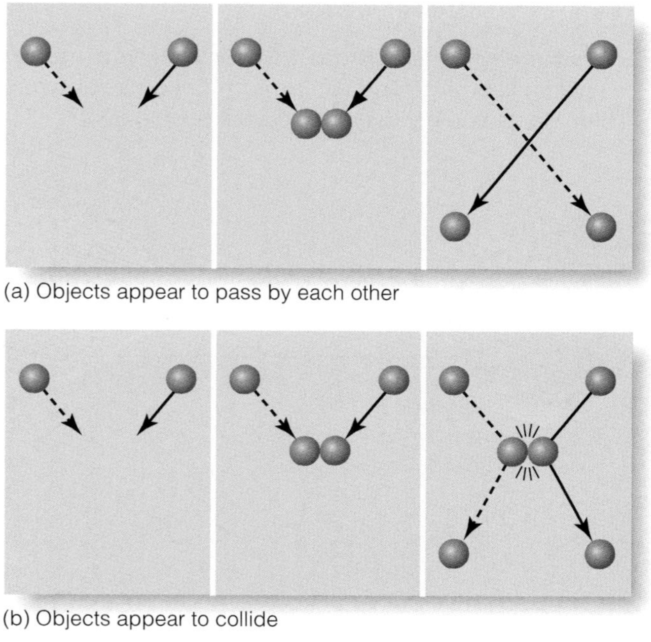

Figure 12.24 ■ Two conditions in the Sekuler et al. (1997) experiment showing successive positions of two balls that were presented so they appeared to be moving. (a) No sound condition: the two balls were perceived to pass each other and continue moving in a straight-line motion. (b) Click added condition: observers were more likely to see the balls as colliding.

TEST YOURSELF 12.2

1. What is auditory scene analysis, and why is it a "problem" for the auditory system?
2. What are the basic principles of auditory grouping that help us achieve auditory scene analysis? Be sure you understand the following experiments: (1) Wessel (Figure 12.14); Bregman and Campbell (Figure 12.16); Bregman and Rudnicky (Figure 12.17); Deutsch (Figure 12.18); good continuation experiments (Figures 12.19, 12.20), and Dowling's experiment on melody schema (Figure 12.21).
3. Why would music played outdoors sound different from music played indoors?
4. What is the precedence effect, and what does it do for us perceptually?
5. What are some basic principles of architectural acoustics that have been developed to help design concert halls?
6. Describe the following demonstrations of the way that vision and hearing can interact: (1) vision influencing sound: visual capture; (2) sound influencing perception of visual collision. What do these demonstrations tell us about the relationship between what we perceive and what usually occurs in the environment?

THINK ABOUT IT

1. What are some situations in which (a) you use one sense in isolation, and (b) the combined use of two or more senses is necessary to accomplish a task?
2. We can perceive space visually, as we saw in the chapter on depth perception, and through the sense of hearing, as we have described in this chapter. How are these two ways of perceiving space similar and different?
3. How is object recognition in vision like stream segregation in hearing?
4. Figure 12.25a shows the principle behind receptive fields in vision. The firing of cortical neuron A is influenced when receptors within its receptive field—area A on the retina—are stimulated. Similarly, neuron B fires when receptors within area B on the retina are stimulated. This occurs because signals are sent along nerve fibers that connect areas A and B on the retina to neurons A and B in the cortex.

   Figure 12.25b shows an analogous situation for hearing. Neurons 1 and 2 in the owl's MLD fire when sound is presented within the receptive fields of these neurons—areas 1 and 2 in space. But how can these MLD neurons fire to sounds coming from specific areas in space when there are no nerve fiber connections between these areas in space and the neurons?

IF YOU WANT TO KNOW MORE

1. ***The Physiology of Auditory Grouping*** New research is looking at how the brain separates sounds.

   Carlyon, R. P. (2004). How the brain separates sounds. *Trends in Cognitive Sciences, 8,* 465–471.

2. ***Multimodal Cells*** One way the brain may coordinate information for different senses in order to create a unified perception of objects and events in the environment is through areas of the brain that are activated by more than one sense.

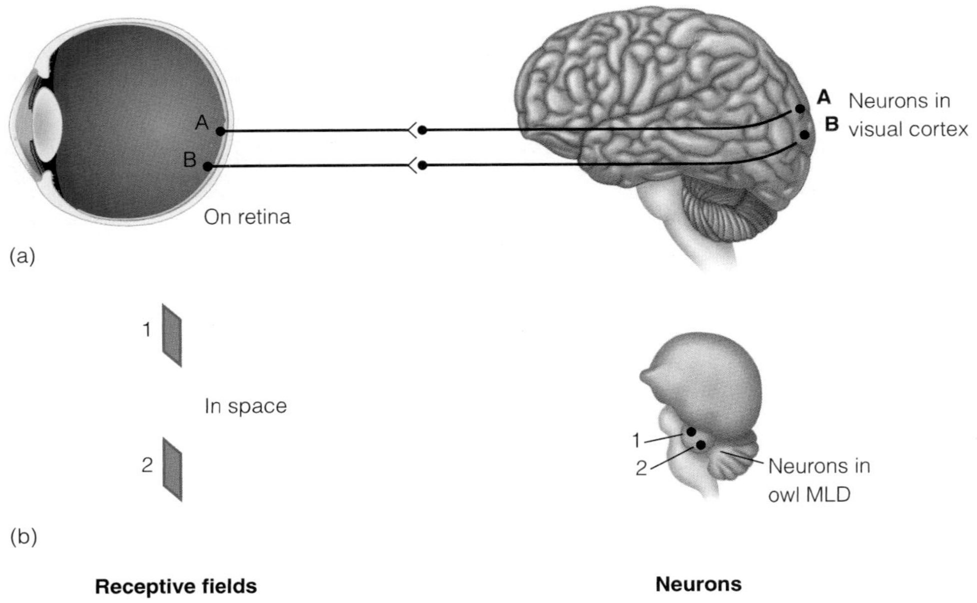

Figure 12.25 ■ (a) In vision, cortical neurons are physically connected to the retina. (b) In hearing, these connections do not exist for neurons that respond to locations in space, as shown here for the owl. How can these owl neurons respond to areas in space even though they aren't physically connected to these areas?

Bushara, K. O. et al. (2003). Neural correlates of cross-modal bonding. *Nature Neuroscience, 6,* 190–195.

3. ***Loss of One Sense Can Enhance Another One*** When one sense is lost or reduced, performance by the other senses can become enhanced. The physiological basis for this appears to be that the remaining senses take over cortical area from the lost one.

Rauschecker. J. P., and Korte, M. (1993). Auditory compensation for early blindness in cat cerebral cortex. *Journal of Neuroscience, 13,* 4538–4548.

KEY TERMS

Acoustic shadow (p. 269)
Architectural acoustics (p. 280)
Auditory localization (p. 266)
Auditory scene (p. 274)
Auditory scene analysis (p. 274)
Auditory space (p. 266)
Auditory stream segregation (p. 275)
Azimuth coordinate (p. 266)
Binaural cue (p. 267)
Direct sound (p. 278)
Distance coordinate (p. 266)
Echo threshold (p. 279)
Elevation coordinate (p. 266)
Externalization (p. 270)
Free-field presentation (p. 269)
Fusion (p. 279)
Headphone presentation (p. 269)
Head-related transfer function (HRTF) (p. 269)
Indirect sound (p. 278)
Interaural level difference (ILD) (p. 268)
Interaural time difference (ITD) (p. 267)
Interaural time difference detectors (p. 272)
Internalization (p. 270)
Location cue (p. 267)
Melodic channeling (p. 276)
Melody schema (p. 278)
Monaural cue (p. 267)
Panoramic neurons (p. 273)
Precedence effect (p. 279)
Principles of auditory grouping (p. 275)
Receptive field for sound location (p. 272)
Reverberation time (p. 280)
Scale illusion (p. 276)
Spectral cue (p. 269)
Topographic map (p. 272)
Ventriloquism effect (p. 281)
Virtual auditory space (VAS) (p. 270)
Visual capture (p. 281)
Wessel effect (p. 275)

VISIT YOUR COMPANION WEBSITE FOR THIS BOOK

http://psychology.wadsworth.com/goldstein7e

Check out this companion website where you'll find online resources—glossary, flashcards, web links, multiple-choice and essay questions, and much more!

VIRTUAL LAB

Your Virtual Lab is designed to help you get the most out of this course. The Virtual Lab icons direct you to specific media demonstrations and experiments designed to help you visualize what you are reading about. The number beside each icon indicates the number of the media element you can access through your CD-ROM, Perception PsychologyNow, or WebTutor resource at http:now.ilrn.com/goldstein_7e.

The following are the lab exercises covering what you've just learned in this chapter:

1 *Interaural Level Difference as a Cue for Sound Localization* How the relative level of two tones presented in different speakers determines the perceived location of the tone.

2 *Grouping by Similarity of Timbre: The Wessel Demonstration* How similarity of timbre can change the perceived organization of a series of tones, if the tones are presented fast enough.

3 *Captor Tone Demonstration* The stimuli used in Bregman and Rudnicki's captor tone experiment.

4 *Grouping by Similarity of Pitch* How the perceptual organization of two sequences of tones changes when their pitches approach each other.

5 *Grouping by Pitch and Temporal Closeness* How our perception of groups of three tones changes as the tones are presented more rapidly. A demonstration of auditory stream segregation.

6 *Effect of Repetition on Grouping by Pitch* How the grouping observed in the "Grouping by Pitch and Temporal Closeness" demonstration can be affected by repeating the sequences.

7 *Auditory Good Continuation* How we hear a tone as continuous when spaces are filled in with noise.

8 *Perceiving Interleaved Melodies* How when two melodies are "interleaved," it becomes easier to hear both when the separation between their tones is increased.

9 *Layering Naturalistic Sounds* How we are able to hear different environmental sounds as being produced by different sound sources, even when they are presented at the same time.

10 *The Precedence Effect* How perception of sound location depends on the lag between sounds presented by two different speakers.

11 *Reverberation Time* How increasing a tone's reverberation time changes its perceived quality.

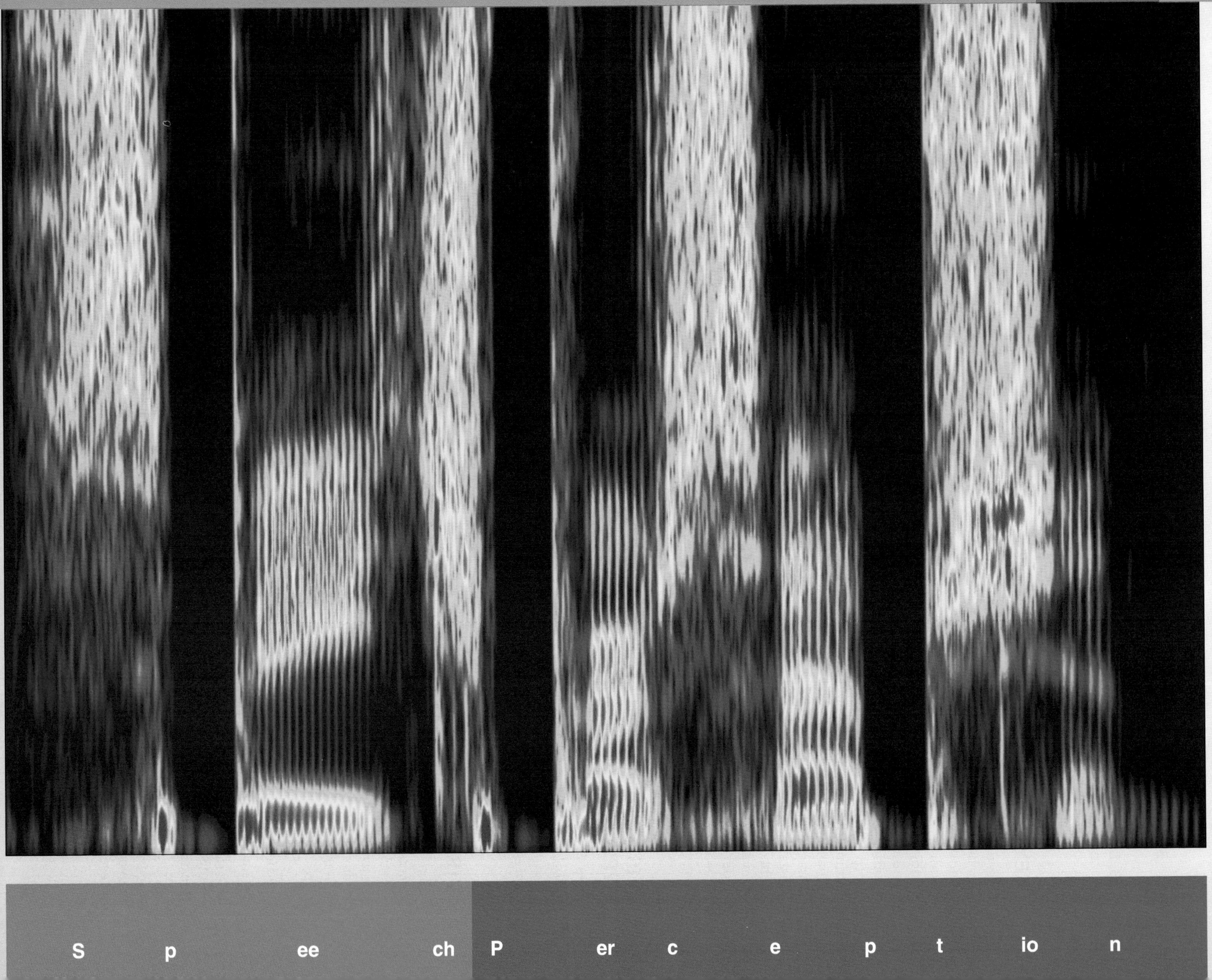
S p ee ch P er c e p t io n

CHAPTER

13

SPEECH PERCEPTION

Chapter Contents

This pattern is a speech spectrogram, which represents the sound energy from speaking the words speech perception*. Spectrograms are usually displayed as black on a white background, with frequency indicated on one axis and speech sounds on the other axis. See page 288 for more details on speech spectrograms.* Original spectrogram (before colorizing) courtesy of David Pisoni, Luis Hernandez, and Tessa Bent.

VL *The Virtual Lab icons direct you to specific animations and videos designed to help you visualize what you are reading about. The number beside each icon indicates the number of the clip you can access through your CD-ROM or your student website.*

Some Questions We Will Consider:

- *Can computers perceive speech as well as humans?* *(p. 286)*
- *Why does an unfamiliar foreign language often sound like a continuous stream of sound, with no breaks between words?* *(p. 289)*
- *Does each word that we hear have a unique pattern of air pressure changes associated with it?* *(p. 289)*
- *Are there specific areas in the brain that are responsible for perceiving speech?* *(p. 297)*

Although we perceive speech easily under most conditions, beneath this ease lurks processes as complex as those involved in perceiving the most complicated visual scenes. One way to appreciate this complexity is to consider attempts to use computers to recognize speech. Many companies now use computer speech recognition systems to provide services such as booking tickets, automated banking, and computer technical support.

But if you've ever used one of these systems, it is likely that a friendly computer voice has told you "I can't understand what you said" on more than one occasion. Computer speech recognition is constantly improving, but it still can't match people's ability to recognize speech. Computers perform well when a person speaks slowly and clearly, and when there is no background noise. However, humans can perceive speech under a wide variety of conditions, including the presence of various background noises, sloppy pronunciation, speakers with different accents, and the often chaotic give-and-take that routinely occurs when people talk with one another (Sinha, 2002; Zue & Glass, 2000).

This chapter will help you appreciate the complex perceptual problems posed by speech and will describe research that has helped us begin to understand how the human speech perception system has solved some of these problems.

THE SPEECH STIMULUS

Think about what you hear when someone speaks to you. You perceive a series of sounds called syllables, which combine to create words. These syllables and words appear strung together one after another like beads on a string. For example, we perceive the phrase "perception is easy" as the sequence of units: "per-sep-shon-iz-ee-z." Although perceiving speech may seem to be just a matter of processing a series of discrete sounds that are lined up one after another, the actual situation is quite different.

Rather than following one another, with the signal for one sound ending and then the next beginning, signals for neighboring sounds overlap one another. In addition, the pattern of air pressure changes for a particular word can vary greatly depending on whether the speaker is male or female, young or old, speaks rapidly or slowly, or has an accent. To understand the way speech sounds overlap and why the same sound can be represented by many different patterns of pressure changes, we need to describe the speech stimulus and how it is produced. We will do this in two ways: (1) in terms of short segments of sound, called phonemes; and (2) in terms of the patterns of frequencies and intensities of the pressure changes in the air, called the acoustic signal.

Phonemes: Sounds and Meanings

Our first task in studying speech perception is to separate speech sounds into manageable units. What are these units? The flow of a sentence? A particular word? A syllable? The sound of a letter? A sentence is too large a unit for easy analysis, and some letters have no sounds at all. Although there are arguments for the idea that the syllable is the basic unit of speech (Mehler, 1981; Segui, 1984), most speech research has been based on a unit called the **phoneme**. The phoneme is the shortest segment of speech that, if changed, would change the meaning of a word. Consider the word *bit*, which contains the phonemes /b/, /i/, and /t/. (Phonemes and other speech sounds are indicated by setting them off with slashes.) We know that /b/, /i/, and /t/ are phonemes because we can change the meaning of the word by changing each phoneme individually. Thus, *bit* becomes *pit* if /b/ is changed to /p/, it becomes *bat* if /i/ is changed to /a/, and it becomes *bid* if /t/ is changed to /d/.

The phonemes of English, listed in Table 13.1, are represented by phonetic symbols that stand for speech sounds: 13 phonemes have vowel sounds, and 24 pho-

Table 13.1 *Major consonants and vowels of English and their phonetic symbols*

Consonants				Vowels	
p	*pull*	s	*sip*	i	heed
b	*bull*	z	*zip*	I	hid
m	*man*	r	*rip*	e	bait
w	*will*	š	*should*	ε	head
f	*fill*	ž	*pleasure*	æ	had
v	*vet*	č	*chop*	u	who'd
θ	*thigh*	ǰ	*gyp*	U	put
ð	*thy*	y	*yip*	ʌ	but
t	*tie*	k	*kale*	o	boat
d	*die*	g	*gale*	ɔ	bought
n	*near*	h	*hail*	a	hot
l	*lear*	ŋ	*sing*	ə	sofa
				ɨ	many

nemes have consonant sounds. Your first reaction to this table may be that there are more vowels than the standard set you learned in grade school (a, e, i, o, u, and sometimes y). But some vowels can have more than one pronunciation, so there are more vowel sounds than vowel letters. For example, the vowel *o* sounds different in *boat* and *hot*, and the vowel *e* sounds different in *head* and *heed*. Phonemes, therefore, refer not to letters but to speech sounds that serve to distinguish meaning.

Because different languages use different sounds, the number of phonemes varies across languages. Although there are only 11 phonemes in Hawaiian, there are 37 in English, and as many as 60 in some African dialects. Thus, phonemes are defined in terms of the sounds that are used to create words in a specific language.

The Acoustic Signal: Patterns of Pressure Changes

Speech sounds are produced by the position or the movement of structures within the vocal apparatus, which produce patterns of pressure changes in the air that are called the **acoustic stimulus**, or the **acoustic signal**. The acoustic signal for most speech sounds is created by air that is pushed up from the lungs past the vocal cords and into the vocal tract. The sound that is produced depends on the shape of the vocal tract as air is pushed through it. The shape of the vocal tract is altered by moving the **articulators**, which include structures such as the tongue, lips, teeth, jaw, and soft palate (Figure 13.1).

Let's first consider the production of vowels. Vowels are produced by vibration of the vocal cords, and the specific sounds of each vowel are created by changing the overall shape of the vocal tract. This change in shape changes the resonant frequency of the vocal tract and produces peaks of pressure at a number of different frequencies (Figure 13.2). The frequencies at which these peaks occur are called **formants**.

Each vowel sound has a characteristic series of for-

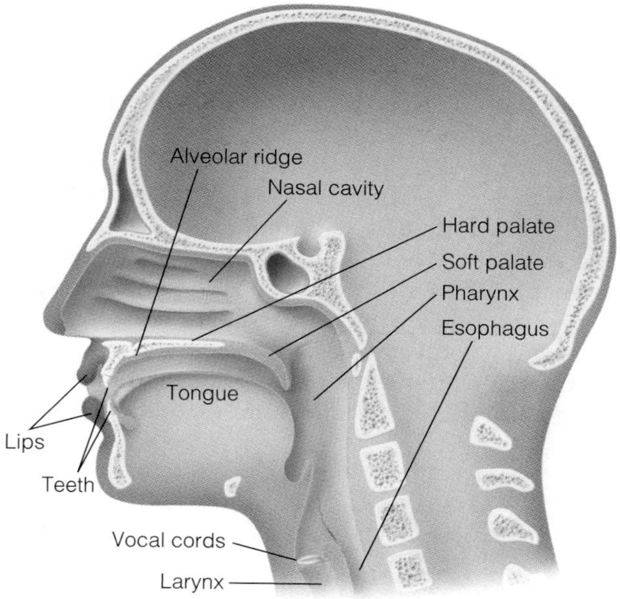

Figure 13.1 ▌ The vocal tract includes the nasal and oral cavities and the pharynx, as well as components that move, such as the tongue, lips, and vocal cords.

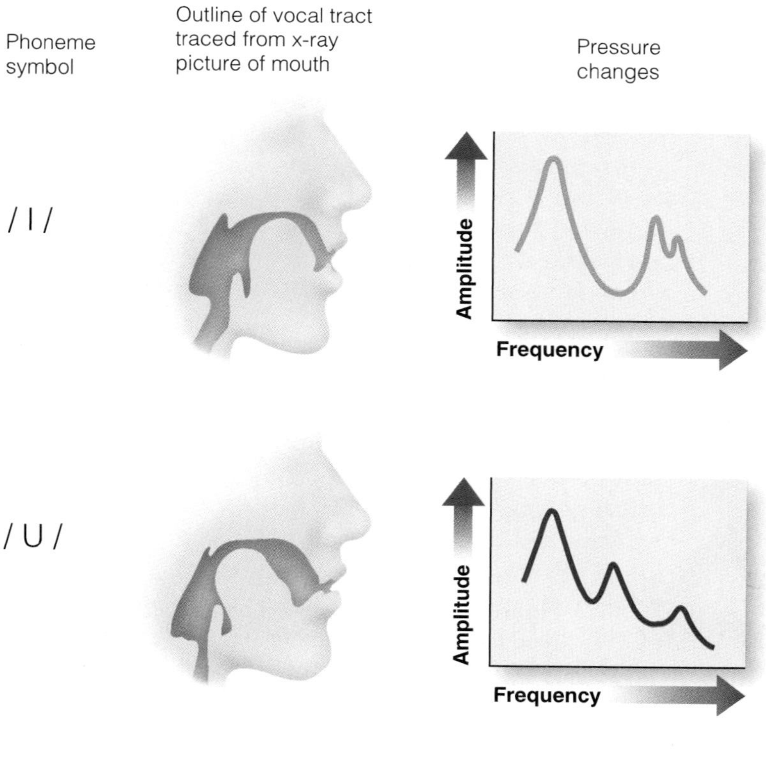

Figure 13.2 ▌ Left: the shape of the vocal tract for the vowels /I/ and /oo/. Right: the amplitude of the pressure changes produced for each vowel. The peaks in the pressure changes are the formants. Each vowel sound has a characteristic pattern of formants that is determined by the shape of the vocal tract for that vowel.
(From The Speech Chain, *2/e by P. B. Denes and E. N. Pinson. Copyright © 1993 by W. H. Freeman and Company. Reprinted by permission.)*

mants. The first formant has the lowest frequency. The second formant is the next highest, and so on. The formants for the vowel /æ/ are shown on a **speech spectrogram** in Figure 13.3. The speech spectrogram indicates the pattern of frequencies and intensities over time that make up the acoustic signal. Frequency is indicated on the vertical axis, time on the horizontal axis, and intensity is indicated by the darkness, with more darkness indicating greater intensity. From Figure 13.3 we can see that /æ/ has formants at 500, 1,700, and 2,500 Hz. The vertical lines in the spectrogram are pressure oscillations caused by vibrations of the vocal cord.

Consonants are produced by a constriction, or closing, of the vocal tract. To illustrate how different consonants are produced, let's focus on the sounds /d/ and /f/. Make these sounds, and notice what your tongue, lips, and teeth are doing. As you produce the sound /d/, you place your tongue against the ridge above your upper teeth (the alveolar ridge of Figure 13.1) and then release a slight rush of air as you move your tongue away from the alveolar ridge (try it). As you produce the sound /f/, you place your bottom lip against your upper front teeth and then push air between the lips and the teeth.

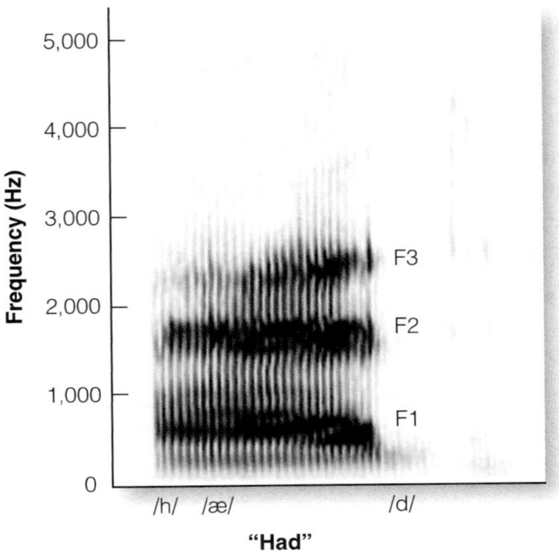

Figure 13.3 ❚ Spectrogram of the word *had* showing the first (F1), second (F2), and third (F3) formants for the vowel /æ/. (Spectrogram courtesy of Kerry Green.)

These movements of the tongue, lips, and other articulators create patterns of energy in the acoustic signal that we can observe on the speech spectrogram. For example, the spectrogram for the sentence "Roy read the will," shown in Figure 13.4, shows aspects of the signal associated with vowels and consonants. The three horizontal bands marked F1, F2, and F3 are the three formants associated with the /e/ sound of *read*. Rapid shifts in frequency preceding or following formants are called **formant transitions** and are associated with consonants. For example, T2 and T3 are formant transitions associated with the /r/ of *read*.

Now that we know how speech is produced and how it is represented on a speech spectrogram, we are ready to look at some of the problems that we must solve in order to understand speech perception.

THE RELATIONSHIP BETWEEN THE SPEECH STIMULUS AND WHAT WE HEAR

The main problem facing researchers trying to understand speech perception is that the relationships between the acoustic signal and the sounds we hear are extremely complex. One reason for this complexity is that the acoustic signal is not neatly separated into individual words.

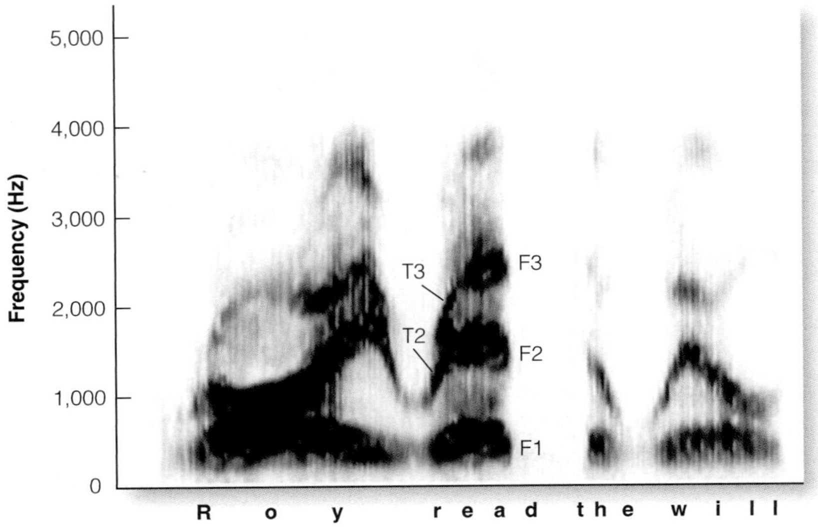

Figure 13.4 ❚ Spectrogram of the sentence "Roy read the will," showing formants such as F1, F2, and F3, and formant transitions such as T2 and T3. (Spectrogram courtesy of Kerry Green.)

This lack of separation between the signals for each word creates the **segmentation problem**: How do we perceptually segregate this continuous stream into individual words?

The Segmentation Problem

In Chapter 5 we saw that one task of the visual system is segmentation—separating a visual scene into individual objects. The auditory system faces a similar problem for speech—separating speech stimuli into individual words.

Just as we effortlessly see objects when we look at a visual scene, we usually have little trouble perceiving individual words when conversing with another person. But when we look at the speech spectrogram, we see that the acoustic signal is continuous, with either no physical breaks in the signal or breaks that don't necessarily correspond to the breaks we perceive between words (Figure 13.5). The fact that there are usually no spaces between words becomes obvious when you listen to someone speaking a foreign language. To someone who is unfamiliar with that language, the words seem to speed by in an unbroken string. However, to a speaker of that language, the words seem separated, just as the words of your native language seem separated to you. The solution to the segmentation problem involves determining how we divide the continuous stream of the acoustic signal into a series of individual words.

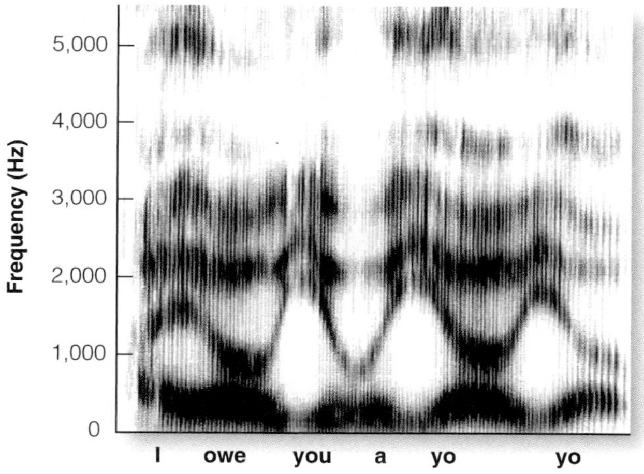

Figure 13.5 ▮ Spectrogram of "I owe you a yo-yo." This spectrogram does not contain pauses or breaks that correspond to the words that we hear. The absence of breaks in the acoustic signal creates the segmentation problem. (Spectrogram courtesy of David Pisoni.)

The Variability Problem

Another problem associated with the speech stimulus is that the acoustic signal is so variable that there is no simple correspondence between the acoustic signal and individual phonemes. This variability comes from a number of different sources.

Variability From a Phoneme's Context The acoustic signal associated with a phoneme changes depending on its context. For example, look at Figure 13.6, which shows spectrograms for the sounds /di/ and /du/. These are smoothed hand-drawn spectrograms that show the two most important characteristics of the sounds: the formants (shown in red) and the formant transitions (shown in blue). Because formants are associated with vowels, we know that the formants at 200 and 2,600 Hz are the acoustic signal for the vowel /i/ in /di/ and that the formants at 200 and 600 Hz are the acoustic signal for the vowel /u/ in /du/.

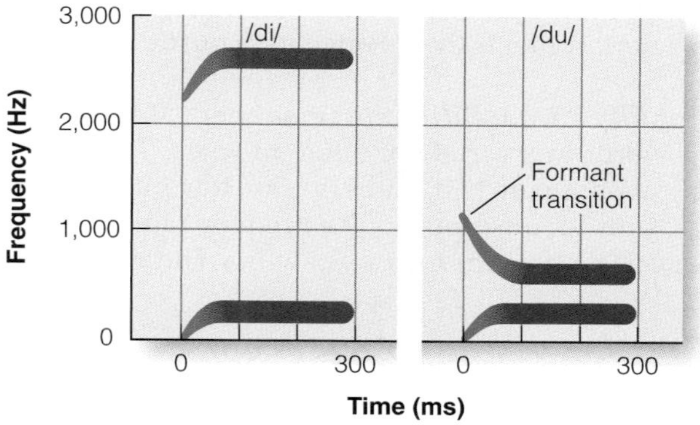

Figure 13.6 ▮ Hand-drawn spectrograms for /di/ and /du/. *(From "Perception of the Speech Code," by A. M. Liberman, 1967,* Psychological Review, *74, 431–461, figure 1. Copyright © 1967 by the American Psychological Association. Reprinted by permission of the author.)*

The formants are the acoustic signals for the vowels in /di/ and /du/, so the formant transitions that precede the formants must be the signal for the consonant /d/. But notice that the formant transitions for the second (higher frequency) formants of /di/ and /du/ are different. For /di/, the formant transition starts at about 2,200 Hz and rises to meet the second formant. For /du/, the second transition starts at about 1,100 Hz and falls to meet the second formant. Thus, even though we perceive the same /d/ sound in /di/ and /du/, the acoustic signals associated with these sounds are different.

This effect of context occurs because of the way speech is produced. The articulators are constantly moving as we talk, so the shape of the vocal tract for a particular phoneme is influenced by the shapes for the phonemes that both precede it and follow it. This overlap between the articulation of neighboring phonemes is called **coarticulation**. You can demonstrate coarticulation to yourself by noting how you produce phonemes in different contexts. For example, say *bat* and *boot*. When you say *bat*, your lips are unrounded, but when you say *boot*, your lips are rounded, even during the initial /b/ sound. Thus, even though the /b/ is the same in both words, you articulate each differently. In this example, the articulation of /oo/ in *boot* overlaps the articulation of /b/, causing the lips to be rounded even before the /oo/ sound is actually produced.

The fact that we perceive the sound of a phoneme as the same even though the acoustic signal is changed by coarticulation, is an example of perceptual constancy. This term may be familiar to you from our observations of constancy phenomena in the sense of vision, such as color constancy (we perceive an object's chromatic color as constant even when the wavelength distribution of the illumination changes) and size constancy (we perceive an object's size as constant even when the size of its image changes on our retina). Perceptual constancy in speech perception is similar. We perceive the sound of a particular phoneme as constant even when the phoneme appears in different contexts that change its acoustic signal.

Variability From Different Speakers People say the same words in a variety of different ways. Some people's voices are high pitched, and some are low pitched; people speak with accents; some talk extremely rapidly, and others speak e-x-t-r-e-m-e-l-y s-l-o-w-l-y. These wide variations in speech mean that for different speakers, a particular phoneme or word can have very different acoustic signals.

Speakers also introduce variability by their sloppy pronunciation. For example, say the following sentence at the speed you would use in talking to a friend: "This was a best buy." How did you say "best buy"? Did you pronounce the /t/ of best, or did you say "bes buy"? What about "She is a bad girl"? While saying this rapidly, notice whether your tongue hits the top of your mouth as you say the /d/ in bad. Many people omit the /d/ and say "ba girl." Finally, what about "Did you go to the store?" Did you say "did you" or "dijoo"? You have your own ways of producing various words and phonemes, and other people have theirs. Analysis of how people actually speak has determined that there are 50 different ways to produce the word "the" (Waldrop, 1988).

That people do not usually articulate each word individually in conversational speech is reflected in the spectrograms in Figure 13.7. The spectrogram in Figure 13.7a is for the question "What are you doing?" spoken slowly

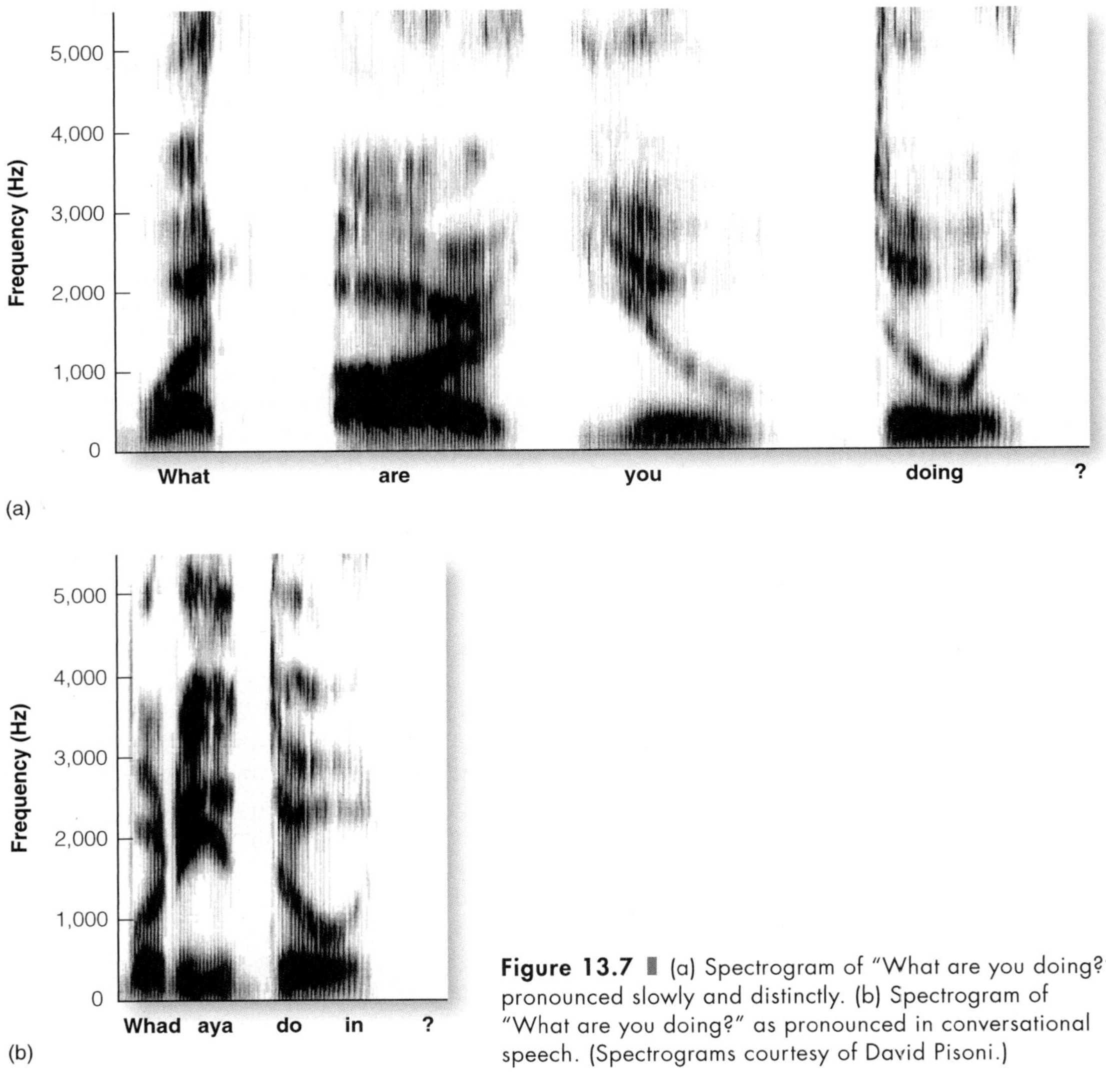

Figure 13.7 ■ (a) Spectrogram of "What are you doing?" pronounced slowly and distinctly. (b) Spectrogram of "What are you doing?" as pronounced in conversational speech. (Spectrograms courtesy of David Pisoni.)

and distinctly, whereas the spectrogram in Figure 13.7b is for the same question taken from conversational speech, in which "What are you doing?" becomes "Whad'aya doin'?" This difference shows up clearly in the spectrogram, which indicates that although the first and last words (*what* and *doing*) create similar patterns in the two spectrograms, the pauses between words are absent or are much less obvious in the spectrogram of Figure 13.7b, and the middle of this spectrogram is completely changed, with a number of speech sounds missing.

The variability in the acoustic signal caused by coarticulation, different speakers, and sloppy pronunciation creates a problem for the listener: He or she must somehow transform the information contained in this highly variable acoustic signal into familiar words. This variability problem, combined with the segmentation problem, is the reason that it has been so difficult to design machines that can recognize speech. But humans somehow recognize speech even in the face of what might seem to be extreme difficulties. Although it's not yet clear exactly how we do it, research conducted over the past 50 years has begun to unravel the mystery of how humans perceive speech. We will describe this research by first considering stimulus dimensions of speech perception and then considering cognitive dimensions of speech perception.

STIMULUS DIMENSIONS OF SPEECH PERCEPTION

What is the connection between the speech stimulus and what we perceive? We have already seen that the connection is not a simple one. We will now describe a number of different ways that speech perception researchers have approached this question.

Invariant Acoustic Cues

One of the unsolved problems of speech perception research has been identifying invariant acoustic cues in the acoustic signal. An **invariant acoustic cue** is a feature of the acoustic signal associated with a particular phoneme that remains constant even when phonemes appear in different contexts or are spoken by different speakers. Because invariant acoustic cues are not that obvious from the normal speech spectrogram, researchers searching for these invariant cues have devised new ways of displaying and analyzing the acoustic signal.

One way of displaying the acoustic signal is called the **short-term spectrum**. A short-term spectrum creates a detailed picture of the frequencies that occur within a short segment of time. For example, see Figure 13.8: On

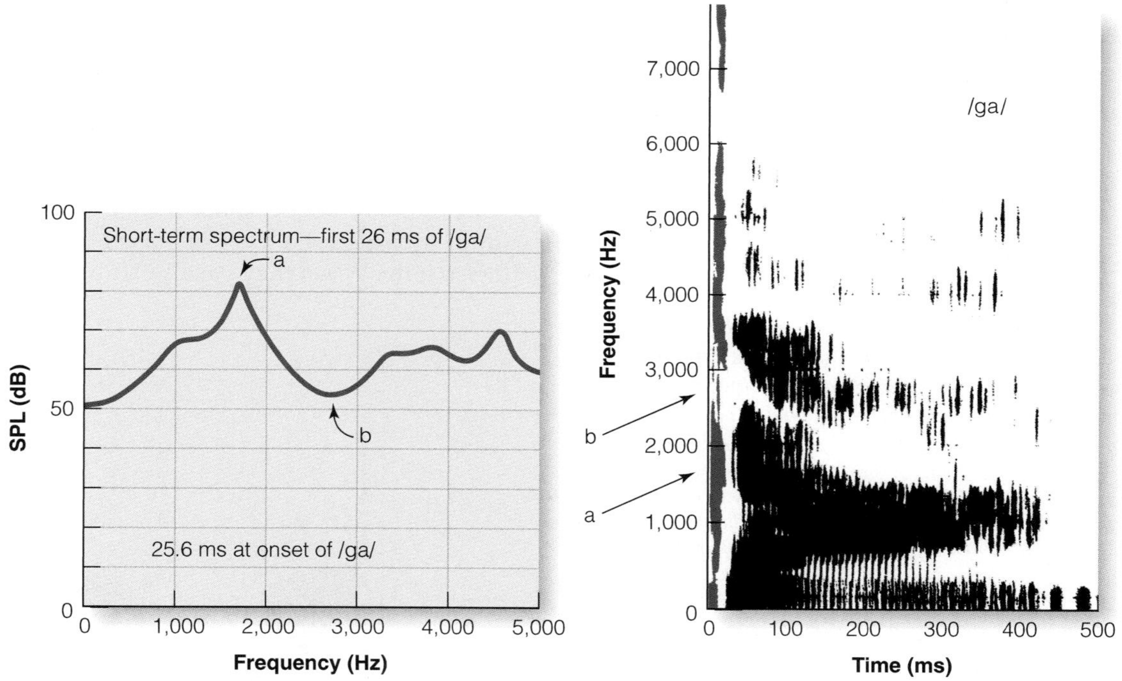

Figure 13.8 ▮ Left: a short-term spectrum of the acoustic energy in the first 26 ms of the phoneme /ga/. Right: sound spectrogram of the same phoneme. The sound for the first 26 ms is indicated in red. The peak in the short-term spectrum, marked *a*, corresponds to the dark band of energy, marked *a* in the spectrogram. The minimum in the short-term spectrum, marked *b*, corresponds to the light area, marked *b* in the spectrogram. The spectrogram on the right shows the energy for the entire 500 ms duration of the sound, whereas the short-term spectrum only shows the first 26 ms at the beginning of this signal. (Courtesy of James Sawusch.)

the left is the short-term spectrum that shows the frequencies that occur during the first 26 ms of the sound /ga/; on the right is the regular spectrogram for /ga/, showing the signal for the first 26 ms in red. The peak in the short-term spectrum, labeled a, and the minimum, labeled b, correspond to the dark and light energy bands a and b during the first 26 ms of the spectrogram. The advantage of the short-term spectrum is that it provides a precise and detailed picture of the acoustic signal. A sequence of short-term spectra can be combined to create a **running spectral display** that shows how the frequencies in the auditory signal change over time (Figure 13.9).

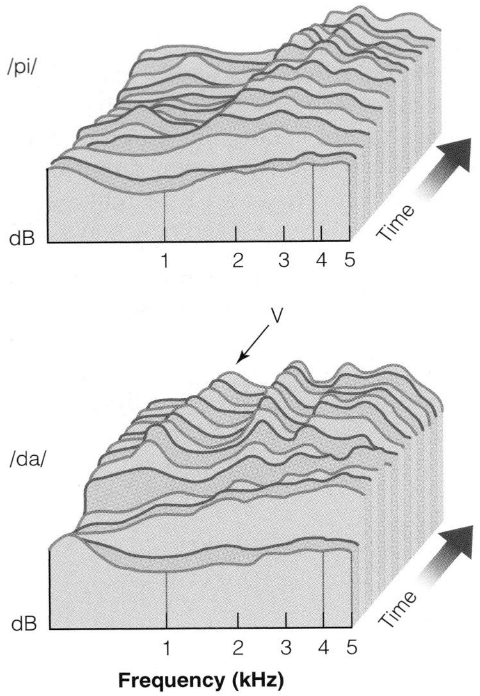

Figure 13.9 ▌ Running spectral displays for /pi/ and /da/. These displays are made up of a sequence of short-term spectra, like the one in Figure 13.8. Each of these spectra is displaced 5 ms on the time axis, so that each step we move along this axis indicates the frequencies present in the next 5 ms. The low-frequency peak (V) in the /da/ display is a cue for voicing. *(From "Time-Varying Features of Initial Stop Consonants in Auditory Running Spectra: A First Report," by D. Kewley-Port and P. A. Luce, 1984, Perception and* Psychophysics, *35, 353–360, figure 1. Copyright © 1984 by Psychonomic Society Publications. Reprinted by permission.)*

Researchers have identified some invariant acoustic cues in these running spectral displays. The invariance of these cues has been demonstrated by showing that people can identify characteristics of phonemes based on these cues, even in different contexts (Blumstein & Stevens, 1979; Kewley-Port, 1983; Kewley-Port & Luce, 1984; Searle, Jacobson, & Rayment, 1979; K. N. Stevens & Blumstein, 1978, 1981). For example, a low-frequency peak that continues in succeeding frames (marked with V in Figure 13.9) indicates that the vocal cords are vibrating. Notice that it occurs for /da/ but not for /pi/. The listener can, therefore, use this information to help differentiate between these two sounds.

Although the search for invariant acoustic cues has yielded some encouraging results, it hasn't been possible to identify invariant cues for all of the speech sounds (Nygaard & Pisoni, 1995). (See also Sussman, Hoemeke, & Ahmed, 1993; Sussman, McCaffrey, & Matthews, 1991, for additional evidence for invariant acoustic cues.) Thus, the search for invariant cues is continuing, but researchers are also looking for other connections between the speech signal and speech perception.

Categorical Perception

While looking for connections between the speech signal and speech perception, researchers have discovered a phenomenon called **categorical perception**—when a wide range of acoustic signals results in perception of a limited number of categories of sounds. We will use a specific example to explain what this means.

The example we will describe involves varying a characteristic of the acoustic signal called **voice onset time (VOT)**. Voice onset time is the time delay between when a sound begins and when the vocal cords begin vibrating. We can illustrate this delay by comparing the spectrograms for the sounds /da/ and /ta/ in Figure 13.10. We can see from these spectrograms that the time between the beginning of the sound /da/ and the beginning of the vocal cord vibrations (indicated by the presence of vertical stripes in the spectrogram) is 17 ms for /da/ and 91 ms for /ta/. Thus, /da/ has a short VOT and /ta/ has a long VOT.

By using computers, researchers have created sound stimuli in which the VOT is varied in small steps from short to long. When they vary VOT, using stimuli like the

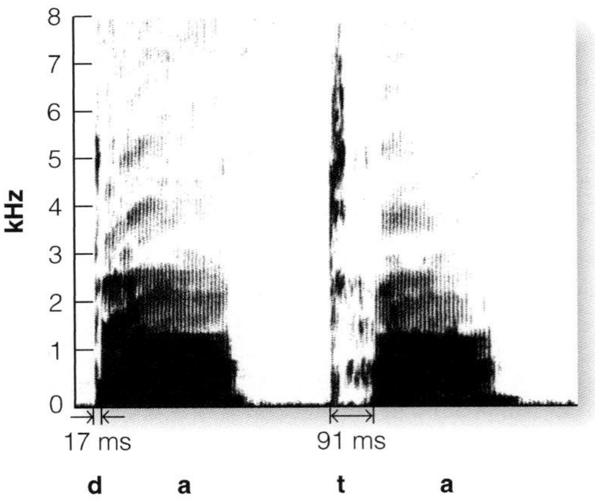

Figure 13.10 ▌ Spectrograms for /da/ and /ta/. The voice onset time—the time between the beginning of the sound and the onset of voicing—is indicated at the beginning of the spectrogram for each sound. (Spectrogram courtesy of Ron Cole.)

ones in Figure 13.10, and ask listeners to indicate what sound they hear, the listeners report hearing only one or the other of the two phonemes, /da/ or /ta/, even though a large number of stimuli with different VOTs are presented.

VIRTUAL LAB 1

This result is shown in Figure 13.11 (Eimas & Corbit, 1973). At short VOTs, listeners report that they hear /da/, and they continue reporting this even when the VOT is increased. But when the VOT reaches about 35 ms, their perception abruptly changes, so at VOTs above 40 ms, they report hearing /ta/. The VOT when the perception changes from /da/ to /ta/ is called the **phonetic boundary**. The key result of the categorical perception experiment is that even though the VOT is changed continuously across a wide range, the listener perceives only two categories: /da/ on one side of the phonetic boundary and /ta/ on the other side.

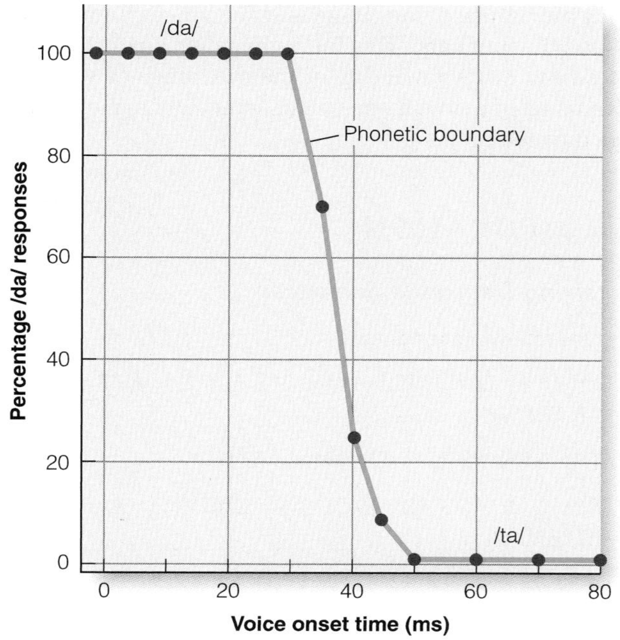

Figure 13.11 ▮ The results of a categorical perception experiment indicate that /da/ is perceived for VOTs to the left of the phonetic boundary, and that /ta/ is perceived at VOTs to the right of the phonetic boundary.
(From "Selective Adaptation of Linguistic Feature Detectors," by P. Eimas and J. D. Corbit, 1973, Cognitive Psychology, *4, 99–109, figure 2. Copyright © 1973 Academic Press, Inc. Reprinted by permission.)*

Once we have demonstrated categorical perception using the procedure above, we can run a discrimination test, in which we present two stimuli with different VOTs and ask the listener whether they sound the same or different. When we present two stimuli that are on the same side of the phonetic boundary, such as 10 and 30 ms VOTs, the listener says they sound the same (Figure 13.12). However, when we present two stimuli on opposite sides of

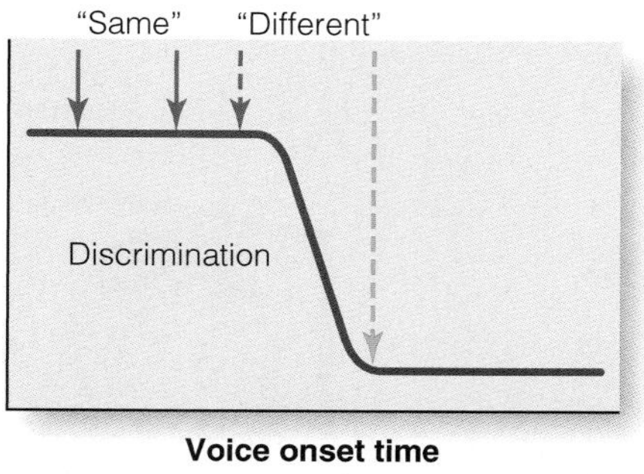

Figure 13.12 ▮ In the discrimination part of a categorical perception experiment, two stimuli are presented, and the listener indicates whether they are the same or different. The typical result is that two stimuli with VOTs on the same side of the phonetic boundary (solid arrows) are judged to be the same, and that two stimuli on different sides of the phonetic boundary (dashed arrows) are judged to be different.

the phonetic boundary, such as 30 and 50 ms VOTs, the listener says they sound different. The fact that all stimuli on the same side of the phonetic boundary are perceived as the same category is an example of perceptual constancy (Figure 13.13). If this constancy did not exist, we would perceive different sounds every time we changed the VOT. Instead, we experience one sound on each side of the phonetic boundary. This simplifies our perception of phonemes and helps us more easily perceive the wide variety of sounds in our environment.

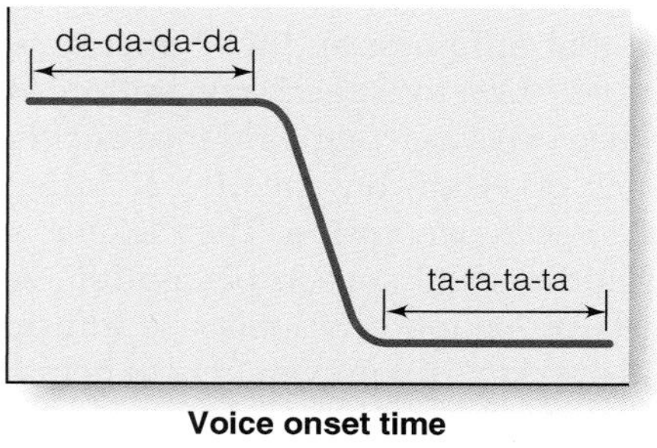

Figure 13.13 ▮ Perceptual constancy occurs when all stimuli on one side of the phonetic boundary are perceived to be in the same category even though their VOT is changed over a substantial range. This diagram symbolizes the constancy observed in the Eimas and Corbit (1973) experiment, in which /da/ was heard on one side of the boundary and /ta/ on the other side.

Speech Perception Is Multimodal

Another property of speech perception is that it is **multimodal**. That is, our perception of speech can be influenced by information from a number of different senses. One illustration of how speech perception can be influenced by visual information is shown in Figure 13.14. At first our listener is hearing the sounds /ba-ba/. But when visual stimulation is added in the form of a videotape

Figure 13.14 ▮ The McGurk effect. The woman's lips are moving as if she is saying /ga-ga/, but the actual sound being presented is /ba-ba/. The listener, however, reports hearing the sound /da-da/. If the listener closes his eyes, so that he no longer sees the woman's lips, he hears /ba-ba/. Thus, seeing the lips moving influences what the listener hears.

showing a person making the lip movements for the sound /ga-ga/, our listener begins hearing the sound /da-da/. Despite the fact that the listener is receiving the acoustic signal for /ba-ba/, he actually hears the sounds /da-da/.

This effect is called the **McGurk effect**, after the person who first described it (McGurk & MacDonald, 1976). It illustrates that although auditory energy is the major source of information for speech perception, visual information can also exert a strong influence on what we hear. This influence of vision on speech perception is called **audiovisual speech perception**. The McGurk effect is one example of audiovisual speech perception. Another example is the way people routinely use information provided by the speaker's lip movements to help understand speech in a noisy environment (also see Massaro, 2003). VL 2

TEST YOURSELF 13.1

1. Describe the speech stimulus. Be sure you understand what phonemes are and how the acoustic signal can be displayed using a sound spectrogram to reveal formants and formant transitions.
2. What are the two major problems posed by the speech stimulus? Be sure you understand the three types of variability in the speech signal.
3. What is an invariant acoustic cue, and how have researchers tried to demonstrate the existence of invariant acoustic cues in the speech signal?
4. What is categorical perception? Be sure you understand how it is measured and what it illustrates.
5. Give an example to illustrate the multimodal nature of speech perception.

COGNITIVE DIMENSIONS OF SPEECH PERCEPTION

Our discussion so far in this chapter has emphasized the relationship between speech perception and the stimuli we receive. But our perception of speech depends on more than just the energy that reaches our receptors. There is a cognitive dimension to speech perception as well, which depends on information stored in the listener's memory about the nature of language and the voice characteristics of specific speakers. The following demonstration illustrates how our knowledge of the meanings of words enables us to perceive these words even when the stimulus is incomplete.

DEMONSTRATION

Perceiving Degraded Sentences

Read the following sentences:

1. M*R* H*D * L*TTL* L*MB I*S FL**C* W*S WH*T* *S SN*W
2. TH* S*N *S N*T SH*N*NG T*D**
3. S*M* W**DS *R* EA*I*R T* U*D*R*T*N* T*A* *T*E*S ■

Your ability to read the sentences, even though up to half of the letters have been eliminated, was aided by your knowledge of English (Denes & Pinson, 1993). This is an example of top-down processing that we have discussed in connection with visual perception (see page 9): Knowledge you bring to the situation is used to supplement the bottom-up information provided by stimulation of the receptors (Figure 13.15). Another example of the effect of top-down processing in speech perception is provided by the process of segmentation, in which the speaker breaks the continuous acoustic signal into individual words.

Meaning and Segmentation

To help you appreciate the role of meaning in achieving segmentation, do the following demonstration.

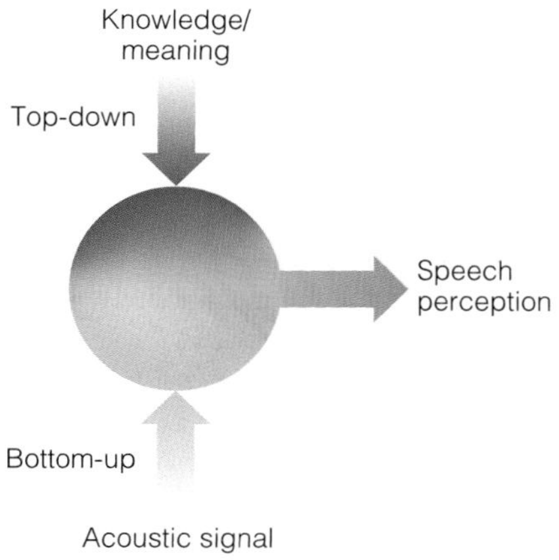

Figure 13.15 ▌ Speech perception is the result of top-down processing (based on knowledge and meaning) and bottom-up processing (based on the acoustic signal) working together.

DEMONSTRATION

Segmenting Strings of Sounds

1. Read the following words: Anna Mary Candy Lights Since Imp Pulp Lay Things. Now that you've read the words, what do they mean? If you think that this is a list of unconnected words beginning with the names of two women, Anna and Mary, you're right; but if you read this series of words a little faster, ignoring the spaces between the words on the page, you may hear a connected sentence that does not begin with the names Anna and Mary. (For the answer, see the bottom of page 296—but don't peek until you've tried reading the words rapidly.)
2. Read the following phrase fairly rapidly to a few people: "In mud eels are, in clay none are," and ask them to write the phrase. ■

If you succeeded in creating a new sentence from the series of words in the first part of the demonstration, you did so by changing the segmentation, and this change was achieved by your knowledge of the meaning of the sounds. When Raj Reddy (1976) asked participants to write their perception of "In mud eels are, in clay none are," he obtained responses like "In muddies, sar, in clay nanar"; "In may deals are, en clainanar"; and "In madel sar, in claynanar." In the absence of any context, some of Reddy's listeners had difficulty figuring out what the phrase meant and therefore forced their own interpretation on the sounds they heard. Had the listeners known that the passage was taken from a book about amphibians, their knowledge about possible meanings of the words would have facilitated segmentation and increased probability of their decoding the sentence correctly. (Another example of a situation in which segmentation would be aided by knowledge of the context in which a phrase or sentence appears are the phrases "How to recognize speech" and "How to wreck a nice beach.")

Pairs of words that flow together in speech also exemplify how segmentation results from meaning: "big girl" can be interpreted as "big Earl." The interpretation you pick will probably depend on the overall meaning of the sentence in which these words appear. This example is similar to the familiar "I scream, you scream, we all scream for ice cream" that many people learn as children. The acoustic stimuli for "I scream" and "ice cream" are identical, so the different segmentations must be achieved by the meaning of the sentence in which these words appear.

Although segmentation is clearly aided by knowing the meanings of words and being aware of the context within which these words occur, listeners use other information as well to achieve segmentation. For example, we learn that certain sounds are more likely to follow one another within a word than they are to occur as the last sound in one word and the first sound in the next. An example of such a case is the sound "bay-be," which is most likely to form the word "baby," and less likely to appear in the two adjacent words, "bay be." What's important about the "baby" example is that even though it is much more likely for "bay" and "be" to be in the same word, it is still possible that they could be in different words. The message here is that although there are many types of information for segmentation, no one type of information is 100-percent foolproof. Therefore, it is likely that listeners use a number of different sources of information to achieve segmentation (Sanders & Neville, 2000).

Meaning and Phoneme Perception

The meanings of words and their context are important not only for helping achieve segmentation, but for helping us understand the phonemes that make up words. A large amount of research has shown it is easier to perceive phonemes that appear in a meaningful context. Philip Rubin, M. T. Turvey, and Peter Van Gelder (1976) showed that meaning enhances a listener's ability to recognize phonemes by presenting a series of short words like SIN, BAT, and LEG, or nonwords like JUM, BAF, and TEG, and asking listeners to respond by pressing a key as rapidly as possible whenever they heard a sound that began with /b/. On the average, participants took 631 ms to respond to the nonwords and 580 ms to respond to the real words. Thus, when a phoneme is at the beginning of a real word, it is identified about 8 percent faster than when it is at the beginning of a meaningless syllable.

The effect of meaning on the perception of phonemes was demonstrated in another way by Richard Warren (1970), who had participants listen to a recording of the sentence "The state governors met with their respective legislatures convening in the capital city." Warren replaced the first /s/ in "legislatures" with the sound of a cough and told his subjects that they should indicate where in the sentence the cough occurred. None of the participants identified the correct position of the cough, and, even more significantly, none noticed that the /s/ in "legislatures" was missing. This effect, which Warren called the **phonemic restoration effect**, was experienced even by students and staff in the psychology department who knew that the /s/ was missing.

Warren not only demonstrated the phonemic restoration effect but also showed that it can be influenced by the meaning of words following the missing phoneme. For example, the last word of the phrase "There was time to *ave . . . " (where the * indicates the presence of a cough or some other sound) could be "shave," "save," "wave," or "rave," but participants heard the word "wave" when the remainder of the sentence had to do with saying goodbye to a departing friend.

The phonemic restoration effect was used by Arthur Samuel (1981) to show that speech perception is determined both by a context that produces expectations in the listener (top-down processing) *and* also by the nature of the acoustic signal (bottom-up processing). Samuel demonstrated top-down processing by masking various phonemes in sentences with a white-noise mask, like the sound produced by a television set tuned to a nonbroadcasting channel, and showing that longer words increase the likelihood of the phonemic restoration effect. Apparently, participants used the additional context provided by the long word to help identify the masked phoneme. Further evidence for the importance of context is Samuel's finding that more restoration occurs for a real word like prOgress (where the capital letter indicates the masked phoneme) than for a similar pseudoword like crOgress (Samuel, 1990).

Samuel demonstrated bottom-up processing by showing that restoration is better when the masking sound and the masked phoneme sound similar. Thus, phonemic restoration is more likely to occur for a phoneme such as /s/, which is rich in high-frequency acoustic energy, when the mask also contains a large proportion of high-frequency energy.

What happens in phonemic restoration, according to Samuel, is that we use the context to develop some expectation of what a sound will be. But before we actually perceive the sound, its presence must be confirmed by the presence of a sound that is similar to it. If the white-noise mask contains frequencies that make it sound similar to the phoneme we are expecting, phonemic restoration occurs, and we are likely to hear the phoneme. If the mask does not sound similar, phonemic restoration is less likely to occur (Samuel, 1990).

Meaning and Word Perception

Meaningfulness also makes it easier to perceive whole words. An early demonstration of this effect by George Miller and Steven Isard (1963) showed that words are more intelligible when heard in the context of a grammatical sentence than when presented as items in a list of unconnected words. They demonstrated this by creating three kinds of stimuli: (1) normal grammatical sentences, such as *Gadgets simplify work around the house;* (2) anomalous sentences that follow the rules of grammar but make no sense, such as *Gadgets kill passengers from the eyes;* and (3) ungrammatical strings of words, such as *Between gadgets highways passengers the steal.*

Miller and Isard used a technique called **shadowing**, in which they presented these sentences to subjects through earphones and asked them to repeat aloud what they were hearing. The participants reported normal sentences with an accuracy of 89 percent, but their accuracy fell to 79 percent for the anomalous sentences and 56 percent for the ungrammatical strings.

The differences among the three types of stimuli became even greater when the listeners heard the stimuli in the presence of a background noise. For example, at a moderately high level of background noise, accuracy was 63 percent for the normal sentences, 22 percent for the anomalous sentences, and only 3 percent for the ungrammatical strings of words.

This result tells us that when words are arranged in a meaningful pattern, we can perceive them more easily. But most people don't realize it is their knowledge of the nature of their language that helps them fill in sounds and words that might be difficult to hear. For example, our knowledge of permissible word structures tells us that ANT, TAN, and NAT are all permissible sequences of letters in English, but that TQN or NQT cannot be English words.

At the level of the sentence, our knowledge of the rules of grammar tells us that "There is no time to question" is a permissible English sentence, but "Question, no time there is" is not permissible or, at best, is extremely awkward (unless you are Yoda, who says this in *Star Wars, Episode III: Revenge of the Sith*). Because we mostly encounter meaningful words and grammatically correct sentences, we are continually using our knowledge of what is permissible in our language to help us understand what is being said. This becomes particularly important when listening under less-than-ideal conditions, such as in noisy environments or when the speaker's voice quality or accent is difficult to understand (see also Salasoo & Pisoni, 1985).

All of these results support the idea that the knowledge a listener brings to a situation helps him or her decode the acoustic signal into phonemes and meaningful words and sentences. In addition, there is also evidence that a listener's experience in listening to specific speakers can enhance his or her ability to perceive what is being said.

Answer to question on page 295: "An American delights in simple playthings."

Speaker Characteristics

When you're having a conversation, hearing a lecture, or listening to dialogue in a movie, you usually focus on determining the meaning of what is being said. But as you are taking in these messages, you are also, perhaps without realizing it, taking in characteristics of the speaker's voice. These characteristics, which are called **indexical characteristics**, carry information about speakers such as their age, gender, place of origin, emotional state, and whether they are being sarcastic or serious. Consider, for example, the following joke:

> A linguistics professor was lecturing to his class one day. "In English," he said, "a double negative forms a positive. In some languages, though, such as Russian, a double negative is still a negative. However, there is no language wherein a double positive can form a negative." A voice from the back of the room piped up, "Yeah, right."

This joke is humorous because "Yeah, right" contains two positive words that, despite the linguistics professor's statement, produce a negative statement that most people who know contemporary English usage would interpret as "I disagree" (or "No way," to use a more colloquial expression). The point of this example is not just that "Yeah, right" can mean "I disagree," but that the meaning of this phrase is determined by our knowledge of current English usage and also (if we were actually listening to the student's remark) by the speaker's tone of voice, which in this case would be highly sarcastic.

The speaker's tone of voice is one factor that helps listeners determine the meaning of what is being said. But most research on indexical characteristics has focused on how speech perception is influenced by the speaker's identity. Thomas Palmeri, Stephen Goldinger, and David Pisoni (1993) demonstrated the effect of speaker identity by presenting listeners with a sequence of words. After each word, listeners indicated whether the word was a new word (this was the first time it appeared) or an old word (it had appeared previously in the sequence). They found that listeners reacted more rapidly and were more accurate when the same speaker said all of the words than when different speakers said the words. This means listeners are taking in two levels of information about the word: (1) its meaning and (2) characteristics of the speaker's voice.

From the results of this experiment and the others we have discussed, we can conclude that speech perception depends both on the bottom-up information provided by the acoustic signal and on the top-down information provided by the meanings of words and sentences, the listener's knowledge of the rules of grammar, and information that the listener has about characteristics of the speaker's voice.

We can appreciate the interaction between the acoustic signal for speech and the meaning of speech when we realize that although we use the meaning to help us to understand the acoustic signal, the acoustic signal is the starting point for determining the meaning. Look at it this way: There may be enough information in my sloppy handwriting so that a person using bottom-up processing can decipher it solely on the basis of the squiggles on the page, but my handwriting is much easier to decipher when, by using top-down processing, the person takes the meanings of the words into account. And just as previous experience in hearing a particular person's voice makes it easier to understand that person later, previous experience in reading my handwriting would make it easier to read the squiggles on the page. Speech perception apparently works in a similar way. Although most of the information is contained in the acoustic signal, taking meaning and indexical properties into account makes understanding speech much easier.

SPEECH PERCEPTION AND THE BRAIN

Investigation of the physiological basis for speech perception stretches back to at least the 19th century, but only recently has considerable progress has been made.

Brain Areas, Neurons, and Speech Perception

Based on their studies of brain-damaged patients, 19th-century researchers Paul Broca and Carl Wernike showed that damage to specific areas of the brain causes language problems, called **aphasias** (Figure 13.16). There are numerous forms of aphasia, with the specific symptoms de-

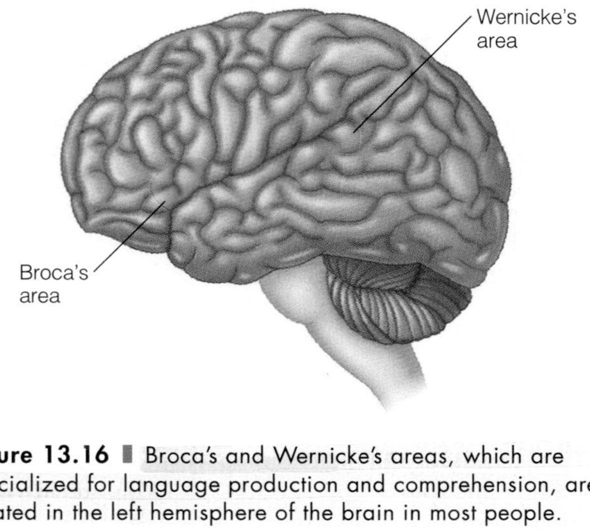

Figure 13.16 ■ Broca's and Wernicke's areas, which are specialized for language production and comprehension, are located in the left hemisphere of the brain in most people.

pending on the area damaged and extent of the damage. Patients with damage to **Broca's area** in the frontal lobe have a condition called **Broca's aphasia**. They have labored and stilted speech and can only speak in short sentences. They are, however, capable of comprehending what others are saying. Patients with damage to **Wernicke's area** in the temporal lobe have **Wernicke's aphasia**. They can speak fluently, but what they say is extremely disorganized and not meaningful. These patients have great difficulty understanding what other people are saying. In the most extreme form of Wernicke's aphasia, the person has a condition called **word deafness**, in which he or she cannot recognize words, even though the ability to hear pure tones remains intact (Kolb & Whishaw, 2003).

Modern research on speech perception and the brain has focused on determining how individual neurons and areas of the brain respond to speech stimuli. Figure 13.17 shows the results of an experiment that compared the short-term spectra for the sound /da/ and the firing of cat auditory nerve fibers with low, medium, and high characteristic frequencies (Sachs et al., 1981). (Remember from Chapter 11 that the neuron's characteristic frequency is the frequency to which this neuron responds best.) The information in this group of neurons clearly mimics the form of the sound stimulus, but what happens to this information when it reaches the auditory cortex?

When we described the *what* and *where* streams in the auditory system in Chapter 11, we saw that there are neurons outside of the core area of auditory cortex that respond to complex sounds, including animal calls and speechlike stimuli (see page 254). Brain-scan experiments have shown that there are areas in the *what* stream that are selectively activated by the human voice (Belin et al., 2000), and, as we will see in the "Something to Consider" section, the *where* stream may play a role in perceiving speech as well.

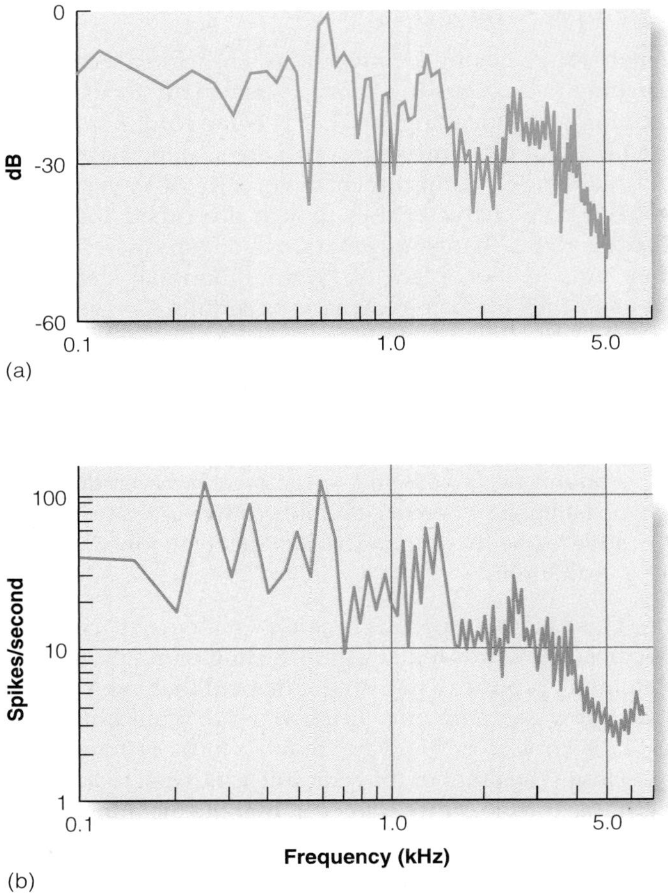

Figure 13.17 (a) Short-term spectrum for /da/. This curve indicates the energy distribution in /da/ between 20 and 40 ms after the beginning of the signal. (b) Nerve firing of a population of cat auditory nerve fibers to the same stimulus. *(From "Encoding of Speech Features in the Auditory Nerve," by M. B. Sachs, E. D. Young & M. I. Miller, 1981. In R. Carlson and B. Granstrom (Eds.)* The Representation of Speech in the Peripheral Auditory System. *pp. 115–130. Copyright ©1981 by Elsevier Science Publishing, New York. Reprinted by permission.)*

Experience-Dependent Plasticity

Young infants in all cultures can tell the difference between sounds that create all of the speech sounds used in the world's languages, but by the age of 1, they have lost the ability to tell the difference between some of these sounds (Kuhl, 2000). The classic example of this phenomenon is provided by Japanese children and adults. Six-month-old Japanese children can tell the difference between the /r/ and /l/ used in American English just as well as American children. However, by 12 months, the Japanese children can no longer do this, whereas, over the same period, the American children have become better at telling the difference between the two sounds (Kuhl et al., 1997; Strange, 1995).

The physiological mechanism responsible for this early shift in speech perception is likely to involve experience-dependent plasticity, in which the brain becomes tuned to respond best to sounds that the infants hear and use (see page 85). Evidence supporting this idea has recently been provided by Maritza Rivera-Gaxiola and coworkers (2005), who recorded electrical potentials from the surface of the cortex of 7- and 11-month-old American infants in response to pairs of sounds that are perceived as different to adult Spanish-speakers, but which sound the same to adult English-speakers. At 7 months of age, the electrical response to these two sounds was different, but by 11 months of age, the response had become the same. This result provides a physiological parallel to the experience of young Japanese children we described in the previous paragraph. Apparently, the brain is shaped by experience to respond to sounds that are used in a language that the child is learning.

SOMETHING TO CONSIDER: IS THERE A CONNECTION BETWEEN SPEECH PERCEPTION AND SPEECH PRODUCTION?

In 1967 Philip Liberman and coworkers proposed a theory called the **motor theory of speech perception**. The motor theory states that there is a close link between how speech is perceived and how it is produced. The basic idea is that when we *hear* a particular speech sound, this activates the motor mechanisms responsible for *producing* the sound *and* the mechanisms that enable us to *perceive* the sound. The rationale behind motor theory is simple: Because the motor action of speaking and the perceptual act of listening are so closely connected, it makes sense to propose that the mechanisms responsible for these two functions are closely linked to one another.

Motor theory has been controversial and has generated a huge amount of research, some of which has supported the theory, and some of which has not. But the recent discovery of mirror neurons, which we described in Chapter 10, provides the physiological link between motor actions and perception that motor theory proposes. Audiovisual mirror neurons fire when a monkey *carries out an action* that produces a sound and when the monkey *hears the sound* that results from the action (Kohler et al., 2002) (see page 227). Interestingly, mirror neurons that have been studied in the monkey are found in an area roughly equivalent to Broca's area in humans.

But is there any evidence that links speech perception and production in humans? K. D. Watkins and coworkers (2003) provided some evidence for this link by using a technique called transcranial magnetic stimulation (TMS) to activate the area of the motor cortex that controls movements of the face. When they stimulated this area, they were able to detect small responses, called motor evoked potentials (MEP), from the lips (Figure 13.18a). This wasn't surprising because stimulating this area of the motor cortex should cause movement potentials in the lips. But what was significant was that the MEP response became larger when the person either listened to speech or watched someone else's lip movements (Figure 13.18b). Watkins also did other experiments that showed that this MEP enhancement occurs only for structures such as the lips, which are part of the motor system for producing speech. He also suggested that perhaps mirror neurons are responsible for this effect.

Although these results support motor theory, many researchers feel that other mechanisms, such as the firing of neurons that respond to speech stimuli, are also involved. In fact, the recent discovery of the *what* and *where* streams for hearing has led to the suggestion that speech perception may be based both on motor movements,

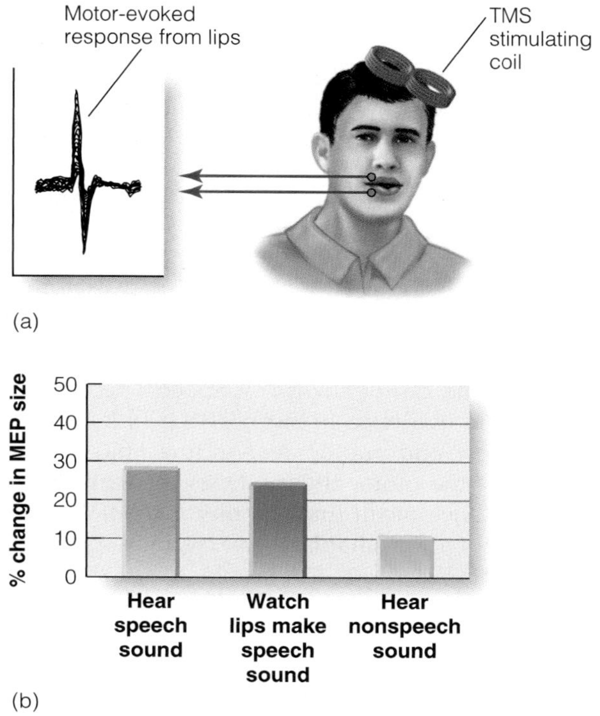

Figure 13.18 ▌ The transcranial magnetic stimulation experiment that provides evidence for a link between speech perception and production in humans. See text for details. *(Reprinted from* Neuropsychologia, 41, *Watkins, K. E., Strafella, A. P., & Paus, T., Seeing and hearing speech excites the motor system involved in speech production, 989–994, (2003), with permission from Elsevier.)*

which are served by the dorsal stream, and on responses to the sound stimulus, which are served by the ventral stream (Scott & Johnsrude, 2003). Thus, it is likely that speech perception will eventually be explained in a way similar to other types of perception—as involving a number of different mechanisms working together.

TEST YOURSELF 13.2

1. What is the evidence that meaning can influence phoneme perception? Describe the Rubin et al.'s (1976) experiment and also some of the things that have been discovered about the phonemic restoration effect.
2. What is the evidence that meaning can influence word perception?
3. How do speaker characteristics influence speech perception?
4. Which type of processing is more important in speech perception—bottom-up or top-down? Describe an experiment that provides evidence for

bottom-up and top-down influences on speech perception in the same study.

5. What did Broca and Wernicke discover about the physiology of speech perception?
6. Describe the following evidence that is relevant to the physiology of speech perception: (1) recording from auditory nerve fibers; (2) determining the brain's response to speech stimuli; (3) the change in speech perception abilities that take place during the first year of life.
7. What is the motor theory of speech perception? Cite some evidence to support the link between perception and motor responding that is proposed by the motor theory. Does the existence of this evidence mean that the motor theory is now the accepted mechanism for explaining speech perception?

THINK ABOUT IT

1. How well can computers recognize speech? You can research this question by getting on the telephone with a computer. Dial a service such as the one that books movie tickets, and then instead of going out of your way to talk slowly and clearly, try talking in a normal conversational voice (but talk clearly enough so a human would still understand you), and see whether you can determine the limits of the computer's ability to understand speech.
2. How do you think your perception of speech would be affected if the phenomenon of categorical perception did not exist?

IF YOU WANT TO KNOW MORE

1. ***Tadoma: "Hearing" with Touch*** People who are both deaf and blind can figure out what people are saying by using a procedure called "Tadoma," which involves touching a person's face while he or she is speaking.

   Reed, C. M., Durlach, N. I., Braida, L. D., & Schultz, M. C. (1982). Analytic study of the Tadoma method: Identification of consonants and vowels by an experienced Tadoma user. *Journal of Speech and Hearing Research, 25,* 108–116.

2. ***Is Speech Special?*** This is a controversy in which some researchers (many of whom are proponents of the motor theory of speech perception) argue that speech perception involves special mechanisms not shared by other auditory mechanisms, and another group of researchers feel that speech perception is served by the same mechanisms that enable us to hear other types of auditory stimuli.

   Fowler, C. A., and Rosenblum, L. D. (1990). Duplex perception: A comparison of monosyllables and slamming doors. *Journal of Experimental Psychology: Human Perception and Performance, 17,* 816–828.

   Trout, J. D. (2003). Biological specializations for speech: What can the animals tell us? *Current Directions in Psychological Science, 5,* 155–159.

KEY TERMS

Acoustic signal (p. 287)
Acoustic stimulus (p. 287)
Aphasia (p. 297)
Articulator (p. 287)
Audiovisual speech perception (p. 294)
Broca's aphasia (p. 298)
Broca's area (p. 298)
Categorical perception (p. 292)
Coarticulation (p. 289)
Formant (p. 287)
Formant transitions (p. 288)
Indexical characteristic (p. 297)
Invariant acoustic cue (p. 291)
McGurk effect (p. 294)
Motor theory of speech perception (p. 299)
Multimodal (p. 293)
Phoneme (p. 286)
Phonemic restoration effect (p. 296)
Phonetic boundary (p. 293)
Running spectral display (p. 292)
Segmentation problem (p. 289)
Shadowing (p. 296)
Short-term spectrum (p. 291)
Speech spectrogram (p. 288)
Voice onset time (VOT) (p. 292)
Wernicke's aphasia (p. 298)
Wernicke's area (p. 298)
Word deafness (p. 298)

VISIT YOUR COMPANION WEBSITE FOR THIS BOOK

http://psychology.wadsworth.com/goldstein7e

Check out this companion website where you'll find online resources—glossary, flashcards, web links, multiple-choice and essay questions, and much more!

VIRTUAL LAB

Your Virtual Lab is designed to help you get the most out of this course. The Virtual Lab icons direct you to specific media demonstrations and experiments designed to help you visualize what you are reading about. The number beside each icon indicates the number of the media element you can access through your CD-ROM, Perception PsychologyNow, or WebTutor resource at http:now.ilrn.com/goldstein_7e.

The following are the lab exercises covering what you've just learned in this chapter:

1 *Categorical Perception* How perception of a tone suddenly changes from one category to another as the tone's characteristics are slowly changed over a wide range.

2 *The McGurk Effect* How seeing a person's lips move can influence what we hear.

CHAPTER 14

THE CUTANEOUS SENSES

Chapter Contents

The fingers of a person reading Braille. Scanning the fingers over the raised Braille dots is an example of active touch.

VL *The Virtual Lab icons direct you to specific animations and videos designed to help you visualize what you are reading about. The number beside each icon indicates the number of the clip you can access through your CD-ROM or your student website.*

Some Questions We Will Consider

- *Are there specialized receptors in the skin for sensing different tactile qualities? (p. 305)*
- *What is the most sensitive part of the body? (p. 311)*
- *Is it possible to reduce pain with your thoughts? (p. 320)*
- *Do all people experience pain in the same way? (p. 321)*

Geerat Vermeij, blind since the age of 4 from a childhood eye disease, had come with his parents from his boyhood home in the Netherlands to live in the United States. After being educated in residential schools for the blind and also the regular school system, he attended Princeton University. During his senior year at Princeton, he applied to a number of graduate schools to study evolutionary biology, with a specialty in mollusks. He was rejected by a number of schools, who said his blindness would make it impossible for him to study biology, but he was granted an interview by Edgar Boell, the director of graduate study in the biology department at Yale. Boell took Vermeij to the museum, introduced him to the curator, and handed him a shell. Here is what happened next, as told by Vermeij (1997):

> "Here's something. Do you know what it is?" Boell asked as he handed me a specimen.
>
> My fingers and mind raced. Widely separated ribs parallel to outer lip; large aperture; low spire; glossy; ribs reflected backward. "It's a Harpa," I replied tentatively. "It must be Harpa major." Right so far.
>
> "How about this one?" inquired Boell, as another fine shell changed hands. Smooth, sleek, channeled suture, narrow opening; could be any olive. "It's an olive. I'm pretty sure it's Oliva sayana, the common one from Florida, but they all look alike."
>
> Both men were momentarily speechless. They had planned this little exercise all along to call my bluff. Now that I had passed, Boell had undergone an instant metamorphosis. Beaming with enthusiasm and warmth, he promised me his full support. (Vermeij, 1997, pp. 79–80)

Vermeij was admitted to graduate study at Yale, graduated with a PhD in evolutionary biology, and is presently a professor of geology at the University of California at Davis and editor of the scientific journal *Evolution*. He does all of his work with his hands, using his exquisitely trained sense of touch to identify the mollusks he studies. It has, for him, provided a window into the world of shells that has enabled him to surpass many of his sighted colleagues, partially because he, of necessity, ignores visual details that might be extraneous and focuses on the physical characteristics that he can feel.

Geerat Vermeij's abilities illustrate the amazing capabilities of touch. Another example of the capabilities of touch is provided by Braille, the system of raised dots that enables blind people to read with their fingertips (Figure 14.1). A Braille character consists of a cell made up of from one to six dots. Different arrangements of dots and blank spaces represent letters of the alphabet, as shown, and, in addition to characters for each letter of the alphabet, there are also characters for numbers, punctuation marks, and common speech sounds and words.

Experienced Braille readers can read at a rate of about 100 words per minute, slower than the rate for visual reading, which averages about 250 to 300 words per minute, but impressive nonetheless when we consider that the a Braille reader transforms an array of raised dots into information that goes far beyond simply feeling sensations on the skin.

But the importance of the sense of touch and the other perceptions we experience through the skin extends beyond its usefulness as a way to take in information. Imagine how your ability to write might change if your hand were anesthetized. Would you know how firmly to grasp your pen if you had no feeling in your hand? Consider all of the other things you do with your hands. How would losing feeling in your hands affect your ability to do these things? We know that a complete loss of our ability to feel

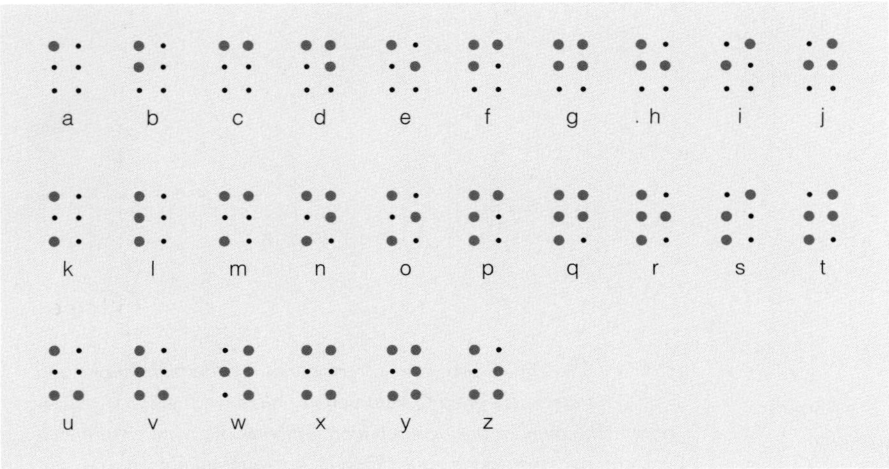

Figure 14.1 ▮ The Braille alphabet consists of raised dots in a 2 × 3 matrix. The large dots indicate the location of the raised dot for each letter. Blind people read these dots by scanning them with their fingertips.

with the skin is dangerous, as demonstrated by people who, because they can't feel touch or pain, suffer constant bruises, burns, and broken bones in the absence of the warnings provided by touch and pain (Melzack & Wall, 1983; Rollman, 1991; Wall & Melzack, 1994). And consider for a moment what sex would be like without the sense of touch. Or perhaps a better way to put this is to ask whether sex without the sense of touch is something people would be capable of or care about at all.

When we recognize that the perceptions we experience through our skin are crucial for protecting ourselves from injury and for motivating sexual activity, we can see that these perceptions are crucial to our survival and to the survival of our species. We could, in fact, make a good case for the idea that perceptions felt through the skin are more important for survival than those provided by vision and hearing.

In this chapter, we will be considering the **cutaneous sensations**—sensations based on the stimulation of receptors in the skin. The cutaneous sensations are served by the **somatosensory system**, which is also responsible for two other types of perception: (1) **proprioception**, the "body sense" in which input from the skin, muscles, tendons, and vestibular (balance) system results in perception of the body, and (2) **kinesthesis**, the sense of the position and movement of the limbs. We will focus our attention primarily on touch and pain. As we look at the anatomy of the somatosensory system by first focusing on the skin, where the receptors for touch and pain are located, we will notice an important parallel with the visual system: the skin, like the retina, contains a number of different kinds of receptors.

OVERVIEW OF THE CUTANEOUS SYSTEM

Just as for vision, we can distinguish between different types of receptors, pathways from receptors to cortex, and a number of different cortical areas. In this section we will describe some basic facts about the anatomy and functioning of the various parts of the cutaneous system.

The Skin

Comel (1953) called the skin the "monumental facade of the human body" for good reason. It is the heaviest organ in the human body, and, if not the largest (the surface areas of the gastrointestinal tract or of the alveoli of the lungs exceed the surface area of the skin), it is certainly the most obvious, especially in humans, whose skin is not obscured by fur or large amounts of hair (Montagna & Parakkal, 1974).

VIRTUAL LAB 1

In addition to its warning function, the skin also prevents body fluids from escaping and at the same time protects us by keeping bacteria, chemical agents, and dirt from penetrating our bodies. Skin maintains the integrity of what's inside and protects us from what's outside, but it also provides us with information about the various stimuli that contact it. The sun's rays heat our skin, and we feel warmth; a pinprick is painful; and, when someone touches us, we experience pressure or other sensations.

Our main experience with the skin is its visible surface, which is actually a layer of tough dead skin cells. (Try sticking a piece of cellophane tape onto your palm and pulling it off. The material that sticks to the tape is dead skin cells.) This layer of dead cells is part of the outer layer of skin, which is called the **epidermis**. Below the epidermis is another layer, called the **dermis** (Figure 14.2). It is in these two layers that we find the **mechanoreceptors**, receptors that respond to mechanical stimulation such as pressure, stretching, and vibration.

Mechanoreceptors

Many of the tactile perceptions that we feel from stimulation of the skin can be traced to the four types of mechanoreceptors that are located in the epidermis and the dermis. We can distinguish between these receptors by their distinctive structures and by how fibers associated with the receptors respond to stimulation (Figure 14.2).

- The **Merkel receptor** is a disk-shaped receptor located near the border between the epidermis and the dermis.
- The **Meissner corpuscle** is a stack of flattened cells located in the dermis just below the epidermis.
- The **Ruffini cylinder** is many-branched fibers inside a roughly cylindrical capsule.
- The **Pacinian corpuscle** is a layered, onionlike capsule that surrounds a nerve fiber; located deep in the skin, the Pacinian corpuscle can also be found in many other places, including the intestines and the joints.

The four types of mechanoreceptors were identified by 19th-century anatomists when they examined the skin under microscopes and saw the different receptor structures. Most modern research on the functions of these receptors has focused not on the receptor structures but on recording from the nerve fibers that are associated with these receptors. What they have found is that the fibers associated with different mechanoreceptors have different properties. Three of the main properties are:

- *Temporal Properties: Adaptation.* Figure 14.3 shows that we can distinguish between two different types of fibers based on how they respond to continuous stimulation of the skin. Fibers associated with the Merkel and Ruffini receptors are **slowly adapting (SA) fibers** (Merkel = **SA1 fiber**; Ruffini = **SA2 fiber**). They fire continuously, as long as pressure is applied. Fibers associated with the Meissner receptor and Pacinian corpuscle are **rapidly adapting**

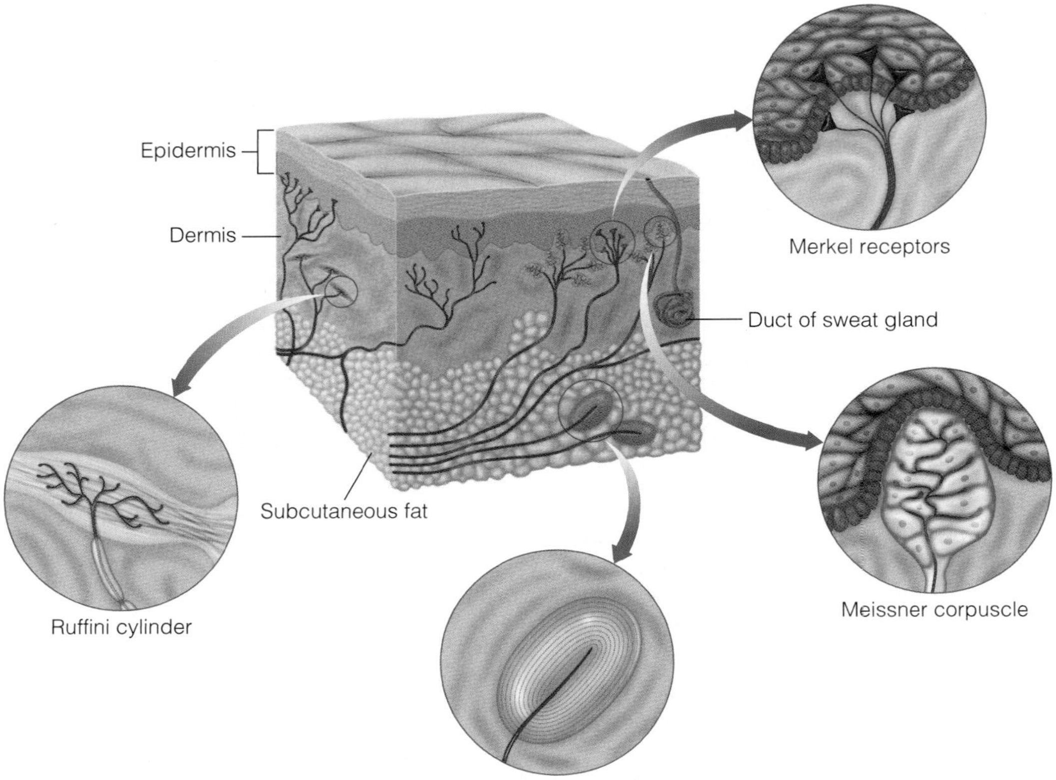

Figure 14.2 ▌ A cross section of glabrous (without hairs or projections) skin, showing the layers of the skin and the four major receptors for tactile perception: the Merkel receptor, Meissner corpuscle, Ruffini cylinder, and Pacinian corpuscle.

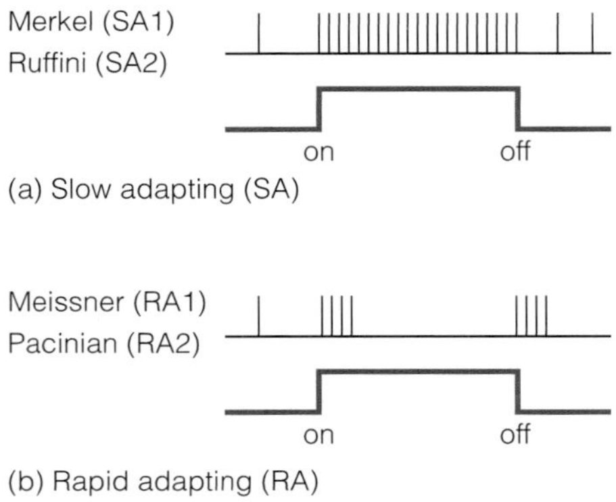

Figure 14.3 ▌ (a) Slowly adapting (SA) fibers continue to fire during a sustained stimulus. (b) Rapidly adapting (RA) fibers fire only at the onset and offset of a sustained stimulus.

(RA) fibers (Meissner = **RA1 fiber**; Pacinian = **RA2 fiber**). They fire only at the onset and offset of stimulation. The second column in Table 14.1 summarizes this property of the mechanoreceptors.

- *Spatial Properties: Detail resolution.* Our ability to perceive details on a surface depends on the ability of receptors to fire to these details. This property can be measured by determining how fibers respond to grooved stimuli presented to the skin. Figure 14.4 shows that the response of the SA1 fiber (Merkel receptor) reflects the pattern of these grooved stimuli, but the response of the RA2 fiber (Pacinian corpuscle) does not indicate the presence of these details.

- *Frequency response.* Our ability to perceive slow movement and rapid vibrations depends on the range of vibration speed over which a fiber responds. The third column of Table 14.1 indicates how the mechanoreceptors respond when vibrating stimuli are presented to the skin. These receptors respond to stimuli having frequencies ranging from 0.3 Hz (Merkel receptor/SA1 fiber), which corresponds to someone pushing and releasing your skin about once every 3 seconds, to over 500 Hz (Pacinian corpuscle/SA2 fiber), which corresponds to an extremely rapid vibration like that created by machinery.

The fourth column of Table 14.1 indicates that the four types of mechanoreceptors provide a way for the skin to register a wide range of different stimuli. The Merkel

Table 14.1 ▮ *Properties of Four Types of Mechanoreceptors*

Receptor (Fiber)	How Fiber Responds	Frequency Response	Perceptions
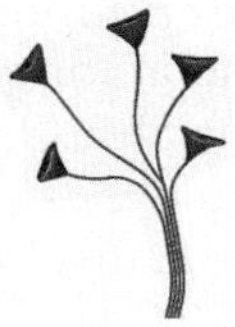 Merkel (SA1)	Continuous (slow adapting)	0.3–3 Hz Slow pushing	Fine details
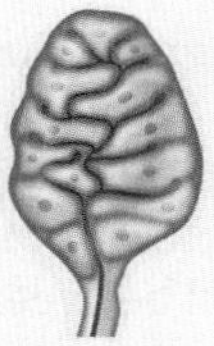 Meissner (RA1)	On Off Responds to change (rapid adapting)	3–40 Hz	"Flutter" Hand-grip control (tools)
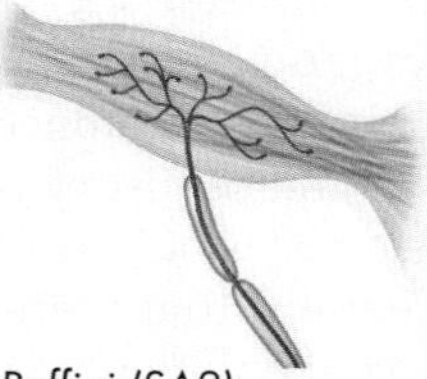 Ruffini (SA2)	Continuous (slow adapting)	15–400 Hz	Stretching
 Pacinian (RA2)	Responds to change (rapid adapting)	10–500 Hz Rapid vibration at upper range	Vibration Texture by moving fingers

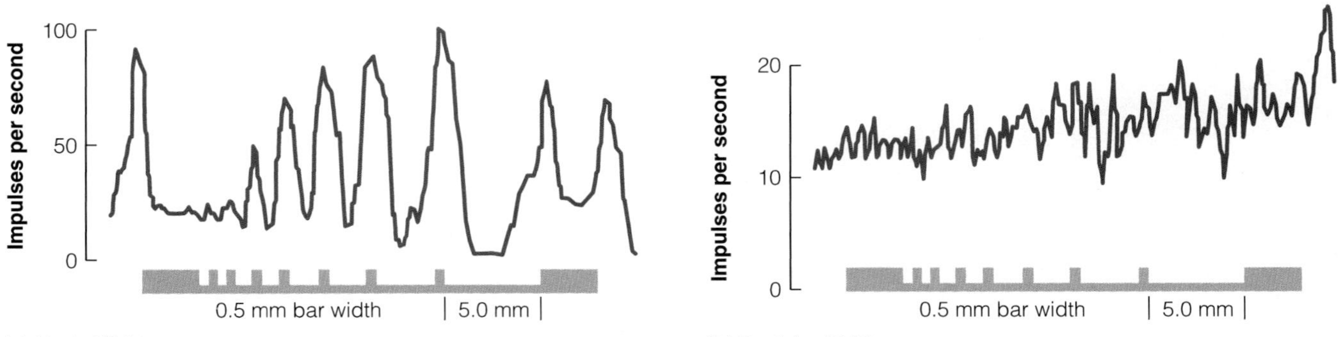

Figure 14.4 ▮ (a) The firing of the Merkel receptor/SA1 fiber signals the grooved stimulus pattern, but (b) the firing of the Pacinian corpuscle/RA2 fiber does not. Results such as these indicate that the Merkel receptor/SA1 fiber signals details *(Johnson, 2002; adapted from Phillips & Johnson, 1981.)*

receptor/SA1 fiber responds to fine details; the Meissner receptor/RA1 fiber responds to fluttering (slowly changing) stimuli on the skin and is also involved in controlling hand-grasp that helps hold and manipulate tools. The Ruffini receptor/SA2 fiber responds to stretching of stimuli as might occur when grasping large objects or when a guitar or piano player stretches his or her fingers to play a chord. The Pacinian corpuscle/RA2 fiber responds to rapid vibrations and fine textures sensed by moving the fingers across a surface.

Pathways From Skin to Cortex

Signals from the mechanoreceptors are transmitted from the skin toward the brain by a web of connections that rival those of the visual and auditory systems in complexity. We will focus on basic characteristics of this system.

Nerve fibers from receptors in the skin travel in bundles called peripheral nerves that enter the spinal cord through the dorsal root (Figure 14.5). Once they enter the spinal cord, the nerve fibers go up the spinal cord in two major pathways: the **medial lemniscal pathway** and the **spinothalamic pathway**. Just as parallel pathways in the visual and auditory systems serve different perceptual functions, so it is with the cutaneous system. The lemniscal pathway has large fibers that carry signals related to sensing the positions of the limbs (proprioception) and perceiving touch. The spinothalamic pathway consists of smaller fibers that transmit signals related to temperature and pain.

Fibers from both pathways cross over to the other side of the body during their upward journey to the thalamus. Most of these fibers synapse in the **ventrolateral nucleus** in the thalamus, but some synapse in other thalamic nuclei. (Remember that fibers from the retina and the cochlea also synapse in the thalamus, in the *lateral geniculate nucleus* for vision and the *medial geniculate nucleus* for hearing.) Because the signals in the spinal cord have crossed over to the opposite side of the body on their way to the thalamus, signals originating from the left side of the body reach the thalamus in the right hemisphere of the brain, and signals from the right side of the body reach the thalamus in the left hemisphere.

Maps of the Body on the Cortex

From the thalamus, signals travel to the **somatosensory receiving area (S1)** in the parietal lobe of the cortex and possibly also to the **secondary somatosensory cortex (S2)** (Rowe et al., 1996; Turman et al., 1998; Figures 14.5 and 14.6). Signals also travel between S1 to S2 and from S1 and S2 to additional somatosensory areas.

An important characteristic of the somatosensory cortex is that it is organized into maps that correspond to locations on the body. The existence of a map of the body on S1, the primary somatosensory receiving area, was determined in a classic series of investigations by the neurosurgeon Wilder Penfield that were carried out while he was operating on awake patients who were having brain surgery to relieve symptoms of epilepsy (Penfield & Rasmissen, 1950). When Penfield stimulated points on S1 and asked patients to report what they perceived, they reported sensations such as tingling and touch on various parts of their body. Penfield found that stimulating the ventral part of S1 (lower on the parietal lobe) caused sensations on the lips and face, stimulating higher on S1 caused sensations in the hands and fingers, and stimulating the dorsal S1 caused sensations in the legs and feet.

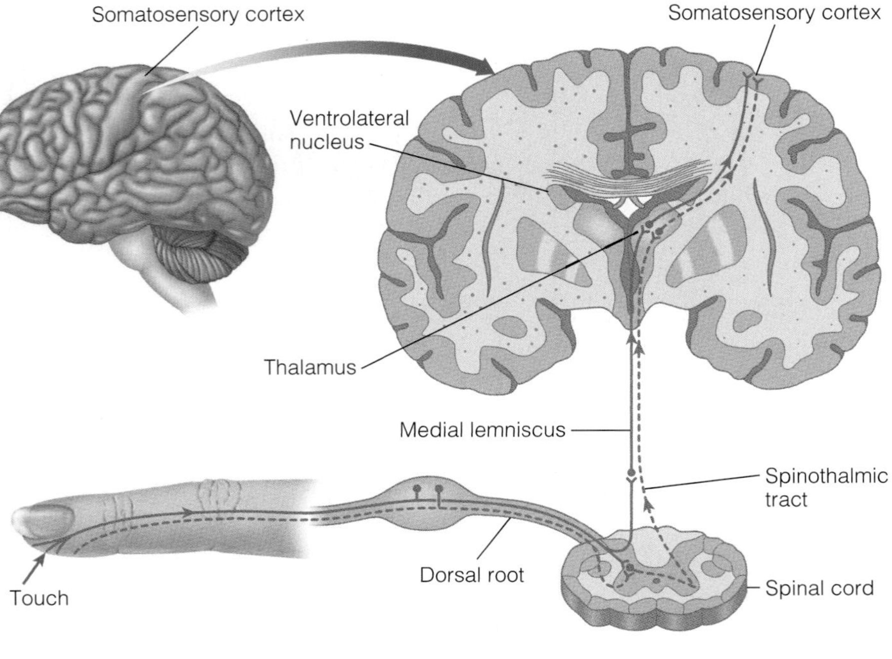

Figure 14.5 ▮ The pathway from receptors in the skin to the somatosensory receiving area of the cortex. The fiber carrying signals from a receptor in the finger enters the spinal cord through the dorsal root and then travels up the spinal cord along two pathways: the medial lemniscus and the spinothalamic tract. These pathways synapse in the ventrolateral nucleus of the thalamus and then send fibers to the somatosensory cortex in the parietal lobe.

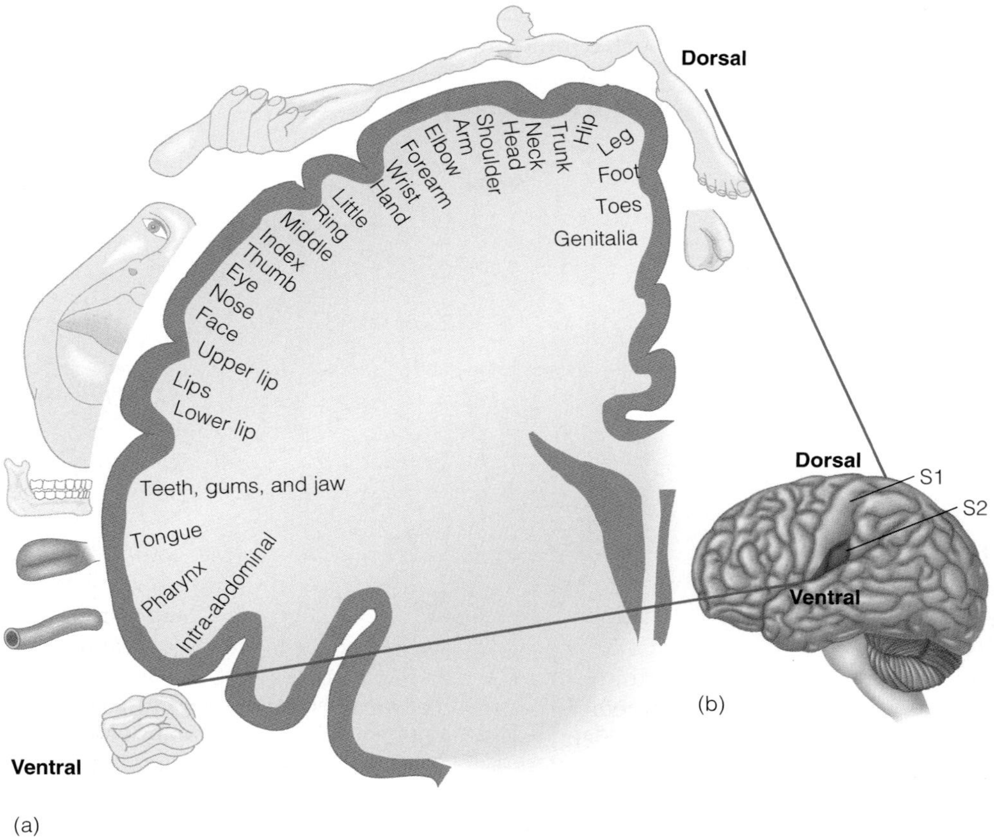

Figure 14.6 ▮ (a) The sensory homunculus on the somatosensory cortex. Parts of the body with the highest tactile acuity are represented by larger areas on the cortex. (b) The somatosensory cortex in the parietal lobe. The primary somatosensory area, S1 (light shading), receives inputs from the ventrolateral nucleus of the thalamus. The secondary somatosensory area, S2 (dark shading), is partially hidden behind the temporal lobe.
(Reprinted with permission of the Gale Group, from The Cerebral Cortex of Man *by Wilder Penfield and Theodore Rasmussen, 1950, p. 214. Copyright ©1950 by Macmillan Publishing Co., renewed 1978 by Theodore Rasmussen.)*

The resulting body map, shown in Figure 14.6, is called the **homunculus**, Latin for "little man." The homunculus shows that some areas on the skin are represented by a disproportionately large area of the brain. The area devoted to the thumb, for example, is as large as the area devoted to the entire forearm. This result is analogous to the magnification factor in vision (p. 73), in which receptors in the fovea, which are responsible for perceiving visual details, are allotted a disproportionate area on the visual cortex. Similarly, parts of the body such as the fingers, which are used to detect details by the sense of touch, are allotted a disproportionate area on the somatosensory cortex.

When the homunculus was originally determined, it was believed that there was one fixed map of the body on the somatosensory cortex. Later research showed that there are a number of maps in both S1 and S2 and that these maps are not totally fixed, but can change in response to stimulation of the skin.

In Chapter 4 we introduced the idea of experience-dependent plasticity (which is also called neural plasticity)—how the properties of neurons can be shaped by stimulation caused by experience. One example of neural plasticity in the visual system is how rearing kittens in a vertical environment caused most of the neurons in their visual cortex to respond best to vertical orientations (see page 65). Another example is how training humans to recognize shapes called Greebles caused neurons in the fusiform face area of the cortex to respond more strongly to Greeble stimuli (see page 85).

Most of the early experiments that demonstrated plasticity were carried out in the somatosensory system. In one of these early experiments, William Jenkins and Michael Merzenich (1987) showed that increasing stimulation of a specific area of the skin causes an expansion of the cortical area receiving signals from that area of skin. When they measured the cortical areas devoted to each of a monkey's fingers and trained monkeys to complete a task that involved the extensive use of a particular location on one fingertip, they obtained the results shown in Figure 14.7. Comparison of the cortical maps of the fingertip measured just before the training and 3 months later shows that the area representing the stimulated fingertip was greatly expanded after the training. Thus, the cortical area representing part of the fingertip, which is large to begin with, becomes even larger when the area receives a large amount of stimulation.

In most animal experiments, like the one we just described, the effect of plasticity is determined by measuring how special training affects the brain. An experiment that measured this effect in humans determined how training has affected the brains of musicians. Consider, for example, players of stringed instruments. A right-handed violin player bows with the right hand and uses

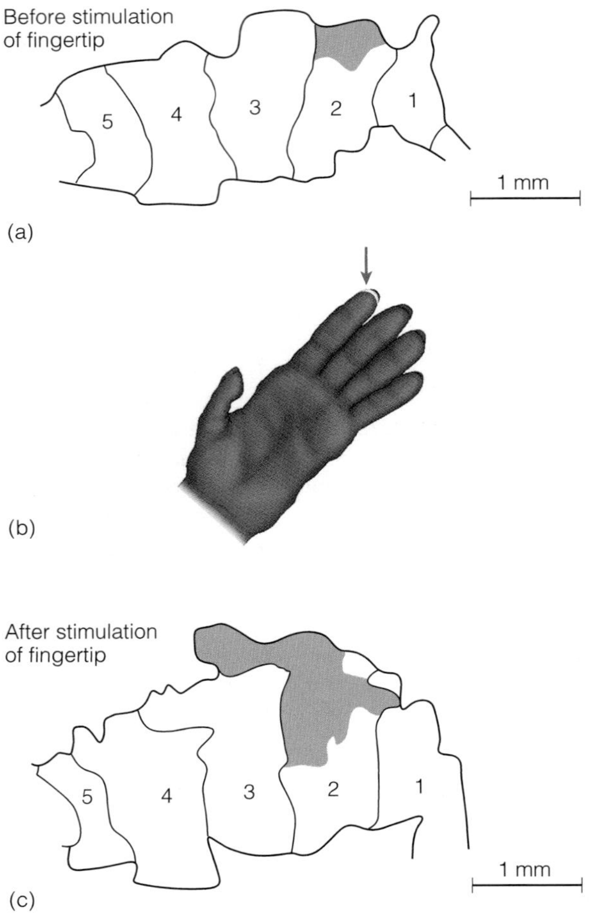

Figure 14.7 ▮ (a) Each numbered zone represents the area in the somatosensory cortex that represents one of a monkey's five fingers. The shaded area on the zone for finger 2 is the part of the cortex that represents the small area on the tip of the finger shown in (b). (c) The shaded region shows how the area representing the fingertip increased in size after this area was heavily stimulated over a 3-month period.
(From "Cortical Representational Plasticity," by M. M. Merzenich, G. Reconzone, W. M. Jenkins, T. T. Allard, & R. J. Nudo, 1988. In P. Rakic and W. Singer (Eds.) Neurobiology of Neocortex, *pp. 42–67, figure 1. Copyright ©1988 John Wiley & Sons. Reproduced by permission of M. M. Merzenich.)*

the fingers of his or her left hand to finger the strings. One result of this tactile experience is that these musicians have a greater than normal cortical representation for the fingers on their left hand (Elbert et al., 1995). Just as in the monkeys, plasticity has created more cortical area for parts of the body that have been used more.

Sometimes, however, neural plasticity can have negative effects, as in the case of "musician's cramp," which is also called **focal dystonia**. Musicians with this condition lose the ability to make skilled hand movements, a situation that usually ends their careers (Lim et al., 2001). A study of musicians with the condition revealed that areas responsible for controlling their fingers were fused in the brain, as shown in Figure 14.8 (Elbert et al., 1998). Luckily, negative outcomes such as this occur in only about 1 percent of musicians. Plasticity usually results in an improvement in functioning.

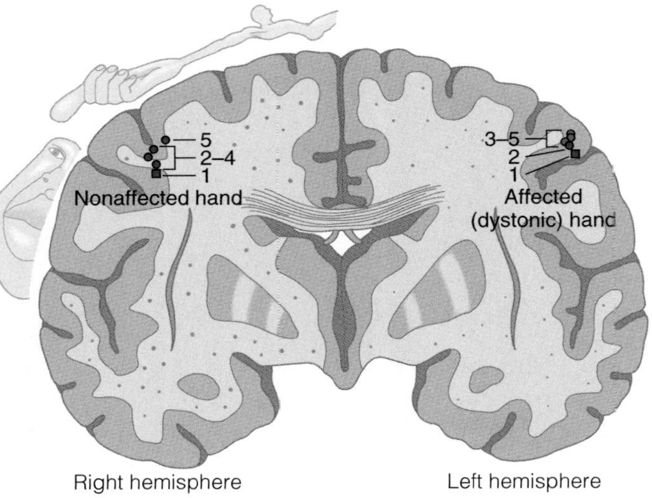

Figure 14.8 ▮ Cross section of the cortex, showing where the five fingers (1–5) are represented in the left and right hemispheres in a musician with focal dystonia (musician's cramp). The areas representing all the fingers of the right hand (on the left side of the brain) are separated, but the areas representing fingers 3, 4, and 5 on the left hand (right side of brain) are superimposed. This superimposition is associated with the dystonia of the left hand.
(Adapted from Elbert et al., 1998)

PERCEIVING DETAILS

The ability of Geerat Vermeij, the biologist we described at the beginning of the chapter, to identify mollusks based just on his sense of touch, attests to the touch system's ability to detect details. The first step in describing research on tactile detail perception is to consider how researchers have measured our capacity to detect details of stimuli presented to the skin.

METHOD ▪ Measuring Tactile Acuity

Just as there are a number of different kinds of eye charts for determining a person's visual acuity, there are a number of ways to measure a person's **tactile acuity**—the ability to detect details on the skin. The classic method of measuring tactile acuity is the **two-point threshold**, the minimum separation between two points on the skin that when stimulated is perceived as two points (Figure 14.9a). The two-point threshold is measured by gently touching the skin with two points and having the person indicate whether he or she feels one point or two points.

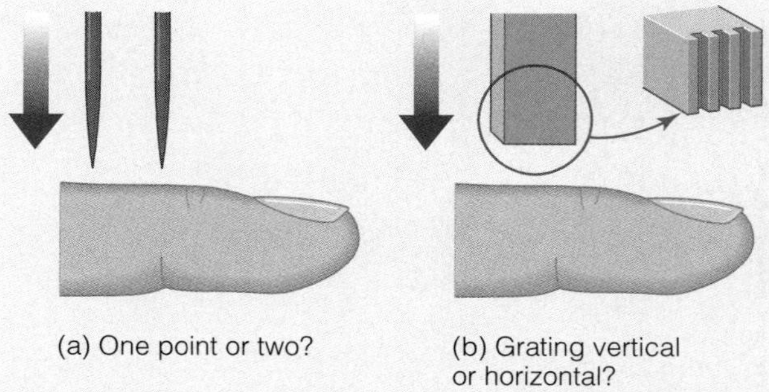

Figure 14.9 ▮ Methods for determining tactile acuity: (a) two-point threshold; (b) grating acuity.

The two-point threshold was the main measure of acuity in most of the early research on touch. Recently, however, other methods have been introduced. **Grating acuity** is measured by presenting a grooved stimulus like the one in Figure 14.9b onto the skin and asking the person to indicate the orientation of the grating. Acuity is measured by determining the narrowest spacing for which orientation can be accurately judged. Finally, acuity can also be measured by pushing raised patterns such as letters onto the skin and determining the smallest sized pattern or letter that can be identified (Cholewaik & Collins, 2003; Craig & Lyle, 2001, 2002).

■ ■ ■

As we consider the role of both receptor mechanisms and cortical mechanisms in determining tactile acuity, we will see that there are a number of parallels between the cutaneous system and the visual system.

Receptor Mechanisms for Tactile Acuity

The properties of the receptors are one of the things that determines what we experience when the skin is stimulated. We will illustrate this by first focusing on the connection between the Merkel receptor/SA1 fiber and tactile acuity. We have already seen from Figure 14.4 that the Merkel receptor/SA1fiber is sensitive to details. It is not surprising, therefore, that there is a high density of SA1 fibers in the fingertips, the area of the body that is most sensitive to details (Vallbo & Johansson, 1978). The relationship between locations on the body and sensitivity to detail has been studied psychophysically by measuring the two-point threshold on different parts of the body. Try this yourself by doing the following demonstration.

DEMONSTRATION

Comparing Two-Point Thresholds

To measure two-point thresholds on different parts of the body, hold two pencils side by side (or better yet, use a drawing compass) so that their points are about 12 mm (0.5 in.) apart; then touch both points simultaneously to the tip of your thumb and determine whether you feel two points. If you feel only one, increase the distance between the pencil points until you feel two; then note the distance between the points. Now move the pencil points to the underside of your forearm. With the points about 12 mm apart (or at the smallest separation you felt as two points on your thumb), touch them to your forearm and note whether you feel one point or two. If you feel only one, how much must you increase the separation before you feel two? ■

When James Craig and Keith Lyle (2001, 2002) measured grating acuity on the fingertips, the base of the fingers, and the palms of the hand, they found that acuity was greatest on the fingertips, as shown in Figure 14.10, and that acuity was related to the spacing between Merkel receptors at each location. Thus, just as is the case of vision, in which acuity is better in the fovea where the cones are most closely packed (see page 48), high tactile acuity is better on parts of the body in which the receptors are most closely packed.

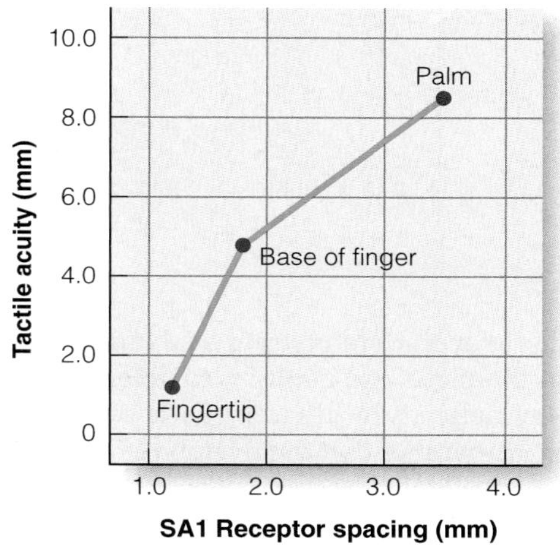

Figure 14.10 ▮ Correlation between density of Merkel receptors/SA1 fiber density and tactile acuity.
(From Craig & Lyte, 2002.)

Cortical Mechanisms for Tactile Acuity

Just as there is a parallel between the packing of receptors in the skin and tactile acuity, there is also a parallel between the representation of the body on the brain and the acuity at different locations on the body. Figure 14.11 indicates the two-point threshold measured on different parts of the male body. We can see that regions of high acuity, like the fingers and lips, are represented by larger areas on the cortex. As we mentioned earlier, "magnification" of the representation on the brain of some areas of the body parallels the magnification factor in vision (p. 73). The map of the body on the brain is distorted to provide the extra neural processing that enables us to accurately sense fine details with our fingers and other parts of the body.

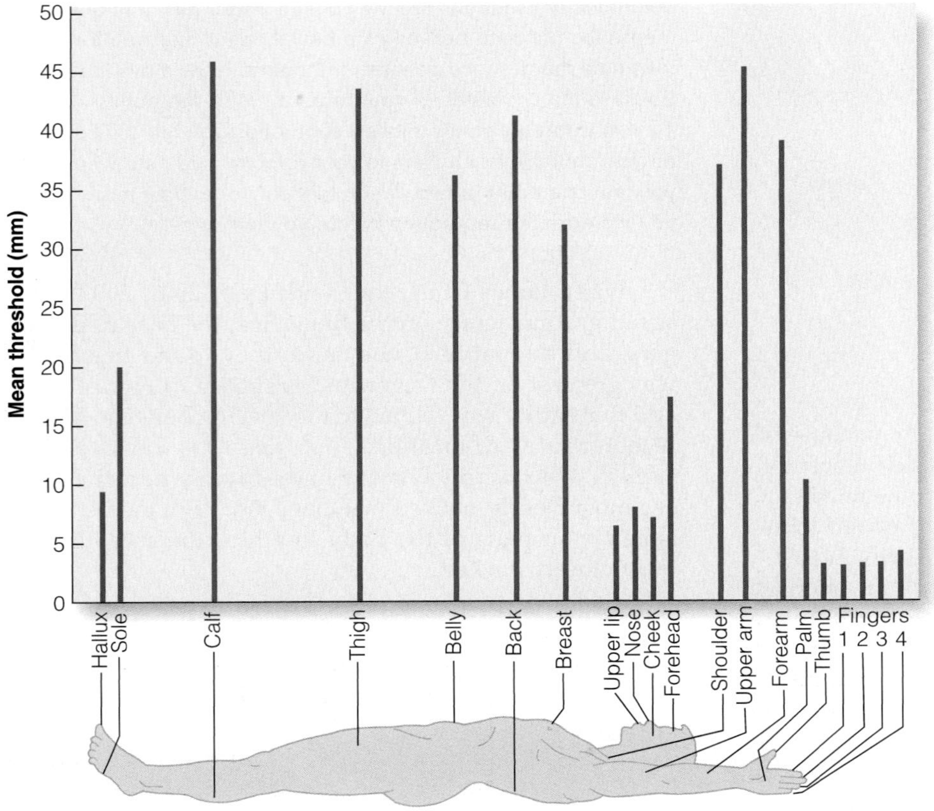

Figure 14.11 ▮ Two-point thresholds for males. Two-point thresholds for females follow the same pattern.
(From "Intensive and Extensive Aspects of Tactile Sensitivity as a Function of Body Part, Sex, and Laterality," by S. Weinstein, 1968. In D. R. Kenshalo (Ed.), The Skin Senses, *pp. 206, 207. Copyright © 1968 by Charles C. Thomas. Courtesy of Charles C. Thomas, Publishers, Springfield, IL.)*

Another way to demonstrate the connection between cortical mechanisms and acuity is to determine the receptive fields of neurons in different parts of the cortical homunculus. Remember that the receptive field for a neuron in the visual system is *the area on the retina that, when stimulated, influences the firing rate of the neuron.* The receptive field for a neuron in the cutaneous system is *the area on the skin that, when stimulated, influences the firing rate of the neuron.* From Figure 14.12, which shows the sizes of receptive fields from cortical neurons that represent a monkey's finger, hand, and arm, we can see that cortical neurons representing parts of the body with better acuity have smaller receptive fields. Thus, the fingers' excellent detail perception is achieved because the fingers are represented by a large number of neurons in the cortex and because each of these neurons receives information from a very small area on the skin.

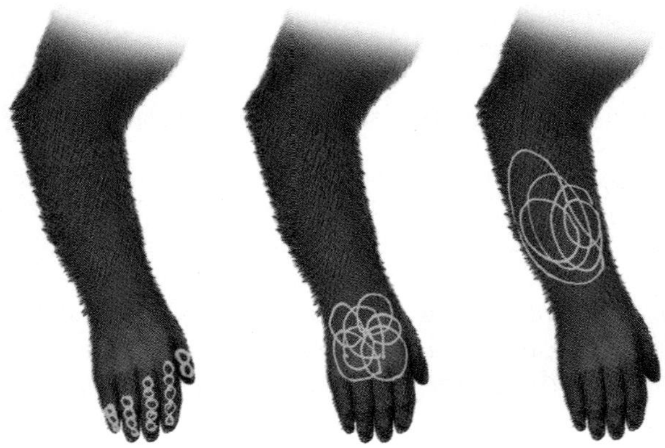

Figure 14.12 ▮ Receptive fields of cortical neurons are smallest on the monkey's fingers and become larger on the hand and the forearm.
(From "Touch," by E. R. Kandel and T. M. Jessell, 1991. In E. R. Kandel, J. H. Schwartz & T. M. Jessell (Eds.) Principles of Neural Science, *3rd ed., figure 26-8a. Copyright © 1991 Appleton & Lange, Norwalk, CT. Reprinted with permission of McGraw-Hill Companies.)*

PERCEIVING VIBRATION

The skin is capable of detecting not only spatial details of objects, but other qualities as well. When you place your hands on mechanical devices that are producing vibration, such as a car, a lawnmower, or an electric toothbrush, you can sense these vibrations with your fingers and hands. The mechanoreceptor that is primarily responsible for sensing vibration is the Pacianian corpuscle.

The most convincing evidence linking the Pacinian corpuscle to vibration is that RA2 fibers associated with the Pacinian corpuscle respond best to high rates of vibration. From Table 14.1 you can see that the Ruffini cylinder also responds to high rates of vibration, but other evidence indicates that the primary function of this receptor is probably sensing the stretching of the skin.

Why do the RA2 fibers associated with the Pacinian corpuscle fire well to rapid vibration? The answer to this question is that the fiber's response is determined by properties of the Pacinian corpuscle receptor. The research that led to this conclusion was made possible by the large size of the Pacinian corpuscle (it is about 1 mm long and 0.6 mm wide) and the fact that it is easily accessible (it can be removed from the cat's mesentery, a membrane attached to the intestine).

Werner Lowenstein (1960) determined the effect of the Pacinian corpuscle receptor on the firing of the RA2 fiber by measuring the response of the fiber under two conditions: (1) when the corpuscle was partially dissected away, so that pressure could be applied closer to the nerve fiber, and (2) when the corpuscle remained, so that pressure could be applied to it. When most of the corpuscle was removed, so the stimulus could be presented near the nerve fiber at B (Figure 14.13), the fiber responded when the pressure was first applied, as the pressure continued, and when the pressure was removed. However, when the corpuscle was present and the stimulus was presented at A on the intact corpuscle, the fiber responded only when the pressure was first applied and when it was removed. Thus, the Pacinian corpuscle gives its nerve fiber the property of rapid adaptation. It causes the fiber to respond poorly to constant stimulation, such as sustained pressure, but to respond well to changes in stimulation that occur at the beginning and end of a pressure or when stimulation is changing rapidly, as occurs in vibration.

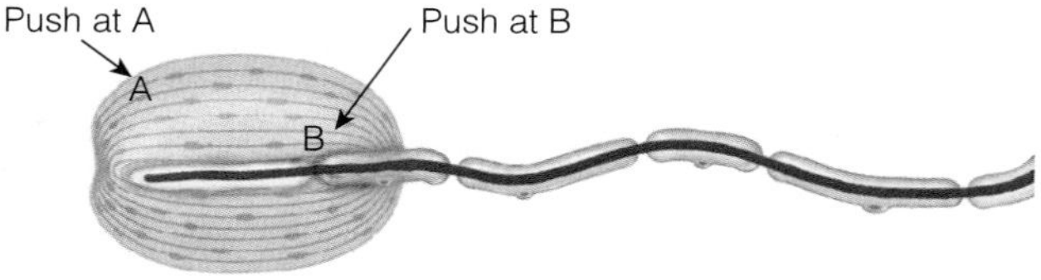

Figure 14.13 ▌ A Pacinian corpuscle.
(From "Biological Transducers," by W. R. Lowenstein, 1960, p. 103. Copyright © 1960 by Scientific American, Inc. All rights reserved.)

PERCEIVING TEXTURE

When you touch an object or run your fingers over the object, you can sense textures ranging from coarse (the spacing of the teeth of a comb) to fine (the surface of the page of this book). Research on texture perception tells an interesting story, which extends from 1925 to the present and which illustrates how psychophysics can be used to discover perceptual mechanisms.

In 1925, David Katz proposed that our perception of texture depends on both spatial cues and temporal cues. **Spatial cues** are determined by the size, shape, and distribution of surface elements, such as bumps and grooves. These cues are responsible for our perception of coarse texture such as Braille dots (Figure 14.1) or the texture you feel when you run your fingers over the teeth of a comb. **Temporal cues** are determined by the rate of vibrations that occur as we move our skin across a finely textured surface like fine sandpaper. These cues are responsible for our perception of fine texture that cannot be detected by touching a surface without moving the fingers.

Although Katz proposed that texture perception is determined by both spatial and temporal cues, research on texture perception has, until recently, focused on spatial cues. An example of this type of research is measurement of the response of different fibers to grooved surfaces that we presented in Figure 14.4. This research linked the SA1 fiber/ Merkel with spatial cues for texture perception.

Temporal Cues and Texture Perception

Recent research by Mark Hollins and coworkers (2002) has provided evidence that temporal cues are responsible for our perception of fine textures. Hollins called Katz's proposal that there are two types of receptors involved in texture perception the **duplex theory of texture perception.**

Hollins and Ryan Risner (2000) presented evidence for the role of temporal cues by showing that when participants touch surfaces without moving their fingers, and judge "roughness" using the procedure of magnitude estimation (see Chapter 1, page 15), they sense little difference between two fine textures (particle sizes of 10 and 100 mm; Figure 14.14a). However, when participants are allowed to move their fingers across the surface, they are able to detect the difference between the fine textures (Figure 14.14b). Thus, movement, which generates vibration as the skin scans a surface, makes it possible to sense the roughness of fine surfaces.

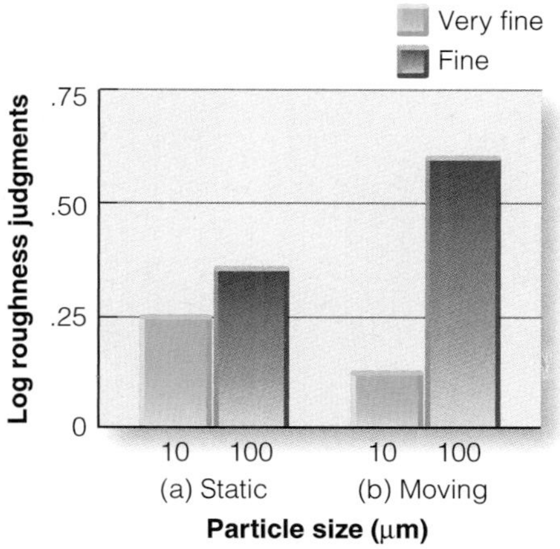

Figure 14.14 ▌ (a) Participants in Hollins and Reisner's (2000) experiment perceived the roughness of two fine surfaces to be essentially the same when felt with stationary fingers, but (b) could perceive the difference between the two surfaces when they were allowed to move their fingers.

Additional evidence for the role of vibration in sensing fine textures was provided by using the selective adaptation procedure we introduced in Chapter 3 (see page 62). This procedure involves presenting a stimulus that adapts a particular type of receptor, and then testing to see how adaptation of that receptor affected perception. Hollins and coworkers (2001) used this procedure by presenting two adaptation conditions: (1) 10-Hz adaptation, in which the skin was vibrated with a 10-Hz stimulus for 6 minutes. This frequency of adaptation was picked to adapt the RA1/Meissner corpuscle. (2) 250-Hz adaptation. This frequency was picked to adapt the RA2/Pacinian corpuscle.

Following each type of adaptation, participants ran their fingers over two fine textures—a "standard" texture and a "test" texture. The participants' task was to indicate which texture was finer. Because there were two surfaces, chance performance would be 50 percent, as indicated by the dashed line in Figure 14.15. The results indicate that participants could tell the difference between the two textures when they had not been adapted, or had received the 10-Hz adaptation. However, after they had been adapted to the 250-Hz vibration, they were unable to tell the difference between two fine textures, as indicated by the participants' chance performance. Thus, adapting the Pacinian corpuscle receptor, which is responsible for perceiving vibration, eliminates the ability to sense fine textures by moving the fingers over a surface. These results and the results of other experiments (Hollins et al., 2002) support the duplex theory of perception—the perception of coarse textures is determined by spatial cues and fine textures by temporal (vibration) cues.

Additional evidence for the role of temporal cues for perceiving texture has been provided by research that shows that vibrations are important for perceiving textures not only when a person directly explores a surface with their fingers, but when they make contact with a surface indirectly, through the use of tools. You can experience this yourself, by doing the following demonstration.

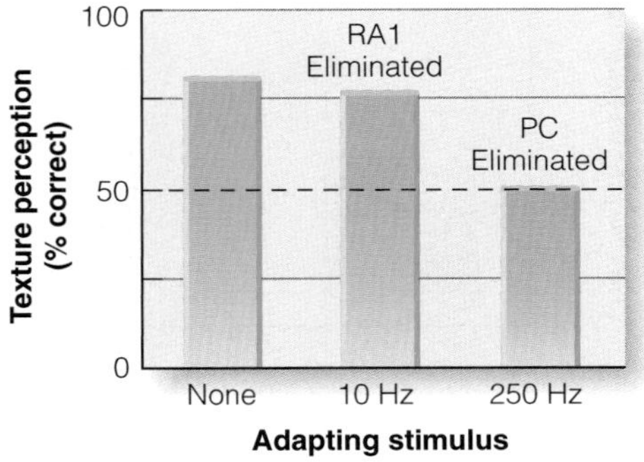

Figure 14.15 ▌ Eliminating the action of RA1 fibers by adaptation to a 10-Hz vibration had no effect on perception of a fine texture, but eliminating the action of the Pacinian corpuscle by adapting to a 250-Hz vibration eliminated the ability to sense the fine textures.
(Data from Hollins et al., 2001.)

DEMONSTRATION

Perceiving Texture With a Pen

Turn your pen over (or cap it) so you can use it as a "probe" (without writing on things!). Hold the pen at one end and move the other end over something smooth, such as this page. As you do this, notice that you can sense the smoothness of the page, even though you are not directly touching it. Then, try the same thing on a rougher surface, such as a rug, fabric, or concrete. ■

Your ability to detect differences in texture by running a pen (or some other "tool," such as a stick) over a surface is determined by vibrations transmitted through the tool to your skin (Klatzky et al., 2003). The most remarkable thing about perceiving texture with a tool is that what you perceive is not the vibrations, but the texture of the surface, even though you are feeling the surface remotely, with the tip of the tool (Carello & Turvey, 2004).

TEST YOURSELF 14.1

1. Describe the four types of mechanoreceptors in the skin, indicating their appearance, where they are located, the type of fiber associated with each receptor, and the type of perception associated with each receptor.
2. Where is the cortical receiving area for touch, and what does the map of the body on the cortical receiving area look like? How can this map be changed by experience?
3. How is tactile acuity measured, and what are the receptor and cortical mechanisms that serve tactile acuity?
4. Which receptor is primarily responsible for the perception of vibration? Describe the experiment that showed that the presence of the receptor structure determines how the fiber fires.
5. Describe the evidence that indicates that the perception of texture depends on both spatial and temporal cues. Be able to describe the series of experiments that led to the conclusion that vibration is responsible for perceiving fine textures and observations that have been made about the experience of exploring an object with a probe.

PERCEIVING OBJECTS

We rarely sit passively while someone else touches us with separated pencil points or presses dots or raised letters into our fingertips. This situation, which is called **passive touch**, does sometimes occur, as when someone gives us a backrub, but we usually take a more active role in determining how our skin is stimulated. We run our fingers across the smooth surface of a table, rhythmically hit the keys of our computer, or feel the contours of a pen as we grip it to write. This way of experiencing touch, in which the person controls the touch stimulation, is called **active touch**, and this is the method we typically use when we are using touch to recognize an object. The following demonstration compares the ability to identify objects using active touch and passive touch.

DEMONSTRATION

Identifying Objects

Ask another person to select five or six small objects for you to identify. Close your eyes and have the person place each object in your hand. Your job is to identify the object by touch alone by moving your fingers and hand over the object. As you do this, be aware of what you are experiencing: your finger and hand movements, the sensations you are feeling, and what you are thinking. Do this for three objects. Then hold out your hand, keeping it still, with fingers outstretched, and let the person move each of the remaining objects around on your hand, moving their surfaces and contours across your skin. Your task is the same as before: to identify the object and to pay attention to what you are experiencing as the object is moved across your hand. ■

You may have noticed that in the active condition, in which you moved your fingers across the object, you were much more involved in the process and had more control over what parts of the objects you were exposed to. In the active part of the demonstration you were engaging in **haptic perception,** perception in which three-dimensional objects are explored with the hand.

Identifying Objects by Haptic Exploration

Haptic perception provides a particularly good example of a situation in which a number of different systems are interacting with each other. As you manipulated the objects in the first part of the demonstration above, you were using three distinct systems to arrive at your goal of identifying the objects: (1) the sensory system, which was involved in detecting cutaneous sensations such as touch, temperature, and texture and the movements and positions of your fingers and hands; (2) the motor system, which was involved in moving your fingers and hands; and (3) the cognitive system, which was involved in thinking about the information provided by the sensory and motor systems.

Haptic perception is an extremely complex process because the sensory, motor, and cognitive systems must all work together. For example, the motor system's control of finger and hand movements is guided by cutaneous feelings in the fingers and the hands, by your sense of the positions of the fingers and hands, and by thought processes that determine what information is needed about the object in order to identify it.

These processes working together create an experience of active touch that is quite different than the experience of passive touch. J. J. Gibson (1962), who championed the importance of movement in perception (see Chapters 9 and 10), compared the experience of active and passive touch by noting that we tend to relate passive touch to the sensation experienced in the skin, whereas we relate active touch to the object being touched. For example, if someone pushes a pointed object into your skin, you might say, "I feel a pricking sensation on my skin"; if, however, you push on the tip of the pointed object yourself, you might say, "I feel a pointed object" (Kruger, 1970). Thus, for passive touch you experience stimulation of the skin, and for active touch you experience the objects you are touching.

Psychophysical research has shown that people can accurately identify most common objects within 1 or 2 seconds (Klatzky, Lederman, & Metzger, 1985). When Susan Lederman and Roberta Klatzky (1987, 1990) observed participants' hand movements as they made these identifications, they found that people use a number of distinctive movements, which the researchers called **exploratory procedures (EPs),** and that the types of EPs used depend on the object qualities the participants are asked to judge.

Figure 14.16 shows four of the EPs observed by Lederman and Klatzky. People tend to use just one or two EPs to determine a particular quality. For example, people use mainly lateral motion and contour following to judge texture, and they use enclosure and contour following to judge exact shape.

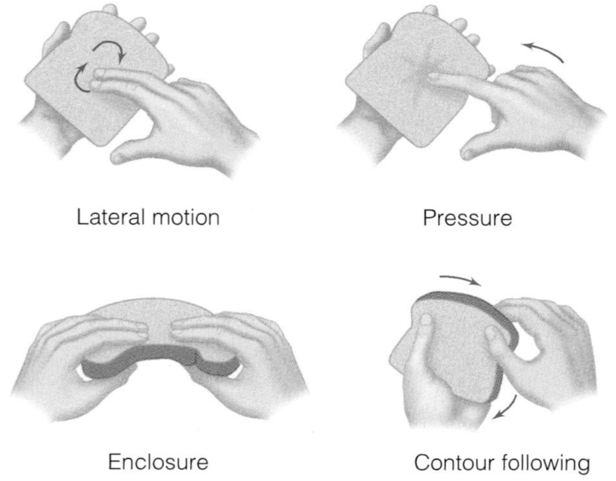

Figure 14.16 ■ Some of the exploratory procedures (EPs) observed by Lederman and Klatzky as participants identified objects.
(From "Hand Movements: A Window into Haptic Object Recognition," by S. J. Lederman and R. L. Klatzky, 1987, Cognitive Psychology, *19, 342–368, figure 1. Academic Press, Inc.)*

The Physiology of Tactile Object Perception

What is happening physiologically as we explore an object with our fingers and hands? Researchers have tried to answer this question by recording from mechanoreceptor fibers in the skin, from neurons in the somatosensory cortex, and from neurons in the parietal and frontal lobes.

In order for the brain to control everyday tasks, such as screwing a lid on a bottle, it needs to have access to information about the size and contour of the lid, and the amount of force needed to grasp the lid. This information is provided by receptors within the body that indicate the position of the joints and by mechanoreceptors in the skin that indicate the textures and contours of the lid.

The information for indicating the contours of the lid is signaled by the pattern of firing of a large number of mechanoreceptors. This is illustrated by the response profiles in Figures 14.17a and 14.17b, which indicate how SA1 fibers in the fingertips respond to contact with two different spheres, one with high curvature relative to the fingertip (14.17a) and one that is more gently curved (14.17b). In both cases, the receptors right at the point where the fingers contact the sphere respond the most, and ones farther away fire less, but the *pattern* of response is different in the two cases. It is this overall pattern that provides information to the brain about the curvature of the sphere (Goodwin, 1998).

As we move from mechanoreceptor fibers in the fingers toward the brain, we see that neurons become more specialized. This is similar to what occurs in the visual system. Neurons in the monkey's thalamus (the ventral posterior nucleus) have center-surround receptive fields that are similar to the center-surround receptive fields in the visual area of the thalamus (the lateral geniculate nucleus; Figure 14.18; Mountcastle & Powell, 1959). In the cortex, we find some neurons with center-surround receptive fields and others that respond to more specialized stimulation of the skin. Figure 14.19 shows stimuli that cause neurons in the monkey's somatosensory cortex to fire. There are neurons that respond to specific orientations (Figure 14.19a) and neurons that respond to movement across the skin in a specified direction (Figure 14.19b; Hyvarinin & Poranen, 1978; see also Costanzo & Gardner, 1980; Romo et al., 1998; Warren, Hamalainen, & Gardner, 1986).

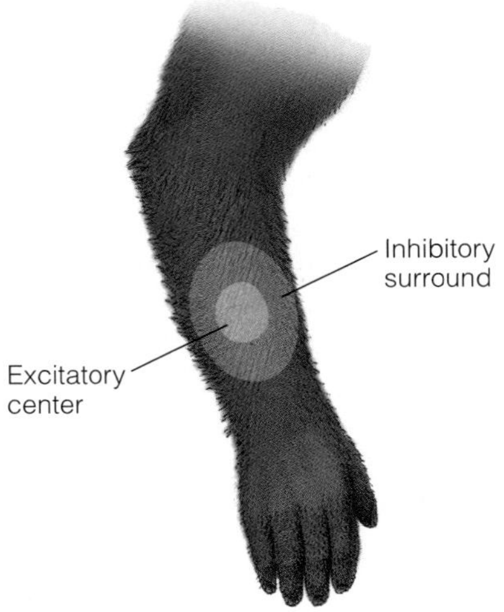

Figure 14.18 ▮ An excitatory-center, inhibitory-surround receptive field of a neuron in a monkey's thalamus.

There are also neurons in the monkey's somatosensory cortex that respond when the monkey grasps a specific object (Sakata & Iwamura, 1978). For example, Figure 14.20 shows the response of one of these neurons. This neuron responds when the monkey grasps the ruler but does not respond when the monkey grasps a ball or a sphere (see also Iwamura, 1998).

Cortical neurons are affected not only by the properties of the object, but by whether or not the perceiver

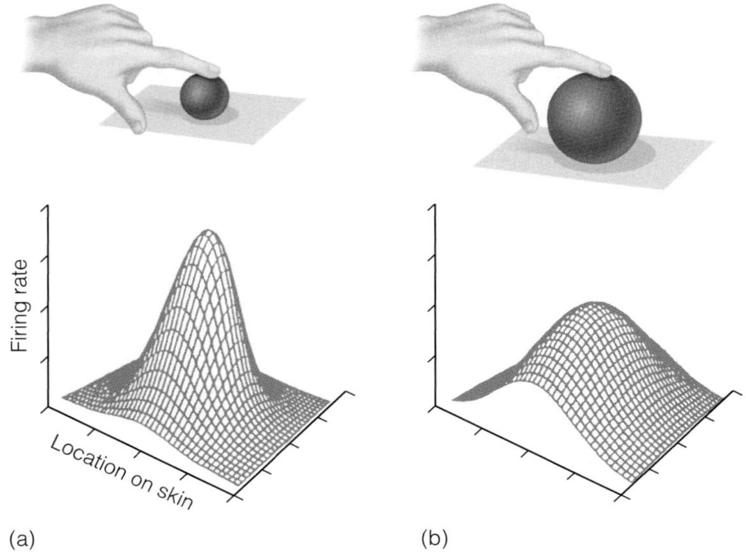

Figure 14.17 ▮ (a) Response of SA1 fibers in the fingertips to touching a high-curvature stimulus. The height of the profile indicates the firing rate at different places across the fingertip. (b) The profile of firing to touching a stimulus with more gentle curvature.

(From A. W. Goodwin (1998). Extracting the shape of an object from the responses of peripheral nerve fibers. In J. W. Morely (Ed.), Neural aspects of tactile sensation. *Elsevier Science, pp. 55–87, Fig. 12a, b. Used with permission.)*

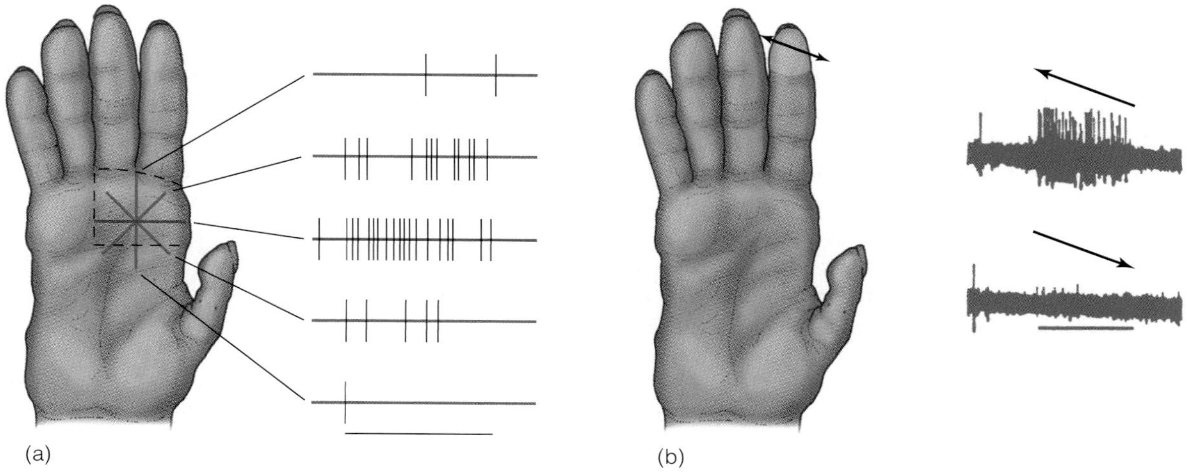

Figure 14.19 ▮ Receptive fields of neurons in the monkey's somatosensory cortex. (a) This neuron responds best when a horizontally oriented edge is presented to the monkey's hand. (b) This neuron responds best when a stimulus moves across the fingertip from right to left.

(From "Movement-Sensitive and Direction and Orientation Selective Cutaneous Receptive Fields in the Hand Area of the Postcentral Gyrus in Monkeys," by L. Hyvarinen and A. Poranen, 1978, Journal of Physiology, 283, *523–537, figure 3. Copyright ©1978 by The Physiological Society, UK. Reprinted by permission.)*

is paying attention. Steven Hsiao and coworkers (1993, 1996) recorded the response of neurons in areas S1 and S2 to raised letters that were scanned across a monkey's finger. In the tactile-attention condition, the monkey had to perform a task that required focusing its attention on the letters being presented to its fingers. In the visual-attention condition, the monkey had to focus its attention on an unrelated visual stimulus. The results, shown in Figure 14.21, show that even though the monkey is receiving exactly the same stimulation on its fingertips in both conditions, the response is larger for the tactile-attention condition. Thus, stimulation of the receptors may trigger a response, but the size of the response can

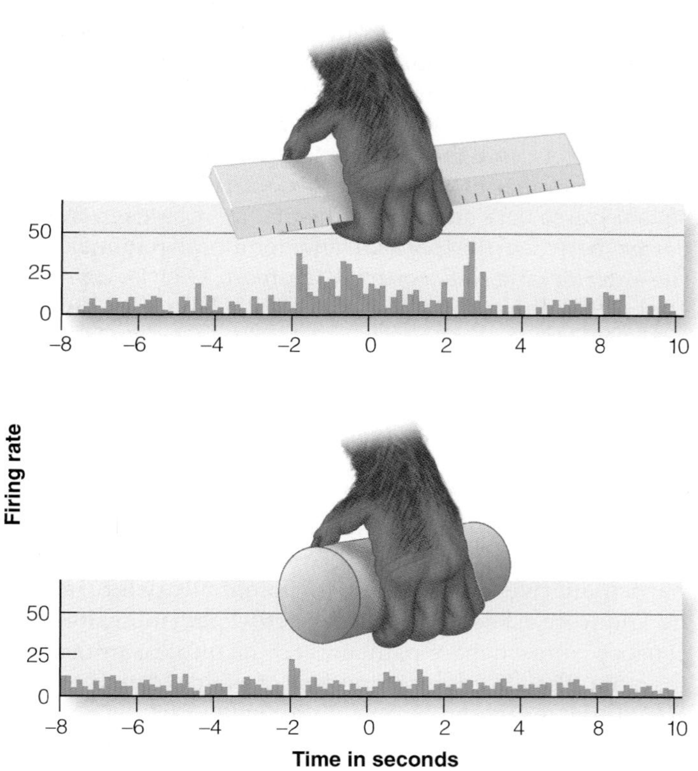

Figure 14.20 ▮ The response of a neuron in a monkey's parietal cortex that fires when the monkey grasps a ruler but that does not fire when the monkey grasps a cylinder.

(From "Cortical Processing of Tactile Information in the First Somatosensory and Parietal Association Areas in the Monkey," by H. Sakata and Y. Iwamura, 1978. In G. Gordon (Ed.), Active Touch, *p. 61. Copyright © 1978 by Pergamon Press, Ltd. Reprinted by permission.)*

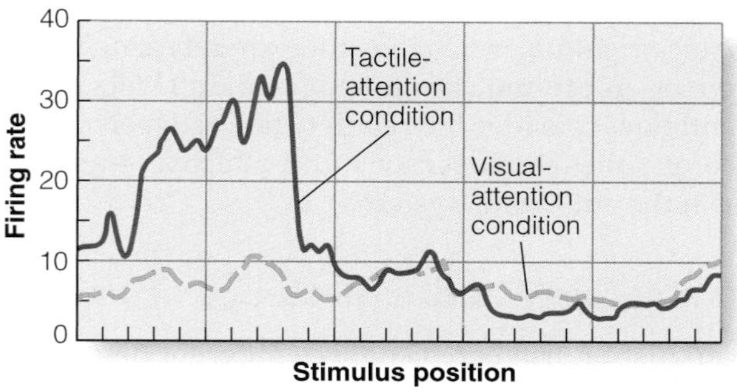

Figure 14.21 ▮ Firing rate of a neuron in area S1 of a monkey's cortex to a letter being rolled across the fingertips. The neuron responds only when the monkey is paying attention to the tactile stimulus.

(From "Effects of Selective Attention on Spatial Form Processing in Monkey Primary and Secondary Somatosensory Cortex," by S. S. Hsiao, D. M. O'Shaughnessy, and K. O. Johnson, 1993, Journal of Neurophysiology, 70, *444–447. Copyright © 1993 by The American Physiological Society. Reprinted by permission.)*

then be affected by processes such as attention, thinking, and other actions of the perceiver.

If the idea that events other than stimulation of the receptors can affect perception sounds familiar, it is because similar situations occur in vision (see pp. 8; 115) and hearing (p. 294). A person's active participation makes a difference in perception, not just by influencing what stimuli stimulate the receptors but by influencing the processing that occurs once the receptors are stimulated. This is perhaps most clearly demonstrated for the experience of pain, which is strongly affected by processes in addition to stimulation of the receptors.

PAIN PERCEPTION: NEURAL FIRING AND COGNITIVE INFLUENCES

As we mentioned at the beginning of this chapter, pain functions to warn us of potentially damaging situations and therefore helps us avoid or deal with cuts, burns, and broken bones. People born without the ability to feel pain might become aware that they are leaning on a hot stove burner only by smelling their burning flesh, or might be unaware of broken bones, infections or internal injuries—situations that could easily be life-threatening (Watkins & Maier, 2003). The signaling function of pain is reflected in the following definition, from the International Association for the Study of Pain: "Pain is an unpleasant sensory and emotional experience associated with actual or potential tissue damage, or described in terms of such damage" (Merskey, 1991).

There are a number of things that are notable about this definition of pain. First, the reference to both sensory *and* emotional experience reflects the **multimodal nature of pain**, which is reflected by how people describe pain. When people describe their pain with words like *throbbing, prickly, hot,* or *dull* they are referring to the **sensory component of pain**. When they use words like *torturing, annoying, frightful,* or *sickening* they are referring to the **affective** or **emotional component of pain** (Melzak, 1999). We will now consider the relationship between our experience of pain—both sensory and affective—and structures in the cutaneous system.

The Anatomy and Experience of Pain

We can distinguish between three different types of pain, each of which are triggered by different types of stimuli.

- **Nociceptive pain**, which serves as a warning of impending damage to the skin, is caused by activation of receptors in the skin called **nociceptors**. There are a number of different types of nociceptors, which respond to different stimuli—heat, chemical, severe pressure, and cold (Figure 14.22a). The threshold for eliciting activity in nociceptors should be high enough so pain doesn't interfere with normal activities, but low enough so pain occurs before tissue damage occurs. Clinical pain syndromes are often associated with shifts in threshold. For example, when the threshold becomes too low, pain can occur in response to light touch (Woolf & Salter, 2000).
- **Inflammatory pain** is caused by damage to tissues and inflammations to joints or by tumor cells. This damage releases chemicals that create an "inflammatory soup" that activates nociceptors (Figure 14.22b).
- **Neuropathic pain** is caused by lesions or other damage to the nervous system. Examples are carpal tunnel syndrome, which is caused by repetitive tasks such as typing; spinal cord injury; and brain damage due to stroke. These sources of pain are usually accompanied by neurological problems, such as paralysis or difficulty in moving limbs (Figure 14.22c).

The fact that pain can be caused in so many different ways complicates the study of pain and poses challenges to discovering ways to control pain. This is one of the reasons that many of the clinical treatments for pain are only partially effective (Scholz & Woolf, 2002).

We will now focus on nociceptive pain. Nociceptive pain occurs when signals from the nociceptors in the skin travel up the spinothalamic pathway to the brain (see Figure 14.5). Signals reaching the brain activate a number of subcortical structures, including the hypothalamus, the limbic system, and the thalamus, and these areas send signals to a number of areas of cortex, including the somatosensory areas, S1 and S2, the insula, an area deep in the cortex between the parietal and temporal regions, and the anterior cingulate cortex (Chapman, 1995; Derbyshire et al., 1997; Price, 2000; Rainville, 2002; Figure 14.23). All of the brain regions that are involved in pain perception, taken together, have been called the **pain matrix** (Melzak, 1999; Wager et al., 2004).

How do researchers determine the functions of each of these brain structures? One way is to have people rate the severity of pain and correlate these ratings with the results of brain-scan experiments. We will describe an experiment by R. K. Hofbauer and coworkers (2001) in which participants were presented with potentially painful stimuli and were asked to rate (1) subjective pain intensity (the sensory component of pain) and (2) the unpleasantness of the pain (the affective component of pain). Hoffauer and coworkers measured brain activity using PET, as participants responded to pain induced by immersing their hands in hot water.

What makes Hofbauer and coworkers' experiment particularly interesting is that they not only asked their participants to rate both the sensory and affective components of their pain, but they also used hypnotic suggestion to decrease or increase each of these components. Figure 14.24a shows that presenting suggestions to de-

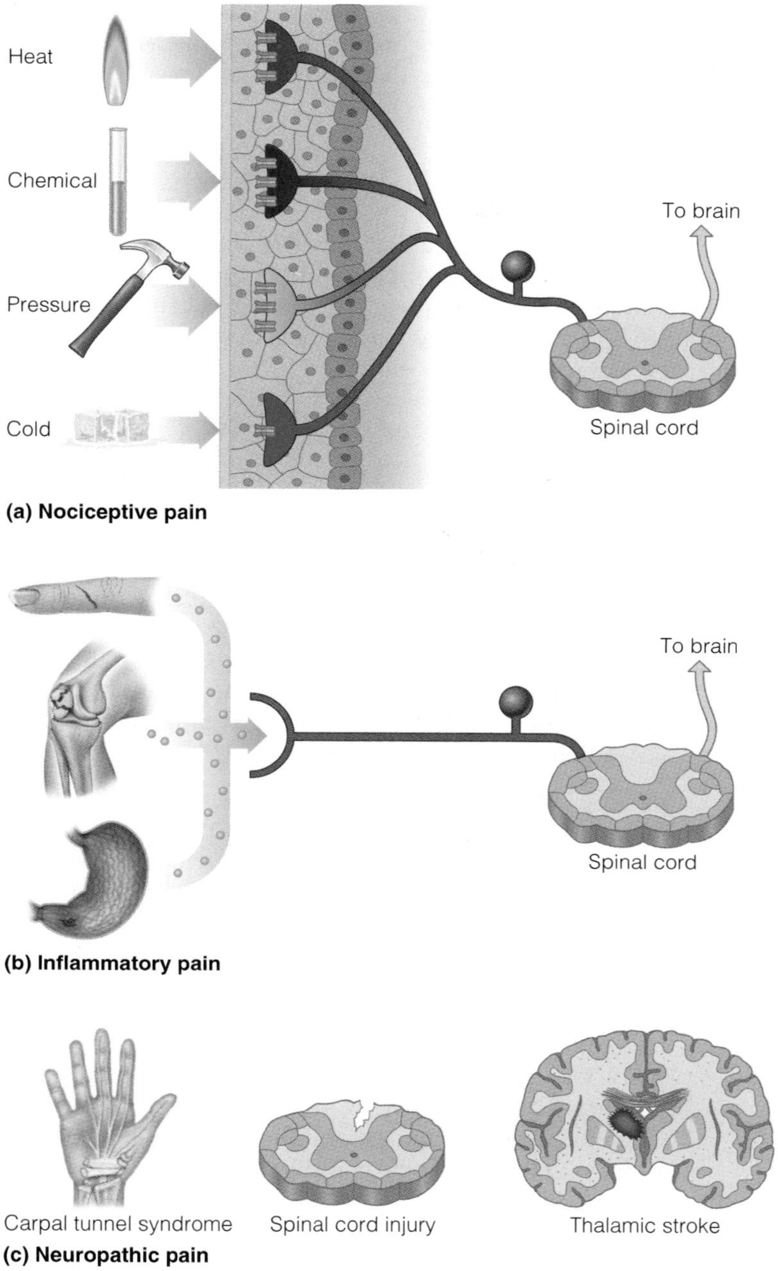

Figure 14.22 ▮ Pain can be created in a number of different ways. See text for details. *(Adapted from Scholz & Woolf, 2002.)*

crease or increase *subjective intensity* changed the participants' ratings of both subjective intensity (left pair of bars) and unpleasantness (right bars). These changes were accompanied by changes in activity in S1, the primary somatosensory receiving area.

Figure 14.24b shows that presenting suggestions to decrease or increase the *unpleasantness* of the pain did not affect ratings of subjective intensity (left bars), but did affect ratings of unpleasantness (right bars). These changes were accompanied by changes in activity in the anterior cingulate cortex.

These results show that area S1 is important for determining pain intensity and that unpleasantness can change as intensity changes. But they also show that the anterior cingulate cortex is important for determining unpleasantness and that unpleasantness can change even when the perceived intensity of pain remains the same. It is clear from this experiment and others that different structures in the pain matrix serve different aspects of pain perception (Rainville, 2002).

Cognitive and Experiential Aspects of Pain Perception

The fact that both the sensory and affective components of pain can be influenced by hypnosis reflects the fact that our perception of pain depends not only on stimulation of neurons in the skin, but on more central influences as

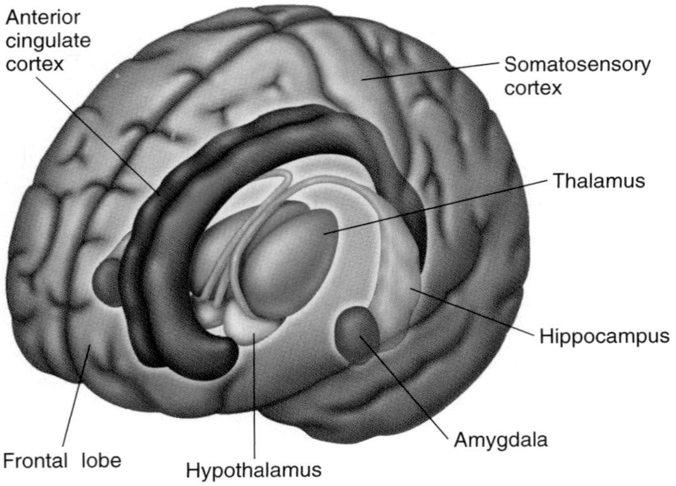

Figure 14.23 ▮ The perception of pain is accompanied by activation of a number of different areas of the brain, including the somatosensory cortex, thalamus, anterior cingulate cortex, amygdala, hippocampus, and thalamus. The ring-like configuration formed by the anterior cingulated cortex, hippocampus and amygdala is called the limbic system.

well. This central influence of pain is illustrated by the following description of a childhood experience by one of the students in my class:

> I remember being around five or six years old, and I was playing Nintendo when my dog ran by and pulled the wire out of the game system. When I got up to plug the wire back in I stumbled and banged my forehead on the radiator underneath the living room window. I got back up and staggered over to the Nintendo and plugged the controller back into the port, thinking nothing of my little fall. . . . As I resumed playing the game, all of a sudden I felt liquid rolling down my forehead, and reached my hand up to realize it was blood. I turned and looked into the mirror on the closet door to see a gash running down my forehead with blood pouring from it. All of a sudden I screamed out, and the pain hit me. My mom came running in, and took me to the hospital to get stitches. (Ian Kalinowski)

The important message of this description is that Ian's pain occurred not when he was injured, but when he *realized* he was injured. The fact that the pain didn't hit him until he saw the gash in his head is consistent with a great deal of evidence that indicates that pain can't be explained just based on stimulation of the skin. This is well known to clinicians who, in their attempt to alleviate their patient's pain, have cut nerve fibers that send signals from the skin to the brain, only to find that the pain persists (Turk & Flor, 1999). We will now consider a few examples of how cognitive factors can influence pain perception.

Expectation In a hospital study in which surgical patients were told what to expect and were instructed to relax to alleviate their pain, the patients requested fewer painkillers following surgery and were sent home 2.7 days earlier than patients who were not provided with this information. Studies have also shown that a significant proportion of patients with pathological pain get relief from taking a **placebo**, a pill that they believe contains painkillers but that, in fact, contains no active ingredients (Finniss & Benedetti, 2005; Weisenberg, 1977).

Shifting Attention The fact that pain can be reduced by shifting attention away from a pain-producing experience has been used in hospitals using virtual reality techniques. Consider, for example, the case of James Pokorny, who had received third-degree burns over 42 percent of his body when the fuel tank of the car he was repairing exploded. While having his bandages changed at the University of Washington Burn Center, he wore a black plastic helmet with a computer monitor inside, on which he saw a virtual world of multicolored, three-dimensional graphics. This world placed him in a virtual kitchen that contained a virtual spider, and he was able to chase the spider into the sink so he could grind it up with a virtual garbage disposal (Robbins, 2000).

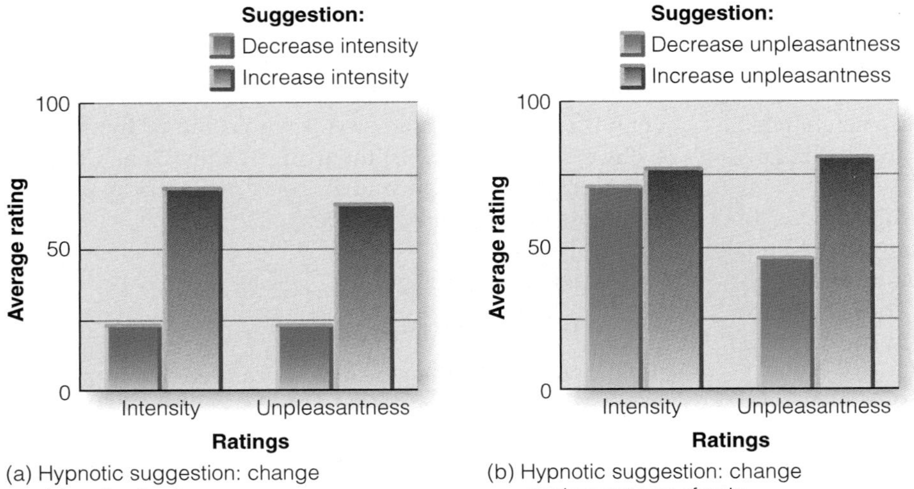

(a) Hypnotic suggestion: change *intensity* of pain

(b) Hypnotic suggestion: change *unpleasantness* of pain

Figure 14.24 ▮ Results of Hofbauer et al.'s (2001) experiment. Participants' ratings of the intensity and the unpleasantness of pain were affected by hypnosis. (a) Results of hypnotic suggestion to decrease or increase the pain's intensity. (b) Results of suggestion to decrease or increase the pain's unpleasantness.

The point of this "game" was to reduce Pokorny's pain by shifting his attention from the bandages to the virtual reality world. Pokorny reports that "you're concentrating on different things, rather than your pain. The pain level went down significantly." Studies of other patients indicate that burn patients using this virtual reality technique experienced much greater pain reduction than patients in a control group who were distracted by playing video games (Hoffman et al., 2000).

Content of Emotional Distraction An experiment by Minet deWied and Marinis Verbaten (2001) shows how the content of distracting materials can influence pain perception. The stimuli they used were pictures that had been previously rated as being positive (sports pictures and attractive females), neutral (household objects, nature, and people), or negative (burn victims and accidents). Male participants looked at the pictures as one of their hands was immersed in cold (2°C) water. They were told to keep the hand immersed for as long as possible but to withdraw the hand when it began to hurt.

The results, shown in Figure 14.25, indicate that the length of time the participants kept their hands in the water depended on the content of the pictures, with longer times associated with more positive pictures. Because the participants' ratings of the intensity of their pain—made immediately after removing their hands from the water—was the same for all three groups, deWied and Verbaten concluded that the content of the pictures influenced the time it took to reach the same pain level in the three groups.

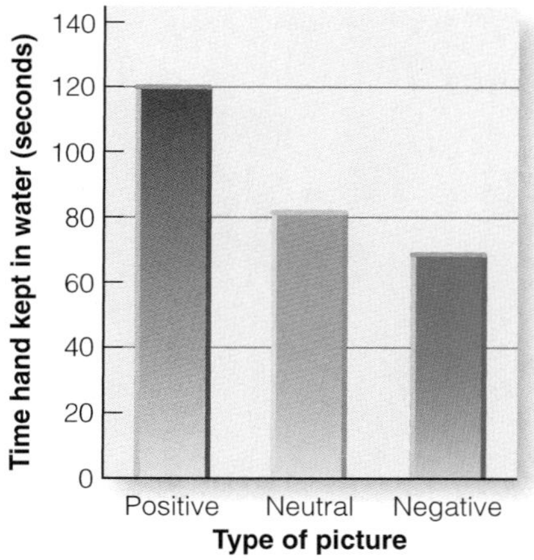

Figure 14.25 ▮ The results of deWied and Verbaten's (2001) experiment showing that participants kept their hands in cold water longer when looking at positive pictures than when looking at neutral or negative pictures.

Individual Differences Individuals or groups of people may describe the experiences associated with painful stimuli differently. Evelyn Hall and Simon Davies (1991) had female varsity track athletes and female nonathletes rate their level of pain in response to immersion of their hands in freezing ice water. Although both groups were exposed to the same stimulus, the athletes rated their pain as less intense (their average rating was 76 on a 150-point pain scale) than the nonathletes (whose average was 130).

Various explanations have been proposed to explain this. One explanation is based on past experience: Perhaps the athletes had learned, during painful training workouts, to withstand higher levels of pain. It is also possible that differences in the ability to withstand pain are associated with physiological differences between people. For example, we will see later in the chapter that differences in the ability to withstand pain have been linked to differences in brain chemistry.

The Physiology of Cognitive and Experiential Aspects of Pain Perception

We have been focusing on the behavioral level of analysis to show that things other than stimulation of nociceptors influence pain. But we can also approach this problem at the physiological level. We will begin by describing an approach to perception called the gate-control model, which proposes a neural circuit that takes into account the fact that pain can be influenced by "central influences" like a person's thoughts and expectations. VL 2

Gate-Control Model The **gate-control model** was proposed by Ronald Melzack and Patrick Wall (1965, 1988) to explain how pain perception can be affected both by central influences, such as those just described, and by nonpainful tactile stimuli, as when rubbing the skin causes a decrease in the perception of pain.

The gate-control system consists of cells in the spinal cord called the **substantia gelatinosa** (Figure 14.26a). These cells are represented by SG− and SG+ in the gate-control circuit in Figure 14.26b. We can understand how this circuit functions by considering the following facts about its operation:

1. Input to the gate-control system can occur along three pathways:
   - *L-fibers.* The **large-diameter fibers (L-fibers)** carry information about nonpainful tactile stimulation.
   - *Central control.* These fibers, which contain information related to cognitive functions such as expectation, attention, and distraction, carry signals down from the cortex.
   - *S-fibers.* The **small-diameter fibers (S-fibers)** are associated with nociceptors—fibers or receptors that fire to damaging and potentially painful stimuli.
2. Activation of each of these pathways sends signals to the T-cell. The intensity of pain is determined by the amount of T-cell activity, with more activity resulting in more pain.
3. Activity in the S-fibers increases T-cell activity. You can see how this works by following the paths along which signals from the S-fibers travel and noting

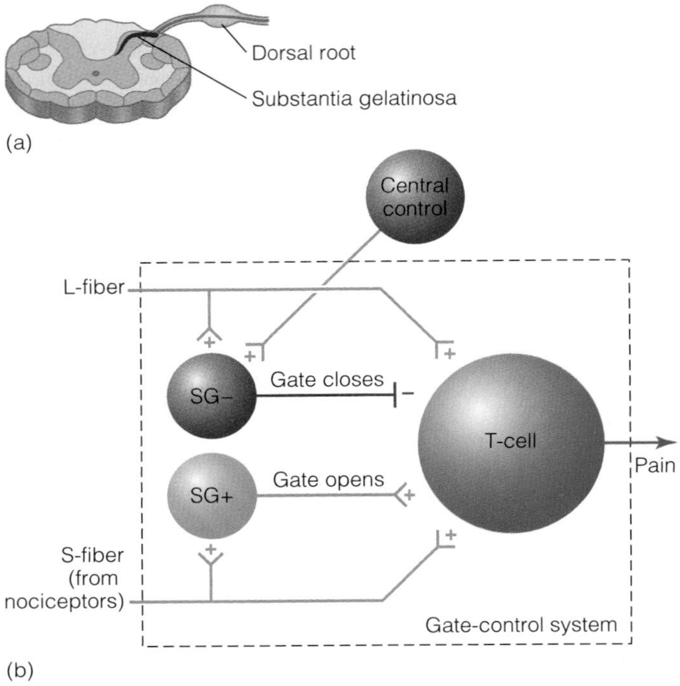

Figure 14.26 ▌ (a) Cross-section of the spinal cord showing fibers entering through the dorsal root and the location of the substantia gelatinosa. (b) The circuit proposed by Melzack and Wall (1988) for their gate-control model of pain perception. See text for details.

that all of the synapses are excitatory. Thus, signals from S-fibers always excite T-cells, and pain increases. This is called "opening the gate."

4. Activity in the L-fibers or from central control fibers can send inhibition to the T-cells. This occurs because signals that have passed through SG− activate an inhibitory synapse. The resulting decrease in T-cell activity decreases pain. This is called "closing the gate."

After introduction of the gate-control model, researchers discovered an effect called **stimulation-produced analgesia**, which showed that signals from the brain can reduce the perception of pain. Stimulation-produced analgesia occurs when electrical stimulation of an area in a rat's midbrain causes the rat to ignore pinching of its tail or paw that would normally cause a strong withdrawal response. In fact, David Reynolds (1969), who first demonstrated this effect, found that he could even perform abdominal surgery on rats with no anesthesia other than the electrical stimulation. The gate-control model explains this by proposing that the electrical stimulation activates "central control," which sends signals to SG− that close the gate.

Since the introduction of the gate-control model in 1965, researchers have determined that the neural circuits that control pain are much more complex than what was proposed by the model (Perl & Kruger, 1996). Nonetheless, this model has helped guide research that has shown that perception of pain depends not only on input from nociceptors, but also on input from fibers usually not concerned with pain (Fields & Basbaum, 1999; Sufka & Price, 2002; Turk & Flor, 1999; Weissberg, 1999).

Another important development in our understanding of how central factors influence pain perception is the discovery of a link between chemicals called **opioids** and pain perception. This can be traced back to research that began in the 1970s on opiate drugs such as opium and heroin, which have been used since the dawn of recorded history to reduce pain and induce feelings of euphoria.

Opioids and Pain By the 1970s researchers had discovered that the opiate drugs act on receptors in the brain, which respond to stimulation by molecules with specific structures. The importance of the molecule's structure for exciting these "opiate receptors" explains why injecting a drug called **naloxone** into a person who has overdosed on heroin can almost immediately revive the victim. Because naloxone's structure is similar to heroin's, it blocks the action of heroin by attaching itself to receptor sites usually occupied by heroin (Figure 14.27a).

Why are there opiate receptor sites in the brain? After all, they most certainly have been present since long before people started taking heroin. Researchers concluded that there must be naturally occurring substances in the body that act on these sites, and in 1975 neurotransmitters were discovered that act on the same receptors that are activated by opium and heroin. One group of these transmitters are the pain-reducing **endorphins**.

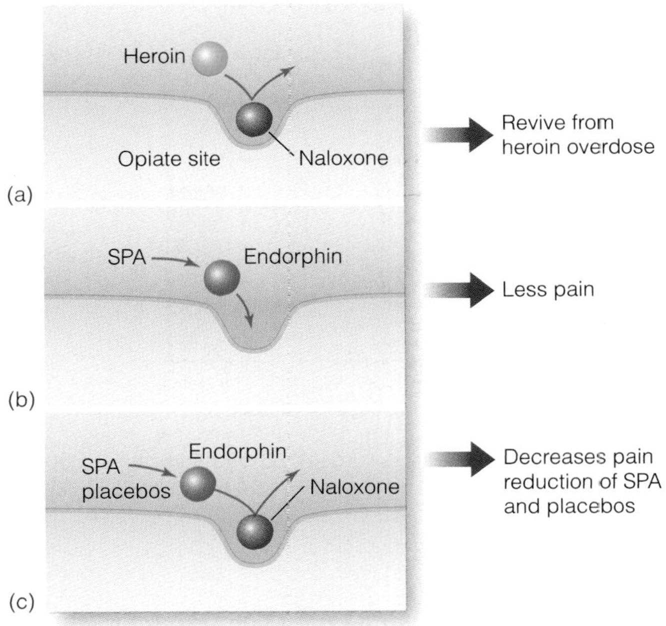

Figure 14.27 ▌ (a) Naloxone reduces the effect of heroin by occupying a receptor site normally stimulated by heroin. (b) Stimulation-produced analgesia (SPA) may work by causing the release of endorphins, which stimulate opiate receptor sites. (c) Naloxone decreases the pain reduction caused by SPA and placebos by displacing endorphins.

Since the discovery of endorphins, researchers have accumulated a large amount of evidence linking endorphins to pain reduction. For example, the effect of stimulation-produced analgesia is increased by stimulating endorphin sites, and is decreased by injecting naloxone. Because stimulating endorphin sites releases endorphins (Figure 14.27b) and injecting naloxone blocks endorphins from reaching their receptor sites (Figure 14.27c), both of these results support the idea that stimulation-produced analgesia works by releasing endorphins.

In addition to decreasing the effect of stimulation-produced analgesia, naloxone also decreases the analgesic effect of placebos (see p. 320). Because placebos contain no active chemicals, their effects have always been thought to be "psychological." However, the idea that placebos cause the release of endorphins provides a physiological basis for what had previously been described in strictly psychological terms. (Also see If You Want to Know More, "The Physiology of Placebos" on p. 325).

Finally, a recent study has identified genetic differences in people that cause their brain to release different amounts of opioids in response to painful stimuli (Zubieta et al., 2003). This study found that people whose brains released more opoids were able to withstand higher levels of pain stimulation.

SOMETHING TO CONSIDER: PAIN IN SOCIAL SITUATIONS

The song lyrics "It only hurts for a little while" refers not to the pain of falling down on the sidewalk but to the pain of ending a romantic relationship. In our society, "pain" goes beyond the physical pain we have been focusing on in this chapter to include, for example, the distress one feels when a relationship ends or the anguish one feels when excluded from a group. Although this may seem more like "social psychology" than "perception," there is new evidence that the pain of social loss may activate some of the brain areas that are activated by physical pain.

Naomi Eisenberger and coworkers (2003) determined how the brain responds to social loss. Participants' brain activity was measured in an fMRI scanner as they either watched or played a computer game called CyberBall. Participants were led to believe that they were playing the game with two other players who were also in fMRI scanners, although in reality there were no other players. After watching the other "players" play the game, the participant was then included in the game. After receiving seven throws from the other players (actually preprogrammed by the experimenter), it became apparent to the participant that he or she was being excluded, because the other players stopped throwing the ball to the participant.

During the exclusion part of the experiment, participants reported feeling ignored and excluded, and reported some distress. When this happened, their brain scan showed increased activation of the anterior cingulate cortex (ACC)—the same area of the brain that is activated by the emotional suffering associated with physical pain (see Figure 14.23). This activation of the ACC was greater in participants who reported feeling greater social distress in response to being excluded.

If being hurt by feeling rejected activates pain-related areas in the brain, what about watching someone else experiencing pain? The answer is that watching another person experience pain also activates the ACC, especially when the person watching feels empathy—an understanding and sharing of the other person's feelings.

Tania Singer and coworkers (2004) demonstrated this by bringing romantically involved couples into the laboratory and having the woman, whose brain activity was being measured by an fMRI scanner, either receive shocks herself or watch her male partner receive shocks. The results, shown in Figure 14.28, show that a number of brain areas were activated when the woman received the shocks (Figure 14.28a), and that some of the same areas were activated when she watched her partner receive shocks (Figure 14.28b).

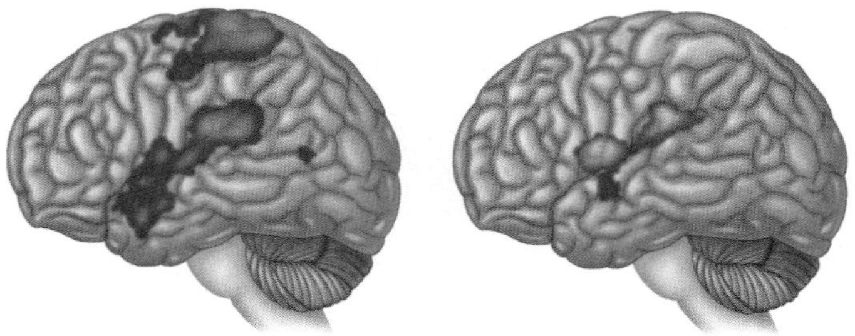

(a) Receive electric shocks (b) Watch partner receive shocks

Figure 14.28 ▮ Singer and coworkers (2004) used fMRI to determine the areas of the brain activated by (a) receiving electric shocks and (b) watching another person receive the shocks. Singer proposes that the activation in (b) is related to empathy for the other person. Empathy did not activate the somatosensory cortex, but did activate other areas that are activated by pain, such as the insula (tucked between the parietal and temporal lobes) and anterior cingulate cortex (see Figure 14.23). *(Adapted with permission from Holden, C., Imaging studies show how brain thinks about pain.* Science, *303, 1121, (2004), AAAS.)*

To show that the brain activity caused by watching their partner was related to empathy, Singer had the women fill out "empathy scales" designed to measure their tendency to empathize with others. As she predicted, women with higher "empathy scores" showed higher activation of their ACC. Thus, although "social" pain may be caused by stimulation that is very different from physical pain, these two types of pain apparently share some physiological mechanisms.

TEST YOURSELF 14.2

1. What processes are involved in identifying objects by haptic exploration?
2. What are some of the physiological processes that are involved in recognition of objects by touch?

3. What does it mean to say that pain is multimodal?
4. Describe the three types of pain.
5. Describe the receptors for nociceptive pain, the pathways from the receptors to the brain, and the areas of the brain that make up the pain matrix.
6. Describe the hypnosis experiments that identified areas involved in the sensory component of pain and the emotional component of pain.
7. Give examples for the following situations, which illustrate how pain is influenced by cognition and experience: expectation; shifting attention; content of emotional distraction; individual differences.
8. Describe the following, which are related physiological mechanisms that are involved in determining cognitive and experiential aspects of pain perception: gate-control model; opiates and pain; the physiology of the placebo effect.
9. What are some parallels between nociceptive pain and the pain associated with social situations?

THINK ABOUT IT

1. Some people report situations in which they were injured but didn't feel any pain until they became aware of their injury. How would you explain this kind of situation in terms of top-down and bottom-up processing? How could you relate this situation to the studies we have discussed?
2. Even though the senses of vision and cutaneous perception are different in many ways, there are a number of parallels between them. Cite examples of parallels between vision and cutaneous sensations (touch and pain) for the following: "tuned" receptors; mechanisms of detail perception; receptive fields; plasticity (changing the environment influences properties of the system); and top-down processing. Also, can you think of situations in which vision and touch interact with one another?
3. One of the themes in this book is that it is possible to use the results of psychophysical experiments to suggest the operation of physiological mechanisms or to link physiological mechanisms to perception. Cite an example of how psychophysics has been used in this way for each of the senses we have considered so far—vision, hearing, and the cutaneous senses.

IF YOU WANT TO KNOW MORE

The length of this list of topics reflects the large amount of research that is being done on touch, pain, and the other cutaneous senses. If space were available, it would be easy to write separate chapters on touch and pain, with an additional chapter on proprioception and kinesthesis. In lieu of these chapters, here are a few of the interesting things that are being done in this extremely active area of research:

1. ***Plastic Effects of Losing a Sense*** When input from one sense is eliminated, the brain area normally devoted to that sense can be taken over by another sense. For example, in people who became blind before the age of 7, the occipital cortex (which is usually associated with vision) is activated by reading Braille.

   Sadato, N., Pascual-Leone, A., Grafman, J., Ibanez, V., Deiber, M-P., Dold, G., & Hallett, M. (1996). Activation of the primary visual cortex by Braille reading in blind subjects. *Nature, 380,* 526–528.

2. ***A Tactile Illusion and the Homunculus*** Recent research on monkeys has shown that tactile illusions on the skin, in which stimulation at one point causes a feeling at another point, activate the area of the brain that corresponds not to where the skin was stimulated, but to where the monkey *felt* the stimulation.

   Chen, L. M., Friedman, R. M., & Roe, A. W. (2003). Optical imaging of a tactile illusion in area 3b of the primate somatosensory cortex. *Science, 302,* 881–885.

   Eysel, U. T. (2003). Illusions and perceived images in the primate brain. *Science, 302,* 789–790.

3. ***Why You Can't Tickle Yourself*** It is generally not possible to tickle yourself. This has to do with differences between a self-produced tactile stimulus and the same stimulus presented externally.

   Blakemore, S. J., Wolpert, D. M., & Frith, C. D. (1998). Central cancellation of self-produced tickle sensation. *Nature Neuroscience, 1,* 635–640.

4. ***How Different Types of Stimulation Affect the Brain*** Research has shown that three types of stimuli—pressure, flutter, and vibration—cause maximum activation of different areas in somatosensory cortex.

   Friedman, R., N., Chen, L. M., & Roe, A. W. (2004). Modality maps within primate somatosensory cortex. *Proceedings of the National Academy of Sciences, 101,* 12724–12729.

5. ***Pain in Phantom Limb*** Many people who have had a limb amputated continue to experience the limb. This experience, which is called a phantom limb, is often accompanied by feelings of pain in the limb, even though the limb is no longer present.

   Katz, J., & Gagliese, L. (1999). Phantom limb pain: A continuing puzzle. In R. J. Gatchel & D. C. Turk (Eds.), *Psychosocial factors in pain* (pp. 284–300). New York: Guilford.

   Ramachandran, V. S., & Hirstein, W. (1998). The perception of phantom limbs. *Brain, 121,* 1603–1630.

6. ***Pathological Pain*** Pathological pain—pain that continues despite medical attempts to relieve it—is a serious problem that disrupts the lives of many people.

   Scholz, J., & Woolf, C. J. (2002). Can we conquer pain? *Nature Neuroscience, 5,* 1062–1067.

   Watkins, L. R., & Maier, S. F. (2003). When good pain turns bad. *Current Directions in Psychological Science, 12,* 232–236.

7. ***Accepting Pain as a Way of Dealing With It*** It has been suggested that one way to deal with pathological pain is by using a strategy that involves acceptance of the pain.

   Vaine, I., Crombez, G., Eccleston, C., Devulder, J., & DeCorte, W. (2004). Acceptance of the unpleasant reality of chronic pain: Effects upon attention to pain and engagement with daily activities. *Pain, 112,* 282–288.

8. ***The Physiology of Placebos*** Research has shown that placebos activate the same brain structures that are activated by opioids.

   Petrovic, P., Kalso, E., Petersson, K. M., & Ingvar, M. (2002). Placebo and opioid analgesia—imaging a shared neuronal network. *Science, 295,* 1737–1740.

   Wager, T. D., Rilling, J. K., Smith, E. E., Sokolik, A., Casey, K. L., Davidson, R. J., et al. (2004). Placebo-induced changes in fMRI in the anticipation and experience of pain. *Science, 303,* 1162–1167.

KEY TERMS

Active touch (p. 315)
Affective (or emotional) component of pain (p. 318)
Cutaneous sensation (p. 305)
Dermis (p. 305)
Duplex theory of texture perception (p. 313)
Emotional component of pain (p. 318)
Endorphin (p. 322)
Epidermis (p. 305)
Exploratory procedures (EPs) (p. 315)
Focal dystonia (p. 310)
Gate-control model (p. 321)
Grating acuity (p. 311)
Haptic perception (p. 315)
Homunculus (p. 309)
Inflammatory pain (p. 318)
Kinesthesis (p. 305)
Large-diameter fibers (L-fibers) (p. 321)
Mechanoreceptor (p. 305)
Medial lemniscal pathway (p. 308)
Meissner corpuscle (p. 305)
Merkel receptor (p. 305)
Multimodal nature of pain (p. 318)
Naloxone (p. 322)
Neuropathic pain (p. 318)
Nociceptive pain (p. 318)
Nociceptor (p. 318)
Opioid (p. 322)
Pacinian corpuscle (p. 305)
Pain matrix (p. 318)
Passive touch (p. 314)
Placebo (p. 320)
Proprioception (p. 305)
RA 1 fiber (p. 306)
RA 2 fiber (p. 306)
Rapidly adapting (RA) fiber (p. 305)
Ruffini cylinder (p. 305)
SA 1 fiber (p. 305)
SA 2 fiber (p. 305)
Secondary somatosensory cortex (S2) (p. 308)
Sensory component of pain (p. 318)
Slowly adapting (SA) fiber (p. 305)
Small-diameter fibers (S-fibers) (p. 321)
Somatosensory receiving area (S1) (p. 308)
Somatosensory system (p. 305)
Spatial cue (p. 313)
Spinothalamic pathway (p. 308)
Stimulation-produced analgesia (SPA) (p. 322)
Substantia gelatinosa (p. 321)
Tactile acuity (p. 310)
Temporal cue (p. 313)
Two-point threshold (p. 310)
Ventrolateral nucleus (p. 308)

VISIT YOUR COMPANION WEBSITE FOR THIS BOOK

http://psychology.wadsworth.com/goldstein7e

Check out this companion website where you'll find online resources—glossary, flashcards, web links, multiple-choice and essay questions, and much more!

VIRTUAL LAB

Your Virtual Lab is designed to help you get the most out of this course. The Virtual Lab icons direct you to specific media demonstrations and experiments designed to help you visualize what you are reading about. The number beside each icon indicates the number of the media element you can access through your CD-ROM, Perception PsychologyNow, or WebTutor resource at http:now.ilrn.com/goldstein_7e.

The following are the lab exercises covering what you've just learned in this chapter:

1 *Anatomy of the Skin* The skin, with drag-and-drop terms to test your knowledge of the locations of basic skin structures.

2 *Gate-Control System* How different types of stimulation are processed by the gate-control system.

BRACIUK
€ al kg. 18,00
Lire al kg. 34.853

CHAPTER

15

THE CHEMICAL SENSES

Chapter Contents

Taste and smell are "molecule detectors" that enable us to sense chemicals in the environment. These odoriferous foods would strongly stimulate our sense of smell, and if we were to take a bite, stimulation of both our smell and taste systems would combine to create the "flavor" of the cheese.

VL *The Virtual Lab icons direct you to specific animations and videos designed to help you visualize what you are reading about. The number beside each icon indicates the number of the clip you can access through your CD-ROM or your student website.*

Some Questions We Will Consider

- Why is a dog's sense of smell so much better than a human's? (p. 329)
- Why does a cold inhibit the ability to taste? (p. 344)
- How do neurons in the cortex combine smell and taste? (p. 345)

> . . . We have five senses, but only two that go beyond the boundaries of ourselves. When you look at someone, it's just bouncing light, or when you hear them, it's just sound waves, vibrating air, or touch is just nerve endings tingling. Know what smell is? . . . It's made up of the molecules of what you're smelling. (Kushner, 1993, p. 17)

The character speaking the these lines in the play *Angels in America* probably did not take a course in sensation and perception and so leaves out the fact that vision and hearing are "just nerve endings tingling" as well. But his point—that smell involves taking molecules into your body—is one of the properties of the chemical senses that distinguishes them from the other senses. Thus, as you drink something, you smell it because molecules in gas form are entering your nose, and you taste it because molecules in liquid form are stimulating your tongue. Smell (which we will refer to as *olfaction*) and taste have been called molecule detectors because they endow these gas and liquid molecules with distinctive smells and tastes (Cain, 1988; Kauer, 1987).

Because the stimuli responsible for tasting and smelling are on the verge of being assimilated into the body, these senses are often seen as "gatekeepers," which (1) identify things that the body needs for survival and that should therefore be consumed and (2) detect things that would be bad for the body and that should therefore be rejected. The gatekeeper function of taste and smell is aided by a large affective, or emotional, component—things that are bad for us often taste or smell unpleasant, and things that are good for us generally taste or smell good. In addition to creating "good" and "bad" affect, smelling an odor associated with a past place or event can trigger memories, which in turn may create emotional reactions.

Because the receptors that serve taste and smell are constantly exposed not only to the chemicals that they are designed to sense but also to harmful materials such as bacteria and dirt, they undergo a cycle of birth, development, and death over 5–7 weeks for olfactory receptors and 1–2 weeks for taste receptors. This constant renewal of the receptors, which is called **neurogenesis**, is unique to these senses. In vision, hearing, and the cutaneous senses, the receptors are safely protected inside structures such as the eye, the inner ear, and under the skin; however, the receptors for taste and smell are relatively unprotected and therefore need to be constantly renewed.

We will consider olfaction first and then taste. We will describe the psychophysics and anatomy of each system and then how different taste and smell qualities are coded in the nervous system. Finally, we will consider flavor, which results from the interaction of taste and smell.

THE OLFACTORY SYSTEM

Functions of Olfaction

Olfaction is extremely important in the lives of many species because it is often their primary window to the environment (Ache, 1991). One important contrast between humans and other species is that many animals are **macrosmatic** (having a keen sense of smell that is important to their survival), whereas humans are **microsmatic** (having a less keen sense of smell that is not crucial to their survival). Many animals use olfaction to survive: It provides cues to orient them in space, to mark territory, and to guide them to specific places, other animals, and food sources (Holley, 1991). Olfaction is also extremely important in sexual reproduction because it triggers mating behavior in many species (Doty, 1976; Pfeiffer & Johnston, 1994).

Although olfaction may not be as central to our sensory experience as vision, hearing, or touch, some of its effects may be occurring without our awareness. Consider, for example, the phenomenon of **menstrual synchrony**—women who live or work together often have menstrual periods at about the same time. In the first systematic investigation of this phenomenon, Martha McClintock (1971) asked 135 females, aged 17 to 22, living in a college dormitory, to indicate when their periods began throughout the school year. She found that women who saw each other often (roommates or close friends) tended to have synchronous periods by the end of the school year. After eliminating other explanations such as awareness of the other person's period, McClintock concluded that "there is some interpersonal physiological process which affects the menstrual cycle" (p. 246).

What might this physiological process be? Twenty-seven years after the dormitory experiment, Kathleen Stern and McClintock (1998) did an experiment that led them to conclude that menstrual synchrony is caused by human **pheromones**—chemical signals released by an individual that affect the physiology and behavior of other individuals. They used cotton pads to collect secretions from the underarms of 9 donor women at various times in their ovulatory cycle. The pads from the donor women were treated with a small amount of alcohol and were wiped on the upper lips of other women (the recipients) who were instructed not to wash their face for 6 hours after the application.

Stern and McClintock found that underarm secretions taken from donor women in the initial phase of their cycle (just after menstruation) shortened the length of the recipients' cycles. In contrast, secretions from the ovulatory phase of the cycle lengthened the recipients' cycles. Women in a control group, who just had alcohol applied to their upper lip, did not show this effect. Apparently, there were two pheromones at work—one that shortens the cycle and one that lengthens it. What is especially interesting about these results is that they occurred even though the recipient women reported that they detected only the alcohol that was added to the pads. Thus the pheromones resulted in "chemical communication" that occurred even though odors were not consciously detected.

Although smell might work "behind the scenes" in determining a phenomenon like menstrual synchrony, there is nothing hidden about the vast sums of money people spend yearly on perfumes and deodorants (Rossiter, 1996). In addition, the emergence of a new billion-dollar-a-year industry called environmental fragrancing, which offers products to add pleasing scents to the air in both homes and businesses, attests to the fact that the role of smell in our daily lives is not inconsequential (Gilbert & Firestein, 2002; Owens, 1994).

But perhaps the most convincing argument for the importance of smell to humans comes from those who suffer from **anosmia**, the loss of the ability to smell due to injury or infection. People suffering from anosmia describe the great void created by their inability to taste many foods because of the close connection between smell and flavor. One woman who suffered from anosmia and then briefly regained her sense of smell stated, "I always thought I would sacrifice smell to taste if I had to choose between the two, but I suddenly realized how much I had missed. We take it for granted and are unaware that everything smells: people, the air, my house, my skin" (Birnberg, 1988; quoted in Ackerman, 1990, p. 42). Olfaction is more important in our lives than most of us realize, and, although it may not be essential to our survival, life is often enhanced by our ability to smell and becomes a little more dangerous if we lose the olfactory warning system that alerts us to spoiled food, leaking gas, or smoke from a fire.

Detecting Odors

Our sense of smell enables us to detect extremely low concentrations of some odorants. The **detection threshold** for odors is the lowest concentration at which an odorant can be detected.

METHOD ▪ Measuring the Detection Threshold

One way to measure the threshold for detecting an odorant is to present the odorant on some trials and to present "blanks" on other trials. The participant responds either "yes" (I smell something) or "no" (I don't smell anything) on each trial. However, one problem with this procedure is that it is susceptible to bias. Some people will respond "yes" at the merest hint of a smell, whereas others wait until they are sure they smell something before saying "yes" (see Appendix, p. 373).

The forced-choice method avoids this problem by presenting the participant with blocks of two trials—one trial contains a weak odorant and the other, no odorant. The participant's task is to indicate which trial has a stronger smell. When using this procedure, it is important to wait at least 30 seconds between trials to allow for recovery if an odorant was presented on the first trial. The forced-choice procedure generally indicates greater sensitivity than the yes/no procedure (Dalton, 2002).

▪ ▪ ▪

Table 15.1 lists thresholds for a number of substances. It is notable that there is a very large range of thresholds. T-butyl mercepatan, the odorant that is added to natural gas, can be detected in concentrations of less than 1 part per billion in air. In contrast, to detect the vapors of acetone (the main component of nail polish remover), the concentration must be 15,000 parts per billion and for the vapor of methanol, the concentration must be 141,000 parts per billion.

Table 15.1 ▮ *Human odor detection thresholds*

Compound	Odor Threshold in Air (parts per billion)
Methanol	141,000
Acetone	15,000
Formaldehyde	870
Menthol	40
T-butyl mercaptan	0.3

Source: From Devos et al. (1990).

Although humans can detect extremely small concentrations of some odorants, they are much less sensitive to odors than many animals. For example, rats are 8 to 50 times more sensitive to odors than humans, and dogs are from 300 to 10,000 times more sensitive, depending on the odorant (Laing, Doty, & Breipohl, 1991). But even though humans are unaware of odors that other animals can detect, humans' individual olfactory receptors are as sensitive as any animal's. H. deVries and M. Stuiver (1961) demonstrated this by showing that human olfactory receptors can be excited by the action of just 1 molecule of odorant. This is similar to the situation in vision, in which a rod receptor can be activated by the action of just 1 quantum of light (see page 35).

Nothing can be more sensitive than 1 molecule per receptor, so humans' lower sensitivity to odors compared to other animals' must be due to something other than the sensitivity of individual receptors. That something else is the number of receptors: Humans have only about 10 million receptors, whereas dogs have about 1 billion (Dodd & Squirrell, 1980; Moulton, 1977).

Another aspect of odor detection is the difference threshold—the smallest difference in the concentration of two odors that can be detected. Measurements of the difference threshold highlight one of the most important problems in olfactory research—the control of concentrations in stimulus presentations. For example, when William Cain (1977) carefully measured the difference threshold by placing two odorants of different concentrations on absorbent cotton balls and asked participants to judge which was more intense, he found that the difference threshold averaged 19 percent. However, when Cain analyzed the stimuli he had presented on the cotton balls, he found that stimuli that were supposed to have the same concentration actually varied considerably. This variation was apparently caused by differences in the airflow pattern through the cotton in different samples.

To deal with this problem, Cain remeasured the difference threshold using a device called an **olfactometer**, which presents olfactory stimuli with much greater precision than cotton balls. Using this more precise method of presenting of stimulus, Cain found that the threshold dropped to 11 percent.

Identifying Odors

When odorant concentrations are near threshold, so a person can just detect the *presence* of an odor, the person usually cannot sense the *quality* of the odor—whether it is "floral" or "pepperminty" or "rancid." The concentration of an odorant has to be increased by as much as a factor of 3 above the threshold concentration before the person can recognize an odor's quality. The concentration at which quality can be recognized is called the **recognition threshold** (Dalton, 2002).

One of the more intriguing facts about odors is that even though humans can discriminate between as many as 100,000 different odors (Firestein, 2001), they often find it difficult to accurately identify specific odors. For example, when people are presented with the odors of familiar substances such as coffee, bananas, and motor oil, they can easily tell the difference between them. However, when they are asked to *identify* the substance associated with the odor, they are successful only about half the time (Engen & Pfaffman, 1960). J. A. Desor and Gary Beauchamp (1974) found, however, that when they presented participants with the names of the substances at the beginning of the experiment and then reminded them of the correct names when they failed to respond correctly on subsequent trials, they could, after some practice, correctly identify 98 percent of the substances.

One of the amazing things about odor identification is that knowing the correct label for the odor actually seems to transform our perception into that odor. Cain (1980) gives the example of an object initially identified by as "fishy-goaty-oily." When the experimenter told the person that the fishy-goaty-oily smell actually came from leather, the smell was then transformed into that of leather.

I had a similar experience when a friend gave me a bottle of Aquavit, a Danish drink with a very interesting smell. As I was sampling this drink with some friends, we tried to identify its smell. Many odors were proposed ("anise," "orange," "lemon"), but it wasn't until someone turned the bottle around and read the label on the back that the truth became known: "Aquavit (Water of Life) is the Danish national drink—a delicious, crystal-clear spirit distilled from grain, with a slight taste of caraway." When we heard the word *caraway,* the previous hypotheses of anise, orange, and lemon were discarded, and the smell became caraway. Thus, when we have trouble identifying odors, this trouble results not from a deficiency in our olfactory system, but from an inability to retrieve the odor's name from our memory.

DEMONSTRATION

Naming and Odor Identification

To demonstrate the effect of naming substances on odor identification, have a friend collect a number of familiar objects for you and, without looking, try to identify the odors. You will find that you can identify some but not others, and when your friend tells you the correct answer for the ones you identified incorrectly, you will wonder how you could have failed to identify such a familiar smell. But don't blame your mistakes on your nose; blame them on your memory. ■

The Puzzle of Olfactory Quality

Although we know that we can discriminate among a huge number of odors, research to determine the mechanisms behind this ability is complicated by difficulties in establishing a system to bring some order to our descriptions of odor quality. Such systems do exist for other senses. For example, we can describe visual stimuli in terms of their colors and can relate our perception of color to the physical property of wavelength. We can describe sound stimuli as having different pitches and relate these pitches to the physical property of frequency. However, attempts to create a way to organize odors and to relate odors to physical properties of molecules has proven to be extremely difficult.

One reason for the difficulty is that we lack a specific language for odor quality. For example, when people smell the chemical ~-ionone they usually say that it smells like violets. This description, it turns out, is fairly accurate, but if you compare ~-ionone to real violets, they smell different. The perfume industry's solution is to use names such as "woody violet" and "sweet violet" to distinguish between different violet smells, but this hardly solves the problem we face in trying to determine how olfaction works.

Many attempts have been made to find a way to classify odors and so bring some order into this confusing situation. One of the best known attempts is Henning's **odor prism** (1916), shown in Figure 15.1. Henning's prism has six corners, at which the qualities putrid, ethereal, resinous, spicy, fragrant, and burned are located. Odors resemble the qualities at the corners of the surface, in proportion to their nearness to each corner. For example, the position of lemon-oil on the prism indicates that it has both ethereal and resinous properties, but that it is more like ethereal because it is closer to the ethereal corner.

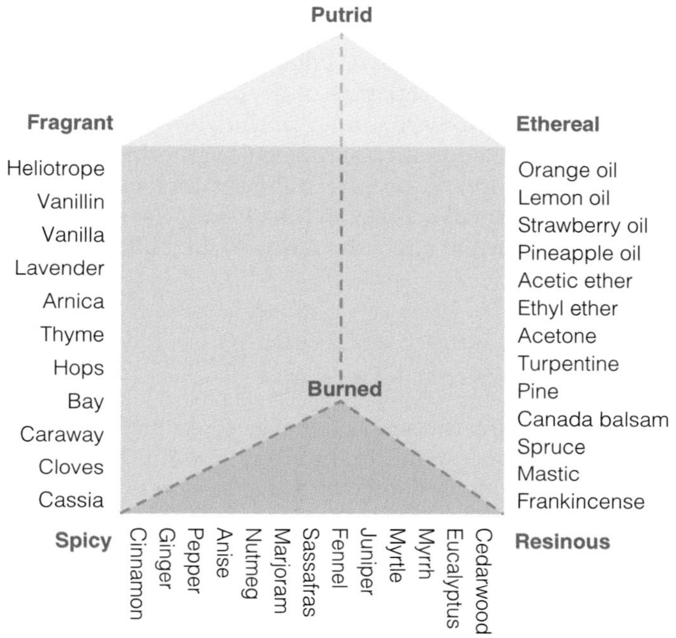

Figure 15.1 ▮ The odor prism proposed by Henning (1916). As described in the text, the position of substances relative to the corners of the prism represents the relative contribution of the qualities at each corner to the substance's smell. *(Adapted from Woodworth, 1938)*

Although Henning's attempt to classify odors based on quality was ambitious and included a large number of odors, his prism has proven to be of little use in helping us to understand olfaction and now only has historical importance (Bartoshuk, Cain, & Pfaffmann, 1985). Unfortunately, other classification schemes are not any better. Many schemes propose too few classifications, thereby making it impossible to find a class for some odors, and others propose categories so broad or ambiguous that one person might judge a particular odor to be in one category, whereas another person would judge the same odor to be in a different category.

Another idea has been to link specific structures to specific types of smells. This tactic also runs into problems because it has been difficult to determine a simple relationship between these physical and chemical properties and the odor qualities we perceive. For example, some molecules that have similar structures can smell different (Figure 15.2a), and molecules that have very different structures can smell similar (Figure 15.2b). As we will see, however, recent research has succeeded in demonstrating some links between (1) structural components of molecules, (2) olfactory quality, and (3) patterns of activation in the olfactory system.

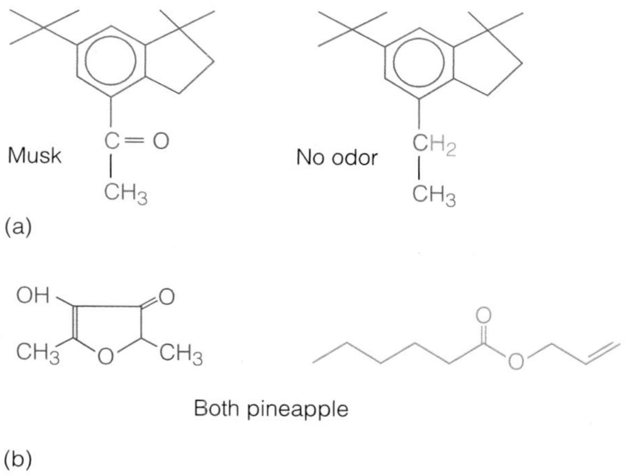

Figure 15.2 ▮ (a) Two molecules that have the same structures, but one smells like musk and the other is odorless. (b) Two molecules with different structures but similar odors.

THE NEURAL CODE FOR OLFACTORY QUALITY

How does the olfactory system know what molecules are entering the nose? Answers to this question have been provided by research on different areas of the olfactory system, from the receptors to the cortex. To describe this research, we need to first describe the structure of the olfactory system.

Structure of the Olfactory System

The picture in Figure 15.3 is not an underwater coral reef or vegetation on the forest floor. It is a picture of the surface of the **olfactory mucosa**, the dime-sized region located high in the nasal cavity that contains the receptors for olfaction. Figure 15.4a shows the location of the mucosa, on the roof of the nasal cavity and just below the olfactory bulb.

Odorant molecules are carried into the nose in an air stream, which brings these molecules into contact with the mucosa. Figure 15.4b shows the **olfactory sensory neurons** (which we will call *sensory neurons*) that are located in the mucosa. The cilia of these sensory neurons, which jut out into the air stream, contain the **olfactory receptors** (Figure 15.4c). Each olfactory receptor is a protein string that crosses the sensory neuron's membrane seven times, just as visual pigment molecules in the rod and cone receptors cross the membrane seven times (see Figure 2.19).

VIRTUAL LAB 1

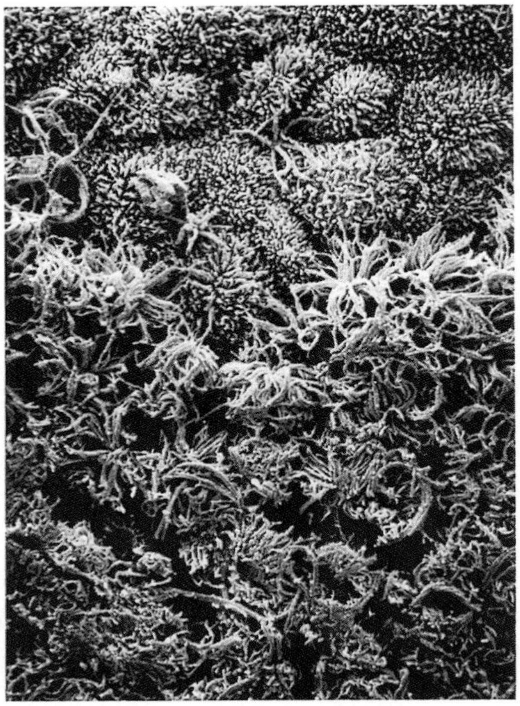

Figure 15.3 ■ A scanning electron micrograph of the surface of the olfactory mucosa. The region in the foreground is densely covered with the cilia of olfactory receptors.
(From Morrison, E. E., & Moran, D. T. (1995). Anatomy and ultrastructure of the human olfactory neuroepithelium. In R. L. Doty (Ed.), Handbook of Olfaction and Gustation *(pp. 75–101). New York: Marcel Dekker.)*

Odorants contacting the olfactory receptors result in transduction, which creates electrical signals in the sensory neurons (Figure 15.4d). The electrical signals travel from the sensory neurons to structures called **glomeruli** in the olfactory bulb (Figure 15.4e). Each glomerulus collects and combines signals from a large number of sensory neurons and then relays signals to the olfactory bulb. The olfactory bulb, which is part of the brain, sends signals to a few different places in the cerebral cortex. One destination is the **primary olfactory cortex**, or **piriform cortex**, a small area under the temporal lobe, and another is the **secondary olfactory cortex**, or **orbitofrontal cortex**, located in the frontal lobe, near the eyes (Figure 15.5; Cinelli, 1993; Dodd & Castellucci, 1991; Frank & Rabin, 1989; McLean & Shipley, 1992; Price et al., 1991; Rolls, 2000; Takagi, 1980). Olfactory signals also reach the **amygdala**, a structure deep in the cortex that is involved in emotional responding.

Describing the Olfactory Receptors

A giant step toward determining the olfactory code was Linda Buck and Richard Axel's (1991) description of the structure of olfactory receptors. Buck and Axel received the Nobel Prize in Physiology and Medicine in 2004 for their research on the olfactory system, and their discoveries led to a groundswell of research by other investigators that has greatly enhanced our understanding of how both the olfactory and taste systems work.

Buck and Axel used techniques of molecular biology to isolate a family of genes that are responsible for creating the olfactory receptors. Once they identified the genes, they determined that there are 1,000 different types of olfactory receptors in the mouse, and about 350 in humans (Buck, 2004). Activation of these receptors by an odorant molecule triggers a sequence of reactions that changes the flow of ions across the membrane and creates an electrical signal in the sensory neuron. Because a particular sensory neuron contains only one type of olfactory receptor, the response of this neuron reflects the properties of the olfactory receptors that dot its cilia.

Describing the properties of the olfactory receptors is just the first step toward understanding how the olfactory system codes the identity of molecules entering the nose. The key question "How are different molecules represented by electrical activity in the olfactory system?" has been studied in the olfactory mucosa, the olfactory bulb, and the cortex.

Activating Receptor Neurons in the Olfactory Mucosa

How do the different types of olfactory receptors in the olfactory mucosa respond to different odorants? One technique that has helped answer this question is called **calcium imaging**.

METHOD ■ Calcium Imaging

When an olfactory receptor responds, the concentration of calcium ions (Ca^{++}) increases inside the receptor. This calcium can be detected by soaking olfactory neurons in a chemical that causes the receptor to fluoresce with a green glow when exposed to ultraviolet (380 nm) light. The increase in Ca^{++} inside the receptor that occurs in response to an odorant *decreases* this fluorescence. Thus, measuring the decrease in fluorescence indicates how strongly the receptor is activated.

■ ■ ■

Bettina Malnic and coworkers (1999), working in Linda Buck's laboratory, determined the response to a large number of odorants using the calcium imaging technique. The results for a few of her odorants are shown in Figure 15.6, which indicates the receptors that are activated by each odorant. The pattern of this activation for each odorant is called the **recognition profile** of the odorant. For example, the recognition profile of octanoic acid is weak firing of receptor 79 and strong firing of receptors 1, 18, 19, 41, 46, 51, and 83, whereas the profile for octanol is strong firing of receptors 18, 19, 41, and 51.

From these receptor profiles, we can see each odorant causes a different pattern of firing across receptors. Also, odorants like octanoic acid and nonanoic acid, which have

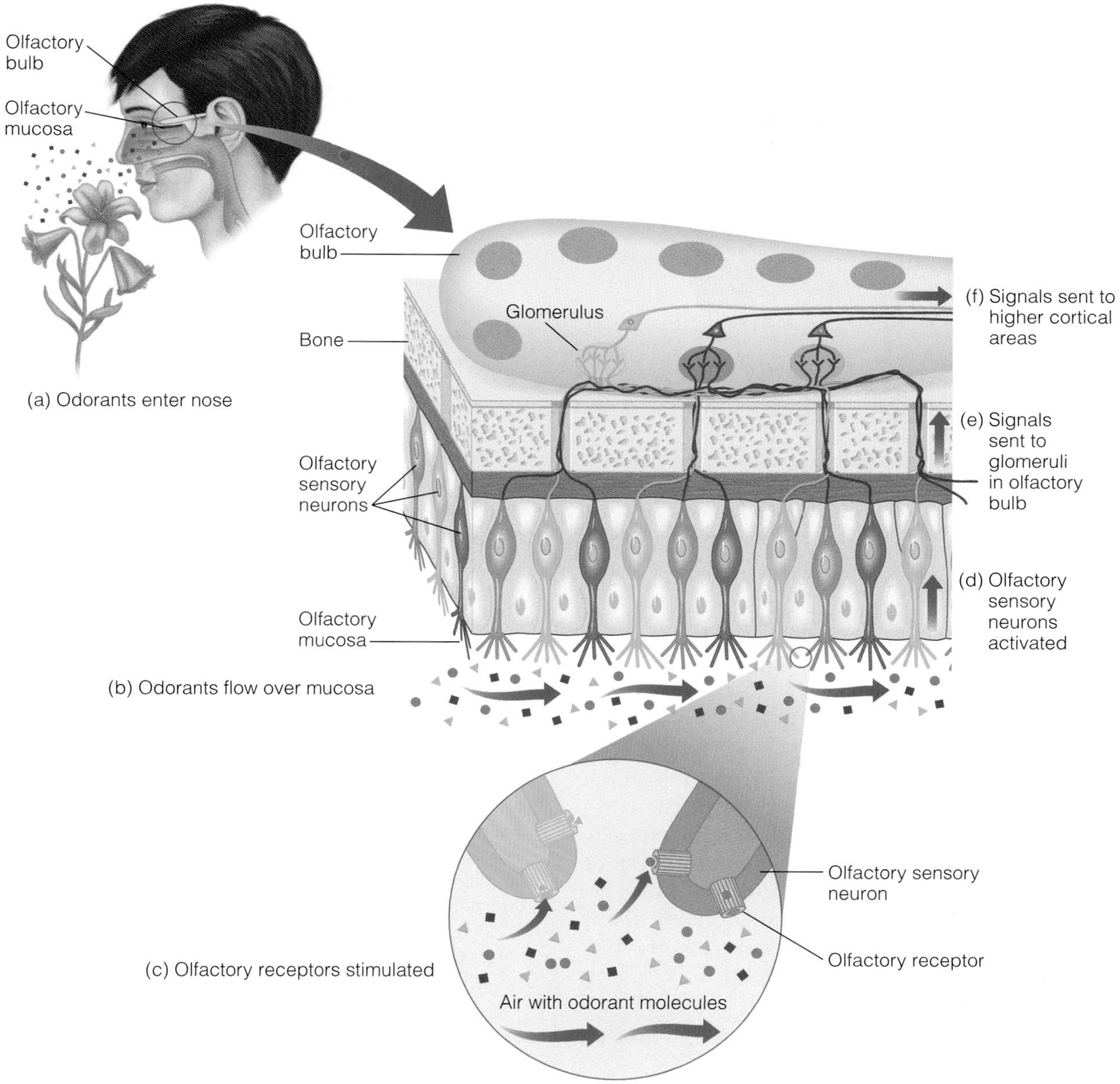

Figure 15.4 ▮ The structure of the olfactory system. See text for details.

similar structures (shown on the right) often have similar profiles. We can also see, however, that this doesn't always occur (compare the patterns for bromohexanoic acid and bromooctanoic acid, which also have similar structures).

Remember that one of the puzzling facts about odor perception is that some molecules have similar structures but smell different (see Figure 15.2a). When Malnic compared such molecules, she found that these molecules had different recognition profiles. For example, octanoic acid and octanol differ only by one oxygen molecule, but the smell of octanol is described as "sweet," "rose," and "fresh," whereas the smell of octanoic acid is described as "rancid," "sour," and "repulsive." This difference in perception is reflected in their different profiles. Although we still can't predict which smells result from specific patterns of response, we do know that when two odorants smell different, they will have different profiles.

The results of these experiments led Malnic and coworkers to propose what they called a **combinatorial code for odor**. In a combinatorial code, different odorants are coded by different combinations of olfactory receptors, but a particular olfactory receptor may participate in the code for many odorants. For example, the top odorant in Figure 15.7 stimulates receptors 1 and 3, and the next odorant activates receptors 3 and 4, so the patterns are different, but receptor 3 is included in the code for both odorants. The beauty of this scheme is that with 350 dif-

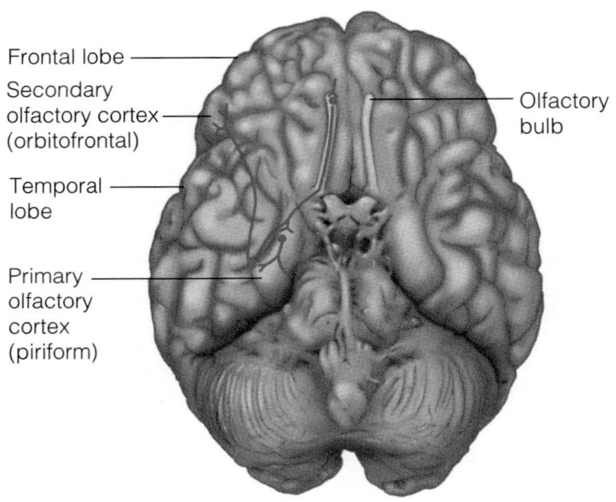

Figure 15.5 ▮ The underside of the brain, showing the neural pathways for olfaction.
(Adapted from "Chemosensory Neuroanatomy and Physiology," by M. E. Frank and M. D. Rabin, 1989, Ear, Nose and Throat Journal, 68.*)*

ferent olfactory receptors, the human olfactory system can create enough combinations to enable us to discriminate among an almost unlimited number of different odorants.

We can compare the combinatorial code for odor to the trichromatic code for color vision that we described in Chapter 7 (see page 147). Remember that each wavelength of light is coded by a different pattern of firing of the three cone pigments, and that a particular cone pigment responds to many wavelengths. The situation for odors is similar—each odorant is coded by a different pattern of firing of olfactory receptors, and a particular olfactory receptor responds to many odorants. What's different about olfaction is that there are over 350 different types of olfactory receptors, compared to just 3 for vision.

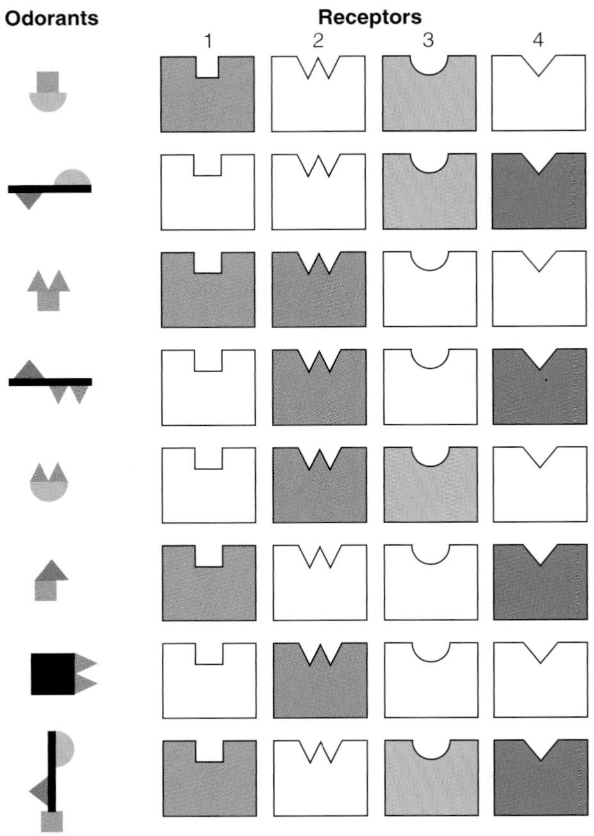

Figure 15.7 ▮ The combinatorial code for odor proposed by Malnic et al. (1999). The receptors that are shown in co or are the ones that respond to the odorant on the left. Notice that each odorant activates a different pattern of receptors, but that a given receptor responds to a number of different odorants.
(Malnic, B., Hirono, J., Sata, T., & Buck, L. B. (1999). Combinctatorial receptor codes for odors. Cell, 96, *713–723.)*

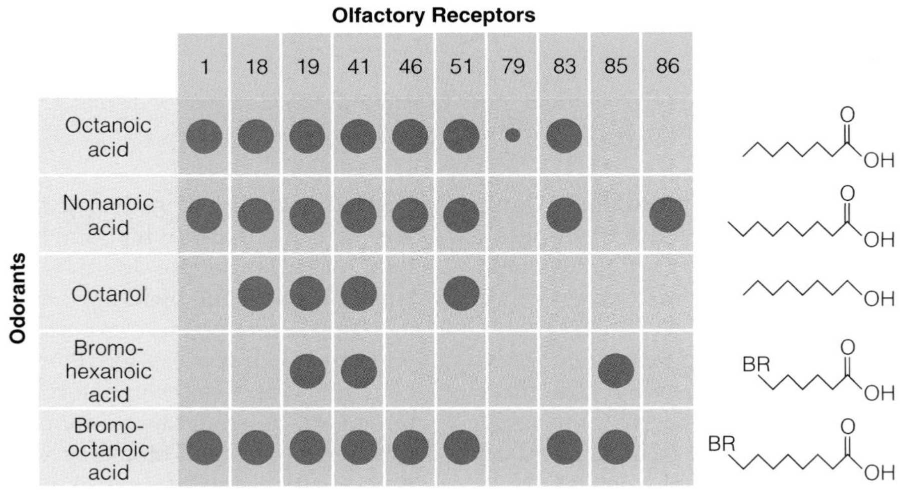

Figure 15.6 ▮ Recognition profiles for some odorants. Large dots indicate that the odorant causes a high firing rate for the receptor listed along the top; small dots indicate lower firing rates for the receptor. The structures of the compounds are shown on the right.
(Adapted from Malnic et al., 1999.)

Activating the Olfactory Bulb

Activation of receptors in the mucosa causes electrical signals in the sensory neurons that are distributed across the mucosa. Figure 15.8 shows that the mucosa is divided into four zones. Each zone contains a number of different types of sensory neurons, but a particular type of sensory neuron is found in only one zone.

When an odorant flows over the olfactory mucosa, the odorant activates a number of different types of olfactory receptors, which, in turn, activate their sensory neurons. A particular odorant usually activates sensory neurons within the same zone. Because there are about 10,000 of each type of sensory neuron, the odorant activates many tens of thousands of these neurons.

Each type of sensory neuron transmits its signals to just one or two glomeruli. This means that the pattern of activation in the olfactory bulb becomes simplified compared to the olfactory mucosa because information from thousands of sensory neurons are collected by just a few glomeruli. Evidence supporting this idea comes from studies that have measured olfactory bulb responding to different chemicals. One of these studies, by Naoshige Uchida and coworkers (2000), used a technique called optical imaging.

METHOD ▪ Optical Imaging

The technique of **optical imaging** can be used to measure the activity of large areas of a structure by measuring how much red light is reflected from the structure. The structure must first be exposed by removing a patch of the skull, so this technique has been used only in animals or in patients undergoing brain surgery. Red light is used because when neurons are activated, they consume oxygen from the blood. Blood that contains less oxygen reflects less red light than blood with oxygen, so areas that have been activated reflect less red light and look slightly darker than areas that have not been activated.

The optical imaging procedure involves illuminating the surface of the structure with red light, measuring how much light is reflected, and then presenting a stimulus to determine which areas become slightly darker. These darker areas are the areas that have been activated by the stimulus.

▪ ▪ ▪

The results of Uchida's optical imaging experiment on the rat are shown in Figure 15.9. Each colored area represents the location of clusters of glomeruli in the olfactory bulb that are activated by the chemicals on the right. Figure 15.9a shows that each type of carboxylic acid activated a small area, and that there is some overlap between areas. Notice that as the length of the carbon chain increases, the area of activation moves to the left. Figure 15.9b shows that a different group of chemicals—aliphatic alcohols—activates a different area of the olfactory bulb and that the same pattern occurs as before: Large chain lengths activate areas farther to the left.

From these results we can conclude that the functional group associated with a particular type of compound (COOH for the acids; OH for the alcohols) determines the general area of the olfactory bulb that is activated, and the compound's chain length determines the position within each area.

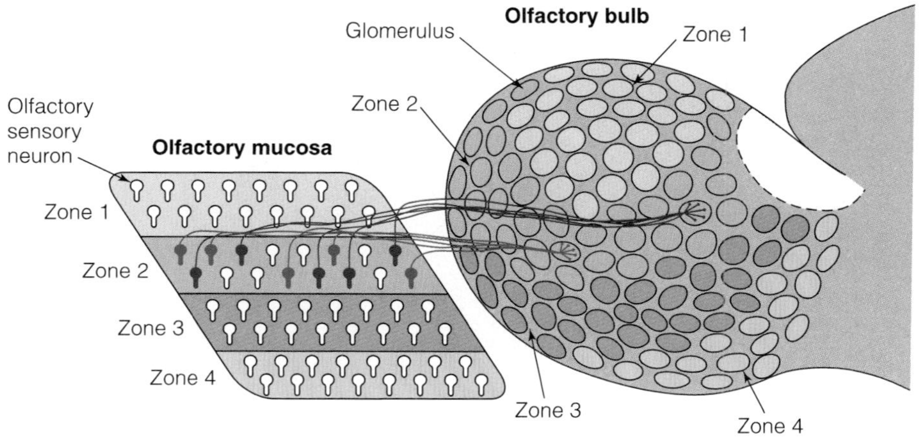

Figure 15.8 ▌ Organization of the olfactory mucosa. The olfactory mucosa, on the left, is divided into four zones. Each zone contains a mixture of different kinds of sensory neurons, as indicated by the red and blue neurons in Zone 2. However, a particular kind of sensory neuron is found only in one zone. The olfactory bulb, on the right, is also divided into zones. Each type of sensory neuron in the olfactory mucosa sends its axons to just one or two glomeruli in the olfactory bulb.
(Adapted from K. Mori, H. Nagao, & Y. Yoshihara (1999). The olfactory bulb: Coding and processing of odor molecule information. Science, 286, *711–715, Fig 2. Reprinted with permission.)*

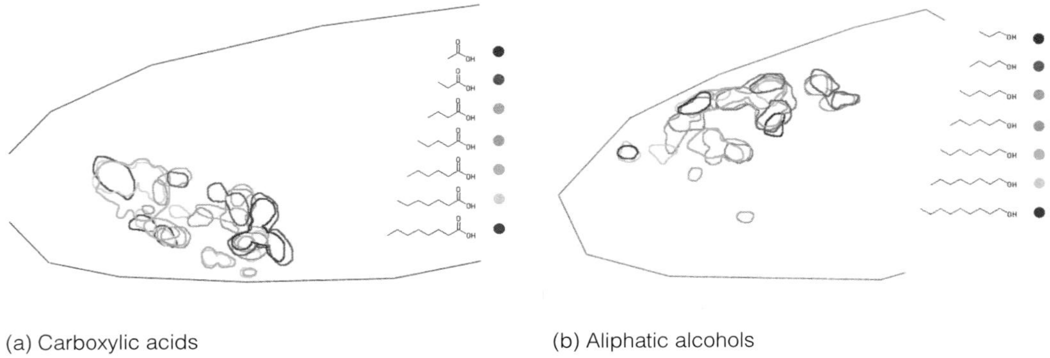

Figure 15.9 ▌ Areas in the rat olfactory bulb that are activated by various chemicals: (a) a series of carbolic acids; (b) a series of aliphatic alcohols.
(Uchida, N., Takahashi, Y. K., Tanifuji, M., & Mori, K. (2000). Odor maps in the mammalian olfactory bulb: Domain organization and odorant structural features. Nature Neuroscience, 3, *1035–1043.)*

Before leaving the olfactory bulb, let's return to a characteristic of odor that we considered for the olfactory receptors—molecules with similar structures can have very different odors. Christiane Linster and coworkers (2001) looked at this phenomenon in the olfactory bulb by studying pairs of molecules that have the same chemical formula, but in which a group within the molecule is rotated to a different position. Figure 15.10a shows two forms of carvone, and Figure 15.10b shows two forms of limonene. Linster studied how these molecules acti-

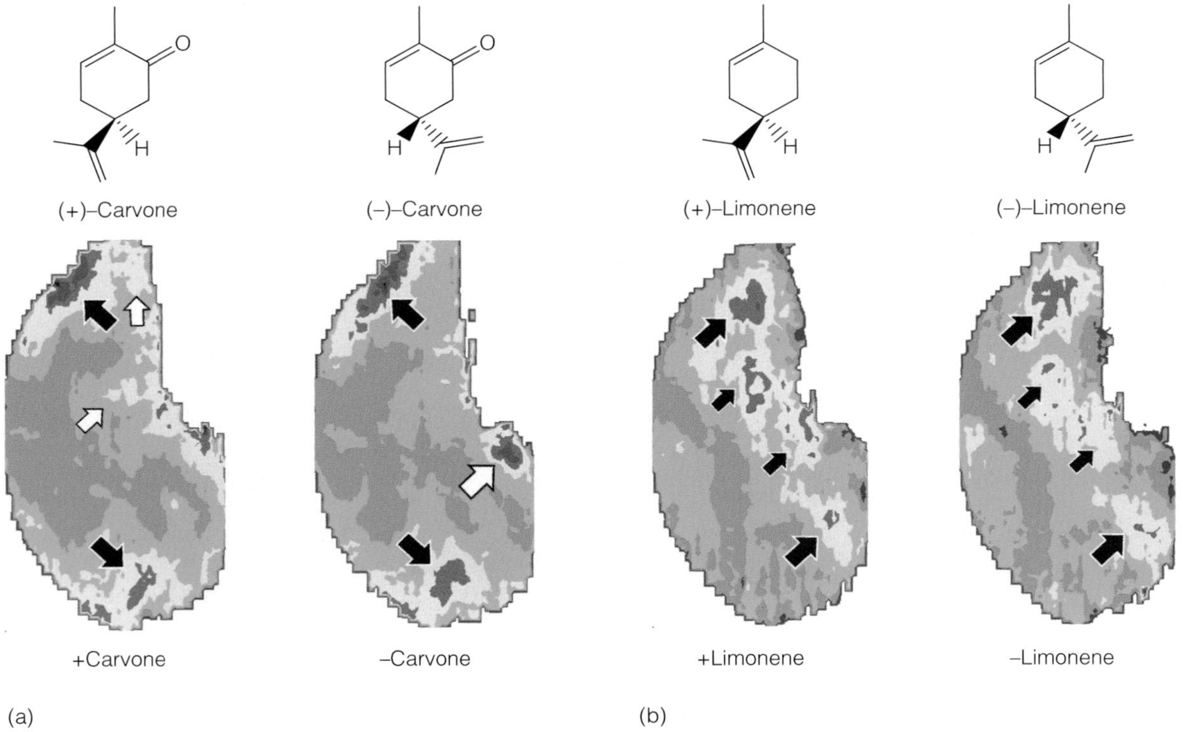

Figure 15.10 ▌ Patterns of activation in the rat olfactory bulb. Red, orange, and yellow indicate high activation. (a) Top: two forms of carvone. These molecules have the same chemical formula, but the molecular group at the bottom is rotated to a different position. Bottom: activation patterns. The black arrows indicate areas activated by both compounds. The white arrows, which indicate areas activated by one compound but not the other, show that the two forms of carvone activate different areas in the olfactory bulb. (b) Top: two forms of limonene. Bottom: activation patterns. The black arrows indicate that the two forms of limonene activate similar areas in the olfactory bulb.
(Linster, C., Johnson, B. A., Yue, E., Morse, A., Xu, Z., Hingco, E. E., Choi, Y., Choi, M., Messiha, A., & Leon, M. (2001). Perceptual correlations of neural representations evoked by odorant enantiomers. Journal of Neuroscience, 21, *9837–9843.)*

vated the olfactory bulb using a technique called the 2-deoxyglucose technique.

METHOD ■ 2-Deoxyglucose Technique

The **2-deoxyglucose technique** involves injecting a radioactive 2-deoxyglucose (2DG) molecule into an animal and exposing the animal to different chemicals. The 2DG contains the sugar glucose, which is taken up by active neurons, so by measuring the amount of radioactivity in the various parts of a structure, we can determine which neurons are most activated by the different chemicals.

■ ■ ■

The patterns of activation in the rat olfactory bulb, determined using the 2DG technique, are shown in Figure 15.10. They indicate that the two forms of carvone have different patterns (the white arrows indicate areas activated by one compound, but not the other), but the two forms of limonene have almost identical patterns. What's important about this result is that behavioral testing of the rats showed that they could tell the difference between the two forms of carvone but could not distinguish between the two forms of limonene. Therefore, the pattern of activation on the OB is related not only to functional groups and structure, but also to the odor that is perceived. Notice that this is similar to Malnic's finding in the olfactory mucosa that molecules with similar structures but different smells have different recognition profiles.

Activating the Cortex

From the olfactory bulb, signals travel to a number of different areas of the cortex. The major area for olfaction is the piriform cortex (Buck, 2004). The way odorants activate the cortex has been determined using a technique called **genetic tracing**.

METHOD ■ Genetic Tracing

This method demonstrates how molecular biological techniques have been used to determine the structure of the olfactory system. Two techniques are involved. First, DNA cloning is used to create cloned mice with a specific receptor. Once the mice with this receptor are created, a tracer molecule is applied to the mucosa. This molecule is called a tracer because it stains the specific receptor that was created by the cloning procedure. The stain is then transferred across synapses to stain the olfactory bulb neurons and cortical neurons that receive signals from the receptor. This sequence of stains therefore "traces" the pathway from receptor to cortex.

■ ■ ■

A group of researchers in Linda Buck's laboratory, headed by Zhihua Zou and Lisa Horowitz (Zou et al., 2001), created two different types of mice. One type had a new receptor in zone 1 of the olfactory mucosa, and another type had a new receptor in zone 4. When Zou and coworkers applied tracers that marked the path from the receptors to the cortex, they found that the pathways from the different receptors led to two different areas of the olfactory bulb (Figure 15.11). However, in the piriform cortex the map was not so precise. Each receptor sent signals to a particular area of the cortex, but the areas activated by the two receptors overlapped. Zou suggests that perhaps this overlap in the cortex, which is different than the separation observed in the olfactory bulb, might be one of the mechanisms involved in perception of more complex odors.

We are just beginning to understand olfactory processing, especially in the cortex. If the olfactory system follows the pattern we observed in the other senses, higher cortical areas will be involved in perception of complex odors. We will see at the end of the chapter that one of

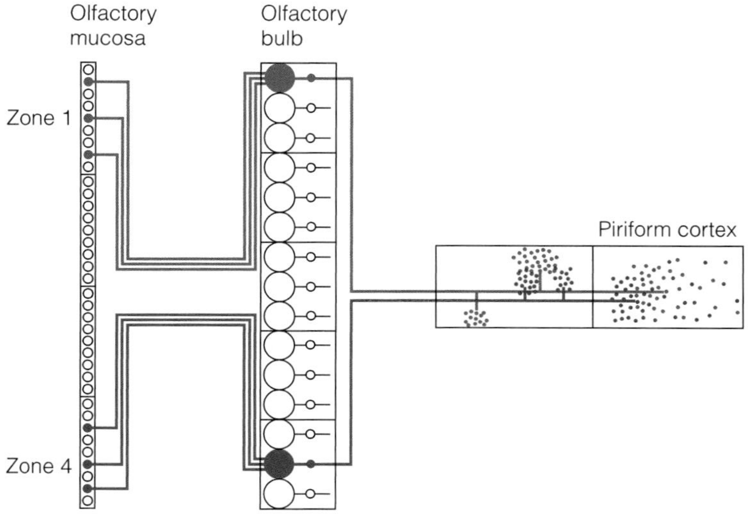

Figure 15.11 ■ The patterns of activation in the olfactory bulb and piriform cortex in a mouse with a new receptor in Zone 1 of the olfactory mucosa, and in a mouse with a new receptor in Zone 4. Activation is indicated by blue for mouse 1 and red for mouse 2. *(Adapted from Zou et al., 2001.)*

these areas is the orbitofrontal cortex, which receives inputs not only for olfaction but for touch, vision, and most important, taste, as well.

TEST YOURSELF 15.1

1. What are some of the functions of odor perception?
2. What is the difference between the detection threshold and recognition threshold? What are some of the factors that need to be taken into account when measuring the detection threshold and the difference threshold?
3. How well can people identify odors? What is the role of memory in odor recognition?
4. Why is it accurate to call odor quality a "puzzle"?
5. Describe the following components of the olfactory system: the olfactory receptors, the olfactory sensory neurons, the olfactory bulb, and the cortex.
6. What is the code for olfactory quality at the level of (a) the olfactory mucosa; (b) the olfactory bulb; and (c) the piriform cortex? Be sure to understand the procedures used to determine the patterns of activation in the olfactory bulb and piriform cortex.

THE TASTE SYSTEM

We will now move from olfaction, which detects molecules that enter the nose in gaseous form, to taste, which detects molecules that enter the mouth in solid or liquid form, usually as components of the foods we eat.

Functions of Taste

At the beginning of this chapter we noted that taste and smell can be thought of as "gatekeepers" that help us determine which substances we should consume and which we should avoid. This is especially true for taste because we often use taste to choose which foods to eat and which to avoid (Breslin, 2001).

Taste accomplishes its gatekeeper function by the connection between taste quality and a substance's effect. Thus, sweetness is often associated with compounds that have nutritive or caloric value, and that are, therefore, important for sustaining life. Sweet compounds cause an automatic acceptance response and also trigger anticipatory metabolic responses that prepares the gastrointestinal system for processing these substances.

Bitter compounds have the opposite effect—they trigger automatic rejection responses to help the organism avoid harmful substances. Examples of harmful substances that taste bitter are the poisons strychnine, arsenic, and cyanide.

Salty tastes often indicate the presence of sodium. When people are deprived of sodium or lose a great deal of sodium due to sweating, they will often seek out foods that taste salty in order to replenish the salt their body needs.

Although there are many examples of connections between a substance's taste and its function in the body, this connection is not perfect. People have often made the mistake of eating good-tasting poisonous mushrooms, and there are artificial sweeteners, such as saccharine and sucralose, that have no metabolic value. There are also bitter foods that are not dangerous and do have metabolic value. People can, however, learn to modify their responses to certain tastes, as when they develop a taste for foods they may have initially found unappealing.

Basic Taste Qualities

When considering taste quality, we are in a much better position than we were for olfaction. Although we have not been able to fit the many olfactory sensations into a small number of categories or qualities, most taste researchers generally describe taste quality in terms of five basic taste sensations: salty, sour, sweet, bitter, and umami (which has been described as meaty, brothy, or savory, and is often associated with the flavor-enhancing properties of MSG, monosodium glutamate).

Early research that supported the idea of basic tastes showed that people can describe most of their taste experiences on the basis of the four basic taste qualities (this research was done before umami became the fifth basic taste). In one study, Donald McBurney (1969) presented taste solutions to participants and asked them to make magnitude estimates of the intensity of each of the four taste qualities. He found that some substances have a predominant taste and that other substances result in combinations of the four tastes. For example, sodium chloride (salty), hydrochloric acid (sour), sucrose (sweet), and quinine (bitter) are compounds that come the closest to having only one of the four basic tastes, but the compound potassium chloride (KCl) has substantial salty and bitter components (Figure 15.12). Similarly, sodium nitrate ($NaNO_3$) results in a taste consisting of a combination of salty, sour, and bitter.

Results such as these have led most researchers to accept the idea of basic tastes. As you will see in our discussion of the code for taste quality, most of the research on this problem takes the idea of basic tastes as the starting point. (Although see Erickson, 2000, for some arguments against the idea of basic tastes.)

THE NEURAL CODE FOR TASTE QUALITY

One of the central questions in taste research has been identification of the physiological code for taste quality. We will first describe the structure of the taste system, and

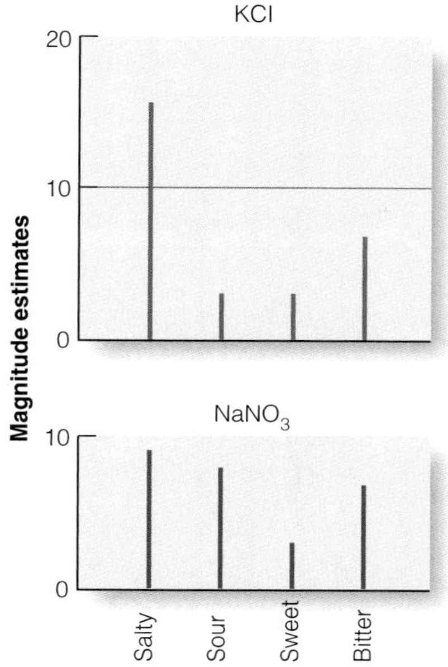

Figure 15.12 ▌ The contribution of each of the four basic tastes to the tastes of KCl and $NaNO_3$, determined by the method of magnitude estimation. The height of the line indicates the size of the magnitude estimate for each basic taste.
(From McBurney, 1969.)

then we will describe two proposals regarding how taste quality is coded in this system.

Structure of the Taste System

The process of tasting begins with the tongue (Figure 15.13a and Table 15.2), when receptors are stimulated by taste stimuli. The surface of the tongue contains many ridges and valleys due to the presence of structures called **papillae**, which fall into four categories: (1) filiform papillae, which are shaped like cones and are found over the entire surface of the tongue, giving it its rough appearance; (2) fungiform papillae, which are shaped like mushrooms and are found at the tip and sides of the tongue; (3) foliate papillae, which are a series of folds along the back of the tongue on the sides; and (4) circumvallate papillae, which are shaped like flat mounds surrounded by a trench and are found at the back of the tongue (see also Figure 15.14). VL 2

All of the papillae except the filiform papillae contain **taste buds** (Figure 15.13b and c), and the whole tongue contains about 10,000 taste buds (Bartoshuk, 1971). Because the filiform papillae contain no taste buds, stimulation of the central part of the tongue, which contains only these papillae, causes no taste sensations. However, stimulation of the back or perimeter of the tongue results in a broad range of taste sensations.

Each taste bud (Figure 15.13c) contains 50–100 of **taste cells**, which have tips that protrude into the **taste pore** (Figure 15.13d). Transduction occurs when chemicals contact **receptor sites** located on the tips of these taste cells (Figure 15.13e). Electrical signals generated in the taste cells are transmitted from the tongue in a number of different nerves: (1) the **chorda tympani nerve** (from taste cells on the front and sides of the tongue); (2) the **glossopharyngeal nerve** (from the back of the tongue); (3) the **vagus nerve** (from the mouth and throat); and (4) the **superficial petronasal nerve** (from the soft palette—the top of the mouth).

Figure 15.15 shows that fibers from the tongue, mouth, and throat make connections in the brain stem in the **nucleus of the solitary tract**, and from there signals travel to the thalamus and then to two areas in the frontal lobe—the **insula** and the **frontal operculum cortex**—that are partially hidden behind the temporal lobe (Finger, 1987; Frank & Rabin, 1989). In addition, fibers serving the taste system also reach the orbital frontal cortex (OFC), which also receives olfactory signals (Rolls, 2000; see Figure 15.5).

Distributed Coding

In Chapter 3 we introduced the idea of sensory coding, and we distinguished between two types: *specificity coding,* the idea that quality is signaled by the activity in neurons that are tuned to respond to specific qualities; and *distributed coding,* the idea that quality is signaled by the pattern of activity distributed across many neurons. In that discussion, and in others throughout the book, we have generally favored distributed coding. The situation for taste, however, is not clear-cut, and there are arguments in favor of both types of coding.

Let's consider some evidence for distributed coding. Robert Erickson (1963) conducted one of the first experiments that demonstrated this type of coding by presenting a number of different taste stimuli to a rat's tongue and recording the response of the chorda tympani nerve. Figure 15.16 shows how 13 nerve fibers responded to ammonium chloride (NH_4Cl), potassium chloride (KCl), and sodium chloride (NaCl). Erickson called these patterns the **across-fiber patterns**, which is another name for distributed coding. The red and green lines show that the across-fiber patterns for ammonium chloride and potassium chloride are similar to each other but are different from the pattern for sodium chloride, indicated by the open circles.

Erickson reasoned that if the rat's perception of taste quality depends on the across-fiber pattern, then two substances with similar patterns should taste similar. Thus, the electrophysiological results would predict that ammonium chloride and potassium chloride should taste similar and that both should taste different from sodium chloride. To test this hypothesis, Erickson shocked rats while they were drinking potassium chloride and then gave them a choice between ammonium chloride and sodium chloride. If potassium chloride and ammonium chloride taste similar, the rats should avoid the ammonium chloride when given a choice. This is exactly what they did. And when the rats were shocked for drinking

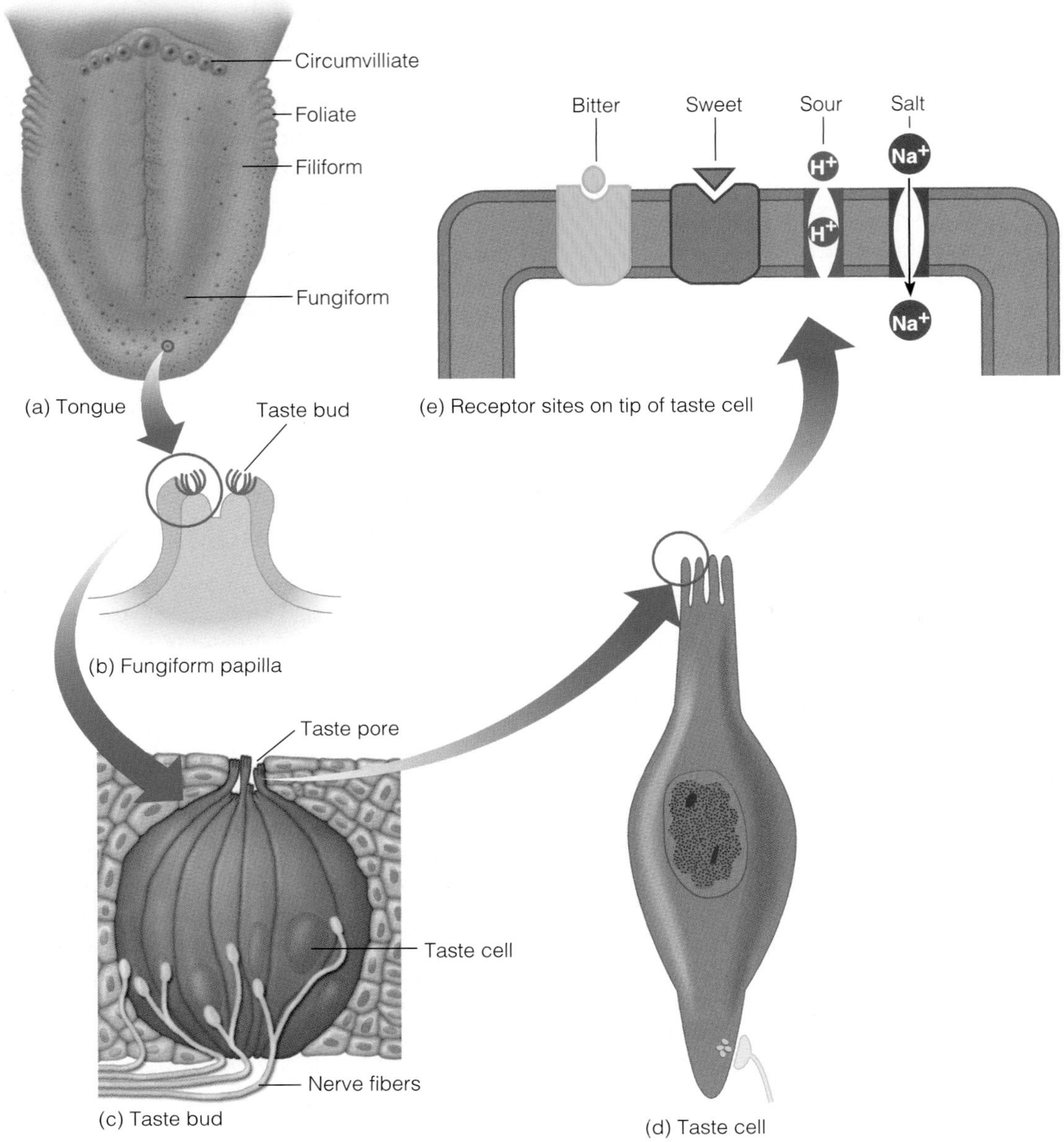

Figure 15.13 ▮ (a) The tongue, showing the four different types of papillae. (b) A fungiform papilla on the tongue; each papilla contains a number of taste buds. (c) Cross section of a taste bud showing the taste pore where the taste stimulus enters. (d) The taste cell; the tip of the taste cell is positioned just under the pore. (e) Close-up of the membrane at the tip of the taste cell, showing the receptor sites for bitter, sour, salty, and sweet substances. Stimulation of these receptor sites, as described in the text, triggers a number of different reactions within the cell (not shown) that lead to movement of charged molecules across the membrane, which creates an electrical signal in the taste cell.

ammonium chloride, they subsequently avoided the potassium chloride, as predicted by the electrophysiological results.

But what about the perception of taste in humans? When Susan Schiffman and Robert Erickson (1971) asked humans to make similarity judgments between a number of different solutions, they found that substances that were perceived to be similar were related to patterns of firing for these same substances in the rat. Solutions judged more similar psychophysically had similar patterns of firing, as distributed coding would predict.

Specificity Coding

Most of the evidence for specificity coding has been obtained from research that has focused on the taste receptors and recording neural activity early in the taste system. We begin at the receptors by describing research that

Table 15.2 ▌ *Structures in the taste system*

Structures	Description
Tongue	The receptor sheet for taste. Contains papillae and all of the other structures described below.
Papillae	The structures that give the tongue its rough appearance. There are four kinds, each with a different shape.
Taste buds	Contained on the papillae. There are about 10,000 taste buds.
Taste cells	Cells that make up a taste bud. There are a number of cells for each bud, and the tip of each one sticks out into a taste pore. One or more nerve fibers are associated with each cell.
Receptor sites	Sites located on the tips of the taste cells. There are different types of sites for different chemicals. Chemicals contacting the sites cause transduction by affecting ion flow across the membrane of the taste cell.

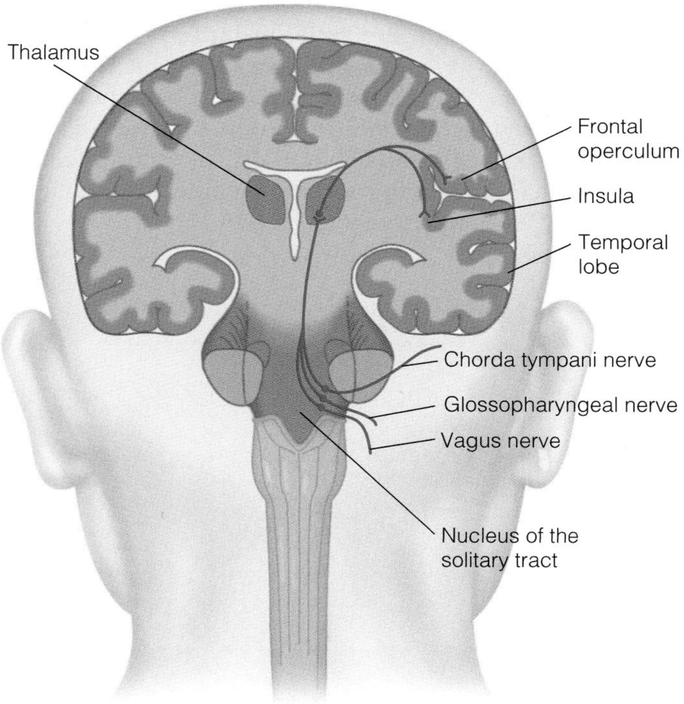

Figure 15.15 ▌ The central pathway for taste signals, showing the nucleus of the solitary tract (NST), where nerve fibers from the tongue and the mouth synapse in the medulla at the base of the brain. From the NST, these fibers synapse in the thalamus and the frontal lobe of the brain.
(From Frank & Rabin, 1989.)

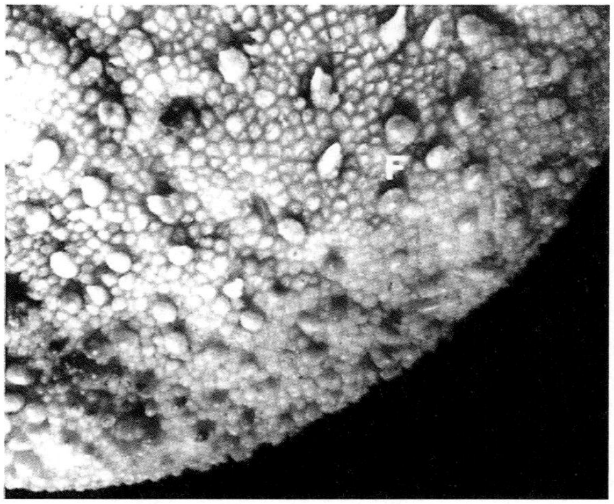

Figure 15.14 ▌ The surface of the tongue, showing fungiform (F) papillae.
(From Miller, I. J. (1995). Anatomy of the peripheral taste system. In R. L. Doty (Ed.), Handbook of Olfaction and Gustation *(pp. 521–548). New York: Marcel Dekker.)*

has used genetic procedures like those we described for olfaction. These experiments have revealed receptors for sweet, bitter, and umami that are protein strings that cross the taste receptor membrane seven times, just like olfactory and visual receptor molecules.

The evidence supporting the idea that these receptors respond specifically to a particular taste has been obtained by using genetic cloning to add or eliminate specific receptors in mice. Ken Mueller and coworkers (2005) did a series of experiments using a chemical compound called PTC that tastes bitter to humans but is not bitter to mice. The lack of bitter PTC taste in mice is inferred by the fact that mice do not avoid even high concentrations of

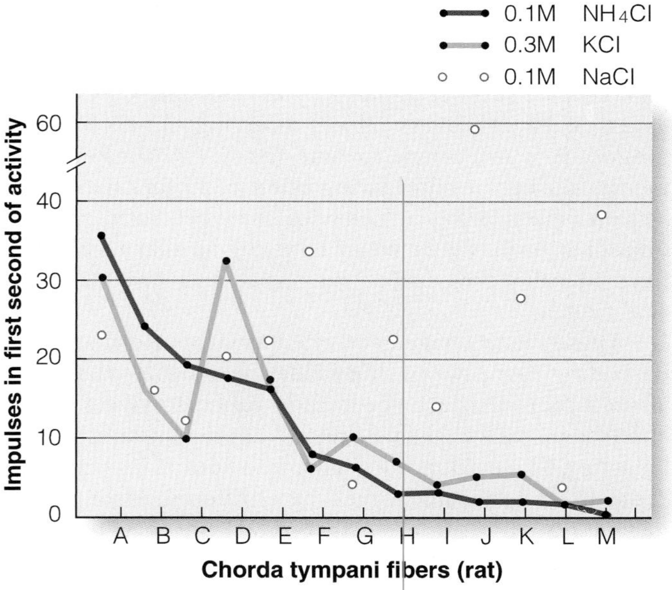

Figure 15.16 ▌ Across-fiber patterns of the response of fibers in the rat's chorda tympani nerve to three salts. Each letter on the horizontal axis indicates a different single fiber.
(From "Sensory Neural Patterns and Gustation," by R. Erickson, 1963. In Y. Zotterman (Ed.), Olfaction and Taste, *Vol. 1, pp. 205–213, figure 4. Copyright © 1963 by Pergamon Press, Ltd. Reprinted by permission.)*

PTC in behavioral tests (blue line in Figure 15.17). Because a specific receptor in the family of bitter receptors had been identified as being responsible for the bitter taste of PTC in humans, Mueller decided to see what would happen if he used genetic cloning techniques to create a strain of mice that had this human bitter-PTC receptor. When he did this, the mice with this receptor avoided high concentrations of PTC (red curve in Figure 15.17).

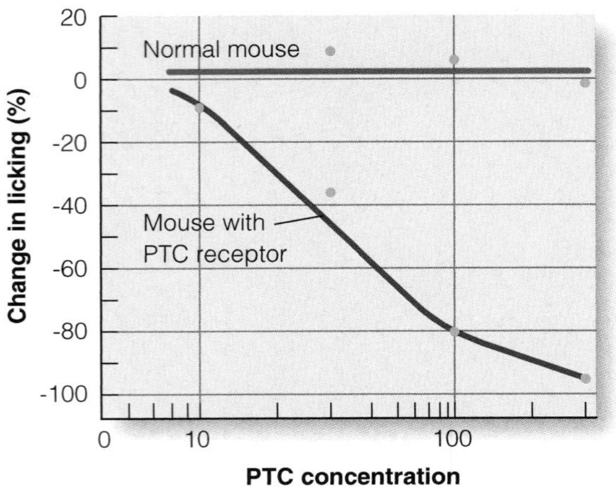

Figure 15.17 ▮ Mouse behavioral response to PTC. The blue curve indicates that a normal mouse will drink PTC even in high concentrations. The red curve indicates that a mouse that has a human bitter-PTC receptor avoids PTC, especially at high concentrations.
(Adapted from Mueller et al., 2005.)

In another experiment, Mueller created a strain of mice that *lacked* a bitter receptor that responds to a compound called cyclohexamide (Cyx). Mice normally have this receptor, and they avoid Cyx. But the mice lacking this receptor did not avoid Cyx. In addition, Cyx no longer caused any firing in nerves receiving signals from the tongue. It is important to note that in all these experiments, adding or eliminating bitter receptors had no effect on neural firing or behavior to sweet, sour, salty, or umami stimuli. Other research using similar techniques have identified receptors for sugar and umami (Zhao et al., 2003).

These results have been cited as support for specificity coding. Simply put, the evidence indicates that there are receptors that are specifically tuned to sweet, bitter, and umami tastes that are linked both to neural firing and behavior. The evidence for salty and sour is less clear because these tastes are served by a different taste mechanism. Salty and sour are called ionic tastes because these compounds act directly on the taste cell membrane to change the flow of sodium ions (Na^+) across the membrane for salty tastes and hydrogen ions (H^+) for "acid" or sour tastes (see Lyall et al., 2004).

Another line of evidence for specificity coding in taste has come from research on how single neurons respond to taste stimuli. For example, Figure 15.18 shows that 66 fibers in the monkey's chorda tympani responded to four substances, each representing one of the basic tastes: sucrose (sweet); salt (NaCl, salty); hydrogen chloride (HCl, sour); and quinine (bitter; Sato et al., 1994). We can see that some fibers responded well to sucrose but poorly to almost all other compounds. For example, look at fiber 5's responses to each substance by following the dashed line across the record for each substance. Fibers 1 to 16 are called sucrose-best because they respond best to sucrose. A similar situation exists for the quinine-best fibers (numbers 56–66), most of which respond only to quinine. The NaCl- and HCl-best fibers fire predominantly to one solution, but some fire to both NaCl and HCl (also see Frank, Bieber, & Smith, 1988, for similar results in the hamster).

Another finding in line with specificity theory is the effect of presenting a substance called **amiloride**, which blocks the flow of sodium into taste receptors. Applying amiloride to the tongue causes a decrease in the responding of neurons in the rat's brainstem (nucleus of the solitary tract) that respond best to salt (Figure 15.19a) but has little effect on neurons that respond best to a combination of salty and bitter tastes (Figure 15.19b; Scott & Giza, 1990). Thus, eliminating the flow of sodium across the membrane selectively eliminates responding of salt-best neurons, but does not affect the response of neurons that respond best to other tastes. As it turns out, the sodium channel that is blocked by amiloride is important for determining saltiness in rats and other animals, but not in humans. Recent research has identified another channel that serves the salty taste in humans (Lyall et al., 2004, 2005).

What does all of this mean? With the discovery of specific receptor mechanisms for bitter, sour, and umami, the balance in the distributed vs. specificity argument appears to be shifting toward specificity. However, the issue is still not settled, especially because the research on specific taste receptors is so recent. More research needs to be done on salty and sour tastes to determine whether or not these are also governed by specific mechanisms. David Smith and Thomas Scott (2003) argue for distributed coding based on the finding that at more central locations in the taste system, neurons are tuned broadly, with many neurons responding to a more than one taste quality.

Smith and coworkers (2000) point out that just because there are neurons that might respond best to one compound like salty or sour, this doesn't mean that these tastes are signaled by just one type of neuron. They illustrate this by drawing an analogy between taste perception and the mechanism for color vision. Even though presenting a long-wavelength light that appears red may cause the highest activation in the long-wavelength cone pigment (Figure 7.9), our perception of red still depends on the combined response of both the long- and medium-wavelength pigments. Similarly, salt stimuli may cause high firing rates in neurons that respond best to salt, but other neurons are probably also involved in creating saltiness as well.

Because of arguments such as this, some researchers

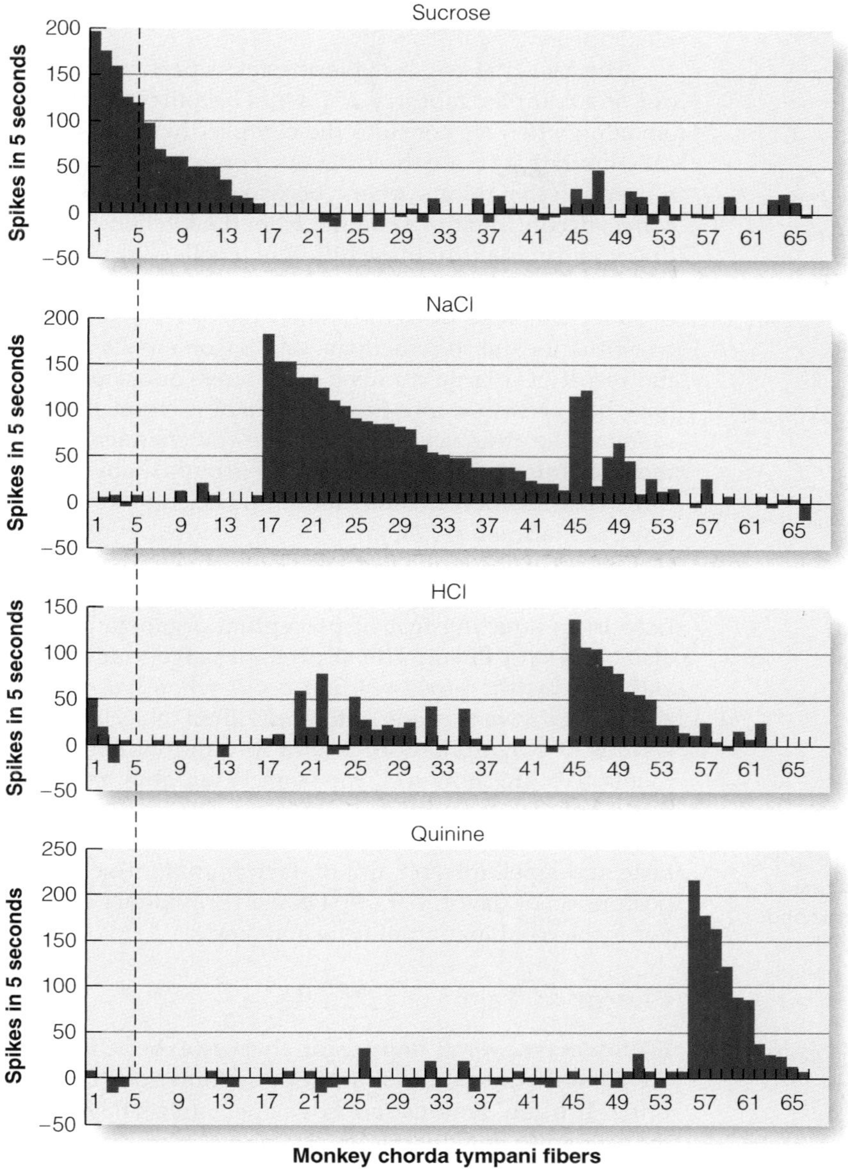

Figure 15.18 ▮ Responses of 66 different fibers in the monkey's chorda tympani nerve to four types of stimuli: sucrose (sweet); sodium chloride (salty); hydrogen chloride (sour); and quinine (bitter). To determine the response of a particular fiber, pick its number and note the height of the bars for each compound. For example, fiber 5 (dashed line) fired well to sucrose but didn't fire to any of the other compounds. Fiber 5 is therefore called a *sucrose-best fiber.*

(Adapted from "Neural Coding of Taste in Macaque Monkeys," by M. Sato and H. Ogawa, 1993. In K. Kurihara, N. Suzuki, & H. Ogawa (Eds.), Olfaction and Taste XI, *p. 398. Copyright © 1993 by Springer-Verlag. Adapted by permission.)*

believe that even though there is good evidence for specific taste receptors, distributed coding is involved in determining taste as well, especially at higher levels of the system. One suggestion is that basic taste qualities could be determined by a specific code, but distributed coding could determine subtle differences between tastes within a category (Pfaffmann, 1974; Scott & Plata-Salaman, 1991). This would help explain why not all substances in a particular category have the same taste. For example, the taste of all sweet substances is not identical (Lawless, 2001).

THE PERCEPTION OF FLAVOR

Our society is obsessed with the taste of food, as evidenced by the numerous cooking shows on TV, shelves of cookbooks at bookstores, and restaurants whose reputations are made or broken based on the taste of the food they serve. Most people look forward to eating not because it is necessary for survival but because of the pleasure it brings. Consider, for example, how Ruth Reichl (1994), then the *New York Times* food critic and currently editor of *Gourmet* magazine, describes her experience at a four-star restaurant:

> It is a surprise to dip your spoon into this mild-mannered soup and experience an explosion of flavor. Mushroom is at the base of the taste sensation, but it is haunted by citric tones—lemongrass, lime perhaps—and high at the top, a resonant note of sweetness. What is it? No single flavor ever dominates a dish. At first you find yourself searching for flavors in this complex tapestry, fascinated by the way they are woven together. In the end, you just give in and allow

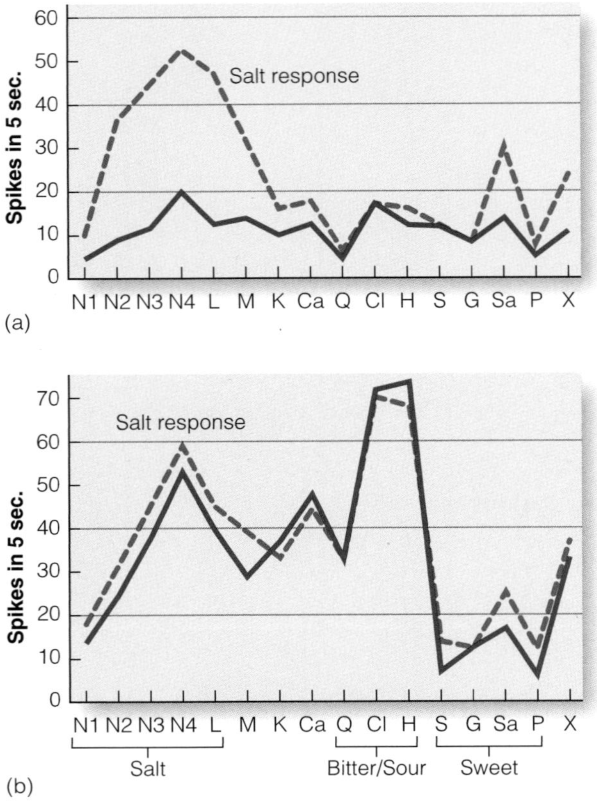

Figure 15.19 ▮ The blue lines show how two neurons in the rat NST respond to a number of different taste stimuli (along the horizontal axis). The neuron in (a) responds strongly to compounds associated with salty tastes. The neuron in (b) responds to a wide range of compounds. The red lines show how these two neurons fire after the sodium-blocker amiloride is applied to the tongue. This compound inhibits the responses to salt of neuron (a) but has little effect on neuron (b).
(Adapted from "Coding Channels in the Taste System of the Rat," by T. R. Scott and B. K. Giza, 1990, Science, 249, 1585–1587, figure 1. Copyright ©1990 by the American Association for the Advancement of Science. Adapted by permission.)

yourself to be seduced. Each meal is a roller coaster of sensations.

Reichl's description captures not only her enjoyment but also the complexity of some of the aspects of perceiving the flavors of food. Notice that she opens the review by commenting on the food's "flavor." What most people refer to as "taste" when describing their experience of food ("That tastes good, Mom") is usually a combination of taste, from stimulation of the receptors in the tongue, and smell, from stimulation of the receptors in the olfactory mucosa. This combination of taste and smell, as well as other sensations—such as those caused by the burning of hot peppers—is called flavor. Another thing Reichl captures in her review is the complexity of the perceptions created by foods. We are usually dealing with not just one or two different flavors, but many, and, as Reichl points out, the flavors often are contained within a "complex tapestry."

The fact that we are able to pick a particular flavor out of a complex tapestry of flavors becomes even more amazing when we consider the complexity of the chemical stimuli that create these flavors. For example, consider a situation that occurs when you wake up to the smells of coffee, bacon, and toast coming from the kitchen. The fact that you can identify these different smells may not seem particularly surprising until we recognize that the smell of coffee can arise from more than 100 different chemical constituents and that the toast and bacon smells are also the result of a large number of different molecules that have been released into the air. Somehow, your olfactory system takes this vast array of airborne chemicals, with their various physical qualities, and groups them into the three classifications: coffee, toast, and bacon (Bartoshuk, Cain, & Pfaffmann, 1985).

This creation of the perception of coffee, toast, and bacon that occurs when hundreds of chemicals enter the nose is an amazing feat of perceptual organization that also occurs for flavor. This process of perceptual organization rivals the processes that occur when we separate a complex visual scene into individual objects or the sounds of a symphony orchestra into individual instruments. We are, however, far from being able to understand how we accomplish this feat for flavor. Most of the basic research on flavor has focused on showing how taste and smell interact and on factors that influence our perception of flavor. Let's first consider evidence that flavor is the combination of taste and smell.

Flavor = Taste + Olfaction

Flavor is the overall impression that we experience from the combination of nasal and oral stimulation (Lawless, 2001). You can demonstrate how smell affects flavor with the following demonstration.

DEMONSTRATION

"Tasting" With and Without the Nose

While pinching your nostrils shut, drink a beverage with a distinctive taste, such as grape juice, cranberry juice, or coffee. Notice both the quality and the intensity of the taste as you are drinking it. (Take just one or two swallows because swallowing with your nostrils closed can cause a buildup of pressure in your ears.) After one of the swallows, open your nostrils, and notice whether you perceive a flavor. Finally, drink the beverage normally with nostrils open, and notice the flavor. You can also do this demonstration with fruits or cooked foods. ■

During this demonstration you probably noticed that when your nostrils were closed, it was difficult to identify the substance you were drinking or eating, but as soon as you opened your nostrils, the flavor became obvious. This occurred because odor stimuli from the food reached the olfactory mucosa by following the **retronasal route**, from the mouth through the **nasal pharynx**, the passage that connects the oral and nasal cavities (Figure 15.20). Although pinching the nostrils shut does not close the nasal pharynx, it prevents vapors from reaching the olfactory receptors by eliminating the circulation of air through this channel (Murphy & Cain, 1980).

The importance of olfaction in the sensing of flavor has been demonstrated experimentally by using both chemical solutions and typical foods. In general, solutions are more difficult to identify when the nostrils are pinched shut (Mozell et al., 1969), and are often judged to be tasteless. For example, Figure 15.21a shows that the chemical sodium oleate has a strong soapy flavor when the nostrils are open but was judged tasteless when they were closed. Similarly, ferrous sulfate (Figure 15.21b) normally has a metallic flavor but is judged predominantly tasteless when the nostrils are closed (Hettinger et al., 1990). However, some compounds are not influenced by olfaction. For example, monosodium glutamate (MSG) has about the same flavor whether or not the nose is clamped (Figure 15.21c). Thus, in this case, the sense of taste predominates.

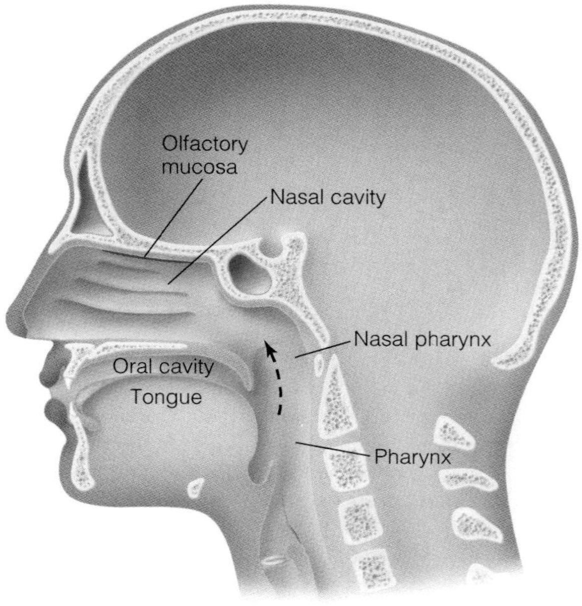

Figure 15.20 ▌ Odorant molecules released by food in the oral cavity and pharynx can travel through the nasal pharynx (dashed arrow) to the olfactory mucosa in the nasal cavity. This is the retronasal route to the olfactory receptors.

The results of these experiments indicate that many of the sensations that we call taste, and that we assume are caused only by stimulation of the tongue, are greatly influenced by stimulation of the olfactory receptors. Apparently, we often mislocate the source of our sensations as being in the mouth, partially because the stimuli physically enter the mouth and partially because we experience the tactile sensations associated with chewing and swallowing (Murphy & Cain, 1980; Rozin, 1982).

The Physiology of Flavor Perception

A number of cortical areas that serve both taste and olfaction are probably involved in the perception of the flavor of food. Presently, however, most of the work on the cortical response to food has focused not on the primary olfactory cortex, but on the orbital frontal cortex (OFC), because it is here that responses from taste and smell are first combined.

The OFC receives inputs from the primary cortical areas for taste and olfaction, plus from the primary somato-

	Sodium oleate (a)		Ferrous sulfate (b)		MSG (c)	
	Clamped	Open	Clamped	Open	Clamped	Open
Sweet	x		x			
Salty	x				xxxxxxxxx	xxxxxxxx
Sour			xx	x	xxx	xxx
Bitter		x	x		xx	x
Soapy	xx	xxxxxxxxx	x	xx		
Metallic		xx	x	xxxxxxxxx		
Sulfurous				x	x	xx
Tasteless	xxxxxxxx		xxxxxx	x		
Other	x	x	x		x	xxx

Figure 15.21 ▌ How people described the flavors of three different compounds when they tasted them with nostrils clamped shut and with nostrils open. Each X represents the judgment of one person.
(Adapted from "Role of Olfaction in Perception of Non-Traditional 'Taste' Stimuli," by T. P. Hettinger, W. E. Myers & M. E. Frank, 1990, Chemical Senses, 15, *755–760, fig. 2. Copyright © 1990 by Oxford University Press. Adapted by permission of Oxford University Press, UK.)*

sensory cortex and from the inferotemporal cortex in the visual *what* pathway (Rolls, 2000; Figure 15.22). Because of this convergence of neurons from different senses, the OFC contains many **bimodal neurons,** those that respond to more than one sense. For example, some bimodal neurons respond to both taste and smell, and other neurons respond to taste and vision.

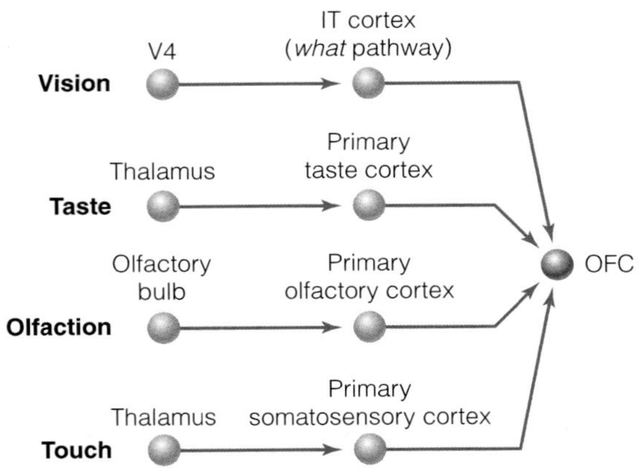

Figure 15.22 ▮ The orbital frontal cortex (OFC) receives inputs from vision, taste, olfaction, and touch, as shown. It is the first area where signals from the taste and smell systems meet. *(Adapted from E. T. Rolls (2000). The orbitofrontal cortex and reward.* Cerebral Cortex, *10, 284–294, Fig. 2. Reprinted with permission from Oxford University Press.)*

An important property of these bimodal neurons is that they often respond to similar qualities. Thus, a cell that responds to the taste of sweet fruits would also respond to the smell of these fruits. Because of these properties, and the fact that the OFC is the first place where taste and smell information is combined, it has been suggested that the OFC is a cortical center for detecting flavor and for the perceptual representation of foods (Rolls & Baylis, 1994).

But there is also another reason to think that the OFC is important for flavor perception: Unlike neurons in the primary taste area, which are not affected by hunger, the firing of neurons in the OFC reflects the extent to which an animal will consume a particular food. Figure 15.23 shows how neurons in the monkey's OFC respond before and after ingesting dairy cream. The top graph shows that this neuron fires at about 10 spikes per second to the odor of dairy cream, and that the response had decreased to 3 spikes per second (the level of spontaneous activity) after 50 ml of the cream had been consumed. The bottom graph shows the monkey's behavioral reaction to presentation of the cream. At the beginning of the experiment, the monkey enthusiastically licked the feeding tube to receive the solution, but at the end it rejected the solution and tried to push it away. Thus, as the monkey's hunger for the cream decreased, the firing of the cell to the cream's odor decreased as well. What this means, according to Edmund Rolls (2004), is that the response of neurons in the OFC are essentially reflecting the pleasantness of flavors, and in doing so, help control food intake.

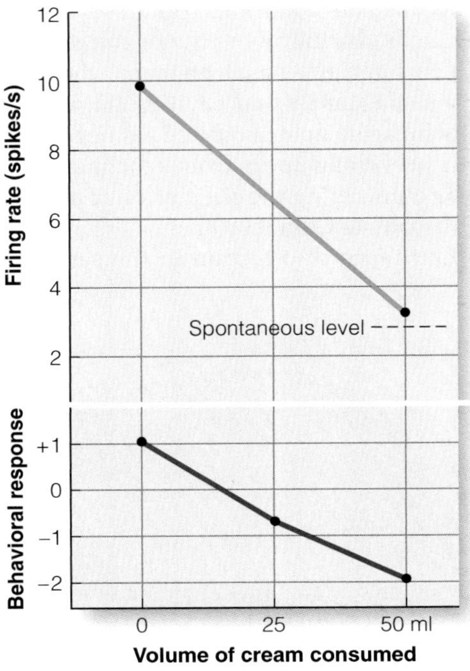

Figure 15.23 ▮ How consuming dairy cream affects the firing rate of neurons in the monkey's OFC (top panel) and the monkey's response to the cream (bottom panel). Consuming the cream causes a decrease in the neuron's response to the cream, but not to other substances (not shown). It also causes the monkey to become less interested in drinking the cream, and eventually to actively reject it.
(Adapted from Critchley & Rolls, 1996.)

SOMETHING TO CONSIDER: INDIVIDUAL DIFFERENCES IN TASTING

Although most people describe their taste preferences in terms of four basic qualities, there are genetic differences that affect people's ability to sense the taste of certain substances. One of the best-documented effects involves people's ability to taste the bitter substance phenylthiocarbamide (PTC), which we discussed earlier. Linda Bartoshuk (1980) describes the discovery of this PTC effect:

> The different reactions to PTC were discovered accidentally in 1932 by Arthur L. Fox, a chemist working at the E. I. DuPont deNemours Company in Wilmington, Delaware. Fox had prepared some PTC, and when he poured the compound into a bottle, some of the dust escaped into the air. One of his colleagues complained about the bitter taste of the dust, but Fox, much closer to the material, noticed nothing. Albert F. Blakeslee,

an eminent geneticist of the era, was quick to pursue this observation. At a meeting of the American Association for the Advancement of Science (AAAS) in 1934, Blakeslee prepared an exhibit that dispensed PTC crystals to 2,500 of the conferees. The results: 28 percent of them described it as tasteless, 66 percent as bitter, and 6 percent as having some other taste. (p. 55)

People who can taste PTC are described as **tasters**, and those who cannot are called **nontasters**. Recently, additional experiments have been done with a substance called 6-*n*-propylthiouracil, or PROP, which has properties similar to those of PTC (Lawless, 1980, 2001). Researchers have found that about one-third of Americans report that PROP is tasteless and that two-thirds can taste it.

What causes these differences in people's ability to taste PROP? One reason is that people have different numbers of taste buds on the tongue. Linda Bartoshuk used a technique called **video microscopy** to count the taste buds on people's tongues that contain the receptors for tasting (Bartoshuk & Beauchamp, 1994). The key result of this study was that people who could taste PROP had higher densities of taste buds than those who couldn't taste it (Figure 15.24).

But the results of an experiment by Jeannine Delwiche and coworkers (2001b) show that the density of taste buds alone cannot explain high sensitivity to PROP. After confirming that PROP-tasters do have a higher density of papillae than nontasters, they devised a system for stimulating the same number of papillae in tasters and nontasters. They accomplished this by presenting stimuli to smaller areas of the tongue for the tasters. When participants rated the bitterness of PROP, the tasters' ratings were much higher than nontasters' ratings, even when the same number of papillae were stimulated.

Apparently, in addition to receptor density, the types of receptors present are also involved in determining individual differences in taste. Genetic studies have shown that PROP and PTC tasters have specialized receptors that are absent in nontasters (Bufe et al., 2005; Kim et al., 2003). Thus, just as we saw that color perception is affected by the presence or absence of different types of cone receptors (see p. 152), people might taste substances differently because of differences in the types of taste receptors.

What does this mean for everyday taste experience? If PROP tasters also perceived other compounds as being more bitter than nontasters, this would indicate that perhaps certain foods would taste more bitter to the tasters. The evidence on this question has, however, been mixed. Some studies have reported differences between how tasters and nontasters rate the bitterness of other compounds (Bartoshuk, 1979; Hall et al., 1975), and others have not observed this difference (Delwiche et al., 2001b). However, it does appear that people who are especially sensitive to PROP, who are called **supertasters**, may actually be more sensitive to most bitter substances, as if the amplification in the bitter taste system is turned up for all bitter compounds (Delwiche et al., 2001a).

Although we don't completely understand the mechanisms responsible for individual differences in tasting, especially when considering everyday foods, there is no question that there is a great deal of variability in taste experience across different people. Thus, the next time you disagree with someone else about the taste of a particular food, don't automatically assume that your disagreement is simply a reflection of the fact that you prefer different tastes. It may reflect not a difference in *preference* (you like sweet things more than John does) but a difference in *taste experience* (you experience more intense sweet tastes than John does) that could be caused by differences in the types and numbers of taste receptors on your tongues.

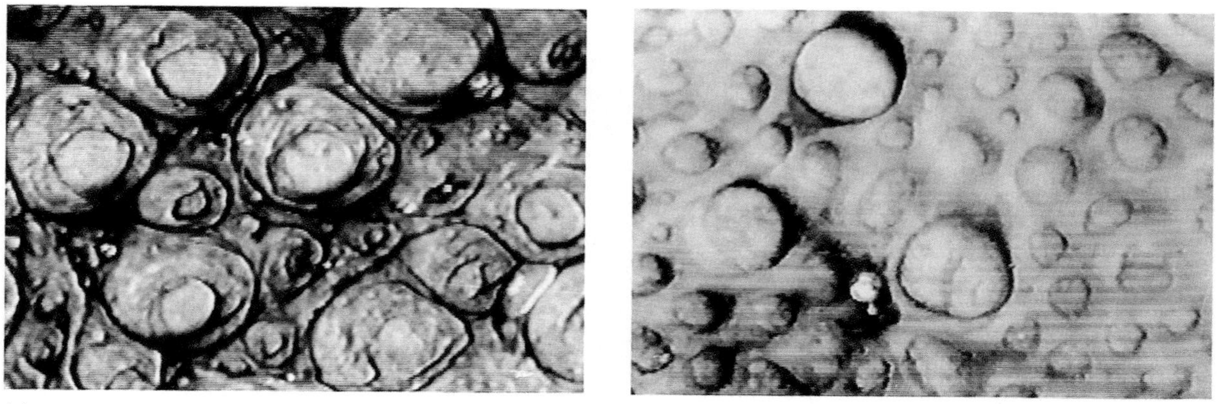

Courtesy of Linda Bartoshuk

(a) (b)

Figure 15.24 ■ (a) Videomicrograph of the tongue showing the fungiform papillae of a "supertaster"—a person who is very sensitive to the taste of PROP. (b) Papillae of a "nontaster"—someone who cannot taste PROP. The supertaster has both more papillae and more taste buds than the nontaster.

TEST YOURSELF 15.2

1. Describe the anatomy of the taste system, including the receptors and central destinations.
2. What are the four basic taste qualities?
3. How can genetics affect taste?
4. What is the evidence for distributed coding and specificity coding in taste? Is it possible to choose between the two?
5. What is flavor perception? Why do we say that the perception of environmental stimuli, such as coffee and eggs that you might be having for breakfast, is an example of perceptual organization?
6. What is the role of taste in flavor perception?
7. Describe the physiology of flavor perception, focusing on the role of the orbital frontal cortex.
8. What kinds of evidence support the idea that different people may have different taste experiences? What mechanisms may be responsible for these differences?

THINK ABOUT IT

1. Can you think of situations in which you have encountered a smell that triggered memories about an event or place that you hadn't thought about in years? What do you think might be the mechanism for this type of experience?
2. Consider the kinds of food that you avoid because you don't like the taste. Do these foods have anything in common that might enable you to explain these taste preferences in terms of the activity of specific types of taste receptors?

IF YOU WANT TO KNOW MORE

1. ***Chemistheses*** In addition to creating experiences associated with tasting and smelling, molecules entering the nose and mouth can cause other experiences, such as the irritation of breathing ammonia or the burning sensation from eating chili peppers. This component of chemical sensitivity, which is called chemesthesis, is related to the cutaneous senses we discussed in Chapter 14.

   Doty, R. L. (1995). Intranasal trigeminal chemoreception. In R. L. Doty (Ed.), *Handbook of olfaction and gustation* (pp. 821–833). New York: Marcel Dekker.

   Silver, W. L., & Finger, T. E. (1991). The trigeminal system. In T. V. Getchell, R. L. Doty, L. M. Bartoshuk, & J. B. Snow (Eds.), *Smell and taste in health and disease* (pp. 97–108). New York: Raven Press.

2. ***Using Smell to Identify People*** Humans generally do not make it a practice to smell other people at close range. However, experiments indicate that we have the capacity to recognize the smell of others and ourselves.

   McBurney, D. H., Levine, J. M., & Cavanaugh, P. H. (1977). Psychophysical and social ratings of human body odor. *Personality and Social Psychology Bulletin, 3,* 135–138.

   Russell, M. J. (1976). Human olfactory communication. *Nature, 260,* 520–522.

3. ***Temporal Coding in the Olfactory Bulb*** The code for odors may involve the way the pattern of nerve firing changes over time.

   Spors, H., & Grinvald, A. (2002). Spatio-temporal dynamics of odor representations in the mammalian olfactory bulb. *Neuron, 34,* 301–315.

4. ***Electronic Nose*** Although we are far from developing a computer that can match human or animal abilities to discriminate and recognize odors, "electronic noses" have been developed that are capable of identifying some odors.

   Gardner, J. W., & Bartlett, P. N. (1999). *Electronic noses.* Oxford, UK: Oxford University Press.

   Rakow, N. A., & Suslick, K. S. (2000). A colorimetric sensory array for odour visualization. *Nature, 406,* 710–713.

5. ***Odor and Memory*** Exposure to odors can bring back long-forgotten memories of places or events. This phenomenon has been confirmed in experiments that show that odors can help retrieve memories.

   Aggelton, J. P., & Waskett, L. (1999). The ability of odours to serve as state-dependent cues for real-world memories: Can Viking smells aid the recall of Viking experiences? *British Journal of Psychology, 90,* 1–7.

   Lyman, B. J., & McDaniel, M. A. (1990). Memory for odors and odor names: Modalities of elaboration and imagery. *Journal of Experimental Psychology: Learning, Memory, and Cognition, 16,* 656–664.

6. ***A Dynamic Code for Taste*** As for olfaction, there is evidence that the way neurons firing changes over time provides information about taste. This information may also help determine whether or not an animal will decide to ingest a substance.

   DiLorenzo, P. M., & Victor, J. D. (2003). Taste response variability and temporal coding in the nucleus of the solitary tract of the rat. *Journal of Neurophysiology, 90,* 1418–1431.

   Katz, D. B., Nicolelis, M. A. L., & Simon, S. A. (2002). Gustatory processing is dynamic and distributed. *Current Opinion in Neurobiology, 12,* 449–454.

7. ***The Human Brain's Response to Taste*** Brain imaging research has located areas that are activated by taste stimuli.

DeAraujo, I. E. T., Kringelbach, M. L., Rolls, E. T., & Hobden, P. (2003). The representation of umami taste in the human brain. *Journal of Neurophysiology, 90,* 313–319.

Rolls, E. T. (2004). Smell, taste, texture, and temperature multimodal representations in the brain, and their relevance to the control of appetite. *Nutrition Reviews, 62,* S193–S204.

KEY TERMS

2-deoxyglucose technique (p. 337)
across-fiber patterns (p. 339)
amiloride (p. 342)
amygdala (p. 332)
anosmia (p. 329)
bimodal neuron (p. 346)
calcium imaging (p. 332)
chorda tympani nerve (p. 339)
combinatorial code for odor (p. 333)
detection threshold (p. 329)
flavor (p. 344)
frontal operculum cortex (p. 339)
genetic tracing (p. 337)
glomeruli (p. 332)
glossopharyngeal nerve (p. 339)
insula (p. 339)
macrosmatic (p. 328)
menstrual synchrony (p. 328)
microsmatic (p. 328)
nasal pharynx (p. 345)
neurogenesis (p. 328)
nontaster (p. 347)
nucleus of the solitary tract (p. 339)
odor prism (p. 331)
olfactometer (p. 330)
olfactory mucosa (p. 331)
olfactory receptors (p. 331)
olfactory sensory neurons (p. 331)
optical imaging (p. 335)
orbitofrontal cortex (p. 332)
papillae (p. 339)
pheromone (p. 328)
piriform cortex (p. 332)
primary olfactory cortex (p. 332)
receptor site (p. 339)
recognition profile (p. 332)
recognition threshold (p. 330)
retronasal route (p. 343)
secondary olfactory cortex (p. 332)
superficial petronasal nerve (p. 339)
supertaster (p. 347)
taste bud (p. 339)
taste cell (p. 339)
taste pore (p. 339)
taster (p. 347)
vagus nerve (p. 339)
video microscopy (p. 347)

VISIT YOUR COMPANION WEBSITE FOR THIS BOOK

http://psychology.wadsworth.com/goldstein7e

Check out this companion website where you'll find online resources—glossary, flashcards, web links, multiple-choice and essay questions, and much more!

VIRTUAL LAB

Your Virtual Lab is designed to help you get the most out of this course. The Virtual Lab icons direct you to specific media demonstrations and experiments designed to help you visualize what you are reading about. The number beside each icon indicates the number of the media element you can access through your CD-ROM, Perception PsychologyNow, or WebTutor resource at http:now.ilrn.com/goldstein_7e.

The following are the lab exercises covering what you've just learned in this chapter:

1 *Olfactory System* A drag-and-drop diagram to test your knowledge of structures in the olfactory system.

2 *Taste System* A drag-and-drop diagram to test your knowledge of structures in the taste system.

MetLife

CHAPTER

16

PERCEPTUAL DEVELOPMENT

Chapter Contents

Two views of the New York skyline. The top picture represents an adult's perception of the scene. The bottom picture simulates how a 1- to 2-month-old infant would perceive this scene.
Photographs and image-processing courtesy of Anthony Movshon.

SOME QUESTIONS WE WILL CONSIDER

- *What can newborns perceive? (p. 352)*
- *When can an infant perceive colors? (p. 356)*
- *Can a newborn recognize his or her mother? (p. 359)*

Our senses endow us with truly amazing capacities. We can see fine details and keep them in focus when an object moves from close to far away. We see something move and can follow the moving object with our eyes, keeping its image on our foveas so we can see the object clearly. We can perceive the location of a sound, transform pressure changes in the air into meaningful sentences, and create myriad tastes and smells from our molecular environment.

As adults, we can do all these things and more. But were we born with these abilities? Most 19th-century psychologists would have answered this question by saying that newborns and young infants experience a totally confusing perceptual world, in which they either perceive nothing or can make little sense of the stimulation to which they are exposed.

One of the things we will do in this chapter is to deal directly with this idea by asking what perceptual capacities are present in the newborn and very young infant. We will see that although newborns have great perceptual deficiencies compared to older children or adults, they can perceive quite a bit more than the 19th-century psychologists believed. But our goal in this chapter goes beyond simply establishing what newborns and young infants can perceive. We will also be considering how their perception develops as they get older and what mechanisms are responsible for early perception and this development.

BASIC VISUAL CAPACITIES

Why did the early psychologists think the newborn's perceptual world was either nonexistent or very confusing, whereas present-day psychologists think that newborns have some perceptual abilities? Did infants learn to see and hear better between the 19th century and now? Obviously not. What did happen is that psychologists learned how to measure infants' perceptual abilities that were there all along. As we describe some of the techniques used to measure infant perceptual abilities, we should not lose sight of the difficulties involved in doing research on human newborns and young infants. The following statement, by a well-known researcher who studies perceptual development in 3- to 5-month-old infants, captures some of these difficulties.

> I admit I've never had the courage to run a full-blown experiment with human newborns. For those who may not be aware of the difficulties involved, running such an experiment can be a formidable task: convincing hospital administrators and personnel in the neonatal nursery that the research is worthwhile; setting up elaborate equipment often in cramped, temporary quarters; obtaining permission from mothers who are still recovering from their deliveries; waiting, sometimes for hours, until the infant to be tested is in a quiet, alert state; coping with the infant's inevitable changes in state after testing has begun; and interpreting the infant's responses that at one moment may seem to be nothing more than a blank stare and at another moment active involvement with the stimulus. (Cohen, 1991, p. 1)

Not only do newborns and young infants exhibit behaviors such as crying, sleeping, and not paying attention while the experimenter is trying to test them, but the fact that they can't understand or respond to verbal instructions presents a special challenge. Even when the infant is cooperating by being quiet and paying attention, the researcher is still faced with the problem of devising methods that will make it possible to determine what the infant is perceiving. As we will see, in the Methods sections in this chapter, they have come up with some ingenious solutions to this problem.

Visual Acuity

One of the most basic questions we can ask about infant perception is how well infants can perceive details. Here we encounter our first measurement challenge—how to determine visual acuity; the ability to see details—in newborns and young infants. Two of the most common methods involving using behavior (preferential looking) and electrical signals recorded from the scalp (visual evoked potential).

METHODS ■ Preferential Looking and Visual Evoked Potential

The key to measuring infant perception is to pose the correct question. To understand what we mean by this, let's consider two questions we can ask to determine visual acuity. One question, "What do you see?" is what you're answering when you read the letters on an eye chart in the doctor's office. Acuity is determined by noting the smallest letters a person can accurately identify. This technique is obviously, however, not suitable for infants. To test infant acuity, we have to ask another question and use another procedure.

A question that works for infants is "Can you tell the difference between the stimulus on the left and the one on the right?" The way infants look at stimuli in their environment provides a way to determine whether they can tell the difference between two stimuli. In the **preferential looking (PL) technique**, two stimuli like the ones the infant is observing in Figure 16.1 are presented, and the experimenter watches the infant's eyes to determine where the infant is looking. If the infant looks at one stimulus more than the other, the experimenter concludes that he or she can tell the difference between them.

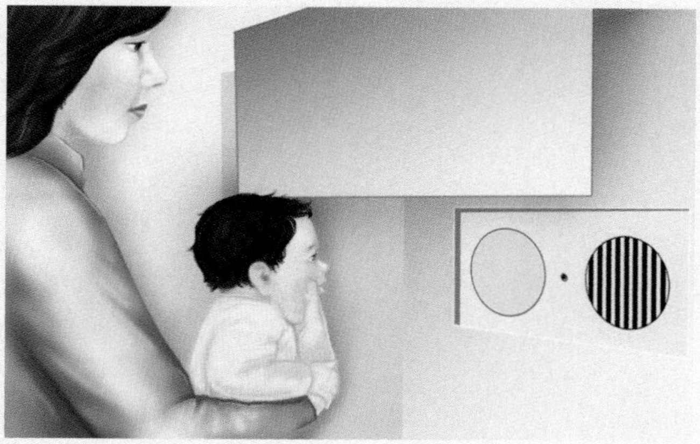

Figure 16.1 ▮ An infant being tested using the preferential looking procedure. The mother holds the infant in front of the display, which consists of a grating on the right and a homogeneous gray field on the left. The grating and the gray field have the same average light intensity. An experimenter, who does not know which side the grating is on in any given trial, looks through the peephole between the grating and the gray field and judges whether the infant is looking to the left or to the right.

The reason preferential looking works is that infants have *spontaneous looking preferences;* that is, they prefer to look at certain types of stimuli. For example, to measure visual acuity, we can use the fact that infants choose to look at objects with contours over ones that are homogeneous (Fantz, Ordy, & Udelf, 1962). Thus, when we present a grating with large bars and a homogeneous field (that reflects the same amount of light that the grating would reflect if the bars were spread evenly over the whole area), the infant can easily see the bars and therefore looks at the side with the bars more than the side with the homogeneous field. This continues to happen when the grating and homogeneous field are switched randomly from side to side on different trials. By preferentially looking at the side with the bars the infant is telling us, "I see the grating."

As we decrease the size of the bars, it becomes more difficult for the infant to tell the difference between the grating and gray stimuli, until, when they become indiscriminable, the infant looks equally at each display. We measure the infant's acuity by determining the narrowest stripe width that results in looking more to one side.

Another method for measuring acuity involves measuring an electrical response called the **visual evoked potential (VEP)**. The VEP, which is recorded by disk electrodes placed on the back of the infant's head, over the visual cortex, is the pooled response of thousands of neurons that are near the electrode. When a researcher is using the VEP to measure acuity, the infant looks at a gray field, which is briefly replaced by either a grating or a checkerboard pattern. If the stripes or checks are large enough to be detected by the visual system, the visual cortex generates an electrical response called the visual evoked potential. If, however, the stripes are too fine to be detected by the visual system, no response is generated. Thus, the VEP provides an objective measure of the ability of the visual system to detect details.

■ ■ ■

Figure 16.2 shows acuity measuring using the preferential looking technique and the visual evoked potential technique. The VEP usually results in higher measurements of acuity, but both techniques indicate that visual acuity is poorly developed at birth (about 20/400 to 20/600 at 1 month). (The expression 20/400 means that the infant must view a stimulus from 20 feet to see the same thing that a normal adult can see from 400 feet.).

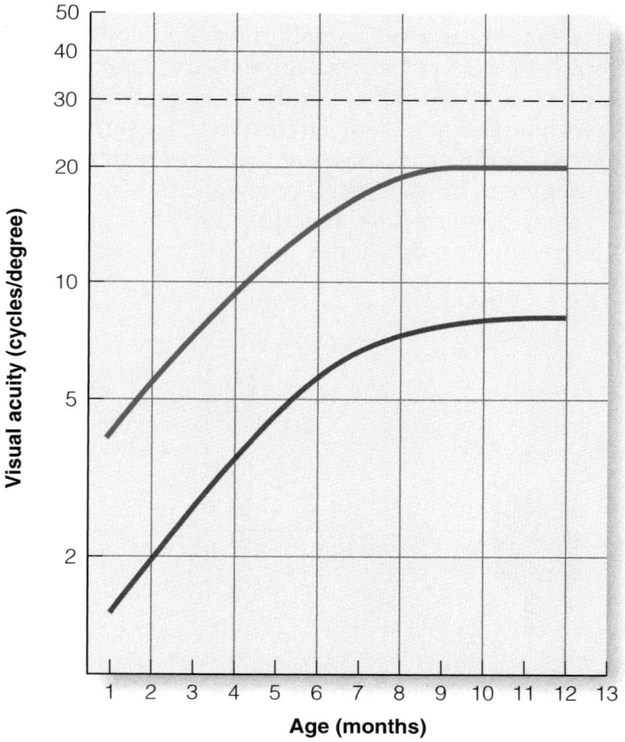

Figure 16.2 ▮ The improvement of acuity over the first year of life, as measured by the visual evoked potential technique (top curve) and the preferential looking technique (bottom curve). The numbers on the vertical axis indicate the fineness of a grating stimulus that can be detected, in cycles per degree of visual angle. Gratings with finer bars have more cycles per degree. (See Figure 16.5 for further details about the cycles-per-degree measure.) The horizontal dashed curve represents adult acuity (20/20 vision).

(VEP curve adapted from Norcia and Tyler, 1985; PL curve adapted from Gwiazda et al., 1980, and Mayer, et al., 1995.)

Acuity then rapidly increases over the first 6 to 9 months (Banks & Salapatek, 1978; Dobson & Teller, 1978; Harris, Atkinson, & Braddick, 1976; Salapatek, Bechtold, & Bushnell, 1976). The initial rapid improvement of acuity is followed by a leveling-off period, and full adult acuity is not reached until sometime after 1 year of age.

The reason for low acuity at birth becomes obvious when we look at the state of the cortex and retina at birth. The infant's visual cortex is not fully developed. Figure 16.3 shows the state of cortical development at birth, at 3 months, and at 6 months (Conel, 1939, 1947, 1951). These drawings indicate that the visual cortex is only partially developed at birth and becomes more developed at 3 and 6 months, the time when significant improvements in visual acuity are occurring. However, the state of the cortex is not the whole explanation for the newborn's low visual acuity. If we look at the newborn's retina, we find that although the rod-dominated peripheral retina appears adultlike in the newborn, the all-cone fovea contains widely spaced and very poorly developed cone receptors (Abramov et al., 1982).

Figure 16.4a compares the shapes of newborn and adult foveal cones (see p. 32). The newborn's cones have fat inner segments and very small outer segments, whereas the adult's inner and outer segments are larger and are about the same diameter (Banks & Bennett, 1988; Yuodelis & Hendrickson, 1986). These differences in shape and size have a number of consequences. The small size of the outer segment means that the newborn's cones contain less visual pigment and therefore do not absorb light as effectively as adult cones. In addition, the fat inner segment creates the coarse receptor lattice shown in Figure 16.4b, with large spaces between the outer segments. In contrast, the thin adult cones are closely packed, creating a fine lattice that is well suited to detecting fine details. Martin Banks and Patrick Bennett (1988) calculated

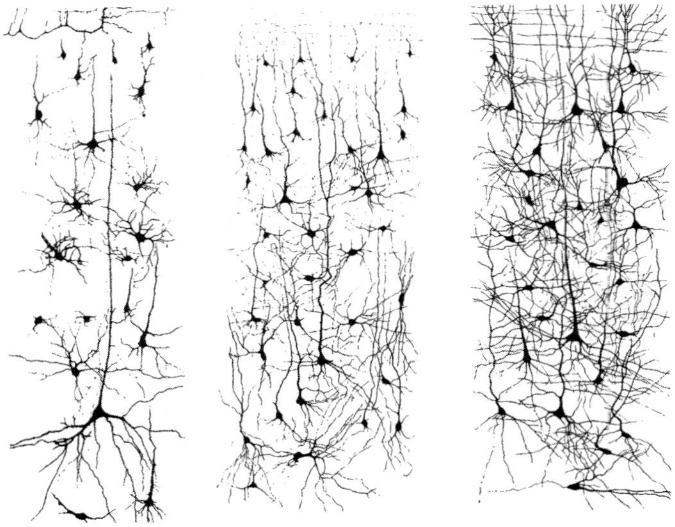

Figure 16.3 ▮ Drawings of neurons in the visual cortex of the newborn, the 3-month-old, and the 6-month-old human infant. *(From* The Postnatal Development of the Cerebral Cortex, *Vol. 1, 1939, and Vol. 3, 1947, and* The Postnatal Development of the Human Cerebral Cortex, *Vol. 4, 1951, by J. L. Conel, plates LVIII, LXIV, and LXIV. Copyright © 1939, 1947, 1951, by Harvard University Press. Reprinted by permission of the publisher.)*

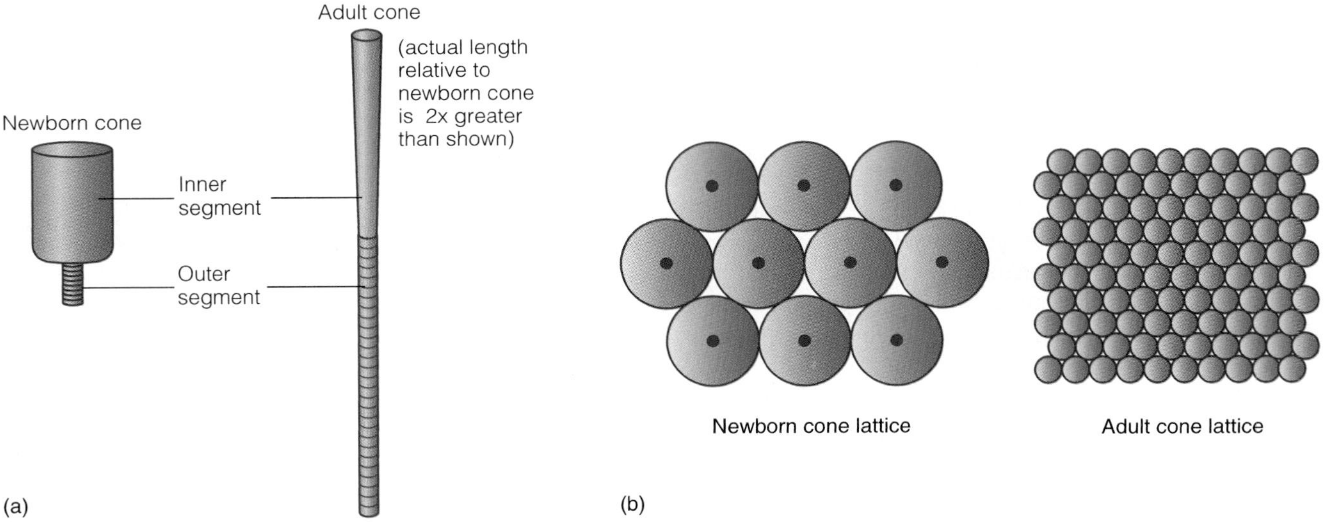

Figure 16.4 ▮ (a) Idealized shapes of newborn and adult foveal cones. (Real cones are not so perfectly straight and cylindrical.) Foveal cones are much narrower and longer than the cones elsewhere in the retina, so these look different from the one shown in Figure 2.13. (b) Receptor lattices for newborn and adult foveal cones. The newborn cone outer segments, indicated by the red circles, are widely spaced because of the fat inner segments. In contrast, the adult cones, with their slender inner segments, are packed closely together.
(Adapted from Banks & Bennett, 1988.)

that the cone receptors' outer segments effectively cover 68 percent of the adult fovea but only 2 percent of the newborn fovea. This means that most of the light entering the newborn's fovea is lost in the spaces between the cones and is therefore not useful for vision.

Visual acuity provides a measure of the ability to see fine details, so an infant's acuity reflects the finest bars that he or she can resolve in a grating. However, objects in the environment come in all sizes, ranging from extremely small to very large. To determine how an infant perceives this environment, we need to determine his or her contrast sensitivity, which we introduced in Chapter 3 (see page 63).

Contrast Sensitivity

Contrast sensitivity is measured by determining the smallest difference between the dark and light bars of a grating at which an observer can still detect the bars (see "Method: Contrast Sensitivity" on page 63). We can determine how an infant perceives objects of different sizes by measuring contrast sensitivity with gratings of different bar sizes. However, rather than describing the grating in terms of fine or wide bars, researchers use a measure called spatial frequency.

The **spatial frequency** of a grating is the number of cycles of the grating (in which one cycle is one light bar and one dark bar) per degree of visual angle. The spatial frequency of the grating in Figure 16.5a is 3 cycles per degree and the spatial frequency of the grating in Figure 16.5b is 6 cycles per degree. Thus, finer bars are generally associated with higher spatial frequencies. However, spatial frequency also depends on the grating's distance from the observer. Moving closer to the grating, as shown in Figure 16.5c, decreases the spatial frequency. Spatial frequency therefore is a measure of how fine the bar pattern is *on the retina.*

Determining the contrast sensitivity of gratings with different spatial frequencies results in a plot of contrast sensitivity versus spatial frequency, which is called the **contrast sensitivity function (CSF**; Figure 16.6). The top curve in this figure is the adult contrast sensitivity function. This function indicates that adults are most sensitive to gratings with spatial frequencies of about 3 cycles per degree. The adult function also indicates that adults can see low spatial frequencies (very wide bars in relation to the eye), but that their ability to see high spatial frequencies (very narrow bars) drops off rapidly above 10 cycles per degree.

Now let's consider the curves for the 1- to 3-month-old infants. These curves indicate that (1) the infants' ability to perceive contrast is restricted to low frequencies; (2) even at these low frequencies the infants' contrast sensitivity is lower than the adult's by a factor of 20 to 100; and (3) infants can see little or nothing at frequencies above about 2 to 3 cycles/degree, the frequencies to which adults are most sensitive (Banks, 1982; Banks & Salapatek, 1978, 1981; Salapatek & Banks, 1978).

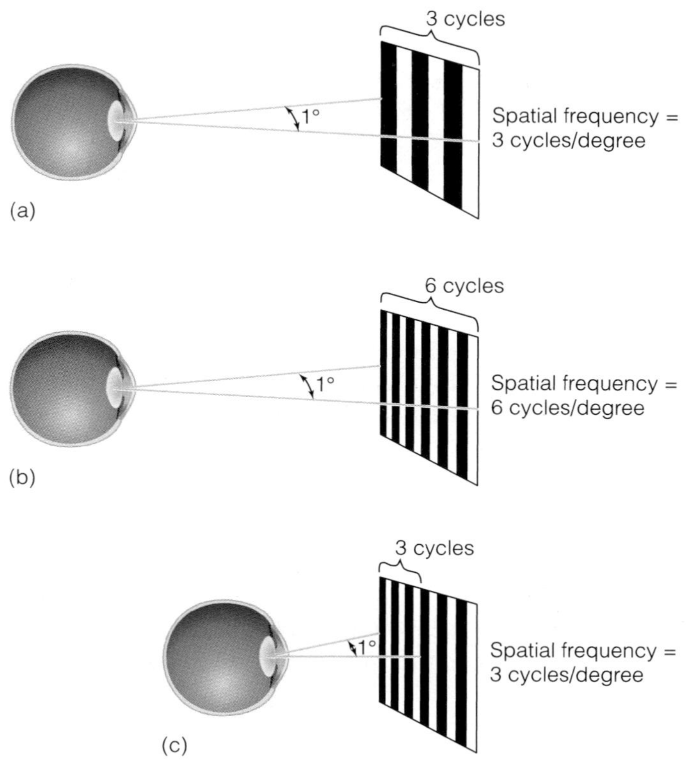

Figure 16.5 An observer's eye looking at a grating stimulus. (a) A grating in which three cycles of bars fall within a visual angle of one degree. (Each cycle includes a black bar and a white bar.) The spatial frequency of this grating is therefore 3 cycles per degree. (b) A grating with spatial frequency of 6 cycles per degree. (c) When the grating from b is moved closer, now just 3 cycles fit within the one-degree viewing angle, so the spatial frequency of this grating is now 3 cycles per degree. These examples illustrate that spatial frequency depends on both the fineness of the grating and the distance from which it is viewed.

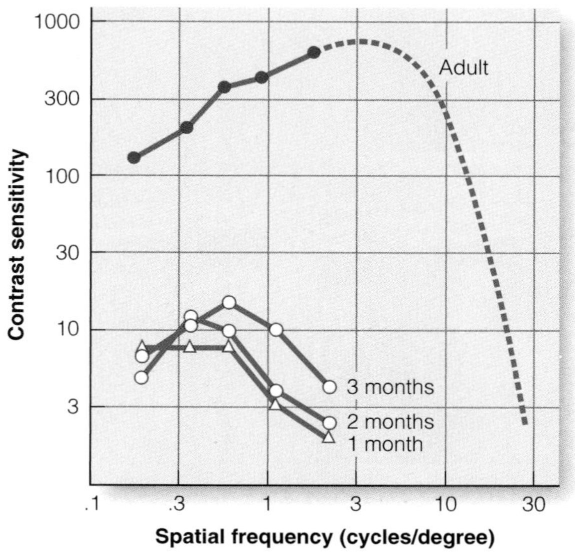

Figure 16.6 Contrast sensitivity functions for an adult and for infants tested at 1, 2, and 3 months of age.

What does the young infants' depressed CSF tell us about their visual world? Clearly, infants are sensitive to only a small fraction of the pattern information available to the adult. At 1 month, infants can see no fine details and can see only relatively large objects with high contrast. Their vision at this age is slightly worse than adult night vision (Fiorentini & Maffei, 1973; Pirchio et al., 1978), a finding consistent with the fact that the undeveloped state of the infant's fovea forces it to see primarily with the rod-dominated peripheral retina. Thus, infants' "window on the world" is very different from adults'; infants see the world as if they are looking through a frosted glass that filters out the high frequencies that would enable them to see fine details but leaves some ability to detect larger, low-frequency forms.

We should not conclude from the young infants' poor vision, however, that they can see nothing at all. At very close distances, a young infant can detect some gross features, as indicated in Figure 16.7, which simulates how infants perceive an object from a distance of about 2 feet. At birth the contrast is so low that it is difficult to determine it is a cat, but it is possible to see very high-contrast areas.

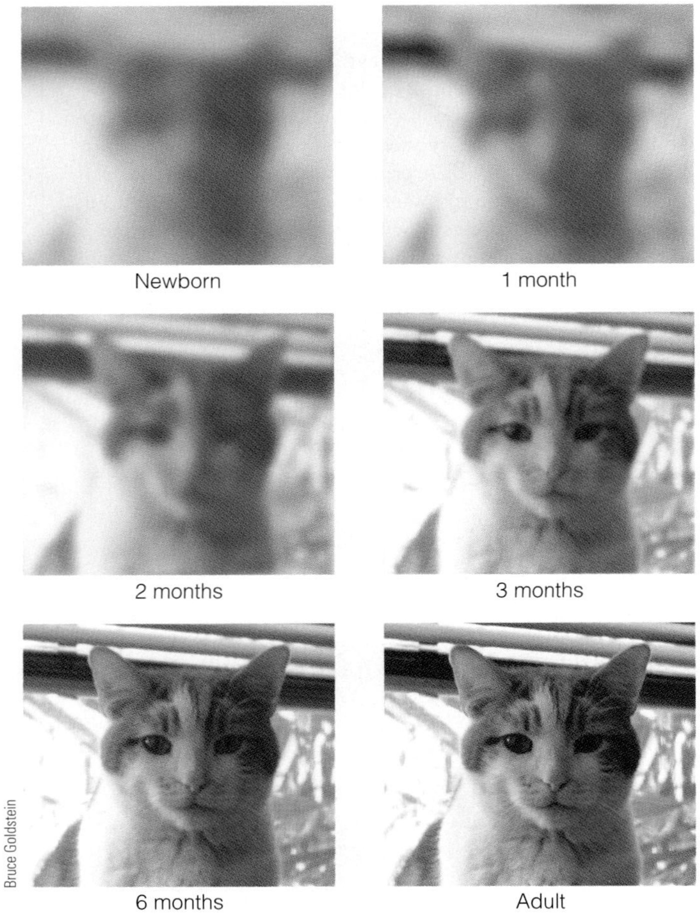

Figure 16.7 ▮ Simulation of perceptions of a cat located 24 inches from an observer, as seen by newborns, 1-, 2-, 3-, and 6-month-old infants, and adults.
(Simulations courtesy of Alex Wade and Bob Dougherty.)

By 3 months, however, the infant's contrast perception has improved so that the image looks clearly catlike. This improvement in contrast sensitivity over the first few months is reflected in the fact that by 3 to 4 months, infants can tell the difference between faces that look happy and those that show surprise, anger, or are neutral (LaBarbera et al., 1976; Young-Browne, Rosenfield, & Horowitz, 1977) and can tell the difference between a cat and a dog (Eimas & Quinn, 1994).

Perceiving Color

We know that our perception of color is determined by the action of three different types of cone receptors (see Figure 7.8). Because the cones are poorly developed at birth, we can guess that the newborn would not have good color vision. However, research has shown that color vision develops early and that appreciable color vision is present within the first 3 to 4 months of life.

One of the challenges in determining whether infants have color vision is created by the fact that perception of a light stimulus can vary on at least two dimensions: (1) its chromatic color and (2) its brightness. Thus, if we present the red and yellow patches in Figure 16.8a to a color-deficient person and ask him whether he could tell the difference between them, he might say yes, because the yellow patch is brighter than the red one.

You can make this observation, if you don't have access to a color-deficient person, by using a "color-blind" black-and-white photocopier as your "observer." Xeroxed pictures of the red and yellow patches (Figure 16.8b) show that the color-blind photocopier can distinguish between the two patches on the basis of differences in brightness. This means that when stimuli with different wavelengths are used to test color vision, their intensity should be adjusted so that they have the same brightness. The experiment we will now describe has done this.

Marc Bornstein, William Kessen, and Sally Weiskopf

Figure 16.8 ▮ (a) Two color patches. (b) The same two patches as "seen" by a photocopy machine.

(1976) assessed the color vision of 4-month-old infants by determining whether they perceive the same color categories in the spectrum as adults. People with normal trichromatic vision see the spectrum as a sequence of color categories, starting with blue at the short-wavelength end and followed by green, yellow, orange, and red, with fairly abrupt transitions between one color and the next (see the spectrum in Figure 2.9). Bornstein and coworkers used a method called habituation to determine whether infants can perceive the difference between these categories.

METHOD ■ Habituation

We have seen that the preferential looking technique is based on the existence of spontaneous looking preferences. But in some cases we want to determine whether an infant perceives a difference between two stimuli that he or she normally looks at equally. Researchers have achieved this by using the following fact about infant looking behavior: When given a choice between a familiar stimulus and a novel one, an infant is more likely to look at the novel one (Fagan, 1976; Slater, Morison, & Rose, 1984).

Because infants are more likely to look at a novel stimulus, we can create a preference for one stimulus over another by familiarizing the infant with one stimulus but not with the other. For this technique, which is called **habituation**, one stimulus is presented to the infant repeatedly, and the infant's looking time is measured on each presentation (Figure 16.9). As the infant becomes more familiar with the stimulus, he or she habituates to it, looking less and less on each trial, as indicated by the green circles in Figure 16.9.

Once the infant has habituated to this stimulus, we determine whether the infant can tell the difference between it and another stimulus by presenting a new stimulus. In Figure 16.9, the new stimulus is presented on the eighth trial. If the infant can tell the difference between the habituation stimulus and the new stimulus, he or she will exhibit **dishabituation**, an increase in looking time when the stimulus is changed, as shown by the red circles in Figure 16.9. If, however, the infant cannot tell the difference between the two stimuli, he or she will continue to habituate to the new stimulus (because it will not be perceived as novel), as indicated by the blue squares in Figure 16.9. Remember that the occurrence of dishabituation means that the second stimulus appears different to the infant from the habituation stimulus.

■ ■ ■

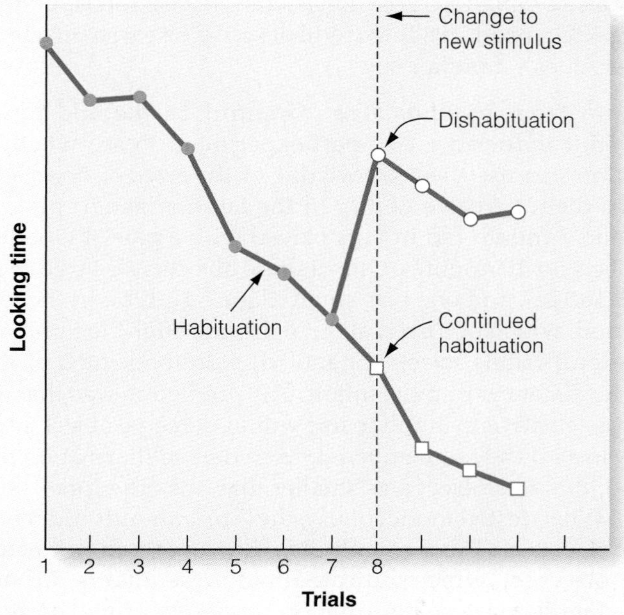

Figure 16.9 ■ Possible results of a habituation experiment. See text for details.

Bornstein and his coworkers habituated infants to a 510-nm light—a wavelength that appears green to a trichromat—and then presented either a 480-nm light, which looks blue to a trichromat, or a 540-nm light, which is on the other side of the blue–green border and therefore appears green to a trichromat (Figure 16.10). Because dishabituation occurred to the 480-nm light but did not occur to the 540-nm light, Bornstein concluded (a) that the 480-nm light looked different than the 510-nm light, and (b) that the 540-nm light looked similar to the 510-nm light. From this result and the results of other experiments, Bornstein concluded that 4-month-old infants categorize colors the same way adult trichromats do.

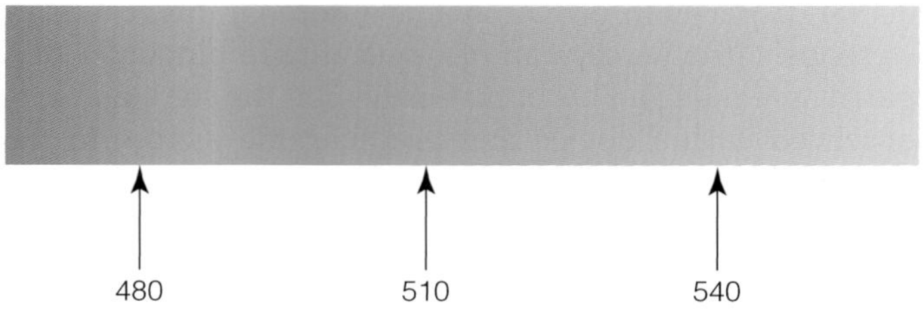

Figure 16.10 ■ Three wavelengths (indicated by arrows) used in Bornstein, Kessen, and Weiskopf's (1976) experiment. The 510- and 480-nm lights are in different perceptual categories (one appears green, the other blue to adults), but the 510 and 540 nm lights are in the same perceptual category (both appear green to adults).

Bornstein and coworkers dealt with the problem of equating brightness by setting the intensity at each wavelength so each stimulus looked equally bright to adults. This is not an ideal procedure because infants may perceive brightness differently from adults. However, as it turns out, Bornstein's result appears to be correct, because later research has confirmed Bornstein's conclusion that young infants have color vision (see Franklin & Davies, 2004; Hamer et al., 1982; Varner et al., 1985).

Perceiving Depth

At what age are infants able to use different kinds of depth information? The answer to this question is that different types of information become operative at different times. Binocular disparity becomes functional early, and pictorial depth cues become functional later.

Using Binocular Disparity One requirement for the operation of binocular disparity is that the eyes must be able to **binocularly fixate** so that the two foveas are directed to exactly the same place. Newborns have only a rudimentary, imprecise ability to fixate binocularly, especially on objects that are changing in depth (Slater & Findlay, 1975).

Richard Aslin (1977) determined when binocular fixation develops by making some simple observations. He filmed infants' eyes while moving a target toward and away from an infant. When the infant is directing both eyes at a target, the eyes should diverge (rotate outward) as the target moves away and should converge (rotate inward) as the target moves closer (See Figure 8.2). Aslin's films indicate that although some divergence and convergence does occur in 1- and 2-month-old infants, these eye movements do not reliably direct both eyes toward the target until about 3 months of age.

Although binocular fixation may be present by 3 months of age, this does not guarantee that the infant can use the resulting disparity information to perceive depth. To determine when infants can use this information to perceive depth, Robert Fox and coworkers (1980) presented random-dot stereograms to infants ranging in age from 2 to 6 months (see page 177 to review random-dot stereograms).

The beauty of random-dot stereograms is that the binocular disparity information in the stereograms results in stereopsis (the perception of depth due to binocular disparity; see p. 173). This occurs only (1) if the stereogram is observed with a device that presents one picture to the left eye and the other picture to the right eye and (2) if the observer's visual system can convert this disparity information into the perception of depth. Thus, if we present a random-dot stereogram to an infant whose visual system cannot yet use disparity information, all he or she sees is a random collection of dots.

In Fox's experiment, an infant wearing special viewing glasses was seated in his or her mother's lap in front of a television screen (Figure 16.11). The child viewed a random-dot stereogram that appeared, to an observer sensitive to disparity information, as a rectangle-in-depth, moving either to the left or to the right. Fox's premise was that an infant sensitive to disparity will move his or her eyes to follow the moving rectangle. He found that infants younger than about 3 months of age would not follow the rectangle, but that infants between 3 and 6 months of age would follow it. He therefore concluded that the ability to use disparity information to perceive depth emerges sometime between 3½ and 6 months of age. This time frame for the emergence of binocular depth perception has been confirmed by other research (Shimojo et al., 1986; Teller, 1997).

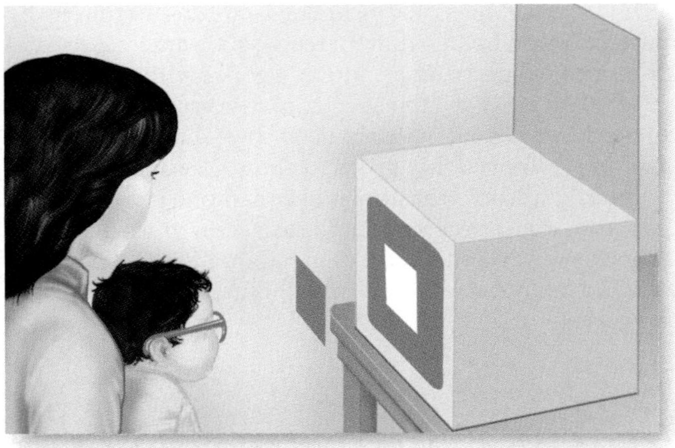

Figure 16.11 ▮ The setup used by Fox et al. (1980) to test infants' ability to use binocular disparity information. If the infant can use disparity information, he or she sees a rectangle moving to the left and right in front of the screen.
(From "Assessment of Stereopsis in Human Infants," by S. L. Shea, R. Fox, R. Aslin, & S. T. Dumais, 1980, Investigative Ophthalmology and Visual Science, *19, 1440–1404, figure 1. Copyright © 1980 C. V. Mosby Company, St. Louis, MO. Reprinted by permission.)*

Another type of depth information is provided by pictorial cues (see Chapter 8, p. 169). These cues develop later than disparity, presumably because they depend on experience with the environment and the development of cognitive capabilities. In general, infants begin to use pictorial cues such as overlap, familiar size, relative size, shading, linear perspective, and texture gradients sometime between about 5 and 7 months of age (Granrud, Haake, & Yonas, 1985; Granrud & Yonas, 1984; Granrud, Yonas, & Opland, 1985; Yonas et al., 1986; Yonas, Pettersen, & Granrud, 1982). We will describe research on one of these cues—familiar size.

Depth From Familiar Size Granrud, Haake, and Yonas (1985) conducted a two-part experiment to see whether infants can use their knowledge of the sizes of objects to help them perceive depth. In the familiarization period, 5- and 7-month-old infants played with a pair of wooden objects for 10 minutes. One of these objects was large (Figure 16.12a), and one was small (Figure 16.12b). In the test period, which occurred about a minute after the familiarization period, objects (c) and (d) were presented at the same distance from the infant. The prediction was that infants sensitive to familiar size would perceive object (c) to be closer if they remembered, from the familiarization period, that this object was smaller than the other one.

When tested monocularly, the 7-month-olds did reach for object (c). The 5-month-olds, however, did not reach for object (c), which indicated that these infants did not use familiar size as information for depth. Thus, the ability to use familiar size to perceive depth appears to develop sometime between 5 and 7 months.

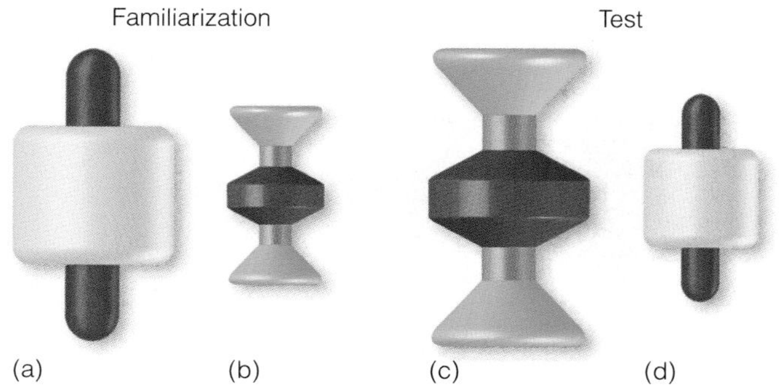

Figure 16.12 ▮ Stimuli for Granrud, Haake, and Yonas's (1985) familiar-size experiment. See text for details.
(From "Infants' Sensitivity to Familiar Size: The Effect of Memory on Spatial Perception," by C. E. Granrud, R. J. Haake, & A. Yonas, 1985, Perception and Psychophysics, *37, 459–466. Copyright © 1985 by Psychonomic Society Publications. Reprinted by permission.)*

This experiment is interesting not only because it indicates when the ability to use familiar size develops, but also because the infant's response in the test phase depends on a cognitive ability—the ability to remember the sizes of the objects that he or she played with in the familiarization phase. The 7-month-old infant's depth response in this situation is therefore based both on what is perceived and what is remembered.

PERCEIVING FACES

Human faces are among the most important stimuli in an infant's environment. As a newborn or young infant stares up from the crib, numerous faces of interested adults appear in the infant's field of view. The face that the infant sees most frequently is usually the mother's, and there is evidence that young infants can recognize their mother's face shortly after they are born.

Recognizing Their Mother's Face

Research on the infant's ability to recognize faces provides an example of how research in perceptual development often progresses. First, an infant's ability to perceive a particular stimulus is demonstrated. Then, the result is confirmed by replicating it, perhaps also using improved procedures to rule out possible sources of bias. Finally, experiments are done to determine the information the infant is using to achieve his or her perception.

Using preferential looking in which 2-day-old infants were given a choice between their mother's face and a stranger's, Ian Bushnell and coworkers (1989) found that newborns looked at the mother about 63 percent of the time. This result is above the 50 percent chance level, so Bushnell concluded that the 2-day-olds could recognize their mother's face.

You may recall from our earlier discussion (p. 357) that infants usually prefer novel stimuli. If that were occurring here, we would expect the infant to look at the stranger more than the mother. Why, then, does the infant prefer to look at the mother? Apparently the infant's preference for the mother is so strong that it overrides the usual tendency to prefer novel stimuli.

Bushnell did control experiments to rule out the possibility that perhaps the mother was doing something to attract the infant's attention or that the infant could detect the mother's familiar smell. But to be sure that distraction and smell were not contributing factors, Gail Walton and coworkers (1992) showed that newborns still responded to the mother more than a stranger when the faces were presented on videotape.

To determine what information the infants might be using to recognize the mother's face, Olivier Pascalis and coworkers (1995) showed that when the mother and stranger wore pink scarves that covered their hairline, the preference for the mother disappeared. The high-contrast border between the mother's dark hairline and light forehead apparently provides important information about the mother's physical characteristics that the infant uses to recognize its mother (see Bartrip et al., 2001, for another experiment that shows this).

The fact that newborns are able to perceive the difference between their mother's face and the face of a stranger raises another question: Is this ability due to a special face-sensitive mechanism that is built in at birth, or is it the result of a general perceptual mechanism?

Is There a Special Mechanism for Perceiving Faces?

The idea of an inborn face-sensitive mechanism has been proposed by John Morton and Mark Johnson (1991). They presented stimuli (see bottom of Figure 16.13) to newborns within an hour after birth and then moved the stim-

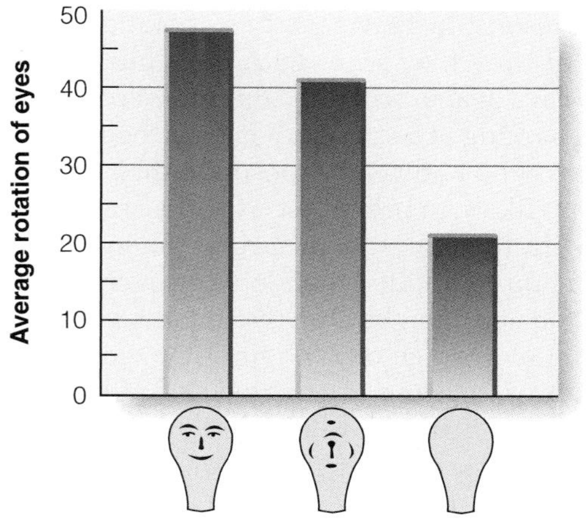

Figure 16.13 ▮ The magnitude of infants' eye movements in response to movement of each stimulus. The average rotation of the infants' eyes was greater for the face-like stimulus than for the scrambled-face stimulus or the blank stimulus.
(Adapted from Morton and Johnson, 1991.)

uli to the left and right. As they did this, they videotaped the infant's face. Later, scorers who were unaware of which stimulus was being presented viewed the tapes and noted whether the infant turned his or her head or eyes to follow the moving stimulus. The results in Figure 16.13 show that the newborns looked at the moving face more than the other moving stimuli.

Support for a special mechanism for face recognition has been provided by Martha Farah and coworkers' (2000) case study of Adam, a 16-year-old boy who contracted meningitis when he was 1 day old. This disease damaged areas in the occipital and temporal lobe usually associated with perceiving faces and left him with a condition called **prosopagnosia**, an inability to recognize faces, which we discussed in Chapter 4. He could, however, still recognize other kinds of objects.

Although Adam scored below normal when tested on pictures of common household objects, vehicles, and toys (87 percent correct; normal performance is close to 100 percent), he was able to identify environmental objects well enough for everyday functioning. Faces, however, were another story. He was unable to identify any of the pictures of faces he was shown, even though many were pictures of people he watched daily on television, and he could identify friends only after hearing them talk.

Because Adam had a dissociation between object perception and face perception (see "Method: Dissociations in Neuropsychology" on page 80), Farah concluded that the mechanism for face perception is different from the mechanism for object perception. What makes Adam's case especially significant is that even after 16 years of observing faces, he was never able to learn to identify them. Thus, the area responsible for object perception was not able to take over the task of identifying faces.

But other evidence leads some researchers to question the idea of a separate face-recognition mechanism. For example, Ian Bushnell (2001) observed newborns over the first 3 days of life to determine whether there was a relationship between their looking behavior and amount of time they were with their mother. He found that at 3 days of age, when the infants were given a choice between looking at a stranger's face or their mother's face, the infants who had been exposed to their mother longer were more likely to prefer her over the stranger. The two infants with the lowest exposure to the mother (an average of 1.5 hours) divided their looking evenly between the mother and stranger, but the two infants with the longest exposure (an average of 7.5 hours) looked at the mother 68 percent of the time. Analyzing the results from all of the infants led Bushnell to conclude that face perception emerges very rapidly after birth, but that experience in looking at faces does have an effect.

Chiara Turati and coworkers (2002) presented additional evidence to support the idea that early face recognition is not based on a special mechanism. They found that 1- to 4-day-old infants look longer at displays with more elements in the top half (Figure 16.14). Notice that infants looked longer at the top-heavy stimuli in pairs (a) and (b) even though in pair (b), the arrangement of the elements in the bottom-heavy stimulus looked more like a face. When two stimuli with the same number of elements on the top were compared, as in (c), the infants showed no preference, even though the display on the right looks more like a face.

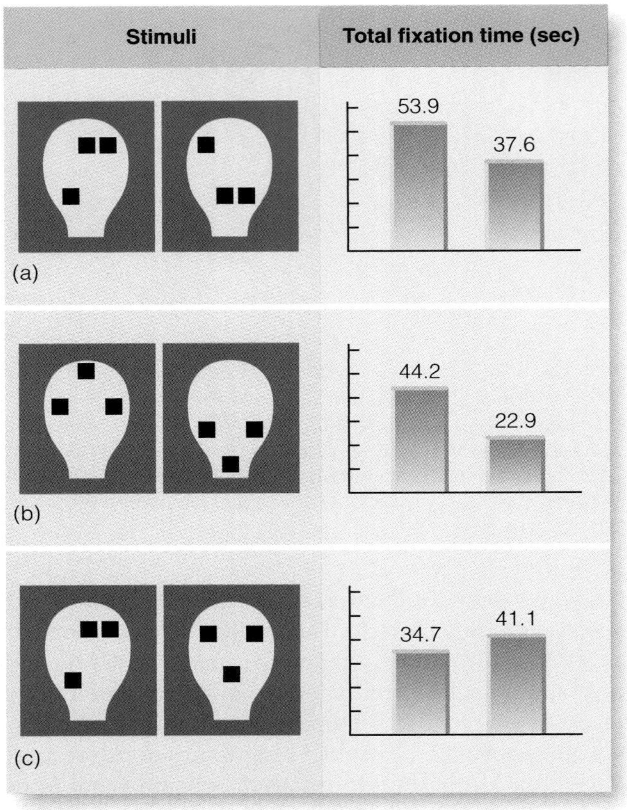

Figure 16.14 ■ Results of Turati et al.'s (2002) measurements of how long infants looked at each stimulus in the pair when they are presented simultaneously. (a) Infants looked longer at top-heavy stimulus. (b) Infants looked longer at top-heavy stimulus. (c) There was no significant difference in looking between these two stimuli, which are equally top-heavy.

This result could mean that infants attend to faces because faces have more elements in their top half. The infants therefore gain more experience in looking at faces, and this experience could help create neurons in the fusiform face area (FFA) that are specialized for faces (see page 85). According to this idea, infants' early preference for faces can be explained by a general mechanism of object perception. No special mechanism for face perception is needed (see Nelson, 2001).

We can summarize our description of infant face perception by noting that there is ample evidence that newborns and young infants can distinguish between different faces, and that very young infants prefer to look at facelike stimuli. There is disagreement, however, about whether this preference for faces is caused by a special mechanism dedicated to perceiving faces or by the same mechanism that serves the perception of objects in general. If this sounds familiar, it is because the same disagreement among researchers exists about the mechanism that is responsible for adults' perception of faces (see page 91). Further research on both infants and adults is needed to resolve this question.

TEST YOURSELF 16.1

1. Why is measuring infant perception more difficult than measuring adult perception?
2. Describe two techniques that have been used to measure infant visual acuity, and the results obtained using these methods.
3. What is the connection between the development of infant visual acuity and the physiology of the cortex and the cone receptors?
4. What information about perception does measuring contrast sensitivity provide that is not provided by measuring visual acuity? What do infant contrast sensitivity functions tell us about the infant's visual world?
5. What do researchers have to take into account when determining whether infants can perceive color? How did Bornstein use the method of habituation to determine that infants can perceive color categories?
6. Describe the experiments that determined the age at which infants can (a) binocularly fixate; and (b) use disparity to perceive depth.
7. How did researchers determine infants' ability to use pictorial depth information? Why do pictorial depth cues become operational at a later age than disparity?
8. Describe research on the infant's ability to recognize faces. What two explanations have been proposed for the finding that infants can recognize faces at a young age?

PERCEIVING OBJECT UNITY

So far, in considering how infants perceive objects, we have focused on faces. Although faces are extremely important to infants, they also see many other things and have to develop the capacity to perceptually organize all of the objects they encounter in the environment. This process of organization includes grouping some things together (see the "Gestalt Laws of Perceptual Organization," page 99) and also being able to perceive different objects as separate from one another (see "Perceptual Segregation," page 103). Because the research on the development of object perception is far too vast to cover here, we will focus on one very important aspect of object perception—the perception of **object unity**.

When adults look at the three men in Figure 16.15, they perceive their bodies as continuing behind the boards on which they are leaning. But would a young infant perceive the upper, middle, and lower parts of their bodies as separate units or as parts of a single object that continues behind the boards? Experiments on the perception of object unity have focused on the conditions under which an infant can perceive an object as a whole even when part of it is obscured by an occluding stimulus

Bruce Goldstein

Figure 16.15 Three men whose bodies are occluded by the two boards. The perception of object unity has occurred if each man is perceived as a single object that continues behind the boards.

Philip Kellman and Elizabeth Spelke (1983) showed that movement helps infants perceive objects as continuing behind an occluding object. They habituated 4-month-old infants to a rod moving back and forth behind a block (left stimulus in Figure 16.16a) and then presented either two separated rods or a single longer rod (right stimuli in Figure 16.16b). Because dishabituation occurred to the two separated rods (top), but not to the whole rod, Kellman and Spelke concluded that 4-month-old infants perceive the partly occluded moving rod as a whole object that continues behind the block. (Remember that dishabituation indicates that the infant perceives the second stimulus as different from the first one.)

This result does not, however, occur when the infant is habituated to a stationary rod and block display. Thus, movement helps 4-month-old infants infer that one object extends behind another. It appears that the 4-month-olds are making the following inference: If the top and bottom

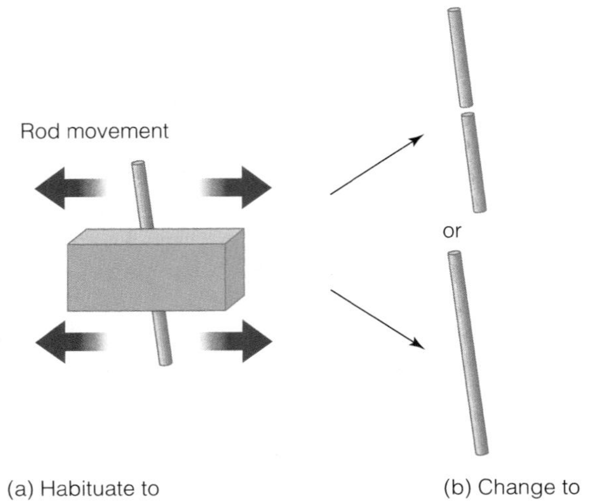

Figure 16.16 ▮ (a) Stimuli used in the habituation phase of the Kellman and Spelke (1983) experiment. A rod moves back and forth behind a rectangular occluder. (b) Two stimuli presented separately in the dishabituation phase of the experiment.
(From "Perception of Partly Occluded Objects in Infancy," by P. J. Kellman and E. S. Spelke, 1983, Cognitive Psychology, 15, *483–524, figure 3. Copyright ©1983 by Academic Press. Reprinted by permission.)*

units are moving together, then they must be part of the same object.

If 4-month-olds perceive a moving object as continuing behind an occluding stimulus, can younger infants do this as well? When Alan Slater and coworkers (1990) repeated Kellman and Spelke's experiment for newborns, they found that when the newborns saw the moving rod during habituation, they looked more at the single rod during dishabituation. This suggests that they saw the moving rods as two separate units and not as a single rod extending behind the occluder. Apparently newborns do *not* make the inference that 4-month-olds make about the moving display.

Thus, the capacity demonstrated at 4 months does not exist (or can't be measured using this particular procedure) at birth. But when does it appear? Scott Johnson and Richard Aslin (1995) helped determine the answer when they tested 2-month-olds and obtained results similar to those for the 4-month-olds. Apparently, the ability to use movement as a way to organize the perceptual world develops rapidly over the first few months of life.

A number of experiments like these show that at 2 months of age infants are able to perceive partially hidden objects as a single object, and that this ability becomes stronger by 4 to 6 months. But simply determining the age when a perceptual capacity emerges is only the first step in understanding the mechanism behind this capacity. Scott Johnson and coworkers (2004) investigated the link between infants' perception of object unity and how they looked at a rod as it moved behind an occluder. They accomplished this by measuring both habituation behavior and eye movements in 3-month-old infants as the infants observed a moving rod display.

The habituation results indicated that some of the infants perceived the moving rod as continuing behind the occluder. Johnson and coworkers called these infants *perceivers.* The results also indicated that other infants did not perceive the moving rod as continuing behind the occluder. These infants were called *nonperceivers.*

Figure 16.17 shows eye fixation records measured during habituation for a perceiver (top) and a nonperceiver (bottom). The two rods in each figure indicate the left- and right-most positions of the moving rod. No-

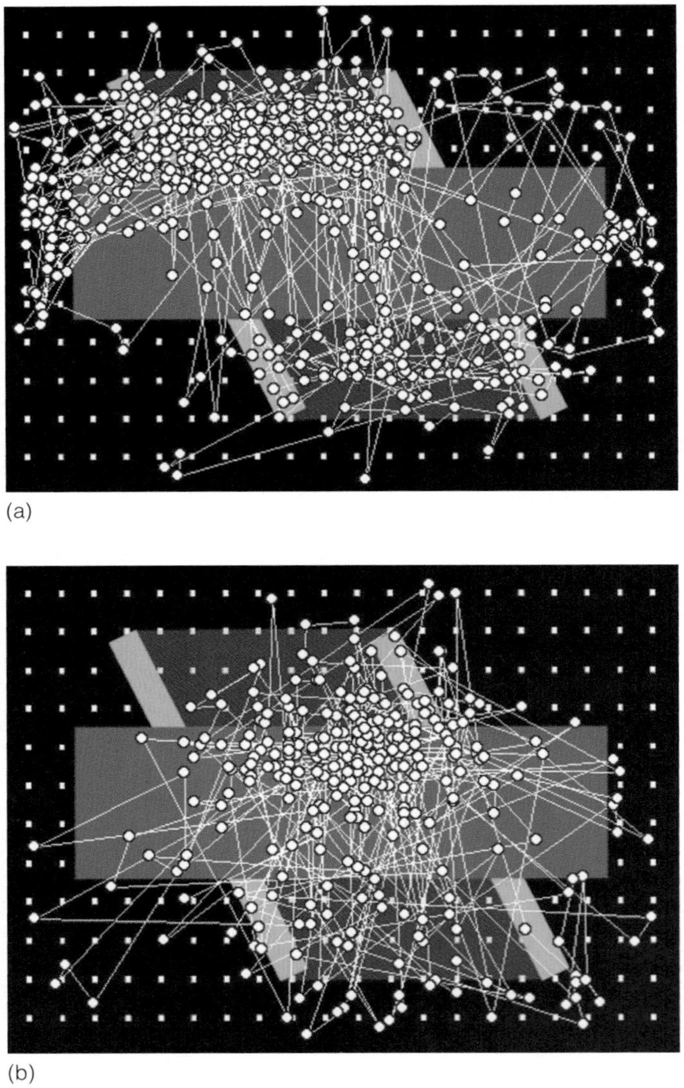

Figure 16.17 ▮ How infants looked at a display during habituation, in which a rod moved back and forth behind a rectangular occluder. (a) Fixations for an infant who perceived the moving rod as a single object (a "perceiver"). (b) Fixations for an infant who did not perceive the moving rod as a single object (a "nonperceiver").
(Johnson, S. P., Slemmer, J. A., & Amso, D. (2004). Where infants look determines how they see: Eye movement and object perception performance in 3-month-olds. Infancy, 6, 185–201.*)*

tice that in these examples, the perceiver fixated mainly on the rod, whereas the nonperceiver fixated on the rectangular occluder. Eye movement records also showed that, as a group, perceivers made more horizontal eye movements than the nonperceivers. The perceivers, therefore, tended to look at the rod and follow its movement, whereas the nonperceivers looked more at the stationary occluder and other parts of the display that were not related to perceiving the rods as extending behind the occluder. These differences between perceivers and nonperceivers mean that the infants' perception of object unity depends on the development of looking behavior that enables the infant to pick up information about the rod's movement.

HEARING

What do newborn infants hear, and how does hearing develop as infants get older? Although some early psychologists felt that newborns were functionally deaf, recent research has shown that newborns do have some auditory capacities and that this capacity improves as the child gets older (Werner & Bargones, 1992).

Threshold for Hearing a Tone

A simple way to find out whether infants can hear is to determine whether they will orient toward the source of a sound. Darwin Muir and Jeffry Field (1979) presented newborn infants with a loud (80-dB) rattle sound 20 cm from either their right or their left ear and found that the infants usually turned toward the sound. Newborns can therefore hear and are capable of at least crude sound localization.

More precise measurements of infants' capacities have been achieved with older infants, who have a wider repertoire of responses to sound. Lynne Werner Olsho and coworkers (1988) used the following procedure to determine infants' audibility curves. An infant is fitted with earphones and sits on the parent's lap. An observer, sitting out of view of the infant, watches the infant through a window. A light blinks on, indicating that a trial has begun, and the infant is either presented with a tone or is not. The observer's task is to decide whether or not the infant heard the tone (Olsho et al., 1987).

How can observers tell whether the infant has heard a tone? They decide by looking for responses such as eye movements, changes in facial expression, a wide-eyed look, a turn of the head, or changes in activity level. Although this determination is not easy for observers, we can see from the data in Figure 16.18a that it works (Olsho et al., 1988).

Observers only occasionally indicated that the 3-month-old infants heard a 2,000-Hz tone that was presented at low intensities or not at all. But observers were more likely to say that the infant had heard the tone when the tone was presented at high intensity. The infant's threshold at 2,000 Hz was determined from this curve, and the results from a number of other frequencies were combined to create audibility functions, such as those in Figure 16.18b. The curves for 3- and 6-month-olds and adults indicate that infant and adult audibility func-

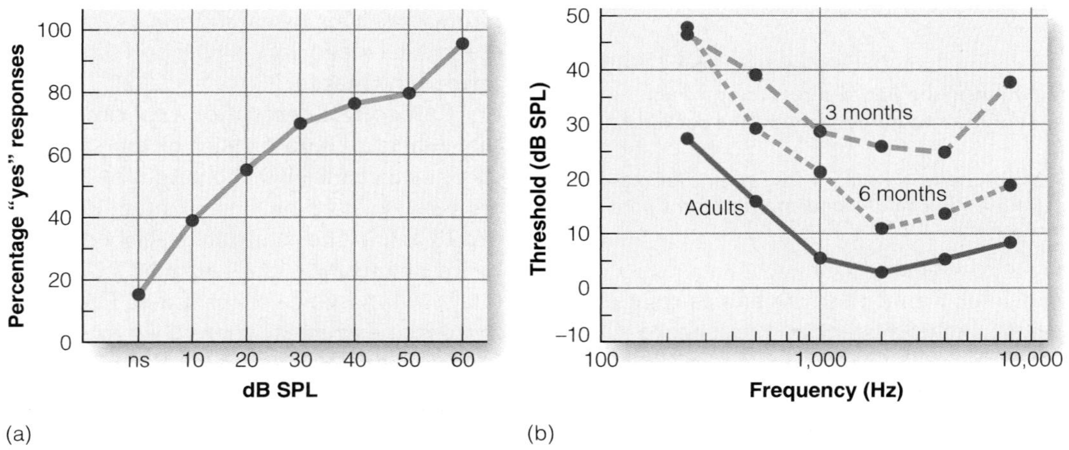

Figure 16.18 ▮ (a) Data obtained from Olsho et al.'s observer-based psychoacoustic procedure that shows the percentage of trials on which the observer indicated that a 3-month-old infant heard tones presented at different intensities. NS indicates no sound. (b) Audibility curves for 3- and 6-month-old infants determined from functions like the one in (a). The curve for 12-month-olds, not shown here, is similar to the curve for 6-month-olds. The adult curve is shown for comparison.
(Adapted from "Pure-Tone Sensitivity of Human Infants," by L. W. Olsho, E. G. Koch, E. A. Carter, C. F. Halpin, & N. B. Spetner, 1988, Journal of the Acoustical Society of America, *84, 1316–1324. American Institute of Physics.)*

tions look similar and that, by 6 months of age, the infant's threshold is within about 10 to 15 dB of the adult threshold.

Recognizing Their Mother's Voice

Another approach to studying hearing in infants has been to show that newborns can identify sounds they have heard before. Anthony DeCasper and William Fifer (1980) demonstrated this capacity in newborns by showing that 2-day-old infants will modify their sucking on a nipple in order to hear the sound of their mother's voice. They first observed that infants usually suck on a nipple in bursts separated by pauses. They fitted infants with earphones and let the length of the pause in the infant's sucking determine whether the infant heard a recording of the mother's voice or a recording of a stranger's voice (Figure 16.19). For half of the infants, long pauses activated the tape of the mother's voice, and short pauses activated the tape of the stranger's voice. For the other half, these conditions were reversed.

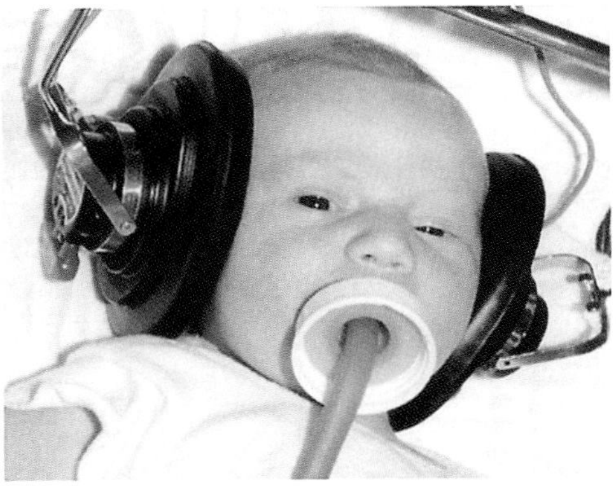

Figure 16.19 ▌ This baby, from DeCasper and Fifer's (1980) study, could control whether she heard a recording of her mother's voice or a stranger's voice by the way she sucked on the nipple.
(Walter Salinger/Photo property of Anthony DeCasper. DeCasper, A. J., & Fifer, W. P. (1980). Of human bonding: Newborns prefer their mothers' voices. Science, 208, *1174–1176.)*

DeCasper and Fifer found that the babies regulated the pauses in their sucking so that they heard their mother's voice more than the stranger's voice. This is a remarkable accomplishment for a 2-day-old, especially because most had been with their mothers for only a few hours between birth and the time they were tested.

Why did the newborns prefer their mother's voice? DeCasper and Fifer suggested that newborns recognize their mother's voice because they heard the mother talking during development in the womb. This suggestion is supported by the results of another experiment, in which DeCasper and M. J. Spence (1986) had one group of pregnant women read from Dr. Seuss's book *The Cat in the Hat* and another group read the same story with the words *cat* and *hat* replaced with *dog* and *fog*. When the children were born, they regulated their sucking pattern to hear the version of the story their mother had read when they were in the womb.

In another experiment, 2-day-old infants regulated their sucking to hear a recording of their native language rather than of a foreign language (Moon, Cooper, & Fifer, 1993). Apparently, even when in the womb, the fetus becomes familiar with the sound cues they hear, possibly the intonation and rhythm of the mother's voice and also the sounds of specific words. (See also DeCasper et al., 1994.)

PERCEIVING SPEECH

Perceiving individual tones and being able to recognize familiar sounds are important basic skills that infants possess at an early age. As the infant develops, another skill becomes important—the infant's ability to discern meaning through words and sentences. This ability emerges long before the infant can produce speech. The starting point for understanding speech perception in infants has been to determine how infants respond to phonemes.

The Categorical Perception of Phonemes

Remember from Chapter 13 that each language is constructed from units called phonemes—the smallest unit that when changed, changes the meaning of a word. Because of the importance of phonemes and their role as elementary units of language, some of the first research on infant speech perception focused on their perception of phonemes. This research took as its starting point the research on categorical perception of phonemes that we described in Chapter 13 (see p. 292).

Categorical perception experiments in adults indicate that when a characteristic of the speech stimulus called voice onset time (VOT) changes over a wide range, listeners tend to hear only two categories of sound (see Figure 13.11). In the example described in Chapter 13, adults heard one sound ("da") at short VOTs and another sound ("ta") at long voice onset times. There is a place between these two extremes where changing the VOT just a little causes people's categorization of the sound to suddenly change from one sound to the other. This place is called the *phonetic boundary*.

Categorical perception was first reported for adults in 1967 (Liberman et al., 1967). In 1971, Peter Eimas and coworkers began the modern era of research on infant speech perception by using the habituation procedure to show that infants as young as 1 month old perform similarly to adults in categorical perception experiments. The basis of these experiments was the observation that an infant will suck on a nipple in order to hear a series of brief speech sounds, but as the same speech sounds are repeated, the infant's sucking eventually habituates to a low level. By presenting a new stimulus after the rate of sucking had decreased, Eimas determined whether the infant perceived the new stimulus as sounding the same as or different from the old one.

The results of Eimas and coworkers' experiment are shown in Figure 16.20. The number of sucking responses when no sound was presented is indicated by the point at B. When a sound with voice onset time (VOT) of 20 ms (sounds like "ba" to an adult) is presented as the infant sucks, the sucking increases to a high level and then begins to decrease. When the VOT is changed to 40 ms (sounds like "pa" to an adult), sucking increases, as indicated by the points to the right of the dashed line. This means that the infant perceives a difference between sounds with VOTs of 20 and 40 ms. The center graph, however, shows that changing the VOT from 60 to 80 ms (both sound like "pa" to an adult) has only a small effect on sucking, indicating that the infants perceive little, if any, difference between the two sounds. Finally, the results for a control group (the right graph) show that when the sound is not changed, the number of sucking responses decreases throughout the experiment.

These results show that when the VOT is shifted across the average adult phonetic boundary (left graph), the infants perceive a change in the sound, and when the VOT is shifted on the same side of the phonetic boundary (center graph), the infants perceive little or no change in the sound. That infants as young as 1 month old are capable of categorical perception is particularly impressive, especially because these infants have had virtually no experience in producing speech sounds and only limited experience in hearing them.

Experience and Speech Perception

When infants are a few months old, they can distinguish between phonemes that make up their native language and also between phonemes from other languages. (Remember that although there are many possible phonemes, each language is created from one particular set of phonemes. For example, there are 11 phonemes in Hawaiian, 37 in English, and as many as 60 in some African languages.) However, by the time infants are 1 year old, their ability to distinguish between phonemes has become "tuned" to the phonemes of the language to which they have been exposed.

This tuning is illustrated by the fact that a 4-month-old Japanese infant can distinguish between the sounds /r/ and /l/, but by the time they are 1 year old they can no longer make this distinction. This occurs because infants become sensitive only to distinctions between sounds that are important in their language, and the Japanese language does not distinguish between these two sounds (Kuhl, 2004; Kuhl et al., 1992, 1997; Werker, 1991; Werker & Tees, 1984).

Thus, infants possess mechanisms for perceiving all speech sounds fairly early in their development, and during the first year of life these mechanisms become tuned to the language that the child hears. We will return to this result at the end of the chapter when we describe research that suggests a similar "tuning" effect for perceiving faces.

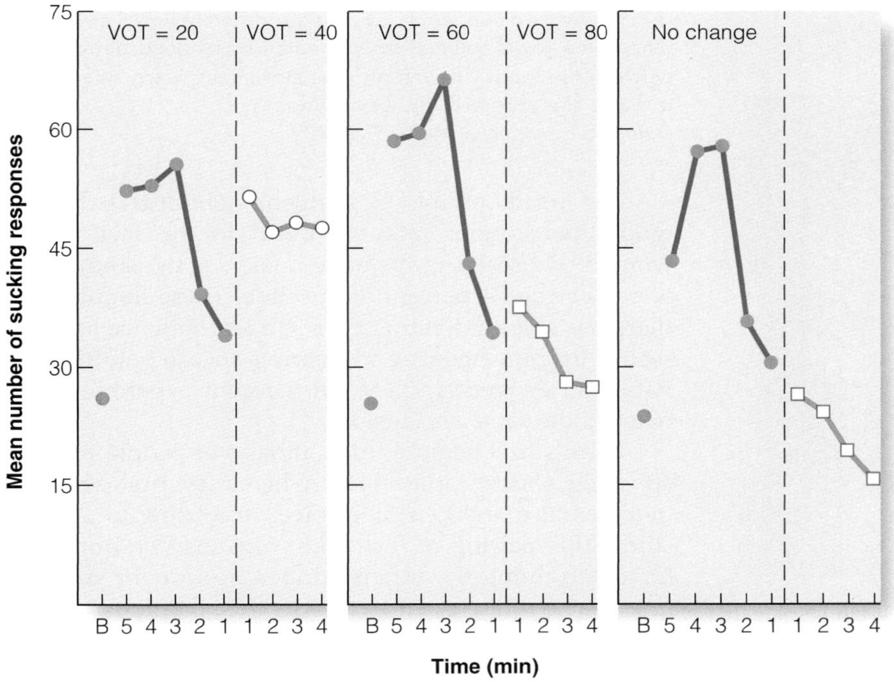

Figure 16.20 Results of a categorical perception experiment on infants using the habituation procedure. In the left panel, VOT is changed from 20 to 40 ms (across the phonetic boundary). In the center panel, VOT is changed from 60 to 80 ms (not across the phonetic boundary). In the right panel, the VOT was not changed. See text for details. *(From "Speech Perception in Infants," by P. Eimas, E. P. Siqueland, P. Jusczyk, J. Vigorito, 1971,* Science*, 171, 303–306, figure 2. Copyright © 1971 by the American Association for the Advancement of Science. Reprinted by permission.)*

INTERMODAL PERCEPTION

So far we have considered perceptual capacities such as seeing details, hearing sound frequencies, perceiving faces and recognizing the mother's voice. But in the real world these things often occur together. We observe a person's face as we hear them speak; we hear an ambulance's siren as we see it racing down the street. These combinations of hearing and vision are examples of **intermodal perception**—coordination of information from different senses into a perceptual whole. This ability to coordinate information from different senses is something that adults routinely accomplish every day, and there is evidence that very young infants are capable of intermodal perception, as well.

For example, Kelly Kaye and T. G. R. Bower (1994) showed that a 1-day-old infant is capable of matching a shape they feel to a shape they can see. They placed one of two pacifiers in the infant's mouth. When the infant began sucking, a large image of the end of one of the pacifiers appeared on a computer monitor located directly in front of the newborn (Figure 16.21). As long as the infant continued sucking, the image remained on the screen. But pausing for longer than 1 second caused the image of the other, differently shaped, pacifier to appear on the screen. Thus, the infant could determine which image appeared on the screen by the way he or she sucked on the pacifier.

The results of this experiment show that infants controlled their sucking so that in their initial exposures to the images of the pacifiers, 11 of the 12 infants caused the image of the pacifier on which they were sucking to appear on the screen longer than the image of the other pacifier. This means that newborns are capable of sensing the shape of a pacifier in their mouths and can generalize this perception from the tactual to the visual mode.

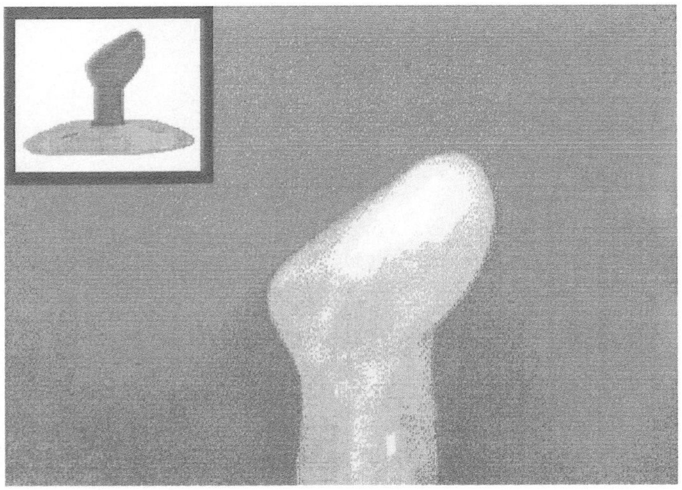

Figure 16.21 ▮ Large image: picture of the end of the pacifier as seen by infants who were looking at a TV monitor. Insert: actual pacifier on which the infant was sucking. See text for details. *(From Kaye and Bower, 1994.)*

An example of intermodal perception involving vision and hearing is Patricia Kuhl and Anthony Meltzoff's (1982) experiment in which $4\frac{1}{2}$-month-old infants observed films of two women's faces (Figure 16.22). One woman was repeating the vowel /i/ as in h*ee*d and the other was repeating /a/ as in h*a*t. As the infant observed both faces, he or she heard just one of these sounds (either the /i/ or the /a/) from a loudspeaker placed between the two faces, and researchers videotaped the infants to determine where they were looking.

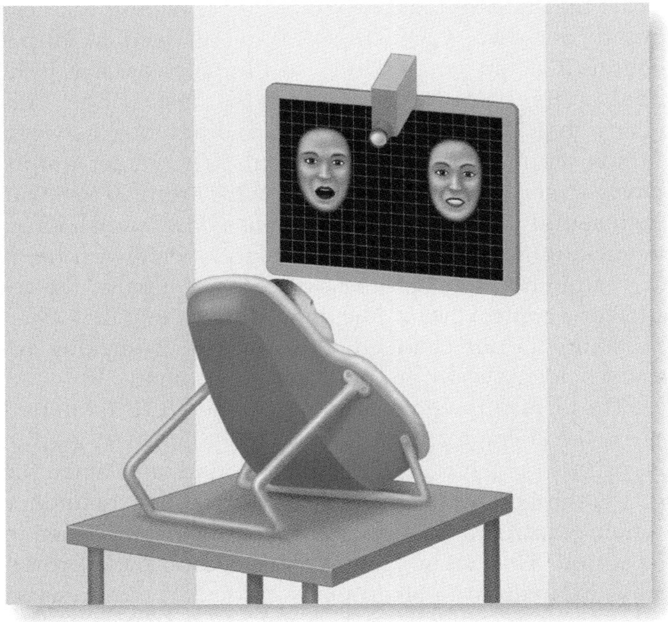

Figure 16.22 ▮ An infant viewing two faces in Kuhl and Meltzoff's (1982) experiment. Infants viewed a film showing the faces of two women, each repeating a different vowel sound. One of the vowel sounds was presented by the loudspeaker, between the faces. The infants' eye movements were videotaped as he or she observed the women's faces. *(Adapted from Kuhl & Meltzoff, 1982.)*

The result of this experiment demonstrated intermodal perception: Infants looked at the face of the woman whose lip movements matched the sound they were hearing 74 percent of the time. These infants were therefore able to determine the correspondence between seeing lip movements and hearing speech sounds. (See Patterson & Werker, 1999, for a recent experiment that reached the same conclusion.)

Infants first begin to look at faces of people who are speaking shortly after birth, when they first see their mother's face and hear her voice. According to a recent study, this pairing of face and voice may be important for determining the infant's preference for the mother's face that we described earlier in this chapter. F. Z. Sai (2005) showed two 12-hour-old newborns two faces—the mother's and a stranger's. The left pair of bars in Figure 16.23 shows that the newborns turned their heads more toward the mother's face, a finding that replicates previous results showing that newborns look more at their mother than at a stranger.

However, Sai also tested a group of newborns whose mothers did not talk to them or make any other sounds until after the infants were tested. Even though the mothers in the "no talking" group had held their infants and played with them in the same way as had the mothers in the "talking" group, the infants who had not heard their mothers talk showed no preference for the mother's face when given a choice between the mother's face and the stranger's face (right pair of bars in Figure 16.23).

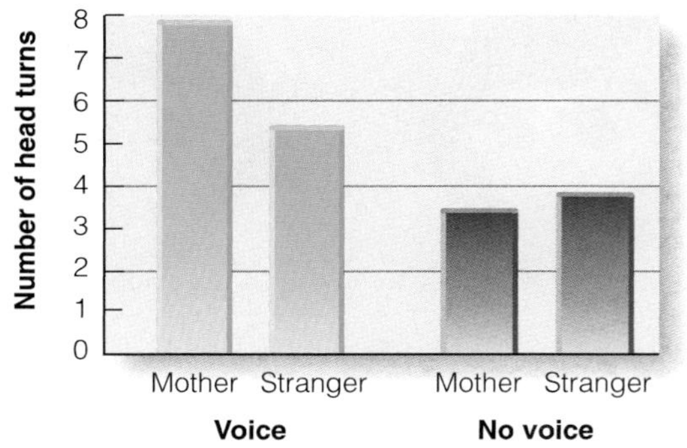

Figure 16.23 ▮ Average number of head turns in the direction of the mother's face or a stranger's face. Left pair of bars: head turns for infants whose mothers talked to them before the experiment. Right pair of bars: head turns for infants whose mothers did not talk to them.
(Adapted from Sai, 2005.)

Why would seeing the mother's face paired with hearing her talk facilitate recognition of the mother's face? Sai suggests that because infants are familiar with the mother's voice even before they are born, from listening to it while in the womb (see p. 364), when they hear this familiar voice paired with the mother's face, this creates a link between the two and helps the infant recognize the mother's face. Thus, intermodal perception is not only present in newborns, but it serves an important function of transferring the infant's familiarity with the mother's voice to the mother's face. (It is important to note, however, that although this result shows that hearing the mother's voice helps the newborn recognize her face, this doesn't mean that recognition cannot be achieved by other means. For example, nonhearing infants' recognition of the mother's face would presumably occur from extended visual experiences and perhaps associating seeing the mother with smelling her odor or with other cues.)

OLFACTION AND TASTE

Do newborn infants perceive odors and tastes? Early researchers, noting that a number of olfactory stimuli elicited responses such as body movements and facial expressions from newborns, concluded that newborns can smell (Kroner, 1881, cited in Peterson & Rainey, 1911). However, some of the stimuli used by these early researchers may have irritated the membranes of the infant's nose, so the infants may have been responding to irritation rather than to smell (Beauchamp, Cowart, & Schmidt, 1991; Doty, 1991).

Modern studies using nonirritating stimuli have, however, provided evidence that newborns can smell and can discriminate between different olfactory stimuli. J. E. Steiner (1974, 1979) used nonirritating stimuli to show that infants respond to banana extract or vanilla extract with sucking and facial expressions that are similar to smiles, and that they respond to concentrated shrimp odor and an odor resembling rotten eggs with rejection or disgust (Figure 16.24).

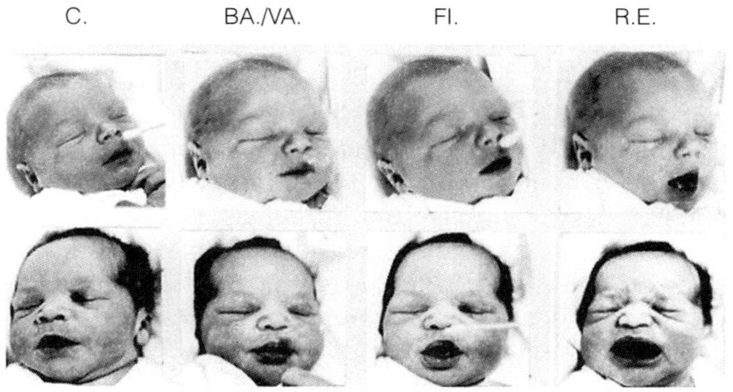

Figure 16.24 ▮ The facial expressions of 3- to 8-hour-old infants in response to some food-related odors. In each of the horizontal rows, the reactions of the same infant can be seen to the following stimulation: C = control, odorless cotton swab; BA/VA = artificial solution of banana or vanilla; FI = artificial fish or shrimp odor; R.E. = artificial rotten egg odor. The infants were tested prior to the first breast- or bottle-feeding.
(Photographs courtesy of J. E. Steiner, The Hebrew University, Jerusalem.)

Research investigating infants' reactions to taste has included numerous studies showing that newborns can discriminate sweet, sour, and bitter stimuli (Beauchamp et al., 1991). For example, newborns react with different facial expressions to sweet, sour, and bitter stimuli but show little or no response to salty stimuli (Figure 16.25; Ganchrow, 1995; Ganchrow, Steiner, & Daher, 1983; Rosenstein & Oster, 1988).

Although responses to taste and olfaction do show some changes as the infant grows into childhood (for example, young infants are indifferent to the taste of salt but develop a response to salty stimuli as they get older; Beauchamp, Bertino, & Engelman, 1991; Beauchamp, Cowart, & Moran, 1986), we could argue that taste and olfaction are the most highly developed of all of the senses at birth.

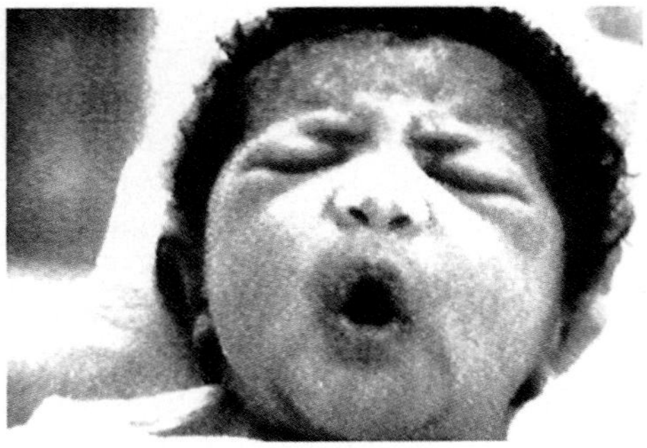

Figure 16.25 ■ The facial expression of an infant who is less than 10 hours old to a sour taste. Specific facial expressions are also associated with bitter and sweet tastes.
(Rosenstein, D., & Oster, H. (1988). Differential facial responses to four basic tastes in newborns. Child Development, *59, 1555–1568.)*

SOMETHING TO CONSIDER: THE UNITY OF PERCEPTION

It is clear that although newborn perception is not as developed as adult perception, the newborn's perceptual abilities far surpass anything imagined by the early psychologists. Not only are infants able to perceive at birth, but they also learn quickly as they experience the environment. This learning often takes the form of perceptual systems becoming tuned to properties of the environment.

We have already described how young infants who can distinguish between a large number of phonemes eventually lose this ability as their hearing becomes tuned to the phonemes of their own language (p. 365). Interestingly enough, the same process appears to occur for distinguishing between faces. Olivier Pascalis and coworkers (2002) demonstrated this by using a procedure called **paired comparison** to determine the ability of infants and adults to recognize human faces and monkey faces.

METHOD ■ Paired Comparison

One stimulus, such as the face on the left in Figure 16.26a, is presented during a familiarization period. Then during the recognition period, this "familiar" stimulus is presented with a new stimulus that the infant has never seen (so both faces in Figure 16.26a are presented together), and the amount of time the infants look at each stimulus is measured. Because infants tend to look more at novel stimuli, if they do look longer at the new face, this means that they can tell the difference between the two faces. Notice that this procedure combines components of the habituation procedure (showing a stimulus until it becomes familiar) and preferential looking (measuring looking time to two side-by-side stimuli).

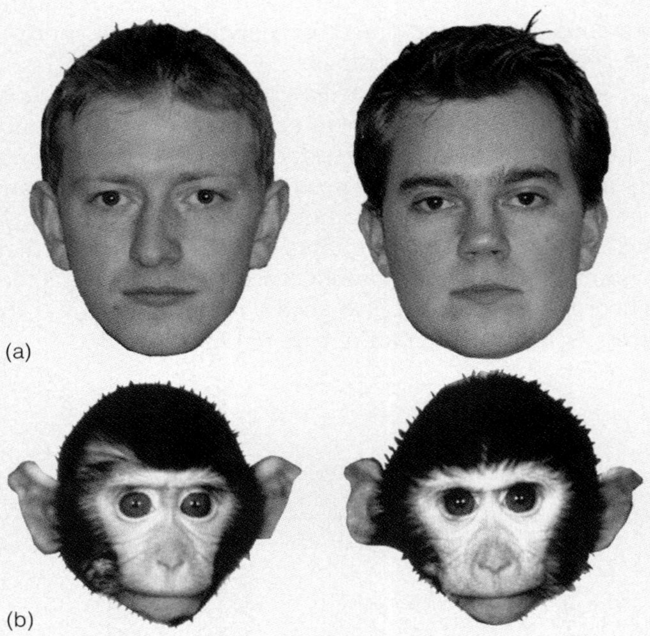

Figure 16.26 ■ Face stimuli presented in the Pascalis et al.'s (2002) experiment. See text for details.
(Pascalis, O., de Haan, M., & Nelson, C. A. (2002). Is face processing species-specific during the first year of life? Science, *296, 1321–1323.)*

■ ■ ■

Pascalis and coworkers first tested adults using the paired-comparison procedure and measured looking time during a 5-second recognition period. The results, shown in Figure 16.27a, reveal that the adults looked more at the novel stimulus when they were familiarized with a human face and then tested with a pair of human faces, but they looked equally when they were familiarized with a monkey face and then tested with a pair of monkey faces like the ones in Figure 16.26b. Thus, adults can distinguish between similar human faces, but not between similar monkey faces.

Figure 16.27b and c shows the results for 6- and 9-month-old infants who were tested in the same way, using a 10-second recognition period. What is striking about these results is that the 6-month-olds discriminated between both human and monkey faces, but the 9-month-olds discriminated only between the human faces. Because the older infants behaved like the adults, Pascalis concluded that, just as for speech, there is an early period during which infants learn, through experience, to discriminate between stimuli that are important in their environment.

As we saw from our discussion of intermodal perception, it may be possible that speech perception and face perception could become tuned in parallel, as infants watch faces that are producing speech. More research is needed, however, to determine whether this does, in fact, occur.

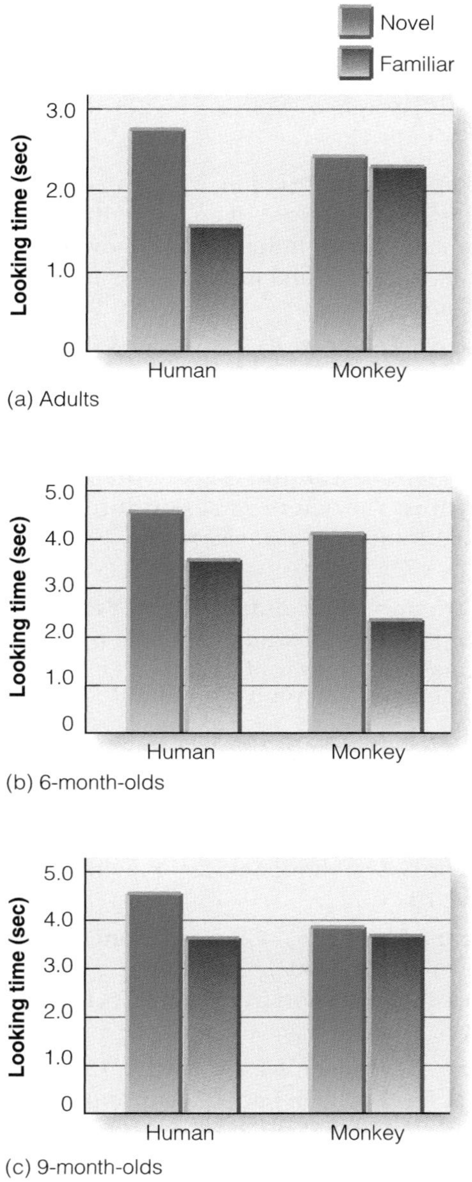

Figure 16.27 ▌ Results of Pascalis et al.'s (2002) experiment. (a) Amount of time adults looked at the face stimuli when a human face they had seen was presented with one they hadn't seen (left pair of bars), and when a monkey face they had seen was presented with one they hadn't seen (right pair of bars). (b) Amount of time 6-month-old infants looked at the human (left) and monkey (right) faces. (c) Amount of time 9-month-old infants looked at the human (left) and monkey (right) faces.

TEST YOURSELF 16.2

1. How have researchers shown that infants can perceive object unity? What type of information is important for the perception of object unity by young infants?
2. How can an infant's threshold for hearing a tone be determined? How do infants' audibility curves compare to adults'?
3. Describe the experiments that showed that newborns can recognize their mother's voice.
4. How did researchers determine that infants are capable of categorical perception of phonemes?
5. What is the evidence that experience in hearing speech tunes the speech-recognition system to become selective to sounds that are used in an infants' native language?
6. What is the evidence for intermodal perception in infants? How might intermodal perception help infants recognize their mother's face?
7. What is the evidence that newborns can perceive odors and tastes?
8. Describe the idea that perception becomes tuned to stimuli in the environment, using examples from perceiving speech and perceiving faces.

THINK ABOUT IT

1. One of the basic principles of perceptual development is that there are some processes that are "built in" or that develop with typical experience (for example, visual acuity), and others that depend more on learning and specific experiences ("tuning" for language and face perception). What are some examples of both of these kinds of processes in object perception (which we discussed in Chapter 5), attention (Chapter 6), movement perception (Chapter 9), and perceiving events (Chapter 10)?
2. The "other race effect" refers to the difficulty people have in distinguishing between members of a different race compared to their own race. Social psychologists have done much of the research on this phenomenon because it plays a role in stereotyping—assigning the same characteristics to all members of a group. Describe how the other race effect relates to (a) your own experience; and (b) developmental processes we have discussed in this chapter.
3. What types of perceptual experiences are possible before birth? Consider smell, taste, touch, hearing and vision.
4. Although measurements of visual acuity indicate that newborns and very young infants see details poorly (page 353), other research shows that young infants can recognize faces. What are some possible explanations for this apparent contradiction?

IF YOU WANT TO KNOW MORE

1. ***Perceptual Segregation*** When you see a coffee cup on a table, you perceive two different objects—the coffee cup and the table. A number of experiments have been done to determine when and under what conditions this ability appears in infants.

Needham, A., & Ormsbee, S. M. (2003). The development of object segregation during the first year of life. In R. Kimchi, M. Behrmann, & C. Olson (Eds.), *Perceptual organization in vision: Behavioral and neural perspectives,* (pp. 205–232). Mahwah, NJ: Erlbaum.

Spelke, E. S., Gutheil, G., & Van de Walle, G. (1995). The development of object perception. In S. M. Kosslyn & D. N. Osherson (Eds.), *Visual cognition* (pp. 297–330). Cambridge, MA: MIT Press.

Wilcox, T., Schweinle, A., & Chapa, C. (2003). Object individuation in infancy. In F. Fagan & H. Hayne (Eds.), *Progress in infancy research* (Vol. 3, pp. 193–243). Mahwah, NJ: Erlbaum.

2. ***Perceptual Organization*** Infants can separate figure from ground and group elements into wholes.

Craton, L. G., & Yonas, A. (1990). The role of motion in infants' perception of occlusion. In J. T. Enns (Ed.), *The development of attention: Research and theory* (pp. 21–46). London: Elsevier.

Quinn, P. C., Burke, S., & Rush, A. (1993). Part-whole perception in early infancy: Evidence for perceptual grouping produced by lightness similarity. *Infant Behavior and Development, 16,* 19–42.

3. ***Preference for Attractive Faces*** Infants' preference for attractive faces suggests that we can't explain "attractiveness" just as something we learn from exposure to the media.

Ramsey, J. L., Langlois, J. H., Hoss, R. A., Rubenstein, A. J., & Griffin, A. M. (2004). Origins of a stereotype: Categorization of facial attributes by 6-month-old infants. *Developmental Science, 7,* 201–211.

Slater et al. (2000). Newborn infants' preference for attractive faces: The role of internal and external facial features. *Infancy, 1,* 265–274.

4. ***Perceiving Movement*** Infants can perceive movement at birth and develop the ability to perceive biological movement later.

Bertenthal, B. I., Proffitt, D. R., Spetner, N. B., & Thomas, M. A. (1985). The development of infant sensitivity to biomechanical motions. *Child Development, 56,* 531–543.

Fox, R., & McDaniel, C. (1982). The perception of biological motion by human infants. *Science, 218,* 486–487.

Nelson, C. A., & Horowitz, F. D. (1987). Visual motion perception in infancy: A review and synthesis. In P. Salapatek & L. Cohen (Eds.), *Handbook of infant perception* (Vol. 2, pp. 123–153). New York: Academic Press.

5. ***Development of Myopia*** Myopia, or nearsightedness, affects 25 percent of adults in the United States. There is evidence linking this condition both to genetic factors (it "runs in families") and to a person's experiences.

Gwiazda, J., Thorn, F., Bauer, J., & Held, R. (1993). Emmetropization and the progression of manifest refraction in children followed from infancy to puberty. *Clinical Visual Science, 8,* 337–344.

Mutti, D. O., Zadnik, K., & Adams, A. J. (1996). Myopia: The nature versus nurture debate goes on. *Investigative Ophthalmology and Visual Science, 37,* 952–957.

Zylbermann, R., Landau, D., & Berson, D. (1993). The influence of study habits on myopia in Jewish teenagers. *Journal of Pediatric Ophthalmology and Strabismus, 30,* 319–322.

6. ***Perceiving Words in Speech*** Young infants can tell the difference between sentences in their native language and sentences in a foreign language. However, they can't do this when cues for separating individual words are eliminated by playing the sentences backward.

Dehaene-Lambertz, G., Dehanene, S., & Hertz-Pannier, L. (2002). Functional neuroimaging of speech perception in primates. *Science, 298,* 2013–2015.

Ramus, F., Hauser, M. D., Miller, C., Morris, D., & Mehler, J. (2000). Language discrimination by human newborns and cotton-top tamarin monkeys. *Science 288,* 349–351.

7. ***Recognizing the Odor of the Mother's Breast*** Just as infants can recognize their mother visually, they can also recognize her by smell.

Balogh, R. D., & Porter, R. H. (1986). Olfactory preferences resulting from mere exposure in human neonates. *Infant Behavior and Development, 9,* 395–401.

Macfarlane, A. (1975). Olfaction in the development of social preferences in the human neonate. In A. Macfarlane (Ed.), *Ciba Foundation Symposium, 33,* 103–117.

Porter, R. H., & Schaal, B. (1995). Olfaction and development of social preferences in neonatal organisms. In R. L. Doty (Ed.), *Handbook of olfaction and gustation* (pp. 299–321). New York: Marcel Dekker.

8. ***Perception and Reasoning About the Physical World*** Infants show "surprise" reactions when an environ-

mentally unlikely event happens, such as when a figure moves behind one object and then emerges from behind another at a different location. This research looks at the links between perception, reasoning, and the knowledge infants have gained by their interactions with the environment.

Baillargeon, R. (2004). Infants' physical world. *Current Directions in Psychological Science, 13,* 89–94.

Wilcox, T., & Schweinle, A. (2002). Object individuation and event mapping: Developmental changes in infants' use of featural information. *Developmental Science, 5,* 132–150.

KEY TERMS

binocularly fixate (p. 358)
contrast sensitivity function (CSF) (p. 355)
dishabituation (p. 357)
habituation (p. 357)
intermodal perception (p. 366)
object unity (p. 361)
paired comparison (p. 368)
preferential looking (PL) technique (p. 352)
prosopagnosia (p. 360)
spatial frequency (p. 355)
visual evoked potential (VEP) (p. 353)

VISIT YOUR COMPANION WEBSITE FOR THIS BOOK

http://psychology.wadsworth.com/goldstein7e

Check out this companion website where you'll find online resources—glossary, flashcards, web links, multiple choice and essay questions, and much more!

APPENDIX

SIGNAL DETECTION: PROCEDURE AND THEORY

In Chapter 1, we surveyed various psychophysical methods for determining the absolute threshold. For example, by randomly presenting tones of different intensities, we can use the method of constant stimuli to determine the intensity to which a person reports "I hear the tone" 50 percent of the time.

But can the experimenter be confident that this intensity truly represents the person's sensory threshold? There are reasons to question the idea of an absolute measure of sensitivity, called the threshold, which is measured by the classic psychophysical methods. We will first discuss why the idea of an absolute threshold has been questioned and will then describe a way of thinking about measuring sensitivity, called signal detection theory, that takes into account both the characteristics of the sensory system and the characteristics of the observer.

IS THERE AN ABSOLUTE THRESHOLD?

To understand why there might be reason to question the idea of an absolute threshold, let's consider a hypothetical experiment. In this experiment, we use the method of constant stimuli to measure two persons' thresholds for hearing a tone. We pick five different tone intensities, present them in random order, and ask our participants to say "yes" if they hear the tone and "no" if they don't hear it.

Julie thinks about these instructions and decides that she wants to appear supersensitive to the tones; because she knows that tones are being presented on every trial, she will answer "yes" if there is even the slightest possibility that she hears the tone. We could call Julie a liberal responder: She is more willing to say "Yes, I hear the tone" than to report that no tone was present.

Regina is given the same instructions, but she doesn't care about being supersensitive. In fact, Regina wants to be totally sure that she hears the tone before saying "yes." We could call Regina a conservative responder: She is not willing to report that she hears the tone unless it is very strong.

The results of this hypothetical experiment are shown in Figure A.1. Julie gives many more "yes" responses than Regina and therefore ends up with a lower threshold. But given what we know about Julie and Regina, should we conclude that Julie is more sensitive to the tones than Regina? It could be that their actual sensitivity to the tones is exactly same, but Julie's apparently lower threshold occurs because she is more willing than Regina to report that she heard a tone.

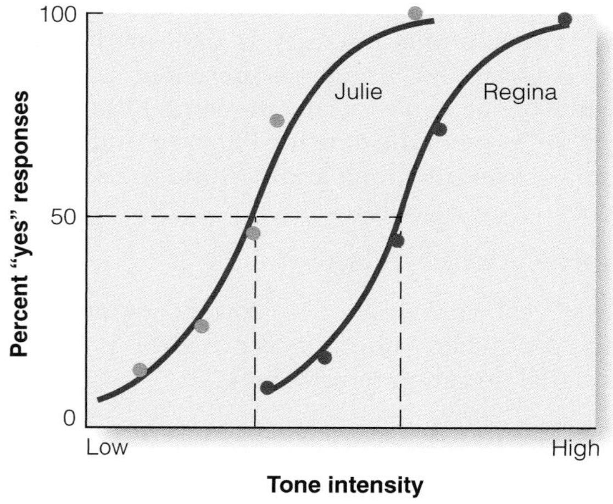

Figure A.1 ▌ Data from experiments in which the threshold for hearing a tone is determined for Julie (green points) and Regina (red points) by means of the method of constant stimuli. These data indicate that Julie's threshold is lower than Regina's. But is Julie really more sensitive to the tone than Regina, or does she just appear to be more sensitive because she is a more liberal responder? Signal detection theory helps provide an answer to this question.

A way to describe the difference between these two people is that each has a different **response criterion**. Julie's response criterion is low (she says "yes" if there is the slightest chance there is a tone present), whereas Regina's response criterion is high (she says "yes" only when she is sure that she heard the tone). That factors other than a person's sensitivity to the signal may influence the results of a psychophysical experiment has caused many researchers to doubt the validity of the absolute threshold, as determined by these psychophysical experiments, and to create new procedures based on a theory called **signal detection theory (SDT)**.

In the next section, we will describe the basic procedure of a signal detection experiment and will show how we can tell whether Regina and Julie are, in fact, equally sensitive to the tone even though their response criteria are very different. After describing the signal detection experiment, we will look at the theory VIRTUAL LAB 1 on which the experiment is based.

A SIGNAL DETECTION EXPERIMENT

Remember that in a psychophysical procedure such as the method of constant stimuli, at least five different tone intensities are presented and that a stimulus is presented on every trial. In a signal detection experiment we use only a single low-intensity tone that is difficult to hear, and we present this tone on some of the trials and present no tone at all on the rest of the trials. Thus, a signal detection experiment differs from a classical psychophysical experiment in two ways: In a signal detection experiment (1) only one stimulus intensity is presented and (2) on some of the trials, no stimulus is presented. Let's consider the results of such an experiment, using Julie as our participant. We present the tone for 100 trials and no tone for 100 trials, mixing the tone and no-tone trials at random. Julie's results are as follows:

When the tone is presented, Julie

- Says "yes" on 90 trials. This correct response—saying "yes" when a stimulus is present—is called a **hit** in signal detection terminology.
- Says "no" on 10 trials. This incorrect response—saying "no" when a stimulus is present—is called a **miss**.

When no tone is presented, Julie

- Says "yes" on 40 trials. This incorrect response—saying "yes" when there is no stimulus—is called a **false alarm**.
- Says "no" on 60 trials. This correct response—saying "no" when there is no stimulus—is called a **correct rejection**.

These results are not very surprising, given that we know Julie has a low criterion and likes to say "yes" a lot. This gives her a high hit rate of 90 percent but also causes her to say "yes" on many trials when no tone is present at all, so her 90 percent hit rate is accompanied by a 40 percent false-alarm rate. If we do a similar experiment on Regina, who has a higher criterion and therefore says "yes" much less often, we find that she has a lower hit rate (say, 60 percent) but also a lower false-alarm rate (say, 10 percent). Note that although Julie and Regina say "yes" on numerous trials on which no stimulus is presented, that result would not be predicted by classical threshold theory. Classical theory would say "no stimulus, no response," but that is clearly not the case here. By adding a new wrinkle to our signal detection experiment, we can obtain another result that would not be predicted by classical threshold theory.

Without changing the tone's intensity at all, we can cause Julie and Regina to change their percentages of hits and false alarms. We do this by manipulating each person's motivation by means of **payoffs**. Let's look at how payoffs might influence Regina's responding. Remember that Regina is a conservative responder who is hesitant to say "yes." But being clever experimenters, we can make Regina say "yes'" more frequently by adding some financial inducements to the experiment. We tell Regina that we are going to reward her for making correct responses and are going to penalize her for making incorrect responses by using the following payoffs:

Hit:	Win $100
Correct rejection:	Win $10
False alarm:	Lose $10
Miss:	Lose $10

What would you do if you were in Regina's position? Being smart, you analyze the payoffs and realize that the way to make money is to say "yes" more. You can lose $10 if a "yes" response results in a false alarm, but this small loss is more than counterbalanced by the $100 you can win for a hit. Although you decide not to say "yes" on every trial—after all, you want to be honest with the experimenter about whether or not you heard the tone—you do decide to stop being so conservative. You decide to change your criterion for saying "yes." The results of this experiment are interesting. Regina becomes a more liberal responder and says "yes" a lot more, responding with 98 percent hits and 90 percent false alarms.

This result is plotted as data point L (for "liberal" response) in Figure A.2, a plot of the percentage of hits versus the percentage of false alarms. The solid curve going through point L is called a **receiver operating characteristic (ROC)** curve. We will see why the ROC curve is important in a moment, but first let's see how we determine the other points on the curve. Doing this is simple: All we have to do is to change the payoffs. We can make Regina raise her criterion and therefore respond more conservatively by means of the following payoffs:

Hit:	Win $10
Correct rejection:	Win $100
False alarm:	Lose $10
Miss:	Lose $10

This schedule of payoffs offers a great inducement to respond conservatively because there is a big reward for

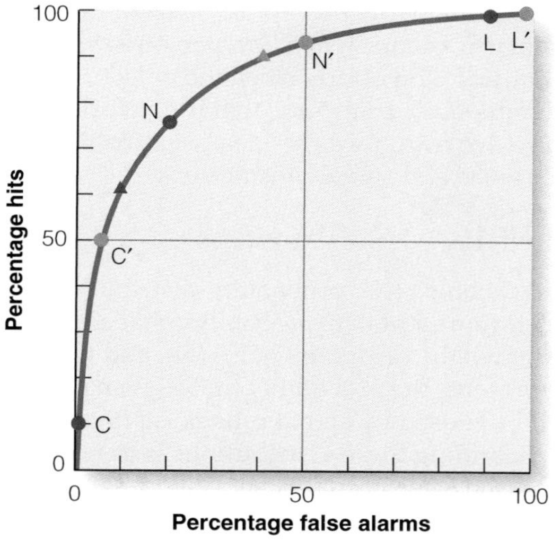

Figure A.2 ▮ A receiver operating characteristic (ROC) curve determined by testing Regina (red data points) and Julie (green data points) under three different criteria: Liberal (L & L′), neutral (N & N′) and conservative (C & C′). The fact that Regina's and Julie's data points all fall on this curve means that they have the same sensitivity to the tone. The triangles indicate the results for Julie and Regina for an experiment that did not use payoffs.

saying "no" when no tone is presented. Regina's criterion is therefore shifted to a much higher level, so Regina now returns to her conservative ways and says "yes" only when she is quite certain that a tone is presented; otherwise she says "no." The result of this newfound conservatism is a hit rate of only 10 percent and a minuscule false-alarm rate of 1 percent, indicated by point C (for "conservative" response) on the ROC curve. We should note that although Regina hits on only 10 percent of the trials in which a tone is presented, she scores a phenomenal 99 percent correct rejections on trials in which a tone is not presented. (This result follows from the fact that, if there are 100 trials in which no tone is presented, then correct rejections + false alarms = 100. Because there was one false alarm, there must be 99 correct rejections.)

Regina, by this time, is rich and decides to put a down payment on the Miata she's been dreaming about. (So far she's won $8,980 in the first experiment and $9,090 in the second experiment, for a total of $18,070! To be sure you understand how the payoff system works, check this calculation yourself. Remember that the signal was presented on 100 trials and was not presented on 100 trials.) However, we point out that she may need a little extra cash to have a satellite audio system installed in her car, so she agrees to stick around for one more experiment. We now use the following neutral schedule of payoffs:

Hit:	Win $10
Correct rejection:	Win $10
False alarm:	Lose $10
Miss:	Lose $10

and obtain point N on the ROC curve: 75 percent hits and 20 percent false alarms. Regina wins $1,100 more and becomes the proud owner of a Miata with a satellite radio system, and we are the proud owners of the world's most expensive ROC curve. (Do not, at this point, go to the psychology department in search of the nearest signal detection experiment. In real life, the payoffs are quite a bit less than in our hypothetical example.)

Regina's ROC curve shows that factors other than sensitivity to the stimulus determine a person's response. Remember that in all of our experiments the intensity of the tone has remained constant. Even though we changed only the person's criterion, we succeeded in drastically changing the person's responses.

Other than demonstrating that people will change how they respond to an unchanging stimulus, what does the ROC curve tell us? Remember, at the beginning of this discussion, we said that a signal detection experiment can tell us whether or not Regina and Julie are equally sensitive to the tone. The beauty of signal detection theory is that the person's sensitivity is indicated by the shape of the ROC curve, so if experiments on two people result in identical ROC curves, their sensitivities must be equal. (This conclusion is not obvious from our discussion so far. We will explain below why the shape of the ROC curve is related to the person's sensitivity.) If we repeat the above experiments on Julie, we get the following results (data points L′, N′, and C′ in Figure A.2):

Liberal payoff:
Hits = 99 percent
False alarms = 95 percent

Neutral payoff:
Hits = 92 percent
False alarms = 50 percent

Conservative payoff:
Hits = 50 percent
False alarms = 6 percent

The data points for Julie's results are shown by the green circles in Figure A.2. Note that although these points are different from Regina's, they fall on the same ROC curve as do Regina's. We have also plotted the data points for the first experiments we did on Julie (green triangle) and Regina (red triangle) before we introduced payoffs. These points also fall on the ROC curve.

That Regina's and Julie's data both fall on the same ROC curve indicates their equal sensitivity to the tones, thus confirming our suspicion that the method of constant stimuli misled us into thinking that Julie is more sensitive, when the real reason for her apparently greater sensitivity is her lower criterion for saying "yes."

Before we leave our signal detection experiment, it is important to note that signal detection procedures can be used without the elaborate payoffs that we described for Regina and Julie. Much briefer procedures, which we will describe shortly, can be used to determine whether differences in the responses of different persons are due to differences in threshold or to differences in the persons' response criteria.

What does signal detection theory tell us about functions such as the spectral sensitivity curve (Figure 2.27) and the audibility function (Figure 11.7), which are usually determined using one of the classical psychophysical methods? When the classical methods are used to determine these functions, it is usually assumed that the person's criterion remains constant throughout the experiment, so that the function measured is due not to changes in their criterion but to changes in the wavelength or some other physical property of the stimulus. This is a good assumption because changing the wavelength of the stimulus probably has little or no effect on factors such as motivation, which would shift the person's criterion. Furthermore, experiments such as the one for determining the spectral sensitivity curve usually use highly experienced people who are trained to give stable results. Thus, even though the idea of an "absolute threshold" may not be strictly correct, classical psychophysical experiments run under well-controlled conditions have remained an important tool for measuring the relationship between stimuli and perception.

SIGNAL DETECTION THEORY

We will now discuss the theoretical basis for the signal detection experiments we have just described. Our purpose is to explain the theoretical bases underlying two ideas: (1) the percentage of hits and false alarms depends on a person's criterion, and (2) a person's sensitivity to a stimulus is indicated by the shape of the person's ROC curve. We will begin by describing two of the key concepts of signal detection theory (SDT): signal and noise. (See Swets, 1964.)

Signal and Noise

The **signal** is the stimulus presented to the person. Thus, in the signal detection experiment we just described, the signal is the tone. The noise is all the other stimuli in the environment, and because the signal is usually very faint, noise can sometimes be mistaken for the signal. Seeing what appears to be a flicker of light in a completely dark room is an example of visual noise. Seeing light where there is none is what we have been calling a false alarm, according to signal detection theory. False alarms are caused by the noise. In the experiment we just described, hearing a tone on a trial in which no tone was presented is an example of auditory noise.

Let's now consider a typical signal detection experiment, in which a signal is presented on some trials and no signal is presented on the other trials. Signal detection theory describes this procedure not in terms of presenting a signal or no signal, but in terms of presenting signal plus noise (S + N) or noise (N). That is, the noise is always present, and on some trials, we add a signal. Either condition can result in the perceptual effect of hearing a tone. A false alarm occurs when the person says "yes" on a noise trial, and a hit occurs when the person says "yes" on a signal-plus-noise trial. Now that we have defined signal and noise, we introduce the idea of probability distributions for noise and signal plus noise.

Probability Distributions

Figure A.3 shows two probability distributions. The one on the left represents the probability that a given perceptual effect will be caused by noise (N), and the one on the right represents the probability that a given perceptual effect will be caused by signal plus noise (S + N). The key to understanding these distributions is to realize that the value labeled "Perceptual effect (loudness)" on the horizontal axis is what the person experiences on each trial. Thus, in an experiment in which the person is asked to indicate whether or not a tone is present, the perceptual effect is the perceived loudness of the tone. Remember that in an SDT experiment the tone always has the same *intensity*. The *loudness* of the tone, however, can vary from trial to trial. The person perceives different loudnesses on different trials, because of either trial-to-trial changes in attention or changes in the state of the person's auditory system.

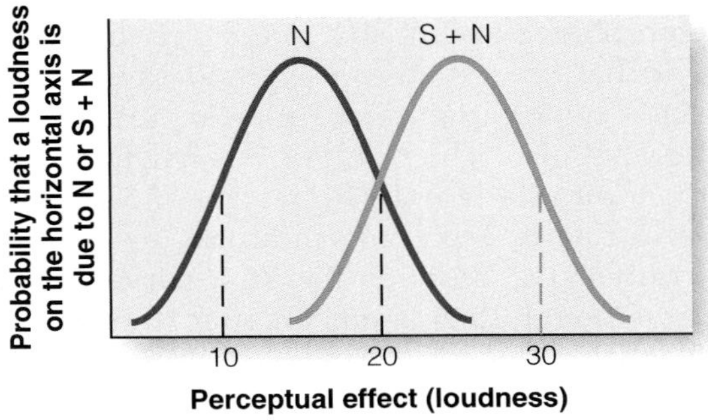

Figure A.3 ▮ Probability distributions for noise alone (N, red curve), and for signal plus noise (S + N, green curve). The probability that any given perceptual effect is caused by the noise (no signal is presented) or by the signal plus noise (signal is presented) can be determined by finding the value of the perceptual effect on the horizontal axis and extending a vertical line up from that value. The place where that line intersects the (N) and (S + N) distributions indicates the probability that the perceptual effect was caused by (N) or by (S + N).

The probability distributions tell us what the chances are that a given loudness of tone is due to (N) or to (S + N). For example, let's assume that a person hears a tone with a loudness of 10 on one of the trials of a signal detection experiment. By extending a vertical dashed line up from 10 on the "Perceptual effect" axis in Figure A.3, we see that the probability that a loudness of 10 is due to (S + N) is extremely low, because the distribution for (S + N) is essentially zero at this loudness. There is, however, a fairly high probability that a loudness of 10 is due to (N), because the (N) distribution is fairly high at this point.

Let's now assume that, on another trial, the person perceives a loudness of 20. The probability distributions indicate that when the tone's loudness is 20, it is equally probable that this loudness is due to (N) or to (S + N). We can also see from Figure A.3 that a tone with a perceived loudness of 30 would have a high probability of being caused by (S + N) and only a small probability of being caused by (N).

Now that we understand the curves of Figure A.3, we can appreciate the problem confronting the person. On each trial, she has to decide whether no tone (N) was present or whether a tone (S + N) was present. However, the overlap in the probability distributions for (N) and (S + N) means that for some perceptual effects this judgment will be difficult. As we saw before, it is equally probable that a tone with a loudness of 20 is due to (N) or to (S + N). So, on a trial in which the person hears a tone with a loudness of 20, how does she decide whether or not the signal was presented? According to signal detection theory, the person's decision depends on the location of her criterion.

The Criterion

We can see how the criterion affects the person's response by looking at Figure A.4. In this figure, we have labeled three different criteria: liberal (L), neutral (N), and conservative (C). Remember that we can cause people to adopt these different criteria by means of different payoffs. According to signal detection theory, once the person adopts a criterion, he or she uses the following rule to decide how to respond on a given trial: If the perceptual effect is greater than (to the right of) the criterion, say, "Yes, the tone was present"; if the perceptual effect is less than (to the left of) the criterion, say, "No, the tone was not present." Let's consider how different criteria influence the person's hits and false alarms.

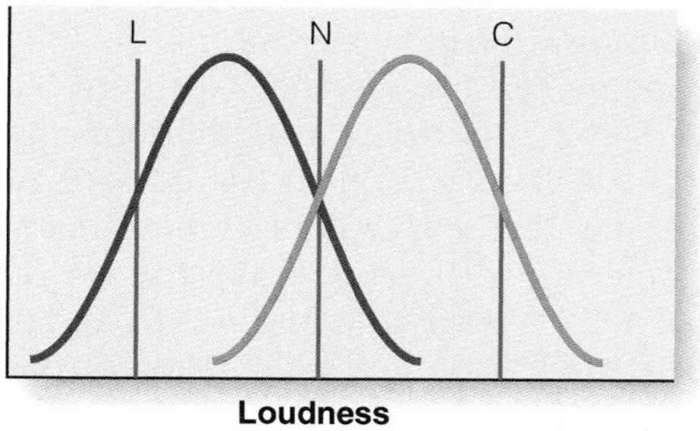

Figure A.4 ▮ The same probability distributions from Figure A.3, showing three criteria: liberal (L), neutral (N), and conservative (C). When a person adopts a criterion, he or she uses the following decision rule: Respond "yes" ("I detect the stimulus") when the perceptual effect is greater than the criterion, and respond "no" ("I do not detect the stimulus") when the perceptual effect is less than the criterion.

Liberal Criterion To determine how criterion L will affect the person's hits and false alarms, we will consider what happens when we present (N) and when we present (S + N):

1. Present (N): Because most of the probability distribution for (N) falls to the right of the criterion, the chances are good that presenting (N) will result in a loudness to the right of the criterion. This means that the probability of saying "yes" when (N) is presented is high; therefore, the probability of a false alarm is high.
2. Present (S + N): Because the entire probability distribution for (S + N) falls to the right of the criterion, the chances are excellent that presenting (S + N) will result in a loudness to the right of the criterion. Thus, the probability of saying "yes" when the signal is presented is high; therefore, the probability of a hit is high. Because criterion L results in high false alarms and high hits, adopting that criterion will result in point L on the ROC curve in Figure A.5.

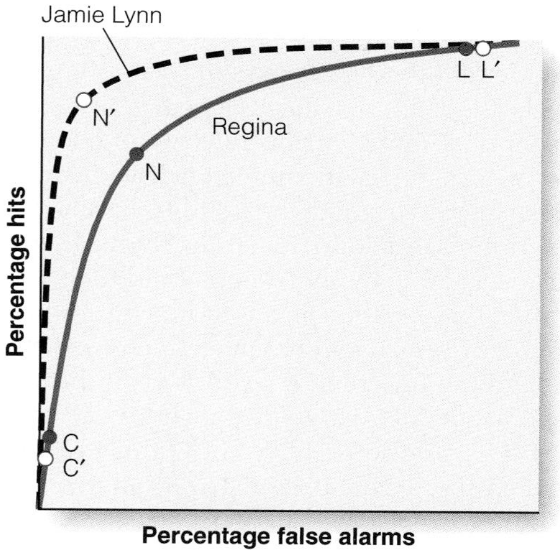

Figure A.5 ▮ ROC curves for Regina (solid curve) and Jamie Lynn (dashed curve) determined using liberal (L, L′), neutral (N, N′) and conservative (C, C′) criteria.

Neutral Criterion

1. Present (N): The person will answer "yes" only rarely when (N) is presented because only a small portion of the (N) distribution falls to the right of the criterion. The false-alarm rate, therefore, will be fairly low.
2. Present (S + N): The person will answer "yes" frequently when (S + N) is presented because most of the (S + N) distribution falls to the right of the criterion. The hit rate, therefore, will be fairly high (but not as high as for the L criterion). Criterion N results in point N on the ROC curve in Figure A.5.

Conservative Criterion

1. Present (N): False alarms will be very low because none of the (N) curve falls to the right of the criterion.
2. Present (S + N): Hits will also be low because only a small portion of the (S + N) curve falls to the right of the criterion. Criterion C results in point C on the ROC curve in Figure A.5.

You can see that applying different criteria to the probability distributions generates the solid ROC curve in Figure A.5. But why are these probability distributions necessary? After all, when we described the experiment with Regina and Julie, we determined the ROC curve simply by plotting the results of the experiment. The reason the (N) and (S + N) distributions are important is that, according to signal detection theory, the person's sensitivity to a stimulus is indicated by the distance (d′) between the peaks of the (N) and (S + N) distributions, and this distance affects the shape of the ROC curve. We will now consider how the person's sensitivity to a stimulus affects the shape of the ROC curve.

The Effect of Sensitivity on the ROC Curve

We can understand how the person's sensitivity to a stimulus affects the shape of the ROC curve by considering what the probability distributions would look like for Jamie Lynn, a person with supersensitive hearing. Jamie Lynn's hearing is so good that a tone barely audible to Regina sounds very loud to Jamie Lynn. If presenting (S + N) causes Jamie Lynn to hear a loud tone, this means that her (S + N) distribution should be far to the right, as shown in Figure A.6. In signal detection terms, we would say that Jamie Lynn's high sensitivity is indicated by the large separation (d′) between the (N) and the (S + N) probability distributions. To see how this greater separation between the probability distributions will affect her

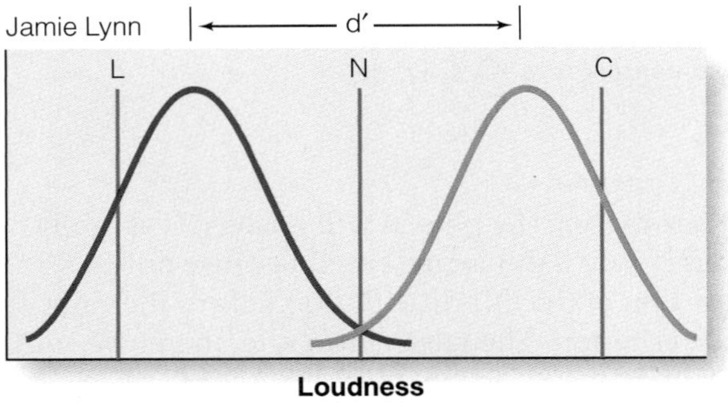

Figure A.6 ▌ Probability distributions for Jamie Lynn, a person who is extremely sensitive to the signal. The noise distribution (red) remains the same, but the (S + N) distribution (green) is shifted to the right compared to the curves in Figure A.4. Liberal (L), neutral (N), and conservative (C) criteria are shown.

ROC curve, let's see how she would respond when adopting liberal, neutral, and conservative criteria.

Liberal Criterion

1. Present (N): high false alarms.
2. Present (S + N): high hits.

The liberal criterion, therefore, results in point L′ on the ROC curve of Figure A.5.

Neutral Criterion

1. Present (N): low false alarms. It is important to note that Jamie Lynn's false alarms for the neutral criterion will be lower than Regina's false alarms for the neutral criterion because only a small portion of Jamie Lynn's (N) distribution falls to the right of the criterion, whereas some of Regina's (N) distribution falls to the right of the neutral criterion (Figure A.4).
2. Present (S + N): high hits. In this case Jamie Lynn's hits will be higher than Regina's because all of Jamie Lynn's (S + N) distribution falls to the right of the neutral criterion, whereas not all of Regina's does (Figure A.4). The neutral criterion, therefore, results in point N′ on the ROC curve in Figure A.5.

Conservative Criterion

1. Present (N): low false alarms.
2. Present (S + N): low hits. The conservative criterion, therefore, results in point C′ on the ROC curve.

The difference between the two ROC curves in Figure A.5 is obvious because Jamie Lynn's curve is more "bowed." But before you conclude that the difference between these two ROC curves has anything to do with where we positioned Jamie Lynn's L, N, and C criteria, see whether you can get an ROC curve like Jamie Lynn's from the two probability distributions of Figure A.4. You will find that, no matter where you position the criteria, there is no way that you can get a point like point N′ (with very high hits and very low false alarms) from the curves of Figure A.4. In order to achieve very high hits and very low false alarms, the two probability distributions must be spaced far apart, as in Figure A.6.

Thus, increasing the distance (d′) between the (N) and the (S + N) probability distributions changes the shape of the ROC curve. When the person's sensitivity (d′) is high, the ROC curve is more bowed. In practice, d′ can be determined by comparing the experimentally determined ROC curve to standard ROC curves (see Gescheider, 1976), or d′ can be calculated from the proportions of hits and false alarms that occur in an experiment by means of a mathematical procedure we will not discuss here. This mathematical procedure for calculating d′ enables us to determine a person's sensitivity by determining only one data point on an ROC curve, thus, using the signal detection procedure without running a large number of trials.

GLOSSARY

The number in parentheses after each item indicates the chapter in which the term is introduced. When more than one chapter is indicated, this means that the term is also discussed at length in the second chapter.

Ablation. Removal of an area of the brain. This is usually done in experiments on animals, to determine the function of a particular area. Also called lesioning. (4)

Absolute threshold. See Threshold, absolute.

Absorption spectrum. A plot of the amount of light absorbed by a visual pigment versus the wavelength of light. (2)

Accidental property. A property of objects that only occurs when viewing the object from a specific, rarely encountered, viewpoint. For example, although three sides of a solid cube are visible from most viewpoints, an accidental property occurs when the cube is viewed end-on, so only one side is visible. (5)

Accommodation (depth cue). A depth cue based on muscular sensations that occur when the eye accommodates to bring objects at different distances into focus. This cue provides information about the distances of nearby objects. (8)

Accommodation (focus). In vision, bringing objects located at different distances into focus by changing the shape of the lens. (2)

Accretion. A cue that provides information about the relative depth of two surfaces. Occurs when the farther object is uncovered by the nearer object due to sideways movement of an observer relative to the objects. See also Deletion. (8)

Achromatic color. Color without hue. White, black, and all the grays between these two extremes are achromatic colors. (7)

Acoustic shadow. The shadow created by the head that decreases the level of high-frequency sounds on the opposite side of the head. The acoustic shadow is the basis of the localization cue of interaural level difference. (12)

Acoustic signal. The pattern of frequencies and intensities of the sound stimulus. (13)

Acoustic stimulus. See Acoustic signal.

Across-fiber patterns. The pattern of firing that a stimulus causes across a number of neurons. This is the same thing as distributed coding. (15)

Action. Motor activities such as moving the head or eyes and locomoting through the environment. Action is one of the major outcomes of the perceptual process. (1)

Action pathway. See Dorsal pathway.

Action potential. Rapid increase in positive charge in a nerve fiber that travels down the fiber. Also called the nerve impulse. (2)

Active touch. Touch in which the observer plays an active role in touching and exploring an object, usually with his or her hands. (14)

Additive color mixture. See Color mixture, additive.

Additive synthesis. In hearing, the process of building a complex tone by starting with the fundamental frequency and adding pure tone harmonics. (11)

Adjustment, method of. A psychophysical method in which the experimenter or the observer adjusts the stimulus intensity in a continuous manner until the observer detects the stimulus. (1)

Affective (or emotional) component of pain. The emotional experience associated with pain—for example, pain described as *torturing, annoying, frightful,* or *sickening.* See also Sensory component of pain. (14)

Affordance. The information specified by a stimulus pattern that indicates how the stimulus can be used. An example of an affordance would be seeing a chair as something to sit on or a flight of stairs as something to climb. (10)

Agnosia. The inability to recognize objects. (1)

Algorithm. A procedure that is guaranteed to result in the solution to a problem. For example, the procedures we learn for addition, subtraction, and long division are algorithms. (5)

Amacrine cell. A neuron that transmits signals laterally in the retina. Amacrine cells synapse with bipolar cells and ganglion cells. (3)

Ames room. A distorted room, first built by Adelbert Ames, which creates an erroneous perception of the sizes of people in the room. The room is constructed so that two people at the far wall of the room appear to stand at the same distance from an observer. In actuality, one of the people is much farther away than the other. (8)

Amiloride. A substance that blocks the flow of sodium into taste receptors. (15)

Amodal representation. An internal description of a stimulus that holds across more than one modality. (16)

Amplitude. In the case of a repeating sound wave, such as the sine wave of a pure tone, amplitude represents the pressure difference between atmospheric pressure and the maximum pressure of the wave. (11)

Amygdala. A subcortical structure that is involved in emotional responding and in processing olfactory signals. (15)

Angle of disparity. The visual angle between the images of an object on the two retinas. When images of an object fall on corresponding points, the angle of disparity is zero. When images fall on noncorresponding points, the angle of disparity indicates the degree of noncorrespondence. (8)

Angular size-contrast theory. An explanation of the moon illusion that states that the perceived size of the moon is determined by the sizes of the objects that surround it. According to this idea, the moon appears small when it is surrounded by large objects, such as the expanse of the sky when the moon is overhead. (8)

Anomalous trichromat. A person who needs to mix a minimum of three wavelengths to match any other wavelength in the spectrum but mixes these wavelengths in different proportions from a trichromat. (7)

Anosmia. Loss of the ability to smell due to injury or infection. (15)

Aperture problem. A situation in which only a portion of a moving stimulus can be seen, as when the stimulus is viewed through a narrow aperture. This results in misleading information about the direction in which the stimulus is moving. (9)

Apex of the cochlea. The end of the basilar membrane farthest from the middle ear. (11)

Aphasia. Difficulties in speaking or understanding speech due to brain damage. (13)

Apparent-distance theory. An explanation of the moon illusion that is based on the idea that the horizon moon, which is viewed across the filled space of the terrain, should appear farther away than the zenith moon, which is viewed through the empty space of the sky. This theory states that because the horizon and zenith moons have the same visual angle, the farther appearing horizon moon should appear larger. (8)

Apparent movement (or **stroboscopic movement).** An illusion of movement that occurs between two objects separated in space when the objects are flashed rapidly on and off, one after another, separated by a brief time interval. (5, 9)

Architectural acoustics. The study of how sounds are reflected in rooms. An important concern of architectural acoustics is how these reflected sounds change the quality of the sounds we hear in rooms. (12)

Articulator. Structure involved in speech production, such as the tongue, lips, teeth, jaw, and soft palate. (13)

Atmospheric perspective. A depth cue. Objects that are farther away look more blurred and bluer than objects that are closer because we must look through more air and particles to see them. (8)

Attack. The buildup of sound at the beginning of a tone. (12)

Attended stimulus. The stimulus that is being attended by a person at a given point in time. (1)

Attention. The process of seeking out and focusing on stimuli that are of interest in a way that causes these features to become more deeply processed than those features that are not receiving our attention. (6)

Audibility curve. A curve that indicates the sound pressure level (SPL) at threshold for frequencies across the audible spectrum. (11)

Audiovisual mirror neuron. Neuron that responds to actions that produce sounds. These neurons respond when a monkey performs a hand-action *and* also when it hears the sound associated with this action. See also Mirror neuron. (10)

Audiovisual speech perception. A perception of speech that is affected by both auditory and visual stimulation, as when a person sees a tape of someone saying /ga/ with the sound /ba/ substituted and perceives /da/. Also called the McGurk effect. (13)

Auditory canal. The canal through which air vibrations travel from the environment to the tympanic membrane. (11)

Auditory grouping, principles of. Principles such as similarity and good continuation that operate to group sounds into perceptual streams. See also Auditory stream segregation; Auditory scene analysis. (12)

Auditory localization. The perception of the location of a sound source. (12)

Auditory masking. See Masking (auditory).

Auditory receiving area (A1). The area of the cortex, located in the temporal lobe, that is the primary receiving area for hearing. (11)

Auditory response area. The psychophysically measured area that defines the frequencies and sound pressure levels over which hearing functions. This area extends between the audibility curve and the curve for the threshold of feeling. (11)

Auditory scene. The sound environment, which includes the locations and qualities of individual sound sources. (12)

Auditory scene analysis. The process by which listeners sort superimposed vibrations into separate sounds. See also Auditory grouping, principles of. (12)

Auditory space. Perception of where sounds are located in space. Auditory space extends around a listener's head in all directions, existing wherever there is a sound. (12)

Auditory stream segregation. The effect that occurs when a series of tones that differ in pitch or timbre are played so these tones become perceptually separated into simultaneously occurring independent streams of sound. (12)

Axon. The part of the neuron that conducts nerve impulses over distances. Also called the nerve fiber. (2)

Azimuth coordinate. In hearing, specifies locations that vary from left to right relative to the listener. (12)

Balint's syndrome. A condition resulting from damage to a person's parietal lobe. One characteristic of this syndrome is an inability to focus attention on individual objects. (6)

Base of the cochlea. The part of the basilar membrane nearest the middle ear. (11)

Basilar membrane. A membrane that stretches the length of the cochlea and controls the vibration of the cochlear partition. (11)

Belongingness. The hypothesis that an area's appearance is influenced by the part of the surroundings that the area appears to belong to. This principle has been used to explain the perception of lightness in the Benary cross and White's illusion. (3)

Belt area. Auditory area in the temporal lobe that receives signals from the core area and sends signals to the parabelt area. (11)

Benary cross. A display in which two gray wavelengths associated with a black cross look different even though they are physically the same. It is perceptually significant because the two areas that appear different both receive the same amount of lateral inhibition. (3)

Bimodal neuron. A neuron that responds to stimuli associated with more than one sense. (15)

Binaural cue. Sound localization cue that involves both ears. (12)

Binding. The process by which features—such as color, form, motion, and location—are combined to create our perception of a coherent object. (6)

Binding problem. The problem of how neural activity in many separated areas in the brain is combined to create a perception of a coherent object. (6)

Binocular depth cell. A neuron in the visual cortex that responds best to stimuli that fall on points separated by a specific degree of disparity on the two retinas. Also called Disparity-selective cell. (8)

Binocular disparity. Occurs when the retinal images of an object fall on disparate points on the two retinas. (8)

Binocularly fixate. Directing the two foveas to exactly the same spot. (16)

Binocular rivalry. A situation in which two different images are simultaneously presented to the left and right eyes and perception alternates back and forth between the two images. (4)

Biological motion. Motion produced by biological organisms. Most of the experiments on biological motion have used walking humans with lights attached to their joints and limbs as stimuli. See also Point-light walkers. (9)

Bipolar cell. A retinal neuron that receives inputs from the visual receptors and sends signals to the retinal ganglion cells. (3)

Blind spot. The small area where the optic nerve leaves the back of the eye; there are no visual receptors in this area so small images falling directly on the blind spot cannot be seen. (2)

Border ownership. When two areas share a border, as occurs in figure–ground displays, the border is usually perceived as belonging to the figure. (5)

Bottom-up processing. Processing in which a person constructs a perception by analyzing the information falling on the receptors. Also called data-based processing. (1)

Brain imaging. Procedures that make it possible to visualize areas of the human brain that are activated by different types of stimuli, tasks, or behaviors. The two most common techniques used in perception research are positron emission tomography (PET) and functional magnetic resonance imaging (fMRI). (4)

Broca's aphasia. Language problems, caused by damage to Broca's area in the frontal lobe, characterized by labored and stilted speech and short sentences. (13)

Broca's area. An area in the frontal lobe that is important for language perception and production. One effect of damage is difficulty in speaking. (13)

Calcium imaging. Technique used to identify olfactory receptors activated by an odorant. (15)

Categorical perception. In speech perception, perceiving one sound at short voice onset times and another sound at longer voice onset times. The listener perceives only two categories across the whole range of voice onset times. (13)

Cell body. The part of a neuron that contains the neuron's metabolic machinery and that receives stimulation from other neurons. (2)

Center-surround antagonism. The competition between the center and surround regions of a center-surround receptive field, caused by the fact that one is excitatory and the other is inhibitory. Stimulating center and surround areas simultaneously decreases responding of the neuron, compared to stimulating the excitatory area alone. (3)

Center-surround receptive field. A receptive field that consists of a roughly circular excitatory area surrounded by an inhibitory area, or a circular inhibitory center surrounded by an excitatory surround. (3)

Central pitch processor. A hypothetical central mechanism that analyzes the pattern of a tone's harmonics and selects the fundamental frequency that is most likely to have been part of that pattern. It has been proposed that this mechanism is involved in our perception of periodicity pitch. (11)

Cerebral achromatopsia. A loss of color vision caused by damage to the cortex. (7)

Change blindness. Difficulty in detecting differences between two visual stimuli that are presented with another stimulus interposed between them. Also occurs when part of a stimulus is changed very slowly. (6)

Change blindness blindness. The finding that people predict that they would detect changes between the stimuli presented in change blindness experiments, even though they usually fail to detect these changes during an actual experiment. (6)

Characteristic frequency. The frequency at which a neuron in the auditory system has its lowest threshold. (11)

Chorda tympani nerve. A nerve that transmits signals from receptors on the front and sides of the tongue. (15)

Chromatic adaptation. Prolonged exposure to light in a specific part of the visible spectrum, which adapts receptors that fire to these wavelengths by selectively bleaching a specific visual pigment. For example, adaptation to a long-wavelength light selectively bleaches the long-wavelength pigment. The perceptual effect of adapting to long-wavelength light is a decrease in sensitivity to these wavelengths. Chromatic adaptation has been proposed as one of the mechanisms responsible for color constancy. (7)

Chromatic color. Color with hue, such as blue, yellow, red, and green. (7)

Cilia. Fine hairs that protrude from the inner and outer hair cells of the auditory system. Bending the cilia of the inner hair cells leads to transduction. (11)

Classical psychophysical methods. The methods of limits, adjustment, and constant stimuli, described by Fechner that are used for measuring thresholds. (1)

Coarticulation. The overlapping articulation that occurs when different phonemes follow one another in speech. Because of these effects, the same phoneme can be articulated differently depending on the context in which it appears. For example, articulation of the /b/ in *boot* is different from articulation of the /b/ in *boat*. (13)

Cochlea. The snail-shaped, liquid-filled structure that contains the structures of the inner ear, the most important of which are the basilar membrane, the tectorial membrane, and the hair cells. (11)

Cochlear implant. A device in which electrodes are inserted into the cochlea to create hearing by electrically stimulating the auditory nerve fibers. This device is used to restore hearing in people who have lost their hearing because of damaged hair cells. (11)

Cochlear nucleus. The nucleus where nerve fibers from the cochlea first synapse. (11)

Cochlear partition. A partition in the cochlea, extending almost its full length, that separates the scala tympani and the scala vestibuli. The organ of Corti, which contains the hair cells, is part of the cochlear partition. (11)

Cognitive influences on perception. How the knowledge, memories, and expectations that a person brings to a situation influence his or her perception. (1)

Coherence. A term used to describe the degree of correlation between the direction of moving objects. In displays containing many moving dots, zero percent coherence means all of the dots are moving independently; 100 percent coherence means all of the dots are moving in the same direction. (9)

Color, achromatic. See Achromatic color.

Color, chromatic. See Chromatic color.

Color-blindness. A condition in which a person perceives no chromatic color. This can be caused by absent or malfunctioning cone receptors or by cortical damage. (7)

Color constancy. The effect in which the perception of an object's hue remains constant even when the wavelength distribution of the illumination is changed. Approximate color constancy means that our perception of hue usually changes a little when the illumination changes, though not as much as we might expect from the change in the wavelengths of light reaching the eye. (7)

Color deficiency. People with this condition (sometimes incorrectly called color blindness) see fewer colors than people with normal color vision and need to mix fewer wavelengths to match any other wavelength in the spectrum. (7)

Color-matching experiment. A procedure in which observers are asked to match the color in one field by mixing two or more lights in another field. (7)

Color mixture, additive. The creation of colors that occurs when lights of different colors are superimposed. (7)

Color mixture, subtractive. The creation of colors that occurs when paints of different colors are mixed together. (7)

Combinatorial code for odor. The concept that different odorants are coded by different combinations of olfactory receptors, but a particular olfactory receptor may participate in the code for many odorants. (15)

Common fate, law of. A Gestalt law of perceptual organization that states that things that are moving in the same direction appear to be grouped together. (5)

Common region, principle of. A modern Gestalt principle that states that elements that are within the same region of space appear to be grouped together. (5)

Comparator. A structure hypothesized by the corollary discharge theory of movement perception. The corollary discharge signal and the sensory movement signal meet at the comparator to determine whether movement will be perceived. (9)

Complex cell. A neuron in the visual cortex that responds best to moving bars with a particular orientation. (3)

Componential recovery, principle of. A principle of the recognition-by-components model that states that we can rapidly and correctly identify an object if we can perceive its individual geons. (5)

Cones. Cone-shaped receptors in the retina that are primarily responsible for vision in high levels of illumination and for color vision and detail vision. (2)

Conflicting cues theory. A theory of visual illusions proposed by R. H. Day, which states that our perception of line length depends on an integration of the actual line length and the overall figure length. (8)

Conjunction search. A visual search task in which it is necessary to search for a combination (or conjunction) of two or more features on the same stimulus to find the target. An example of a conjunction search would be looking for a horizontal green line among vertical green lines and horizontal red lines. (6)

Constant stimuli, method of. A psychophysical method in which a number of stimuli with different intensities are presented repeatedly in a random order. (1)

Contextual modulation. When the neural response to a stimulus is influenced by the context within which the stimulus occurs. This term has been used to refer to the situation in which a neuron's response is influenced by stimulation of an area outside its receptive field. (5)

Contralateral eye. The eye on the opposite side of the head from a particular structure. (4)

Contrast. The difference in light intensity between two areas. For a visual grating stimulus, the contrast is the amplitude of the grating divided by its mean intensity. (3)

Contrast sensitivity. Sensitivity to the difference in the light intensities in two adjacent areas. Contrast sensitivity is usually measured by taking the reciprocal of the minimum intensity difference between two bars of a grating necessary to see the bars. (3)

Contrast sensitivity function (CSF). A plot of contrast sensitivity versus the spatial frequency of a grating stimulus. (16)

Contrast threshold. The intensity difference that can just barely be seen between two areas. This is often measured using gratings with alternating light and dark bars. (3)

Convergence (depth cue). See Perspective convergence.

Convergence (neural). When many neurons synapse onto a single neuron. (3)

Core area. The area in the temporal lobe that includes the primary auditory cortex (A1) and some nearby areas. Signals from the core area are transmitted to the belt area of auditory cortex. (11)

Cornea. The transparent focusing element of the eye that is the first structure through which light passes as it enters the eye. The cornea is the eye's major focusing element. (2)

Corollary discharge signal (CDS). A copy of the signal sent from the motor area of the brain to the eye muscles. The corollary discharge signal is sent to the hypothetical comparator of corollary discharge theory. (9)

Corollary discharge theory. According to this theory of motion perception, a corollary discharge signal, which is a copy of the signal sent from the motor area to initiate an eye movement, is sent to a structure called the comparator. At the comparator, information in the corollary discharge is compared to the sensory movement signal. If the corollary discharge signal and the sensory movement signal do not cancel each other, movement is perceived. (9)

Correct rejection. In a signal detection experiment, saying, "No, I don't detect a stimulus" on a trial in which the stimulus is not presented (a correct response). (Appendix)

Correspondence problem. The visual system's matching of points on one image with similar points on the other image in order to determine binocular disparity. (8)

Corresponding retinal points. The points on each retina that would overlap if one retina were slid on top of the other. Receptors at corresponding points send their signals to the same location in the brain. (8)

Cortical magnification factor. See Magnification factor.

Crossed disparity. Binocular disparity in which objects are located in front of the horopter. (8)

Cue approach to depth perception. The approach to explaining depth perception that identifies information in the retinal image, and also information provided by aiming and focusing the eyes on an object that is correlated with depth in the scene. Some of the depth cues that have been identified are overlap, relative height, relative size, atmospheric perspective, convergence, and accommodation. (8)

Cutaneous sensations. Sensations based on the stimulation of receptors in the skin. (14)

Dark adaptation. Visual adaptation that occurs in the dark, during which the sensitivity to light increases. This increase in sensitivity is associated with regeneration of the rod and cone visual pigments. (2)

Dark adaptation curve. The function that traces the time course of the increase in visual sensitivity that occurs during dark adaptation. (2)

Dark-adapted sensitivity. The sensitivity of the eye after it has completely adapted to the dark. (2)

Data-based processing. Another name for bottom-up processing. Refers to processing that is based on incoming data, as opposed to top-down, or knowledge-based, processing, which is based on prior knowledge. (1)

Decay. The decrease in the sound signal that occurs at the end of a tone. (11)

Decibel (dB). A unit that indicates the presence of a tone relative to a reference pressure: $dB = 20 \log (p/p_o)$ where p is the pressure of the tone and p_o is the reference pressure. (11)

Delayed-matching-to-sample procedure. A procedure in which a sample stimulus is presented, followed by a delay period, followed by a test period. During the test period, the same stimulus or a different one is presented. The task is to indicate whether the test stimulus is the same as or different from the sample stimulus. (5)

Deletion. A cue that provides information about the relative depth of the two surfaces. Deletion occurs when a farther object is covered by a nearer object due to sideways movement of an observer relative to the objects. See also Accretion. (8)

Dendrites. Nerve processes on the cell body that receive stimulation from other neurons. (2)

Depolarization. When the inside of a neuron becomes more positive, as occurs during the initial phases of the action potential. Depolarization is often associated with the action of excitatory neurotransmitters. (2)

Dermis. The inner layer of skin that contains nerve endings and receptors. (14)

Desaturated. Low saturation in chromatic colors as would occur when white is added to a color. For example, pink is not as saturated as red. (7)

Detached retina. A condition in which the retina is detached from the back of the eye. (2)

Detection threshold. See Threshold, detection.

Deuteranopia. A form of red–green color dichromatism caused by lack of the middle-wavelength cone pigment. (7)

Dichromat. A person who has a form of color deficiency. Dichromats can match any wavelength in the spectrum by mixing two other wavelengths. Deuteranopes, protanopes, and tritanopes are all dichromats. (7)

Difference threshold. See Threshold, difference.

Direct sound. Sound that is transmitted directly from a sound source to the ears. (12)

Discriminability. Generally, the ability to distinguish between one stimulus and another. In the recognition-by-components theory of object perception, discriminability is a property of geons, which indicates that each geon can be distinguished from other geons from almost all viewpoints. (5)

Dishabituation. An increase in looking time that occurs when a stimulus is changed. This response is used in testing infants to see whether they can differentiate two stimuli. (16)

Disparate points. See Noncorresponding points.

Disparity detectors. Neurons that respond best to stimuli that fall on retinal points separated by a specific angle of disparity. Also called binocular depth cells. (8)

Disparity-selective cell. See Binocular depth cell.

Dissociation. A situation that occurs as a result of brain damage in which one function is present and another is absent. See also Double dissociation; Single dissociation. (4)

Distance coordinate. In hearing, this coordinate specifies how far the sound source is from the listener. (12)

Distributed coding. Type of neural code in which different perceptions are signaled by the pattern of activity that is distributed across many neurons. See also Specificity coding. (4)

Divided attention. Directing attention to a number of things at once. (6)

Doctrine of specific nerve energies. A principle proposed by Mueller, which states that our perceptions depend on "nerve energies" reaching the brain and that the specific quality we experience depends on which nerves are stimulated. For example, activating the optic nerve results in seeing, and activating the auditory nerve results in hearing. (2)

Dorsal pathway. Pathway that conducts signals from the striate cortex to the parietal lobe. This is also called the *where,* the *how,* and the *action* pathway to indicate its function. (4)

Double dissociation. In brain damage, when function A is present and function B is absent, and, in another person, when function A is absent and function B is present. Presence of a double dissociation means that the two functions involve different mechanisms and operate independently of one another. (4)

Duplex theory of texture perception. The idea that texture perception is determined by both spatial and temporal cues that are detected by two types of receptors. Originally proposed by David Katz and named the "duplex theory" by Hollins. (14)

Eardrum. Another term for the tympanic membrane, the membrane located at the end of the auditory canal that vibrates in response to sound. (11)

Echo threshold. The time separation at which two sounds presented at different locations are no longer fused, so two separate sounds are heard. At separations shorter than the echo threshold, the two sound sources are heard as one. (12)

Ecological approach to perception. This approach focuses on studying perception as it occurs in natural settings, particularly emphasizing the role of observer movement. (10)

Effect of the missing fundamental. Removing the fundamental frequency and other lower harmonies from a musical tone does not change the tone's pitch. See also Periodicity pitch. (11)

Electromagnetic spectrum. Continuum of electromagnetic energy that extends from very-short-wavelength gamma rays to long-wavelength radio waves. Visible light is a narrow band within this spectrum. (2)

Elevation coordinate. In hearing, sound locations that are up and down relative to the listener. (12)

Emmert's law. A law stating that the size of an afterimage depends on the distance of the surface against which the afterimage is viewed. The farther away the surface, the larger the afterimage appears. (8)

Emotional component of pain. See *Affective component of pain.* (14)

Endorphin. Chemical that is naturally produced in the brain and that causes analgesia. (14)

End-stopped cell. A cortical neuron that responds best to lines of a specific length that are moving in a particular direction. (3)

Envelope of the traveling wave. A curve that indicates the maximum displacement at each point along the basilar membrane caused by a traveling wave. (11)

Environmental stimulus. All of the things in our environment that we can potentially perceive at a given point in time. (1)

Enzyme cascade. Sequence of reactions triggered by an activated visual pigment molecule that results in transduction. (2)

Epidermis. The outer layers of the skin, including a layer of dead skin cells. (14)

Equal loudness curve. A curve that indicates the sound pressure levels that result in a perception of the same loudness at frequencies across the audible spectrum. (11)

Excitatory area. Area of a receptive field that is associated with excitation. Stimulation of this area causes an increase in the rate of nerve firing. (3)

Excitatory-center-inhibitory-surround receptive field. A center-surround receptive field in which stimulation of the center area causes an excitatory response and stimulation of the surround causes an inhibitory response. (3)

Excitatory response. The response of a nerve fiber in which the firing rate increases. (2)

Excitatory transmitters. Neurotransmitters that cause the inside of a neuron to become more positively charged. Excitatory neurotransmitters increase the probability that an action potential will be generated and are also associated with increases in the rate of nerve firing. (2)

Experience-dependent plasticity. A process by which neurons adapt to the specific environment within which a person or animal lives. This is achieved when neurons change their response properties so they become tuned to respond best to stimuli that have been repeatedly experienced in the environment. See also Neural plasticity; Selective rearing. (4)

Exploratory procedures (EPs). People's movements of their hands and fingers while they are identifying three-dimensional objects by touch. (14)

Externalization. In hearing, the situation in which sounds are heard as originating in space, as in the space surrounding a listener. This occurs in the normal listening environment, and when a person's head-related transfer function (HRTF) is taken into account in processing sounds heard through headphones. (12)

Extrastriate body area (EBA). An area of the temporal lobe that is activated by pictures of bodies and parts of bodies. (4)

Extrastriate cortex. Areas in the cerebral cortex outside the striate cortex. This term is most commonly used to refer to areas associated with vision that are outside the primary visual receiving area in the striate cortex. (3)

Eye. The eyeball and its contents, which include focusing elements, the retina, and supporting structures. (2)

False alarm. In a signal detection experiment, saying, "Yes, I detect the stimulus" on a trial in which the stimulus is not presented (an incorrect response). (Appendix)

Familiarity, law of. A Gestalt law of perceptual organization that states that things are more likely to form groups when the groups appear familiar or meaningful. (5)

Familiar size. A depth cue. Our knowledge of an object's actual size sometimes influences our perception of an object's distance. (8)

Feature detector. A neuron that responds selectively to a specific feature of the stimulus. (3)

Feature integration theory. A sequence of steps proposed by Treisman to explain how objects are broken down into features and how these features are recombined to result in a perception of the object. (6)

Feature search. A visual search task in which a person can find a target by searching for only one feature. An example would be looking for a horizontal green line amongst vertical green lines. (6)

Feedback (nervous system). When signals are transmitted "backward" from "higher" areas, such as the temporal or parietal lobe, to "earlier" areas such as the primary visual receiving area in the occipital lobe. (5)

Figure. When an object is seen as separate from the background (the "ground"), it is called a figure. See also Figure-ground segregation. (5)

Figure–ground segregation. The perceptual separation of an object from its background. (5)

Fixation. The pause of the eye that occurs between eye movements as a person scans a scene. (6)

Flavor. The perception that occurs from the combination of taste and olfaction. (15)

Flow. See Gradient of flow; Optic flow.

Focal dystonia. A condition in which a person loses the ability to make skilled hand movements. (14)

Focused-attention stage (of perceptual processing). The stage of processing in feature integration theory in which the features are combined. This stage requires focused attention. (6)

Focusing power. The degree to which a structure such as the lens or the cornea bends light. The greater the focusing power, the more the light passing through the structure is bent. (2)

Focus of expansion (FOE). The point in the flow pattern caused by observer movement in which there is no expansion. According to J. J. Gibson, the focus of expansion always remains centered on the observer's destination. (10)

Formant. Horizontal band of energy in the speech spectrogram associated with vowels. (13)

Formant transition. In the speech stimulus, the rapid shift in frequency that precedes a formant. (13)

Fourier analysis. A mathematical technique that analyzes complex periodic waveforms into a number of sine-wave components. (11)

Fovea. A small area in the human retina that contains only cone receptors. The fovea is located on the line of sight, so that when a person looks at an object, the center of its image falls on the fovea. (2)

Free-field presentation. In hearing experiments, presenting sounds at various positions around a listener's head. This is usually accomplished by moving speakers to different positions in space, and testing the listener in the dark. The listener indicates the position of the sound, either by pointing to it, or by indicating azimuth and elevation coordinates. (12)

Frequency. In the case of a sound wave that repeats itself, such as the sine wave of a pure tone, frequency is the number of times per second that the wave repeats itself. (11)

Frequency spectrum. A plot that indicates the amplitudes of the various harmonics that make up a complex tone. Each harmonic is indicated by a line that is positioned along the frequency axis, with the height of the line indicating the amplitude of the harmonic. (11)

Frequency tuning curve. Curve relating frequency and the threshold intensity for activating an auditory neuron. (11)

Frontal operculum cortex. An area in the frontal lobe of the cortex that receives signals from the taste system. (15)

Functional magnetic resonance imaging (fMRI). A brain imaging technique that indicates brain activity in awake behaving humans in response to perceptual stimuli. (4)

Fundamental frequency. Usually the lowest frequency in the Fourier spectrum of a complex tone. The fundamental frequency is also called the first harmonic. The tone's other components, called higher harmonics, have frequencies that are multiples of the fundamental frequency. (11)

Fusiform face area (FFA). An area in the human inferotemporal (IT) cortex that contains neurons that are specialized to respond to faces. (4)

Fusion. In hearing, when sounds that are presented simultaneously at two different locations are perceived as one sound coming from a single location. (12)

Ganglion cell. A neuron in the retina that receives inputs from bipolar and amacrine cells. The axons of the ganglion cells that travel out of the eye in the optic nerve. (3)

Gate-control model. Melzack and Wall's idea that our perception of pain is controlled by a neural circuit that takes into account the relative amount of activity in large (L) fibers and small (S) fibers. This model has been used to explain how pain can be influenced by factors in addition to stimulation of receptors in the skin. (14)

Genetic tracing. Molecular biological technique that has used genetic cloning procedures and staining to determine the structure of the olfactory and taste systems. (15)

Geon. The volumetric features of Biederman's recognition-by-components theory of object perception. (5)

Gestalt psychology. An approach to psychology that focuses on developing principles of perceptual organization, proposing that "the whole differs from the sum of its parts." (5)

Global optic flow. Information for movement that occurs when all elements in a scene move. The perception of global optic flow indicates that it is the observer that is moving and not the scene. (9)

Glomeruli. Small structures in the olfactory bulb that receive signals from similar olfactory receptor neurons. One function of each glomerulus is to collect information about a small group of odorants. (15)

Glossopharyngeal nerve. A nerve that transmits signals from receptors located at the back of the tongue. (15)

Good continuation, law of. A Gestalt law of perceptual organization that states that points that, when connected, result in straight or smoothly curving lines are seen as belonging together, and lines tend to be seen in such a way as to follow the smoothest path. (5)

Good figure, law of. See Pragnanz, law of.

Gradient of flow. In an optic flow pattern, a gradient is created by movement of an observer through the environment. The "gradient" refers to the fact that the optic flow is rapid in the foreground and becomes slower as distance from the observer increases. (10)

Grandmother cell. A hypothesized type of neuron that responds only to a very specific stimulus, such as a person's grandmother. (4)

Grating. A stimulus pattern consisting of alternating bars with different lightnesses or colors. (3)

Grating acuity. The narrowest spacing of a grooved surface on the skin for which orientation can be accurately judged; a measure of acuity on the skin. See also Two-point threshold. (14)

Ground. In object perception, the background is called the ground. See also Figure. (5)

Habituation. The result when the same stimulus is presented repeatedly. For example, infants look at a stimulus less and less on each succeeding trial. See also Dishabituation. (16)

Hair cell. Neuron in the cochlea that contains small hairs, or cilia, that are displaced by vibration of the basilar membrane and fluids inside the inner ear. There are two kinds of hair cells: inner and outer. (11)

Hair cell, inner. Auditory receptor cell in the inner ear that is primarily responsible for auditory transduction and the perception of pitch. (11)

Hair cells, outer. Auditory receptor cells in the inner ear that amplify the response of the inner hair cells. See also Motile response. (11)

Haptic perception. The perception of three-dimensional objects by touch. (14)

Harmonics. Fourier components of a complex tone with frequencies that are multiples of the fundamental frequency. (11)

Headphone presentation. In hearing experiments, presenting sounds through headphones. This way of presenting sound has the advantage that the experimenter has precise control over the stimuli. For example, it is possible to vary the timing and intensities of the signals reaching the left and right ears. (12)

Head-related transfer function (HRTF). The difference between the sound from a source and the sound actually entering the ears that is caused by interaction of the sound with the head and the pinnae. This difference provides a cue for auditory localization because a specific pattern of frequencies is associated with each location in space relative to the listener. See also Externalization; Spectral cues. (12)

Hearing. The experience of perceiving sound. (11)

Hering grid. A geometrical display that results in the illusion of dark areas at the intersection of two white "corridors." This perception can be explained by lateral inhibition. (3)

Hertz (Hz). The unit for designating the frequency of a tone. One Hertz equals one cycle per second. (11)

Heuristic. In perception, a rule of thumb that provides a "best guess" estimate of the identity of a particular stimulus. (5)

Hierarchical processing. Processing signals through a sequence of areas. This occurs in the visual system as signals are transmitted from the LGN to primary visual receiving area, and then to higher areas. It occurs in the auditory system as signals are transmitted from the core to the belt to the parabelt regions of the cortex. (11)

Hit. In a signal detection experiment, saying, "Yes, I detect a stimulus" on a trial in which the stimulus is present (a correct response). (Appendix)

Homunculus. Latin for "little man," refers to the topographic the map of the body in the somatosensory cortex. (14)

Horizontal cell. A neuron that transmits signals laterally across the retina. Horizontal cells synapse with receptors and bipolar cells. (3)

Horopter. An imaginary surface that passes through the point of fixation. Images caused by a visual stimulus on this surface fall on corresponding points on the two retinas. (8)

***How* pathway.** See Dorsal pathway.

Hue. The experience of a chromatic color such as red, green, yellow, or blue or combinations of these colors. (7)

Hyperpolarization. When the inside of a neuron becomes more negative. Hyperpolarization is often associated with the action of inhibitory neurotransmitters. (2)

Illumination edge. The border between two areas created by different light intensities in the two areas. (7)

Illusory conjunction. Illusory combination of features that are perceived when stimuli containing a number of features are presented briefly and under conditions in which focused attention is difficult. For example, presenting a red square and a blue triangle could potentially create the perception of a red triangle. (6)

Illusory contour. Contour that is perceived even though they are not present in the physical stimulus. (5)

Image-description model. An approach to object perception that states that our ability to recognize objects from different viewpoints is based on stored two-dimensional views of the object as it would appear from different viewpoints. For another approach, see Structural-description models. (5)

Image movement signal (IMS). In corollary discharge theory, the signal that occurs when an image stimulates the receptors by moving across them. (9)

Implied motion. When a still picture depicts an action that involves motion, so that an observer could potentially extend the action depicted in the picture in his or her mind, based on what will most likely happen next. (9)

Inattentional blindness. A situation in which a stimulus that is not attended is not perceived, even though a person is looking directly at it. (6)

Incus. The second of the three ossicles of the middle ear. It transmits vibrations from the malleus to the stapes. (11)

Indexical characteristic. Characteristics of the speech stimulus that indicates information about a speaker such as the speaker's age, gender, and emotional state. (13)

Indirect sound. Sound that reaches the ears after being reflected from a surface such as a room's walls. (12)

Induced movement. The illusory movement of one object that is caused by the movement of another object that is nearby. (9)

Inferior colliculus. A nucleus in the hearing system along the pathway from the cochlea to the auditory cortex. The inferior colliculus receives inputs from the superior olivary nucleus. (11)

Inflammatory pain. Caused by damage to tissues and inflammations to joints or by tumor cells, this damage releases chemicals that create an "inflammatory soup" that activates nociceptors. (14)

Inhibition. A condition that decreases the likelihood that nerve impulses will be generated. (2)

Inhibitory area. Area of a receptive field that is associated with inhibition. Stimulation of this area causes a decrease in the rate of nerve firing. (3)

Inhibitory-center-excitatory-surround receptive field. A center-surround receptive field in which stimulation of the center causes an inhibitory response and stimulation of the surround causes an excitatory response. (3)

Inhibitory response. The response of a nerve fiber in which the firing rate decreases due to inhibition from another neuron. (2)

Inhibitory transmitters. Neurotransmitters that cause the inside of a neuron to become negatively charged. Inhibitory transmitters decrease the possibility that an action potential will be generated and are also associated with decreases in the rate of nerve firing. (2)

Inner ear. The innermost division of the ear, containing the cochlea and the receptors for hearing. (11)

Inner hair cell. See Hair cell, inner.

Insula. An area in the frontal lobe of the cortex that receives signals from the taste system. (15)

Interaural level difference (ILD). The greater level of a sound at the closer ear when a sound source is positioned closer to one ear than to the other. This effect is most pronounced for high-frequency tones. The ILD provides a cue for sound localization. (12)

Interaural time difference (ITD). When a sound is positioned closer to one ear than to the other, the sound reaches the close ear slightly before reaching the far ear, so there is a difference in the time of arrival at the two ears. The ITD provides a cue for sound localization. (12)

Interaural time difference detector. A neuron that fires only when a stimulus is presented first to one ear and then to the other, with a specific delay between the stimulation of the two ears. (12)

Intermodel perception. Coordination of information from different senses into a perceptual whole. (16)

Internalization. In hearing experiments, when a listener perceives outside sounds as originating inside his or her head. This can occur when listening through headphones. See also Externalization. (12)

Invariant acoustic cues. In speech perception, a feature of an auditory signal that remains constant even in different contexts. (13)

Invariant information. Environmental properties that do not change as the observer moves relative to an object or scene. For example, the spacing, or texture, of the elements in a texture gradient does not change as the observer moves on the gradient. The texture of the gradient therefore supplies invariant information for depth perception. See also View-invariant properties. (10)

Inverse projection problem. The idea that a particular image on the retina could have been caused by an infinite number of different objects. Thus, the retinal image does not unambiguously specify a stimulus. (5)

Ions. Charged molecules found floating in the liquid that surrounds nerve fibers. (2)

Ipsilateral eye. The eye on the same side of the head of the structure to which the eye sends inputs. (4)

Ishihara plate. A display of colored dots used to test for the presence of color deficiency. The dots are colored so that people with normal (trichromatic) color vision can perceive numbers in the plate, but people with color deficiency cannot perceive these numbers or perceive different numbers than someone with trichromatic vision. (7)

Isomerization. Change in shape of the retinal part of the visual pigment molecule that occurs when the molecule absorbs a quantum of light. Isomerization triggers the enzyme cascade that results in transduction from light energy to electrical energy in the retinal receptors. (2)

Kinesthesis. The sense that enables us to feel the motions and positions of the limbs and body. (14)

Kinetic depth effect. Occurs when a stimulus's three-dimensional structure becomes apparent from viewing a two-dimensional image of a stimulus as it rotates. See also Structure-from-motion. (9)

Knowledge. Any information that the perceiver brings to a situation. See also Top-down processing. (1)

Knowledge-based processing. Another name for top-down processing. Refers to processing that is based on knowledge, as opposed to bottom-up, or data-based, processing, which is based on incoming data. (1)

Landmark discrimination problem. The behavioral task used in Ungerleider and Mishkin's experiment in which they provided evidence for the dorsal, or "where," visual processing stream. Monkeys were required to respond to a previously indicated location. (4)

Large-diameter fiber (L-fiber). According to gate-control model, activity in L-fibers closes the gate control mechanism and therefore decreases the perception of pain. (14)

Lateral geniculate nucleus (LGN). The nucleus in the thalamus that receives inputs from the optic nerve and, in turn, sends fibers to the cortical receiving area for vision. (3)

Lateral inhibition. Inhibition that is transmitted laterally across a nerve circuit. In the retina, lateral inhibition is transmitted by the horizontal and amacrine cells. (3)

Laws of perceptual organization. See Perceptual organization, laws of.

Lens. The transparent focusing element of the eye through which light passes after passing through the cornea and the aqueous humor. The lens's change in shape to focus at different distances is called accommodation. (2)

Lesioning. Removal of an area of the brain. This is usually done in experiments on animals to determine the function of a particular area. Also called ablation. (4)

Level. Short for sound level. Indicates the decibels or sound pressure of a sound stimulus. (11)

Level of analysis. The idea that we can observer processes at different scales. Perception can be studied at the psychophysical and physiological levels of analysis. (1)

Light-adapted sensitivity. The sensitivity of the eye when in the light-adapted state. Usually taken as the starting point for the dark adaptation curve because it is the sensitivity of the eye just before the lights are turned off. (2)

Light-from-above heuristic. The assumption that light is usually coming from above, which influences our perception of form in some situations. (5)

Lightness. Perception of reflectance. Usually objects with high reflectance are perceived as white and objects with low reflectance are perceived as gray or black. (7)

Lightness constancy. The constancy of our perception of an object's lightness under different intensities of illumination. (7)

Likelihood principle. The idea proposed by Helmholtz that we perceive the object that is *most likely* to have caused the pattern of stimuli we have received. (5)

Limits, method of. A psychophysical method for measuring threshold in which the experimenter presents stimuli in alternating ascending and descending order. (1)

Linear optical trajectory (LOT) strategy. A strategy for catching a fly ball based on the idea that if the ballplayer runs so the ball appears to be following a straight-line path, the ball will always be directly above, so when the ball reaches the ground, the outfielder will be there to catch it. (10)

Local disturbance in the optic array. Occurs when one object moves relative to the environment, so that the stationary background is covered and uncovered by the moving object. This local disturbance indicates that the object is moving relative to the environment. (9)

Location column. A column in the visual cortex that contains neurons with the same receptive field locations on the retina. (4)

Location cue. In hearing, characteristics of the sound reaching the listener that provide information regarding the location of a sound source. (12)

Loudness. The quality of sound that ranges from soft to loud. For a tone of a particular frequency, loudness usually increases with increasing decibels. (11)

Mach band. Perception of a thin dark band on the dark side of a light–dark border and a thin light band on the light side of the border. These bands are an illusion because they occur even though corresponding intensity changes do not exist. (3)

Macrosmatic. Having a keen sense of smell that is important to an animal's survival. (15)

Macular degeneration. A clinical condition that causes degeneration of the macula, an area of the retina that includes the fovea and a small surrounding area. (2)

Magnification factor. The apportioning of proportionally more space in a structure, such as the cortex, to the representation of specific areas of sensory receptors. For example, a small area on the retina in or near the fovea receives more space on the cortex than the same area of peripheral retina. Similarly, the fingertips receive more space on the somatosensory cortex than the forearm or leg. (4, 13)

Magnitude estimation. A psychophysical method in which the subject assigns numbers to a stimulus that are proportional to the subjective magnitude of the stimulus. (1)

Magnocellular (or magno) layers. Layers 1 and 2 of the lateral geniculate nucleus that receive inputs from the M ganglion cells. (4)

Malleus. The first of the ossicles of the middle ear. Receives vibrations from the tympanic membrane and transmits these vibrations to the incus. (11)

Masking (auditory). Occurs when presentation of one sound decreases a listener's ability to hear another sound. (11)

Masking stimulus. A visual pattern that, when presented immediately after a visual stimulus decreases a person's ability to perceive the stimulus. This stops the persistence of vision and therefore limits the effective duration of the stimulus. (5)

M-cell. Retinal ganglion cells that have medium-sized cell bodies and that respond with sustained firing. M-cells synapse in the magnocellular layer of the LGN. (4)

McGurk effect. See Audiovisual speech perception.

Mechanoreceptor. Receptor that responds to mechanical stimulation of the skin, such as pressure, stretching, and vibration. (14)

Medial geniculate nucleus. An auditory nucleus in the thalamus that is part of the pathway from the cochlea to the auditory cortex. The medial geniculate nucleus receives inputs from the inferior colliculus and transmits signals to the auditory cortex. (11)

Medial lemniscal pathway. A pathway in the spinal cord that transmits signals from the skin toward the thalamus. (14)

Meissner corpuscle. A receptor in the skin, associated with RA 1 mechanoreceptors. It has been proposed that the Meissner corpuscle is important for perceiving tactile slip and for controlling the force needed to grip objects. (14)

Melodic channeling. See Scale illusion.

Melody schema. A representation of a familiar melody that is stored in a person's memory. Existence of a melody schema makes it more likely that the tones associated with a melody will be perceptually grouped. (12)

Memory color. The idea that an object's characteristic color influences our perception of that object's color. (7)

Menstrual synchrony. Women who live together experience menstrual periods that begin at approximately the same time. There is evidence that the sense of smell is involved in determining this effect. (15)

Merkel receptor. A disk-shaped receptor in the skin associated with slowly adapting fibers, and the perception of fine details. (14)

Metamerism. The situation in which two physically different stimuli are perceptually identical. In vision, this refers to two lights with different wavelength distributions that are perceived as having the same color. (7)

Metamers. Two lights that have different wavelength distributions but are perceptually identical. (7)

Method of adjustment. See Adjustment, method of.

Method of constant stimuli. See Constant stimuli, method of.

Method of limits. See Limits, method of.

Microelectrode. A thin piece of wire that is small enough to record electrical signals from a single neuron. (2)

Microsmatic. Having a weak sense of smell. This usually occurs in animals like humans, for which the sense of smell is not crucial for survival. (15)

Microstimulation. A procedure in which a small electrode is inserted into the cortex and an electrical current is passed through the electrode that activates the neurons near the electrode. This procedure has been used to determine how activating specific groups of neurons affects perception. (8, 9)

Middle ear. The small air-filled space between the auditory canal and the cochlea that contains the ossicles. (11)

Middle-ear muscles. Muscles attached to the ossicles in the middle ear. The smallest skeletal muscles in the body, they contract in response to very intense sounds and dampen the vibration of the ossicles. (11)

Mirror neuron. Neuron in the premotor area of the monkey's cortex that responds when the monkey grasps an object and also when the monkey observes someone else (another monkey or the experimenter) grasping the object. See also Audiovisual mirror neurons. (10)

Misapplied size constancy scaling. A principle, proposed by Richard Gregory, that when mechanisms that help maintain size constancy in the three-dimensional world are applied to two-dimensional pictures, an illusion of size sometimes results. (8)

Miss. In a signal detection experiment, saying, "No, I don't detect a stimulus" on a trial in which the stimulus is present (an incorrect response). (Appendix)

Modularity. Specialization of the brain in which specific cortical areas processes information about specific perceptual qualities. (4)

Modular organization. The organization of specific functions into specific brain structures. (2)

Module. A structure that processes information about a specific behavior or perceptual quality. Often identified as a structure that contains a large proportion of neurons that respond selectively to a particular quality. (4)

Monaural cue. Sound localization cue that involves one ear. (12)

Monochromat. A person who is completely color-blind and therefore sees everything as black, white, or shades of gray. A monochromat can match any wavelength in the spectrum by adjusting the intensity of any other wavelength. Monochromats generally have only one type of functioning receptors, usually rods.

Monochromatic light. Light that contains only a single wavelength. (2)

Monocular cue. Depth cue, such as overlap, relative size, relative height, familiar size, linear perspective, movement parallax, and accommodation, that works when we use only one eye. (8)

Moon illusion. An illusion in which the moon appears to be larger when it is on or near the horizon than when it is high in the sky. (8)

Morphing. A computerized method of combining two stimuli which involves locating corresponding points on two "prototype" stimuli and combining the features that exist at these points in different amounts. (5)

Motile response. A response to sound of the outer hair cells in which these cells move. The cells tilt and get slightly longer, which increases basilar membrane vibration and therefore amplifies the response of the inner hair cells. (11)

Motion agnosia. An effect of brain damage in which the ability to perceive motion is disrupted. (9)

Motor-dominant neuron. Neuron in the anterior intraparietal cortex (AIP) of the monkey that responds well when a monkey carries out a motor action like pushing a button but doesn't respond well when the monkey looks at the button. (10)

Motor signal (MS). In corollary discharge theory, the signal that is sent to the eye muscles when the observer moves or tries to move his or her eyes. (9)

Motor theory of speech perception. A theory that proposes a close link between how speech is perceived and how it is produced. The idea behind this theory is that when we *hear* a particular speech sound, this activates the motor mechanisms that are responsible for *producing* that sound and it is the activation of these motor mechanisms that enable us to perceive the sound. (13)

Movement aftereffect. An illusion that occurs after a person views a moving stimulus and then sees movement in the opposite direction when viewing a stationary stimulus. See also Waterfall illusion. (9)

Movement parallax. A depth cue based on the fact that as an observer moves, nearby objects appear to move rapidly whereas far objects appear to move slowly. (8)

Müller-Lyer illusion. An illusion consisting of two lines of equal length that appear to be different lengths because of the addition of "fins" to the ends of the lines. (8)

Multimodal. The involvement of a number of different senses in determining perception. For example, speech perception can be influenced by information from a number of different senses, including audition, vision, and touch. (13)

Multimodal nature of pain. The fact that the experience of pain has both sensory and emotional components. (14)

Naloxone. A substance that inhibits the activity of opiates. It is hypothesized that naloxone also inhibits the activity of endorphins and therefore can have an effect on pain perception. (14)

Nasal pharynx. A passageway that connects the mouth cavity and the nasal cavity. (15)

Nearness, law of. See Proximity, law of.

Near point. The distance at which the lens can no longer accommodate enough to bring close objects into focus. Objects nearer than the near point can be brought into focus only by corrective lenses. (2)

Nerve. A group of nerve fibers traveling together. (2)

Nerve fiber. In most sensory neurons, the long part of the neuron that transmits electrical impulses from one point to another. Also called the axon. (2)

Nerve impulse. The rapid increase in positive charge that travels down the nerve fiber. Also called the action potential. (2)

Neural circuit. A number of neurons that are connected by synapses. (3)

Neural plasticity. The capacity of the nervous system to change in response to experience. Examples are how early visual experience can change the orientation selectivity of neurons in the visual cortex and how tactile experience can change the sizes of areas in the cortex that represent different parts of the body. See also Experience-dependent plasticity; Selective rearing. (3, 14)

Neural processing. Operations that transform electrical signals within a network of neurons or that transform the response of individual neurons. (1)

Neurogenesis. The cycle of birth, development, and death of a neuron. This process occurs for the receptors for olfaction and taste. (15)

Neuron. A cell in the nervous system that generates and transmits electrical impulses. (2)

Neuropathic pain. Pain caused by lesions or other damage to the nervous system. (14)

Neuropsychology. The study of the behavioral effects of brain damage in humans. (4)

Neurotransmitter. A chemical stored in synaptic vesicles that is released in response to a nerve impulse and has an excitatory or inhibitory effect on another neuron. (2)

Neutral point. The wavelength at which a dichromat perceives gray. (7)

Nociceptive pain. This type of pain, which serves as a warning of impending damage to the skin, is caused by activation of receptors in the skin called nociceptors. (14)

Nociceptor. A fiber that responds to stimuli that are damaging to the skin. (14)

Noncorresponding (disparate) points. Two points, one on each retina, that would not overlap if the retinas were slid onto each other. (8)

Nontaster. A person who cannot taste the compound phenylthiocarbamide (PTC). (15)

Nucleus of the solitary tract (NST). The nucleus in the brain stem that receives signals from the tongue, the mouth, and the larynx transmitted by the chorda tympani, glossopharyngeal, and vagus nerves. (15)

Object discrimination problem. The behavioral task used in Ungerleider and Mishkin's experiment in which they provided evidence for the ventral, or "what," visual processing stream. Monkeys were required to respond to an object with a particular shape. (4)

Object unity. Perception of a partially occluded object as a single object that continues behind the occluder. (16)

Oblique effect. Enhanced sensitivity to vertically and horizontally oriented visual stimuli. This effect has been demonstrated by measuring both perception and neural responding. (5)

Occipital lobe. A lobe at the back of the cortex that is the site of the cortical receiving area for vision. (2)

Occlusion. Depth cue in which one object hides or partially hides another object from view, causing the hidden object to be perceived as being farther away. (8)

Occlusion heuristic. The assumption that a moving object will cover and uncover the background and that when the background is covered, it still exists. Thus, when a large object is occluded by a smaller one, we see the larger one as continuing to exist behind the occluder. (9)

Octave. Tones that have frequencies that are binary multiples of each other (2, 4, etc.). For example, an 800-Hz tone is 1 octave above a 400-Hz tone. (11)

Ocular dominance. The degree to which a neuron is influenced by stimulation of each eye. A neuron has a large amount of ocular dominance if it responds only to stimulation of one eye. There is no ocular dominance if the neuron responds equally to stimulation of both eyes. (4)

Ocular dominance column. A column in the visual cortex that contains neurons that respond best to stimulation of the same eye. (4)

Oculomotor cue. Depth cue that depends on our ability to sense the position of our eyes and the tension in our eye muscles. Accommodation and convergence are oculomotor cues. (8)

Odor prism. Henning's six-corner prism that separates odors into the categories of putrid, ethereal, resinous, spicy, fragrant, and burned. (15)

Odotope. A group of odorants that share a specific chemical feature that determines neural firing. (15)

Olfactometer. A device that presents olfactory stimuli with great precision. (15)

Olfactory mucosa. The region inside the nose that contains the receptors for the sense of smell. (15)

Olfactory receptor. A protein string that responds to odor stimuli. (15)

Olfactory sensory neuron. A sensory neuron located in the olfactory mucosa that contains the olfactory receptors. (15)

Ommatidium. A structure in the eye of the *Limulus* that contains a small lens, located directly over a visual receptor. The Limulus eye is made up of hundreds of these ommatidia. The *Limulus* eye has been used for research on lateral inhibition because its receptors are large enough so that stimulation can be applied to individual receptors. (3)

Opioid. A chemical, such as opium, heroin, and other molecules with related structures that reduce pain and induce feelings of euphoria. (14)

Opponent neuron. A neuron that has an excitatory response to wavelengths in one part of the spectrum and an inhibitory response to wavelengths in the other part of the spectrum. (7)

Opponent-process theory of color vision. A theory originally proposed by Hering, which claimed that our perception of color is determined by the activity of two opponent mechanisms: a blue–yellow mechanism and a red–green mechanism. The responses to the two colors in each mechanism oppose each other, one being an excitatory response and the other an inhibitory response. In addition, this theory also includes a black–white mechanism, which is concerned with the perception of brightness. See also Opponent neurons. (7)

Opsin. The protein part of the visual pigment molecule, to which the light-sensitive retinal molecule is attached. (2)

Optical imaging. A technique to measure the activity of large areas of the cortex by measuring the intensity of red light reflected from the cortex. (15)

Optic array. The structured pattern of light created by the presence of objects, surfaces, and textures in the environment. (9)

Optic ataxia. A problem in carrying out actions relative to visual stimuli that occurs in some patients with parietal lobe damage. People with optic ataxia reach for objects slowly and inaccurately and often also have trouble forming their hands to match the shape of an object they are trying to grasp. (10)

Optic flow. The flow of stimuli in the environment that occurs when an observer moves relative to the environment. Forward movement causes an expanding optic flow, whereas backward movement causes a contracting optic flow. The term *optic flow field* is used by some researchers to refer to this flow. (10)

Optic nerve. Bundle of nerve fibers that carry impulses from the retina to the lateral geniculate nucleus and other structures. Each optic nerve contains about 1 million ganglion cell fibers. (2)

Orbitofrontal cortex (OFC). An area in the frontal lobe, near the eyes, that receives signals originating in the olfactory receptors. Also known as the secondary olfactory cortex. (15)

Organization, laws of. See Auditory grouping, principles of; Auditory scene analysis; Perceptual organization, laws of.

Organ of Corti. The major structure of the cochlear partition, containing the basilar membrane, the tectorial membrane, and the receptors for hearing. (11)

Orientation. The angle of a stimulus relative to vertical. (3)

Orientation column. A column in the visual cortex that contains neurons with the same orientation preference. (4)

Orientation tuning curve. A function relating the firing rate of a neuron to the orientation of the stimulus. (3)

Ossicles. Three small bones in the middle ear that transmit vibrations from the outer to the inner ear. (11)

Outer ear. The pinna and the external auditory meatus. (11)

Outer hair cell. See Hair cell, outer.

Outer segments. Part of the rod and cone visual receptors that contain the light-sensitive visual pigment molecules. (2)

Oval window. A small, membrane-covered hole in the cochlea that receives vibrations from the stapes. (11)

Pacinian corpuscle. A receptor with a distinctive elliptical shape associated with RA2 mechanoreceptors. It transmits pressure to the nerve fiber inside it only at the beginning or end of a pressure stimulus, and is responsible for our perception of vibration and fine textures that are perceived when moving the fingers over a surface. (14)

Pain matrix. The network of structures in the brain that are responsible for pain perception. (14)

Paired comparison. A procedure in which a participant is first familiarized with one stimulus, and then is given a choice between that stimulus and a new stimulus. Measurement of looking time indicates whether participants can tell the difference between the two stimuli. (16)

Panoramic neuron. A neuron in the auditory system that fires to sounds originating in any direction and that indicates each location by its temporal pattern of firing. (12)

Papillae. Ridges and valleys on the tongue, some of which contain taste buds. There are four types of papillae: filiform, fungiform, foliate, and circumvallate. (15)

Parabelt area. Auditory area in the temporal lobe that receives signals from the belt area. (11)

Parahippocampal place area (PPA). An area in the temporal lobe that is activated by pictures of indoor and outdoor scenes. (4)

Parietal lobe. A lobe at the top of the cortex that is the site of the cortical receiving area for touch and is the termination point of the dorsal (*where* or *how*) stream for visual processing. (2)

Parietal reach region. A network of areas in the parietal cortex that contains neurons that are involved in reaching behavior. (10)

Parvocellular (or parvo) layer. Layers 3, 4, 5, and 6 of the lateral geniculate nucleus. These neurons receive inputs from the P ganglion cells (P-cell). (4)

Passive touch. A situation in which a person passively receives tactile stimulation that is presented by someone else. (14)

Payoffs. A system of rewards and punishments used to influence a participant's motivation in a signal detection experiment. (Appendix)

P-cell. Retinal ganglion cells that have larger cell bodies than the M-cells and that respond with brief bursts of firing. P-cells synapse in the parvocellular area of the LGN. (4)

Penumbra. The fuzzy border at the edge of a shadow. (7)

Perception. Conscious sensory experience. (1)

Perceptual organization. The process by which small elements become perceptually grouped into larger objects. (5)

Perceptual organization, laws of. Series of rules proposed by the Gestalt psychologists that specify how we organize small parts into wholes. Some of these laws are common fate, familiarity, good continuation, good figure, nearness, and similarity. Most of these laws were originally proposed by the Gestalt psychologists, but modern researchers have proposed some additional laws. (5)

Perceptual process. A sequence of steps leading from the environment to perception of a stimulus, recognition of the stimulus, and action with regard to the stimulus. (1)

Perceptual segregation. Perceptual organization in which one object is seen as separate from other objects. (5)

Periodicity pitch. The constancy of a complex tone's pitch when the fundamental frequency and other lower harmonics are eliminated. See also Effect of the missing fundamental. (11)

Peripheral retina. All of the retina except the fovea and a small area surrounding the fovea. (2)

Permeability. A property of a membrane that refers to the ability of molecules to pass through it. If the permeability to a molecule is high, the molecule can easily pass through the membrane. (2)

Persistence of vision. A phenomenon in which perception of any stimulus persists for about 250 ms after the stimulus is physically terminated. (5)

Perspective convergence. The perception that parallel lines in the distance converge as distance increases. (8)

PET. See Positron emission tomography (PET).

Phase locking. Firing of auditory neurons in synchrony with the phase of an auditory stimulus. (11)

Phenomenological method. Method of determining the relationship between stimuli and perception in which the observer describes what he or she perceives. (1)

Pheromone. Chemical signal released by an individual that affects the physiology and behavior of other individuals. (15)

Phoneme. The shortest segment of speech that, if changed, would change the meaning of a word. (13)

Phonemic restoration effect. An effect that occurs in speech perception when listeners perceive a phoneme in a word even though the acoustic signal of that phoneme is obscured by another sound, such as white noise or a cough. (13)

Phonetic boundary. The voice onset time when perception changes from one speech category to another in a categorical perception experiment. (13)

Physiological level of analysis. Analyzing perception by determining how a person's perception is related to physiological processes that are occurring within the person. This approach focuses on determining the relationship between stimuli and physiological responding and between physiological responding and perception. (1)

Pictorial cue. Depth cue, such as overlap, relative height, and relative size, that can be depicted in pictures. (8)

Pigment bleaching. The process that begins when a visual pigment molecule absorbs light. The molecule changes shape, and the color of the rod visual pigment changes from red to transparent. Visual transduction occurs at some point, early in this process. (2)

Pineal gland. Gland at the base of the brain that René Descartes identified as being the seat of the soul. (2)

Pinna. The part of the ear that is visible on the outside of the head. (11)

Piriform cortex. An area under the temporal lobe that receives signals from glomeruli in the olfactory bulb. Also called the primary olfactory cortex. (15)

Pitch. The quality of sound, ranging from low to high, that is most closely associated with the frequency of a tone. (11)

Placebo. A substance that a person believes will relieve symptoms such as pain but that contains no chemicals that actually act on these symptoms. (14)

Place theory of hearing. The proposal that the frequency of a sound is indicated by the place along the organ of Corti at which nerve firing is highest. Modern place theory is based on Békésy's traveling wave theory of hearing. (11)

Point-light walker. A biological motion stimulus created by placing lights on a number of places on a person's body and having an observer view the moving-light stimulus that results as the person moves in the dark. (9)

Ponzo illusion. An illusion of size in which two objects of equal size that are positioned between two converging lines appear to be different in size. Also called the railroad track illusion. (8)

Positron emission tomography (PET). A brain mapping technique that is used in awake human subjects to determine which brain areas are activated by various tasks. (4)

Power function. A mathematical function of the form $P = KS^n$, where P is perceived magnitude, K is a constant, S is the stimulus intensity, and n is an exponent. (1)

Pragnanz, law of. A Gestalt law of perceptual organization that states that every stimulus pattern is seen in such a way that the resulting structure is as simple as possible. Also called the law of good figure or the law of simplicity. (5)

Preattentive stage (of perceptual processing). An automatic and rapid stage of processing, proposed by feature integration theory, during which a stimulus is decomposed into individual features. (6)

Precedence effect. The effect that occurs when two identical or very similar sounds reach a listener's ears separated by a time interval of less than about 50 to 100 ms, and the listener hears the sound that reaches his or her ears first. (12)

Precueing. A procedure in which a cue stimulus is presented to direct an observer's attention to a specific location where a test stimulus is likely to be presented. This procedure was used by Posner to show that attention enhances the processing of a stimulus presented at the cued location. (6)

Preferential looking (PL) technique. A technique used to measure perception in infants. Two stimuli are presented, and the infant's looking behavior is monitored for the amount of time the infant spends viewing each stimulus. (16)

Presbyopia ("old eye"). The inability of the eye to accommodate due to the hardening of the lens and a weakening of the ciliary muscles. It occurs as people get older. (2)

Primary olfactory cortex. A small area under the temporal lobe that receives signals from glomeruli in the olfactory bulb. Also called the piriform cortex. (15)

Primary receiving areas. Areas of the cerebral cortex that first receive most of the signals initiated by a sense's receptors. For example, the occipital cortex is the site of the primary receiving area for vision and the temporal lobe is the site of the primary receiving area for hearing. (2)

Principle of componential recovery. See Componential recovery, principle of.

Principle of univariance. See Univariance, principle of.

Principles of auditory grouping. See Auditory grouping, principles of.

Propagated response. A response, such as a nerve impulse, that travels all the way down the nerve fiber without decreasing in amplitude. (2)

Proprioception. The sensing of the position of the limbs. (14)

Prosopagnosia. A form of visual agnosia in which the person can't recognize faces. (4, 15)

Protanopia. A form of red-green dichromatism caused by a lack of the long-wavelength cone pigment. (7)

Proximity, law of. A Gestalt law of perceptual organization that states that things that are near to each other appear to be grouped together. Also called the law of nearness. (5)

Psychophysical level of analysis. Analyzing perception by determining how a person's perception is related to stimuli in the environment. This approach focuses on determining the relationship between stimuli in the environment and perceptual responding. (1)

Psychophysical tuning curve (hearing). A function that indicates the intensity of masking tones of different frequencies that cause a low-intensity pure tone to become just barely detectable. (11)

Psychophysics. Traditionally, the term "psychophysics" refers to quantitative methods for measuring the relationship between properties of the stimulus and the subject's experience. In this book, all methods that are used to determine the relationship between stimuli and perception will be broadly referred to as pychophysical methods. (1)

Pure tone. A tone with pressure changes that can be described by a single sine wave. (11)

Purkinje shift. The shift from cone spectral sensitivity to rod spectral sensitivity that takes place during dark adaptation. See also Spectral sensitivity. (2)

RA1 fiber. This fiber responds to slowly changing stimuli on the skin and is also involved in controlling hand-grasp that helps hold and manipulate tools. This fiber is associated with the Meissner receptor. (14)

RA2 fiber. This fiber responds to rapid vibrations and fine textures. Associated with the Pacinian corpuscle. (14)

Random-dot stereogram. A pair of stereoscopic images made up of random dots. When one section of this pattern is shifted slightly in one direction, the resulting disparity causes the shifted section to appear above or below the rest of the pattern when the patterns are viewed in a stereoscope. (8)

Rapidly adapting fiber (RA fiber). A mechanoreceptive fiber that adapts rapidly to continuous stimulation of the skin. Rapidly adapting fibers are associated with Meissner corpuscle and Pacinian corpuscle receptors. (14)

Ratio principle. A principle stating that two areas that reflect different amounts of light will look the same if the ratios of their intensities to the intensities of their surroundings are the same. (7)

Rat–man demonstration. The demonstration in which presentation of a "ratlike" or "manlike" picture influences an observer's perception of a second picture, which can be interpreted either as a rat or as a man. This demonstration illustrates an effect of top-down processing on perception. (1)

Reaction time. The time between presentation of a stimulus and an observer's or listener's response to the stimulus. Reaction time is often used in experiments as a measure of speed of processing. (1)

Real movement. The physical movement of a stimulus. (9)

Real-movement neuron. Neuron in the monkey's cortex that responds when movement of an image across the retina is caused by movement of a stimulus, but does not respond when movement across the retina is caused by movement of the eyes. (9)

Receiver operating characteristic (ROC) curve. A graph in which the results of a signal detection experiment are plotted as the proportion of hits versus the proportion of false alarms for a number of different response criteria. (Appendix)

Receptive field. A neuron's receptive field is the area on the receptor surface (the retina, for vision; the skin, for touch) that, when stimulated, affects the firing of that neuron. There are some exceptions, however, such as receptive fields for auditory space perception in the owl (Chapter 12). In this case, the receptive fields are locations in space rather than in areas on the receptor surface. (3)

Receptive field for sound location. The location in space from which sound influences the firing of the neuron. (12)

Receptor. A sensory receptor is a neuron sensitive to environmental energy that changes this energy into electrical signals in the nervous system. (2)

Receptor site. Small area on the postsynaptic neuron that is sensitive to specific neurotransmitters. (2)

Recognition. The ability to place an object in a category that gives it meaning; for example, recognizing a particular red object as a tomato. (1)

Recognition-by-components (RBC) theory. A theory of object perception proposed by Biederman, which proposes that we recognize objects by decomposing them into volumetric features called geons. See also Structural-description models. (5)

Recognition profile. The pattern of activation of olfactory receptors caused by a particular odorant. (15)

Recognition threshold. See Threshold, recognition.

Reflectance. The percentage of light reflected from a surface. (7)

Reflectance curve. A plot showing the percentage of light reflected from an object versus wavelength. (7)

Reflectance edge. An edge between two areas where the reflectance of two surfaces changes. (7)

Refractory period. The time period of about 1/1,000th of a second that a nerve fiber needs to recover from conducting a nerve impulse. No new nerve impulses can be generated in the fiber until the refractory period is over. (2)

Region-of-interest (ROI) approach. A procedure used in brain imaging in which subjects are pretested on the stimuli to be studied. This enables researchers to establish the precise location in the brain that they will be studying for each individual person. (5)

Regularities in the environment. Characteristics of the environment that occur regularly and in many different situations. (5)

Relative height. A depth cue. Objects that have bases below the horizon appear to be farther away when they are higher in the field of view. Objects that have bases above the horizon appear to be farther away when they are lower in the field of view. (8)

Relative size. A cue for depth perception. When two objects are of equal size, the one that is farther away will take up less of the field of view. (8)

Representational momentum. Occurs when an observer views two pictures depicting the same motion, one after another, and is asked to indicate whether the second picture is the same as or different from the first picture. Representational momentum occurs when the second picture depicts the action *later in time* but is identified by the observer as being identical to the first picture. (9)

Resonance. A mechanism that enhances the intensity of certain frequencies because of the reflection of sound waves in a closed tube. Resonance in the auditory canal enhances frequencies between about 2,000 and 5,000 Hz. (11)

Resonant frequency. The frequency that is most strongly enhanced by resonance. The resonance frequency of a closed tube is determined by the length of the tube. (11)

Response compression. The result when doubling the physical intensity of a stimulus less than doubles the subjective magnitude of the stimulus. (1)

Response criterion. In a signal detection experiment, the subjective magnitude of a stimulus above which the participant will indicate that the stimulus is present. (Appendix)

Response expansion. The result when doubling the physical intensity of a stimulus more than doubles the subjective magnitude of the stimulus. (1)

Resting potential. The difference in charge between the inside and the outside of the nerve fiber when the fiber is not conducting electrical signals. Most nerve fibers have resting potentials of about –70 mV, which means the inside of the fiber is negative relative to the outside. (2)

Retina. A complex network of cells that covers the inside back of the eye. These cells include the receptors, which generate an electrical signal in response to light, as well as the horizontal, bipolar, amacrine, and ganglion cells. (2)

Retinal. The light-sensitive part of the visual pigment molecule. Retinal is attached to the protein molecule, opsin, to form the visual pigment. (2)

Retinitis pigmentosa. A retinal disease that causes a gradual loss of vision. (2)

Retinotopic map. A map on a structure in the visual system, such as the lateral geniculate nucleus or the cortex, that indicates locations on the structure that correspond to locations on the retina. In retinotopic maps, locations adjacent to each other on the retina are usually represented by locations that are adjacent to each other on the structure. See also Topographic map. (4)

Retronasal route. The opening from the oral cavity, through the nasal pharnyx, and into the nasal cavity. This route is the basis for the way smell combines with taste to create flavor. (15)

Reverberation time. The time it takes for a sound produced in an enclosed space to decrease to 1/1,000th of its original pressure. (12)

Reversible figure–ground. A figure–ground pattern that perceptually reverses as it is viewed, so that the figure becomes the ground and the ground becomes the figure. The most well-known reversible figure–ground pattern is Rubin's vase–face pattern. (5)

Rod. Rod-shaped receptor in the retina primarily responsible for vision at low levels of illumination. The rod system is extremely sensitive in the dark but cannot resolve fine details. (2)

Rod-and-frame illusion. An illusion in which the perception of the perceived orientation of a rod is affected by the orientation of a surrounding frame. (4)

Rod-cone break. The point on the dark adaptation curve at which vision shifts from cone vision to rod vision. (2)

Rod monochromat. A person who has a retina in which the only functioning receptors are rods. (2)

Ruffini cylinder. A receptor structure in the skin associated with slowly adapting fibers. It has been proposed that the Ruffini cylinder is involved in perceiving "stretching." (14)

Running spectral display. A way of representing the speech stimulus in which a number of short-term spectra are arranged to show how the frequencies in the speech stimulus change as time progresses. (13)

SA1 fiber. This fiber responds to skin stimuli with fine details, such as grooved textures. Associated with the Merkel receptor. (14)

SA2 fiber. This fiber responds to an extremely rapid vibration like that created by machinery. Associated with the Pacinian corpuscle. (14)

Saccade. Small, rapid eye movement. (6)

Saliency map. A "map" of a visual display that takes into account characteristics of the display such as color, contrast, and orientation that are associated with capturing attention. This map predicts which areas a person is most likely to attend to. (6)

Saturation (color). The relative amount of whiteness in a chromatic color. The less whiteness a color contains, the more saturated it is. (7)

Scale illusion. An illusion that occurs when successive notes of a scale are presented alternately to the left and the right ears. Even though each ear receives notes that jump up and down in frequency, smoothly ascending or descending scales are heard in each ear. Also called melodic channeling. (12)

Scene schema. A person's knowledge about what is contained in typical scenes. An example of a scene schema is knowing that an office usually contains a computer, books, and a desk. This knowledge can help guide attention in familiar scenes. (6)

Secondary olfactory cortex. An area in the frontal lobe, near the eyes, that receives signals originating in the olfactory receptors. Also known as the orbitofrontal cortex. (15)

Secondary somatosensory cortex (S2). The area in the parietal lobe next to the primary somatosensory area (S1) that processes neural signals related to touch, temperature, and pain. (14)

Segmentation problem. The problem of perceptually segmenting the continuous speech stimulus into individual words. (13)

Selective adaptation. A procedure in which a person or animal is selectively exposed to one stimulus and then the effect of this exposure is assessed by testing with a wide range of stimuli. Exposing a person to vertical bars and then testing a person's sensitivity to bars of all orientations is an example of selective adaptation to orientation. (3)

Selective attention. Focusing attention on specific objects and ignoring others. (6)

Selective rearing. A procedure in which animals are reared in special environments. An example of selective rearing is the experiment in which kittens were reared in an environment of vertical stripes to determine the effect on orientation-selectivity of cortical neurons. (3)

Selective reflection. When an object reflects some wavelengths of the spectrum more than others. (7)

Selective transmission. When some wavelengths pass through visually transparent objects or substances and others do not. Selective transmission is associated with the perception of chromatic color. See also Selective reflection. (7)

Self-produced information. Generally, environmental information that is produced by actions of the observer. An example is optic flow, which occurs as a result of a person's movement and which, in turn, provides information that can be used to guide that movement. (10)

Sensations. Elementary elements that according to the structuralists, combine to create perceptions. (5)

Sensory code. The information contained in the firing of neurons, which represents what we perceive. (4)

Sensory component of pain. Pain perception described with terms such as *throbbing, prickly, hot,* or *dull.* See also Affective (or emotional) component of pain. (14)

Shadowing. Listeners' repetition aloud of what they hear as they are hearing it. (13)

Shortest-path constraint. The principle that apparent movement occurs along the shortest path between two stimuli when they are flashed on and off with the appropriate timing. (9)

Short-term spectrum. A plot that indicates the frequencies in a sound stimulus during a short period, usually at the beginning of the stimulus. (13)

Signal. The stimulus presented to a participant. A concept in signal detection theory. (Appendix)

Signal detection theory (SDT). A theory stating that the detection of a stimulus depends both on the participant's sensitivity to the stimulus and on the participant's response criterion. (Appendix)

Similarity, law of. A Gestalt law stating that similar things appear to be grouped together. (5)

Simple cortical cell. A neuron in the visual cortex that responds best to bars of a particular orientation. (3)

Simplicity, law of. See Pragnanz, law of.

Simultaneous contrast. The effect that occurs when surrounding one color with another changes the appearance of the surrounded color. (3, 7)

Single dissociation. When, as a result of brain damage, one function is present and another is absent. Existence of a single dissociation indicates that the two functions involve different mechanisms but may not be totally independent of one another. (4)

Size constancy. Occurs when the size of an object is perceived to remain the same even when it is viewed from different distances. (8)

Size-distance scaling. A hypothesized mechanism that helps maintain size constancy by taking an object's perceived distance into account. According to this mechanism, an object's perceived size, *S*, is determined by multiplying the size of the retinal image, R, times the object's perceived distance, *D*. (8)

Size-tuning curves. A function that indicates a neuron's response to stimuli of different sizes. Gratings, in which the size of the bars width can be varied, are usually used as stimuli to determine size-tuning curves. (3)

Slowly adapting fiber (SA fiber). A mechanoreceptive fiber in the skin that adapts slowly to continuous stimulation of the skin. Slowly adapting fibers are associated with Merkel receptors and Ruffini cylinders. (14)

Small-diameter fiber (S-fiber). According to gate control theory, activity in S-fibers opens the gate control mechanism and therefore increases the perception of pain. (14)

Somatosensory receiving area (S1). An area in the parietal lobe of the cortex that receives inputs from the skin and the viscera that are associated with somatic senses such as touch, temperature, and pain. See also Secondary somatosensory receiving area. (14)

Somatosensory system. The system that includes the cutaneous senses (senses involving the skin), proprioception (the sense of position of the limbs), and kinesthesis (sense of movement of the limbs). (14)

Sound (perceptual). The perceptual experience of hearing. The statement "I hear a sound" is using "sound" in that sense. (11)

Sound (physical). The physical stimulus for hearing. The statement, "The sound's level was 10 dB" is using "sound" in that sense. (11)

Sound level. The pressure of a sound stimulus, expressed in decibels. See also Sound pressure level. (11)

Sound pressure level (SPL). A designation used to indicate that the reference pressure used for calculating a tone's decibel rating is set at 20 micropascals, near the threshold in the most sensitive frequency range for hearing. (11)

Sound spectrogram. A plot showing the pattern of intensities and frequencies of a speech stimulus. (13)

Sound wave. Pattern of pressure changes in a medium. Most of the sounds we hear are due to pressure changes in the air, although sound can be transmitted through water and solids as well. (11)

Spatial cue. In tactile perception, information about the texture of a surface that is determined by the size, shape, and distribution of surface elements, such as bumps and grooves. (14)

Spatial frequency. For a grating stimulus, the frequency with which the grating repeats itself per degree of visual angle. (One cycle of a grating includes one light bar and one dark bar.) For more natural stimuli, high spatial frequencies are associated with fine details, and low spatial frequencies are associated with grosser features. (16)

Specificity coding. Type of neural code in which different perceptions are signaled by activity in specific neurons. See also Distributed coding. (4)

Spectral cue. In hearing, the distribution of frequencies reaching the ear that are associated with specific locations of a sound. One of the major spectral cues is the head-related transfer function (HRTF), which indicates the spectrum of frequencies at each location that are caused by interaction of sound with the listener's head and pinnae. See also Head-related transfer function. (12)

Spectral sensitivity. The sensitivity of visual receptors to different parts of the visible spectrum. See also Spectral sensitivity curve. (2)

Spectral sensitivity curve. The function relating a subject's sensitivity to light to the wavelength of the light. The spectral sensitivity curves for rod and cone vision indicates that the rods and cones are maximally sensitive at 500nm and 560nm, respectively. See also Purkinje shift. (2)

Spinothalamic pathway. One of the nerve pathways in the spinal cord that conducts nerve impulses from the skin to the somatosensory area of the thalamus. (14)

Spontaneous activity. Nerve firing that occurs in the absence of environmental stimulation. (2)

Staining. A technique in which neurons take up a dye that make their structure visible. (2)

Stapes. The last of the three ossicles in the middle ear. It receives vibrations from the incus and transmits these vibrations to the oval window of the inner ear. (11)

Stereopsis. The impression of depth that results from binocular disparity—the difference in the position of images of the same object on the retinas of the two eyes. (8)

Stereoscope. A device that presents pictures to the left and the right eyes so that the binocular disparity a person would experience when viewing an actual scene is duplicated. The result is a convincing illusion of depth. (8)

Stevens's power law. A law concerning the relationship between the physical intensity of a stimulus and the perception of the subjective magnitude of the stimulus. The law states that $P = KS^n$, where P is perceived magnitude, K is a constant, S is the stimulus intensity, and n is an exponent. (1)

Stimulation-produced analgesia (SPA). Brain stimulation that eliminates or strongly decreases the perception of pain. (14)

Stimulus salience. Characteristics such as bright colors, high contrast, and highly visible orientations that cause stimuli to stand out and therefore attract attention. (6)

Striate cortex. The visual receiving area of the cortex, located in the occipital lobe. (3)

Stroboscopic movement. See Apparent movement.

Structural-description model. An approach to object perception that states that our ability to recognize three-dimensional objects is based on three-dimensional volumes that can be combined to create the overall shape of the object. This approach is associated with Biederman's recognition-by-components theory of object perception. For another approach, see Image-description models. (5)

Structuralism. The approach to psychology, prominent in the late 19th and early 20th centuries, that postulated that perceptions result from the summation of many elementary sensations. The Gestalt approach to perception was, in part, a reaction to structuralism. (5)

Structure-from-motion. A situation in which movement of a stimulus creates the perception of an object that was not perceived when the stimulus was stationary. See also Kinetic depth effect. (9)

Subcortical structure. Structure below the cerebral cortex. For example, the superior colliculus is a subcortical structure in the visual system. The cochlear nucleus and superior olivary nucleus are among the subcortical structures in the auditory system. (11)

Substantia gelatinosa. A nucleus in the spinal cord that, according to the gate-control model, receives inputs from S-fibers and L-fibers and sends inhibition to the T-cell. (14)

Subtraction technique. A technique used to analyze the results of brain imaging experiments, in which brain activity elicited by a control condition is subtracted from the activity elicited by an experimental condition to determine the activity that can be attributed to the experimental condition alone. (4)

Subtractive color mixture. See Color mixture, subtractive.

Superficial petronasal nerve. A nerve in the taste system that transmits signals from the receptors located at the top of the mouth toward the brain. (15)

Superior colliculus. An area in the brain that is involved in controlling eye movements and other visual behaviors. This area receives about 10 percent of the ganglion cell fibers that leave the eye in the optic nerve. (3)

Superior olivary nucleus. A nucleus along the auditory pathway from the cochlea to the auditory cortex. The superior olivary nucleus receives inputs from the cochlear nucleus. (11)

Supertaster. A person who is especially sensitive to 6-*n*-propylthiouracil (PROP), a bitter substance. (15)

Synapse. A small space between the end of one neuron (the presynaptic neuron) and the cell body of another neuron (the postsynaptic neuron). See also Synaptic vesicles. (2)

Synchrony hypothesis. The idea that when an object causes neurons in different parts of the cortex to fire, the timing of the firing of these neurons will be synchronized. This synchrony indicates that all of these neurons are responding to the same object. This idea has been proposed as a solution to the binding problem. (6)

Synchrony, principle of. A modern principle of perceptual organization that states that visual events that occur at the same time will be perceived as belonging together. (5)

Tactile actuity. The smallest details that can be detected on the skin. (14)

Taste-blind. A person who is taste-blind cannot taste phenylthiocarbamide (PTC) and also tends to be less sensitive to certain other tastes than someone who is not taste-blind. (15)

Taste bud. A structure located within papillae on the tongue that contains the taste cells. (15)

Taste cell. Cell located in taste buds that causes the transduction of chemical to electrical energy when chemicals contact receptor sites or channels located at the tip of this cell. (15)

Taste pore. An opening in the taste bud through which the tips of taste cells protrude. When chemicals enter a taste pore, they stimulate the taste cells and result in transduction. (15)

Taster. A person who can taste the compound phenylthiocarbamide (PTC). (15)

Tectorial membrane. A membrane that stretches the length of the cochlea and is located directly over the hair cells. Vibrations of the cochlear partition cause the tectorial membrane to bend the hair cells by rubbing against them. (11)

Temporal cue. In tactile perception, information about the texture of a surface that is determined by the rate of vibrations that occur as we move our fingers across the surface. (14)

Temporal lobe. A lobe on the side of the cortex that is the site of the cortical receiving area for hearing and the termination point for the ventral, or *what* stream for visual processing. There are a number of areas in the temporal lobe, such as the fusiform face area and the extrastriate body area, that serve functions related to perceiving and recognizing objects. (2)

Texture gradient. The visual pattern formed by a regularly textured surface that extends away from the observer. This pattern provides information for distance because the elements in a texture gradient appear smaller as distance from the observer increases. (8, 10)

Theory of natural selection. The idea that genetically based characteristics that enhance an animal's ability to survive, and therefore reproduce, will be passed on to future generations. (4)

Theory of unconscious inference. The idea proposed by Helmholtz that some of our perceptions are the result of unconscious assumptions that we make about the environment. See also Likelihood principle. (5)

Threshold, absolute. The minimum stimulus energy necessary for an observer to detect a stimulus. (1)

Threshold, detection. The minimum amount of energy that can be detected. The detection threshold for smell is the lowest concentration at which an odorant can be detected. This threshold is distinguished from the recognition threshold, which requires a higher concentration of odorant. (15)

Threshold, difference. The minimal detectable difference between two stimuli. (1)

Threshold, recognition. For smell, the concentration at which the quality of an odor can be recognized. (15)

Timbre. The quality that distinguishes between two tones that sound different even though they have the same loudness, pitch, and duration. Differences in timbre are illustrated by the sounds made by different musical instruments. (11)

Tone chroma. The perceptual similarity of notes separated by one or more octaves. (11)

Tone height. The increase in pitch that occurs as frequency is increased. (11)

Tonotopic map. An ordered map of frequencies created by the responding of neurons within structures in the auditory system. There is a tonotopic map of neurons along the length of the cochlea, with neurons at the apex responding best to low frequencies and neurons at the base responding best to high frequencies. (11)

Top-down processing. Processing that starts with the analysis of high-level information, such as the knowledge a person brings to a situation. Also called knowledge-based processing. Distinguished from bottom-up, or data-based processing, which is based on incoming data. (1)

Topographic map. A map on a structure such as the cortex in which points on the structure correspond in a systematic way to locations in space for vision and hearing, and to locations on the body for touch. See also Homunculus. (12)

Transduction. In the senses, the transformation of environmental energy into electrical energy. For example, the retinal receptors transduce light energy into electrical energy. (1)

Traveling wave. In the auditory system, vibration of the basilar membrane in which the peak of the vibration travels from the base of the membrane to its apex. (11)

Trichromat. A person with normal color vision. Trichromats can match any wavelength in the spectrum by mixing three other wavelengths in various proportions. (5)

Trichromatic theory of color vision. A theory proposing that our perception of color is determined by the ratio of activity in three receptor mechanisms with different spectral sensitivities. (7)

Tritanopia. A form of dichromatism thought to be caused by a lack of the short-wavelength cone pigment. (7)

Tuning curve, frequency. See Frequency tuning curve.

Tuning curve, orientation. See Orientation tuning curve.

2-deoxyglucose technique. A procedure that involves injecting a radioactive 2-deoxyglucose (2DG) molecule into an animal and exposing the animal to oriented stimuli. The 2DG is taken up by neurons that respond to the orientation. This procedure is used to visualize orientation columns in the cortex. (15)

Two-point threshold. The smallest separation between two points on the skin that is perceived as two points; a measure of acuity on the skin. See also Grating acuity. (14)

Tympanic membrane (eardrum). A membrane at the end of the auditory canal that vibrates in response to vibrations of the air and transmits these vibrations to the ossicles in the middle ear. (11)

Uncrossed disparity. Binocular disparity that occurs when objects are located beyond the horopter. (8)

Uniform connectedness, principle of. A modern Gestalt principle that states that connected regions of a visual stimulus are perceived as a single unit. (5)

Unilateral dichromat. A person who has dichromatic vision in one eye and trichromatic vision in the other eye. People with this condition (which is extremely rare) have been tested to determine what colors a dichromat perceives by asking them to compare the perceptions they experience with their dichromatic eye and their trichromatic eye. (7)

Univariance, principle of. Absorption of a photon by a visual pigment molecule causes the same effect no matter what the wavelength. (7)

Vagus nerve. A nerve that conducts signals from taste receptors in the mouth and larynx. (15)

Ventral pathway. Pathway that conducts signals from the striate cortex to the temporal lobe. Also called the *what* pathway because it is involved in recognizing objects. (4)

Ventricles. Cavities located at the center of the brain which were identified by Galen as the source of "spirits" that determined human health, thoughts, and emotions. (2)

Ventriloquism effect. See Visual capture.

Ventrolateral nucleus. Nucleus in the thalamus that receives signals from the cutaneous system. (14)

Veridical perception. Perception that matches the actual physical situation. An example of veridical perception would be perceiving a line to be vertical when it is vertical. Examples of nonveridical perception are provided by illusions, in which what is perceived does not match the physical stimulus. (8)

Video microscopy. A technique that has been used to take pictures of papillae and taste buds on the tongue. (15)

View-invariant properties. Properties of objects that remain visible even when an object is viewed from different angles. For example, a view-invariant property of a rectangular solid is its three parallel edges, which are visible from most viewing angles. (5)

Viewpoint invariance. Objects that have properties that don't change when viewed from different angles. The geons in the recognition-by-components theory of object perception are view invariant. (5)

Virtual auditory space (VAS). Occurs when a listener wearing headphones experiences externalization, so sounds are heard as originating in space, as in the normal listening environment. This occurs only when sounds heard in the headphones have been processed, taking the listener's head related transfer function (HRTF) into account. See also Externalization. (12)

Visible light. The band of electromagnetic energy that activates visual system and which we can, therefore, perceive. For humans, visible light has wavelengths between 400 and 700 nanometers. (2)

Visual acuity. The ability to resolve small details. (3)

Visual angle. The angle of an object relative to an observer's eyes. This angle can be determined by extending two lines from the eye—one to one end of an object and the other to the other end of the object. Because an object's visual angle is always determined relative to an observer, its visual angle changes as the distance between the object and the observer changes. (8)

Visual capture. When sound is heard coming from its seen location, even though it is actually originating somewhere else. Also called the ventriloquism effect. (8)

Visual direction strategy. A strategy used by moving observers to reach a destination by keeping their body oriented toward the target. (10)

Visual-dominant neuron. Neuron in the monkey's anterior intraparietal cortex that responds when a monkey looks at a button or presses the button in the light, but does not respond to pushing the button in the dark. (10)

Visual evoked potential. An electrical response to visual stimulation recorded by the placement of disk electrodes on the back of the head. This potential reflects the activity of a large population of neurons in the visual cortex. (16)

Visual pigment. A light-sensitive molecule contained in the rod and cone outer segments. The reaction of this molecule to light results in the generation of an electrical response in the receptors. (2)

Visual pigment molecules. Light-sensitive molecules in the outer segments of the rod and cone visual receptors that are responsible for the transformation of light energy into electrical energy. The molecule consists of a large protein component called opsin and a small light-sensitive component called retinal. (2)

Visual pigment regeneration. Occurs after the visual pigment's two components—opsin and retinal—have become separated due to the action of light. Regeneration, which occurs in the dark, involves a rejoining of these two components to reform the visual pigment molecule. This process depends on enzymes located in the pigment epithelium. (2)

Visual search. A procedure in which a person's task is to find a particular element in a display that contains a number of elements. (1, 6)

Visual transduction. Transformation of light energy into electrical energy that occurs in the rod and cone receptors in the retina. (2)

Voice onset time (VOT). In speech production, the time delay between the beginning of a sound and the beginning of the vibration of the vocal chords. (13)

Volumetric features. Three-dimensional features that can be combined to create objects. The geons of the recognition-by-components theory of recognition are volumetric features. (5)

Waterfall illusion. An aftereffect of movement that occurs after viewing a stimulus moving in one direction, such as a waterfall. Viewing the waterfall creates other objects to appear to move in the opposite direction. (9)

Wavelength. For light energy, the distance between one peak of a light wave and the next peak. (2)

Weber fraction. The ratio of the difference threshold to the value of the standard stimulus in Weber's law. (1)

Weber's law. A law stating that the ratio of the difference threshold (*DL*) to the value of the stimulus (DL/S) is constant. According to this relationship, doubling the value of a stimulus will cause a doubling of the difference threshold. The ratio DL/S is called the Weber fraction. (1)

Wernicke's aphasia. An inability to comprehend words or arrange sounds into coherent speech, caused by damage to Wernicke's area. (13)

Wernicke's area. An area in the temporal lobe involved in speech perception. Damage to this area causes Wernicke's aphasia, which is characterized by a difficulty in understanding speech.

Wessel effect. In hearing, grouping by similarity of timbre that occurs when three-note ascending scales of tones alternating in timbre are played rapidly. The resulting grouping based on timbre creates a perception of descending three-note scales. (12)

***What* pathway.** See Ventral pathway.

***Where* pathway.** See Dorsal pathway.

White's illusion. A display in which two rectangles are perceived as differing in lightness even though they both reflect the same amount of light and even though the rectangle that is perceived as lighter receives more lateral inhibition than the one perceived as darker. (3)

Word deafness. Occurs in the most extreme form of Wernicke's aphasia, when a person cannot recognize words, even though the ability to hear pure tones remains intact. (13)

Young-Helmholtz theory of color vision. See Trichromatic theory of color vision.

REFERENCES

Abbott, L. F., Rolls, E. T., & Tovee, M. J. (1996). Representational capacity of face coding in monkeys. *Cerebral Cortex, 6,* 498–505.

Abramov, I., & Gordon, J. (1994). Color appearance: On seeing red, or yellow, or green, or blue. *Annual Review of Psychology, 45,* 451–485.

Abramov, I., Gordon, J., Hendrickson, A., Hainline, L., Dobson, V., & LaBossiere, E. (1982). The retina of the newborn human infant. *Science, 217,* 265–267.

Ache, B. W. (1991). Phylogeny of smell and taste. In T. V. Getchell, R. L. Doty, L. M. Bartoshuk, & J. B. Snow (Eds.), *Smell and taste in health and disease* (pp. 3–18). New York: Raven Press.

Ackerman, D. (1990). *A natural history of the senses.* New York: Vintage Books.

Adelson, E. H. (1993). Perceptual organization and the judgment of brightness. *Science, 262,* 2042–2044.

Adelson, E. H. (1999). Light perception and lightness illusions. In M. Gazzaniga (Ed.), *The new cognitive neurosciences* (pp. 339–351). Cambridge, MA: MIT Press.

Adrian, E. D. (1928). *The basis of sensation.* New York: Norton.

Adrian, E. D. (1932). *The mechanism of nervous action.* Philadelphia: University of Pennsylvania Press.

Aggelton, J. P., & Waskett, L. (1999). The ability of odours to serve as state-dependent cues for real-world memories: Can Viking smells aid the recall of Viking experiences? *British Journal of Psychology, 90,* 1–7.

Aguirre, G. K., Zarahn, E., & D'Esposito, M. (1998). An area within human ventral cortex sensitive to "building" stimuli: Evidence and implications. *Neuron, 21,* 373–383.

Alain, C., Arnott, S. R., Hevenor, S., Graham, S., & Grady, C. L. (2001). "What" and "where" in the human auditory system. *Proceedings of the National Academy of Sciences, 98,* 12301–12306.

Albrecht, D. G., DeValois, R. L., & Thorell, L. G. (1980). Visual cortical neurons: Are bars or gratings the optimal stimuli? *Science, 207,* 88–90.

Albright, T. D., Desimone, R., & Gross, C. A. (1984). Columnar organization of directionally selective cells in visual area MT of the macaque. *Journal of Neurophysiology, 51,* 16–31.

Alpern, M., Kitahara, K., & Krantz, D. H. (1983). Perception of color in unilateral tritanopia. *Journal of Physiology, 335,* 683–697.

Ambridge, E., Cowey, A., & Wade, D. (1999). Does parietal cortex contribute to feature binding? *Neuropsychologia, 37,* 999–1004.

Anderson, B. L., & Winawer, J. (2005). Image segmentation and lightness perception. *Nature, 434,* 79–83.

Anstis, S. M., Verstraten, F. A. J., & Mather, G. (1998). The motion aftereffect: A review. *Trends in Cognitive Science, 2,* 111–117.

Appelle, S. (1972). Perception and discrimination as a function of stimulus orientation: The "oblique effect" in man and animals. *Psychological Bulletin, 78,* 266–278.

Ashbridge, E., Cowey, A., & Wade, D. (1999). Does parietal cortex contribute to feature binding? *Neuropsychologia, 37,* 999–1004.

Aslin, R. N. (1977). Development of binocular fixation in human infants. Journal of *Experimental Child Psychology, 23,* 133–150.

Azzopardi, P., & Cowey, A. (1993). Preferential representation of the fovea in the primary visual cortex. *Nature, 361,* 719–721.

Backhaus, W. G. K. (1998). Physiological and psychophysical simulations of color vision in humans and animals. In W. G. K. Backhaus, R. Kliegl, & J. S. Werner (Eds.), *Color vision: Perspectives from different disciplines* (pp. 45–77). New York: Walter de Gruyter.

Backus, B. T., Fleet, D. J., Parker, A. J., & Heeger, D. J. (2001). Human cortical activity correlates with stereoscopic depth perception. *Journal of Neuropshysiology, 86,* 2054–2068.

Baillargeon, R. (2004). Infants' physical world. *Current Directions in Psychological Science, 13,* 89–94.

Baird, J. C., Wagner, M., & Fuld, K. (1990). A simple but powerful theory of the moon illusion. *Journal of Experimental Psychology: Human Perception and Performance, 16,* 675–677.

Balogh, R. D., & Porter, R. H. (1986). Olfactory preferences resulting from mere exposure in human neonates. *Infant Behavior and Development, 9,* 395–401.

Banks, M. S. (1982). The development of spatial and temporal contrast sensitivity. *Current Eye Research, 2,* 191–198.

Banks, M. S., & Bennett, P. J. (1988). Optical and photoreceptor immaturities limit the spatial and chromatic vision of human neonates. *Journal of the Optical Society of America, A5,* 2059–2079.

Banks, M. S., & Salapatek, P. (1978). Acuity and contrast sensitivity in 1-, 2-, and 3-month-old human infants. *Investigative Ophthalmology and Visual Science, 17,* 361–365.

Banks, M. S., & Salapatek, P. (1981). Infant pattern vision: A new approach based on the contrast sensitivity function. *Journal of Experimental Child Psychology, 31,* 1–45.

Bardy, B. G., & Laurent, M. (1998). How is body orientation controlled during somersaulting? *Journal of Experimental Psychology: Human Perception and Performance, 24,* 963–977.

Barinaga, M. (1994). Neurons tap out a code that may help locate sounds. *Science, 264,* 775.

Barlow, H. B. (1972). Single units and sensation: A neuron doctrine for perceptual psychology. *Perception, 1,* 371–394.

Barlow, H. B. (1995). The neuron in perception. In Gazzaniga, M. S. (Ed.), *The cognitive neurosciences* (pp. 415–434). Cambridge, MA: MIT Press.

Barlow, H. B., Blakemore, C., & Pettigrew, J. D. (1967). The neural mechanism of binocular depth discrimination. *Journal of Physiology, 193,* 327–342.

Barlow, H. B., & Mollon, J. D. (Eds.). (1982). *The senses.* Cambridge, England: University of Cambridge Press.

Bartoshuk, L. M. (1971). The chemical senses: I. Taste. In J. W. Kling & L. A. Riggs (Eds.), *Experimental psychology* (3rd ed.). New York: Holt, Rinehart and Winston.

Bartoshuk, L. M. (1979). Bitter taste of saccharin: Related to the genetic ability to taste the bitter substance propylthioural (PROP). *Science, 205,* 934–935.

Bartoshuk, L. M. (1980, September). Separate worlds of taste. *Psychology Today, 243,* 48–56.

Bartoshuk, L. M., & Beauchamp, G. K. (1994). Chemical senses. *Annual Review of Psychology, 45,* 419–449.

Bartoshuk, L. M., Cain, W. S., & Pfaffmann, C. (1985). Taste and olfaction. In G. A. Kimble & K. Schlesinger (Eds.), *Topics in the history of psychology* (Vol. 1, pp. 221–260). Hillsdale, NJ: Erlbaum.

Bartrip, J., Morton, J., & deSchonen, S. (2001). Responses to mother's face in 3-week to 5-month-old infants. *British Journal of Developmental Psychology, 19,* 219–232.

Battaglini, P. P., Galletti, C., & Fattori, P. (1996). Cortical mechanisms for visual perception of object motion and position in space. *Behavioural Brain Research, 76,* 143–154.

Baylis, G. C., & Driver, J. (1993). Visual attention and objects: Evidence for hierarchical coding of location. *Journal of Experimental Psychology: Human Perception and Performance, 19,* 451–470.

Baylis, G. C., & Driver, J. (2001). Shape-coding in IT cells generalizes over contrast and mirror reversal, but not figure–ground reversal *Nature Neuroscience, 4,* 937–942.

Baylor, D. (1992). Transduction in retinal photoreceptor cells. In P. Corey & S. D. Roper (Eds.), *Sensory transduction* (pp. 151–174). New York: Rockefeller University Press.

Beauchamp, G. K., Bertino, M., & Engelman, K. (1991). Human salt appetite. In M. I. Friedman, M. G. Tordoff, & M. R. Kare (Eds.), *Chemical senses: Appetite and nutrition* (pp. 85–107). New York: Marcel Dekker.

Beauchamp, G. K., Cowart, B. J., & Moran, M. (1986). Developmental changes in salt acceptability in human infants. *Developmental Psychobiology, 19,* 17–25.

Beauchamp, G. K., Cowart, B. J., & Schmidt, H. J. (1991). Development of chemosensory sensitivity and preference. In T. V. Getchell, R. L. Doty, L. M. Bartoshuk, & J. B. Snow (Eds.), *Smell and taste in health and disease* (pp. 405–416). New York: Raven Press.

Behrmann, M., Geng, J. J., & Shomstein, S. (2004). Parietal cortex and attention. *Current Opinion in Neurobiology, 14,* 212–217.

Békésy, G. von (1960). *Experiments in hearing.* New York: McGraw-Hill.

Belin, P., Zatorre, R. J., Lafaille, P., Ahad, P., & Pike, B. (2000). Voice-selective areas in human auditory cortex. *Nature 403,* 309–312.

Benary, W. (1924). Beobachtungen zu einem. Experiment uber Helligkeitz-kontrast (Observations concerning an experiment on brightness contrast). *Psychologische Forschung, 5,* 131–142.

Beranek, L. L. (1996). *Concert and opera halls: How they sound.* Woodbury, NY: Acoustical Society of America.

Berger, K. W. (1964). Some factors in the recognition of timbre. *Journal of the Acoustical Society of America, 36,* 1881–1891.

Bertenthal, B. I., Proffitt, D. R., Spetner, N. B., & Thomas, M. A. (1985). The development of infant sensitivity to biomechanical motions. *Child Development, 56,* 531–543.

Berthenthal, B. I., Rose, J. L., & Bai, D. L. (1997). Perception-action coupling in the development of visual control of posture. *Journal of Experimental Psychology: Human Perception and Performance, 23,* 1631–1643.

Biederman, I. (1981). On the semantics of a glance at a scene. In M. Kubovy & J. R. Pomerantz (Eds.), *Perceptual organization* (pp. 213–253). Hillsdale, NJ: Erlbaum.

Biederman, I. (1987). Recognition-by-components: A theory of human image understanding. *Psychological Review, 94,* 115–147.

Biederman, I., & Cooper, E. E. (1991). Priming contour-deleted images: Evidence for intermediate representations in visual object recognition. *Cognitive Psychology, 23,* 393–419.

Birnberg, J. R. (1988). My turn. *Newsweek,* March 21.

Bisley, J. W., & Goldberg, M. E. (2003). Neuronal activity in the lateral intraparietal area and spatial attention. *Science, 299,* 81–86.

Blake, R. (1993). Cats perceive biological motion. *Psychological Science, 4,* 54–57.

Blake, R., & Hirsch, H. V. B. (1975). Deficits in binocular depth perception in cats after alternating monocular deprivation. *Science, 190,* 1114–1116.

Blake, R., & Wilson, H. R. (1991). Neural models of stereoscopic vision. *Trends in Neuroscience, 14,* 445–452.

Blakemore, C. (1973). The language of vision. *New Scientist, 58,* 674–677.

Blakemore, C., & Cooper, G. G. (1970). Development of the brain depends on the visual environment. *Nature, 228,* 477–478.

Blakemore, S. J., Wolpert, D. M., & Frith, C. D. (1998). Central cancellation of self-produced tickle sensation. *Nature Neuroscience, 1,* 635–640.

Blakemore, S-J, & Decety, J. (2001). From the perception of action to the understanding of intention. *Nature Reviews Neuroscience, 2,* 561–567.

Blasdel, G., Obermayer, K., & Kiorpes, L. (1995). Organization of ocular dominance and orientation columns in the striate cortex of neonatal macaque monkeys. *Visual Neuroscience, 12,* 589–603.

Blauert, J. (1997). *Spatial hearing: The psychophysics of human sound localization,* (Rev. ed.). Cambridge, MA: MIT Press.

Blumstein, S. E., & Stevens, K. N. (1979). Acoustic invariance in speech production: Evidence from measurements of the spectral characteristics of stop consonants. *Journal of the Acoustical Society of America, 66,* 1001–1007.

Boring, E. G. (1942). *Sensation and perception in the history of experimental psychology.* New York: Appleton-Century-Crofts.

Bornstein, M. H., Kessen, W., & Weiskopf, S. (1976). Color vision and hue categorization in young human infant. *Journal of Experimental Psychology: Human Perception and Performance, 2,* 115–119.

Bowmaker, J. K., & Dartnall, H. J. A. (1980). Visual pigments of rods and cones in a human retina. *Journal of Physiology, 298,* 501–511.

Boynton, R. M. (1979). *Human color vision.* New York: Holt, Rinehart and Winston.

Bradley, D. R., & Petry, H. M. (1977). Organizational determinants of subjective contour: The subjective Necker cube. *American Journal of Psychology, 90,* 253–262.

Brainard, D. H., & Wandell, B. A. (1986). Analysis of the retinex theory of color vision. *Journal of the Optical Society of America, A3,* 1651–1661.

Bregman, A. S. (1990). *Auditory scene analysis.* Cambridge: MIT Press.

Bregman, A. S. (1993). Auditory scene analysis: Hearing in complex environments. In S. McAdams & E. Bigand (Eds.), *Thinking in sound: The cognitive psychology of human audition* (pp. 10–36). Oxford, England: Oxford University Press.

Bregman, A. S., & Campbell, J. (1971). Primary auditory stream segregation and perception of order in rapid sequence of tones. *Journal of Experimental Psychology, 89,* 244–249.

Bregman, A. S., & Pinker, S. (1978). Auditory streaming and the building of timbre. *Canadian Journal of Psychology, 32,* 19–31.

Bregman, A. S., & Rudnicky, A. I. (1975). Auditory segregation: Stream or streams? *Journal of Experimental Psychology: Human Perception and Performance, 1,* 263–267.

Breslin, P. A. S. (2001). Human gustation and flavour. *Flavour and Fragrance Journal, 16,* 439–456.

Bridgeman, B., & Stark, L. (1991). Ocular proprioception and efference copy in registering visual direction. *Vision Research, 31,* 1903–1913.

Britten, K. H., & van Wezel, R. J. A. (2002). Area MST and heading perception in macaque monkeys. *Cerebral Cortex, 12,* 692–701.

Broadbent, D. E. (1958). *Perception and communication.* London: Pergammon.

Brosch, M., Bauer, R., & Eckhorn, R. (1997). Stimulusdependent modulations of correlated high-frequency oscillations in cat visual cortex. *Cerebral Cortex, 7,* 70–76.

Brown, A. A., Dowell, R. C., & Clark, G. M. (1987). Clinical results for postlingually deaf patients implanted with multichannel cochlear prosthetics. *Annals of Otology, Rhinology, and Laryngology, 96* (Suppl. 128), 127–128.

Brown, P. K., & Wald, G. (1964). Visual pigments in single rods and cones of the human retina. *Science, 144,* 45–52.

Brownell, W. E., Bader, C. R., Bertrand, D., & Ribaupierre, Y. D. (1985). Evoked mechanical responses of isolated cochlear outer hair cells. *Science, 227,* 194–196.

Brugge, J. F., & Merzenich, M. M. (1973). Responses of neurons in auditory cortex of the macaque monkey to monaural and binaural stimulation. *Journal of Neurophysiology, 36,* 1138–1158.

Buck, L. B. (2004). Olfactory receptors and coding in mammals. *Nutrition Reviews, 62,* S184–S188.

Buck, L., & Axel, R. (1991). A novel multigene family may encode odorant receptors: A molecular basis for odor recognition. *Cell, 65,* 175–187.

Bufe, B., Breslin, P. A. S., Kuhn, C., Reed, D. R., Tharp, C. D., Slack, J. P., Kim, Un-Kyun, Drayna, D., & Meyerhof, W. (2005). The molecular basis of individual differences in phenylthiocarbamide and propylthiouracil bitterness perception. *Current Biology, 15,* 322–327.

Bugelski, B. R., & Alampay, D. A. (1961). The role of frequency in developing perceptual sets. *Canadian Journal of Psychology, 15,* 205–211.

Burns, M., & Lamb, T. D. (2004). Visual transduction by rod and cone photoreceptors. In L. M. Chalupa & J. S. Werner (Eds.), *The visual neurosciences* (pp. 215–233). Cambridge, MA: MIT Press.

Burton, A. M., Young, A. W., Bruce, V., Johnston, R. A., & Ellis, A. W. (1991). Understanding covert recognition. *Cognition, 39,* 129–166.

Bushara, K. O., Hanakawa, T., Immisch, I., Toma, K., Kansaku, K., & Hallett, M. (2003). Neural correlates of cross-modal binding. *Nature Neuroscience, 6,* 190–195.

Bushnell, I. W. R. (2001). Mother's face recognition in newborn infants: Learning and memory. *Infant and Child Development, 10,* 67–74.

Bushnell, I. W. R., Sai, F., & Mullin, J. T. (1989). Neonatal recognition of the mother's face. *British Journal of Developmental Psychology, 7,* 3–15.

Cain, W. S. (1977). Differential sensitivity for smell: "Noise" at the nose. *Science, 195,* 796–798.

Cain, W. S. (1980). *Sensory attributes of cigarette smoking* (Branbury Report: 3. A safe cigarette?, pp. 239–249). Cold Spring Harbor, NY: Cold Spring Harbor Laboratory.

Cain, W. S. (1988). Olfaction. In R. A. Atkinson, R. J. Herrnstein, G. Lindzey, & R. D. Luce (Eds.), *Stevens' handbook of experimental psychology: Vol. 1. Perception and motivation* (Rev. ed., pp. 409–459). New York: Wiley.

Calton, J. L., Dickenson, A. R., & Snyder, L. H. (2002). Nonspatial, motor-specific activation in posterior parietal cortex. *Nature Neuroscience, 5,* 580–588.

Calvert, G. A., Bullmore, E. T., Brammer, M. J., Campbell, R., Williams, S. C. R., McGuire, P. K., Woodruff, P. W. R., Iversen, S. D., & David, A. S. (1997). Activation of auditory cortex during silent lip-reading. *Science, 276,* 593–595.

Campbell, F. W., Kulikowski, J. J., & Levinson, J. (1966). The effect of orientation on the visual resolution of gratings. *Journal of Physiology (London), 187,* 427–436.

Campbell, F. W., & Robson, J. G. (1968). Application of Fourier analysis to the visibility of gratings. *Journal of Physiology, 197,* 551–566.

Carello, C., & Turvey, M. T. (2004). Physics and psychology of the muscle sense. *Current Directions in Psychological Science, 13,* 25–28.

Carlyon, R. P., Cusack, R., Foxton, J. M., & Robertson, I. H. (2001). Effects of attention and unilateral neglect on auditory stream segregation. *Journal of Experimental Psychology: Human Perception and Performance, 27,* 115–127.

Carr, R. E., & Ripps, H. (1967). Rhodopsin kinetics and rod adaptation in Oguchi's disease. *Investigative Ophthalmology, 6,* 426–436.

Carrasco, M., Ling, S., & Read, S. (2004). Attention alters appearance. *Nature Neuroscience, 7,* 308–313.

CBS News. (2001, September 4). The cochlear implant controversy. CBS Sunday Morning. Retrieved from http://www.cbsnews.com/stories/1998/06/01/sunday/main10719.shtml

Chapman, C. R. (1995). The affective dimension of pain: A model. In B. Bromm & J. Desmedt (Eds.), *Pain and the brain:*

From nociception to cognition: Advances in pain research and therapy, Volume 22 (pp. 283–301). New York: Raven.

Chatterjee, S. H., Freyd, J. J., & Shiffrar, M. (1996). Configural processing in the perception of apparent biological motion. *Journal of Experimental Psychology: Human Perception and Performance, 22,* 916–929.

Chella, A., Frixione, M., & Gaglio, S. (2000). Understanding dynamic scenes. *Artificial Intelligence, 123,* 89–132.

Chen, L. M., Friedman, R. M., & Roe, A. W. (2003). Optical imaging of a tactile illusion in area 3b of the primate somatosensory cortex. *Science, 302,* 881–885.

Chino, Y., Smith, E., Hatta, S., & Cheng, H. (1997). Postnatal development of binocular disparity sensitivity in neurons of the primate visual cortex. *Journal of Neuroscience, 17,* 296–307.

Chodosh, L. A., Lifson, L. E., & Tabin, C. (1995). Play ball! *Science, 268,* 1682–1683.

Cholewaik, R. W., & Collins, A. A. (2003). Vibrotactile localization on the arm: Effects of place, space, and age. *Perception & Psychophysics, 65,* 1058–1077.

Churchland, P. S., & Ramachandran, V. S. (1996). Filling in: Why Dennett is wrong. In K. Atkins (Ed.), *Perception.* Oxford, England: Oxford University Press.

Cinelli, A. R. (1993). Review of "Science of olfaction." *Trends in Neurosciences, 16,* 123–124.

Clarke, S., Thiran, A. B., Maeder, P., Adriani, M., Vernet, O., Regli, L., Cuisenaire, O., & Thiran, J.-P. (2002). What and where in human auditory: Selective deficits following focal hemispheric lesions. *Experimental Brain Research, 147,* 8–15.

Clulow, F. W. (1972). *Color: Its principles and their applications.* New York: Morgan & Morgan.

Cohen, J. D., & Tong, F. (2001). The face of controversy. *Science, 293,* 2405–2407.

Cohen, L. B. (1991). Infant attention: An information processing approach. In M. J. Weiss & P. R. Zelazo (Eds.), *Newborn attention: Biological constraints and the influence of experience* (pp. 1–21). Norwood, NJ: Ablex.

Cohen, M. R., & Newsome, W. T. (2004). What electrical microstimulation has revealed about the neural basis of cognition. *Current Opinion in Neurobiology, 14,* 169–177.

Colby, C. L., Duhamel, J.-R., & Goldberg, M. E. (1995). Oculocentric spatial representation in parietal cortex. *Cerebral Cortex, 5,* 470–481.

Collett, T. S., & Harkness, L. I. K. (1982). Depth vision in animals. In D. J. Ingle, M. A. Goodale, & R. J. W. Mansfield (Eds.), *Analysis of visual behavior* (pp. 111–176). Cambridge, MA: MIT Press.

Coltheart, M. (1970). The effect of verbal size information upon visual judgments of absolute distance. *Perception and Psychophysics, 9,* 222–223.

Comel, M. (1953). *Fisiologia normale e patologica della cute umana.* Milan, Italy: Fratelli Treves Editori.

Conel, J. L. (1939). *The postnatal development of the cerebral cortex* (Vol. 1). Cambridge, MA: Harvard University Press.

Conel, J. L. (1947). *The postnatal development of the cerebral cortex* (Vol. 2). Cambridge, MA: Harvard University Press.

Conel, J. L. (1951). *The postnatal development of the cerebral cortex* (Vol. 3). Cambridge, MA: Harvard University Press.

Coppola, D. M., White, L. E., Fitzpatrick, D., & Purves, D. (1998). Unequal distribution of cardinal and oblique contours in ferret visual cortex. *Proceedings of the National Academy of Sciences, 95,* 2621–2623.

Costanzo, R. M., & Gardner, E. B. (1980). A quantitative analysis of responses of direction-sensitive neurons in somatosensory cortex of awake monkeys. *Journal of Neurophysiology, 43,* 1319–1341.

Cox, D., Meyers, E., & Sinha, P. (2004). Contextually evoked object-specific responses in human visual cortex. *Science, 304,* 115–117.

Craig, J. C., & Lyle, K. B. (2001). A comparison of tactile spatial sensitivity on the palm and fingerpad. *Perception & Psychophysics, 63,* 337–347.

Craig, J. C., & Lyle, K. B. (2002). A correction and a comment on Craig and Lyle (2001). *Perception & Psychohysics, 64,* 504–506.

Craton, L. G., & Yonas, A. (1990). The role of motion in infants' perception of occlusion. In J. T. Enns (Ed.), *The development of attention: Research and theory* (pp. 21–46). London: Elsevier.

Critchley, H. D., & Rolls, E. T. (1996). Hunger and satiety modify the responses of olfactory and visual neurons in the primate orbitofrontal cortex. *Journal of Neurophysiology,* 75, 1673–1686.

Culler, E. A., Coakley, J. D., Lowy, K., & Gross, N. (1943). A revised frequency-map of the guinea-pig cochlea. *American Journal of Psychology, 56,* 475–500.

Cutting, J. E., & Vishton, P. M. (1995). Perceiving layout and knowing distances: The integration, relative potency, and contextual use of different information about depth. In W. Epstein & S. Rogers (Eds.), *Handbook of perception and cognition: Perception of space and motion* (pp. 69–117). New York: Academic Press.

Dallos, P. (1996). Overview: Cochlear neurobiology. In P. Dallos, A. N. Popper, & R. R. Fay (Eds.), *The cochlea* (pp. 1–43). New York: Springer.

Dalton, J. (1948). Extraordinary facts relating to the vision of colour: With observations. In W. Dennis (Ed.), *Readings in the history of psychology* (pp. 102–111). New York: Appleton-Century-Crofts. (Original work published 1798)

Dalton, P. (2002). Olfaction. In S. Yantis (Ed.), *Stevens' handbook of experimental psychology: Sensation and perception* (3rd ed., pp. 691–756). New York: Wiley.

Dartnall, H. J. A., Bowmaker, J. K., & Mollon, J. D. (1983). Human visual pigments: Microspectrophotometric results from the eyes of seven persons. *Proceedings of the Royal Society of London, 220B,* 115–130.

Darwin, C. J. (1997). Auditory grouping. *Trends in Cognitive Sciences, 1,* 327–333.

David, A. S., & Senior, C. (2000). Implicit motion and the brain. *Trends in Cognitive Sciences, 4,* 293–295.

Day, R. H. (1989). Natural and artificial cues, perceptual compromise and the basis of veridical and illusory perception. In D. Vickers & P. L. Smith (Eds.), *Human information processing: Measures and mechanisms* (pp. 107–129). North Holland, The Netherlands: Elsevier Science.

Day, R. H. (1990). The Bourdon illusion in haptic space. *Perception and Psychophysics, 47,* 400–404.

DeAngelis G. C., Cumming B. G., & Newsome, W. T. (1998). Cortical area MT and the perception of stereoscopic depth. *Nature, 394,* 677–680.

DeAraujo, I. E. T., Kringelbach, M. L., Rolls, E. T., & Hobden, P. (2003). The representation of umami taste in the human brain. *Journal of Neurophysiology, 90,* 313–319.

DeCasper, A. J., & Fifer, W. P. (1980). Of human bonding: Newborns prefer their mothers' voices. *Science, 208,* 1174–1176.

DeCasper, A. J., Lecanuet, J.-P., Busnel, M.-C., Deferre- Granier, C., & Maugeais, R. (1994). Fetal reactions to recurrent maternal speech. *Infant Behavior and Development, 17,* 159–164.

DeCasper, A. J., & Spence, M. J. (1986). Prenatal maternal speech influences newborn's perception of speech sounds. *Infant Behavior and Development, 9,* 133–150.

Dehaene-Lambertz, G., Dehanene, S., & Hertz-Pannier, L. (2002). Functional neuroimaging of speech perception in primates. *Science, 298,* 2013–2015.

Delahunt, P. B., & Brainard, D. H. (2004). Does human color constancy incorporate the statistical regularity of natural daylight? *Journal of Vision, 4,* 57–81.

DeLucia, P., & Hochberg, J. (1985). Illusions in the real world and in the mind's eye [Abstract]. *Proceedings of the Eastern Psychological Association, 56,* 38.

DeLucia, P., & Hochberg, J. (1986). Real-world geometrical illusions: Theoretical and practical implications [Abstract]. *Proceedings of the Eastern Psychological Association, 57,* 62.

DeLucia, P., & Hochberg, J. (1991). Geometrical illusions in solid objects under ordinary viewing conditions. *Perception and Psychophysics, 50,* 547–554.

Delwiche, J. F., Buletic, Z., & Breslin, P. A. S. (2001a). Covariation in individuals' sensitivities to bitter compounds: Evidence supporting multiple receptor/transduction mechanisms. *Perception & Psychophysics, 63,* 761–776.

Delwiche, J. F., Buletic, Z., & Breslin, P. A. S. (2001b). Relationship of papillae number to bitter intensity of quinine and PROP within and between individuals. *Physiology and Behavior, 74,* 329–337.

deMonasterio, F. M., Schein, S. J., & McCrane, E. P. (1981). Staining of blue-sensitive cones of the macaque by a fluorescent dye. *Science, 213,* 1278–1281.

Denes, P. B., & Pinson, E. N. (1993). *The speech chain* (2nd ed.). New York: Freeman.

Derbyshire, S. W. G., Jones, A. K. P., Gyulia, F., Clark, S., Townsend, D., & Firestone, L. L. (1997). Pain processing during three levels of noxious stimulation produces differential patterns of central activity. *Pain, 73,* 431–445.

Desor, J. A., & Beauchamp, G. K. (1974). The human capacity to transmit olfactory information. *Perception and Psychophysics, 13,* 271–275.

Deutsch, D. (1975). Two-channel listening to musical scales. *Journal of the Acoustical Society of America, 57,* 1156–1160.

Deutsch, D. (1996). The perception of auditory patterns. In W. Prinz & B. Bridgeman (Eds.), *Handbook of perception and action* (Vol. 1, pp. 253–296). San Diego, CA: Academic Press.

DeValois, K. K., DeValois, R. L., & Yund, E. W. (1979). Responses of striate cortex cells to gratings and checkerboard patterns. *Journal of Physiology, 291,* 483–505.

DeValois, R. L. (1960). Color vision mechanisms in monkey. *Journal of General Physiology, 43,* 115–128.

DeValois, R. L., Abramov, I., & Jacobs, G. H. (1966). Analysis of response of LGN cells. *Journal of the Optical Society of America, 56,* 966–977.

DeValois, R. L., & Jacobs, G. H. (1968). Primate color vision. *Science, 162,* 533–540.

DeValois, R. L., Yund, E. W., & Hepler, N. (1982). The orientation and direction selectivity of cells in macaque visual cortex. *Vision Research, 22,* 531–544.

Devos, M., Patte, F., Rouault, J., Laffert, P., & van Gemert, L. J. (1990). *Standardized human olfactory thresholds.* Oxford, UK: IRL Press.

deVries, H., & Stuiver, M. (1961). The absolute sensitivity of the human sense of smell. In W. A. Rosenblith (Ed.), *Sensory communication.* Cambridge, MA: MIT Press.

deWeid, M., & Verbaten, M. N. (2001). Affective pictures processing, attention, and pain tolerance. *Pain, 90,* 163–172.

DiLorenzo, P. M., & Victor, J. D. (2003). Taste response variability and temporal coding in the nucleus of the solitary tract of the rat. *Journal of Neurophysiology, 90,* 1418–1431.

Dobson, V., & Teller, D. (1978). Visual acuity in human infants: Review and comparison of behavioral and electrophysiological studies. *Vision Research, 18,* 1469–1483.

Dodd, G. G., & Squirrell, D. J. (1980). Structure and mechanism in the mammalian olfactory system. *Symposium of the Zoology Society of London, 45,* 35–56.

Dodd, J., & Castellucci, V. F. (1991). Smell and taste: The chemical senses. In E. R. Kandel, J. H. Schwartz, & T. M. Jessell (Eds.), *Principles of neural science* (3rd ed., pp. 512–529). New York: Elsevier.

Doty, R. L. (1991). Olfactory system. In T. V. Getchell, R. L. Doty, L. M. Bartoshuk, & J. B. Snow (Eds.), *Smell and taste in health and disease* (pp. 175–203). New York: Raven Press.

Doty, R. L. (1995). Intranasal trigeminal chemoreception. In R. L. Doty (Ed.), *Handbook of olfaction and gustation* (pp. 821–833). New York: Marcel Dekker.

Doty, R. L. (Ed.). (1976). *Mammalian olfaction, reproductive processes and behavior.* New York: Academic Press.

Dougherty, R. F., Koch, V. M., Brewer, A. A., Fischer, B., Modersitzki, J., & Wandell, B. A. (2003). Visual field representations and locations of visual areas V1/2/3 in human visual cortex. *Journal of Vision, 3,* 586–598.

Dowling, J. E., & Boycott, B. B. (1966). Organization of the primate retina. *Proceedings of the Royal Society of London, 166B,* 80–111.

Dowling, W. J. (1973). The perception of interleaved melodies. *Cognitive Psychology, 5,* 322–337.

Dowling, W. J., & Harwood, D. L. (1986). *Music cognition.* New York: Academic Press.

Downar, J., Crawley, A. P., Mikulis, D. J., & Davis, K. D. (2001). The effect of task relevance on the cortical response to changes in visual and auditory stimuli: An event-related fMRI study. *Neuroimage, 14,* 1256–1267.

Downing, P. E., Jiang, Y., Shuman, M., & Kanwisher, N. (2001). Cortical area selective for visual processing of the human body. *Science, 293,* 2470–2473.

Driver, J., & Baylis, G. C. (1989). Movement and visual attention: The spotlight metaphor breaks down. *Journal of Experimental Psychology: Human Perception and Performance, 15,* 448–456.

Driver, J., & Baylis, G. C. (1998). Attention and visual object segmentation. In R. Parasuraman (Ed.), *The attentive brain* (pp. 299–325). Cambridge, MA: MIT Press.

Duffy, C. J., & Wurtz, R. H. (1991). Sensitivity of MST neurons to optic flow stimuli: 2. Mechanisms of response selectivity revealed by small-field stimuli. *Journal of Neurophysiology, 65,* 1346–1359.

Duncan, R. O., & Boynton, G. M. (2003). Cortical magnification within human primary visual cortex correlates with acuity thresholds. *Neuron, 36,* 659–671.

Durrant, J., & Lovrinic, J. (1977). *Bases of hearing science.* Baltimore: Williams & Wilkins.

Dyde, R. T., & Milner, A. D. (2002). Two illusions of perceived orientation: One fools all of the people some of the time, but the other fools all of the people all of the time. *Experimental Brain Research, 144,* 518–527.

Egan, J. P., & Hake, H. W. (1950). On the masking pattern of a simple auditory stimulus. *Journal of the Acoustical Society of America, 22,* 622–630.

Egly, R., Driver, J., & Rafal, R. D. (1994). Shifting visual attention between objects and locations: Evidence from normal and parietal lesion subjects. *Journal of Experimental Psychology: General, 123,* 161–177.

Eimas, P. D., & Corbit, J. D. (1973). Selective adaptation of linguistic feature detectors. *Cognitive Psychology, 4,* 99–109.

Eimas, P. D., & Quinn, P. C. (1994). Studies on the formation of perceptually based basic-level categories in young infants. *Child Development, 65,* 903–917.

Eimas, P. D., Siqueland, E. R., Jusczyk, P., & Vigorito, J. (1971). Speech perception in infants. *Science, 171,* 303–306.

Eisenberger, N. I., Lieberman, M. D., & Williams, K. D. (2003). Does rejection hurt? An fMRI study of social exclusion. *Science, 302,* 290–292.

Elbert, T., Candia, V., Altenmuller, E., Rau, H., Sterr, A., Rockstroh, B., et al. (1998). Alteration of digital representations in somatosensory cortex in focal hand dystonia. *Neuroreport, 9,* 3571–3575.

Elbert, T., Pantev, C., Wienbruch, C., Rockstroh, B., & Taub, E. (1995). Increased cortical representation of the fingers of the left hand in string players. *Science, 270,* 305–307.

Emmert, E. (1881). Grossenverhaltnisse der Nachbilder. *Klinische Monatsblaetter fuer Augenheilkunde, 19,* 443–450.

Engel, A. K., Fries, P., Konig, P., Brecht, M., & Singer, W. (1999). *Consciousness and Cognition, 8,* 128–151.

Engel, S., Zhang, X., & Wandell, B. (1997). Colour tuning in human visual cortex measured with functional magnetic resonance imaging. *Nature, 388,* 68–71.

Engen, T. (1972). Psychophysics. In J. W. Kling & L. A. Riggs (Eds.), *Experimental psychology* (3rd ed., pp. 1–46). New York: Holt, Rinehart and Winston.

Engen, T., & Pfaffmann, C. (1960). Absolute judgments of odor quality. *Journal of Experimental Psychology, 59,* 214–219.

Epstein, R., Harris, A., Stanley, D., & Kanwisher, N. (1999). The parahippocampal place area: Recognition, navigation, or encoding? *Neuron, 23,* 115–125.

Epstein, R., & Kanwisher, N. (1998). A cortical representation of the local visual environment. *Nature, 392,* 598–601.

Epstein, W. (1965). Nonrelational judgments of size and distance. *American Journal of Psychology, 78,* 120–123.

Erickson, R. (1975). *Sound structure in music.* Berkeley: University of California Press.

Erickson, R. P. (1963). Sensory neural patterns and gustation. In Y. Zotterman (Ed.), *Olfaction and taste* (Vol. 1, pp. 205–213). Oxford, England: Pergamon Press.

Erickson, R. P. (2000). The evolution of neural coding ideas in the chemical senses. *Physiology & Behavior, 69,* 3–13.

Evans, E. F. (1978). Place and time coding of frequency in the peripheral auditory system: Some physiological pros and cons. *Audiology, 17,* 369–420.

Eysel, U. T. (2003). Illusions and perceived images in the primate brain. *Science, 302,* 789–790.

Fadiga, L., Fogassi, L., Pavesi, G., & Rizzolatti, G. (1995). Motor facilitation during action observation: A magnetic stimulation study. *Journal of Neurophysiology, 73,* 2608–2611.

Fagan, J. F. (1976). Infant's recognition of invariant features of faces. *Child Development, 47,* 627–638.

Fajen, B. R., & Warren, W. H. (2003). Behavioral dynamics of steering, obstacle avoidance and route selection. *Journal of Experimental Psychology: Human Perception and Performance, 29,* 343–362.

Fantz, R. L., Ordy, J. M., & Udelf, M. S. (1962). Maturation of pattern vision in infants during the first six months. *Journal of Comparative and Physiological Psychology, 55,* 907–917.

Farah, M. J., Rabinowitz, C., Quinn, G. E., & Liu, G. T. (2000). Early commitment of neural substrates for face recognition. *Cognitive Neuropsychology, 17,* 117–123.

Fernald, R. D. (2000). Evolution of eyes. *Current Opinion in Neurobiology, 10,* 444–450.

Fields, H. L., & Basbaum, A. I. (1999). Central nervous system mechanisms of pain modulation. In P. D. Wall & R. Melzak (Eds.), *Textbook of pain* (pp. 309–328). New York: Churchill Livingstone.

Finger, T. E. (1987). Gustatory nuclei and pathways in the central nervous system. In T. E. Finger & W. L. Silver (Eds.), *Neurobiology of taste and smell* (pp. 331–353). New York: Wiley.

Finniss, D. G., & Benedetti, F. (2005). Mechanisms of the placebo response and their impact on clinical trials and clinical practice. *Pain, 114,* 3–6.

Fiorentini, A., & Maffei, L. (1973). Contrast in night vision. *Vision Research, 13,* 73–80.

Firestein, S. (2001). How the olfactory system makes sense of scents. *Nature, 413,* 211–218.

Fletcher, H., & Munson, W. A. (1933). Loudness: Its definition, measurement, and calculation. *Journal of the Acoustical Society of America, 5,* 82–108.

Fowler, C. A., & Rosenblum, L. D. (1990). Duplex perception: A comparison of monosyllables and slamming doors. *Journal of Experimental Psychology: Human Perception and Performance, 16,* 742–754.

Fox, C. R. (1990). Some visual influences on human postural equilibrium: Binocular versus monocular fixation. *Perception and Psychophysics, 47,* 409–422.

Fox, R., & McDaniel, C. (1982). The perception of biological motion by human infants. *Science, 218,* 486–487.

Fox, R., Aslin, R. N., Shea, S. L., & Dumais, S. T. (1980). Stereopsis in human infants. *Science, 207,* 323–324.

Frank, M. E., Bieber, S. L., & Smith, D. V. (1988). The organization of taste sensibilities in hamster chorda tympani nerve fibers. *Journal of General Physiology, 91,* 861–896.

Frank, M. E., & Rabin, M. D. (1989). Chemosensory neuroanatomy and physiology. *Ear, Nose and Throat Journal, 68,* 291–292; 295–296.

Franklin, A., & Davies, R. L. (2004). New evidence for infant colour categories. *British Journal of Developmental Psychology, 22,* 349–377.

Freedman, D. J., et al. (2003). A comparison of primate prefrontal and inferior temporal cortices during visual categorization. *Journal of Neuroscience, 23,* 5235–5246.

Freedman, D. J., Riesenhuber, M., Poggio, T., & Miller, E. K. (2002). Visual categorization and the primate prefrontal cortex: Neurophysiology and behavior. *Journal of Neurophysiology, 88,* 929–941.

Freyd, J. (1983). The mental representation of movement when static stimuli are viewed. *Perception & Psychophysics. 33,* 575–581.

Friedman, R., N., Chen, L. M., & Roe, A. W. (2004). Modality maps within primate somatosensory cortex. *Proceedings of the National Academy of Sciences, 101,* 12724–12729.

Frisina, R. D. (2001). Subcortical neural coding mechanisms for auditory temporal processing. *Hearing Research, 158,* 1–27.

Friedman-Hill, S. R., Robertson, L. C., & Treisman, A. (1995). Parietal contributions to visual feature binding: Evidence from a patient with bilateral lesions. *Science, 269,* 853–855.

Fritz, J., Shamma, S., Elhilali, M., & Klein, D. (2003). Rapid task-related plasticity of spectrotemporal receptive fields in primary auditory cortex. *Nature Neuroscience, 6,* 1216–1223.

Fuld, K., Wooten, B. R., & Whalen, J. J. (1981). Elemental hues of short-wave and spectral lights. *Perception and Psychophysics, 29,* 317–322.

Furmanski, C. S., & Engel, S. A. (2000). An oblique effect in human primary visual cortex. *Nature Neuroscience, 3,* 535–536.

Gallese, V., Fadiga, L., Fogassi, L., & Rizzolatti, G. (1996). Action recognition in the premotor cortex. *Brain, 119,* 593–609.

Galletti, C., & Fattori, P. (2003). Neuronal mechanisms for detection of motion in the field of view. *Neuropsychologia, 41,* 1717–1727.

Ganchrow, J. R. (1995). Ontogeny of human taste perception. In R. L. Doty (Ed.), *Handbook of olfaction and gustation* (pp. 715–729). New York: Marcel Dekker.

Ganchrow, J. R., Steiner, J. E., & Daher, M. (1983). Neonatal facial expressions in response to different qualities and intensities of gustatory stimuli. *Infant Behavior and Development, 6,* 473–484.

Gardner, J. W., & Bartlett, P. N. (1999). *Electronic noses.* Oxford, UK: Oxford University Press.

Gardner, M. B., & Gardner, R. S. (1973). Problem of localization in the median plane: Effect of pinnae cavity occlusion. *Journal of the Acoustical Society of America, 53,* 400–408.

Gauthier, I., Skudlarski, P., Gore, J. C., & Anderson, A. W. (2000). Expertise for cars and birds recruits brain areas involved in face recognition. *Nature Neuroscience, 3,* 191–197.

Gauthier, I., Tarr, M. J., Anderson, A. W., Skudlarski, P., & Gore, J. C. (1999). Activation of the middle fusiform "face area" increases with expertise in recognizing novel objects. *Nature Neuroscience, 2,* 568–573.

Gegenfurtner, K. (2001). Color in the cortex revisited. *Nature Neuroscience, 4,* 339–340.

Gescheider, G. A. (1976). *Psychophysics: Method and theory.* Hillsdale, NJ: Erlbaum.

Getty, D. J., & Howard, J. H. (Eds.). (1981). *Auditory and visual pattern recognition.* Hillsdale, NJ: Erlbaum.

Gibson, B. S., & Peterson, M. A. (1994). Does orientation-independent object recognition precede orientation-dependent recognition? Evidence from a cuing paradigm. *Journal of Experimental Psychology: Human Perception and Performance, 20,* 299–316.

Gibson, J. J. (1950). *The perception of the visual world.* Boston: Houghton Mifflin.

Gibson, J. J. (1962). Observations on active touch. *Psychological Review, 69,* 477–491.

Gibson, J. J. (1966). *The senses considered as perceptual systems.* Boston: Houghton Mifflin.

Gibson, J. J. (1979). *The ecological approach to visual perception.* Boston: Houghton Mifflin.

Gilbert, A. N., & Firestein, S. (2002). Dollars and scents: Commercial opportunities in olfaction and taste. *Nature Neuroscience, 5,* 1043–1045.

Gilbert, C. D., & Wiesel, T. N. (1989). Columnar specificity of intrinsic horizontal and corticocortical connections in cat visual cortex. *Journal of Neuroscience, 9,* 2432–2442.

Gilchrist, A. L. (Ed.). (1994). *Lightness, brightness, and transparency.* Hillsdale, NJ: Erlbaum.

Gilchrist, A., Kossyfidis, C., Agostini, T., Li, Xiaojun, Bonato, F., Cataliotti, J., Spehar, B., Annan, V., & Economou, E. (1999). An anchoring theory of lightness perception. *Psychological Review, 106,* 795–834.

Gilinsky, A. S. (1951). Perceived size and distance in visual space. *Psychological Review, 58,* 460–482.

Girard, P., Lomber, S. G., & Bullier, J. (2002). Shape discrimination deficits during reversible deactivation of area V4 in the macaque monkey. *Cerebral Cortex, 12,* 1146–1156.

Glanz, J. (2000, April 18). Art + physics = beautiful music. *New York Times,* pp. D1–D4.

Glickstein, M. (1988, September). The discovery of the visual cortex. *Scientific American, 259,* 118–127.

Gold, J. I., & Mazurek, M. E. (2002). Posterior parietal cortex: Not just where, but how. *Nature Neuroscience, 5,* 506–508.

Goldstein, E. B. (2001a). Cross-talk between psychophysics and physiology in the study of perception. In E. B. Goldstein (Ed.), *Blackwell handbook of perception* (pp. 1–23). Oxford, UK: Blackwell.

Goldstein, E. B. (2001b). Pictorial perception and art. In E. B Goldstein (Ed.), *Blackwell handbook of perception* (pp. 344–378). Oxford, UK: Blackwell.

Goldstein, E. B., & Fink, S. I. (1981). Selective attention in vision: Recognition memory for superimposed line drawings. *Journal of Experimental Psychology: Human Perception and Performance, 7,* 954–967.

Goldstein, J. L. (1978). Mechanisms of signal analysis and pattern perception in periodicity pitch. *Audiology, 17,* 421–445.

Goodale, M. A., & Humphrey, G. K. (1998). The objects of action and perception. *Cognition, 67,* 181–207.

Goodale, M. A., & Humphrey, G. K. (2001). Separate visual systems for action and perception. In E. B. Goldstein (Ed.), *Blackwell handbook of perception* (pp. 311–343). Oxford, UK: Blackwell.

Goodwin, A. W. (1998). Extracting the shape of an object from the responses of peripheral nerve fibers. In J. W. Morley (Ed.), *Neural aspects of tactile sensation* (pp. 55–87). New York: Elsevier Science.

Gordon, J., & Abramov, I. (2001). *Color vision.* In E. B. Goldstein (Ed.), *Blackwell handbook of perception* (pp. 92–127). Oxford: Blackwell.

Gottlieb, J. P., Kununoki, M., & Goldberg, M. (2002). The representation of visual salience in monkey parietal cortex. *Nature, 391,* 481–483.

Gouras, P. (1991). Color vision. In E. R. Kandel, J. H. Schwartz, & T. M. Jessell (Eds.), *Principles of neural science* (3rd ed., pp. 467–480). New York: Elsevier.

Graham, C. H., Sperling, H. G., Hsia, Y., & Coulson, A. H. (1961). The determination of some visual functions of a unilaterally color-blind subject: Methods and results. *Journal of Psychology, 51,* 3–32.

Graham, N. (1992). Breaking the visual stimulus into parts. *Current Directions in Psychological Science,* 1, 55–61.

Granrud, C. E., & Yonas, A. (1984). Infants' perception of pictorially specified interposition. *Journal of Experimental Child Psychology, 37,* 500–511.

Granrud, C. E., Haake, R. J., & Yonas, A. (1985). Infants' sensitivity to familiar size: The effect of memory on spatial perception. *Perception and Psychophysics, 37,* 459–466.

Granrud, C. E., Yonas, A., & Opland, E. A. (1985). Infants' sensitivity to the depth cue of shading. *Perception and Psychophysics, 37,* 415–419.

Graziano, M. S. A., Andersen, R. A., & Snowden, R. J. (1994). Tuning of MST neurons to spiral motions. *Journal of Neuroscience, 14,* 54–67.

Graziano, M. S. A., & Gross, C. G. (1995). The representation of extrapersonal space: A possible role for bimodal, visual-tactile neurons. In M. S. Gazzaniga (Ed.), *The cognitive neurosciences* (pp. 1021–1034).Cambridge, MA: MIT Press.

Green, G. S., & Bavelier, D. (2003). Action video game modifies visual selective attention. *Nature, 423,* 534–537.

Gregory, R. L. (1966). *Eye and brain.* New York: McGraw-Hill.

Griffin, D. R. (1944). Echolocation by blind men and bats. *Science, 100,* 589–590.

Griffiths, T. D., Rees, A., Witton, C., Shakir, R. A., Henning, G. B., & Green, G. G. R. (1996). Evidence for a sound movement area in the human cerebral cortex. *Nature, 383,* 425–427.

Grill-Spector, K., Knouf, N., & Kanwisher, N. (2004). The fusiform face area subserves face perception, not generic within-category identification. *Nature Neuroscience, 7,* 555–562.

Gross, C. G. (2002). The genealogy of the "grandmother cell." *The Neuroscientist, 8,* 512–518.

Grossman, E. D., & Blake, R. (2001). Brain activity evoked by inverted and imagined biological motion. *Vision Research, 41,* 1475–1482.

Gulick, W. L., Gescheider, G. A., & Frisina, R. D. (1989). *Hearing.* New York: Oxford University Press.

Gwiazda, J., Brill, S., et al. (1980). Preferential looking acuity in infants from two to fifty-eight weeks of age. *American Journal of Optometry and Physiological Optics, 57,* 428–432.

Gwiazda, J., Thorn, F., Bauer, J., & Held, R. (1993). Emmetropization and the progression of manifest refraction in children followed from infancy to puberty. *Clinical Visual Science, 8,* 337–344.

Gyr, J. W. (1972). Is a theory of direct perception adequate? *Psychological Bulletin, 77,* 246–261.

Haarmeier, T., Their, P., Repnow, M., & Petersen, D. (1997). False perception of motion in a patient who cannot compensate for eye movements. *Nature, 389,* 849–852.

Hall, E. G., & Davies, S. (1991). Gender differences in perceived intensity and affect of pain between athletes and nonathletes. *Perceptual and Motor Skills, 73,* 779–786.

Hall, J. L. (1965). Binaural interaction in the accessory superior-olivary nucleus of the cat. *Journal of the Acoustical Society of America, 37,* 814–823.

Hall, M. J., Bartoshuk, L. M., Cain, W. S., & Stevens, J. C. (1975). PTC taste blindness and the taste of caffeine. *Nature, 253,* 442–443.

Hamer, R. D., Alexander, K. R., & Teller, D. Y. (1982). Rayleigh discriminations in young human infants. *Vision Research, 22,* 575–587.

Handford, M. (1997). *Where's Waldo?* Cambridge, MA: Candlewick Press.

Hari, R., Forss, N., Avikainen, S., Kirveskari, E., Salenious, S., & Rizzolatti, G. (1998). Activation of human primary motor cortex during action observation: A neuromagnetic study. *Proceedings of the National Academy of Sciences USA, 95,* 15061–15065.

Harris, J. M., & Rogers, B. J. (1999). Going against the flow. *Trends in Cognitive Sciences, 3,* 449–450.

Harris, L., Atkinson, J., & Braddick, O. (1976). Visual contrast sensitivity of a 6-month-old infant measured by the evoked potential. *Nature, 246,* 570–571.

Hartline, H. K., Wagner, H. G., & Ratliff, F. (1956). Inhibition in the eye of *Limulus. Journal of General Physiology, 39,* 651–673.

Hasson, U., Nir, Y., Levy, I., Fuhrmann, G., & Malach, R. (2004). Intersubject synchronization of cortical activity during natural vision. *Science, 303,* 1634–1640.

Haueisen, J., & Knosche, T. R. (2001). Involuntary motor activity in pianists evoked by music perception. *Journal of Cognitive Neuroscience, 136,* 786–792.

Haxby, J. V., Horwitz, B., Ungerleider, L. G., Maisog, J. M., Pietrini, P., & Grady, C. L. (1994). The functional organization of human extrastriate cortex: A PET-rCBF study of selective attention to faces and locations. *Journal of Neuroscience, 14,* 6336-6353.

Hecaen, H., & Angelerques, R. (1962). Agnosia for faces (prosopagnosia). *Archives of Neurology, 7,* 92–100.

Hecht, S., Shlaer, S., & Pirenne, M. H. (1942). Energy, quanta, and vision. *Journal of General Physiology, 25,* 819–840.

Heffner, H. E., & Heffner, R. S. (1990). Effect of bilateral auditory cortex lesions on sound localization in Japanese macaques. *Journal of Neurophysiology, 64,* 915–931.

Heise, G. A., & Miller, G. A. (1951). An experimental study of auditory patterns. *American Journal of Psychology, 57,* 243–249.

Helmholtz, H. von (1852). On the theory of compound colors. *Philosophical Magazine, 4,* 519–534.

Helmholtz, H. von (1911). *Treatise on physiological optics* (J. P. Southall, Ed. & Trans.) (3rd ed., Vols. 2 & 3). Rochester, NY: Optical Society of America. (Original work published 1866)

Helson, H. (1933). The fundamental propositions of Gestalt psychology. *Psychological Review, 40,* 13–32.

Henderson, J. M. (2003). Human gaze control during real-world scene perception. *Trends in Cognitive Sciences, 7,* 498–503.

Henderson, J. M., & Hollingworth, A. (2003). Eye movements, visual memory, and scene representation. In M. Peterson & G. Rhodes (Eds.), *Perception of faces, objects, and scenes: Analytic and holistic processes.* Oxford University Press.

Henning, H. (1916). *Der Geruch.* Leipzig: Barth.

Hering, E. (1878). *Zur Lehre vom Lichtsinn.* Vienna: Gerold.

Hering, E. (1905). Grundzuge der Lehre vom Lichtsinn. In *Handbuch der gesamter Augenheilkunde* (Vol. 3, Chap. 13). Berlin.

Hering, E. (1964). *Outlines of a theory of the light sense* (L. M. Hurvich & D. Jameson, Trans.). Cambridge, MA: Harvard University Press.

Hershenson, M. (Ed.). (1989). *The moon illusion.* Hillsdale, NJ: Erlbaum.

Hess, E. H. (1965). Attitude and pupil size. *Scientific American, 212,* 46–54.

Hettinger, T. P., Myers, W. E., & Frank, M. E. (1990). Role of olfaction in perception of nontraditional "taste" stimuli. *Chemical Senses, 15,* 755–760.

Heywood, C., & Cowey, A. (1998). With color in mind. *Nature Neuroscience, 1,* 171–173.

Heywood, C. A., Cowey, A., & Newcombe, F. (1991). Chromatic discrimination in a cortically colour blind observer. *European Journal of Neuroscience, 3,* 802–812.

Hinkle, D. A., & Connor, C. E. (2002). Three-dimensional orientation tuning in macaque area V4. *Nature Neuroscience, 5,* 665–670.

Hochberg, J. E. (1971). Perception. In J. W. Kling & L. A. Riggs (Eds.), *Experimental psychology* (3rd ed., pp. 396–550). New York: Holt, Rinehart and Winston.

Hochberg, J. E. (1987). Machines should not see as people do, but must know how people see. *Computer Vision, Graphics and Image Processing, 39,* 221–237.

Hofbauer, R. K., Rainville, P., Duncan, G. H., & Bushnell, M. C. (2001). Cortical representation of the sensory dimension of pain. *Journal of Neurophysiology, 86,* 402–411.

Hoffman, E. J., Phelps, M. E., Mullani, N. A., Higgins, C. S., & Ter-Pogossian, M. M. (1976). Design and performance characteristics of a whole-body positron tranxial tomograph. *Journal of Nuclear Medicine, 17,* 493–502.

Hoffman, H. G., Doctor, J. N., Patterson, D. R., Carrougher, G. J., & Furness, T. A. III (2000). Virtual reality as an adjunctive pain control during burn wound care in adolescent patients. *Pain, 85,* 305–309.

Hofman, F. M., Van Riswick, J. G. A., & Van Opstal, A. J. (1998). Relearning sound localization with new ears. *Nature Neuroscience, 1,* 417–421.

Holden, C. (2004). Imaging studies show how brain thinks about pain. *Science, 303,* 1121.

Holley, A. (1991). Neural coding of olfactory information. In T. V. Getchell, R. L. Doty, L. M. Bartoshuk, & J. B. Snow (Eds.), *Smell and taste in health and disease* (pp. 329–343). New York: Raven Press.

Hollins, M., Bensmaia, S. J., & Roy, E. A. (2002). Vibrotaction and texture perception. *Behavioural Brain Research, 135,* 51–56.

Hollins, M., Bensmaia, S. J., & Washburn, S. (2001). Vibrotactile adaptation impairs discrimination of fine, but not coarse, textures. *Somatosensory & Motor Research, 18,* 253–262.

Hollins, M., & Risner, S. R. (2000). Evidence for the duplex theory of texture perception. *Perception & Psychophysics, 62,* 695–705.

Holway, A. H., & Boring, E. G. (1941). Determinants of apparent visual size with distance variant. *American Journal of Psychology, 54,* 21–37.

Houtsma, A. J. M., & Goldstein, J. L. (1972). Perception of musical intervals: Evidence for the central origin of the pitch of complex tones. *Journal of the Optical Society of America, 51,* 520–529.

Hsiao, S. S., Johnson, K. O., Twombly, A., & DiCarlo, J. (1996). Form processing and attention effects in the somatosensory system. In O. Franzen, R. Johannson, & L. Terenius (Eds.), *Somesthesis and the neurobiology of the somatosensory cortex* (pp. 229–247). Basel, Switzerland: Biorkhauser Verlag.

Hsiao, S. S., O'Shaughnessy, D. M., & Johnson, K. O. (1993). Effects of selective attention on spatial form processing in monkey primary and secondary somatosensory cortex. *Journal of Neurophysiology, 70,* 444–447.

Hubel, D. H. (1982). Exploration of the primary visual cortex, 1955–1978. *Nature, 299,* 515–524.

Hubel, D. H., & Wiesel, T. N. (1959). Receptive fields of single neurons in the cat's striate cortex. *Journal of Physiology, 148,* 574–591.

Hubel, D. H., & Wiesel, T. N. (1961). Integrative action in the cat's lateral geniculate body. *Journal of Physiology, 155,* 385–398.

Hubel, D. H., & Wiesel, T. N. (1965). Receptive fields and functional architecture in two non-striate visual areas (18 and 19) of the cat. *Journal of Neurophysiology, 28,* 229–289.

Hubel, D. H., & Wiesel, T. N. (1970). Cells sensitive to binocular depth in area 18 of the macaque monkey cortex. *Nature, 225,* 41–42.

Hubel, D. H., Wiesel, T. N., & Stryker, M. P. (1978). Anatomical demonstration of orientation columns in macaque monkey. *Journal of Comparative Neurology, 177,* 361–379.

Hudspeth, A. J. (1983). The hair cells of the inner ear. *Scientific American, 248*(1), 54–64.

Hudspeth, A. J. (1989). How the ear's works work. *Nature, 341,* 397–404.

Hurvich, L. (1981). *Color vision.* Sunderland, MA: Sinauer Associates.

Hyvarinin, J., & Poranen, A. (1978). Movement-sensitive and direction and orientation-selective cutaneous receptive fields in the hand area of the postcentral gyrus in monkeys. *Journal of Physiology, 283,* 523–537.

Iacobini, M., Woods, R. P., Brass, M., Bekkering, H., Mazziotta, J. C., & Rizzolatti, G. (1999). Cortical mechanism of human imitation. *Science, 286,* 2526–2528.

Ilg, U. J., Bridgeman, B., & Hoffmann, K. P. (1989). Influence of mechanical disturbance on oculomotor behavior. *Vision Research, 29,* 545–551.

Ishai, A., Ungerleider, L. G., Martin, A., & Haxby, J. V. (2000). The representation of objects in the human occipital and temporal cortex. *Journal of Cognitive Neuroscience, 12,* 35–51.

Ishai, A., Ungerleider, L. G., Martin, A., Schouten, J. L., & Haxby, J. V. (1999). Distributed representation of objects in the human ventral visual pathway. *Proceedings of the National Academy of Sciences, USA, 96,* 9379–9384.

Ito, M., Tamura, H., Fujita, I., & Tanaka, K. (1995). Size and position invariance of neuronal responses in monkey inferotemporal cortex. *Journal of Neurophysiology, 73,* 218–226.

Ittleson, W. H. (1952). *The Ames demonstrations in perception.* Princeton, NJ: Princeton University Press.

Iwamura, Y. (1998). Representation of tactile functions in the somatosensory cortex. In J. W. Morley (Ed.), *Neural aspects of tactile sensation* (pp. 195–238). New York: Elsevier Science.

Jacobs, G. H. (1993). The distribution and nature of colour vision among the mammals. *Biological Review, 68,* 413–471.

Jacobs, T. M., Lawrence, M. D., Hong, K., Giordano, N., Jr., & Giordano, N., Sr. (1996). On catching fly balls. *Science, 273,* 257–258.

Jacobson, A., & Gilchrist, A. (1988). The ratio principle holds over a million-to-one range of illumination. *Perception and Psychophysics, 43,* 1–6.

James, W. (1981). *The principles of psychology* (Rev. ed.). Cambridge, MA: Harvard University Press. (Original work published 1890)

Jameson, D. (1985). Opponent-colors theory in light of physiological findings. In D. Ottoson & S. Zeki (Eds.), *Central and* *peripheral mechanisms of color vision* (pp. 8–102). New York: Macmillan.

Janzen, G., & van Turennout, M. (2004). Selective neural representation of objects relevant for navigation. *Nature Neuroscience, 7,* 673–677.

Jenkins, W. M., & Merzenich, M. M. (1987). Reorganization of neocortical representations after brain injury: A neurophysiological model of the bases of recovery from stroke. *Progress in Brain Research, 71,* 249–266.

Jin, E. W., & Shevell, S. K. (1996). Color memory and color constancy. *Journal of the Optical Society of America, A, 13,* 1981–1991.

Johansson, G. (1975). Visual motion perception. *Scientific American, 232,* 76–89.

Johnson, K. O. (2002). Neural basis of haptic perception. In H. Pashler and S. Yantis (Eds.), *Steven's handbook of experimental psychology, 3rd ed. Vol. 1. Sensation and perception* (pp. 537–583). New York: Wiley.

Johnson, M. H., Dziurawiec, S., Ellis, H., & Morton, J. (1991). Newborns' preferential tracking of face-like stimuli and its subsequent decline. *Cognition, 90,* 1–19.

Johnson, S. P., & Aslin, R. N. (1995). Perception of object unity in 2-month-old infants. *Developmental Psychology, 31,* 739–745.

Johnson, S. P., Slemmer, J. A., & Amso, D. (2004). Where infants look determines how they see: Eye movement and object perception performance in 3-month-olds. *Infancy, 6,* 185–201.

Johnstone, B. M., & Boyle, A. J. F. (1967). Basilar membrane vibrations examined with the Mossbauer technique. *Science, 158,* 390–391.

Jones, K. S. (2003). What is an affordance? *Ecological Psychology, 15,* 107–114.

Jones, M. R., & Yee, W. (1993). Attending to auditory events: The role of temporal organization. In S. McAdams & E. Bigand (Eds.), *Thinking in sound: The cognitive psychology of human audition* (pp. 69–112). Oxford, England: Oxford University Press.

Judd, D. B., MacAdam, D. L., & Wyszecki, G. (1964). Spectral distribution of typical daylight as a function of correlated color temperature. *Journal of the Optical Society of America, 54,* 1031–1040.

Julesz, B. (1971). *Foundations of cyclopean perception.* Chicago: University of Chicago Press.

Kaas, J. H., & Hackett, T. A. (1999). "What" and "where" processing in auditory cortex. *Nature Neuroscience, 2,* 1045–1047.

Kaas, J. H., Hackett, T. A., & Tramo, M. J. (1999). Auditory processing in primate cerebral cortex. *Current Opinion in Neurobiology, 9,* 164–170.

Kanwisher, N. (2000). Domain specificity in face perception. *Nature, 3,* 759–763.

Kanwisher, N. (2004). The ventral visual object pathway in humans: Evidence from fMRI. In L. M. Chalupa & J. S. Werner (Eds.), *The visual neurosciences* (pp. 1179–1190). Cambridge, MA: MIT Press.

Kanwisher, N., McDermott, J., & Chun, M. M. (1997). The fusiform face area: A module in human extrastriate cortex specialized for face perception. *Journal of Neuroscience, 17,* 4302–4311.

Kaplan, E., Mukherjee, P., & Shapley, R. (1993). Information filtering in the lateral geniculate nucleus. In R. Shapley & D. Man-Kit Lam (Eds.), *Contrast sensitivity* (Vol. 5). Cambridge, MA: MIT Press.

Kaplan, G. (1969). Kinetic disruption of optical texture: The perception of depth at an edge. *Perception and Psychophysics, 6,* 193–198.

Kastner, S., Pinsk, M. A., DeWeerd, P. Desimone, R., & Ungerleider, L. G. (1999). Increased activity in human visual cortex during directed attention in the absence of visual stimulation. *Neuron, 22,* 751–761.

Katz, D. (1989). *The world of touch* (L.E. Krueger, Ed. & Trans.). Hillsdale, NJ: Erlbaum. (Original work published in 1925)

Katz, D. B., Nicolelis, M. A. L., & Simon, S. A. (2002). Gustatory processing is dynamic and distributed. *Current Opinion in Neurobiology, 12,* 449–454.

Katz, J., & Gagliese, L. (1999). Phantom limb pain: A continuing puzzle. In R. J. Gatchel & D. C. Turk (Eds.), *Psychosocial factors in pain* (pp. 284–300). New York: Guilford.

Kauer, J. S. (1987). Coding in the olfactory system. In T. E. Finger & W. C. Silver (Eds.), *Neurobiology of taste and smell* (pp. 205–231). New York: Wiley.

Kaufman, L., & Rock, I. (1962a). The moon illusion. *Science, 136,* 953–961.

Kaufman, L., & Rock, I. (1962b). The moon illusion. *Scientific American, 207,* 120–132.

Kaye, K. L., & Bower, T. G. R. (1994). Learning and intermodal transfer of information in newborns. *Psychological Science, 5,* 286–288.

Kellman, P., & Spelke, E. (1983). Perception of partly occluded objects in infancy. *Cognitive Psychology, 15,* 483–524.

Kewley-Port, D. (1983). Time-varying features as correlates of place of articulation in stop consonants. *Journal of the Acoustical Society of America, 73,* 322–335.

Kewley-Port, D., & Luce, P. A. (1984). Time-varying features of initial stop consonants in auditory running spectra: A first report. *Perception and Psychophysics, 35,* 353–360.

Khanna, S. M., & Leonard, D. G. B. (1982). Basilar membrane tuning in the cat cochlea. *Science, 215,* 305–306.

Kiefer, J, von Ilberg, C., Reimer, B., Knecht, R., Gall, V., Diller, G., Sturzebecher, E., Pfenningdorff, T., & Spelsberg, A. (1996). Results of cochlear implantation in patients with severe to profound hearing loss: Implications for the indications. *Audiology, 37,* 382–395.

Kim, U. K., Jorgenson, E., Coon, H., Leppert, M., Risch, N., & Drayna, D. (2003). Positional cloning of the human quantitative trait locus underlying taste sensitivity to phenylthiocarbamide. *Science, 299,* 1221–1225.

King, A. J., Schnupp, J. W. H., & Doubell, T. P. (2001). The shape of ears to come: Dynamic coding of auditory space. *Trends in Cognitive Sciences, 5,* 261–270.

King, W. L., & Gruber, H. E. (1962). Moon illusion and Emmert's law. *Science, 135,* 1125–1126.

Klatzky, R. L., Lederman, S. J., Hamilton, C., Grindley, M., & Swendsen, R. H. (2003). Feeling textures through a probe: Effects of probe and surface geometry and exploratory factors. *Perception & Psychophysics, 65,* 613–631.

Klatzky, R. L., Lederman, S. J., & Metzger, V. A. (1985). Identifying objects by touch: An "expert system." *Perception and Psychophysics, 37,* 299–302.

Kleffner, D. A., & Ramachandran, V. S. (1992). On the perception of shape from shading. *Perception and Psychophysics,* 52, 18–36.

Knill, D. C., & Kersten, D. (1991). Apparent surface curvature affects lightness perception. *Nature, 351,* 228–230.

Knudsen, E. I., & Konishi, M. (1978a). Center-surround organization of auditory receptive fields in the owl. *Science, 202,* 778–780.

Knudsen, E. I., & Konishi, M. (1978b). A neural map of auditory space in the owl. *Science, 200,* 795–797.

Kobatake, E., & Tanaka, K. (1994). Neuronal selectivities to complex object features in the ventral visual pathway of the macaque cerebral cortex. *Journal of Neurophysiology, 71,* 856–867.

Kobatake, E., Wang, G., & Tanaka, K. (1998). Effects of shape-discrimination training on the selectivity of inferotemporal cells in adult monkeys. *Journal of Neurophysiology, 80,* 324–330.

Kohler, E., Keysers, C., Umilta, M. A., Fogassi, L., Gallese, V., & Rizzonatti, G. (2002). Hearing sounds, understanding actions: Action representation in mirror neurons. *Science, 297,* 846–848.

Kolb, B., & Whishaw, I. Q. (1990). *Fundamentals of human neuropsychology* (3rd ed.). New York: Freeman.

Kolb, N., & Whishaw, I. Q. (2003). *Fundamentals of human neuropsychology* (5th ed.). New York: Worth.

Kong, S. G., Heo, J., Abidi, B. R., Paik, J., & Abidi, M. A. (2005). Recent advances in visual and infrared face recognition review. *Computer Vision and Image Understanding, 97,* 103–135.

Konorski, J. (1967). *Integrative activity of the brain: An interdisciplinary approach.* Chicago: University of Chicago Press.

Kosaki, H., Hashikawa, T., He, J., & Jones, E. G. (1997). Tonotopic organization of auditory cortical fields delineated by parvalbumin immunoreactivity in macaque monkeys. *Journal of Comparative Neurology,* 386, 304–316.

Kosslyn, S. M. (1994). *Image and brain: The resolution of the imagery debate.* Cambridge, MA: MIT Press.

Kourtzi, Z., Erb, M., Grodd, W., & Bulthoff, H. H. (2003). Representation of the perceived 3-D object shape in the human lateral occipital complex. *Cerebral Cortex, 13,* 911–920.

Kourtzi, Z., & Kanwisher, N. (2000). Activation on human MT/MST by static images with implied motion. *Journal of Cognitive Neuroscience, 12,* 48–55.

Kreiman, G., Koch, C., & Fried, I. (2000). Category-specific visual responses of single neurons in the human medial temporal lobe. *Nature Neuroscience, 3,* 946–953.

Kruger, L. E. (1970). David Katz: Der Aufbau der Tastwelt [The world of touch: A synopsis]. *Perception and Psychophysics, 7,* 337–341.

Kuhl, P. K. (2000). Language, mind and brain: Experience alters perception. In M. Gazzaniga (Ed.), *The new cognitive neurosciences.* Cambridge, MA: MIT Press, pp. 99–115.

Kuhl, P. K. (2004). Early language acquisition: Cracking the speech code. *Nature Reviews: Neuroscience, 5,* 831–843.

Kuhl, P. K., Kirtani, S., Deguchi, T., Hayashi, A., Stevens, E. B., Dugger, C. D., & Iverson, P. (1997). Effects of language experience on speech perception: American and Japanese infants' perception of /ra/ and /la/. *Journal of the Acoustical Society of America, 102,* 3125.

Kuhl, P. K., & Meltzoff, A. N. (1982). The bimodal perception of speech in infancy. *Science, 218,* 1138–1141.

Kuhl, P. K., Williams, K. A., Lacerda, F., Stevens, K. N., & Lindblom, B. (1992). Linguistic experience alters phonetic perception in infants by 6 months of age. *Science, 255,* 606–608.

Kushner, T. (1993). *Angels in America.* New York: Theatre Communications Group.

Kwee, I., Fujii, Y., Matsuzawa, H., & Nakada, T. (1999). Perceptual processing of stereopsis in humans: GH High-field (3.0 tesla) functional MRI study. *Neurology, 53,* 1599–1601.

LaBarbera, J. D., Izard, C. E., Vietze, P., & Parisi, S. A. (1976). Four- and six-month-old infants' visual responses to joy, anger, and neutral expressions. *Child Development, 47,* 535–538.

Laing, D. D., Doty, R. L., & Breipohl, W. (Eds.). (1991). *The human sense of smell.* New York: Springer.

Lamme, V. A. F. (1995). The neurophysiology of figure–ground segregation in primary visual cortex. *Journal of Neuroscience, 15,* 1605–1615.

Lamme, V. A. F., & Roelfesma, P. R. (2000). The distinct modes of vision offered by feedforward and recurrent processing. *Trends in Neurosciences, 23,* 571–579.

Land, E. H. (1983). Recent advances in retinex theory and some implications for cortical computations: Color vision and the natural image. *Proceedings of the National Academy of Sciences, USA, 80,* 5163–5169.

Land, E. H. (1986). Recent advances in retinex theory. *Vision Research, 26,* 7–21.

Land, E. H., & McCann, J. J. (1971). Lightness and retinex theory. *Journal of the Optical Society of America, 61,* 1–11.

Land, M., & Horwood, J. (1995). Which parts of the road guide steering? *Nature, 377,* 339–340.

Land, M. F., & Hayhoe, M. (2001). In what ways do eye movements contribute to everyday activities? *Vision Research, 41,* 3559–3565.

Land, M. F., & Lee, D. N. (1994). Where we look when we steer. *Nature, 369,* 742–744.

Land, M. F., Mennie, N., & Rusted, J. (1999). The roles of vision and eye movements in the control of activities of daily living. *Perception, 28,* 1311–1328.

Lavie, N. (1995). Perceptual load as a necessary condition for selective attention. *Journal of Experimental Psychology: Human Perception and Performance, 21,* 451–486.

Lavie, N., & Driver, J. (1996). On the spatial extend of attention in object-based visual selection. *Perception and Psychophysics, 58,* 1238–1251.

Lawless, H. (1980). A comparison of different methods for assessing sensitivity to the taste of phenylthiocarbamide PTC. *Chemical Senses, 5,* 247–256.

Lawless, H. (2001). Taste. In E. B. Goldstein (Ed.), *Blackwell handbook of perception* (pp. 601–635). Oxford, UK: Blackwell.

Lederman, S. J., & Klatzky, R. L. (1987). Hand movements: A window into haptic object recognition. *Cognitive Psychology, 19,* 342–368.

Lederman, S. J., & Klatzky, R. L. (1990). Haptic classification of common objects: Knowledge-driven exploration. *Cognitive Psychology, 22,* 421–459.

Lee, D. N. (1980). The optic flow field: The foundation of vision. *Transactions of the Royal Society, 290B,* 169–179.

Lee, D. N., & Aronson, E. (1974). Visual proprioceptive control of standing in human infants. *Perception and Psychophysics, 15,* 529–532.

Lee, D. N., & Reddish, P. E. (1976). Plummeting gannets: A paradigm of ecological optics. *Nature, 293,* 293–294.

LeGrand, Y. (1957). *Light, color and vision.* London: Chapman & Hall.

Lennie, P., Krauskopf, J., & Sclar, G. (1990). Chromatic mechanisms in striate cortex of macaque. *Journal of Neuroscience,* 649–669.

Leventhal A. G., Thompson, K. G., Liu, D., Zhou, Y., & Ault, S. J. (1995). Concomitant sensitivity to orientation, direction, and color of cells in layers 2, 3, and 4 of monkey striate cortex. *Journal of Neuroscience, 15,* 1808–1818.

Levin, D., & Simons, D. (1997). Failure to detect changes in attended objects in motion pictures. *Psychonomic Bulletin and Review, 4,* 501–506.

Levin, D. T., Momen, N., Drivdahl, S. B., & Simons, D. (2000). Change blindness blindness: The metacognitive error of overestimating change-detection ability. *Visual Cognition. 7,* 397–412.

Lewis, E. R., Zeevi, Y. Y., & Werblin, F. S. (1969). Scanning electron microscopy of vertebrate visual receptors. *Brain Research, 15,* 559–562.

Li, F. F., VanRullen, R., Koch, C., & Perona, P. (2002). Rapid natural scene categorization in the near absence of attention. *Proceedings of the National Academy of Sciences, 99,* 9506–9601.

Liberman, A. M., Cooper, F. S., Shankweiler, D. P., & Studdert-Kennedy, M. (1967). Perception of the speech code. *Psychological Review, 74,* 431–461.

Lim, V. K., Altenmuller, E., & Bradshaw, J. L. (2001). Focal dystonia: Current theories. *Human Movement Science, 20,* 875–914.

Lindsay, P. H., & Norman, D. A. (1977). *Human information processing* (2nd ed.). New York: Academic Press.

Linster, C., Johnson, B. A., Yue, E., Morse, A., Xu, Z., Hingco, E. E. , Choi, Y., Choi, M., Messiha, A., & Leon, M. (2001). *Journal of Neuroscience, 21,* 9837–9843.

Litovsky, R. Y., Colburn, H. S., Yost, W. A., & Guzman, S. J. (1999). The precedence effect. *Journal of the Acoustical Society of America,* 106, 1633–1654.

Litovsky, R. Y., Fligor, B. J., & Tramo, M. J. (2002). Functional role of the human inferior colliculus in binaural hearing. *Hearing Research, 165,* 177–188.

Litovsky, R. Y., Rakerd, B., Yin, T. C. T., & Hartmann, W. M. (1997). Psychophysical and physiological evidence for a precedence effect in the median saggital plane. *Journal of Neurophysiology, 77,* 2223–2226.

Litovsky, R. Y., & Yin, T. C. T. (1998). Physiological studies of the precedence effect in the inferior colliculus of the cat. *Journal of Neurophysiology, 80,* 1302–1316.

Livingstone, M. S., & Hubel, D. H. (1988). Segregation of form, color, movement, and depth: Anatomy, physiology, and perception. *Science, 240,* 740–749.

Logothetis, N. K., & Pauls, J. (1995). Psychophysical and physiological evidence for viewer-centered object representations in the primate. *Cerebral Cortex, 5,* 270–288.

Loomis, J. M., DaSilva, J. A., Fujita, N., & Fulusima, S. S. (1992). Visual space perception and visually directed action. *Journal of Experimental Psychology: Human Perception and Performance, 18,* 906–921.

Lowenstein, W. R. (1960). Biological transducers. *Scientific American, 203,* 98–108.

Luck, S. J. (2004). Understanding awareness: One step closer. *Nature Neuroscience, 7,* 208–209.

Lumer, E. D., Friston, K. J., & Rees, G. (1998). Neural correlates of perceptual rivalry in the human brain. *Science, 280,* 1930–1934.

Lumer, E. D., & Rees, G. (1999). Covariation of activity in visual and prefrontal cortex associated with subjective visual perception. *Proceedings of the National Academy of Sciences, USA, 96,* 1669–1673.

Lyall, V., Heck, G. L., Phan, T. H., Mummalaneni, S., Malik, S. A., Vinnikova, A. K., & DeSimone, J. A. (2005). Ethanol modulates the VR-1 variant amiloride-insensitive salt taste receptor. I. Effect on TRC volume and Na+ flux. *Journal of General Physiology,125,* 569–585.

Lyall, V., Heck, G. L., Vinnikova, A. K., Ghosh, S., Phan, T.-H. T., Alam, R. I., Russell, O. F., Malik, S. A., Bigbee, J. W., & De-Simone, J. A. (2004). The mammalian amiloride-insensitive non-specific salt taste receptor is a vanilloid receptor-1 variant. *Journal of Physiology, 558,* 147–159.

Lyman, B. J., & McDaniel, M. A. (1990). Memory for odors and odor names: Modalities of elaboration and imagery. *Journal of Experimental Psychology: Learning, Memory, and Cognition, 16,* 656–664.

Mach, E. (1959). *The analysis of sensations.* New York: Dover. (Original work published 1914)

Mack, A., & Rock, I. (1998). *Inattentional blindness.* Cambridge, MA: MIT Press.

Maeder, P., Meuli, R., Adriani, M., Bellmann, A., Fornari, E., Thiran, J.-P., Pittet, A., & Clarke, S. (2001). Distinct pathways involved in sound recognition and localization: A human fMRI study. *Neuroimage, 14,* 802–816.

Maffei, L., & Fiorentini, A. (1973). The visual cortex as a spatial frequency analyzer. *Vision Research, 13,* 1255–1267.

Maguire, E. A., Frith, C. D., Burgess, N., Donnett, J. G., & O'Keefe, J. (1998). Knowing where things are: Parahippocampal involvement in encoding object locations in virtual large-scale space. *Journal of Cognitive Neuroscience, 10,* 61–76.

Makous, J. C., & Middlebrooks, J. C. (1990). Two-dimensional sound localization by human listeners. *Journal of the Acoustical Society of America, 87,* 2188–2200.

Malnic, B., Hirono, J., Sata, T., & Buck, L. B. (1999). Combinatorial receptor codes for odors. *Cell, 96,* 713–723.

Mamassian, P., Knill, D., & Kersten, D. (1998). The perception of cast shadows. *Trends in Cognitive Sciences, 2,* 288–295.

Marks, L. E. (1975). On colored-hearing synesthesia: Cross-modal translations of sensory dimensions. *Psychological Bulletin, 82,* 303–331.

Marr, D. (1982). *Vision.* San Francisco: Freeman.

Massaro, D. W. (1998). Perceiving talking faces: From speech perception to a behavioral principle. Cambridge MA: MIT Press.

Massaro, D. W. (2003). Speech perception and recognition, theories and models of. In L. Nadel (Ed.). *Encyclopedia of cognitive science* (pp. 169–177). New York: Nature Publishing Group.

Matin, L., Picoult, E., Stevens, J., Edwards, M., & MacArthur, R. (1982). Oculoparalytic illusion: Visual-field dependent spatial mislocations by humans partially paralyzed with curare. *Science, 216,* 198–201.

Maunsell, J. H. R. (2004). The role of attention in visual cerebral cortex. In L. M. Chalupa & J. S. Werner (Eds.), *The visual neurosciences* (pp. 1538–1545). Cambridge, MA: MIT Press.

Mayer, D. L., Beiser, A. S., Warner, A. F., Pratt, Raye, K. N., & Lang, J. M. (1995). Monocular acuity norms for the Teller Acuity Cards between ages one month and four years. *Investigative Ophthalmology and Visual Science, 36,* 671–685.

McBeath, M. K., Shaffer, D. M., & Kaiser, M. K. (1995). How baseball outfielders determine where to run to catch fly balls. *Science, 268,* 569–573.

McBurney, D. H. (1969). Effects of adaptation on human taste function. In C. Pfaffmann (Ed.), *Olfaction and taste* (pp. 407–419). New York: Rockefeller University Press.

McBurney, D. H., Levine, J. M., & Cavanaugh, P. H. (1977). Psychophysical and social ratings of human body odor. *Personality and Social Psychology Bulletin, 3,* 135–138.

McClintock, M. K. (1971). Menstrual synchrony and suppression. *Nature, 229,* 244–245.

McFadden, S. A. (1987). The binocular depth stereoacuity of the pigeon and its relation to the anatomical resolving power of the eye. *Vision Research, 27,* 1967–1980.

McGurk, H., & MacDonald, T. (1976). Hearing lips and seeing voices. *Nature, 264,* 746–748.

McKeefry, D. J., & Zeki, S. (1997). The position and topography of the human colour centre as revealed by functional magnetic resonance imaging. *Brain, 120,* 2229–2242.

McLean, J. H., & Shipley, M. T. (1992). Neuroanatomical substrates of olfaction. In M. J. Serby & K. L. Chobor (Eds.), *Science of olfaction* (pp. 126–171). New York: Springer-Verlag.

McLeod, P., Dittrich, W., Driver, J., Perrett, D., & Zihl, J. (1996). Preserved and impaired detection of structure from motion by a "motion-blind" patient. *Visual Cognition, 3,* 363–391.

McLeod, P., Reed, N., & Dienes, Z. (2002). The optic trajectory is not a lot of use if you want to catch the ball. *Journal of Experimental Psychology: Human Perception and Performance, 28,* 1499–1501.

Meader, P. P., Meuli, R. A., Adriani, M., Bellmann, A., Fornari, E., Thiran, J. P., Pittet, A., & Clarke, S. (2001). Pathways involved in sound recognition and localization: A human fMRI study. *Neuroimage, 14,* 802–816.

Meddis, R., & Hewitt, M. J. (1991). Virtual pitch and phase sensitivity of a computer model of the auditory periphery: I. Pitch identification. *Journal of the Acoustical Society of America, 89,* 2866–2882.

Mehler, J. (1981). The role of syllables in speech processing: Infant and adult data. *Transactions of the Royal Society of London, B295,* 333–352.

Melzack, R. (1999). From the gate to the neuromatrix. *Pain, Suppl. 6, S121–S126.*

Melzack, R., & Wall, P. D. (1965). Pain mechanisms: A new theory. *Science, 150,* 971–979.

Melzack, R., & Wall, P. D. (1983). *The challenge of pain.* New York: Basic Books.

Melzack, R., & Wall, P. D. (1988). *The challenge of pain* (Rev. ed.). New York: Penguin Books.

Menz, M. D., & Freeman, R. D. (2003). Stereoscopic depth processing in the visual cortex: A coarse-to-fine mechanism. *Nature Neuroscience, 6,* 59–65.

Menzel, R., & Backhaus, W. (1989). Color vision in honey bees: Phenomena and physiological mechanisms. In D. G. Stavenga & R. C. Hardie (Eds.), *Facets of vision* (pp. 281–297). Berlin: Springer-Verlag.

Menzel, R., Ventura, D. F., Hertel, H., deSouza, J., & Greggers, U. (1986). Spectral sensitivity of photoreceptors in insect compound eyes: Comparison of species and methods. *Journal of Comparative Physiology, 158A,* 165–177.

Merigan, W. H., & Maunsell, J. H. R. (1993). How parallel are the primate visual pathways? *Annual Review of Neuroscience, 16,* 369–402.

Merskey, H. (1991). The definition of pain. *European Journal of Psychiatry, 6,* 153–159.

Merzenich, M. M., Recanzone, G., Jenkins, W. M., Allard, T. T., & Nudo, R. J. (1988). Cortical representational plasticity. In P. Rakic & W. Singer (Eds.), *Neurobiology of neocortex* (pp. 42–67). Berlin: Wiley.

Middlebrooks, J. C. (1997). Spectral shape cues for sound localization. In R. H. Gilkey & T. R. Anderson (Eds.), *Binaural and spatial hearing in real and virtual environments* (pp. 77–97). Hillsdale, NJ: Erlbaum.

Middlebrooks, J. C. (2000). Cortical representations of auditory space. In M. Gazzaniga (Ed.), *The new cognitive neurosciences* (pp. 425–436). Cambridge, MA: MIT Press.

Middlebrooks, J. C., Clock, A. E., Xu, L., & Green, D. M. (1994). A panoramic code for sound location by cortical neurons. *Science, 264,* 842–844.

Middlebrooks, J. C., & Green, D. M. (1991). Sound localization by human listeners. *Annual Review of Psychology, 42,* 135–159.

Middlebrooks, J . C., Xu, L., Eddins, C., & Green, D. M. (1998). Codes for sound-source location in nontonotopic auditory cortex. *Journal of Neurophysiology, 80,* 863–881.

Miller, G. A., & Heise, G. A. (1950). The trill threshold. *Journal of the Acoustical Society of America, 22,* 637–683.

Miller, G. A., & Isard, S. (1963). Some perceptual consequences of linguistic rules. *Journal of Verbal Learning and Verbal Behavior, 2,* 212–228.

Miller, I. J. (1995). Anatomy of the peripheral taste system. In R. L. Doty (Ed.), *Handbook of olfaction and gustation* (pp. 521–548). New York: Marcel Dekker.

Milner, A. D., & Goodale, M. A. (1995). *The visual brain in action.* New York: Oxford University Press.

Mishkin, M., Ungerleider, L. G., & Macko, K. A. (1983). Object vision and spatial vision: Two central pathways. *Trends in Neuroscience, 6,* 414–417.

Mollon, J. D. (1989). "Tho' she kneel'd in that place where they grew . . . ." *Journal of Experimental Biology, 146,* 21–38.

Mollon, J. D. (1990). The club-sandwich mystery. *Nature, 343,* 16–17.

Mollon, J. D. (1993). Mixing genes and mixing colours. *Current Biology, 3,* 82–85.

Montagna, W., & Parakkal, P. F. (1974). *The structure and function of skin* (3rd ed.). New York: Academic Press.

Mon-Williams, M., & Tresilian, J. R. (1999). Some recent studies on the extraretinal contribution to distance perception. *Perception, 28,* 167–181.

Moon, C., Cooper, R. P., & Fifer, W. P. (1993). Two-day-olds prefer their native language. *Infant Behavior and Development, 16,* 495–500.

Moore, B. C. J. (2001). Basic auditory processes. In E. B. Goldstein (Ed.), *Blackwell handbook of perception* (pp. 379–407). Oxford, UK: Blackwell.

Moore, B. C. J. (2001). Loudness, pitch and timbre. In E. B. Goldstein (Ed.), *Blackwell handbook of perception* (pp. 408–436). Oxford, UK: Blackwell.

Moore, C. M., Yantis, S., & Vaughan, B. (1998). Object-based visual selection: Evidence from perceptual completion. *Psychological Science, 9,* 104–110.

Moran, J., & Desimone, R. (1985). Selective attention gates visual processing in the extrastriate cortex. *Science, 229,* 782–784.

Mori, K., Nagao, H., & Yoshihara, Y. (1999). The olfactory bulb: Coding and processing of odor molecule information. *Science, 286,* 711–715.

Morimoto, C. H., & Mimica, M. R. M. (2005). Eye gaze tracking techniques for interactive applications. *Computer Vision and Image Understanding, 98,* 4–24.

Morrison, E. E., & Moran, D. T. (1995). Anatomy and ultrastructure of the human olfactory neuroepithelium. In R. L. Doty (Ed.). *Handbook of olfaction and gustation* (pp. 75–101). New York: Marcel Dekker.

Morton, J., & Johnson, M. H. (1991). CONSPEC and CONLEARN: A two-process theory of infant face recognition. *Psychological Review, 98,* 164–181.

Moulton, D. G. (1977). Minimum odorant concentrations detectable by the dog and their implications for olfactory receptor sensitivity. In D. Miller-Schwarze & M. M. Mozell (Eds.), *Chemical signals in vertebrates* (pp. 455–464). New York: Plenum Press.

Mountcastle, V. B., & Powell, T. P. S. (1959). Neural mechanisms subserving cutaneous sensibility, with special reference to the role of afferent inhibition in sensory perception and discrimination. *Bulletin of the Johns Hopkins Hospital, 105,* 201–232.

Movshon, J. A., & Newsome, W. T. (1992). Neural foundations of visual motion perception. *Current Directions in Psychological Science, 1,* 35–39.

Mozell, M. M., Smith, B. P., Smith, P. E., Sullivan, R. L., & Swender, P. (1969). Nasal chemoreception in flavor identification. *Archives of Otolaryngology, 90,* 131–137.

Mueller, K. L., Hoon, M. A., Erlenbach, I., Chandrashekar, J., Zuker, C. S., & Ryba, N. J. P. (2005). The receptors and coding logic for bitter taste. *Nature, 434,* 225–229.

Muir, D., & Field, J. (1979). Newborn infants orient to sounds. *Child Development, 50,* 431–436.

Murata, A., Gallese, V., Kaseda, M., & Sakata, H. (1996). Parietal neurons related to memory-guided hand manipulation. *Journal of Neurophysiology, 75,* 2180–2186.

Murphy, C., & Cain, W. S. (1980). Taste and olfaction: Independence vs. interaction. *Physiology and Behavior, 24,* 601–606.

Murphy, K. J., Racicot, C. I., & Goodale, M. A. (1996). The use of visuomotor cues as a strategy for making perceptual judgements in a patient with visual form agnosia. *Neuropsychology, 10,* 396–401.

Musseler, J., van der Heijden, A. H. C., & Kerzel, D. (2004). Visual space perception and action: Introductory remarks. *Visual Cognition, 11,* 129–136.

Mutti, D. O., Zadnik, K., & Adams, A. J. (1996). Myopia: The nature versus nurture debate goes on. *Investigative Ophthalmology and Visual Science, 37,* 952–957.

Nakayama, K. (1994). James J. Gibson: An appreciation. *Psychological Reviews, 10,* 329–335.

Narayan, S. S., Temchin, A. N., Recio, A., & Ruggero, M. A. (1998). Frequency tuning of basilar membrane and auditory nerve fibers in the same cochleae. *Science, 282,* 1882–1884.

Nathans, J., Thomas, D., & Hogness, D. S. (1986). Molecular genetics of human color vision: The genes encoding blue, green, and red pigments. *Science, 232,* 193–202.

Needham, A., & Ormsbee, S. M. (2003). The development of object segregation during the first year of life. In R. Kimchi, M. Behrmann, & C. Olson (Eds.), *Perceptual organization in vision: Behavioral and neural perspectives,* (pp. 205–232). Mahwah, NJ: Erlbaum.

Neff, W., Diamond, I., & Cassedy, J. (1975). Behavioral studies of auditory discrimination: Central nervous system. In W. D. Keider & D. Neff (Eds.) *Handbook of sensory psychology, Vol V/2* (p. 307–400). New York: Springer.

Neisser, U., & Becklen, R. (1975). Selective looking: Attending to visually specified events. *Cognitive Psychology, 7,* 480–494.

Neitz, J., Geist, T., & Jacobs, G. H. (1989). Color vision in the dog. *Visual Neuroscience, 3,* 119–125.

Neitz, M., Neitz, J., & Jacobs, G. H. (1991). Spectral tuning of pigments underlying red-green color vision. *Science, 252,* 971–974.

Nelken, I. (2004). Processing of complex stimuli and natural scenes in the auditory cortex. *Current Opinion in Neurobiology, 14,* 474–480.

Nelson, C. A. (2001). The development and neural basis of face recognition. *Infant and Child Development, 10,* 3–18.

Nelson, C. A., & Horowitz, F. D. (1987). Visual motion perception in infancy: A review and synthesis. In P. Salapatek & L. Cohen (Eds.), *Handbook of infant perception* (Vol. 2, pp. 123–153). New York: Academic Press.

Neuenschwander, S., & Singer, W. (1996). Long-range synchronization of oscillatory light responses in the cat retina and lateral geniculate nucleus. *Nature, 379,* 728–733.

Newsome, W. T., Britten, K. H., & Movshon, J. A. (1989). Neuronal correlates of a perceptual decision. *Nature, 341,* 52–54.

Newsome, W. T., & Paré, E. B. (1988). A selective impairment of motion perception following lesions of the middle temporal visual area (MT). *Journal of Neuroscience, 8,* 2201–2211.

Newton, I. (1704). *Optiks.* London: Smith and Walford.

Nobre, A., Allison, T., & McCarthy, G. (1994). Word recognition in the human inferior temporal lobe. *Nature 372,* 260–263.

Noe, A., Pessoa, L., & Thompson, E. (2000). Beyond the grand illusion: What change blindness really teaches us about vision. *Visual Cognition, 7,* 93–106.

Norcia, A. M., & Tyler, C. W. (1985). Spatial frequency sweep VEP: Visual acuity during the first year of life. *Vision Research, 25,* 1399–1408.

Nordby, K. (1990). Vision in a complete achromat: A personal account. In R. F. Hess, L. T. Sharpe, & K. Nordby (Eds.), *Night vision* (pp. 290–315). Cambridge, England: Cambridge University Press.

Nygaard, L. C., & Pisoni, D. B. (1995). Speech perception: New directions in research and theory. In J. L. Miller & P. D. Eimas (Eds.), *Speech, language, and communication* (pp. 63–97). San Diego, CA: Academic Press.

Ohzawa, I. (1998). Mechanisms of stereoscopic vision: The disparity energy model. *Current Opinion in Neurobiology, 8,* 509–515.

Olsho, L. W., Koch, E. G., Carter, E. A., Halpin, C. F., & Spetner, N. B. (1988). Pure-tone sensitivity of human infants. *Journal of the Acoustical Society of America, 84,* 1316–1324.

Olsho, L. W., Koch, E. G., Halpin, C. F., & Carter, E. A. (1987). An observer-based psychoacoustic procedure for use with young infants. *Developmental Psychology, 23,* 627–640.

Olson, C. R., & Freeman, R. D. (1980). Profile of the sensitive period for monocular deprivation in kittens. *Experimental Brain Research, 39,* 17–21.

Olson, H. (1967). *Music, physics, and engineering* (2nd ed.). New York: Dover.

Ooi, T. L., Wu, B., & He, Z. J. (2001). Distance determined by the angular declination below the horizon. *Nature, 414,* 197–200.

Oram, M. W., & Perrett, D. I. (1994). Responses of anterior superior temporal polysensory (STPa) neurons to "biological motion" stimuli. *Journal of Cognitive Neuroscience, 6,* 99–116.

Orban, G. A., Lagae, L., Verri, A., Raiguel, S., Xiao, D., Maes, H., & Torre, V. (1992). First-order analysis of optical flow in monkey brain. *Proceedings of the National Academy of Sciences, 89,* 2595–2599.

Orban, G. A., Vandenbussche, E., & Vogels, R. (1984). Human orientation discrimination tested with long stimuli. *Vision Research, 24,* 121–128.

Orban, G. A., & Vanduffell, W. (2004). Functional mapping of motion regions. In L. M. Chalupa & J. S. Werner, (Eds.), *The visual neurosciences* (pp. 1229–1246). Cambridge, MA: MIT Press.

Owen, D. (2000, August 21–28). The chosen one. *The New Yorker,* pp. 106–119.

Owens, E. (1989). Present status of adults with cochlear implants. In E. Owens & D. K. Kessler (Eds.), *Cochlear implants in young deaf children* (pp. 25–52). Boston: Little, Brown.

Owens, M. (1994, June 6). Designers discover the sweet smell of success. *New York Times.*

Pack, C. C., & Born, R. T. (2001). Temporal dynamics of a neural solution to the aperture problem in visual area MT of macaque brain. *Nature, 409,* 1040–1042.

Palmer, S. E. (1975). The effects of contextual scenes on the identification of objects. *Memory and Cognition, 3,* 519–526.

Palmer, S. E. (1992). Common region: A new principle of perceptual grouping. *Cognitive Psychology, 24,* 436–447.

Palmer, S. E. (1999). *Vision science.* Cambridge, MA: MIT Press.

Palmer, S. E., & Rock, I. (1994). Rethinking perceptual organization: The role of uniform connectedness. *Psychonomic Bulletin & Review, 1,* 29–55.

Palmeri, T. J., & Gauthier, I. (2004). Visual object understanding. *Nature Review: Neuroscience, 5,* 291–304.

Palmeri, T. J., Goldinger, S. D., & Pisoni, D. B. (1993). Episodic encoding of voice attributes and recognition memory for spoken words. *Journal of Experimental Psychology: Learning Memory and Cognition, 19,* 309–328.

Pantev, C., Oostenveld, R., Engelien, A., Ross, B., Roberts, L. E., & Hoke, M. (1998). Increased auditory cortical representation in musicians. *Nature, 392,* 811–814.

Parkhurst, D., Law, K., & Niebur, E. (2002). Modeling the role of salience in the allocation of overt visual attention. *Vision Research, 42,* 107–123.

Parkin, A. J. (1996). *Explorations in cognitive neuropsychology.* Oxford, England: Blackwell.

Pascalis, O., de Haan, M., & Nelson, C. A. (2002). Is face processing species-specific during the first year of life? *Science, 296,* 1321–1323.

Pascalis, O., deSchonen, S., Morton, J., Deruelle, C., & Fabre-Grenet, M. (1995). Mother's face recognition by neonates: A replication and an extension. *Infant Behavior and Development, 18,* 79–85.

Pasternak, T. (1990). Vision following loss of cortical directional selectivity. In M. A. Berkley & W. C. Stebbins (Eds.), *Comparative perception* (Vol. 1, pp. 407–428). New York: Wiley.

Pasternak, T., & Merigan, E. H. (1994). Motion perception following lesions of the superior temporal sulcus in the monkey. *Cerebral Cortex, 4,* 247–259.

Patterson, M. L., & Werker, J. F. (1999). Matching phonetic information in lips and voice is robust in 4.5 month old infants. *Infant Behavior and Development,* 22, 237–247.

Patterson, R. D., et al. (2002). The processing of temporal pitch and melody information in auditory cortex. *Neuron, 36,* 767–776.

Patuzzi, R. (1996). Cochlear micromechanics and macromechanics. In P. Dallos, A. N. Popper, & R. R. Fay (Eds.), *The cochlea* (pp. 186–257). New York: Springer.

Paulesu, E., Harrison, J., Baron-Cohen, S., Watson, J. D. G., Goldstein, L., Heather, J., Frackowiak, R. S. J., & Frith, C. D. (1995). The physiology of colored hearing. *Brain, 118,* 661–676.

Penfield, W., & Rasmussen, T. (1950). *The cerebral cortex of man.* New York: Macmillan.

Perl, E. R., & Kruger, L. (1996). Nociception and pain: Evolution of concepts and observations In L. Kruger (Ed.), *Pain and touch* (pp. 179–221). San Diego, CA: Academic Press.

Perrett, D. I., Hietanen, J. K., Oram, M. W., & Benson, P. J. (1992). Organization and function of cells responsive to faces in the temporal cortex. *Transactions of the Royal Society of London, B225,* 23–30.

Perrett, D. I., & Oram, M. W. (1993). Neurophysiology of shape processing. *Image and visual computing, 11,* 317–333.

Pessoa, L. (2004). Seeing the world in the same way. *Science, 303,* 1617–1618.

Peterson, F., & Rainey, L. H. (1911). The beginnings of mind in the newborn. *Bulletin of the Lying-In Hospital, 7,* 99–122.

Peterson, M. A. (1994). Object recognition processes can and do operate before figure–ground organization. *Current Directions in Psychological Science, 3,* 105–111.

Peterson, M. A. (2001). Object perception. In E. B. Goldstein (Ed.), *Blackwell handbook of perception.* Oxford, UK: Blackwell.

Petrovic, P., Kalso, E., Petersson, K. M., & Ingvar, M. (2002). Placebo and opioid analgesia—imaging a shared neuronal network. *Science, 295,* 1737–1740.

Pfaffmann, C. (1974). Specificity of the sweet receptors of the squirrel monkey. *Chemical Senses, 1,* 61–67.

Pfeiffer, C. A., & Johnston, R. E. (1994). Hormonal and behavioral responses of male hamsters to females and female odors: Roles of olfaction, the vemeronasal system, and sexual experience. *Physiology and Behavior, 55,* 129–138.

Philbeck, J. W., Loomis, J. M., & Beall, A. C. (1997). Visually perceived location is an invariant in the control of action. *Perception & Psychophysics, 59,* 601–612.

Phillips, J. R., & Johnson, K. O. (1981). Tactile spatial resolution: II: Neural representation of bars, edges, and gratings in monkey primary afferent. *Journal of Neurophysiology, 46,* 1177–1191.

Pirchio, M., Spinelli, D., Fiorentini, A., & Maffei, L. (1978). Infant contrast sensitivity evaluated by evoked potentials. *Brain Research, 141,* 179–184.

Plack, C. J., & Carlyon, R. P. (1995). Loudness perception and intensity coding. In B. C. J. Moore (Ed.), *Hearing* (pp. 123–160). San Diego: Academic Press.

Plug, C., & Ross, H. E. (1994). The natural moon illusion: A multifactor account. *Perception, 23,* 321–333.

Pokorny, J., Shevell, S. K., & Smith, V. C. (1991). Color appearance and color constancy. In P. Gouras (Ed.), *The perception of color: Vol. 6. Vision and visual dysfunction* (pp. 43–61). Boca Raton, FL: CRC Press.

Poremba, A., Saunders, R. C., Crane, A. M., Cook, M., Sokoloff, L., & Mishkin, M. (2003). Functional mapping of the primate auditory system. *Science, 299,* 568–572.

Porter, R. H., & Schaal, B. (1995). Olfaction and development of social preferences in neonatal organisms. In R. L. Doty

(Ed.), *Handbook of olfaction and gustation* (pp. 299–321). New York: Marcel Dekker.
Posner, M. I., Snyder, C. R. R., & Davidson, B. J. (1980). Attention and the detection of signals. *Journal of Experimental Psychology: General, 109,* 160–174.
Price, D. D. (2000). Psychological and neural mechanisms of the affective dimension of pain. *Science, 288,* 1769–1772.
Price, J. L., Carmichael, S. T., Carnes, K. M., Clugnet, M. C., Kuroda, M., & Ray, J. P. (1991). Olfactory output to the prefrontal cortex. In J. L. Davis & H. Eichenbaum (Eds.), *Olfaction: A model system for computational neuroscience* (pp. 101–120). Cambridge, MA: MIT Press.
Prinzmetal, W., Shimamura, A. P., & Mikolinski, M. (2001). The Ponzo illusion and the perception of orientation. *Perception & Psychophysics, 63,* 99–114.
Proffitt, D. R., Stefanucci, J., Banton, T., & Epstein, W. (2003). The role of effort in perceiving distance. *Psychological Science, 14,* 106–112.

Quinn, P. C., Burke, S., & Rush, A. (1993). Part-whole perception in early infancy: Evidence for perceptual grouping produced by lightness similarity. *Infant Behavior and Development, 16,* 19–42.
Quinn, P. C., Rosano, J. L., & Wooten, B. R. (1988). Evidence that brown is not an elemental color. *Perception and Psychophysics, 43,* 156–164.
Quiroga, R. Q., Reddy., L., Kreiman, G., Koch, C., & Fried, I. (2005). Invariant visual representation by single neurons in the human brain. *Nature, 435,* 1102–1107.
Quittner, A. L., Smith, L. B., Osberger, M. J., Mitchell, T. V., & Katz, D. B. (1994). The impact of audition on the development of visual attention. *Psychological Science, 5,* 347–353.

Rainville, P. (2002). Brain mechanisms of pain affect and pain modulation. *Current Opinion in Neurobiology, 12,* 195–204.
Rakow, N. A., & Suslick, K. S. (2000). A colorimetric sensory array for odour visualization. *Nature, 406,* 710–713.
Ramachandran, V. S., & Anstis, S. M. (1986, May). The perception of apparent motion. *Scientific American,* 102–109.
Ramachandran, V. S., & Hirstein, W. (1998). The perception of phantom limbs. *Brain, 121,* 1603–1630.
Ramsey, J. L., Langlois, J. H., Hoss, R. A., Rubenstein, A. J., & Griffin, A. M. (2004). Origins of a stereotype: Categorization of facial attributes by 6-month-old infants. *Developmental Science, 7,* 201–211.
Ramus, F., Hauser, M. D., Miller, C., Morris, D., & Mehler, J. (2000). Language discrimination by human newborns and cotton-top tamarin monkeys. *Science 288,* 349–351.
Ratliff, F. (1965). *Mach bands: Quantitative studies on neural networks in the retina.* New York: Holden-Day.
Ratner, C., & McCarthy, J. (1990). Ecologically relevant stimuli and color memory. *Journal of General Psychology, 117,* 369–377.
Rauschecker, J. P. (1997). Processing of complex sounds in the auditory cortex of cat, monkey, and man. *Acta Otolaryngol, Suppl. 532,* 34–38.
Rauschecker, J. P. (1998). Cortical processing of complex sounds. *Current Opinion in Neurobiology, 8,* 516–521.
Rauschecker, J. P., & Korte, M. (1993). Auditory compensation for early blindness in cat cerebral cortex. *Journal of Neuroscience, 13,* 4538–4548.
Rauschecker, J. P., & Shannon, R. V. (2002). Sending sound to the brain. *Science, 295,* 1025–1029.
Rauschecker, J. P., & Tian, B. (2000). Mechanisms and streams for processing of "what" and "where" in auditory cortex. *Proceedings of the National Academy of Sciences, USA 97,* 11800–11806.
Reale, R. A., & Imig, T. J. (1980). Tonotopic organization in auditory cortex of the cat. *Journal of Comparative Neurology, 192,* 265–291.
Recanzone, G. H., Schreiner, C. E., & Merzenich, M. M. (1993). Plasticity in the frequency representation of primary auditory cortex following discrimination training in adult owl monkeys. *Journal of Neuroscience, 13,* 87–103.
Reddy, D. R. (1976). Speech recognition by machine: A review. *Proceedings of the Institute of Electrical and Electronic Engineers, 64,* 501–531.
Reddy, L., Wilken, P., & Koch, C. (2004). Face-gender discrimination is possible in the near-absence of attention. *Journal of Vision, 4,* 106–117.
Reed, C. L., & Vinson, N. G. (1996). Conceptual effects on representational momentum. *Journal of Experimental Psychology: Human Perception and Performance, 22,* 839–850.
Reed, C. M., Durlach, N. I., Braida, L. D., & Schultz, M. C. (1982). Analytic study of the Tadoma method: Identification of consonants and vowels by an experienced Tadoma user. *Journal of Speech and Hearing Research, 25,* 108–116.
Regan, D. (1986). Luminance contrast: Vernier discrimination. *Spatial Vision, 1,* 305–318.
Regan, D., & Cynader, M. (1979). Neurons in area 18 of cat visual cortex selectively sensitive to changing size: Nonlinear interactions between responses to two edges. *Vision Research, 19,* 699–711.
Reichl, R. (1994, March 11). Dining in New York. *New York Times.*
Rensink, R. A. (2000). The dynamic representation of scenes. *Visual Cognition, 7,* 17–42.
Rensink, R. A. (2002). Change blindness. *Annual Review of Psychology. 53,* 245–277.
Rensink, R. A., O'Regan, J. K., & Clark, J. J. (1997). To see or not to see: The need for attention to perceive changes in scenes. *Psychological Science, 8,* 368–373.
Reynolds, D. V. (1969). Surgery in the rat during electrical analgesia induced by focal brain stimulation. *Science, 164,* 444–445.
Reynolds, J. H., & Desimone, R. (2003). Interacting roles of attention and visual salience in V4. *Neuron, 37,* 853–863.
Riesenhuber, M., and Poggio, T. (1999). Hierarchical models of object recognition in cortex. *Nature Neuroscience, 2,* 1019–1025.
Riesenhuber, M., & Poggio, T. (2002). Neural mechanisms of object recognition. *Current Opinion in Neurobiology, 12,* 162–168.
Rind, F. C., & Simmons, P. J. (1999). Seeing what is coming: Building collision-sensitive neurones. *Trends in Neurosciences, 22,* 215–220.
Ringbach, D. L. (2003). Look at the big picture (details will follow). *Nature Neuroscience, 6,* 7–8.
Risset, J. C., & Mathews, M. W. (1969). Analysis of musical instrument tones. *Physics Today, 22,* 23–30.
Rivera-Gaxiola, M., Silva-Pereyra, J., & Kuhl, P. K. (2005). Brain potentials to native and non-native speech contrasts in 7- and 11-month-old American infants. *Developmental Science, 8,* 162–172.
Rizzolatti, G., & Arbib, M. A. (1998). *Trends in Neurosciences, 21,* 188–194.

Rizzolatti, G., Forgassi, L., & Gallese, V. (2000). Cortical mechanisms subserving object grasping and action recognition: A new view on the cortical motor functions. In M. Gazzaniga (Ed.), *The new cognitive neurosciences* (pp. 539–552). Cambridge, MA: MIT Press.

Robbins, J. (2000, July 4). Virtual reality finds a real place as a medical aid. Retrieved September 30, 2005, from http://query.nytimes.com/gst/health/article-page.html?res=9C0DE2DF1339F937A35754C0A9669C8B63]

Robertson, L., Treisman, A., Friedman-Hill, S., & Grabowecky, M. (1997). The interaction of spatial and object pathways: Evidence from Balint's syndrome. *Journal of Cognitive Neuroscience, 9,* 295–317.

Robinson, D. L., & Wurtz, R. (1976). Use of an extra-retinal signal by monkey superior colliculus neurons to distinguish real from self-induced stimulus movement. *Journal of Neurophysiology, 39,* 852–870.

Robson, J. G., Tolhurst, D. J., Freeman, R. D., & Ohzawa, I. (1988). Simple cells in the visual cortex of the cat can be narrowly tuned for spatial frequency. *Visual Neuroscience, 1,* 415–419.

Rock, I. (1983). *The logic of perception.* Cambridge, MA: MIT Press.

Rock, I., & Kaufman, L. (1962). The moon illusion: Part 2. *Science, 136,* 1023–1031.

Rollman, G. B. (1991). Pain responsiveness. In M. A. Heller & W. Schiff (Eds.), *The psychology of touch* (pp. 91–114). Hillsdale, NJ: Erlbaum.

Rolls, E. T. (1992). Neurophysiological mechanisms underlying face processing within and beyond the temporal cortical visual areas. *Transactions of the Royal Society of London, B335,* 11–21.

Rolls, E. T. (2000). The orbitofrontal cortex and reward. *Cerebral Cortex, 10,* 284–294.

Rolls, E. T. (2004). Invariant object and face recognition. In L. M. Chalupa & J. S. Werner (Eds.), *The visual neurosciences* (pp. 1165–1177). Cambridge, MA: MIT Press.

Rolls, E. T. (2004). Smell, taste, texture, and temperature multimodal representations in the brain, and their relevance to the control of appetite. *Nutrition Reviews, 62,* S193–S204.

Rolls, E. T., & Baylis, L. L. (1994). Gustatory, olfactory, and visual convergence within the primate orbitofrontal cortex. *Journal of Neuroscience, 14,* 5437–5452.

Rolls, E. T., & Tovee, M. J. (1995). Sparseness of the neuronal representation of stimuli in the primate temporal visual cortex. *Journal of Neurophysiology, 73,* 713–726.

Romanski, L. M., Tian, B., Fritz, J., Mishkin, M., Goldman-Rakic, P. S., & Rauschecker, J. P. (1999). Dual streams of auditory afferents target multiple domains in the prefrontal cortex. *Nature Neuroscience, 2,* 1131–1136.

Romo, R., Hernandez, A., Zainos, A., & Salinas, E. (1998). Somatosensory discrimination based on cortical microstimulation. *Nature, 392,* 387–390.

Rose, D. (1996). Reflections on (or by?) grandmother cells. *Perception, 25,* 881.

Rosenstein, D., & Oster, H. (1988). Differential facial responses to four basic tastes in newborns. *Child Development, 59,* 1555–1568.

Roskies, A. L. (1999). The binding problem. *Neuron, 24,* 7–9.

Rossiter, K. J. (1996). Structure-odor relationships. *Chemical Reviews, 96,* 3201–3240.

Rowe, M. J., Turman, A. A., Murray, G. M., & Zhang, H. Q. (1996). Parallel processing in somatosensory areas I and II of the cerebral cortex. In O. Franzen, R. Johansson, & L. Terenius (Eds.), *Somesthesis and the neurobiology of the somatosensory cortex* (pp. 197–212). Basel, Switzerland: Birkhauser Verlag.

Rozin, P. (1982). "Taste-smell confusions" and the duality of the olfactory sense. *Perception and Psychophysics, 31,* 397–401.

Rubin, E. (1915). *Synoplevde Figurer.* Copenhagen: Gyldendalske.

Rubin, P., Turvey, M. T., & Van Gelder, P. (1976). Initial phoneme are detected faster in spoken words than in spoken nonwords. *Perception and Psychophysics, 19,* 394–398.

Rushton, S. K., Harris, J. M., Jloyd, M. R., & Wann, J. P. (1998). Guidance of locomotion on foot uses perceived target location rather than optic flow. *Current Biology, 8,* 1191–1194.

Rushton, S. K., & Salvucci, D. D. (2001). An egocentric account of the visual guidane of locomotion. *Trends in Cognitive Sciences, 5,* 6–7.

Rushton, W. A. H. (1961). Rhodopsin measurement and dark adaptation in a subject deficient in cone vision. *Journal of Physiology, 156,* 193–205.

Rushton, W. A. H. (1964). Color blindness and cone pigments. *American Journal of Optometry and Archives of the American Academy of Optometry, 41,* 265–282.

Russell, M. J. (1976). Human olfactory communication. *Nature, 260,* 520–522.

Sachs, M. B., Young, E. D., & Miller, M. I. (1981). Encoding of speech features in the auditory nerve. In R. Carson & B. Grandstrom (Eds.), *The representation of speech in the peripheral auditory system* (pp. 115–139). New York: Elsevier.

Sackett, B. (1972). Counting every quantum. *Journal of Physiology, 223,* 131–150.

Sacks, O. (1985). *The man who mistook his wife for a hat.* London: Duckworth.

Sadato, N., Pascual-Leone, A., Grafman, J., Ibanez, V., Deiber, M-P., Dold, G., & Hallett, M. (1996). Activation of the primary visual cortex by Braille reading in blind subjects. *Nature, 380,* 526–528.

Sai, F. Z. (2005). The role of the mother's voice in developing mother's face preference: Evidence for intermodal perception at birth. *Infant and Child Development, 14,* 29–50.

Sakata, H., & Iwamura, Y. (1978). Cortical processing of tactile information in the first somatosensory and parietal association areas in the monkey. In G. Gordon (Ed.), *Active touch* (pp. 55–72). Elmsford, NY: Pergamon Press.

Sakada, H., Taira, M., Kusunoki, M., Murata, A., & Tanaka. (1997). The parietal association cortex in depth perception and visual control of hand action. *Trends in Neurosciences, 20,* 350–357.

Sakata, H., Taira, M., Mine, S., & Murata, A. (1992). Hand-movement-related neurons of the posterior parietal cortex of the monkey: Their role in visual guidance of hand movements. In R. Caminiti, P. B. Johnson, & Y. Burnod (Eds.), *Control of arm movement in space: Neurophysiological and computational approaches* (pp. 185–198). Berlin: Springer-Verlag.

Salapatek, P., & Banks, M. S. (1978). Infant sensory assessment: Vision. In F. D. Minifie & L. L. Lloyd (Eds.), *Communicative and cognitive abilities: Early behavioral assessment* (pp. 61–106). Baltimore: University Park Press.

Salapatek, P., Bechtold, A. G., & Bushnell, E. W. (1976). Infant visual acuity as a function of viewing distance. *Child Development, 47,* 860–863.

Salasoo, A., & Pisoni, D. B. (1985). Interaction of knowledge sources in spoken word identification. *Journal of Memory and Language, 24,* 210–231.

Samuel, A. G. (1981). Phonemic restoration: Insights from a new methodology. *Journal of Experimental Psychology: General, 110,* 474–494.

Samuel, A. G. (1990). Using perceptual-restoration effects to explore the architecture of perception. In G. T. M. Altmann (Ed.), *Cognitive models of speech processing* (pp. 295–314). Cambridge, MA: MIT Press.

Sanders, L. D., & Neville, H. J. (2000). Lexical, syntactic, and stress-pattern cues for speech segmentation. *Journal of Speech, Language, and Hearing Research, 43,* 1301–1321.

Sato, M., & Ogawa, H. (1994). Neural coding of taste in macaque monkeys. In K. Kurihara, N. Suzuki, & H. Ogawa (Eds.), *Olfaction and taste* (Vol. 11, pp. 388–392). Tokyo: Springer-Verlag.

Sato, M., Ogawa, H., & Yamashita, S. (1994). Gustatory responsiveness of chorda tympani fibers in the cynomolgus monkey. *Chemical Senses, 19,* 381–400.

Scheinberg, D. L., & Logothetis, N. K. (2001). Noticing familiar objects in real world scenes: The role of temporal cortical neurons in natural vision. *Journal of Neuroscience, 21,* 1340–1350.

Schiff, W., & Detwiler, M. L. (1979). Information used in judging impending collision. *Perception, 8,* 647–658.

Schiffman, H. R. (1967). Size-estimation of familiar objects under informative and reduced conditions of viewing. *American Journal of Psychology, 80,* 229–235.

Schiffman, S. S., & Erickson, R. P. (1971). A psychophysical model for gustatory quality. *Physiology and Behavior, 7,* 617–633.

Schiller, P. H., Logothetis, N. K., & Charles, E. R. (1990). Functions of the colour-opponent and broad-band channels of the visual system. *Nature, 343,* 68–70.

Schindler, I., Rice, N. J., McIntosh, R. D., Rossetti, Y., Vighetto, A., & Milner, A. D. (2004). Automatic avoidance of obstacles is a dorsal stream function: evidence from optic ataxia. *Nature Neuroscience, 7,* 779–784.

Schnapf, J. L., Kraft, T. W., & Baylor, D. A. (1987). Spectral sensitivity of human cone photoreceptors. *Nature, 325,* 439–441.

Schneider, P., Scherg, M., Dosch, H. G., Specht, H. J., Gutschalk, A., & Rupp, A. (2002). Morphology of Heschl's gyrus reflects enhanced activation in the auditory cortex of musicians. *Nature Neuroscience, 3,* 688–694.

Scholz, J., & Woolf, C. J. (2002). Can we conquer pain? *Nature Neuroscience, 5,* 1062–1067.

Schreiner, C. H., & Mendelson, J. R. (1990). Functional topography of cat primary auditory cortex: Distribution of integrated excitation. *Journal of Neurophysiology, 64,* 1442–1459.

Schubert, E. D. (1980). *Hearing: Its function and dysfunction.* Wien, Austria: Springer-Verlag.

Schyns, P. G., & Oliva, A. (1994). From blobs to boundary edges: Evidence for time- and spatial-scale-dependent scene recognition. *Psychological Science, 5,* 195–200.

Scientific American Frontiers. (2001, November 13). *Growing up different.* Public Broadcasting System.

Scott, S. K., & Johnsrude, I. S. (2003). The neuroanatomical and functional organization of speech perception. *Trends in Neuroscience, 26,* 100–107.

Scott, T. R., & Giza, B. K. (1990). Coding channels in the taste system of the rat. *Science, 249,* 1585–1587.

Scott, T. R., & Giza, B. K. (2000). Issues of gustatory neural coding: Where they stand today. *Physiology and Behavior, 69,* 65–76.

Scott, T. R., & Plata-Salaman, C. R. (1991). Coding of taste quality. In T. V. Getchell, R. L. Doty, L. M. Bartoshuk, & J. B. Snow (Eds.), *Smell and taste in health and disease* (pp. 345–368). New York: Raven Press.

Searle, C. L., Jacobson, J. Z., & Rayment, S. G. (1979). Stop consonant discrimination based on human audition. *Journal of the Acoustical Society of America, 65,* 799–809.

Sedgwick, H. (2001). Visual space perception. In E. B. Goldstein (Ed.), *Blackwell handbook of perception* (pp. 128–167). Oxford: Blackwell.

Segui, J. (1984). The syllable: A basic perceptual unit in speech processing? In H. Bouma & D. G. Gouwhuis (Eds.), *Attention and performance X* (pp. 165–181). Hillsdale, NJ: Erlbaum.

Sekuler, R., Sekuler, A. B., & Lau, R. (1997). Sound alters visual motion perception. *Nature, 385,* 308.

Senior, C., Barnes, J., Giampietro, V., Simmons, A., Bullmore, E. T., Brammer, M., & David, A. S. (2000). The functional neuoroanatomy of implicit-motion perception or "representational momentum." *Current Biology, 10,* 16–22.

Sereno, M. E., Trinath, T., Augath, M., & Logothetis, N. K. (2002). Three dimensional shape representation in monkey cortex. *Neuron, 33,* 635–652.

Servos, P., Osu, R., Santi, A., & Kawato, M. (2002). The neural substrates of biological motion perception: An fMRI study. *Cerebral Cortex, 12,* 772–782.

Shaffer, D. M., Krauchunas, S. M., Eddy, M., & McBeath, M. K. (2004). How dogs navigate to catch Frisbees. *Psychological Science, 15,* 437–441.

Shaffer, D. M., & McBeath, M. K. (2002). Baseball outfielders maintain a linear optical trajectory when tracking uncatchable fly balls. *Journal of Experimental Psychology: Human Perception and Performance, 28,* 335–348.

Shafritz, K. M., Gore, J. C., & Marois, R. (2002). The role of the parietal cortex in visual feature binding. *Proceedings of the National Academy of Sciences, 99,* 10917–10922.

Shaw, R. E. (2003). The agent-environment interface: Simon's indirect or Gibson's direct coupling? *Ecological Psychology, 15,* 37–106.

Shein, S. J., & DeSimone, R. (1990). Spectral properties of V4 neurons in the macaque. *Journal of Neuroscience, 10,* 3369–3389.

Sheinberg, D. L., & Logothetis, N. K. (1997). The role of temporal cortical areas in perceptual organization. *Proceedings of the National Academy of Sciences, 94,* 3408–3413.

Shiffrar, M., & Freyd, J. J. (1990). Apparent motion of the human body. *Psychological Science, 1,* 257–264.

Shiffrar, M., & Freyd, J. J. (1993). Timing and apparent motion path choice with human body photographs. *Psychological Science, 4,* 379–384.

Shimamura, A. P., & Prinzmetal, W. (1999). The mystery spot illusion and its relation to other visual illusions. *Psychological Science, 10,* 501–507.

Shimojo, S., Bauer, J. , O'Connell, K. M., & Held, R. (1986). Prestereoptic binocular vision in infants. *Vision Research, 26,* 501–510.

Silver, W. L., & Finger, T. E. (1991). The trigeminal system. In T. V. Getchell, R. L. Doty, L. M. Bartoshuk, & J. B. Snow (Eds.), *Smell and taste in health and disease* (pp. 97–108). New York: Raven Press.

Simons, D. J., & Chabris, C. F. (1999). Gorillas in our midst: Sustained inattentional blindness for dynamic events. *Perception, 28,* 1059–1074.

Singer, T., Seymour, B., O'Doherty, J., Kaube, H., Dolan, R. J., & Frith, C. D. (2004). Empathy for pain involves the affective but not sensory components of pain. *Science, 303,* 1157–1162.

Sinha, P. (2002). Recognizing complex patterns. *Nature Neuroscience 5,* 1093–1097.

Slater, A. M., & Findlay, J. M. (1975). Binocular fixation in the newborn baby. *Journal of Experimental Child Psychology, 20,* 248–273.

Slater, A. M., Morison, V., & Rose, D. (1984). Habituation in the newborn. *Infant Behavior and Development, 7,* 183–200.

Slater, A. M., Morison, V., Somers, M., Mattock, A., Brown, E., & Taylor, D. (1990). Newborn and older infants' perception of partly occluded objects. *Infant Behavior and Development, 13,* 33–49.

Slater et al. (2000). Newborn infants' preference for attractive faces: The role of internal and external facial features. *Infancy, 1,* 265–274.

Sloan, L. L., & Wollach, L. (1948). A case of unilateral deuteranopia. *Journal of the Optical Society of America, 38,* 502–509.

Smith, D. V., St. John, S. J., & Boughter, J. D., Jr. (2000). Neuronal cell types and taste quality coding. *Physiology & Behavior, 69,* 77–85.

Smith, D., V., & Scott, T. R. (2003). Gustatory neural coding. In R. L. Doty (Ed). *Handbook of olfaction and gustation* (2nd ed.). New York: Marcel Dekker.

Snyder, L. H., Batista, A. P., & Andersen, R. A. (2000). Intention-related activity in the posterior parietal cortex: A review. *Vision Res., 40,* 1433–1441.

Soto-Faraco, S., Lyons, J., Gazzaniga, M., Spence, C., & Kingstone, A. (2002). The ventriloquist in motion: Illusory capture of dynamic information across sensory modalities. *Cognitive Brain Research, 14,* 139–146.

Soto-Faraco, S., Spence, C., Lloyd, D., & Kingstone, A. (2004). Moving multisenosry research along: Motion perception across sensory modalities. *Current Directions in Psychological Science, 13,* 29–32.

Spelke, E. S., Gutheil, G., & Van de Walle, G. (1995). The development of object perception. In S. M. Kosslyn & D. N. Osherson (Eds.), *Visual cognition* (pp. 297–330). Cambridge, MA: MIT Press.

Spors, H., & Grinvald, A. (2002). Spatio-temporal dynamics of odor representations in the mammalian olfactory bulb. *Neuron, 34,* 301–315.

Srivinisan, M V., Chahl, J. S., Nagle, M. G., & Zhang, S. W. (1997). Embodying natural vision into machines. In M. V. Srinivasan & S. Ventatesh (Eds.), *From living eyes to seeing machines.* New York: Oxford.

Srinivasan, M. V., & Ventatesh, S. (Eds.). (1997). *From living eyes to seeing machines.* New York: Oxford.

Srulovicz, P., & Goldstein, J. L. (1983). A central spectrum model: A synthesis of auditory-nerve timing and place cues in monaural communication of frequency spectrum. *Journal of the Acoustical Society of America, 73,* 1266–1276.

Stark, L., & Bridgeman, B. (1983). Role of corollary discharge in space constancy. *Perception and Psychophysics, 34,* 371–380.

Steiner, J. E. (1974). Innate, discriminative human facial expressions to taste and smell stimulation. *Annals of the New York Academy of Sciences, 237,* 229–233.

Steiner, J. E. (1979). Human facial expressions in response to taste and smell stimulation. *Advances in Child Development and Behavior, 13,* 257–295.

Stern, K., & McKlintock, M. K. (1998). Regulation of ovulation by human pheromones. *Nature, 392,* 177–179.

Stevens, J. A., Fonlupt, P., Shiffrar, M., & Decety, J. (2000). New aspects of motion perception: Selective neural encoding of apparent human movements. *NeuroReport, 11,* 109–115.

Stevens, J. K., Emerson, R. C., Gerstein, G. L., Kallos, T., Neufeld, G. R., Nichols, C. W., & Rosenquist, A. C. (1976). Paralysis of the awake human: Visual perceptions. *Vision Research, 16,* 93–98.

Stevens, K. N., & Blumstein, S. (1978). Invariant cues for place of articulation in stop consonants. *Journal of the Acoustical Society of America, 64,* 1358–1368.

Stevens, K. N., & Blumstein, S. (1981). The search for invariant acoustic correlates of phonetic features. In P. D. Eimas & L. L. Miller (Eds.), *Perspectives on the study of speech.* Hillsdale, NJ: Erlbaum.

Stevens, S. S. (1957). On the psychophysical law. *Psychological Review, 64,* 153–181.

Stevens, S. S. (1961). To honor Fechner and repeal his law. *Science, 133,* 80–86.

Stevens, S. S. (1962). The surprising simplicity of sensory metrics. *American Psychologist, 17,* 29–39.

Stiles, W. S. (1953). Further studies of visual mechanisms by the two-color threshold method. Coloquio sobre problemas opticos de la vision. Madrid: *Union Internationale de Physique Pure et Appliqué, 1,* 65.

Stoerig, P. (1998). Wavelength information processing versus color perception: Evidence from blindsight and color-blind sight. In W. G. K. Backhaus, R. Kliegl, & J. S. Werner (Eds.), *Color vision: Perspectives from different disciplines* (pp. 131–147). New York: Walter de Gruyter.

Stoffregen, T. A., Smart, J. L., Bardy, B. G., & Pagulayan, R. J. (1999). Postural stabilization of looking. *Journal of Experimental Psychology: Human Perception and Performance, 25,* 1641–1658.

Strange, W. (Ed.). (1995). *Speech perception and linguistic experience: Issues in cross-language research.* Timonium, MD: York.

Stryker, M. P. (1989). Is grandmother an oscillation? *Nature, 338,* 297–298.

Sufka, K. J., & Price, D. D. (2002). Gate control theory reconsidered. *Brain and Mind, 3,* 277–290.

Suga, N. (1990, June). Biosonar and neural computation in bats. *Scientific American,* 60–68.

Sumner, P., & Mollon, J. D. (2000). Catarrhine photopigments are optimized for detecting targets against a foliage background. *Journal of Experimental Biology, 23,* 1963–1986.

Sun, H.-J., Campos, J., Young, M., Chan, G. S. W., & Ellard, C. G. (2004). The contributions of static visual cues, nonvisual cues, and optic flow in distance estimation. *Perception, 33,* 49–65.

Sussman, H. M., Hoemeke, K. A., & Ahmed, F. S. (1993). A cross-linguistic investigation of locus equations as a phonetic descriptor for place of articulation. *Journal of the Acoustical Society of America, 94,* 1256–1268.

Sussman, H. M., McCaffrey, H. A., & Matthews, S. A. (1991). An investigation of locus equations as a source of relational variance for stop place categorization. *Journal of the Acoustical Society of America, 90,* 1309–1325.

Svaetichin, G. (1956). Spectral response curves from single cones. *Acta Physiologica Scandinavica Supplementum, 134,* 17–46.

Swets, J. A. (1964). *Signal detection and recognition by human observers.* New York: Wiley.

Taira, M., Mine, S., Georgopoulos, A. P., Murata, A., & Sakata, H. (1990). Parietal cortex neurons of the monkey related to the visual guidance of hand movement. *Experimental Brain Research, 83,* 29–36.

Takagi, S. F. (1980). Dual nervous systems for olfactory functions in mammals. In H. Van der Starre (Ed.), *Olfaction and taste* (Vol. 7, pp. 275–278). London: IRC Press.

Tanaka, J., Weiskopf, D., & Williams, P. (2001). The role of color in high-level vision. *Trends in Cognitive Sciences, 5,* 211–215.

Tanaka, J. W., & Presnell, L. M. (1999). Color diagnosticity in object recognition. *Perception & Psychophysics, 61,* 1140–1153.

Tanaka, K. (1993). Neuronal mechanisms of object recognition. *Science, 262,* 684–688.

Tanaka, K. (2003). Columns for complex visual object features in the interotemporal cortex: Clustering of cells with similar but slightly different stimulus selectivities. *Cerebral Cortex, 13,* 90–99.

Tanaka, K. (2004). Inferotemporal response properties. In L. M. Chalupa & J. S. Werner (Eds.), *The visual neurosciences* (pp. 1151–1164). Cambridge, MA: MIT Press.

Tanaka, K., Siato, H.-A., Fukada, Y., & Moriya, M. (1991). Coding visual images of objects in inferotemporal cortex of the macaque monkey. *Journal of Neurophysiology, 66,* 170–189.

Tarr, M. J. (1995). Rotating objects to recognize them: A case study of the role of view-point dependency in the recognition of three-dimensional objects. *Psychonomic Bulletin and Review, 2,* 55–82.

Tarr, M. J., & Gauthier, I. (2000). FFA: A flexible fusiform area for subordinate-level visual processing automatized by expertise. *Nature, 3,* 764–769.

Tarr, M. J., & Vuong, Q. C. (2002). Visual object recognition. In S. Yantis (Ed.), *Stevens' handbook of experimental psychology: Sensation and perception* (3rd ed., pp. 287–314). New York: Wiley.

Teghtsoonian, R. (1971). On the exponents in Stevens' Law and the constant in Ekman's Law. *Psychological Review, 78,* 78–80.

Teller, D. Y. (1990). The domain of visual science. In L. Spellman & J. S. Werner (Eds.), *Visual perception: The neurophysiological foundations* (pp. 11–21). San Diego, CA: Academic Press.

Teller, D. Y. (1997). First glances: The vision of infants. *Investigative Ophthalmology and Visual Science, 38,* 2183–2199.

Ter-Pogossian, M. M., Phelps, M. E., Hoffman, E. J., & Mullani, N. A. (1975). A positron-emission tomograph for nuclear imaging (PET). *Radiology, 114,* 89–98.

Terwogt, M. M., & Hoeksma, J. B. (1994). Colors and emotions: Preferences and combinations. *Journal of General Psychology, 122,* 5–17.

Teuber, H. L. (1960). Perception. In J. Field, H. W. Magoun, & V. E. Hall (Eds.), *Handbook of physiology* (Sect. 1, Vol. 3). Washington, DC: American Physiological Society.

Tian, B., Reser, D., Durham, A., Kustov, A., & Rauschecker, J. P. (2001). Functional specialization in rhesus monkey auditory cortex. *Science, 292,* 290–293.

Tonndorf, J., & Khanna, S. M. (1968). Submicroscopic displacement amplitudes of the tympanic membrane (cat) measured by laser interferometer. *Journal of the Acoustical Society of America, 44,* 1546–1554.

Tramo, M. J., Gaurav, D. S., & Braida, L. D., (2002). Functional role of auditory cortex in frequency processing and pitch perception. *Journal of Neurophysiology, 87,* 122–139.

Treisman, A. (1986). Features and objects in visual processing. *Scientific American, 255,* 114B–125B.

Treisman, A. (1998). The perception of features and objects. In R. D. Wright (Ed.), *Visual attention* (pp. 26-54). New York: Oxford University Press.

Treisman, A. (1999). Solutions to the binding problem: Progress through controversy and convergence. *Neuron, 24,* 105–110.

Treisman, A., & Schmidt, H. (1982). Illusory conjunctions in the perception of objects. *Cognitive Psychology 14,* 107–141.

Treisman, A. M. (1964). Selective attention in man. *British Medical Bulletin, 20,* 12–16.

Treisman, A. M. (1988). Features and objects: The fourteenth Bartlett memorial lecture. *Quarterly Journal of Experimental Psychology, 40A,* 207–237.

Treisman, A. M. (2005, February 4). Attention and binding. Presentation to the Cognitive Science Group, University of Arizona.

Treisman, A. M., & Galade, G. (1980). A feature-integration theory of attention. *Cognitive Psychology, 12,* 97–136.

Tresilian, J., R., Mon-Williams, M., & Kelly, B. (1999). Increasing confidence in vergence as a cue to distance. *Proceedings of the Royal Society of London, 266B,* 39–44.

Trout, J. D. (2003). Biological specializations for speech: What can the animals tell us? *Current Directions in Psychological Science, 12,* 155–159.

Truax, B. (1984). *Acoustic communication.* Norwood, NJ: Ablex.

Ts'o, D. Y., Roe, A. R., & Gilbert, C. D. (2001). A hierarchy of the functional organization for color, form, and disparity in primate visual area V2. *Vision Research, 41,* 1333–1349.

Tsunoda, K., Yamane, Y., Nishizaki, M., & Tanifuji, M. (2001). Complex objects are represented in macaque inferotemporal cortex by the combination of feature columns. *Nature Neuroscience, 4,* 832–838.

Tsutsui, K. I., Sakata, H., Naganuma, T., & Taira, M., (2002). Neural correlates for perception of 3D surface orientation from texture gradient. *Science, 298,* 409–412.

Tsutsui, K. I., Taira, M., & Sakata, H. (2005). Neural mechanisms of three-dimensional vision. *Neuroscience Research, 51,* 221–229.

Turati, C., Simion, F., Milani, I., & Umilta, C. (2002). Newborns' preference for faces: What is crucial? *Developmental Psychology, 38,* 875–882.

Turk, D. C., & Flor, H. (1999). Chronic pain: A biobehavioral perspective. In R. J. Gatchel & D. C. Turk (Eds.), *Psychosocial factors in pain* (pp. 18–34). New York: Guilford.

Turman, A. B., Morley, J. W., & Rowe, M. J. (1998). Functional organization of the somatosensory cortex in the primate. In J. W. Morley (Ed.), *Neural aspects of tactile sensation* (pp. 167–193). New York: Elsevier Science.

Turvey, M. T. (2004). Space (and its perception): The first and final frontier. *Ecological Psychology, 16,* 25–29.
Tye-Murray, N., Spencer, L., & Woodworth, G. G. (1995). Acquisition of speech by children who have prolonged cochlear implant experience. *Journal of Speech and Hearing Research, 38,* 327–337.
Tyler, C. W. (1997a). Analysis of human receptor density. In V. Lakshminarayanan (Ed.), *Basic and clinical applications of vision science* (pp. 63–71). Norwell, MA: Kluwer Academic.
Tyler, C. W. (1997b). *Human cone densities: Do you know where all your cones are?* Unpublished manuscript.

Uchida, N., Takahashi, Y. K., Tanifuji, M., & Mori, K. (2000). Odor maps in the mammalian olfactory bulb: Domain organization and odorant structural features. *Nature Neuroscience, 3,* 1035–1043.
Uchikawa, K., Uchikawa, H., & Boynton, R. M. (1989). Partial color constancy of isolated surface colors examined by a color-naming method. *Perception, 18,* 83–91.
Uka, T., & DeAngelis, G. C. (2003). Contribution of middle temporal area to coarse depth discrimination: Comparison of neuronal and psychophysical sensitivity. *Journal of Neuroscience, 23,* 3515–3530.
Ullman, S. (1989). Aligning pictorial descriptions: An approach to object recognition. *Cognition, 32,* 193–254.
Ungerleider, L. G., & Haxby, J. V. (1994). "What" and "where" in the human brain. *Current Opinion in Neurobiology, 4,* 157–165.
Ungerleider, L. G., & Mishkin, M. (1982). Two cortical visual systems. In D. J. Ingle, M. A. Goodale, & R. J. Mansfield (Eds.), *Analysis of visual behavior* (pp. 549–580). Cambridge, MA: MIT Press.
Ungerleider, L. G., & Pasternak, T. (2004). Ventral and dorsal cortical processing streams. In L. M. Chalupa & J. S. Werner (Eds.), *The visual neurosciences.* (pp. 541–562). Cambridge, MA: MIT Press.

Vaine, I., Crombez, G., Eccleston, C., Devulder, J., & DeCorte, W. (2004). Acceptance of the unpleasant reality of chronic pain: Effects upon attention to pain and engagement with daily activities. *Pain, 112,* 282–288.
Valdez, P., & Mehribian, A. (1994). Effect of color on emotions. *Journal of Experimental Psychology: General, 123,* 394–409.
Vallbo, A. B., & Johansson, R. S. (1978). The tactile sensory innervation of the glabrous skin of the human hand. In G. Gordon (Ed.), *Active touch* (pp. 29–54). New York: Oxford University Press.
Van Essen, D. C., & Anderson, C. H. (1995). Information processing strategies and pathways in the primate visual system. S. F. Zornetzer, J. L. Davis, & C. Lau (Eds.), *An introduction to neural and electronic networks* (2nd ed., pp. 45–75). San Diego: Academic Press.
Varela, F. J., Palacios, A. G., & Goldsmith, T. H. (1993). Color vision of birds. In H. P. Zeigler & H-J. Bishof (Eds.), *Vision, brain and behavior in birds* (pp. 77–98). Cambridge: MIT Press.
Varner, D., Cook, J. E., Schneck, M. E., McDonald, M., & Teller, D. Y. (1985). Tritan discriminations by 1- and 2-month-old human infants. *Vision Research, 25,* 821–831.
Vecera, S. P., Vogel, E. K., & Woodman, G. F. (2002). Lower region: A new cue for figure–ground assignment. *Journal of Experimental Psychology: General, 131,* 194–205.
Vermeij, G. (1997). *Privileged hands: A scientific life.* New York: Freeman.
Viana , L. M., Solomon, J., Chowdhury, Sanjida, Sinha, P., & Belliveau, J. W. (2001). Functional neuroanatomy of biological motion perception in humans. *Proceedings of the National Academy of Sciences, USA, 98,* 11656–11661.
Vinje, B. V., & Gallant, J. L. (2002). Natural stimulation of the non-classical receptive field increases information transmission efficiency in V1. *Journal of Neuroscience, 22,* 2904–2915.
Vogten, L. L. M. (1974). Pure-tone masking: A new result from a new method. In E. Zwicker & E. Terhardt (Eds.), *Facts and models in hearing* (pp. 142–155). Berlin: Springer-Verlag.
von Holst, E. (1954). Relations between the central nervous system and the peripheral organs. *British Journal of Animal Behaviour, 2,* 89–94.

Wachmuth, E., Oram, M. W., & Perrett, D. I. (1994). Recognition of objects and their component parts: Responses of single units in the temporal cortex of the macaque. *Cerebral Cortex, 4,* 509–522.
Wager, T. D., Rilling, J. K., Smith, E. E., Sokolik, A., Casey, K. L., Davidson, R. J., et al. (2004). Placebo-induced changes in fMRI in the anticipation and experience of pain. *Science, 303,* 1162–1167.
Wald, G. (1964). The receptors of human color vision. *Science, 145,* 1007–1017.
Wald, G., & Brown, P. K. (1958). Human rhodopsin. *Science, 127,* 222–226.
Waldrop, M. M. (1988). A landmark in speech recognition. *Science, 240,* 1615.
Wall, P. D., & Melzack, R. (Eds.). (1994). *Textbook of pain* (3rd ed.). Edinburgh, UK: Churchill Livingstone.
Wallach, H. (1963). The perception of neutral colors. *Scientific American, 208*(1), 107–116.
Wallach, H., Newman, E. B., & Rosenzweig, M. R. (1949). The precedence effect in sound localization. *American Journal of Psychology, 62,* 315–336.
Wallach, H., & O'Connell, D. N. (1953). The kinetic depth effect. *Journal of Experimental Psychology, 45,* 205–217.
Walls, G. L. (1942). *The vertebrate eye.* New York: Hafner. (Reprinted in 1967)
Walls, G. L. (1953). *The lateral geniculate nucleus and visual histophysiology.* Berkeley: University of California Press.
Walton, G. E., Bower, N. J. A., & Power, T. G. R. (1992). Recognition of familiar faces by newborns. *Infant Behavior and Development, 15,* 265–269.
Wann, J., & Land, M. (2000). Steering with or without the flow: Is the retrieval of heading necessary? *Trends in Cognitive Science, 4,* 319–324.
Warren, J. D., Uppenkamp, S., Patterson, R. D., & Griffiths, T. D. (2003). Separating pitch chroma and pitch height in the human brain. *Proceedings of the National Academy of Sciences, 100,* 10038–10042.
Warren, R. M. (1970). Perceptual restoration of missing speech sounds. *Science, 167,* 392–393.
Warren, R. M., Obuseck, C. J., & Acroff, J. M. (1972). Auditory induction of absent sounds. *Science, 176,* 1149.
Warren, S., Hamalainen, H., & Gardner, E. P. (1986). Objective classification of motion- and direction-sensitive neurons in primary somatosensory cortex of awake monkeys. *Journal of Neurophysiology, 56,* 598–622.

Warren, W. (2004). Optic flow. In L. M. Chalupa & J. S. Werner (Eds.), *The visual neurosciences.* (pp. 1247–1259). Cambridge, MA: MIT Press.

Warren, W. H. (1995). Self-motion: Visual perception and visual control. In W. Epstein & S. Rogers (Eds.), *Handbook of perception and cognition: Perception of space and motion* (pp. 263–323). New York: Academic Press.

Warren, W. H., Kay, B. A., & Yilmaz, E. H. (1996). Visual control of posture during walking: Functional specificity. *Journal of Experimental Psychology: Human Perception and Performance, 22,* 818–838.

Watkins, K. E., Strafella, A. P., & Paus, T. (2003). Seeing and hearing speech excites the motor system involved in speech production. *Neuropsychologia, 41,* 989–994.

Watkins, L. R., & Maier, S. F. (2003). When good pain turns bad. *Current Directions in Psychological Science, 12,* 232–236.

Weisenberg, M. (1977). Pain and pain control. *Psychological Bulletin, 84,* 1008–1044.

Weissberg, M. (1999). Cognitive aspects of pain. In P. D. Wall & R. Melzak (Eds.), *Textbook of pain* (4th ed.). New York: Churchill Livingstone, pp. 345–358.

Werker, J. (1991). The ontogeny of speech perception. In I. G. Mattingly & M. Studdert-Kennedy (Eds.), *Modularity and the motor theory of speech perception* (pp. 91–109). Hillsdale, NJ: Erlbaum.

Werker, J. F., & Tees, R. C. (1984). Cross-language speech perception: Evidence for perceptual reorganization during the first year of life. *Infant Behavior and Development, 7,* 49–63.

Werner, L. A., & Bargones, J. Y. (1992). Psychoacoustic development of human infants. In C. Rovee-Collier & L. Lipsett (Eds.), *Advances in infancy research* (Vol. 7, pp. 103–145). Norwood, NJ: Ablex.

Wertheimer, M. (1912). Experimentelle Stuidien uber das Sehen von Beuegung. *Zeitchrift fuer Psychologie, 61,* 161–265.

Wessel, D. L. (1979). Timbre space as a musical control structure. *Computer Music Journal, 3,* 45–52.

Wever, E. G. (1949). *Theory of hearing.* New York: Wiley.

Wexler, M., Panerai, I. L., & Droulez, J. (2001). Self-motion and the perception of stationary objects. *Nature, 409,* 85–88.

White, M. (1981). The effect of the nature of the surround on the perceived lightness of grey bars within squarewave test gratings. *Perception, 10,* 215–230.

Wightman, F., & Kistler, D. (1997). Monaural sound localization revisited. *Journal of the Acoustical Society of America, 101,* 1050–1063.

Wightman, F., & Kistler, D. (1998). Of Vulcan ears, human ears and "earprints." *Nature Neuroscience, 1,* 337–339.

Wightman, F. L. (1973). Pitch and stimulus fine structure. *Journal of the Acoustical Society of America, 54,* 397–406.

Wightman, F. L., & Kistler, D. J. (1993). Sound localization. In W. Yost, R. R. Fay, & A. N. Popper (Eds.), *Human psychophysics* (pp. 155–192). New York: Springer-Verlag.

Wilcox, T., & Schweinle, A. (2002). Object individuation and event mapping: Developmental changes in infants' use of featural information. *Developmental Science, 5,* 132–150.

Wilcox, T., Schweinle, A., & Chapa, C. (2003). Object individuation in infancy. In F. Fagan & H. Hayne (Eds.), *Progress in Infancy Research* (Vol. 3, pp. 193–243). Mahwah, NJ: Erlbaum.

Wilkie, R. M., & Wann, J. P. (2003). Eye-movements aid the control of locomotion. *Journal of Vision, 3,* 677–684.

Williams, D. R., & Hofer, H. (2003). Formation and acquisition of the retinal image. In L. M. Chalupa & J. S. Werner (Eds.), *The visual neurosciences* (pp. 795–810). Cambridge, MA: MIT Press.

Williams, S. M., McCoy, A. N., & Purves, D. (1998). The influence of depicted illumination on brightness. *Proceedings of the National Academy of Sciences USA, 95,* 13296–13300.

Willis, T. (1665/1965). *The anatomy of the brain and nerves* [Cerebri anatome, cui accessit Nervorum descriptio etusus] (W. Feindel, Ed.). Montreal, Canada: McGill University Press.

Wissinger, C. M., VanMeter, J., Tian, B., Van Lare, J., Pekar, J., & Rauschecker, J. P. (2001). Hierarchical organization of the human auditory cortex revealed by functional magnetic resonance imaging. *Journal of Cognitive Neuroscience, 13,* 1–7.

Witt, J. K., Proffitt, D. R., & Epstein, W. (2004). Perceiving distance: A role of effort and intent. *Perception, 33,* 577–590.

Woolf, C. J., & Salter, M. W. (2000). Neuronal plasticity: Increasing the gain in pain. *Science, 288,* 1765–1768.

Wrightman, F. L., & Kistler, D. J. (1992). The dominant role of low-frequency interaural time difference in sound localization. *Journal of the Acoustical Society of America, 91,* 1648–1661.

Wysecki, G., & Stiles, W. S. (1965). *Color science: Concepts and methods, quantitative data and formulae.* New York: Wiley.

Yarbus, A. (1967). *Eye movements and vision.* New York: Plenum.

Yonas, A., Granrud, C. E., Arterberry, M. E., & Hanson, B. L. (1986). Infant's distance from linear perspective and texture gradients. *Infant Behavior and Development, 9,* 247–256.

Yonas, A., Pettersen, L., & Granrud, C. E. (1982). Infant's sensitivity to familiar size as information for distance. *Child Development, 53,* 1285–1290.

Yost, W. A. (1997). The cocktail party problem: Forty years later. In R. H. Kilkey & T. R. Anderson (Eds.), *Binaural and spatial hearing in real and virtual environments* (pp. 329–347). Hillsdale, NJ: Erlbaum.

Yost, W. A. (2001). Auditory localization and scene perception. In E. B. Goldstein (Ed.), *Blackwell handbook of perception* (pp. 437–468). Oxford, UK: Blackwell.

Yost, W. A., & Guzman, S. J. (1996). Auditory processing of sound sources: Is there an echo in here? *Current Directions in Psychological Science, 5,* 125–131.

Yost, W. A., & Sheft, S. (1993). Auditory processing. In W. A. Yost, A. N. Popper, & R. R. Fay (Eds.), *Handbook of auditory research* (Vol. 3). New York: Springer-Verlag.

Young, R. S. L., Fishman, G. A., & Chen, F. (1980). Traumatically acquired color vision defect. *Investigative Ophthalmology and Visual Science, 19,* 545–549.

Young, T. (1802). On the theory of light and colours. *Transactions of the Royal Society of London, 92,* 12–48.

Young-Browne, G., Rosenfield, H. M., & Horowitz, F. D. (1977). Infant discrimination of facial expression. *Child Development, 48,* 555–562.

Yuodelis, C., & Hendrickson, A. (1986). A qualitative and quantitative analysis of the human fovea during development. *Vision Research, 26,* 847–855.

Zapadia, M. K., Ito, M., Gilbert, C. G., & Westheimer, G. (1995). Improvement in visual sensitivity by changes in local context: Parallel studies in human observers and in V1 of alert monkeys. *Neuron, 15,* 843–856.

Zatorre, A. J. (1988). Pitch perception of complex tones and human temporal-lobe function. *Journal of the Acoustical Society of America, 84,* 566–572.

Zeki, S. M. (1983a). Colour coding in the cerebral cortex: The reaction of cells in monkey visual cortex to wavelengths and colours. *Neuroscience, 9,* 741–765.

Zeki, S. M. (1983b). The distribution of wavelength and orientation selective cells in different areas of monkey visual cortex. *Proceedings of the Royal Society of London 217B,* 449–470.

Zeki, S. M. (1990). A century of cerebral achromatopsia. *Brain, 113,* 1721–1777.

Zeki, S., & Marini, L. (1998). Three cortical stages of colour processing in the human brain. *Brain, 121,* 1669–1685.

Zenner, H. P. (1986). Motile responses in outer hair cells. *Hearing Research, 22,* 83–90.

Zhao, G. Q., Zhang, Y., Hoon, M., Chandrashekar, J., Erienbach, I., Ryba, N. J. P., & Zuker, C. S. (2003). The receptors for mammalian sweet and umami taste. *Cell, 115,* 255–266.

Zhou, H., Friedman, H. S., & von der Heydt, R. (2000). Coding of border ownership in monkey visual cortex. *Journal of Neuroscience, 20,* 6594–6611.

Zihl, J., von Cramon, D., & Mai, N. (1983). Selective disturbance of movement vision after bilateral brain damage. *Brain, 106,* 313–340.

Zihl, J., von Cramon, D., Mai, N., & Schmid, C. (1991). Disturbance of movement vision after bilateral posterior brain damage. *Brain, 114,* 2235–2252.

Zimmer, C. (2004). A distant mirror for the brain. *Science, 303,* 43–44.

Zipser, K., Lamme, V. A. F., & Schiller, P. H. (1996). Contextual modulation in primary visual cortex. *Journal of Neuroscience, 15,* 7376–7389.

Zou, Z., Horowitz, L. F., Montmayeur, J-P., Snapper, S., & Buck, L. B. (2001). Genetic tracing reveals a stereotyped sensory map in the olfactory cortex. *Nature, 414,* 173–179.

Zubieta, J-K., Heitzeg, M. M., Smith, Y. R., Buyeller, J. A., Xu, K., Xu, Y., Koeppe, R. A., Stohler, C. S. & Goldman, D. (2003). COMT val^{158}met genotype affects mu-opioid neurotransmitter responses to a pain stressor. *Science, 299,* 1240–1243.

Zue, V. W., & Glass, J. R. (2000). Conversational interfaces: Advances and challenges. *Proceedings of the IEEE, 88,* 1166–1180.

Zylbermann, R., Landau, D., & Berson, D. (1993). The influence of study habits on myopia in Jewish teenagers. *Journal of Pediatric Ophthalmology and Strabismus, 30,* 319–322.

AUTHOR INDEX

H

I

J

K

SUBJECT INDEX

D

E

F

G

H

I

N

O

P

R

S